elementary
Statistics

A STEP BY STEP APPROACH

CANADIAN EDITION

Allan G. Bluman
Community College of Allegheny County

John G. Mayer
Southern Alberta Institute of Technology

McGraw-Hill
Ryerson

Toronto Montréal Boston Burr Ridge, IL Dubuque, IA Madison, WI New York San
Francisco St. Louis Bangkok Bogotá Caracas Kuala Lumpur Lisbon London Madrid
Mexico City Milan New Delhi Santiago Seoul Singapore Sydney Taipei

Elementary Statistics
A Step-by-Step Approach
Canadian Edition

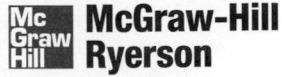

Statistics Canada information is used with the permission of Statistics Canada. Users are forbidden to copy this material and/or redisseminate the data, in an original or modified form, for commercial purposes, without the expressed permission of Statistic Canada. Information on the availability of the wide range of data from Statistics Canada can be obtained from Statistics Canada's Regional Offices, its World Wide Web site at http://www.statcan.ca and its toll-free access number 1-800-263-1136.

ISBN-13: 978-0-07-096305-4
ISBN-10: 0-07-096305-3

1 2 3 4 5 6 7 8 9 10 QPD 0 9 8

Printed and bound in the United States of America.

Care has been taken to trace ownership of copyright material contained in this text; however, the publisher will welcome any information that enables them to rectify any reference or credit for subsequent editions.

Editorial Director: Joanna Cotton
Executive Editor: Leanna MacLean
Developmental Editors: Sarah Fulton & Emma Gain
Marketing Manager: Claire Morrison
Editorial Associate: Stephanie Hess
Copy Editor: Erin Moore
Senior Production Coordinator: Jennifer Hall
Cover and Interior Design: Dave Murphy/Valid Design & Layout
Cover Image Credit: © Stone/Alan Hicks (AR6365-001)
Page Layout: Aptara, Inc.
Printer: Quebecor Printing Dubuque

Library and Archives Canada Cataloguing in Publication Bluman, Allan G.

Elementary statistics : a step by step approach / Allan G. Bluman, John Mayer — Canadian ed.

Includes index.
ISBN 978-0-07-096305-4

1. Statistics—Textbooks.   I. Mayer, John, 1953-   II. Title.

QA276.B58 2007   519.5   C2007-906065-X

This text is dedicated to my wife, Janice, and our children, Tara, Jason, Christian, and Adam, and grandchild, Emily, who provided the inspiration and encouragement to promote our extraordinary Canadian heritage.

Brief Contents

Preface x

CHAPTER 1 The Nature of Probability and Statistics 1

CHAPTER 2 Frequency Distributions and Graphs 29

CHAPTER 3 Data Description 77

CHAPTER 4 Probability and Counting Rules 143

CHAPTER 5 Discrete Probability Distributions 205

CHAPTER 6 The Normal Distribution 247

CHAPTER 7 Confidence Intervals and Sample Size 295

CHAPTER 8 Hypothesis Testing 333

CHAPTER 9 Testing the Difference Between Two Means, Two Variances, and Two Proportions 397

CHAPTER 10 Correlation and Regression 451

CHAPTER 11 Other Chi-Square Tests 499

CHAPTER 12 Analysis of Variance 529

CHAPTER 13 Nonparametric Statistics 563

CHAPTER 14 Sampling and Simulation 605

APPENDIX A Algebra Review 633

APPENDIX B-1 Writing the Research Report 639

APPENDIX B-2 Bayes' Theorem 641

APPENDIX B-3 Alternate Approach to the Standard Normal Distribution 645

APPENDIX C Tables 649

APPENDIX D Data Bank 679

APPENDIX E Technology Step-by-Step 687

APPENDIX F Glossary 709

APPENDIX G Bibliography 717

APPENDIX H Photo Credits 719

APPENDIX I Credits for Unusual Stats, Interesting Facts, Historical Notes, and Exercises (End-of-Sections and End-of-Chapters) 721

APPENDIX J Selected Answers 727

Index 771

Contents

Preface x

CHAPTER **1**

The Nature of Probability and Statistics 1

1–1 Introduction 2

1–2 Descriptive and Inferential Statistics 3

1–3 Variables and Types of Data 6

1–4 Data Collection and Sampling Techniques 9

    Random Sampling 10

    Systematic Sampling 12

    Stratified Sampling 12

    Cluster Sampling 12

    Other Sampling Methods 13

1–5 Observational and Experimental Studies 13

1–6 Uses and Misuses of Statistics 16

    Suspect Samples 17

    Ambiguous Averages 17

    Changing the Subject 17

    Detached Statistics 17

    Implied Connections 18

    Misleading Graphs 18

    Faulty Survey Questions 18

1–7 Computers and Calculators 18

1–8 Summary 21

CHAPTER **2**

Frequency Distributions and Graphs 29

2–1 Introduction 30

2–2 Organizing Data 31

    Categorical Frequency Distributions 32

    Grouped Frequency Distributions 33

2–3 Histograms, Frequency Polygons, and Ogives 41

    The Histogram 42

    The Frequency Polygon 43

    The Ogive 45

    Relative Frequency Graphs 46

    Distribution Shapes 48

2–4 Other Types of Graphs 52

    Pareto Charts 52

    The Time Series Graph 54

    The Pie Graph 56

    Misleading Graphs 58

    Stem and Leaf Plots 61

2–5 Summary 69

CHAPTER **3**

Data Description 77

3–1 Introduction 78

3–2 Measures of Central Tendency 80

    The Mean 80

    The Median 84

    The Mode 85

    The Midrange 87

    The Weighted Mean 88

    Distribution Shapes 90

3–3 Measures of Variation 96

    Range 97

    Population Variance and Standard Deviation 98

    Sample Variance and Standard Deviation 101

    Variance and Standard Deviation for Grouped Data 103

    Coefficient of Variation 105

    Range Rule of Thumb 106

    Chebyshev's Theorem 107

    The Empirical (Normal) Rule 109

3–4 Measures of Position 114

Standard Scores 114

Percentiles 115

Quartiles and Deciles 122

Outliers 123

3–5 Exploratory Data Analysis 127

The Five-Number Summary and Boxplots 127

3–6 Summary 134

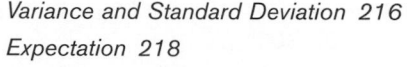

CHAPTER 4

Probability and Counting Rules 143

4–1 Introduction 144

4–2 Sample Spaces and Probability 145

Basic Concepts 145

Classical Probability 148

Complementary Events 151

Empirical Probability 153

Law of Large Numbers 155

Subjective Probability 155

Probability and Risk Taking 156

4–3 The Addition Rules for Probability 161

4–4 The Multiplication Rules and Conditional Probability 168

The Multiplication Rules 168

Conditional Probability 173

Probabilities for "At Least" 176

4–5 Counting Rules 181

The Fundamental Counting Rule 181

Factorial Notation 184

Permutations 184

Combinations 186

4–6 Probability and Counting Rules (Optional) 191

4–7 Summary 196

CHAPTER 5

Discrete Probability Distributions 205

5–1 Introduction 206

5–2 Probability Distributions 207

5–3 Mean, Variance, Standard Deviation, and Expectation 213

Mean 213

Variance and Standard Deviation 216

Expectation 218

5–4 The Binomial Distribution 223

5–5 Other Types of Distributions (Optional) 232

The Multinomial Distribution 233

The Poisson Distribution 234

The Hypergeometric Distribution 236

5–6 Summary 241

CHAPTER 6

The Normal Distribution 247

6–1 Introduction 248

6–2 Properties of a Normal Distribution 250

Empirical Rule and Areas Under the Normal Curve 251

6–3 The Standard Normal Distribution 252

Formula for Standard Score 252

Finding Areas Under the Standard Normal Distribution Curve 253

Rounding Areas 253

A Normal Distribution Curve as a Probability Distribution Curve 255

Probability Notation 255

Finding z Scores When Given Areas 256

Area and Probability Relationship 257

6–4 Applications of the Normal Distribution 260

Finding Data Values Given Specific Probabilities 264

Normality Assumption 266

6–5 The Central Limit Theorem 270

Distribution of Sample Means 270

Finite Population Correction Factor (Optional) 276

6–6 The Normal Approximation to the Binomial Distribution 280

6–7 Summary 287

CHAPTER 7

Confidence Intervals and Sample Size 295

7–1 Introduction 296

7–2 Confidence Intervals for the Mean (σ Known or $n \geq 30$) and Sample Size 297

Confidence Intervals 297

Sample Size 303

7–3 Confidence Intervals for the Mean (σ Unknown and $n < 30$) 307

7–4 Confidence Intervals and Sample Size for Proportions 313

Confidence Intervals 314

Sample Size for Proportions 316

7–5 Confidence Intervals for Variances and Standard Deviations (Optional) 320

7–6 Summary 326

CHAPTER 8

Hypothesis Testing 333

8–1 Introduction 334

8–2 Steps in Hypothesis Testing–Traditional Method 335

8–3 z Test for a Mean 346

P-Value Method for Hypothesis Testing 351

8–4 t Test for a Mean 358

8–5 z Test for a Proportion 366

8–6 χ^2 Test for a Variance or Standard Deviation 373

8–7 Additional Topics Regarding Hypothesis Testing 382

Confidence Intervals and Hypothesis Testing 382

Type II Error and the Power of a Test 384

8–8 Summary 388

CHAPTER 9

Testing the Difference Between Two Means, Two Variances, and Two Proportions 397

9–1 Introduction 398

9–2 Testing the Difference Between Two Means: Large Samples 398

9–3 Testing the Difference Between Two Variances 408

9–4 Testing the Difference Between Two Means: Small Independent Samples 416

9–5 Testing the Difference Between Two Means: Small Dependent Samples 423

9–6 Testing the Difference Between Proportions 433

9–7 Summary 439

Hypothesis-Testing Summary 1 447

CHAPTER 10

Correlation and Regression 451

10–1 Introduction 452

10–2 Scatter Plots 453

10–3 Correlation 457

Correlation Coefficient 457

The Significance of the Correlation Coefficient 460

Correlation and Causation 464

10–4 Regression 468

Line of Best Fit 469

Determination of the Regression Line Equation 469

10–5 Coefficient of Determination and Standard Error of the Estimate 477

Types of Variation for the Regression Model 477

Coefficient of Determination 480

Standard Error of the Estimate 480

Prediction Interval 482

10–6 Multiple Regression (Optional) 485

The Multiple Regression Equation 487

Testing the Significance of R 489

Adjusted R^2 489

10–7 Summary 492

CHAPTER 11

Other Chi-Square Tests 499

11–1 Introduction 500

11–2 Test for Goodness of Fit 501

P-Value Method for Chi-Square Tests 505

11–3 Tests Using Contingency Tables 509

Test for Independence 510

Decision Rule–P-Value Method 512

Test for Homogeneity of Proportions 516

11–4 Summary 523

CHAPTER 12

Analysis of Variance 529

12–1 Introduction 530

12–2 One-Way Analysis of Variance 531

P-Values for ANOVA 536

12–3 The Scheffé Test and the Tukey Test 536

Scheffé Test 537

Tukey Test 538

12–4 Two-Way Analysis of Variance 543

12–5 Summary 555

Hypothesis-Testing Summary 2 561

CHAPTER **13**

Nonparametric Statistics 563

13–1 Introduction 564

13–2 Advantages and Disadvantages of Nonparametric Methods 565

Advantages 565

Disadvantages 565

Ranking 565

13–3 The Sign Test 567

Single-Sample Sign Test 567

Paired-Sample Sign Test 569

13–4 The Wilcoxon Rank Sum Test 574

13–5 The Wilcoxon Signed-Rank Test 578

13–6 The Kruskal-Wallis Test 583

13–7 The Spearman Rank Correlation Coefficient and the Runs Test 587

Rank Correlation Coefficient 588

The Runs Test 590

13–8 Summary 597

Hypothesis-Testing Summary 3 602

CHAPTER **14**

Sampling and Simulation 605

14–1 Introduction 606

14–2 Common Sampling Techniques 606

Simple Random Sampling 607

Systematic Sampling 611

Stratified Sampling 612

Cluster Sampling 614

Other Types of Sampling Techniques 615

14–3 Surveys and Questionnaire Design 618

14–4 Simulation Techniques 621

The Monte Carlo Method 621

14–5 Summary 628

APPENDIX **A**   Algebra Review 633

APPENDIX **B–1**   Writing the Research Report 639

APPENDIX **B–2**   Bayes' Theorem 641

APPENDIX **B–3**   Alternate Approach to the Standard Normal Distribution 645

APPENDIX **C**   Tables 649

APPENDIX **D**   Data Bank 679

APPENDIX **E**   Technology Step-by-Step 687

APPENDIX **F**   Glossary 709

APPENDIX **G**   Bibliography 717

APPENDIX **H**   Photo Credits 719

APPENDIX **I**   Credits for Unusual Stats, Interesting Facts, Historical Notes, and Exercises (End-of-Sections and End-of-Chapters) 721

APPENDIX **J**   Selected Answers 727

Index 771

Preface

Approach

Elementary Statistics: A Step by Step Approach was written to help students in the beginning statistics course whose mathematical background is limited to basic algebra. The book follows a nontheoretical approach without formal proofs, explaining concepts intuitively and supporting them with abundant examples. The applications span a broad range of topics certain to appeal to the interests of students of diverse backgrounds and include problems in business, sports, health, architecture, education, entertainment, political science, psychology, history, criminal justice, the environment, transportation, physical sciences, demographics, eating habits, and travel and leisure.

About This Book

The Canadian Edition of *Elementary Statistics: A Step by Step Approach* goes beyond the obvious grammar changes, metrication, new examples, and exercise questions expected in a Canadian adaptation. Although the learning system remains untouched, many of the procedures have been streamlined and standardized.

Key features in this text include the following:

- **Over 1800** exercises with additional Canadian content are located at the end of major sections within each chapter.
- **Hypothesis-Testing Summaries** are found at the end of Chapter 9 (z, t, x^2, and F tests for testing means, proportions, and variances), Chapter 12 (correlation, chi-square, and ANOVA), and Chapter 13 (nonparametric tests) to show students the different types of hypotheses and the types of tests to use.
- A **Data Bank** listing various attributes (educational level, cholesterol level, gender, etc.) for 100 people and 13 additional data sets using real data and SI units are included and referenced in various exercises and projects throughout the book, including the projects presented in Data Projects sections.
- End-of-chapter **Summaries**, **Important Terms**, and **Important Formulas** give students a concise summary of the chapter topics and provide a good source for quiz or test preparation.
- **Review Exercises** are found at the end of each chapter.
- Special sections called **Data Analysis** require students to work with a data set to perform various statistical tests or procedures and then summarize the results. The data are included in the Data Bank in Appendix D and can be downloaded from the book's website at www.mcgrawhill.ca/olc/bluman.
- **Chapter Quizzes**, found at the end of each chapter, include multiple-choice, true/false, and completion questions along with exercises to test students' knowledge and comprehension of chapter content.
- The **Appendices** provide students with an essential algebra review, an outline for report writing, Bayes' theorem, extensive reference tables, a technology review, a

glossary, and answers to all quiz questions, all odd-numbered exercises, selected even-numbered exercises, and an alternate method for using the standard normal distribution with examples.

Changes to the Canadian Edition

The Canadian Edition of *Elementary Statistics: A Step by Step Approach* features all of the updates and improvements of the U.S. Edition plus the inclusion of feedback provided by expert statistics specialists throughout Canada.

- **Over 300** new Canadian exercises and examples have been inserted, **most using real data**, and many questions now incorporate thought-provoking questions requiring students to interpret their results.
- The text is updated with **Canadian content throughout** with current data and statistics including *Unusual Stats* and *Interesting Facts*; *Speaking of Statistics*; *Critical Thinking Challenges*; *Statistics Today* openers; worked examples; *Data Analysis Exercises*; and Data Sets with SI units.

Based on Canadian reviewer comments, the following improvements were made:

Technology-Step-by-Step: Procedures for Minitab, Excel and the TI-83 Plus / TI-84 Plus were simplified and moved to the Online Learning Centre from the end of each chapter. A brief overview of these technologies is available in **Appendix E**. SPSS procedures were added to the technology section based on reviewer feedback.

Canadian Perspective: This edition includes examples drawn from Canadian business, industry, health-care and other diverse fields. All changes to Canadian content utilize new data sets with source reference information.

Acknowledgments

It is important to acknowledge the many people whose contributions have gone into the Canadian Edition of *Elementary Statistics.* Very special thanks are due to Developmental Editors Emma Gain and Sarah Fulton, Supervising Editor Kelly Dickson, Sponsoring Editor Leanna MacLean, and Copy Editor Erin Moore.

Special thanks for their advice and recommendations for revisions found in the Canadian Edition go to:

Nancy Clarke, *Acadia University*

Rick Elliott, *Wilfrid Laurier University*

Nancy Morrison, *University of Calgary*

John O'Connor, *Grant MacEwan College*

Wendy Kelly, *Trent University*

Dot Miners, *Brock University*

Geoff Salloum, *Camosun College*

Peter LaFleur, *Trent University*

Gord Sarty, *University of Saskatchewan*

Michael Kozdron, *University of Regina*

John Holt, *University of Guelph*

Manny Estabrooks, *Red Deer College*

Gord Robertson, *University of Ottawa*

Zbigniew J. Pasek, *University of Windsor*

Guided Tour: Features and Supplements

Each chapter begins with an **outline** and a list of **learning objectives**. The objectives are repeated at the beginning of each section to help students focus on the concepts presented within that section.

CHAPTER 9

Testing the Difference Between Two Means, Two Variances, and Two Proportions

Objectives

After completing this chapter, you should be able to

1. Test the difference between two large sample means, using the z test.
2. Test the difference between two variances or standard deviations.
3. Test the difference between two means for small independent samples.
4. Test the difference between two means for small dependent samples.
5. Test the difference between two proportions.

Outline

9–1 Introduction

9–2 Testing the Difference Between Two Means: Large Samples

9–3 Testing the Difference Between Two Variances

9–4 Testing the Difference Between Two Means: Small Independent Samples

9–5 Testing the Difference Between Two Means: Small Dependent Samples

9–6 Testing the Difference Between Proportions

9–7 Summary

---

78   Chapter 3 Data Description

Statistics Today

Do You Live as Well as Other Canadians?

The United Nations ranked Canada fifth in the world on its Human Development Index for 2005, ahead of the United States and Japan but trailing Norway and Australia. Unfortunately this reputation for outstanding living conditions merely represents the well-being of the average Canadian. Regional disparities abound. One measure of quality of life is economic well-being. In 2005, the average Canadian income per capita was $42,464. How did your province compare to this average? See Statistics Today—Revisited, page 137, at the end of the chapter.

This chapter will show you how to obtain and interpret descriptive statistics such as measures of average, measures of variation, and measures of position.

3–1 Introduction

Chapter 2 showed how one can gain useful information from raw data by organizing them into a frequency distribution and then presenting the data by using various graphs. This chapter shows the statistical methods that can be used to summarize data. The most familiar of these methods is the finding of averages.

For example, an average NHL hockey player earned $1.46 million dollars in the 2005–06 season[1] or Canadian university student graduates, in 2002, had an average debt of $18,900.[2] By 2010, the life expectancy of Canadian males will average 79.0 years whereas it is expected that females, on average, will live to 83.1 years.[3]

Canadian nationalist writer and humourist Pierre Berton, once described a typical Canadian as "*someone who knows how to make love in a canoe without tipping it.*" Are you an average Canadian? Statistics Canada and market researchers collect descriptive statistics from all facets of Canadian life. Here are some findings of a typical Canadian.

Canadian brides marry at an average age of 31.7 years and their grooms at 34.3 years.[4]
Typical Canadian households spend $121.20 on food each week.
Average Canadians eat 27.1 kg of red meat, 13.5 kg of poultry, and 13 dozen eggs per year.[4]
Canadians consume 63.2 litres of milk, 160.1 litres of coffee or tea, and 65.8 litres of beer per capita each year.[5]
Doctor visits by Canadians average 4.5 per year.
The average Canadian browses the Internet for 75 minutes every day.

Interesting Fact
A person has on average 1460 dreams in one year.

[1] http://prohockey.about.com/od/collectivebargaining/aq/IntL_salaries.htm;
http://www.thehockeynews.com/en/newscenter/news.asp?idNews=20062.
[2] http://www.strathconardnahshire.ca/images/Press/releases/doc292002.pdf.
[3] Office of the Superintendent of Financial Institutions Canada—Population Projections 2005;
http://www.osfi-bsif.gc.ca/app/DocRepository/1/eng/oca/studies/popccdn_e.pdf.
[4] Adapted from Statistics Canada publication *Food Statistics*, Catalogue 21-020, 2004, vol. 4, no. 1, released May 26, 2005, pages 6 and 7 and www.statcan.ca/bsolc/english/bsolc?catno=21-020-X.
[5] Adapted from Statistics Canada publication *The Daily*, Catalogue 11-001, released May 26, 2005, www.statcan.ca/Daily/English/050526/d050526e.htm.

The outline and learning objectives are followed by a feature titled **Statistics Today,** in which a **real-life problem** shows students the relevance of the material in the chapter. This problem is subsequently solved near the end of the chapter by using the statistical techniques presented in the chapter.

Over 300 **examples** with detailed solutions serve as models to help students solve problems on their own. Examples are solved by using a step-by-step explanation, and illustrations provide a clear display of results for students.

Categorical Frequency Distributions

The **categorical frequency distribution** is used for data that can be placed in specific categories, such as nominal- or ordinal-level data. For example, data such as political affiliation, religious affiliation, or major field of study would use categorical frequency distributions.

Example 2–1

Twenty-five armed forces recruits were given a blood test to determine their blood type. The data set is

A	B	B	AB	O
B	O	B	AB	O
B	O	O	A	B
A	B	O	O	AB
AB	A	O	B	A

Construct a frequency distribution for the data.

Solution

Since the data are categorical, discrete classes can be used. There are four blood types: A, B, O, and AB. These types will be used as the classes for the distribution.

The procedure for constructing a frequency distribution for categorical data is given next.

Step 1 Make a table as shown.

A Class	B Tally	C Frequency	D Percent
A			
B			
O			
AB			

Step 2 Tally the data and place the results in column B.

Step 3 Count the tallies and place the results in column C.

Step 4 Find the percentage of values in each class by using the formula

$$\% = \frac{f}{n} \cdot 100\%$$

where f = frequency of the class and n = total number of values in the data set. For example, in the class of type A blood, the percentage is

$$\% = \frac{5}{25} \cdot 100\% = 20\%$$

Percentages are not normally part of a frequency distribution, but they can be added since they are used in certain types of graphs such as pie graphs. Also, the decimal equivalent of a percent is called a *relative frequency*.

Step 5 Find the totals for columns C (frequency) and D (percent). The completed table is shown.

---

14. An environmentalist wants to determine the relationships between the number (in thousands) of forest fires over the year and the number (in hundreds of thousands) of hectares burned. The data for 8 recent years are shown. Describe the relationship.

Number of fires x	72	69	58	47	84	62	57	45
Number of hectares burned y	25	17	8	11	21	6	12	6

Source: National Emergency Fire Causes.

(The information in this exercise will be used for Exercises 14 and 36 in Section 10–4 and Exercises 14 and 18 in Section 10–5.)

15. The director of an alumni association for a small college wants to determine whether there is any type of relationship between the amount of an alumnus's contribution (in dollars) and the years the alumnus has been out of school. The data follow. (The information in this exercise will be used for Exercises 15, 36, and 37 in Section 10–4 and Exercises 15 and 19 in Section 10–5.)

Years x	1	5	3	10	7	6
Contribution y	500	100	300	50	75	80

16. A store manager wishes to find out whether there is a relationship between the age of her employees and the number of sick days they take each year. The data for the sample are shown. (The information in this exercise will be used for Exercises 16 and 37 in Section 10–4 and Exercises 16 and 20 in Section 10–5.)

Age x	18	26	39	48	53	58
Days y	16	12	9	5	6	2

17. A criminology student wants to determine if there is a relationship between the robbery and homicide crime rates in Canada. Data is collected from 7 randomly selected cities. Crime rates are calculated per 100,000 population. Is there a relationship between the two types of crimes in Canada's cities?

Robbery crimes x	229	148	141	150	91	88	84
Homicide crimes y	4.9	2.6	3.4	1.7	1.9	1.3	1.1

Source: Statistics Canada.

(The information in this exercise will be used for Exercise 17 of Section 10–4.)

18. A football fan wishes to see how the number of pass attempts (not completions) relates to the number of yards gained for quarterbacks in past National Football League (NFL) season playoff games. The data are shown for five quarterbacks. Describe the relationships.

Pass attempts x	116	90	82	108	92
Yards gained y	1001	823	851	873	839

(The information in this exercise will be used for Exercises 18 and 38 in Section 10–4.)

19. A meteorologist wants to see if there is a relationship between the number of tornadoes that occur each year and the number of deaths attributed to the tornadoes. The data are shown for 10 recent years. Is there a relationship?

No. of tornadoes x	1133	1132	1297	1173	1082
No. of deaths y	53	39	39	33	69
No. of tornadoes x	1234	1148	1424	1342	898
No. of deaths y	30	67	130	94	40

(The information in this exercise will be used for Exercise 19 of Section 10–4.)

20. An emergency medical service wishes to see whether a relationship exists between the outside temperature (°C) and the number of emergency calls it receives for an 8-hour period. The data are shown. (The information in this exercise will be used for Exercises 20 and 38 in Section 10–4.)

Temperature (°C) x	20	23	28	31	34	37	38
Number of calls y	7	4	8	10	11	9	13

21. A random sample of cities in Eastern Canada is selected to determine if there is a relationship between the number of Black and number of Asian visible minorities. (The information in this exercise will be used for Exercises 21 and 36 in Section 10–4.)

Black x	350	13,085	1,440	325	3,640
Asian y	1,735	9,665	1,110	425	5,065

Source: Statistics Canada.

22. The results of a survey of the average monthly rents (in dollars) for one-bedroom apartments and two-bedroom apartments in randomly selected metropolitan areas are shown. Determine if there is a relationship between the rents. (The information in this exercise will be used for Exercise 22 in Section 10–4.)

One-bedroom x	782	486	451	529	618	520	845
Two-bedroom y	1223	902	739	954	1055	875	1455

Source: N.Y. Times Almanac.

23. The average daily temperature (°C) and the corresponding average monthly precipitation (cm) for the month of July are shown for 7 randomly selected Canadian cities. Determine if there is a relationship between the two variables. (The information in this exercise will be used for Exercise 23 in 10–4.)

Numerous examples and exercises use **real data.** The icon shown here indicates that the data set for the exercise is available in a variety of file formats on the text's Online Learning Centre.

Numerous **Procedure Tables** summarize processes for students' quick reference. All use the step-by-step method.

e. Find the standard deviation of the differences.

$$s_D = \sqrt{\frac{\sum D^2 - \frac{(\sum D)^2}{n}}{n-1}} = \sqrt{\frac{4890 - \frac{(100)^2}{6}}{5}} \approx 25.4$$

f. Find the test statistic.

$$t = \frac{\overline{D} - \mu_D}{s_D/\sqrt{n}} = \frac{16.7 - 0}{25.4/\sqrt{6}} \approx 1.610$$

Step 4 Make the decision. The decision is to not reject the null hypothesis, since the test statistic 1.610 is in the noncritical region, as shown in Figure 9–12.

Figure 9–12
Critical Values and Test Statistic for Example 9–13

−2.015   0   1.610 2.015

Step 5 Summarize the results. There is not enough evidence to support the claim that the mineral changes a person's cholesterol level.

The steps for this t test are summarized in the Procedure Table.

Procedure Table

Testing the Difference Between Means for Dependent Samples

Step 1 State the hypotheses and identify the claim.
Step 2 Find the critical value(s).
Step 3 Compute the test statistic.

  a. Make a table, as shown.

X_1	X_2	A $D = X_1 - X_2$	B $D^2 = (X_1 - X_2)^2$
⋮	⋮		
		$\sum D =$ ___	$\sum D^2 =$ ___

  b. Find the differences and place the results in column A.
  $$D = X_1 - X_2$$
  c. Find the mean of the differences.
  $$\overline{D} = \frac{\sum D}{n}$$
  d. Square the differences and place the results in column B. Complete the table.
  $$D^2 = (X_1 - X_2)^2$$

Unusual Stat
2% of Canadian women younger than 45 years of age are grandparents.

---

62 **Chapter 2** Frequency Distributions and Graphs

Speaking of
Statistics

How much money is held at the Bank of Canada as unclaimed balances?

At the end of December 2004, approximately 804,000 unclaimed balances, worth some $245 million, were on the Bank's books. Over 88% of these were under $500, representing 22% of the total value outstanding. The oldest balance dates back to 1900.

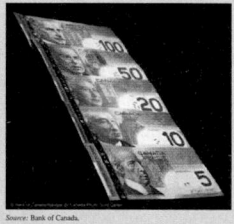
Source: Bank of Canada.

Solution

Step 1 Arrange the data in order:

02, 13, 14, 20, 23, 25, 31, 32, 32, 32, 32, 33, 36, 43, 44, 44, 45, 51, 52, 57

Note: Arranging the data in order is not essential and can be cumbersome when the data set is large; however, it is helpful in constructing a stem and leaf plot. The leaves in the final stem and leaf plot should be arranged in order.

Step 2 Separate the data according to the first digit, as shown.

02   13, 14   20, 23, 25   31, 32, 32, 32, 32, 33, 36
43, 44, 44, 45   51, 52, 57

Step 3 A display can be made by using the leading digit as the *stem* and the trailing digit as the *leaf*. For example, for the value 32, the leading digit, 3, is the stem and the trailing digit, 2, is the leaf. For the value 14, the 1 is the stem and the 4 is the leaf. Now a plot can be constructed as shown in Figure 2–18.

Leading digit (stem)	Trailing digit (leaf)
0	2
1	3 4
2	0 3 5
3	1 2 2 2 2 3 6
4	3 4 4 5
5	1 2 7

Figure 2–18
Stem and Leaf Plot for Example 2–11

0	2
1	3 4
2	0 3 5
3	1 2 2 2 2 3 6
4	3 4 4 5
5	1 2 7

Figure 2–18 shows that the distribution peaks in the centre and that there are no gaps in the data. For 7 of the 20 days, the number of patients receiving cardiograms was between 31 and 36. The plot also shows that the testing centre treated from a minimum of 2 patients to a maximum of 57 patients in any one day.

The **Speaking of Statistics** sections invite students to think about poll results and other statistics-related news stories in another connection between statistics and the real world.

Historical Notes, Unusual Stats, and **Interesting Facts,** located in the margins, make statistics come alive for the reader.

Rules and definitions are set off for easy referencing by the student.

Critical Thinking sections at the end of each chapter challenge students to apply what they have learned to new situations. The problems presented are designed to deepen conceptual understanding and/or to extend topical coverage.

---

4 Chapter 1 The Nature of Probability and Statistics

Objective ②

Differentiate between the two branches of statistics.

Historical Note

The origin of descriptive statistics can be traced to data collection methods used in censuses taken by the Babylonians and Egyptians between 4500 and 3000 B.C. In addition, the Roman Emperor Augustus (27 B.C.–A.D. 17) conducted surveys on births and deaths of the citizens of the empire, as well as the number of livestock each owned and the crops each citizen harvested yearly.

Unusual Stat

...even percent ...lottery ...d their ...cket in their

Suppose that an insurance company studies its records over the past several years and determines that, on average, 3 out of every 100 automobiles the company insured were involved in accidents during a one-year period. Although there is no way to predict the specific automobiles that will be involved in an accident (random occurrence), the company can adjust its rates accordingly, since the company knows the general pattern over the long run. (That is, on average, 3% of the insured automobiles will be involved in an accident each year.)

A collection of data values forms a **data set.** Each value in the data set is called a **data value** or a **datum.**

Data can be used in different ways. The body of knowledge called statistics is sometimes divided into two main areas, depending on how data are used. The two areas are

1. Descriptive statistics
2. Inferential statistics

Consider the national census conducted every five years in Canada by the federal government agency, Statistics Canada. Results of this census provide governments, businesses, researchers, and other interested parties with important data such as average age, income, and other characteristics of Canada's population. To obtain this information, Statistics Canada must have some means to collect relevant data. Once data are collected, the agency must organize and summarize them. Finally, the agency needs a method of presenting the data in some meaningful form, such as charts, graphs, or tables.

Descriptive statistics consists of the collection, organization, summarization, and presentation of data.

The second area of statistics is called *inferential statistics.* Here, the statistician tries to make inferences from *samples* to *populations.* Inferential statistics uses **probability,** i.e., the chance of an event occurring. Many people are familiar with the concepts of probability through various forms of gambling. People who play cards, dice, bingo, and lotteries win or lose according to the laws of probability. Probability theory is also used in the insurance industry and other areas.

It is important to distinguish between a sample and a population.

A **population** consists of all subjects (human or otherwise) that are being studied.

Most of the time, due to the expense, time, size of population, medical concerns, etc., it is not possible to use the entire population for a statistical study; therefore, researchers use samples.

A **sample** is a group of subjects selected from a population.

If the subjects of a sample are properly selected, most of the time they should possess the same or similar characteristics as the subjects in the population. The techniques used to properly select a sample will be explained in Section 1–4.

An area of inferential statistics called **hypothesis testing** is a decision-making process for evaluating claims about a population, based on information obtained from samples. For example, a researcher may wish to know if a new drug will reduce the number of heart attacks in men over 70 years of age. For this study, two groups of men over 70 would be selected. One group would be given the drug, and the other

---

84 Chapter 3 Data Description

The Median

An article recently reported that the median income for college and university professors was $81,104. This measure of central tendency means that one-half of all the professors surveyed earned more than $81,104, and one-half earned less than $81,104.[6]

The *median* is the halfway point in a data set. Before one can find this point, the data must be arranged in order. When the data set is ordered, it is called a **data array.** The median either will be a specific value in the data set or will fall between two values, as shown in Examples 3–4 and 3–5.

> The **median** is the midpoint of the data array. The symbol for the median is MD.

Steps in computing the median of a data array

Step 1   Arrange the data in order.

Step 2   Select the middle point.

Example 3–4   Whistler, British Columbia, will host the downhill ski events in the 2010 Winter Olympic Games. This data represents pre-Olympic hotel rates (per night) in select hotels. Find the median.

$134, $149, $179, $330, $170, $208, $170, $99, $159

Source: www.expedia.com.

Solution

Step 1   Arrange the data in order.

99, 134, 149, 159, 170, 170, 179, 208, 330

Step 2   Select the middle value.

99, 134, 149, 159, 170, 170, 179, 208, 330
↑
Median

Hence, the median hotel price is $170.

Example 3–4 had an odd number of values in the data set; hence, the median was an actual data value. When there are an even number of values in the data set, the median will fall between two given values, as illustrated in Example 3–5.

Example 3–5   The number of residential home sales per month in Calgary over a 12-month period is listed below. Find the median.

1877, 2408, 3060, 3497, 3389, 3550, 3388, 2586, 2516, 2180, 2122, 2394

Source: Calgary Real Estate Board.

_____
[6]University of Toronto Faculty Association Comparative Study.

Data Projects **393**

28. Find the *P*-value for the *z* test in Exercise 16.

29. A copyeditor thinks the standard deviation for the number of pages in a romance novel is greater than 6. A sample of 25 novels has a standard deviation of 9 pages. At $\alpha = 0.05$, is it higher, as the editor hypothesized?

30. It has been hypothesized that the standard deviation of the germination time of radish seeds is 8 days. The standard deviation of a sample of 60 radish plants' germination times was 6 days. At $\alpha = 0.01$, test the claim.

31. The standard deviation of the pollution by-products released in the burning of 1 gallon of gas is 2.3 ounces.

A sample of 20 automobiles tested produced a standard deviation of 1.9 ounces. Is the standard deviation really less than previously thought? Use $\alpha = 0.05$.

32. A manufacturer claims that the standard deviation of the strength of wrapping cord is 4.1 kilograms (kg). A sample of 10 wrapping cords produced a standard deviation of 5.0 kg. At $\alpha = 0.05$, test the claim. Use the *P*-value method.

33. Find the 90% confidence interval of the mean in Exercise 15. Is μ contained in the interval?

34. Find the 95% confidence interval for the mean in Exercise 16. Is μ contained in the interval?

Critical Thinking Challenges

The power of a test $(1 - \beta)$ can be calculated when a specific value of the mean is hypothesized in the alternative hypothesis; for example, let H_0: $\mu = 50$ and let H_1: $\mu = 52$. To find the power of a test, it is necessary to find the value of β. This can be done by the following steps:

Step 1   For a specific value of α find the corresponding value of $\overline{X}$, $z = \dfrac{\overline{X} - \mu}{\sigma/\sqrt{n}}$, where μ is the hypothesized value given in H_0. Use a right-tailed test.

Step 2   Using the value of $\overline{X}$ found in step 1 and the value of μ in the alternative hypothesis, find the area corresponding to z in the formula $z = \dfrac{\overline{X} - \mu}{\sigma/\sqrt{n}}$.

Figure 8–40

Relationship Among α, β, and the Power of a Test

Step 3   Subtract this area from 0.5000. This is the value of β.

Step 4   Subtract the value of β from 1. This will give you the power of a test. See Figure 8–40.

1. Find the power of a test, using the hypotheses given previously and $\alpha = 0.05$, $\sigma = 3$, and $n = 30$.

2. Select several other values for μ in H_1 and compute the power of the test. Generalize the results.

Data Projects

Use Minitab, SPSS, the TI-83 Plus, the TI-84 Plus, or a computer program of your choice to complete these exercises.

1. Choose a variable such as the number of kilometres students live from the college or the number of daily admissions to an ice skating rink for a 1-month period. Before you collect the data, decide what a likely average might be. Then complete the following.

a. Write a brief statement of the purpose of the study.
b. Define the population.

Applying the Concepts exercises are found at the end of each section, and their purpose is to reinforce the concepts explained in the section. They give the student an opportunity to think about the concepts and apply them to hypothetical examples similar to real-life ones found in newspapers, magazines, and professional journals. Most contain open-ended questions—questions that require interpretation and may have more than one correct answer. These exercises can also be used as classroom discussion topics for instructors who like to use this type of teaching technique.

Data Projects further challenge students' understanding and application of the material presented in the chapter. Many of these require the student to gather, analyze, and report on real data. These projects, which appear at the end of each chapter, may include a World Wide Web icon, indicating that websites are listed as possible sources of data.

A brief overview of each of the principle **statistics technologies** is included in Appendix E for easy reference. More detailed technology manuals are available for download on the Online Learning Centre.

Student Supplements

*i*Interact *i*Learn *i*Succeed

Instructor's Supplements

*i*Study

Available 24/7: providing instant feedback when you want, how you want, and where you want. This online *i*Study space was developed to help you master concepts and achieve better grades with all the learning tools you've come to expect, including robust tutorial practice and quizzing, step-by-step solved problems, and multimedia modules for conceptual development. This study tool allows for extra practice and develops problem solving skills. *i*Study offers the best, most convenient way to interact, learn, and succeed.

*i*Study can be purchased through the Online Learning Centre or by purchasing a PIN code card through the campus bookstore. Instructors: Please contact your *i*Learning Sales Specialist for more information on how to make *i*Study part of your students' success.

Online Learning Centre

Available at www.mcgrawhill.ca/olc/bluman, the Online Learning Centre provides a range of resources to help you succeed in your studies, including a searchable glossary, self-study quizzes, and downloadable technology manuals.

Instructor's Online Learning Centre

The Instructor's Online Learning Centre (OLC) at www.mcgrawhill.ca/olc/bluman offers downloadable instructor's supplements in a password protected environment.

Computerized Test Bank

The computerized test bank has been extensively revised and technically checked for accuracy. Available on the Instructor's CD-ROM, it contains a variety of questions including true/false, multiple choice, short answer, and short problems requiring analysis and written answers.

Instructor Solutions Manual

Adapted to reflect the Canadian Edition, this manual includes worked-out solutions to all the exercises in the text and answers to all quiz questions.

CHAPTER 1

The Nature of Probability and Statistics

Objectives

After completing this chapter, you should be able to

1. Demonstrate knowledge of statistical terms.

2. Differentiate between the two branches of statistics.

3. Identify types of data.

4. Identify the measurement level for each variable.

5. Identify the four basic sampling techniques.

6. Explain the difference between an observational and an experimental study.

7. Explain how statistics can be used and misused.

8. Explain the importance of computers and calculators in statistics.

Outline

1–1   Introduction

1–2   Descriptive and Inferential Statistics

1–3   Variables and Types of Data

1–4   Data Collection and Sampling Techniques

1–5   Observational and Experimental Studies

1–6   Uses and Misuses of Statistics

1–7   Computers and Calculators

1–8   Summary

Statistics Today

Are We Improving Our Diet?

Canada's Guide To Healthy Eating and Physical Activity suggests that the benefits of a healthy diet and an active lifestyle improves the quality of life and may prevent the onset of illnesses such as stroke, heart disease, and some types of cancer. Nutritionists recommend consumption of five or more servings of fruits and vegetables per day as part of a healthy diet. North American researchers from the Division of Nutrition, the National Center for Chronic Disease Control and Prevention, the National Cancer Institute, and the National Institutes of Health decided to use statistical procedures to see how much progress is being made toward this goal.

The procedures they used and the results of the study will be explained in this chapter. See Statistics Today— Revisited, page 24, at the end of this chapter.

Source: Healthy Living: Canada's Guide to Healthy Eating and Physical Activity. Health Canada, 2004. Adapted and reproduced with the permission of the Minister of Public Works and Government Services Canada, 2007.

1–1 Introduction

Most people become familiar with probability and statistics through radio, television, newspapers, and magazines. For example, the following statements were found in electronic and print media.

Unusual Stat

Most Canadian women animal owners (82%) embrace or stroke their pets at least four times a day.

- Eating 10 grams (g) of fibre a day reduces the risk of heart attack by 14%. Source: Archives of Internal Medicine, *Reader's Digest,* May 2004.
- Average Canadian student debt, among those who borrow and graduate from four-year programs, is $22,700. Source: www.cbc.ca (*CBC Marketplace*), February 2005.
- On average, the Geological Survey of Canada (GSC) records and locates over 1500 earthquakes in Canada each year. Source: Reproduced with the permission of the Minister of Public Works and Government Services Canada, 2007 and Courtesy of Natural Resources Canada, Geological Survey of Canada.
- Of the 20 hottest years on record, 19 occurred in the 1980s or later. Source: *Time* magazine, April 3, 2006.
- Five percent of Canadians have at least one firearm registration certificate. Source: Government of Canada—Canada Firearms Centre.[1]
- Canadian median age is 38.54 years compared to Japan at 42.64 years and Uganda at 14.97 years. Source: *CIA—World Factbook 2005.*
- Seventy-nine percent of Canadians support the constitutional monarchy as Canada's form of government. Source: *The Globe and Mail,* February 2002.

---

[1]Quick Facts about the Canadian Firearms Program as of March 2007, www.cfc-cafc.gc.ca/media/program_statistics/default_e.asp, Canadian Firearms Centre, 2007. Reproduced with the permission of the Minister of Public Works and Government Services Canada, 2007.

Statistics is used in almost all fields of human endeavour. In sports, for example, a statistician may keep records of the number of yards a running back gains during a football game, or the number of hits a baseball player gets in a season. In other areas, such as public health, an administrator might be concerned with the number of residents who contract a new strain of flu virus during a certain year. In education, a researcher might want to know if new methods of teaching are better than old ones. These are only a few examples of how statistics can be used in various occupations.

Furthermore, statistics is used to analyze the results of surveys and as a tool in scientific research to make decisions based on controlled experiments. Other uses of statistics include industrial operations research, quality engineering, manufacturing quality control, scientific estimation, and prediction.

> **Statistics** is the science of conducting studies to collect, organize, summarize, analyze, and draw conclusions from data.

Students study statistics for several reasons:

1. Students, like professional people, must be able to read and understand the various statistical studies performed in their fields. To have this understanding, they must be knowledgeable about the vocabulary, symbols, concepts, and statistical procedures used in these studies.

2. Students and professional people may be called on to conduct research in their fields, since statistical procedures are basic to research. To accomplish this, they must be able to design experiments, collect, organize, summarize, and analyze data, and possibly make reliable predictions or forecasts for future use. They must also be able to communicate the results of the study in their own words.

3. Students and professional people can also use the knowledge gained from studying statistics to become better consumers and citizens. For example, they can make intelligent decisions about what products to purchase based on consumer studies, about government spending based on utilization studies, and so on.

These reasons can be considered the goals for students and professionals who study statistics.

It is the purpose of this chapter to introduce the student to the basic concepts of *probability* and *statistics* by answering questions such as the following:

What are the branches of statistics?

What are data?

How are samples selected?

1–2 Descriptive and Inferential Statistics

Objective 1

Demonstrate knowledge of statistical terms.

To gain knowledge about seemingly haphazard events, statisticians collect information for *variables,* which describe the event.

> An **element** is an object contained in a set of data. A **variable** is a characteristic or attribute of that element capable of assuming any value within the data set.

Data are the values (measurements or observations) that the variables assume. Variables whose values are determined by chance are called **random variables.**

Objective 2

Differentiate between the two branches of statistics.

Suppose that an insurance company studies its records over the past several years and determines that, on average, 3 out of every 100 automobiles the company insured were involved in accidents during a one-year period. Although there is no way to predict the specific automobiles that will be involved in an accident (random occurrence), the company can adjust its rates accordingly, since the company knows the general pattern over the long run. (That is, on average, 3% of the insured automobiles will be involved in an accident each year.)

A collection of data values forms a **data set.** Each value in the data set is called a **data value** or a **datum.**

Data can be used in different ways. The body of knowledge called statistics is sometimes divided into two main areas, depending on how data are used. The two areas are

1. Descriptive statistics
2. Inferential statistics

Consider the national census conducted every five years in Canada by the federal government agency, Statistics Canada. Results of this census provide governments, businesses, researchers, and other interested parties with important data such as average age, income, and other characteristics of Canada's population. To obtain this information, Statistics Canada must have some means to collect relevant data. Once data are collected, the agency must organize and summarize them. Finally, the agency needs a method of presenting the data in some meaningful form, such as charts, graphs, or tables.

> **Descriptive statistics** consists of the collection, organization, summarization, and presentation of data.

The second area of statistics is called *inferential statistics.* Here, the statistician tries to make inferences from *samples* to *populations.* Inferential statistics uses **probability,** i.e., the chance of an event occurring. Many people are familiar with the concepts of probability through various forms of gambling. People who play cards, dice, bingo, and lotteries win or lose according to the laws of probability. Probability theory is also used in the insurance industry and other areas.

It is important to distinguish between a sample and a population.

> A **population** consists of all subjects (human or otherwise) that are being studied.

Most of the time, due to the expense, time, size of population, medical concerns, etc., it is not possible to use the entire population for a statistical study; therefore, researchers use samples.

> A **sample** is a group of subjects selected from a population.

If the subjects of a sample are properly selected, most of the time they should possess the same or similar characteristics as the subjects in the population. The techniques used to properly select a sample will be explained in Section 1–4.

An area of inferential statistics called **hypothesis testing** is a decision-making process for evaluating claims about a population, based on information obtained from samples. For example, a researcher may wish to know if a new drug will reduce the number of heart attacks in men over 70 years of age. For this study, two groups of men over 70 would be selected. One group would be given the drug, and the other

Speaking of
Statistics

This Snapshot shows the percentages of adults who say these activities are extremely important. Based on the information shown in the Snapshot, do you think people take better care of their automobiles than they do of themselves?

SNAPSHOTS®

A look at statistics that shape our lives

Medical visits take a back seat

Percentage of adults who say these activities are extremely important:

3000-mile oil change	Annual dentist visit	Annual doctor visits for kids	Annual eye exam	Annual checkup for pet
65%	**59%**	**46%**	**44%**	**38%**

Source: Roper/ASW for TLC Laser Eye Centers

Source: Copyright 2002, USA TODAY. Reprinted with permission.

Historical Note

Inferential statistics originated in the 1600s, when John Graunt published his book on population growth, *Natural and Political Observations Made upon the Bills of Mortality.* About the same time, another mathematician/astronomer, Edmund Halley, published the first complete mortality tables. (Insurance companies use mortality tables to determine life insurance rates.)

would be given a placebo (a substance with no medical benefits or harm). Later, the number of heart attacks occurring in each group of men would be counted, a statistical hypothesis test would be run, and a decision would be made about the effectiveness of the drug.

Statisticians also use statistics to determine *relationships* among variables. For example, relationships were the focus of one of the most noted studies in the past few decades, "Smoking and Health," published by the Surgeon General of the United States in 1964. He stated that after reviewing and evaluating the data, his group found a definite relationship between smoking and lung cancer. He did not say that cigarette smoking actually causes lung cancer, but that there is a relationship between smoking and lung cancer. This conclusion was based on a study done in 1958 by Hammond and Horn. In this study, 187,783 men were observed over a period of 45 months. The death rate from lung cancer in this group of volunteers was ten times as great for smokers as for nonsmokers.

Finally, by studying past and present data and conditions, statisticians try to make predictions based on this information. For example, a car dealer may look at past sales records for a specific month to decide what types of automobiles and how many of each type to order for that month next year.

Inferential statistics consists of generalizing from samples to populations, performing estimations and hypothesis tests, determining relationships among variables, and making predictions.

Applying the Concepts 1–2

Attendance and Grades

Read the following on attendance and grades, and answer the questions.

A study conducted at Red Deer Community College revealed that students who attended class 95 to 100% of the time usually received an A in the class. Students who attended class 80 to 90% of the time usually received a B or C in the class. Students who attended class less than 80% of the time usually received a D or an F or eventually withdrew from the class.

Based on this information, attendance and grades are related. The more you attend class, the more likely you will receive a higher grade. If you improve your attendance, your grades will probably improve. Many factors affect your grade in a course. One factor that you have considerable control over is attendance. You can increase your opportunities for learning by attending class more often.

1. What are the variables under study?
2. What are the data in the study?
3. Are descriptive, inferential, or both types of statistics used?
4. What is the population under study?
5. Was a sample collected? If so, from where?
6. From the information given, comment on the relationship between the variables.

See page 27 for the answers.

Unusual Stat

Only one-third of crimes committed are reported to the police.

1–3   Variables and Types of Data

Objective ③

Identify types of data.

As stated in Section 1–2, statisticians gain information about a particular situation by collecting data for random variables. This section will explore in greater detail the nature of variables and types of data.

Variables can be classified as qualitative or quantitative. **Qualitative variables** are variables that can be placed into distinct categories, according to some characteristic or attribute. For example, if subjects are classified according to gender (male or female), then the variable *gender* is qualitative. Other examples of qualitative variables are religious preference and geographic locations.

Quantitative variables are numerical and can be ordered, ranked, or measured. For example, the variable *age* is numerical, and people can be ranked in order according to the value of their ages. Other examples of quantitative variables are heights, weights, and body temperatures.

Quantitative variables can be further classified into two groups: discrete and continuous. *Discrete variables* can be assigned values such as 0, 1, 2, 3 and are said to be countable. Examples of discrete variables are the number of children in a family, the number of students in a classroom, and the number of calls received by a switchboard operator each day for a month.

> **Discrete variables** assume values that can be counted.

Continuous variables, by comparison, can assume an infinite number of values in an interval between any two specific values. Temperature, for example, is a continuous variable, since the variable can assume an infinite number of values between any two given temperatures.

> **Continuous variables** can assume an infinite number of values between any two specific values. They are obtained by measuring. They often include fractions and decimals.

The classification of variables can be summarized as follows:

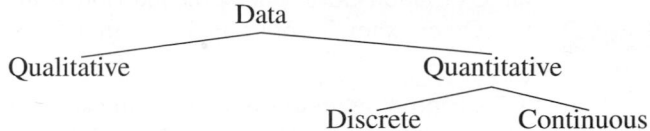

Data

Qualitative · Quantitative

Discrete · Continuous

Since continuous data must be measured, answers must be rounded because of the limits of the measuring device. Usually, answers are rounded to the nearest given unit. For example, heights might be rounded to the nearest centimetre (cm), weights to the nearest gram (g), etc. Hence, a recorded height of 186 cm could mean any measure from 185.5 cm up to but not including 186.6 cm. Thus, the boundary of this measure is given as 185.5–186.5 cm. *Boundaries are written for convenience at 185.5–186.5 but are understood to mean all values up to but not including 186.5.* Actual data values of 186.5 would be rounded to 187 and would be included in a class with boundaries 186.5 up to but not including 187.5, written as 186.5–187.5. As another example, if a recorded weight is 39 kilograms (kg), the exact boundaries are 38.5 up to but not including 39.5 kg. Table 1–1 helps to clarify this concept. The boundaries of a continuous variable are given in one additional decimal place and always end with the digit 5.

Table 1–1	Recorded Values and Boundaries	
Variable	**Recorded value**	**Boundaries**
Length	15 centimetres (cm)	14.5–15.5 cm
Temperature	30 degrees Celsius (°C)	29.5–30.5 °C
Time	0.43 seconds (sec)	0.425–0.435 sec
Mass	1.6 grams (g)	1.55–1.65 g

In addition to being classified as qualitative or quantitative, variables can be classified by how they are categorized, counted, or measured. For example, can the data be organized into specific categories, such as area of residence (rural, suburban, or urban)? Can the data values be ranked, such as first place, second place, etc.? Or are the values obtained from measurement, such as heights, IQs, or temperature? This type of classification—i.e., how variables are categorized, counted, or measured—uses **measurement scales,** and four common types of scales are used: nominal, ordinal, interval, and ratio.

Objective

Identify the measurement level for each variable.

The first level of measurement is called the *nominal level* of measurement. A sample of college instructors classified according to subject taught (e.g., English, history, psychology, or mathematics) is an example of nominal-level measurement. Classifying residents according to telephone numbers is also an example of the nominal level of measurement. Even though numbers are assigned as phone numbers, there is no meaningful order of ranking. Other examples of nominal-level data are political party (Liberal, Conservative, Bloc Quebecois, New Democratic Party, etc.), religious preference (Christian, Muslim, Jewish, nonreligious, etc.), and marital status (single, married, common-law, divorced, etc.).

The **nominal level of measurement** classifies data into mutually exclusive (nonoverlapping), exhausting categories in which no order or ranking can be imposed on the data.

The next level of measurement is called the *ordinal level.* Data measured at this level can be placed into categories, and these categories can be ordered, or ranked. For example, from student evaluations, guest speakers might be ranked as superior, average, or poor. Floats in a homecoming parade might be ranked as first place, second place, etc. *Note that precise measurement of differences in the ordinal level of measurement* does not *exist.* For instance, when people are classified according to their build (small, medium, or large), a large variation exists among the individuals in each class.

Other examples of ordinal data are letter grades (A, B, C, D, F).

> The **ordinal level of measurement** classifies data into categories that can be ranked; however, precise differences between the ranks do not exist.

The third level of measurement is called the *interval level*. This level differs from the ordinal level in that precise differences do exist between units. For example, many standardized psychological tests yield values measured on an interval scale. IQ is an example of such a variable. There is a meaningful difference of 1 point between an IQ of 109 and an IQ of 110. Temperature is another example of interval measurement, since there is a meaningful difference of 1°C between each unit, such as 29°C and 30°C. *One property is lacking in the interval scale: There is no true zero.* For example, IQ tests do not measure people who have no intelligence. For temperature, 0°C does not mean no heat at all.

> The **interval level of measurement** ranks data, and precise differences between units of measure do exist; however, there is no meaningful zero.

The final level of measurement is called the *ratio level*. Examples of ratio scales are those used to measure height, weight, area, and number of phone calls received. Ratio scales have differences between units (1 cm, 1 kg, etc.) and a true zero. In addition, the ratio scale contains a true ratio between values. For example, if one person can lift 100 kg and another can lift 50 kg, then the ratio between them is 2 to 1. Put another way, the first person can lift twice as much as the second person.

> The **ratio level of measurement** possesses all the characteristics of interval measurement, and there exists a true zero. In addition, true ratios exist when the same variable is measured on two different members of the population.

There is not complete agreement among statisticians about the classification of data into one of the four categories. For example, some researchers classify IQ data as ratio data rather than interval. Also, data can be altered so that they fit into a different category. For instance, if the incomes of all professors of a college are classified into the three categories of low, average, and high, then a ratio variable becomes an ordinal variable. Table 1–2 gives some examples of each type of data.

Table 1–2	Examples of Measurement Scales		
Nominal-level data	**Ordinal-level data**	**Interval-level data**	**Ratio-level data**
Postal code	Grade (A, B, C, D, F)	SAT or GMAT score	Height
Gender (male, female)	Judging (first place, second place, etc.)	IQ	Weight
Eye colour (blue, brown, green, hazel)	Rating scale (poor, good, excellent)	Temperature	Time
Political preference	Ranking of tennis players		Salary
Religious affiliation			Age
Major field (mathematics, computers, etc.)			
Nationality			

Applying the Concepts 1–3

Safe Travel

Read the following information about the transportation industry and answer the questions.

Transportation Safety

The chart shows the number of job-related injuries for each of the transportation industries for 1998.

Industry	Number of injuries
Railroad	4520
Intercity bus	5100
Subway	6850
Trucking	7144
Airline	9950

1. What are the variables under study?

2. Categorize each variable as quantitative or qualitative.

3. Categorize each quantitative variable as discrete or continuous.

4. Identify the level of measurement for each variable.

5. The railroad is shown as the safest transportation industry. Does that mean railroads have fewer accidents than the other industries? Explain.

6. What factors other than safety influence a person's choice of transportation?

7. From the information given, comment on the relationship between the variables.

See page 27 for the answers.

1–4 Data Collection and Sampling Techniques

Objective

Identify the four basic sampling techniques.

In research, statisticians use data in many different ways. As stated previously, data can be used to describe situations or events. For example, a manufacturer might want to know something about the consumers who will be purchasing his product so he can plan an effective marketing strategy. In another situation, the management of a company might survey its employees to assess their needs in order to negotiate a new contract with the employees' union. Data can be used to determine whether the educational goals of a school district are being met. Finally, trends in various areas, such as the stock market, can be analyzed, enabling prospective buyers to make more intelligent decisions concerning what stocks to purchase. These examples illustrate a few situations where collecting data will help people make better decisions on courses of action.

Data can be collected in a variety of ways. One of the most common methods is through the use of surveys. Surveys can be done by using a variety of methods. Three of the most common methods are the telephone survey, the mailed questionnaire, and the personal interview.

Telephone surveys have an advantage over personal interview surveys in that they are less costly. Also, people may be more candid in their opinions since there is no face-to-face contact. A major drawback to the telephone survey is that some people in the population will not have phones or will not answer when the calls are made; hence, not all people have a chance of being surveyed. Also, many people now have unlisted numbers and cellphones, so they cannot be surveyed. Finally, even the tone of the voice of the interviewer might influence the response of the person who is being interviewed.

Mailed questionnaire surveys can be used to cover a wider geographic area than telephone surveys or personal interviews since mailed questionnaire surveys are less expensive to conduct. Also, respondents can remain anonymous if they desire. Disadvantages of mailed questionnaire surveys include a low number of responses and inappropriate answers to questions. Another drawback is that some people may have difficulty reading or understanding the questions.

Personal interview surveys have the advantage of obtaining in-depth responses to questions from the person being interviewed. One disadvantage is that interviewers must be trained in asking questions and recording responses, which makes the personal interview survey more costly than the other two survey methods. Another disadvantage is that the interviewer may be biased in his or her selection of respondents.

Data can also be collected in other ways, such as *surveying records* or *direct observation* of situations.

As stated in Section 1–2, researchers use samples to collect data and information about a particular variable from a large population. Using samples saves time and money and, in some cases, enables the researcher to get more detailed information about a particular subject. Samples cannot be selected in haphazard ways because the information obtained might be biased. For example, interviewing people on a street corner during the day would not include responses from people working in offices at that time or from people attending school; hence, not all subjects in a particular population would have a chance of being selected.

To obtain samples that are unbiased—i.e., give each subject in the population an equally likely chance of being selected—statisticians use four basic methods of sampling: random, systematic, stratified, and cluster sampling.

Random Sampling

Random samples are selected by using chance methods or random numbers. One such method is to number each subject in the population. Then place numbered cards in a bowl, mix them thoroughly, and select as many cards as needed. The subjects whose numbers are selected constitute the sample. Since it is difficult to mix the cards thoroughly, there is a chance of obtaining a biased sample. For this reason, statisticians use another method of obtaining numbers. They generate random numbers with a computer or calculator. Before the invention of computers, random numbers were obtained from tables.

Table 1–3	Random Numbers										
79	41	71	93	60	35	04	67	96	04	79	10	86
26	52	53	13	43	50	92	09	87	21	83	75	17
18	13	41	30	56	20	37	74	49	56	45	46	83
19	82	02	69	34	27	77	34	24	93	16	77	00
14	57	44	30	93	76	32	13	55	29	49	30	77
29	12	18	50	06	33	15	79	50	28	50	45	45
01	27	92	67	93	31	97	55	29	21	64	27	29
55	75	65	68	65	73	07	95	66	43	43	92	16
84	95	95	96	62	30	91	64	74	83	47	89	71
62	62	21	37	82	62	19	44	08	64	34	50	11
66	57	28	69	13	99	74	31	58	19	47	66	89
48	13	69	97	29	01	75	58	05	40	40	18	29
94	31	73	19	75	76	33	18	05	53	04	51	41
00	06	53	98	01	55	08	38	49	42	10	44	38
46	16	44	27	80	15	28	01	64	27	89	03	27
77	49	85	95	62	93	25	39	63	74	54	82	85
81	96	43	27	39	53	85	61	12	90	67	96	02
40	46	15	73	23	75	96	68	13	99	49	64	11

Some two-digit random numbers are shown in Table 1–3. To select a random sample of, say, 15 subjects out of 85 subjects, it is necessary to number each subject from 1 to 85. Then select a starting number by closing your eyes and placing your finger on a number in the table. (Although this may sound somewhat unusual, it enables us to find a starting number at random.) In this case suppose your finger landed on the number 12 in the second column. (It is the sixth number down from the top.) Then proceed downward until you have selected 15 different numbers between 01 and 85. When you reach the bottom of the column, go to the top of the next column. If you select a number greater than 85 or the number 00 or a duplicate number, just omit it. In our example, we will use the subjects numbered 12, 27, 75, 62, 57, 13, 31, 06, 16, 49, 46, 71, 53, 41, and 02. A more detailed procedure for selecting a random sample using a table of random numbers is given in Chapter 14, using Table D in Appendix C.

Systematic Sampling

Researchers obtain **systematic samples** by numbering each subject of the population and then selecting every kth subject. For example, suppose there were 2000 subjects in the population and a sample of 50 subjects were needed. Since $2000 \div 50 = 40$, then $k = 40$, and every 40th subject would be selected; however, the first subject (numbered between 1 and 40) would be selected at random. Suppose subject 12 were the first subject selected; then the sample would consist of the subjects whose numbers were 12, 52, 92, etc., until 50 subjects were obtained. When using systematic sampling, one must be careful about how the subjects in the population are numbered. If subjects were arranged in a manner such as wife, husband, wife, husband, and every 40th subject were selected, the sample would consist of all husbands. Numbering is not always necessary. For example, a researcher may select every tenth item from an assembly line to test for defects.

Stratified Sampling

Researchers obtain **stratified samples** by dividing the population into groups (called strata) according to some characteristic that is important to the study, then sampling from each group. Samples within the strata should be randomly selected. For example, suppose the president of a two-year college wants to learn how students feel about a certain issue. Furthermore, the president wishes to see if the opinions of the first-year students differ from those of the second-year students. The president will select students from each group to use in the sample.

Cluster Sampling

Researchers also use **cluster samples.** Here the population is divided into groups called clusters by some means such as geographic area or schools in a large school district, etc. Then the researcher randomly selects some of these clusters and uses all members of the selected clusters as the subjects of the samples. Suppose a researcher wishes to survey apartment dwellers in a large city. If there are ten apartment buildings in the city, the researcher can select at random two buildings from the ten and interview all the residents of these buildings. Cluster sampling is used when the population is large or when it involves subjects residing in a large geographic area. For example, if one wanted to do a study involving the patients in the hospitals in Montreal, it would be very costly and time-consuming to try to obtain a random sample of patients since they would be spread over a large area. Instead, a few hospitals could be selected at random, and the patients in these hospitals would be interviewed in a cluster.

The four basic sampling methods are summarized in Table 1–4.

Historical Note

In Canada's 2004 federal election, pollsters predicted Paul Martin's Liberals and Stephen Harper's Conservatives neck-and-neck in a race too close to call. Final results had the Liberals winning 135 seats versus 99 seats for the Conservatives. Environics Research Group stated that pollsters did not blow it; voters simply changed their minds on Election Day.

Table 1–4	Summary of Sampling Methods
Random	Subjects are selected by random numbers.
Systematic	Subjects are selected by using every kth number after the first subject is randomly selected from 1 through k.
Stratified	Subjects are selected by dividing up the population into groups (strata), and subjects within groups are randomly selected.
Cluster	Subjects are selected by using an intact group that is representative of the population.

Interesting Fact

Older Americans are less likely to sacrifice happiness for a higher-paying job. According to one survey, 38% of those aged 18–29 said they would choose more money over happiness, while only 3% of those over 65 would.

Other Sampling Methods

In addition to the four basic sampling methods, researchers use other methods to obtain samples. One such method is called a **convenience sample.** Here a researcher uses subjects that are convenient. For example, the researcher may interview subjects entering a local mall to determine the nature of their visit or perhaps what stores they will be patronizing. This sample is probably not representative of the general customers for several reasons. For one thing, it was probably taken at a specific time of day, so not all customers entering the mall have an equal chance of being selected since they were not there when the survey was being conducted. But convenience samples can be representative of the population. If the researcher investigates the characteristics of the population and determines that the sample is representative, then it can be used.

Other sampling techniques, such as *sequential sampling, double sampling,* and *multistage sampling,* are explained in Chapter 14, along with a more detailed explanation of the four basic sampling techniques.

Applying the Concepts 1–4

Canadian Culture and Drug Abuse

Assume you are a member of the National Research Council and have become increasingly concerned about the drug use by professional sports players. You set up a plan and conduct a survey on how people believe the Canadian culture (television, movies, magazines, and popular music) influences illegal drug use. Your survey consists of 2250 adults and adolescents from around the country. A consumer group petitions you for more information about your survey. Answer the following questions about your survey.

1. What type of survey did you use (phone, mail, or interview)?
2. What are the advantages and disadvantages of the surveying methods you did not use?
3. What type of scores did you use? Why?
4. Did you use a random method for deciding who would be in your sample?
5. Which of the methods (stratified, systematic, cluster, or convenience) did you use?
6. Why was that method more appropriate for this type of data collection?
7. If a convenience sample were obtained, consisting of only adolescents, how would the results of the study be affected?

See page 27 for the answers.

1–5   Observational and Experimental Studies

Objective

Explain the difference between an observational and an experimental study.

There are several different ways to classify statistical studies. This section explains two types of studies: *observational studies* and *experimental studies.*

> In an **observational study,** the researcher merely observes what is happening or what has happened in the past and tries to draw conclusions based on these observations.

For example, data from the Motorcycle Industry Council (*USA TODAY*) stated that "Motorcycle owners are getting older and richer." Data were collected on the ages and incomes of motorcycle owners for the years 1980 and 1998 and then compared. The findings showed considerable differences in the ages and incomes of motorcycle owners for the two years.

In this study, the researcher merely observed what had happened to the motorcycle owners over a period of time. There was no type of research intervention.

> In an **experimental study,** the researcher manipulates one of the variables and tries to determine how the manipulation influences other variables.

For example, a study conducted at Virginia Polytechnic Institute and presented in *Psychology Today* divided 56 female undergraduate students into two groups and had the students perform as many sit-ups as possible in 90 sec. The first group was told only to "Do your best," while the second group was told to try to increase the actual number of sit-ups done each day by 10%. After four days, the subjects in the group who were given the vague instructions to "Do your best" averaged 43 sit-ups, while the group that was given the more specific instructions to increase the number of sit-ups by 10% averaged 56 sit-ups by the last day's session. The conclusion then was that athletes who were given specific goals performed better than those who were not given specific goals.

This study is an example of a statistical experiment since the researchers intervened in the study by manipulating one of the variables, namely, the type of instructions given to each group.

In a true experimental study, the subjects should be assigned to groups randomly. Also, the treatments should be assigned to the groups at random. In the sit-up study, the article did not mention whether the subjects were randomly assigned to the groups.

Sometimes when random assignment is not possible, researchers use intact groups. These types of studies are done quite often in education where already intact groups are available in the form of existing classrooms. When these groups are used, the study is said to be a **quasi-experimental study.** The treatments, though, should be assigned at random. Most articles do not state whether random assignment of subjects was used.

Statistical studies usually include one or more *independent variables* and one *dependent variable.*

> The **independent variable** in an experimental study is the one that is being manipulated by the researcher. The independent variable is also called the **explanatory variable.** The response variable is called the **dependent variable** or the **outcome variable.**

The outcome variable is the variable that is studied to see if it has changed significantly due to the manipulation of the independent variable. For example, in the sit-up study, the researchers gave the groups two different types of instructions, general and specific. Hence, the independent variable is the type of instruction. The dependent variable, then, is the response variable, that is, the number of sit-ups each group was able to perform after four days of exercise. If the differences in the dependent or outcome variable are large and other factors are equal, these differences can be attributed to the manipulation of the independent variable. In this case, specific instructions were shown to increase athletic performance.

In the sit-up study, there were two groups. The group that received the special instruction is called the **treatment group** while the other is called the **control group.** The treatment group receives a specific treatment (in this case, instructions for improvement) while the control group does not.

Both types of statistical studies have advantages and disadvantages. Experimental studies have the advantage that the researcher can decide how to select subjects and how to assign them to specific groups. The researcher can also control or manipulate the independent variable. For example, in studies that require the subjects to consume a certain amount of medicine each day, the researcher can determine the precise dosages and, if necessary, vary the dosage for the groups.

There are several disadvantages to experimental studies. First, they may occur in unnatural settings, such as laboratories and special classrooms. This can lead to several problems. One such problem is that the results might not apply to the natural setting. The age-old question then is, "This mouthwash may kill 10,000 germs in a test tube, but how many germs will it kill in my mouth?"

Another disadvantage with an experimental study is the **Hawthorne effect.** This effect was discovered in 1924 in a study of workers at the Hawthorne plant of the Western Electric Company. In this study, researchers found that the subjects who knew they were participating in an experiment actually changed their behaviour in ways that affected the results of the study.

Another problem is called *confounding of variables.*

Two variables are **confounded** when their effects on a response variable cannot be distinguished from each other.

Researchers try to control most variables in a study, but this is not possible in some studies. For example, subjects who are put on an exercise program might also improve their diet unbeknownst to the researcher and perhaps improve their health in other ways not due to exercise alone. Then diet becomes a confounding variable.

Observational studies also have advantages and disadvantages. One advantage of an observational study is that it usually occurs in a natural setting. For example, researchers can observe people's driving patterns on streets and highways in large cities. Another advantage of an observational study is that it can be done in situations where it would be unethical or downright dangerous to conduct an experiment. Using observational studies, researchers can study suicides, rapes, murders, etc. In addition, observational studies can be done using variables that cannot be manipulated by the researcher, such as drug users versus nondrug users and right-handedness versus left-handedness.

Observational studies have disadvantages, too. As mentioned previously, since the variables are not controlled by the researcher, a definite cause-and-effect situation cannot be shown since other factors may have had an effect on the results. Observational studies can be expensive and time-consuming. For example, if one wanted to study the habitat of lions in Africa, one would need a lot of time and money, and there would be a certain amount of danger involved. Finally, since the researcher may not be using his or her own measurements, the results could be subject to the inaccuracies of those who collected the data. For example, if the researchers were doing a study of events that occurred in the 1800s, they would have to rely on information and records obtained by others from a previous era. There is no way to ensure the accuracy of these records.

When you read the results of statistical studies, decide if the study was observational or experimental. Then see if the conclusion follows logically, based on the nature of these studies.

No matter what type of study is conducted, two studies on the same subject sometimes have conflicting conclusions. Why might this occur? An article entitled "Bottom Line: Is It Good for You?" (*USA TODAY Weekend*) states that in the 1960s studies suggested that margarine was better for the heart than butter since margarine contains less saturated fat and users had lower cholesterol levels. In a 1980 study, researchers found that butter was better than margarine since margarine contained trans-fatty acids, which are worse for the heart than butter's saturated fat. Then in a 1998 study, researchers found that margarine was better for a person's health. Now, what is to be believed? Should one use butter or margarine?

The answer here is to take a closer look at these studies. Actually, it is not a choice between butter or margarine that counts, but the type of margarine used. In the 1980s, studies showed that solid margarine contains trans-fatty acids, and scientists believe that they are worse for the heart than butter's saturated fat. In the 1998 study, liquid margarine was used. It is very low in trans-fatty acids, and hence it is more healthful than butter because trans-fatty acids have been shown to raise cholesterol. Hence, the conclusion is to use liquid margarine instead of solid margarine or butter.

Before decisions based on research studies are made, it is important to get all the facts and examine them in light of the particular situation.

Applying the Concepts 1–5

Just a Pinch Between Your Cheek and Gum

As the evidence on the adverse effects of cigarette smoke grew, people tried many different ways to quit smoking. Some people tried chewing tobacco or, as it was called, smokeless tobacco. A small amount of tobacco was placed between the cheek and gum. Certain chemicals from the tobacco were absorbed into the bloodstream and gave the sensation of smoking cigarettes. This prompted studies on the adverse effects of smokeless tobacco. One study in particular used 40 university students as subjects. Twenty were given smokeless tobacco to chew, and 20 given a substance that looked and tasted like smokeless tobacco, but did not contain any of the harmful substances. The students were randomly assigned to one of the groups. The students' blood pressure and heart rate were measured before they started chewing and 20 minutes after they had been chewing. A significant increase in heart rate occurred in the group that chewed the smokeless tobacco. Answer the following questions.

1. What type of study was this (observational, quasi-experimental, or experimental)?
2. What are the independent and dependent variables?
3. Which was the treatment group?
4. Could the students' blood pressures be affected by knowing that they are part of a study?
5. List some possible confounding variables.
6. Do you think this is a good way to study the effect of smokeless tobacco?

See page 28 for the answers.

1–6   Uses and Misuses of Statistics

Objective

Explain how statistics can be used and misused.

As explained previously, statistical techniques can be used to describe data, compare two or more data sets, determine if a relationship exists between variables, test hypotheses, and make estimates about population characteristics. However, there is another aspect of statistics, and that is the misuse of statistical techniques to sell products that don't work properly, to attempt to prove something true that is really not true, or to get our attention by using statistics to evoke fear, shock, and outrage.

There are two sayings that have been around for a long time that illustrate this point:

"There are three types of lies—lies, damn lies, and statistics."

"Figures don't lie, but liars figure."

Just because we read or hear the results of a research study or an opinion poll in the media, this does not mean that these results are reliable or that they can be applied to any and all situations. For example, reporters sometimes leave out critical details such as the size of the sample used or how the research subjects were selected. Without this information, one cannot properly evaluate the research and properly interpret the conclusions of the study or survey.

It is the purpose of this section to show some ways that statistics can be misused. One should not infer that all research studies and surveys are suspect, but that there are many factors to consider when making decisions based on the results of research studies and surveys. Here are some ways that statistics can be misrepresented.

Suspect Samples

The first thing to consider is the sample that was used in the research study. Sometimes researchers use very small samples to obtain information. Several years ago, advertisements contained such statements as "Three out of four doctors surveyed recommend brand such and such." If only four doctors were surveyed, the results could have been obtained by chance alone; however, if 100 doctors were surveyed, the results might be quite different.

Not only is it important to have a sample size that is large enough, but also it is necessary to see how the subjects in the sample were selected. Studies using volunteers sometimes have a built-in bias. Volunteers generally do not represent the population at large. Sometimes they are recruited from a particular socioeconomic background, and sometimes unemployed people volunteer for research studies to get a stipend. Studies that require the subjects to spend several days or weeks in an environment other than their home or workplace automatically exclude people who are employed and cannot take time away from work. Sometimes only college students or retirees are used in studies. In the past, many studies have used only men, but have attempted to generalize the results to both men and women. Opinion polls that require a person to phone or mail in a response most often are not representative of the population in general, since only those with strong feelings for or against the issue usually call or respond by mail.

Another type of sample that may not be representative is the convenience sample. Educational studies sometimes use students in intact classrooms since it is convenient. Quite often, the students in these classrooms do not represent the student population of the entire school district.

When results are interpreted from studies using small samples, convenience samples, or volunteer samples, care should be used in generalizing the results to the entire population.

Ambiguous Averages

In Chapter 3, you will learn that there are four commonly used measures that are loosely called *averages.* They are the *mean, median, mode,* and *midrange.* For the same data set, these averages can differ markedly. People who know this can, without lying, select the one measure of average which lends the most evidence to support their position. This fact is explained on page 88 of Chapter 3.

Changing the Subject

Another type of statistical distortion can occur when different values are used to represent the same data. For example, one political candidate who is running for reelection might say, "During my administration, expenditures increased a mere 3%." His opponent, who is trying to unseat him, might say, "During my opponent's administration, expenditures have increased a whopping $6,000,000." Here both figures are correct; however, expressing a 3% increase as $6,000,000 makes it sound like a very large increase. Here again, ask yourself, Which measure best represents the data?

Detached Statistics

A claim that uses a detached statistic is one in which no comparison is made. For example, you may hear a claim such as "Our brand of crackers has one-third fewer calories." Here, no comparison is made. One-third fewer calories than what? Another example is a claim that uses a detached statistic such as "Brand A aspirin works four times faster." Four times faster than what? When you see statements such as this, always ask yourself, Compared to what?

Implied Connections

Many claims attempt to imply connections between variables that may not actually exist. For example, consider the following statement: "Eating fish may help to reduce your cholesterol." Notice the words *may help*. There is no guarantee that eating fish will definitely help you reduce your cholesterol.

"Studies suggest that using our exercise machine will reduce your weight." Here the word *suggest* is used; and again, there is no guarantee that you will lose weight by using the exercise machine advertised.

Another claim might say, "Taking calcium will lower blood pressure in some people." Note the word *some* is used. You may not be included in the group of "some" people. Be careful when you draw conclusions from claims that use words such as *may, in some people,* and *might help*.

Misleading Graphs

Statistical graphs give a visual representation of data that enables viewers to analyze and interpret data more easily than by simply looking at numbers. In Chapter 2, you will see how some graphs are used to represent data. However, if graphs are drawn inappropriately, they can misrepresent the data and lead the reader to false conclusions. The misuse of graphs is also explained in Chapter 2, on pages 58–61.

Faulty Survey Questions

When analyzing the results of a survey using questionnaires, you should be sure that the questions are properly written since the way questions are phrased can often influence the way people answer them. For example, the responses to a question such as "Do you feel that the North Huntingdon School District should build a new football stadium?" might be answered differently than a question such as "Do you favour increasing school taxes so that the North Huntingdon School District can build a new football stadium?" Each question asks something a little different, and the responses could be radically different. When you read and interpret the results obtained from questionnaire surveys, watch out for some of these common mistakes made in the writing of the survey questions.

In Chapter 14, you will find some common ways that survey questions could be misinterpreted by those responding and could therefore result in incorrect conclusions.

To restate the premise of this section, statistics, when used properly, can be beneficial in obtaining much information, but when used improperly, can lead to much misinformation. It is like your automobile. If you use your automobile to get to school or work or to go on a vacation, that's good. But if you use it to run over your neighbour's dog because it barks all night long and tears up your flower garden, that's not so good!

1–7   Computers and Calculators

Objective 8

Explain the importance of computers and calculators in statistics.

Statistical computing continues to evolve with the advent of more powerful computers and calculators. Modern statistical software takes advantage of this computing power, allowing for easy, fast, and accurate analysis on simple and complex data sets.

Affordable tools available to students to perform data analysis include portable hand-held graphing calculators with built-in or downloadable statistical software. One of the most widely used models is the Texas Instruments TI-83 Plus and TI-84 Plus series.

Figure 1–1

Texas Instruments T1-83 Plus graphing calculator with statistics menu displayed

Hewlett-Packard (HP 39g or HP 49g+), Sharp (EL-9900C), and Casio (FX9750) are also excellent models for both descriptive and inferential statistics. Be aware that many academic programs disallow the use of graphing calculators during examinations due to their storage and display capabilities.

Computer-based application software is an indispensable resource for statisticians. Statistical software is available on a variety of hardware platforms—notebook, personal computer, or network server, and operating systems—Windows, Mac OS, or UNIX. The Microsoft Excel spreadsheet application is one of the most widely used software for statistical data analysis and charting due to its ease of use and prevalence in the marketplace. Although not as versatile as dedicated statistical programs, Excel's built-in functions can be enhanced with a wide array of add-in programs, such as the Analysis ToolPak. Many third party add-in programs are available that enhance Excel's already impressive statistical feature set. Other statistical solutions include mathematics programs, such as MATLAB, Mathematica, Maple, Mathcad, and open-source software, such as "R."

Dedicated statistical application software offers all, or at least most, of the required tools for statisticians without the need for optional add-in products. These programs can range from a non-graphical command line interface to the more intuitive menu-driven, spreadsheet-oriented graphical user interface. Popular dedicated programs incorporate both interfaces. Depending on the field of study, there are numerous choices for the statistician. Minitab uses a cross-discipline approach and targets entry-level scientists and business and industrial users. Experimental researchers may opt for the SAS System for Statistical Analysis. The SPSS software focuses on marketing, scientific, government, and education researchers. Many other statistical applications are prevalent in the marketplace.

The purpose of this elementary statistics textbook is to teach the student the concepts and methodologies required to make informed statistical decisions. Statistical software used on either calculators or computers represent tools that ease the burden of time-consuming computations. Learning procedures, formulas, and table-lookup will give the student a much better understanding of the underlying work performed by the chosen

Figure 1–2

Microsoft Excel statistical data analysis output with chart

Figure 1–3

Minitab statistical
software with
command-line and
menu interface

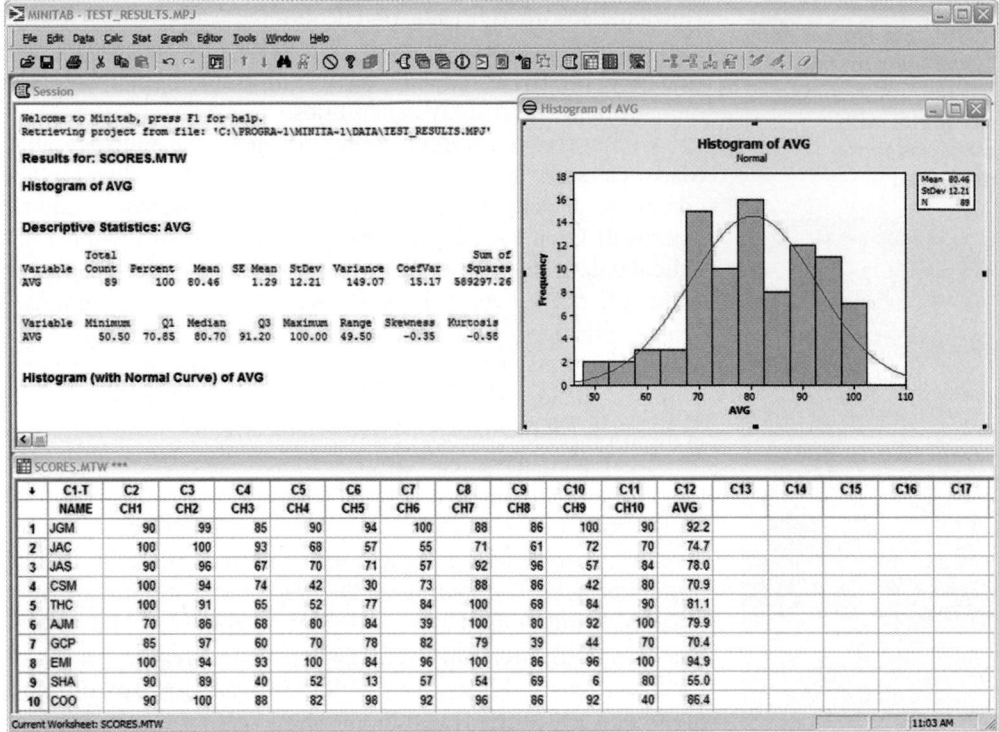

technology. To assist the learning of these tools, a Technology-Step-by-Step section is available in Appendix E of this text. Currently the TI-83 Plus and TI-84 Plus, Excel, MINITAB, and SPSS procedures are described.

The author has left it up to each instructor to choose how much technology he or she will incorporate into the course.

1–8   Summary

The two major areas of statistics are descriptive and inferential. Descriptive statistics includes the collection, organization, summarization, and presentation of data. Inferential statistics includes making inferences from samples to populations, estimations and hypothesis testing, determining relationships, and making predictions. Inferential statistics is based on *probability theory*.

Since in most cases the populations under study are large, statisticians use subgroups called samples to get the necessary data for their studies. There are four basic methods used to obtain samples: random, systematic, stratified, and cluster.

Data can be classified as qualitative or quantitative. Quantitative data can be either discrete or continuous, depending on the values they can assume. Data can also be measured by various scales. The four basic levels of measurement are nominal, ordinal, interval, and ratio.

There are two basic types of statistical studies: observational studies and experimental studies. When conducting observational studies, researchers observe what is happening or what has happened and then draw conclusions based on these observations. They do not attempt to manipulate the variables in any way.

When conducting an experimental study, researchers manipulate one or more of the independent or explanatory variables and see how this manipulation influences the dependent or outcome variable.

Finally, the applications of statistics are many and varied. People encounter them in everyday life, such as in reading newspapers or magazines, listening to the radio, or watching television. Since statistics is used in almost every field of endeavour, the educated individual should be knowledgeable about the vocabulary, concepts, and procedures of statistics.

Today, computers and calculators are used extensively in statistics to facilitate the computations.

Unusual Stat

Twenty percent of Canadians believe that extraterrestrials visit the earth on a regular basis.

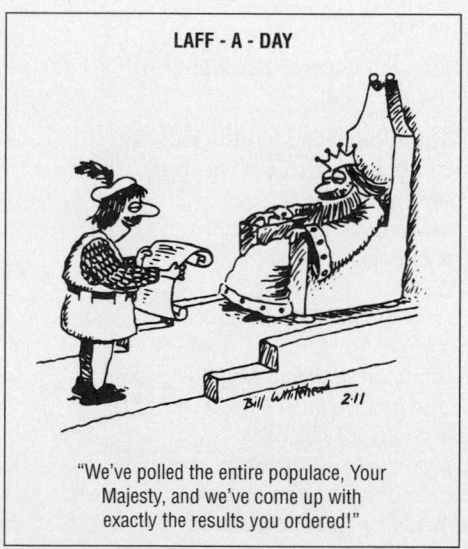

LAFF - A - DAY

"We've polled the entire populace, Your Majesty, and we've come up with exactly the results you ordered!"

Source: © 1993 King Features Syndicate, Inc. World Rights reserved. Reprinted with special permission of King Features Syndicate.

For step-by-step guidance on the use of technology for this chapter, visit the Online Learning Centre at www.mcgrawhill.ca/olc/bluman. Summary procedures for Minitab, SPSS, Excel, and TI-83 Plus or TI-84 Plus can also be found in Appendix E.

Important Terms

cluster sample 12

confounded variables 15

continuous variables 6

control group 14

convenience sample 13

data 3

data set 4

data value or datum 4

dependent variable 14

descriptive statistics 4

discrete variables 6

element 3

experimental study 14

explanatory variable 14

Hawthorne effect 15

hypothesis testing 4

independent variable 14

inferential statistics 5

interval level of
measurement 8

measurement scales 7

nominal level of
measurement 7

observational study 13

ordinal level of
measurement 8

outcome variable 14

population 4

probability 4

qualitative variables 6

quantitative variables 6

quasi-experimental study 14

random sample 10

random variable 3

ratio level of measurement 8

sample 4

statistics 3

stratified sample 12

systematic sample 12

treatment group 14

variable 3

Review Exercises

Note: **All odd-numbered problems and even-numbered problems marked with "ans" are included in the answer section at the end of this book.**

1. Name and define the two areas of statistics.

2. What is probability? Name two areas where probability is used.

3. Suggest some ways statistics can be used in everyday life.

4. Explain the differences between a sample and a population.

5. Why are samples used in statistics?

6. In each of these statements, tell whether descriptive or inferential statistics have been used.

   a. By the year 2010, 87 million homes worldwide will be watching high-definition television broadcasts (HDTV) (Source: www.electronics.ca).

   b. 83% of Canadian drowning victims are male. (Source: www.lifesaving.org)

   c. The value of Canada's building permits in December 2005 set a new record at $6.5 billion (Source: Statistics Canada).

   d. The median length of prison sentences in adult criminal court for property crimes in Canada in 2003 was 42 days (Source: Statistics Canada).

   e. Flu shots may also protect against heart disease and stroke (Source: Heart and Stroke Foundation).

   f. By 2031, 25% of Canada's population will be 65 years of age or over (Source: Statistics Canada).

   g. Average health-care spending per capita by provincial and territorial governments in 2005–2006 was $2845 (Source: Canadian Institute for Healthcare Information).

   h. The projected budget surplus in 2006–2007 for Alberta was $4.1 billion (Source: Government of Alberta).

7. Classify each as nominal-level, ordinal-level, interval-level, or ratio-level measurement.

   a. Pages in the city of Winnipeg telephone book.
   b. Rankings of tennis players.
   c. Weights of air conditioners.
   d. Temperatures inside ten refrigerators.
   e. Salaries of the top five CEOs in the United States.
   f. Ratings of eight local plays (poor, fair, good, excellent).
   g. Times required for mechanics to do a tune-up.
   h. Ages of students in a classroom.
   i. Marital status of patients in a doctor's office.
   j. Horsepower of tractor engines.

8. **(ans)** Classify each variable as qualitative or quantitative.

   a. Number of bicycles sold in one year by a large sporting goods store.
   b. Colours of baseball caps in a store.
   c. Time it takes to cut a lawn.
   d. Capacity in cubic metres of six truck beds.
   e. Classification of children in a day-care centre (infant, toddler, preschool).
   f. Weights of fish caught in Lake George.
   g. Marital status of faculty members in a large university.

9. Classify each variable as discrete or continuous.

   a. Number of doughnuts sold each day by Doughnut Heaven.
   b. Water temperatures of six swimming pools in Saskatoon on a given day.
   c. Weights of cats in a pet shelter.
   d. Lifetime (in hours) of 12 flashlight batteries.
   e. Number of cheeseburgers sold each day by a hamburger stand on a college campus.
   f. Number of DVDs rented each day by a video store.
   g. Daily volume of raw sewage and storm water (in litres) entering St. John's Harbour.

10. Give the boundaries of each value.

    a. 42.8 kilometres
    b. 1.6 millilitres
    c. 5.36 grams
    d. 18 kilograms
    e. 13.8 °C
    f. 40 centimetres

11. Name and define the four basic sampling methods.

12. **(ans)** Classify each sample as random, systematic, stratified, or cluster.

    a. In a large school district, all teachers from two buildings are interviewed to determine whether they believe the students have less homework to do now than in previous years.
    b. Every seventh customer entering a shopping mall is asked to select her or his favourite store.
    c. Nursing supervisors are selected using random numbers in order to determine annual salaries.
    d. Every 100th hamburger manufactured is checked to determine its fat content.
    e. Mail carriers of a large city are divided into four groups according to gender (male or female) and according to whether they walk or ride on their routes. Then ten are selected from each group and interviewed to determine whether they have been bitten by a dog in the last year.

13. Give three examples each of nominal, ordinal, interval, and ratio data.

14. For each of these statements, define a population and state how a sample might be obtained.

    a. The average cost of an airline meal is $4.55 (Source: *Everything Has Its Price,* Richard E. Donley, Simon and Schuster).
    b. Some 25% of Canadian children are obese today (Source: *Reader's Digest, Canada*).
    c. Every ten minutes, two people die in car crashes and 170 are injured (Source: National Safety Council estimates).
    d. When older people with mild to moderate hypertension were given mineral salt for six months, the average blood pressure reading dropped by 8 points systolic and 3 points diastolic (Source: *Prevention*).
    e. The average amount spent per gift for Mom on Mother's Day is $25.95 (Source: The Gallup Organization).

15. Select a newspaper or magazine article that involves a statistical study, and write a paper answering these questions.

    a. Is this study descriptive or inferential? Explain your answer.
    b. What are the variables used in the study? In your opinion, what level of measurement was used to obtain the data from the variables?
    c. Does the article define the population? If so, how is it defined? If not, how could it be defined?
    d. Does the article state the sample size and how the sample was obtained? If so, determine the size of the sample and explain how it was selected. If not, suggest a way it could have been obtained.
    e. Explain *in your own words* what procedure (survey, comparison of groups, etc.) might have been used to determine the study's conclusions.
    f. Do you agree or disagree with the conclusions? State your reasons.

16. Information from research studies is sometimes taken out of context. Explain why the claims of these studies might be suspect.

    a. The average salary of the graduates of the class of 1980 is $32,500.
    b. It is estimated that in Podunk there are 27,256 cats.
    c. Only 3% of the men surveyed read *Cosmopolitan* magazine.
    d. Based on a recent mail survey, 85% of the respondents favoured gun control.
    e. A recent study showed that high school dropouts drink more coffee than students who graduated; therefore, coffee dulls the brain.
    f. Since most automobile accidents occur within 24 kms of a person's residence, it is safer to make long trips.

17. Identify each study as being either observational or experimental.

    a. Subjects were randomly assigned to two groups, and one group was given an herb and the other group a placebo. After six months, the numbers of respiratory tract infections each group had were compared.
    b. A researcher stood at a busy intersection to see if the colour of the automobile that a person drives is related to running red lights.
    c. A researcher finds that people who are more hostile have higher total cholesterol levels than those who are less hostile.
    d. Subjects are randomly assigned to four groups. Each group is placed on one of four special diets—a low-fat diet, a high-fish diet, a combination of low-fat diet and high-fish diet, and a regular diet. After six months, the blood pressures of the groups are compared to see if diet has any effect on blood pressure.

18. Identify the independent variable(s) and the dependent variable for each of the studies in Exercise 17.

19. For each of the studies in Exercise 17, suggest possible confounding variables.

20. According to a pilot study of 20 people conducted at the University of Minnesota, daily doses of a compound called arabinogalactan over a period of six months resulted in a significant increase in the beneficial lactobacillus species of bacteria. Why can't it be concluded that the compound is beneficial for the majority of people?

21. Comment on the following statement, taken from a magazine advertisement: "In a recent clinical study, Brand ABC [actual brand will not be named] was proved to be 1950% better than creatine!"

22. In an ad for women, the following statement was made: "For every 100 women, 91 have taken the road less travelled." Comment on this statement.

23. In many ads for weight loss products, under the product claims and in small print, the following statement is made: "These results are not typical." What does this say about the product being advertised?

24. In an ad for moisturizing lotion, the following claim is made: " . . . it's the #1 dermatologist-recommended brand." What is misleading about this claim?

25. An ad for an exercise product stated: "Using this product will burn 74% more calories." What is misleading about this statement?

26. "Vitamin E is a proven antioxidant and may help in fighting cancer and heart disease." Is there anything ambiguous about this claim? Explain.

27. "Just 1 capsule of Brand X can provide 24 hours of acid control." (Actual brand will not be named.) What needs to be more clearly defined in this statement?

28. ". . . Male children born to women who smoke during pregnancy run a risk of violent and criminal behaviour that lasts well into adulthood." Can we infer that smoking during pregnancy is responsible for criminal behaviour in people?

29. In the 1980s, a study linked coffee to a higher risk of heart disease and pancreatic cancer. In the early 1990s, studies showed that drinking coffee posed minimal health threats. However, in 1994, a study showed that pregnant women who drank 3 or more cups of tea daily may be at risk for spontaneous abortion. In 1998, a study claimed that women who drank more than a half-cup of caffeinated tea every day may actually increase their fertility. In 1998, a study showed that over a lifetime, a few extra cups of coffee a day can raise blood pressure, heart rate, and stress (Source: "Bottom Line: Is It Good for You? Or Bad?" by Monika Guttman, *USA TODAY Weekend*). Suggest some reasons why these studies appear to be conflicting.

Extending the Concepts ● ● ●

30. Find an article that describes a statistical study, and identify the study as observational or experimental.

31. For the article that you used in Exercise 30, identify the independent variable(s) and dependent variable for the study.

32. For the article that you selected in Exercise 30, suggest some confounding variables that may have an effect on the results of the study.

Are We Improving Our Diet?–Revisited

Statistics Today

Researchers selected a *sample* of 23,699 adults in the United States, using phone numbers selected at *random,* and conducted a *telephone survey.* All respondents were asked six questions:

1. How often do you drink juices such as orange, grapefruit, or tomato?
2. Not counting juice, how often do you eat fruit?
3. How often do you eat green salad?
4. How often do you eat potatoes (not including french fries, fried potatoes, or potato chips)?
5. How often do you eat carrots?
6. Not counting carrots, potatoes, or salad, how many servings of vegetables do you usually eat?

Researchers found that men consumed fewer servings of fruits and vegetables per day (3.3) than women (3.7). Only 20% of the population consumed the recommended five or more daily servings. In addition, they found that youths and less-educated people consumed an even lower amount than the average.

Based on this study, they recommend that greater educational efforts are needed to improve fruit and vegetable consumption by North Americans and to provide environmental and institutional support to encourage increased consumption.

Source: Mary K. Serdula, M.D., et al., "Fruit and Vegetable Intake Among Adults in 16 States: Results of a Brief Telephone Survey," *American Journal of Public Health* 85, no. 2. Copyright by the American Public Health Association; Government of Canada.

Chapter Quiz

● ● ●

Determine whether each statement is true or false. If the statement is false, explain why.

1. Probability is used as a basis for inferential statistics.

2. The height of Sir John A. Macdonald is an example of a variable.

3. The highest level of measurement is the interval level.

4. When the population of college professors is divided into groups according to their rank (instructor, assistant professor, etc.) and then several are selected from each group to make up a sample, the sample is called a cluster sample.

5. The variable *age* is an example of a qualitative variable.

6. The weight of pumpkins is considered to be a continuous variable.

7. The boundary of a value such as 6 centimetres would be 5.9–6.1 centimetres.

Select the best answer.

8. The number of absences per year that a worker has is an example of what type of data?

   a. Nominal
   b. Qualitative
   c. Discrete
   d. Continuous

9. What are the boundaries of 25.6 grams?

   a. 25–26 grams
   b. 25.55–25.65 grams
   c. 25.5–25.7 grams
   d. 20–39 grams

10. A researcher divided subjects into two groups according to gender and then selected members from each group for her sample. What sampling method was the researcher using?

    a. Cluster
    b. Random
    c. Systematic
    d. Stratified

11. Data that can be classified according to colour are measured on what scale?

    a. Nominal
    b. Ratio
    c. Ordinal
    d. Interval

12. A study that involves no researcher intervention is called

    a. An experimental study.
    b. A noninvolvement study.
    c. An observational study.
    d. A quasi-experimental study.

13. A variable that interferes with other variables in the study is called

    a. A confounding variable.
    b. An explanatory variable.
    c. An outcome variable.
    d. An interfering variable.

Use the best answer to complete these statements.

14. Two major branches of statistics are _____ and _____.

15. Two uses of probability are _____ and _____.

16. The group of all subjects under study is called a(n) _____.

17. A group of subjects selected from the group of all subjects under study is called a(n) _____.

18. Three reasons why samples are used in statistics are

    a. _____ b. _____ c. _____.

19. The four basic sampling methods are

    a. _____ b. _____ c. _____ d. _____.

20. A study that uses intact groups when it is not possible to randomly assign participants to the groups is called a(n) _____ study.

21. In a research study, participants should be assigned to groups using _____ methods, if possible.

22. For each statement, decide whether descriptive or inferential statistics is used.

    a. The average life expectancy in New Zealand is 78.49 years. Source: *World Factbook 2004.*
    b. A diet high in fruits and vegetables will lower blood pressure. Source: Institute of Medicine.
    c. The total amount of estimated losses from hurricane Hugo was $4.2 billion. Source: Insurance Service Office.
    d. Researchers stated that the shape of a person's ears is related to the person's aggression. Source: *American Journal of Human Biology.*
    e. In 2013, the number of high school graduates will be 3.2 million students. Source: National Center for Education.

23. Classify each as nominal-level, ordinal-level, interval-level, or ratio-level measurement.

    a. Rating of movies as G, PG, and R.
    b. Number of candy bars sold on a fund drive.
    c. Classification of automobiles as subcompact, compact, standard, and luxury.
    d. Temperatures of hair dryers.
    e. Weights of suitcases on a commercial airline.

24. Classify each variable as discrete or continuous.

   a. Ages of people working in a large factory.
   b. Number of cups of coffee served at a restaurant.
   c. The amount of a drug injected into a guinea pig.
   d. The time it takes a student to drive to school.

   e. The number of litres of milk sold each day at a grocery store.

25. Give the boundaries of each.

   a. 48 seconds   *d.* 13.7 kilograms
   b. 0.56 centimetre   *e.* 7 metres
   c. 9.1 litres

Critical Thinking Challenges

● ● ●

1. A study of the world's busiest airports was conducted by *Airports Council International.* Describe three variables that one could use to determine which airports are the busiest. What *units* would one use to measure these variables? Are these variables categorical, discrete, or continuous?

2. The results of a study published in *Archives of General Psychiatry* stated that male children born to women who smoke during pregnancy run a risk of violent and criminal behaviour that lasts into adulthood. The results of this study were challenged by some people in the media. Give several reasons why the results of this study would be challenged.

3. The results of a study published in *Neurological Research* stated that second-graders who took piano lessons and played a computer math game more readily grasped math problems in fractions and proportions than a similar group who took an English class and played the same math game. What type of inferential study was this? Give several reasons why the piano lessons could improve a student's math ability.

4. A study of 2958 collegiate soccer players showed that in 46 anterior cruciate ligament (ACL) tears, 36 were in women. Calculate the percentages of tears for each gender.

   a. Can it be concluded that female athletes tear their knees more often than male athletes?
   b. Comment on how this study's conclusion might have been reached.

5. Read the article entitled "Anger Can Cause Snap Judgments" and answer the following questions.

   a. Is the study experimental or observational?
   b. What is the independent variable?
   c. What is the dependent variable?
   d. Do you think the sample sizes are large enough to merit the conclusion?
   e. Based on the results of the study, what changes would you recommend to persons to help them reduce their anger?

6. Read the article entitled "Hostile Children Fight Unemployment" and answer the following questions.

   a. Is the study experimental or observational?
   b. What is the independent variable?
   c. What is the dependent variable?
   d. Suggest some confounding variables that may have influenced the results of the study.
   e. Identify the three groups of subjects used in the study.

ANGER CAN CAUSE SNAP JUDGMENTS

Anger can make a normally unbiased person act with prejudice, according to a forthcoming study in the journal *Psychological Science.*

 Assistant psychology professors David DeSteno at Northeastern University in Boston and Nilanjana Dasgupta at the University of Massachusetts, Amherst, randomly divided 81 study participants into two groups and assigned them a writing task designed to induce angry, sad or neutral feelings. In a subsequent test to uncover nonconscious associations, angry subjects were quicker to connect negatively charged words —like war, death and vomit—with members of the opposite group—even though the groupings were completely arbitrary.

 "These automatic responses guide our behavior when we're not paying attention," says DeSteno, and they can lead to discriminatory acts when there is pressure to make a quick decision. "If you're aware that your emotions might be coloring these gut reactions," he says, "you should take time to consider that possibility and adjust your actions accordingly."

—*Eric Strand*

UNEMPLOYMENT

Hostile Children Fight Unemployment

Aggressive children may be destined for later long-term unemployment. In a study that began in 1968, researchers at the University of Jyvaskyla in Finland examined about 300 participants at ages 8, 14, 27, and 36. They looked for aggressive behaviors like hurting other children, kicking objects when angry, or attacking others without reason.

Their results, published recently in the *International Journal of Behavioral Development*, suggest that children with low self-control of emotion —especially aggression—were significantly more prone to long-term unemployment. Children with behavioral inhibitions—such as passive and anxious behaviors—were also indirectly linked to unemployment as they lacked the preliminary initiative needed for school success. And while unemployment rates were high in Finland during the last data collection, jobless participants who were aggressive as children were less likely to have a job two years later than their nonaggressive counterparts.

Ongoing unemployment can have serious psychological consequences, including depression, anxiety and stress. But lead researcher Lea Pulkkinen, Ph.D., a Jyvaskyla psychology professor, does have encouraging news for parents: Aggressive children with good social skills and child-centered parents were significantly less likely to be unemployed for more than two years as adults.

—*Tanya Zimbardo*

Source: Reprinted with permission from *Psychology Today,* Copyright © (2001) Sussex Publishers, Inc.

Answers to Applying the Concepts   ● ● ●

Section 1–2 Attendance and Grades

1. The variables are grades and attendance.

2. The data consist of specific grades and attendance numbers.

3. These are descriptive statistics.

4. The population under study is students at Red Deer Community College (RDCC).

5. While not specified, we probably have data from a sample of RDCC students.

6. Based on the data, it appears that in general, the better your attendance the higher your grade.

Section 1–3 Safe Travel

1. The variables are industry and number of job-related injuries.

2. The type of industry is a qualitative variable, while the number of job-related injuries is quantitative.

3. The number of job-related injuries is discrete.

4. Type of industry is nominal, and the number of job-related injuries is ratio.

5. The railroads do show fewer job-related injuries; however, there may be other things to consider. For example, railroads employ fewer people than the other transportation industries in the study.

6. A person's choice of transportation might also be affected by convenience issues, cost, service, etc.

7. Answers will vary. One possible answer is that the railroads have the fewest job-related injuries, while the airline industry has the most job-related industries (more than twice those of the railroad industry). The numbers of job-related industries in the subway and trucking industries are fairly comparable.

Section 1–4 Canadian Culture and Drug Abuse

Answers will vary, so this is one possible answer.

1. I used a telephone survey. The advantage to my survey method is that this was a relatively inexpensive survey method (although more expensive than using the mail) that could get a fairly sizable response. The disadvantage to my survey method is that I have not included anyone without a telephone. (*Note:* My survey used a random dialing method to include unlisted numbers and cellphone exchanges.)

2. A mail survey also would have been fairly inexpensive, but my response rate may have been much lower than what I got with my telephone survey. Interviewing would have allowed me to use follow-up questions and to clarify any questions of the respondents at the time of the interview. However, interviewing is very labour- and cost-intensive.

3. I used ordinal data on a scale of 1 to 5. The scores were 1 = strongly disagree, 2 = disagree, 3 = neutral, 4 = agree, 5 = strongly agree.

4. The random method that I used was a random dialing method.

5. To include people from each province, I used a stratified random sample, collecting data randomly from each of the area codes and telephone exchanges available.

6. This method allowed me to make sure that I had representation from each area of Canada.

7. Convenience samples may not be representative of the population, and a convenience sample of adolescents would probably differ greatly from the general population with regard to the influence of Canadian culture on illegal drug use.

Section 1–5 Just a Pinch Between Your Cheek and Gum

1. This was an experiment, since the researchers imposed a treatment on each of the two groups involved in the study.

2. The independent variable is whether the participant chewed tobacco or not. The dependent variables are the students' blood pressures and heart rates.

3. The treatment group is the tobacco group—the other group was used as a control.

4. A student's blood pressure might not be affected by knowing that he or she was part of a study. However, if the student's blood pressure were affected by this knowledge, all the students (in both groups) would be affected similarly. This might be an example of the placebo effect.

5. Answers will vary. One possible answer is that confounding variables might include the way that the students chewed the tobacco, whether or not the students smoked (although this would hopefully have been evened out with the randomization), and that all the participants were university students.

6. Answers will vary. One possible answer is that the study design was fine, but that it cannot be generalized beyond the population of university students (or people around that age).

Objectives

After completing this chapter, you should be able to

1 Organize data using frequency distributions.

2 Represent data in frequency distributions graphically using histograms, frequency polygons, and ogives.

3 Represent data using Pareto charts, time series graphs, and pie graphs.

4 Draw and interpret a stem and leaf plot.

Outline

2–1 Introduction

2–2 Organizing Data

2–3 Histograms, Frequency Polygons, and Ogives

2–4 Other Types of Graphs

2–5 Summary

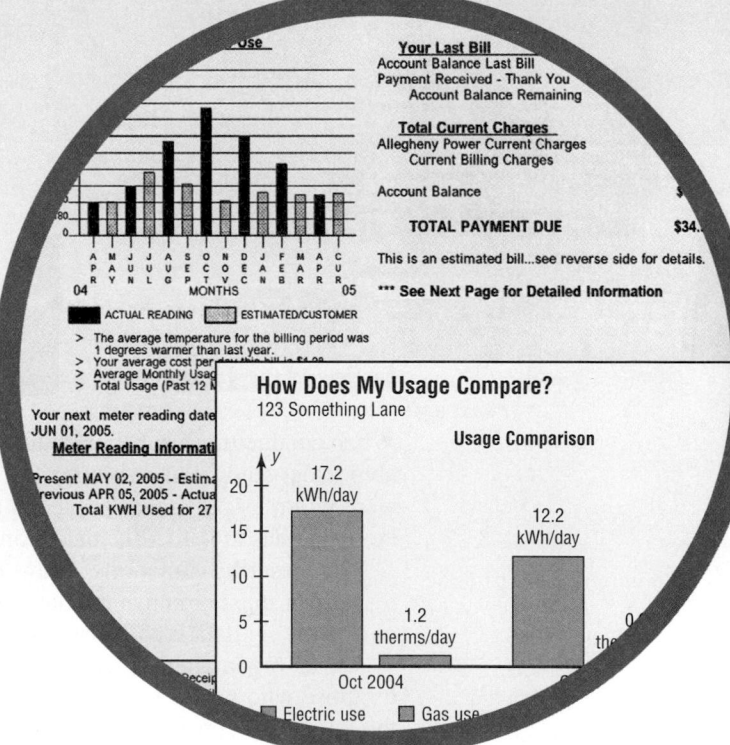

Statistics Today

How Serious Are Hospital Infections?

According to a fact sheet published by the Canadian Union of Public Employees (CUPE), the union estimates that as many as 250,000 patients in Canada contract hospital-acquired infections every year. How serious a problem is this? The fact sheet goes on to say that these infections result in up to 12,000 deaths or almost 5% of infected patients. These figures may be low. In the United States, a Pennsylvania health-care study provided some eye-opening data. In 2004, the state hospitals reported 11,668 patients had hospital-acquired infections with 1797 deaths caused by these infections. That figure represents almost 15.4%. The following table shows the type and number of infections in this study.

Type of infection	Infections reported	Number of deaths	Death rate
Multiple infections	945	527	55.80%
Pneumonia	1,335	393	29.40%
Bloodstream	1,932	446	23.10%
Urinary tract	6,139	423	6.90%
Surgical site	1,317	8	0.10%
	11,668	1,797	

Although the data represents an alarming scenario for hospital patients, the impact of the data may be lost in the numbers. A more powerful presentation using a well-drawn chart or graph would enhance the numeric data. This chapter will demonstrate procedures to organize data and to construct appropriate charts and graphs to represent data and emphasize key points in the data set.

See Statistics Today—Revisited, page 72, at the end of the chapter for some suggestions on how to represent the data graphically.

2-1   Introduction

When conducting a statistical study, the researcher must gather data for the particular variable under study. For example, if a researcher wishes to study the number of people who were bitten by poisonous snakes in a specific geographic area over the past several years, he or she has to gather the data from various doctors, hospitals, or health departments.

To describe situations, draw conclusions, or make inferences about events, the researcher must organize the data in some meaningful way. The most convenient method of organizing data is to construct a *frequency distribution.*

After organizing the data, the researcher must present them so they can be understood by those who will benefit from reading the study. The most useful method of presenting the data is by constructing *statistical charts* and *graphs.* There are many different types of charts and graphs, and each one has a specific purpose.

This chapter explains how to organize data by constructing frequency distributions and how to present the data by constructing charts and graphs. The charts and graphs illustrated here are histograms, frequency polygons, ogives, pie graphs, Pareto charts, and time series graphs. A graph that combines the characteristics of a frequency distribution and a histogram, called a stem and leaf plot, is also explained.

| **2–2** | # Organizing Data |

Objective 1

Organize data using frequency distributions.

 Suppose a researcher wished to do a study on the number of kilometres that the employees of a large department store travelled to work each day. The researcher first would have to collect the data by asking each employee the approximate distance the store is from his or her home. When data are collected in original form, they are called **raw data.** In this case, the data are

1	2	6	7	12	13	2	6	9	5
18	7	3	15	15	4	17	1	14	5
4	16	4	5	8	6	5	18	5	2
9	11	12	1	9	2	10	11	4	10
9	18	8	8	4	14	7	3	2	6

Since little information can be obtained from looking at raw data, the researcher organizes the data into what is called a *frequency distribution.* A frequency distribution consists of *classes* and their corresponding *frequencies.* Each raw data value is placed into a quantitative or qualitative category called a **class.** The **frequency** of a class then is the number of data values contained in a specific class. A frequency distribution is shown for the data set above.

Class limits (in kilometres)	Tally	Frequency
1–3	𝟋𝟋𝟋 𝟋𝟋𝟋	10
4–6	𝟋𝟋𝟋 𝟋𝟋𝟋 ////	14
7–9	𝟋𝟋𝟋 𝟋𝟋𝟋	10
10–12	𝟋𝟋𝟋 /	6
13–15	𝟋𝟋𝟋	5
16–18	𝟋𝟋𝟋	5
		Total 50

Now some general observations can be made from looking at the data in the form of a frequency distribution. For example, the majority of employees live within nine kilometres of the store.

> A **frequency distribution** is the organization of raw data in table form, using classes and frequencies.

The classes in this distribution are 1–3, 4–6, etc. These values are called *class limits.* The data values 1, 2, 3 can be tallied in the first class; 4, 5, 6 in the second class; and so on.

Two types of frequency distributions that are most often used are the *categorical frequency distribution* and the *grouped frequency distribution.* The procedures for constructing these distributions are shown now.

Categorical Frequency Distributions

The **categorical frequency distribution** is used for data that can be placed in specific categories, such as nominal- or ordinal-level data. For example, data such as political affiliation, religious affiliation, or major field of study would use categorical frequency distributions.

Example 2–1

Twenty-five armed forces recruits were given a blood test to determine their blood type. The data set is

A	B	B	AB	O
O	O	B	AB	B
B	B	O	A	O
A	O	O	O	AB
AB	A	O	B	A

Construct a frequency distribution for the data.

Solution

Since the data are categorical, discrete classes can be used. There are four blood types: A, B, O, and AB. These types will be used as the classes for the distribution.

The procedure for constructing a frequency distribution for categorical data is given next.

Step 1   Make a table as shown.

A Class	B Tally	C Frequency	D Percent
A			
B			
O			
AB			

Step 2   Tally the data and place the results in column B.

Step 3   Count the tallies and place the results in column C.

Step 4   Find the percentage of values in each class by using the formula

$$\% = \frac{f}{n} \cdot 100\%$$

where f = frequency of the class and n = total number of values in the data set. For example, in the class of type A blood, the percentage is

$$\% = \frac{5}{25} \cdot 100\% = 20\%$$

Percentages are not normally part of a frequency distribution, but they can be added since they are used in certain types of graphs such as pie graphs. Also, the decimal equivalent of a percent is called a *relative frequency*.

Step 5   Find the totals for columns C (frequency) and D (percent). The completed table is shown.

A Class	B Tally	C Frequency	D Percent
A	/////\	5	20
B	/////\ //	7	28
O	/////\ ////	9	36
AB	////	4	16
		Total 25	100

For the sample, more people have type O blood than any other type.

Grouped Frequency Distributions

When the range of the data is large, the data must be grouped into classes that are more than one unit in width, in what is called a **grouped frequency distribution.** For example, a distribution of the number of hours that boat batteries lasted is the following.

Class limits	Class boundaries	Tally	Frequency	Cumulative frequency
24–30	23.5–30.5	///	3	3
31–37	30.5–37.5	/	1	4
38–44	37.5–44.5	/////\	5	9
45–51	44.5–51.5	/////\ ////	9	18
52–58	51.5–58.5	/////\ /	6	24
59–65	58.5–65.5	/	1	25
			25	

The procedure for constructing the preceding frequency distribution is given in Example 2–2; however, several things should be noted. In this distribution, the values 24 and 30 of the first class are called *class limits*. The **lower class limit** is 24; it represents the smallest data value that can be included in the class. The **upper class limit** is 30; it represents the largest data value that can be included in the class. The numbers in the second column are called **class boundaries**. These numbers are used to separate the classes so that there are no gaps in the frequency distribution. The gaps are due to the limits; for example, there is a gap between 30 and 31.

Students sometimes have difficulty finding class boundaries when given the class limits. The basic rule of thumb is that *the class limits should have the same decimal place value as the data, but the class boundaries should have one additional place value and end in a 5.* For example, if the values in the data set are whole numbers, such as 24, 32, 18, the limits for a class might be 31–37, and the boundaries are 30.5–37.5. Find the boundaries by subtracting 0.5 from 31 (the lower class limit) and adding 0.5 to 37 (the upper class limit).

$$\text{Lower limit} - 0.5 = 31 - 0.5 = 30.5 = \text{lower boundary}$$

$$\text{Upper limit} + 0.5 = 37 + 0.5 = 37.5 = \text{upper boundary}$$

If the data are in tenths, such as 6.2, 7.8, and 12.6, the limits for a class hypothetically might be 7.8–8.8, and the boundaries for that class would be 7.75–8.85. Find these values by subtracting 0.05 from 7.8 and adding 0.05 to 8.8.

Finally, the **class width** for a class in a frequency distribution is found by subtracting the lower (or upper) class limit of one class from the lower (or upper) class limit of the next class. For example, the class width in the preceding distribution on the duration of boat batteries is 7, found from $31 - 24 = 7$.

The class width can also be found by subtracting the lower boundary from the upper boundary for any given class. In this case, $30.5 - 23.5 = 7$.

Note: Do not subtract the limits of a single class. It will result in an incorrect answer.

The researcher must decide how many classes to use and the width of each class. To construct a frequency distribution, follow these rules:

1. *There should be between 5 and 20 classes.* Although there is no hard-and-fast rule for the number of classes contained in a frequency distribution, it is of the utmost importance to have enough classes to present a clear description of the collected data.

2. *It is preferable but not absolutely necessary that the class width be an odd number.* This ensures that the midpoint of each class has the same place value as the data. The **class midpoint** X_m is obtained by adding the lower and upper boundaries and dividing by 2, or adding the lower and upper limits and dividing by 2:

$$X_m = \frac{\text{lower boundary} + \text{upper boundary}}{2}$$

or

$$X_m = \frac{\text{lower limit} + \text{upper limit}}{2}$$

For example, the midpoint of the first class in the example with boat batteries is

$$\frac{24 + 30}{2} = 27 \quad \text{or} \quad \frac{23.5 + 30.5}{2} = 27$$

The midpoint is the numeric location of the centre of the class. Midpoints are necessary for graphing (see Section 2–3). If the class width is an even number, the midpoint is in tenths. For example, if the class width is 6 and the boundaries are 5.5 and 11.5, the midpoint is

$$\frac{5.5 + 11.5}{2} = \frac{17}{2} = 8.5$$

Rule 2 is only a suggestion, and it is not rigorously followed, especially when a computer is used to group data.

3. *The classes must be mutually exclusive.* Mutually exclusive classes have nonoverlapping class limits so that data cannot be placed into two classes. Many times, frequency distributions such as

Age
10–20
20–30
30–40
40–50

are found in the literature or in surveys. If a person is 40 years old, into which class should she or he be placed? A better way to construct a frequency distribution is to use classes such as

Age
10–20
21–31
32–42
43–53

4. *The classes must be continuous.* Even if there are no values in a class, the class must be included in the frequency distribution. There should be no gaps in a

frequency distribution. The only exception occurs when the class with a zero frequency is the first or last class. A class with a zero frequency at either end can be omitted without affecting the distribution.

5. *The classes must be exhaustive.* There should be enough classes to accommodate all the data.

6. *The classes must be equal in width.* This avoids a distorted view of the data.

One exception occurs when a distribution has a class that is open-ended. That is, the class has no specific beginning value or no specific ending value. A frequency distribution with an open-ended class is called an **open-ended distribution.** Here are two examples of distributions with open-ended classes.

Age	Frequency		Minutes	Frequency
10–20	3		Below 110	16
21–31	6		110–114	24
32–42	4		115–119	38
43–53	10		120–124	14
54 and above	8		125–129	5

The frequency distribution for age is open-ended for the last class, which means that anybody who is 54 years or older will be tallied in the last class. The distribution for minutes is open-ended for the first class, meaning that any minute values below 110 will be tallied in that class.

Example 2–2 shows the procedure for constructing a grouped frequency distribution, i.e., when the classes contain more than one data value.

Example 2–2

The following data represents final grades for Professor Fisher's introductory statistics course. Construct a frequency distribution using 7 classes.

74	73	71	55	91	62	78	83	63	81
68	93	37	78	57	56	65	67	81	95
65	58	83	65	72	76	81	53	57	67
88	85	73	97	73	82	43	69	62	31
75	75	62	41	68	87	78	41	98	73

Solution

The procedure for constructing a grouped frequency distribution for numerical data follows.

Step 1 Determine the classes.

Find the highest value and lowest value: $H = 98$ and $L = 31$.

Find the range: $R = $ highest value $-$ lowest value $= H - L$, so $R = 98 - 31 = 67$

Select the number of classes desired (usually between 5 and 20). In this case, 7 is arbitrarily chosen.

Find the class width by dividing the range by the number of classes.

$$\text{Width} = \frac{R}{\text{number of classes}} = \frac{67}{7} = 9.6$$

Round the answer up to the nearest whole number if there is a remainder: $9.6 \approx 10$. (Rounding *up* is different from rounding *off*. A number is rounded up if there is any decimal remainder when dividing. For example, $85 \div 6 = 14.167$ and is rounded up to 15. Also, $53 \div 4 = 13.25$ and is rounded up to 14. Also, after dividing, if there is no remainder, you will need to add an extra class to accommodate all the data.)

Select a starting point for the lowest class limit. This can be the smallest data value or any convenient number less than the smallest data value. In this case, 30 is used. Add the width to the lowest score taken as the starting point to get the lower limit of the next class. Keep adding until there are 7 classes, as shown, 30, 40, 50, etc.

Subtract one unit from the lower limit of the second class to get the upper limit of the first class. Then add the width to each upper limit to get all the upper limits.

$40 - 1 = 39$

The first class is 30–39, the second class is 40–49, etc.

Find the class boundaries by subtracting 0.5 from each lower class limit and adding 0.5 to each upper class limit:

29.5–39.5, 39.5–49.5, etc.

Step 2 Tally the data and place the tally for each data point in the appropriate class.

Step 3 Find the numerical frequencies (f) from the tallies for each class.

Step 4 Find the cumulative frequencies.

A cumulative frequency (cf) column can be added to the distribution by adding the frequency in each class to the total of the frequencies of the classes preceding that class, such as $0 + 2 = 2, 2 + 3 = 5, 5 + 6 = 11$, and $11 + 12 = 23$, etc. (Note: "Σf" is "sum of frequencies.")

The completed frequency distribution is

Class limits	Class boundaries	Tally	Frequency	Cumulative frequency
30–39	29.5–39.5	//	2	2
40–49	39.5–49.5	///	3	5
50–59	49.5–59.5	⊬⊬ /	6	11
60–69	59.5–69.5	⊬⊬ ⊬⊬ //	12	23
70–79	69.5–79.5	⊬⊬ ⊬⊬ ///	13	36
80–89	79.5–89.5	⊬⊬ ////	9	45
90–99	89.5–99.5	⊬⊬	5	50
			$n = \overline{\Sigma f} = 50$	

The frequency distributions shows that the class 69.5–79.5 contains the largest number of grades (13) followed by the class 59.5–69.5 with 12 grades. Hence, exactly one-half of the grades (25) fall between 59.5 and 79.5.

Cumulative frequencies are used to show how many data values are accumulated up to and including a specific class. In Example 2–2, 11 of the final grades are less than 60. Thirty-six of the student's grades are less than 80.

After the raw data have been organized into a frequency distribution, it will be analyzed by looking for peaks and extreme values. The peaks show which class or classes have the most data values compared to the other classes. Extreme values, called outliers, show large or small data values that are relative to other data values.

When the range of the data values is relatively small, a frequency distribution can be constructed using single data values for each class. This type of distribution is called an **ungrouped frequency distribution** and is shown next.

Example 2–3	The data shown here represents highway fuel economy ratings, L/100 km (rounded to the nearest whole number), for 30 selected special purpose vehicles (sports utility vehicles, hybrids, etc.) from various manufacturers with sales in Canada. Construct a frequency distribution, and analyze the distribution.

9	11	12	8	10	14
10	11	8	11	11	10
11	10	7	10	8	11
9	9	12	8	12	8
13	8	11	8	11	12

Source: Natural Resources Canada, *Fuel Consumption Guide, 2006.*

Solution

Step 1 Determine the classes. Since the range of the data set is small (14 − 7 = 7), classes consisting of a single data value can be used. They are 7, 8, 9, 10, 11, 12, 13, and 14.

Note: If the data are continuous, class boundaries can be used. Subtract 0.5 from each class value to get the lower class boundary, and add 0.5 to each class value to get the upper class boundary.

Step 2 Tally the data and place the tally in the appropriate class.

Step 3 Count and record the numerical frequencies from the tallies.

Step 4 Determine the cumulative frequencies beginning with the lowest class.

Class limits	Class boundaries	Tally	Frequency	Cumulative frequency
7	6.5–7.5	/	1	1
8	7.5–8.5	ℍℍ //	7	8
9	8.5–9.5	///	3	11
10	9.5–10.5	ℍℍ	5	16
11	10.5–11.5	ℍℍ ///	8	24
12	11.5–12.5	////	4	28
13	12.5–13.5	/	1	29
14	13.5–14.5	/	1	30

$$n = \Sigma f = 30$$

In this case more than one-half (16/30) of the special purpose vehicles are fuel efficient with 10 or less L/100 km highway fuel consumption.

The steps for constructing a grouped frequency distribution are summarized in the following Procedure Table.

Procedure Table

Constructing a Grouped Frequency Distribution

Step 1   Determine the classes.

Find the highest and lowest value.

Find the range.

Select the number of classes desired.

Find the width by dividing the range by the number of classes and rounding up.

Select a starting point (usually the lowest value or any convenient number less than the lowest value); add the width to get the lower limits.

Find the upper class limits.

Find the boundaries.

Step 2   Tally the data.

Step 3   Find the numerical frequencies from the tallies.

Step 4   Find the cumulative frequencies.

Interesting Fact

Male dogs bite children more often than female dogs do; however, female cats bite children more often than male cats do.

When one is constructing a frequency distribution, the guidelines presented in this section should be followed. However, one can construct several different but correct frequency distributions for the same data by using a different class width, a different number of classes, or a different starting point.

Furthermore, the method shown here for constructing a frequency distribution is not unique, and there are other ways of constructing one. Slight variations exist, especially in computer packages. But regardless of what methods are used, classes should be mutually exclusive, continuous, exhaustive, and of equal width.

In summary, the different types of frequency distributions were shown in this section. The first type, shown in Example 2–1, is used when the data are categorical (nominal), such as blood type or political affiliation. This type is called a categorical frequency distribution. The second type of distribution is used when the range is large and classes several units in width are needed. This type is called a grouped frequency distribution and is shown in Example 2–2. Another type of distribution is used for numerical data and when the range of data is small, as shown in Example 2–3. Since each class is only one unit, this distribution is called an ungrouped frequency distribution.

All the different types of distributions are used in statistics and are helpful when one is organizing and presenting data.

The reasons for constructing a frequency distribution are as follows:

1. To organize the data in a meaningful, intelligible way.
2. To enable the reader to determine the nature or shape of the distribution.
3. To facilitate computational procedures for measures of average and spread (shown in Chapter 3, Sections 3–2 and 3–3).
4. To enable the researcher to draw charts and graphs for the presentation of data (shown in Section 2–3).
5. To enable the reader to make comparisons among different data sets.

The factors used to analyze a frequency distribution are essentially the same as those used to analyze histograms and frequency polygons, which are shown in Section 2–3.

Applying the Concepts 2-2

Prime Minister Ages at Swearing-In

The data represent the ages of Canada's prime ministers at their swearing-in ceremony.

52	51	70	47	69	74
54	57	46	47	60	66
61	66	48	39	55	45
46	59	65	46		

Source: Parliament of Canada.

1. Were the data obtained from a population or a sample? Explain your answer.
2. What was the age of the oldest prime minister?
3. What was the age of the youngest prime minister?
4. Construct a frequency distribution for the data. (Use your own judgment as to the number of classes and class size.)
5. Are there any peaks in the distribution?
6. Identify any possible outliers.
7. Write a brief summary of the nature of the data as shown in the frequency distribution.

See page 76 for the answers.

Exercises 2-2

1. List five reasons for organizing data into a frequency distribution.

2. Name the three types of frequency distributions, and explain when each should be used.

3. Find the class boundaries, midpoints, and widths for each class.

　a. 12–18

　b. 56–74

　c. 695–705

　d. 13.6–14.7

　e. 2.15–3.93

4. How many classes should frequency distributions have? Why should the class width be an odd number?

5. Shown here are four frequency distributions. Each is incorrectly constructed. State the reason why.

a.

Class	Frequency
27–32	1
33–38	0
39–44	6
45–49	4
50–55	2

b.

Class	Frequency
5–9	1
9–13	2
13–17	5
17–20	6
20–24	3

c.

Class	Frequency
123–127	3
128–132	7
138–142	2
143–147	19

d.

Class	Frequency
9–13	1
14–19	6
20–25	2
26–28	5
29–32	9

6. What are open-ended frequency distributions? Why are they necessary?

7. A survey was taken on how much trust people place in the information they read on the Internet. Construct a categorical frequency distribution for the data, A = trust in everything they read, M = trust in most of what they read, H = trust in about one-half of what they read, S = trust in a small portion of what they read. (Based on information from the *UCLA Internet Report.*)

M	M	M	A	H	M	S	M	H	M
S	M	M	M	M	A	M	M	A	M
M	M	H	M	M	M	H	M	H	M
A	M	M	M	H	M	M	M	M	M

8. At a Prince Edward County, Ontario, pumpkinfest, the heaviest pumpkin contest had the following entries. Weights are in kilograms. Construct a frequency distribution using 8 classes beginning at 30. (*Trivia: The 2005 Guinness Book of Records lists the heaviest pumpkin grown at 666.32 kg.*)

215	342	266	233	158	134	362
405	240	417	228	276	422	134
396	287	251	366	150	254	
34	113	245	215	147	94	
347	269	153	177	140	48	

Source: www.pec.on.ca/pumpkinfest/.

9. The National Hockey League expanded from six to 12 teams in 1967. The data shown represents the NHL leading scorer point total since the expansion. Construct a frequency distribution for the data beginning at the minimum data value and use a class width of 20.

125	122	199	164	130
94	161	168	137	133
106	70	183	134	152
96	130	215	132	120
121	160	208	136	126
96	131	205	125	87
127	163	196	135	97
102	142	212	145	

Source: National Hockey League.

10. The Earth Policy Institute's study of global warming trends (1956–2005) published the following data. Temperatures shown are in °C. Construct a frequency distribution using 6 classes, and analyze the nature of the data.

1956–1965	1966–1975	1976–1985	1986–1995	1996–2005
13.8	13.9	13.8	14.2	14.4
14.1	14.0	14.2	14.4	14.4
14.1	13.9	14.1	14.4	14.7
14.1	14.0	14.1	14.3	14.4
14.0	14.0	14.3	14.5	14.4
14.1	13.9	14.4	14.4	14.6
14.1	14.0	14.1	14.2	14.7
14.0	14.2	14.3	14.2	14.6
13.7	13.9	14.2	14.3	14.6
13.8	14.0	14.1	14.5	14.8

Source: Earth Policy Institute.

11. The average quantitative Graduate Records Exam (GRE) scores for the top 30 graduate schools of engineering are listed. Construct a frequency distribution with 6 classes.

767	770	761	760	771	768	776	771	756	770
763	760	747	766	754	771	771	778	766	762
780	750	746	764	769	759	757	753	758	746

Source: *U.S. News & World Report Best Graduate Schools.*

12. In 2003, Canadian Mike Weir won golf's prestigious Masters Championship in an exciting playoff. Below are the final results for the tournament. Construct a frequency distribution with 7 classes beginning at 280. (The data in this exercise will be used in Exercise 22 in Section 3–2.)

281	288	290	292	294	295	297
281	288	290	293	294	296	298
283	288	290	293	294	296	301
284	288	290	293	294	297	301
286	288	290	293	295	297	302
287	289	290	293	295	297	304
287	289	291	294	295	297	305

Source: www.augusta.com.

13. The data below represents the term served (in months) of Canada's prime ministers since Confederation. Five prime ministers served multiple non-consecutive terms. Construct a frequency distribution using 24 month intervals. (The data for this exercise will be used for Exercise 5 in Section 2–3 and Exercise 23 in Section 3–2.)

26	121	5	105	3	9
51	134	60	70	103	62
157	47	54	3	17	33
72	183	14	16	24	17
59	152	76			

Source: Parliament of Canada.

14. The data below represents the number of automobile fatalities in Canada over the past 20 years. Construct a frequency distribution using 7 classes beginning at 2400. (The data for this exercise will be used for Exercise 6 in Section 2–3 and Exercise 24 in Section 3–2.)

3774	3651	3121	2646	2434
3510	3445	2869	2612	2593
3729	3228	2854	2636	2484
3610	3073	2708	2569	2434

Source: Transport Canada.

15. The following data represents the quarterly exchange (in cents) for Canada to United States dollars over a ten-year period. Construct a frequency distribution using 7 classes starting at the minimum value. (The information in this exercise will be used for Exercise 9 in Section 2–3 and Exercise 25 in Section 3–2.)

90	82	76	63	66	68	66	72
86	82	73	65	64	68	68	72
86	78	74	63	66	68	68	73
85	74	68	63	67	68	71	73
81	75	64	64	68	66	71	73

Source: Bank of Canada.

16. The area, in square kilometres, of Canada's National Parks under 10,000 km^2 is shown here. Construct a frequency distribution for the data using 7 classes.

(The data in this exercise will be used in Exercise 11 in Section 2–3.)

6641	16	206	4766	3050
1349	1406	400	1943	1495
1313	3874	404	1878	4345
505	2973	239	907	1138
194	26	544	151	33
260	948	500	154	
9	22	240	112	

Source: Parks Canada.

17. The heights (in metres above sea level) for the top 50 of the world's highest mountains are given here. Construct a frequency distribution for the data using 8 classes beginning at 7000. (The data is this exercise will be used in Exercise 19 in Section 3–2 and Exercise 17 in Section 3–3.)

8848	8068	7785	7654	7313
8611	8047	7756	7619	7291
8586	8035	7756	7555	7285
8511	8012	7756	7553	7273
8463	7885	7546	7546	7245
8201	7852	7742	7495	7150
8167	7820	7723	7485	7142
8163	7816	7720	7439	7135
8125	7815	7719	7406	7134
8091	7788	7690	7398	7129

Source: : http://www.scaruffi.com/travel/tallest.html

18. During the 1998 baseball season, Mark McGwire and Sammy Sosa both broke Roger Maris's home run record of 61. The distances (in feet) for each home run follow. Construct a frequency distribution for each player, using 8 classes. (The information in this exercise will be used for Exercise 12 in Section 2–3, Exercise 10 in Section 3–2, and Exercise 14 in Section 3–3.)

McGwire				Sosa			
306	370	370	430	371	350	430	420
420	340	460	410	430	434	370	420
440	410	380	360	440	410	420	460
350	527	380	550	400	430	410	370
478	420	390	420	370	410	380	340
425	370	480	390	350	420	410	415
430	388	423	410	430	380	380	366
360	410	450	350	500	380	390	400
450	430	461	430	364	430	450	440
470	440	400	390	365	420	350	420
510	430	450	452	400	380	380	400
420	380	470	398	370	420	360	368
409	385	369	460	430	433	388	440
390	510	500	450	414	482	364	370
470	430	458	380	400	405	433	390
430	341	385	410	480	480	434	344
420	380	400	440	410	420		
377	370						

Source: *USA TODAY.*

Extending the Concepts

19. A researcher conducted a survey asking people if they believed more than one person was involved in the assassination of United States President John F. Kennedy in 1963. The results were as follows: 73% said yes, 19% said no, and 9% had no opinion. Is there anything suspicious about the results?

2–3   Histograms, Frequency Polygons, and Ogives

Objective ②

Represent data in frequency distributions graphically using histograms, frequency polygons, and ogives.

After the data have been organized into a frequency distribution, they can be presented in graphical form. The purpose of graphs in statistics is to convey the data to the viewers in pictorial form. It is easier for most people to comprehend the meaning of data presented graphically than data presented numerically in tables or frequency distributions. This is especially true if the users have little or no statistical knowledge.

Statistical graphs can be used to describe the data set or to analyze it. Graphs are also useful in getting the audience's attention in a publication or a speaking presentation. They can be used to discuss an issue, reinforce a critical point, or summarize a data set. They can also be used to discover a trend or pattern in a situation over a period of time.

The three most commonly used graphs in research are as follows:

1. The histogram.

2. The frequency polygon.

3. The cumulative frequency graph, or ogive (pronounced o-jive).

An example of each type of graph is shown in Figure 2–1. The data for each graph represent the distribution of record high temperatures, in °C, for each of the 50 states in the United States.

Figure 2–1

Examples of Commonly Used Graphs

(a) Histogram

(b) Frequency polygon

(c) Cumulative frequency graph—Ogive

The Histogram

The **histogram** is a bar chart in which vertical bars represent class frequencies.

Example 2–4   Construct a histogram to represent the data shown for final grades in Professor Fisher's introductory statistics course.

Class boundaries	Frequency
29.5–39.5	2
39.5–49.5	3
49.5–59.5	6
59.5–69.5	12
69.5–79.5	13
79.5–89.5	9
89.5–99.5	5

Solution

Step 1   Draw and label the x and y axes. The x axis is always the horizontal axis, and the y axis is always the vertical axis.

Step 2   Represent the frequency on the y axis and the class boundaries on the x axis.

Step 3   Using the frequencies as the heights, draw vertical bars for each class. See Figure 2–2.

Figure 2–2

Histogram for Example 2–4

Historical Note

Graphs originated when ancient astronomers drew the position of the stars in the heavens. Roman surveyors also used coordinates to locate landmarks on their maps.

The development of statistical graphs can be traced to William Playfair (1748–1819), an engineer and drafter who used graphs to present economic data pictorially.

As the histogram shows, the class with the greatest number of data values (13) is 69.5–79.5, followed by 12 for 59.5–69.5. The graph also has one peak with the data clustering around it.

The Frequency Polygon

Another way to represent the same data set is by using a frequency polygon.

The **frequency polygon** is a graph that displays the data by using lines that connect points plotted for the frequencies at the midpoints of the classes. The frequencies are represented by the heights of the points.

Example 2–5 shows the procedure for constructing a frequency polygon.

Example 2–5

Using the frequency distribution given in Example 2–4, construct a frequency polygon.

Solution

Step 1 Find the midpoints of each class. Recall that midpoints are found by adding the upper and lower boundaries and dividing by 2:

$$\frac{29.5 + 39.5}{2} = 34.5 \qquad \frac{39.5 + 49.5}{2} = 44.5$$

and so on. The midpoints are

Class boundaries	Midpoints	Frequency
29.5–39.5	34.5	2
39.5–49.5	44.5	3
49.5–59.5	54.5	6
59.5–69.5	64.5	12
69.5–79.5	74.5	13
79.5–89.5	84.5	9
89.5–99.5	94.5	5

Step 2 Draw the x and y axes. Label the x axis with the midpoint of each class, and then use a suitable scale on the y axis for the frequencies.

Step 3 Using the midpoints for the x values and the frequencies as the y values, plot the points.

Step 4 Connect adjacent points with line segments. Draw a line back to the x axis at the beginning and end of the graph, at the same distance that the previous (24.5) and next (104.5) midpoints would be located, as shown in Figure 2–3.

Figure 2–3

Frequency Polygon for
Example 2–5

The frequency polygon and the histogram are two different ways to represent the same data set. The choice of which one to use is left to the discretion of the researcher.

The Ogive

The third type of graph that can be used represents the cumulative frequencies for the classes. This type of graph is called the *cumulative frequency graph* or *ogive*. The **cumulative frequency** is the sum of the frequencies accumulated up to the upper boundary of a class in the distribution.

> The **ogive** is a graph that represents the cumulative frequencies for the classes in a frequency distribution.

Example 2–6 shows the procedure for constructing an ogive.

Example 2–6	Construct an ogive for the frequency distribution described in Example 2–4.

Solution

Step 1 Find the cumulative frequency for each class.

Class boundaries	Cumulative frequency
29.5–39.5	2
39.5–49.5	5
49.5–59.5	11
59.5–69.5	23
69.5–79.5	36
79.5–89.5	45
89.5–99.5	50

Step 2 Draw the *x* and *y* axes. Label the *x* axis with the class boundaries, beginning with the lower class boundary of the first class and ending with the upper class boundary of the last class. Use an appropriate scale for the *y* axis for the cumulative frequency column.

Step 3 Plot the cumulative frequencies at each upper class boundary as the cumulative frequency represents the number of data values below each upper class boundary.

Step 4 Starting with the first upper class boundary, 39.5, connect the adjacent points with line segments. Extend the graph to the first lower class boundary, 29.5, on the *x* axis. Refer to Figure 2–4.

Figure 2–4
Ogive for Example 2–6

Cumulative frequency graphs are used to visually represent how many values are below a certain upper class boundary. For example, to find out how many grades are less then 79.5, locate 79.5 on the x axis, draw a vertical line up until it intersects the graph, and then draw a horizontal line at that point to the y axis. The y axis value is 36. Therefore, 36 grades are less than 79.5.

The steps for drawing these three types of graphs are shown in the following Procedure Table.

Unusual Stat

Thirty-seven percent of Canadian teens report talking to friends on their cellphone while in school.

Procedure Table

Constructing Statistical Graphs

Step 1   Draw and label the x and y axes.

Step 2   Choose a suitable scale for the frequencies or cumulative frequencies, and label it on the y axis.

Step 3   Represent the class boundaries for the histogram or ogive, or the midpoint for the frequency polygon, on the x axis.

Step 4   Plot the points and then draw the bars or lines.

Relative Frequency Graphs

The histogram, the frequency polygon, and the ogive shown previously were constructed by using frequencies in terms of the raw data. These distributions can be converted to distributions using *proportions* instead of raw data as frequencies. These types of graphs are called **relative frequency graphs.**

Graphs of relative frequencies instead of frequencies are used when the proportion of data values that fall into a given class is more important than the actual number of data values that fall into that class. For example, if one wanted to compare the age distribution of adults in Toronto, Ontario, with adults in Niagara Falls, Ontario, one would use relative frequency distributions. The reason is that since the population of the City of Toronto is 2,480,000 whereas the City of Niagara Falls (not including tourists) is 78,815, the bars using the actual data values for Toronto would be much taller than those for the same classes for Niagara Falls.

To convert a frequency into a proportion or relative frequency, divide the frequency for each class by the total of the frequencies. The sum of the relative frequencies will always be 1. These graphs are similar to the ones that use raw data as frequencies, but the values on the y axis are in terms of proportions. Example 2–7 shows the three types of relative frequency graphs.

Example 2–7

Construct a histogram, frequency polygon, and ogive using relative frequencies for the distribution (shown here) of the kilometres that 20 randomly selected runners ran during a given week.

Class boundaries	Frequency	Cumulative frequency
5.5–10.5	1	1
10.5–15.5	2	3
15.5–20.5	3	6
20.5–25.5	5	11
25.5–30.5	4	15
30.5–35.5	3	18
35.5–40.5	2	20
	20	

Solution

Step 1 Convert each frequency to a proportion or relative frequency by dividing the frequency for each class by the total number of observations.

For class 5.5–10.5, the relative frequency is $\frac{1}{20} = 0.05$; for class 10.5−15.5, the relative frequency is $\frac{2}{20} = 0.10$; for class 15.5–20.5, the relative frequency is $\frac{3}{20} = 0.15$; and so on.

Place these values in the column labelled Relative frequency.

Step 2 Find the cumulative relative frequencies. To do this, add the frequency in each class to the total frequency of the preceding class. In this case, $0 + 0.05 = 0.05$, $0.05 + 0.10 = 0.15$, $0.15 + 0.15 = 0.30$, $0.30 + 0.25 = 0.55$, etc. Place these values in the column labelled Cumulative relative frequency.

Using the same procedure, find the relative frequencies for the Cumulative frequency column. The relative frequencies are shown here.

Class boundaries	Midpoints	Relative frequency	Cumulative relative frequency
5.5–10.5	8	0.05	0.05
10.5–15.5	13	0.10	0.15
15.5–20.5	18	0.15	0.30
20.5–25.5	23	0.25	0.55
25.5–30.5	28	0.20	0.75
30.5–35.5	33	0.15	0.90
35.5–40.5	38	0.10	1.00
		1.00	

Step 3 Draw each graph as shown in Figure 2–5. For the histogram and ogive, use the class boundaries along the x axis. For the frequency polygon, use the midpoints on the x axis. The scale on the y axis uses proportions.

Figure 2–5

Graphs for
Example 2–7

(a) Histogram

Figure 2–5

(Continued)

(b) Frequency polygon

(c) Ogive

Distribution Shapes

When one is describing data, it is important to be able to recognize the shapes of the distribution values. In later chapters you will see that the shape of a distribution also determines the appropriate statistical methods used to analyze the data.

A distribution can have many shapes, and one method of analyzing a distribution is to draw a histogram or frequency polygon for the distribution. Several of the most common shapes are shown in Figure 2–6: *the bell-shaped or mound-shaped, the uniform-shaped, the positively or right-skewed shaped, the negatively or left-skewed shaped, and the bimodal-shaped.*

Distributions are most often not perfectly shaped, so it is not necessary to have an exact shape but rather to identify an overall pattern.

A *bell-shaped distribution* shown in Figure 2–6(a) has a single peak and tapers off at either end. It is approximately symmetric; i.e., it is roughly the same on both sides of a line running through the centre.

A *uniform distribution* is basically flat or rectangular. See Figure 2–6(b).

When the peak of a distribution is to the left and the data values taper off to the right, a distribution is said to be *positively or right-skewed*. See Figure 2–6(c). When the data values are clustered to the right and taper off to the left, a distribution is said to be *negatively or left-skewed*. See Figure 2–6(d). Skewness will be explained in detail in Chapter 3, pages 90–91. Distributions with one peak, such as those shown in Figure 2–6(a), (c), and (d), are

Figure 2–6

Distribution Shapes

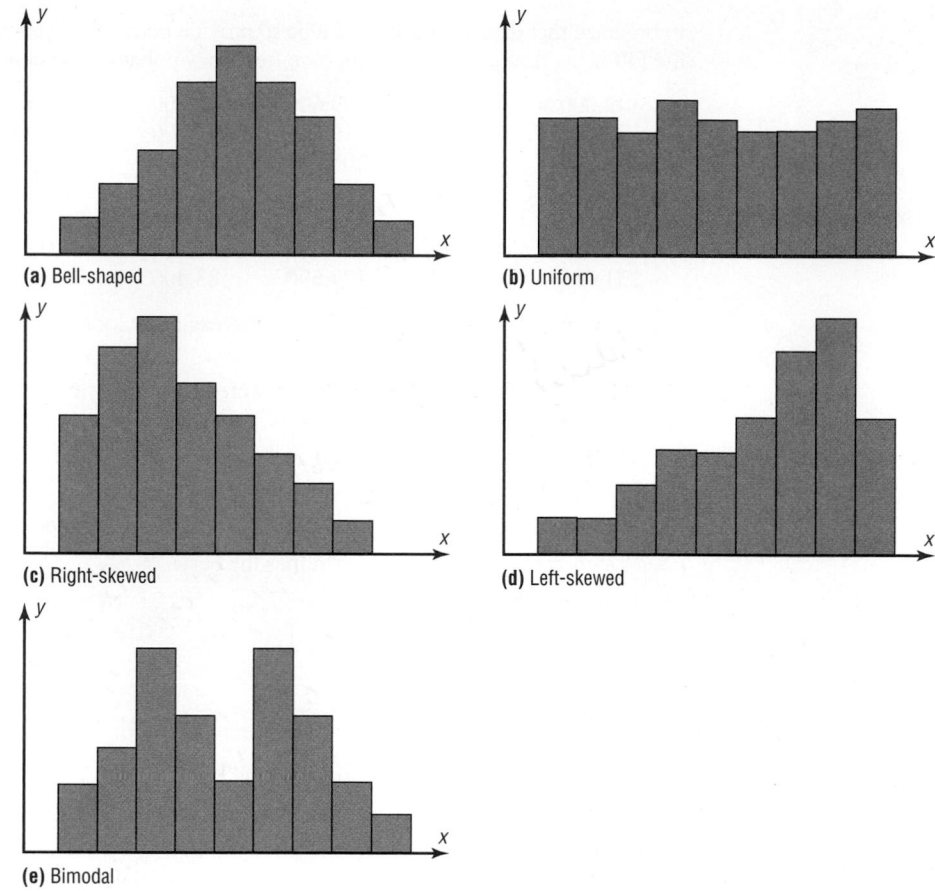

(a) Bell-shaped

(b) Uniform

(c) Right-skewed

(d) Left-skewed

(e) Bimodal

said to be *unimodal*. (The highest peak of a distribution indicates where the mode of the data values is. The mode is the data value that occurs more often than any other data value. Modes are explained in Chapter 3.) When a distribution has two peaks of the same height, it is said to be *bimodal*. See Figure 2–6(e).

Distributions can have other shapes in addition to the ones shown here; however, these are some of the more common ones that you will encounter in analyzing data.

When you are analyzing histograms and frequency polygons, look at the shape of the curve. For example, does it have one peak or two peaks? Is it relatively flat, or is it bimodal? Are the data values spread out on the graph, or are they clustered around the centre? Are there data values in the extreme ends? These may be *outliers*. (See Section 3–4 for an explanation of outliers.) Are there any gaps in the histogram, or does the frequency polygon touch the *x* axis somewhere other than the ends? Finally, are the data clustered at one end or the other, indicating a *skewed distribution*?

For example, the histogram for the statistics final grades shown in Figure 2–2 shows a single peaked distribution, with the class 69.5–79.5 containing the largest number of grades. The distribution has no gaps, and there are fewer grades in the lowest class than in the highest class.

Applying the Concepts 2–3

Selling Real Estate

Assume you are a realtor in St. John's, Newfoundland and Labrador. You have recently obtained a listing of the selling prices of the homes that have sold in that area in the last six months. You wish to organize that data so you will be able to provide potential buyers with useful information. Use the following data to create a histogram, frequency polygon, and cumulative frequency polygon.

142,000	127,000	99,600	162,000	89,000	93,000	99,500
73,800	135,000	119,500	67,900	156,300	104,500	108,650
123,000	91,000	205,000	110,000	156,300	104,000	133,900
179,000	112,000	147,000	321,550	87,900	88,400	180,000
159,400	205,300	144,400	163,000	96,000	81,000	131,000
114,000	119,600	93,000	123,000	187,000	96,000	80,000
231,000	189,500	177,600	83,400	77,000	132,300	166,000

1. What questions could be answered more easily by looking at the histogram rather than the listing of home prices?

2. What different questions could be answered more easily by looking at the frequency polygon rather than the listing of home prices?

3. What different questions could be answered more easily by looking at the cumulative frequency polygon rather than the listing of home prices?

4. Are there any extremely large or extremely small data values compared to the other data values?

5. Which graph displays these extremes the best?

6. Is the distribution skewed?

See page 76 for the answers.

Exercises 2–3

1. For 108 randomly selected college applicants, the following frequency distribution for entrance exam scores was obtained. Construct a histogram, frequency polygon, and ogive for the data. (The data for this exercise will be used for Exercise 13 in this section.)

Class limits	Frequency
90–98	6
99–107	22
108–116	43
117–125	28
126–134	9

Applicants who score above 107 need not enroll in a summer developmental program. In this group, how many students do not have to enroll in the developmental program?

2. For 75 employees of a large department store, the following distribution for years of service was obtained. Construct a histogram, frequency polygon, and ogive for the data. (The data for this exercise will be used for Exercise 14 in this section.)

Class limits	Frequency
1–5	21
6–10	25
11–15	15
16–20	0
21–25	8
26–30	6

A majority of the employees have worked for how many years or less?

3. Calgarian Stephen Ames won The Players Championship in 2006. This victory earned the Canadian golfer US$1.44 million or C$1,682,928. The final results represent player scores after four completed rounds of golf and are shown as a frequency distribution.

Class limits	Frequency
280–283	5
284–287	13
288–291	16
292–295	20
296–299	13
300–303	4
304–307	2

Source: www.pgatour.com.

Construct a histogram, frequency polygon, and ogive for the distribution. Comment on the skewness of the distribution.

4. The salaries (in millions of dollars) for 31 NFL teams for a specific season are given in this frequency distribution.

Class limits	Frequency
39.9–42.8	2
42.9–45.8	2
45.9–48.8	5
48.9–51.8	5
51.9–54.8	12
54.9–57.8	5

Source: NFL.com.

Construct a histogram, frequency polygon, and ogive for the data; and comment on the shape of the distribution.

5. Federal elections in Canada are not held at fixed dates, and so prime ministers serve for terms of variable lengths. The following distribution illustrates the number of months served by prime ministers since Confederation. Construct a histogram, frequency polygon, and ogive for the data.

Term (months)	Class boundaries	Frequency
1–24	0.5–24.5	9
25–48	24.5–48.5	3
49–72	48.5–72.5	7
73–96	72.5–96.5	1
97–120	96.5–120.5	2
121–144	120.5–144.5	2
145–168	144.5–168.5	2
169–192	168.5–192.5	1

Source: Parliament of Canada.

6. Construct a histogram, frequency polygon, and ogive for the data in Exercise 14 in Section 2–2, and analyze the results.

7. The air quality measured for selected cities in the United States for 1993 and 2002 is shown. The data are the number of days per year that the cities failed to meet acceptable standards. Construct a histogram for both years and see if there are any notable changes. If so, explain. (The data in this exercise will be used for Exercise 17 in this section.)

1993		2002	
Class	**Frequency**	**Class**	**Frequency**
0–27	20	0–27	19
28–55	4	28–55	6
56–83	3	56–83	2
84–111	1	84–111	0
112–139	1	112–139	0
140–167	0	140–167	3
168–195	1	168–195	0

Source: *World Almanac and Book of Facts.*

8. In a study of reaction times of dogs to a specific stimulus, an animal trainer obtained the following data, given in seconds. Construct a histogram, frequency polygon, and ogive for the data, and analyze the results. (The histogram in this exercise will be used for Exercise 18 in this section, Exercise 16 in Section 3–2, and Exercise 26 in Section 3–3.)

Class limits	Frequency
2.3–2.9	10
3.0–3.6	12
3.7–4.3	6
4.4–5.0	8
5.1–5.7	4
5.8–6.4	2

9. Construct a histogram, frequency polygon, and ogive for the data in Exercise 15 of Section 2–2, and analyze the results.

10. The following data shows the percentage of drivers and passenger fatalities in Canada by age group. Draw histograms for each category using age groups as *x* axis labels. Decide if there is any difference in age group fatalities.

Age group	Drivers	Passengers
0–4	0	1.4
5–14	0.2	7.7
15–19	8.8	19.0
20–24	14.6	15.5
25–34	17.5	12.0
35–44	17.0	9.5
45–54	14.9	9.6
55–64	11.1	7.7
65+	15.4	16.6

Source: Transport Canada.

11. Construct a histogram, frequency polygon, and ogive for the data in Exercise 16 in Section 2–2, and analyze the results.

12. For the data in Exercise 18 in Section 2–2, construct a histogram for the home run distances for each player and compare them. Are they basically the same, or are there any noticeable differences? Explain your answer.

13. For the data in Exercise 1 in this section, construct a histogram, frequency polygon, and ogive, using relative frequencies. What proportion of the applicants need to enroll in the summer developmental program?

14. For the data in Exercise 2 in this section, construct a histogram, frequency polygon, and ogive, using relative frequencies. What proportion of the employees have been with the store for more than 20 years?

15. The number of calories per serving for selected ready-to-eat cereals is listed here. Construct a frequency distribution using 7 classes. Draw a histogram, frequency polygon, and ogive for the data, using relative frequencies. Describe the shape of the histogram.

130	190	140	80	100	120	220	220	110	100
210	130	100	90	210	120	200	120	180	120
190	210	120	200	130	180	260	270	100	160
190	240	80	120	90	190	200	210	190	180
115	210	110	225	190	130				

Source: *The Doctor's Pocket Calorie, Fat, and Carbohydrate Counter.*

16. The amount of protein (in grams) for a variety of fast-food sandwiches is reported here. Construct a frequency distribution using 6 classes. Draw a

histogram, frequency polygon, and ogive for the data, using relative frequencies. Describe the shape of the histogram.

23	30	20	27	44	26	35	20	29	29
25	15	18	27	19	22	12	26	34	15
27	35	26	43	35	14	24	12	23	31
40	35	38	57	22	42	24	21	27	33

Source: *The Doctor's Pocket Calorie, Fat, and Carbohydrate Counter.*

17. For the data for year 2002 in Exercise 7 in this section, construct a histogram, frequency polygon, and ogive, using relative frequencies.

18. The animal trainer in Exercise 8 in this section selected another group of dogs who were much older than the first group and measured their reaction times to the same stimulus. Construct a histogram, frequency polygon, and ogive for the data.

Class limits	Frequency
2.3–2.9	1
3.0–3.6	3
3.7–4.3	4
4.4–5.0	16
5.1–5.7	14
5.8–6.4	4

Analyze the results and compare the histogram for this group with the one obtained in Exercise 8 in this section. Are there any differences in the histograms? (The data in this exercise will be used for Exercise 16 in Section 3–2 and Exercise 26 in Section 3–3.)

Extending the Concepts

19. Using the histogram shown here, do the following.

a. Construct a frequency distribution; include class limits, class frequencies, midpoints, and cumulative frequencies.

b. Construct a frequency polygon.

c. Construct an ogive.

20. Using the results from Exercise 19, answer these questions.

a. How many values are in the class 27.5–30.5?

b. How many values fall between 24.5 and 36.5?

c. How many values are below 33.5?

d. How many values are above 30.5?

2–4   Other Types of Graphs

In addition to the histogram, the frequency polygon, and the ogive, several other types of graphs are often used in statistics. They are the Pareto chart, the time series graph, and the pie graph. Figure 2–7 shows an example of each type of graph.

Pareto Charts

Objective ③

Represent data using Pareto charts, time series graphs, and pie graphs.

In Section 2–3, graphs such as the histogram, frequency polygon, and ogive showed how data can be represented when the variable displayed on the horizontal axis is quantitative, such as heights and weights.

On the other hand, when the variable displayed on the horizontal axis is qualitative or categorical, a *Pareto chart* can be used.

Figure 2–7

Other Types of Graphs Used in Statistics

(a) Pareto chart

(b) Time series graph

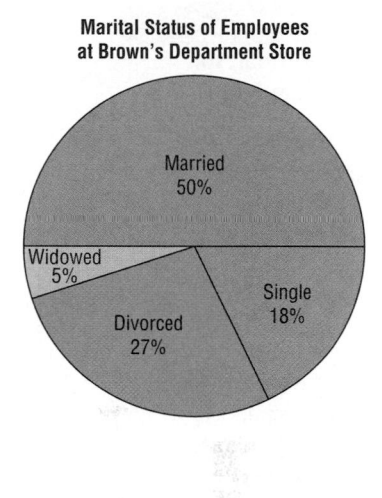

(c) Pie graph

A **Pareto chart** is used to represent a frequency distribution for a categorical variable, and the frequencies are displayed by the heights of vertical bars, which are arranged in order from highest to lowest.

Example 2–8

The table shown represents the usual source from which student smokers, Grades 5 to 9, obtain their cigarettes. Construct and analyze a Pareto chart for the data.

Source	Number
Take from family	9
Friend gives	30
Family gives	14
Buy from friends/other	25
Store	22

Source: Youth Smoking Survey, Technical Report, Health Canada, 2002. Adapted and reproduced with the permission of the Minister of Public Works and Government Services Canada, 2007.

Solution

Step 1 Arrange the data from the largest to the smallest according to frequency.

Source	Number
Friend gives	30
Buy from friends/other	25
Store	22
Family gives	14
Take from family	9

Step 2 Draw and label the *x* and *y* axes.

Step 3 Draw the bars corresponding to the frequencies. See Figure 2–8. The Pareto chart shows that the usual source from which student smokers, Grades 5 to 9, obtain cigarettes is from friends. This source is more than triple the source of taking cigarettes from family.

Figure 2–8

Pareto Chart for Example 2–8

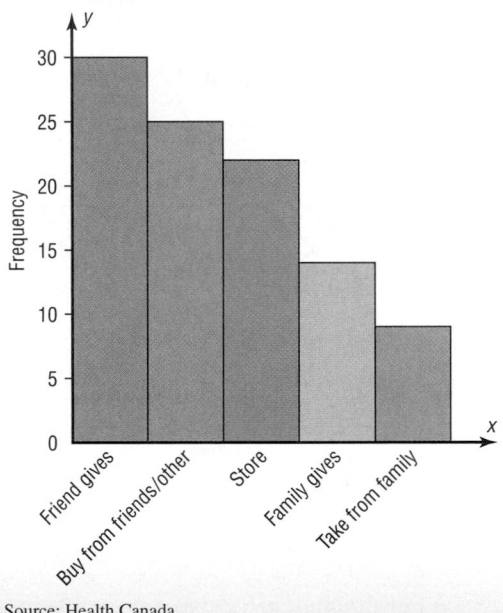

Usual Source of Cigarettes for Smokers (Grades 5 to 9)

Source: Health Canada.

Historical Note

Vilfredo Pareto (1848–1923) was an Italian scholar who developed theories in economics, statistics, and the social sciences. His contributions to statistics include the development of a mathematical function used in economics. This function has many statistical applications and is called the Pareto distribution. In addition, he researched income distribution, and his findings became known as Pareto's law.

Suggestions for Drawing Pareto Charts

1. Make the bars the same width.
2. Arrange the data from largest to smallest according to frequency.
3. Make the units that are used for the frequency equal in size.

When you analyze a Pareto chart, make comparisons by looking at the heights of the bars.

The Time Series Graph

When data are collected over a period of time, they can be represented by a time series graph.

A **time series graph** represents data that occur over a specific period of time.

Example 2–9 shows the procedure for constructing a time series graph.

Example 2–9	Fuelled by high oil prices and Alberta's booming economy, Calgary's population is sharply rising. The following data (in thousands) illustrates Calgary's rapid growth. Construct and analyze a time series graph for the data.

Year	Population
1980	560.6
1985	625.1
1990	692.9
1995	749.1
2000	860.7
2005	956.1

Source: CMHC and City of Calgary.

Solution

Step 1 Draw and label the x and y axes.

Step 2 Label the x axis for years and the y axis for the number of vehicles.

Step 3 Plot each point according to the table.

Step 4 Draw line segments connecting adjacent points. Do not try to fit a smooth curve through the data points. See Figure 2–9. The graph shows a steady increase over the 25-year period.

Figure 2–9

Time Series Graph for Example 2–9

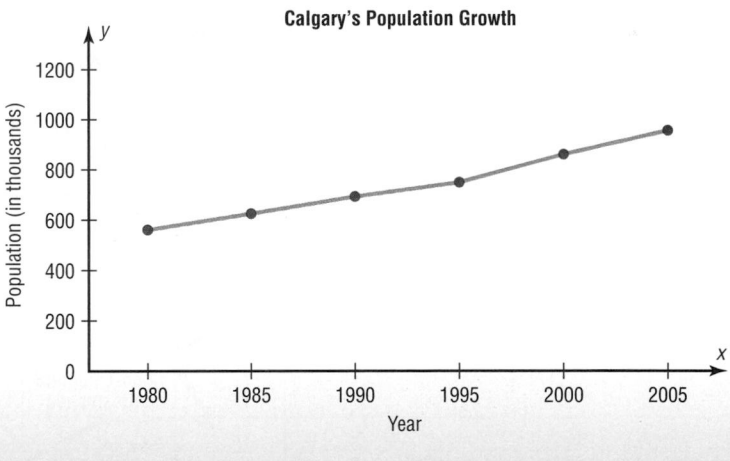

When you analyze a time series graph, look for a trend or pattern that occurs over the time period. For example, is the line ascending (indicating an increase over time) or descending (indicating a decrease over time)? Another thing to look for is the slope, or steepness, of the line. A line that is steep over a specific time period indicates a rapid increase or decrease over that period.

Two data sets can be compared on the same graph (called a *compound time series graph*) if two lines are used, as shown in Figure 2–10. This graph shows the population trend for India and China over a 100-year period.

Figure 2–10

Two Time Series Graphs for Comparison

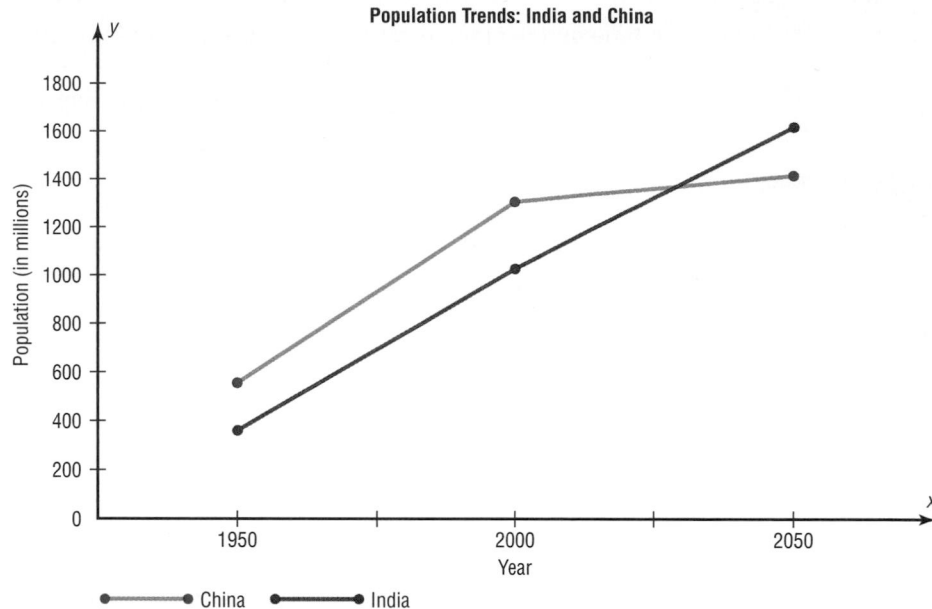

Source: United Nations Department of Economic and Social Affairs, Population Division.

The Pie Graph

Pie graphs are used extensively in statistics. The purpose of the pie graph is to show the relationship of the parts to the whole by visually comparing the sizes of the sections. Percentages or proportions can be used. The variable is nominal or categorical.

A **pie graph** is a circle that is divided into sections or wedges according to the percentage of frequencies in each category of the distribution.

Example 2–10 shows the procedure for constructing a pie graph.

Speaking of

Statistics

This time series graph compares the number of DVD units and the number of VHS units shipped to retailers, using a compound time series graph. Explain in your own words the information that is presented in the graph.

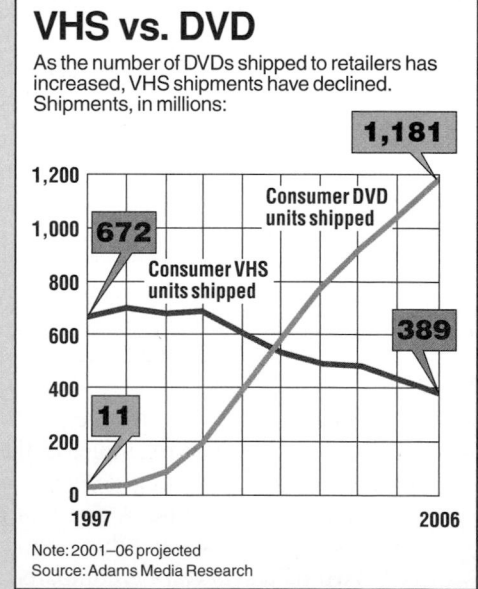

Source: Copyright 2001, *USA TODAY*. Reprinted with permission.

Example 2–10   Construct a pie graph showing the blood types of the armed forces recruits described in Example 2–1. The frequency distribution is repeated here.

Class	Frequency	Percent
A	5	20
B	7	28
O	9	36
AB	4	16
	25	100

Solution

Step 1   Find the number of degrees for each class, using the formula

$$\text{Degree} = \frac{f}{n} \cdot 360°$$

For each class, then, the following results are obtained.

A $\dfrac{5}{25} \cdot 360° = 72°$

B $\dfrac{7}{25} \cdot 360° = 100.8°$

O $\dfrac{9}{25} \cdot 360° = 129.6°$

AB $\dfrac{4}{25} \cdot 360° = 57.6°$

Step 2   Find the percentages. (This was already done in Example 2–1.)

Step 3   Using a protractor, graph each section and write its name and corresponding percentage, as shown in Figure 2–11.

Figure 2–11

Pie Graph for
Example 2–10

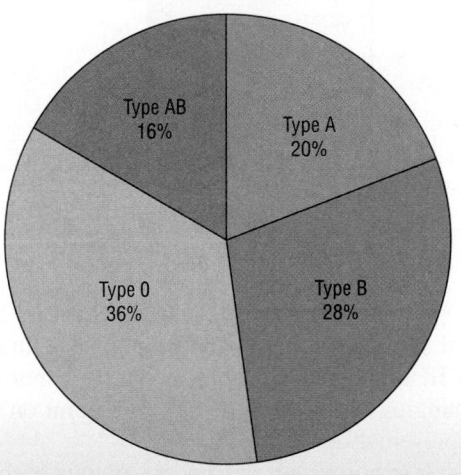

Blood Types for Armed Forces Recruits

The graph in Figure 2–11 shows that in this case the most common blood type is type O.

To analyze the nature of the data shown in the pie graph, compare the sections. For example, are any sections relatively large compared to the rest?

Figure 2–11 shows that among the recruits, type O blood is more prevalent than any other type. People who have type AB blood are in the minority. More than twice as many people have type O blood as type AB.

Misleading Graphs

Graphs give a visual representation that enables readers to analyze and interpret data more easily than they could simply by looking at numbers. However, inappropriately drawn graphs can misrepresent the data and lead the reader to false conclusions. For example, a car manufacturer's ad stated that 98% of the vehicles it had sold in the past ten years were still on the road. The ad then showed a graph similar to the one in Figure 2–12. The graph shows the percentage of the manufacturer's automobiles still on the road and the percentage of its competitors' automobiles still on the road. Is there a large difference? Not necessarily.

Figure 2–12

Graph of Automaker's Claim Using a Scale from 95 to 100%

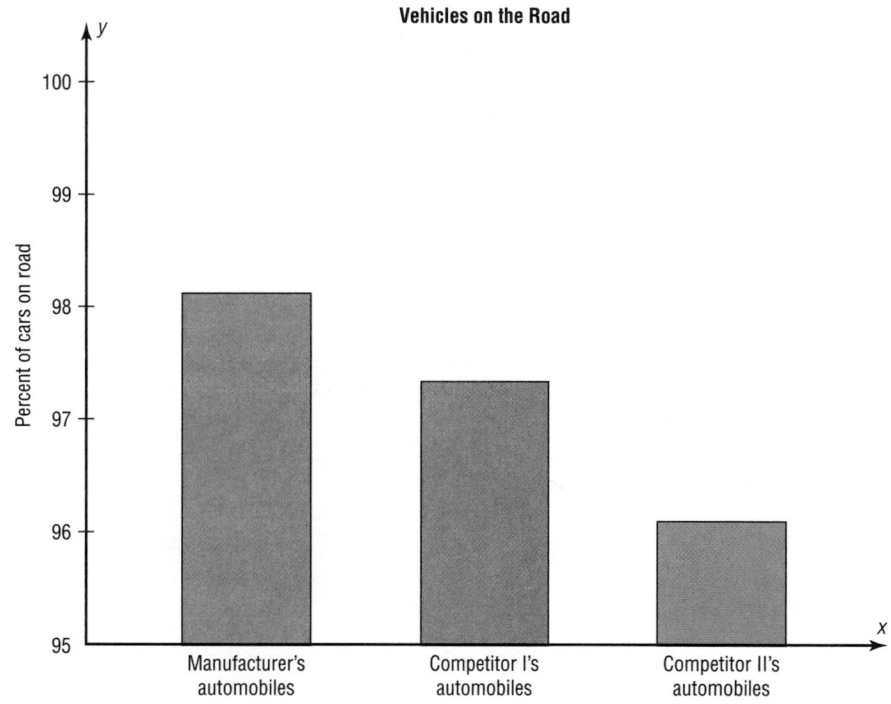

Notice the scale on the vertical axis in Figure 2–12. It has been cut off (or truncated) and starts at 95%. When the graph is redrawn using a scale that goes from 0 to 100%, as in Figure 2–13, there is hardly a noticeable difference in the percentages. Thus, changing the units at the starting point on the y axis can convey a very different visual representation of the data.

It is not wrong to truncate an axis of the graph; many times it is necessary to do so. However, the reader should be aware of this fact and interpret the graph accordingly. Do not be misled if an inappropriate impression is given.

Let's consider another example. The percentage of the world's total motor vehicles produced by manufacturers in the United States declined from 24% in 1998 to 21.5% in 2000, as shown by the data on the next page.

Graph in Figure 2–12
Redrawn Using a Scale
from 0 to 100%

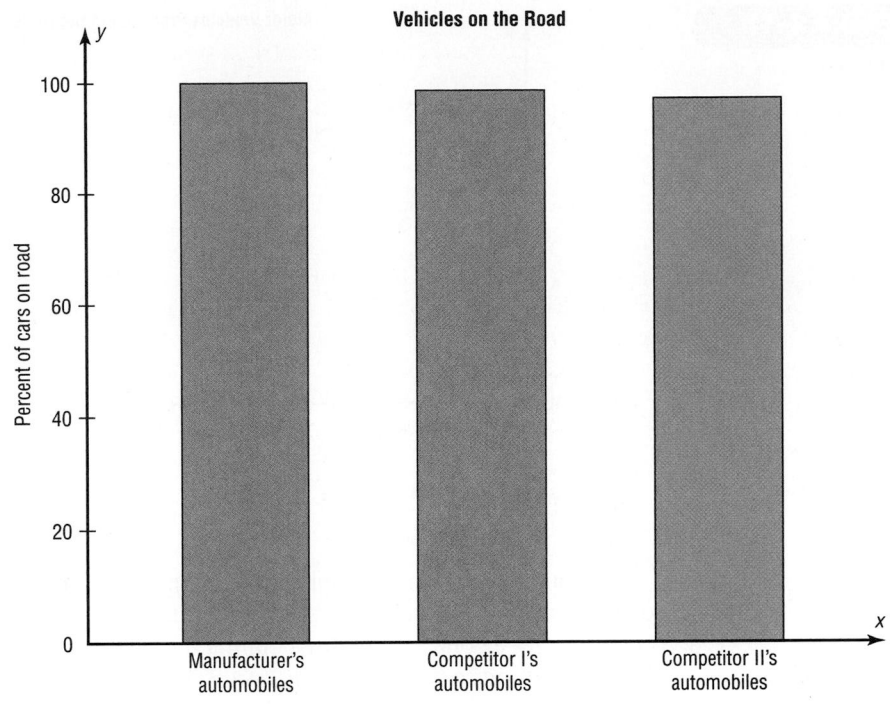

nteresting Fact

The most popular
flavour of ice cream is
vanilla, and about one-
fourth of the ice cream
sold is vanilla.

Year	1995	1996	1997	1998	1999	2000
Percent produced in United States	24.0	23.0	22.7	22.4	22.7	21.5

Source: *The World Almanac and Book of Facts.*

When one draws the graph, as shown in Figure 2–14(a), a scale ranging from 0 to
100% shows a slight decrease. However, this decrease can be emphasized by using a
scale that ranges from 15 to 25%, as shown in Figure 2–14(b). Again, by changing the
units or the starting point on the *y* axis, one can change the visual message.

Figure 2–14

Percent of World's
Motor Vehicles
Produced by
Manufacturers in the
United States

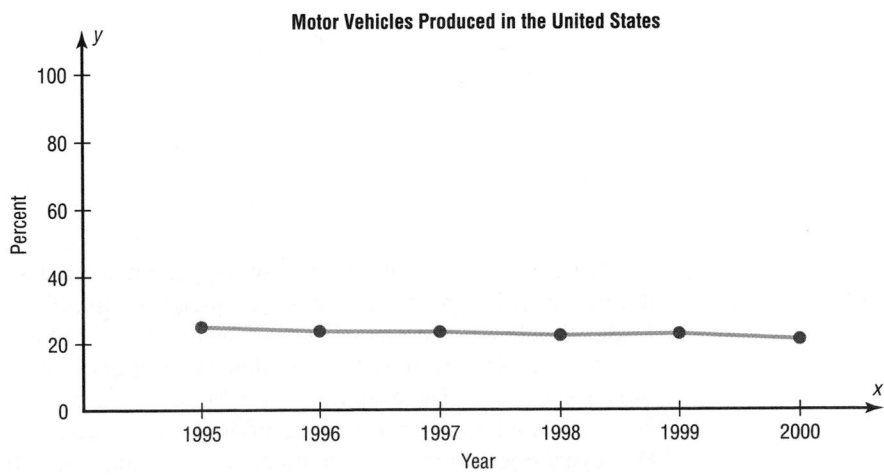

(a) Using a scale from 0% to 100%

Figure 2–14

(Continued)

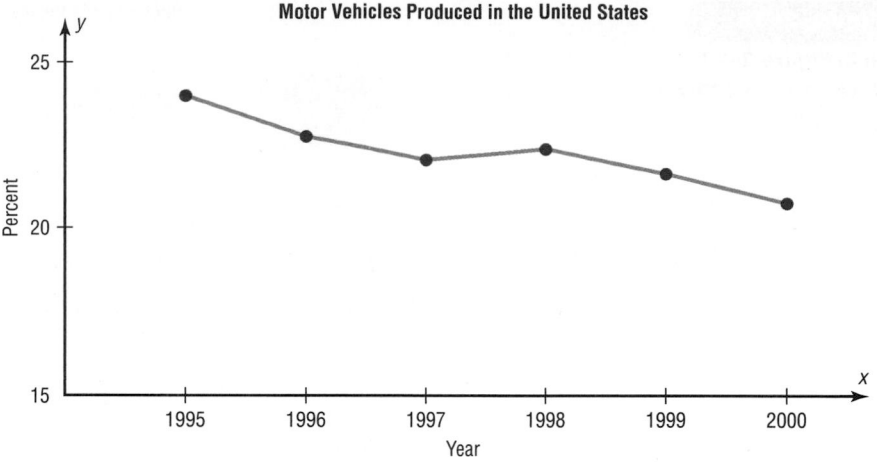

(b) Using a scale from 15% to 25%

Another misleading graphing technique sometimes used involves exaggerating a one-dimensional increase by showing it in two dimensions. For example, the average cost of a 30-second Super Bowl commercial has increased from US$42,000 in 1967 to US$1.9 million in 2002 (Source: *USA TODAY*).

The increase shown by the graph in Figure 2–15(a) represents the change by a comparison of the heights of the two bars in one dimension. The same data are shown two-dimensionally with circles in Figure 2–15(b). Notice that the difference seems much larger because the eye is comparing the areas of the circles rather than the lengths of the diameters.

Figure 2–15

Comparison of Costs for a 30-Second Super Bowl Commercial

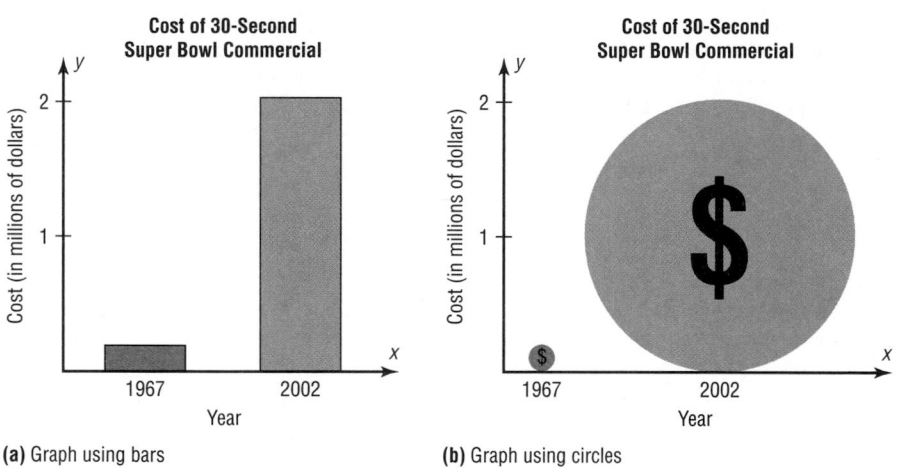

(a) Graph using bars   **(b)** Graph using circles

Note that it is not wrong to use the graphing techniques of truncating the scales or representing data by two-dimensional pictures. But when these techniques are used, the reader should be cautious of the conclusion drawn on the basis of the graphs.

Another way to misrepresent data on a graph is by omitting labels or units on the axes of the graph. The graph shown in Figure 2–16 compares the cost of living, economic growth, population growth, etc., of four main geographic areas in the United States. However, since there are no numbers on the *y* axis, very little information can be gained from this graph, except a crude ranking of each factor. There is no way to decide the actual magnitude of the differences.

Figure 2-16

A Graph with No Units on the *y* Axis

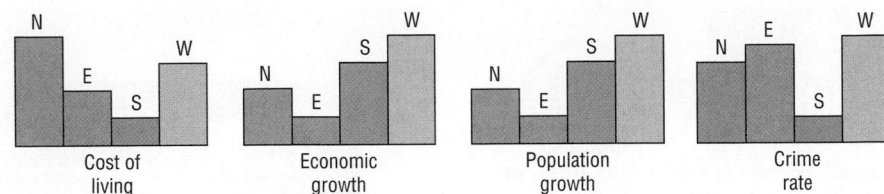

Finally, all graphs should contain a source for the information presented. The inclusion of a source for the data will enable you to check the reliability of the organization presenting the data. A summary of the types of graphs and their uses is shown in Figure 2-17.

Figure 2-17

Summary of Graphs and Uses of Each

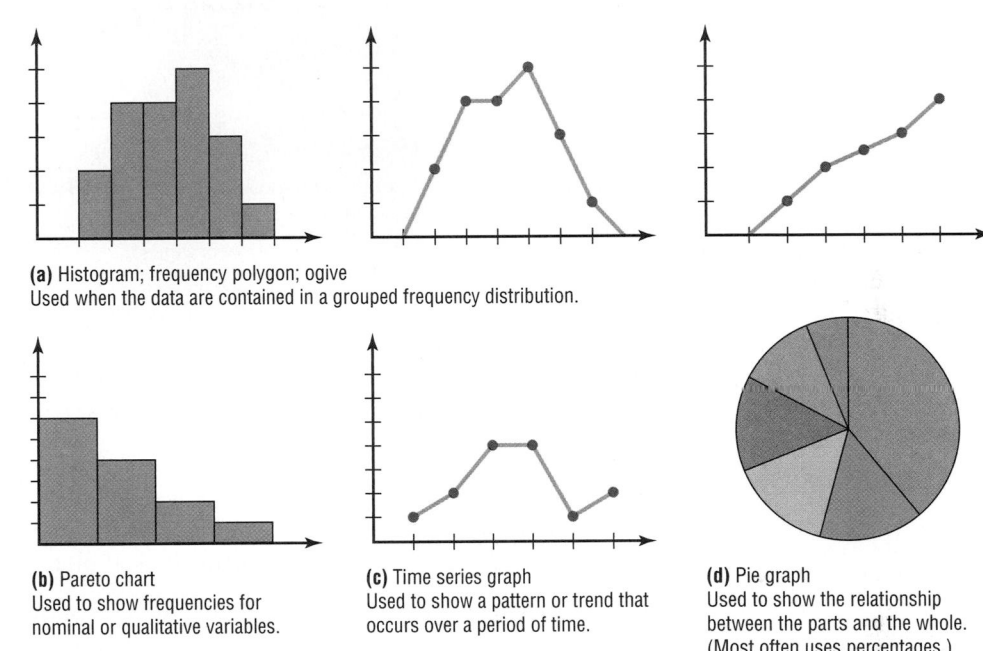

(a) Histogram; frequency polygon; ogive
Used when the data are contained in a grouped frequency distribution.

(b) Pareto chart
Used to show frequencies for nominal or qualitative variables.

(c) Time series graph
Used to show a pattern or trend that occurs over a period of time.

(d) Pie graph
Used to show the relationship between the parts and the whole. (Most often uses percentages.)

Stem and Leaf Plots

The stem and leaf plot is a method of organizing data and is a combination of sorting and graphing. It has the advantage over a grouped frequency distribution of retaining the actual data while showing them in graphical form.

Objective ④

Draw and interpret a stem and leaf plot.

A **stem and leaf plot** is a data plot that uses the stem as the leading part of the data value with the leaf as the remaining part of the data value to form groups or classes.

Example 2-11 shows the procedure for constructing a stem and leaf plot.

Example 2-11

At an outpatient testing centre, the number of cardiograms performed each day for 20 days is shown. Construct a stem and leaf plot for the data.

25	31	20	32	13
14	43	02	57	23
36	32	33	32	44
32	52	44	51	45

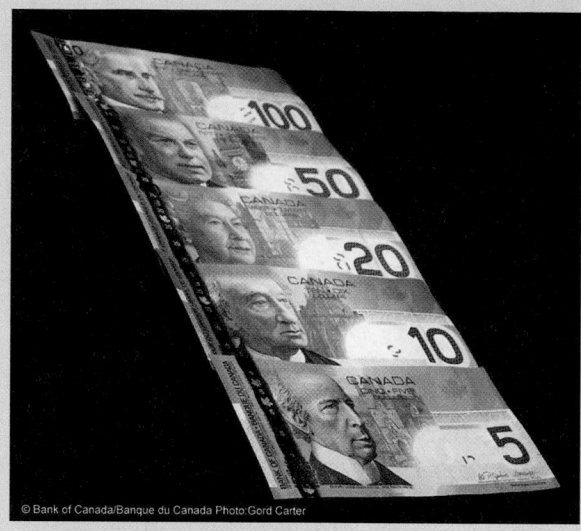
Solution

Step 1   Arrange the data in order:

> 02, 13, 14, 20, 23, 25, 31, 32, 32, 32,
> 32, 33, 36, 43, 44, 44, 45, 51, 52, 57

> *Note:* Arranging the data in order is not essential and can be cumbersome when the data set is large; however, it is helpful in constructing a stem and leaf plot. The leaves in the final stem and leaf plot should be arranged in order.

Step 2   Separate the data according to the first digit, as shown.

> 02   13, 14   20, 23, 25   31, 32, 32, 32, 32, 33, 36
> 43, 44, 44, 45   51, 52, 57

Step 3   A display can be made by using the leading digit as the *stem* and the trailing digit as the *leaf*. For example, for the value 32, the leading digit, 3, is the stem and the trailing digit, 2, is the leaf. For the value 14, the 1 is the stem and the 4 is the leaf. Now a plot can be constructed as shown in Figure 2–18.

Figure 2–18

Stem and Leaf Plot for Example 2–11

0	2
1	3 4
2	0 3 5
3	1 2 2 2 2 3 6
4	3 4 4 5
5	1 2 7

Leading digit (stem)	Trailing digit (leaf)
0	2
1	3 4
2	0 3 5
3	1 2 2 2 2 3 6
4	3 4 4 5
5	1 2 7

Figure 2–18 shows that the distribution peaks in the centre and that there are no gaps in the data. For 7 of the 20 days, the number of patients receiving cardiograms was between 31 and 36. The plot also shows that the testing centre treated from a minimum of 2 patients to a maximum of 57 patients in any one day.

If there are no data values in a class, you should write the stem number and leave the leaf row blank. Do not put a zero in the leaf row.

Example 2–12

An insurance company researcher conducted a survey on the number of car thefts in a large city for a period of 30 days last summer. The raw data are shown. Construct a stem and leaf plot by using classes 50–54, 55–59, 60–64, 65–69, 70–74, and 75–79.

52	62	51	50	69
58	77	66	53	57
75	56	55	67	73
79	59	68	65	72
57	51	63	69	75
65	53	78	66	55

Solution

Step 1   Arrange the data in order.

50, 51, 51, 52, 53, 53, 55, 55, 56, 57, 57, 58, 59, 62, 63, 65, 65, 66, 66, 67, 68, 69, 69, 72, 73, 75, 75, 77, 78, 79

Step 2   Separate the data according to the classes.

50, 51, 51, 52, 53, 53   55, 55, 56, 57, 57, 58, 59
62, 63   65, 65, 66, 66, 67, 68, 69, 69   72, 73
75, 75, 77, 78, 79

Figure 2–19

Stem and Leaf Plot
for Example 2–12

5	0 1 1 2 3 3
5	5 5 6 7 7 8 9
6	2 3
6	5 5 6 6 7 8 9 9
7	2 3
7	5 5 7 8 9

Step 3   Plot the data as shown here.

Leading digit (stem)	Trailing digit (leaf)
5	0 1 1 2 3 3
5	5 5 6 7 7 8 9
6	2 3
6	5 5 6 6 7 8 9 9
7	2 3
7	5 5 7 8 9

The graph for this plot is shown in Figure 2–19.

When the data values are in the hundreds, such as 325, the stem is 32 and the leaf is 5. For example, the stem and leaf plot for the data values 325, 327, 330, 332, 335, 341, 345, and 347 looks like this.

32	5 7
33	0 2 5
34	1 5 7

When you analyze a stem and leaf plot, look for peaks and gaps in the distribution. See if the distribution is symmetric or skewed. Check the variability of the data by looking at the spread.

Related distributions can be compared by using a back-to-back stem and leaf plot. The back-to-back stem and leaf plot uses the same digits for the stems of both distributions, but the digits that are used for the leaves are arranged in order out from the stems on both sides. Example 2–13 shows a back-to-back stem and leaf plot.

Example 2–13

The number of stories in two selected samples of skyscrapers in North America and Asia are shown. Construct a back-to-back stem and leaf plot, and compare the distributions.

North America			Asia		
108	72	65	105	78	70
102	72	64	101	75	69
100	72	64	88	75	69
83	71	64	88	73	68
77	70	64	88	73	68
76	69	62	88	73	68
75	68	61	85	72	66
75	67	60	85	72	66
74	66	60	80	70	66
73	66	60	80	70	66

Source: www.emporis.com.

Solution

Step 1 Arrange the data for both data sets in order.

Step 2 Construct a stem and leaf plot using the same digits as stems. Place the digits for the leaves for North America on the left side of the stem and the digits for the leaves for Asia on the right side, as shown. See Figure 2–20.

Figure 2–20

Back-to-Back Stem and Leaf Plot for Example 2–13

North America		Asia
9 8 7 6 6 6 5 4 4 4 4 2 1 0 0 0	**6**	6 6 6 6 8 8 8 8 9
7 6 5 5 4 3 2 2 2 1 0	**7**	0 0 2 2 3 3 3 5 5 8
3	**8**	0 0 5 5 8 8 8 8
	9	
8 2 0	**10**	1 5

Step 3 Compare the distributions. Both the buildings in North America and Asia have a large variation in the number of stories per building. The North American buildings are congested in the 60- to 79-storey class, whereas the Asian buildings are more evenly distributed in the 60- to 89-storey class.

Stem and leaf plots are part of the techniques called *exploratory data analysis*. More information on this topic is presented in Chapter 3.

Applying the Concepts 2–4

Trends in Cancer Deaths

The following graph shows mortality rates for selected cancer sites for Canadian females from 1977 to 2006. The rates are per 100,000 females. Answer the following questions about the graph.

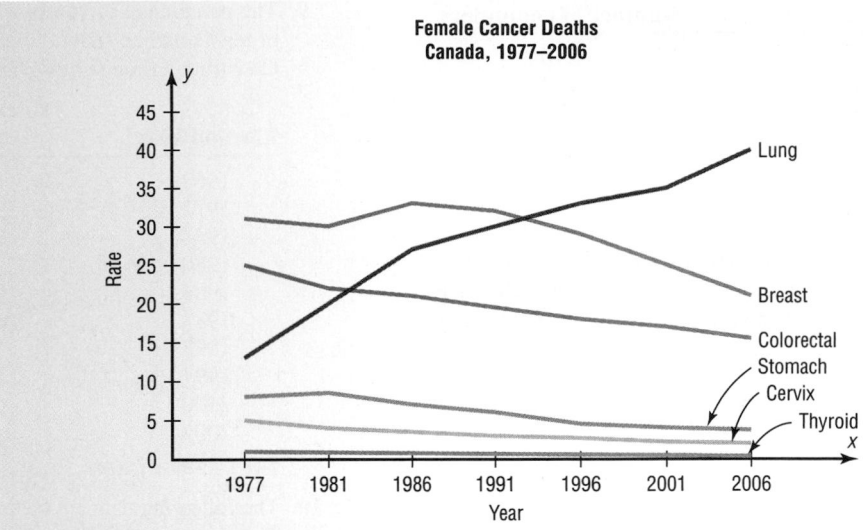

**Female Cancer Deaths
Canada, 1977–2006**

Source: Canadian Cancer Statistics, 2006.

1. What are the variables in the graph?

2. Are the variables qualitative or quantitative?

3. Are the variables discrete or continuous?

4. What type of graph was used to display the data?

5. Could a Pareto chart be used to display the data?

6. Could a pie chart be used to display the data?

7. List some typical uses for the Pareto chart.

8. List some typical uses for the time series chart.

See page 76 for the answers.

Exercises 2–4

1. The population of the United States federal prisons, according to the most serious offences, consists of the following. Make a Pareto chart of the population. Based on the Pareto chart, where should most of the money for rehabilitation be spent?

Violent offences	12.6%
Property offences	8.5
Drug offences	60.2
Public order offences	
Weapons	8.2
Immigration	4.9
Other	5.6

Source: *N.Y. Times Almanac.*

2. Construct a Pareto chart illustrating the overall homicide rate (per 100,000 population) reported for the following Canadian cities in 2005. Rates are based on incidents reported to the police in each of Canada's census metropolitan areas (CMA).

City	Homicide rate
Vancouver	2.9
Winnipeg	3.7
Edmonton	4.3
Montréal	1.3
Calgary	2.4
Ottawa	1.3
Hamilton	1.6
Toronto	2.0
Québec	0.7

Source: *Statistics Canada, The Daily,* July 20, 2006.

3. The following data represent the estimated number (in millions) of computers connected to the Internet worldwide. Construct a Pareto chart for the data. Based on the data, suggest the best place to market appropriate Internet products.

Location	Number of computers
Homes	240
Small companies	102
Large companies	148
Government agencies	33
Schools	47

Source: IDC.

4. The World Roller Coaster Census Report lists the following number of roller coasters on each continent. Represent the data graphically, using a Pareto chart.

Africa	17
Asia	315
Australia	22
Europe	413
North America	643
South America	45

Source: www.rcdb.com.

5. The following percentages indicate the source of energy used worldwide. Construct a Pareto chart for the energy used.

Petroleum	39.8%
Coal	23.2
Dry natural gas	22.4
Hydroelectric	7.0
Nuclear	6.4
Other (wind, solar, etc.)	1.2

Source: N.Y. Times Almanac.

6. Draw a time series graph to represent the data for the number of airline departures (in millions) for the given years. Over the years, is the number of departures increasing, decreasing, or about the same?

Year	1996	1997	1998	1999	2000	2001	2002
Number of departures	7.9	9.9	10.5	10.9	11.0	9.8	10.1

Source: The World Almanac and Book of Facts.

7. The data represent the personal consumption (in billions of dollars) for tobacco in the United States. Draw a time series graph for the data and explain the trend.

Year	1995	1996	1997	1998	1999	2000	2001	2002
Amount	8.5	8.7	9.0	9.3	9.6	9.9	10.2	10.4

Source: The World Almanac and Book of Facts.

8. Draw a time series graph for the data shown and comment on the trend. The data represent the number of active nuclear reactors.

Year	1992	1994	1996	1998	2000	2002
Number	109	109	109	104	104	104

Source: The World Almanac and Book of Facts.

9. The percentage of voters who turned out for a selection of ten Canadian federal elections is shown below. Construct a time series graph and analyze the results.

Election Year	Voter Turnout (%)
1968	75.7
1972	76.7
1974	71.0
1980	69.3
1984	75.3
1988	75.3
1993	69.9
1997	67.0
2000	61.3
2004	60.9

Source: Elections Canada.

10. The following data are based on a survey from American Travel Survey on why people travel. Construct a pie graph for the data and analyze the results.

Purpose	Number
Personal business	146
Visit friends or relatives	330
Work-related	225
Leisure	299

Source: USA TODAY.

11. The assets of the richest 1% of Americans are distributed as follows. Make a pie graph for the percentages.

Principal residence	7.8%
Liquid assets	5.0
Pension accounts	6.9
Stock, mutual funds, and personal trusts	31.6
Businesses and other real estate	46.9
Miscellaneous	1.8

Source: The New York Times.

12. The following elements comprise the earth's crust, the outermost solid layer. Illustrate the composition of the earth's crust with a pie graph.

Oxygen	45.6%
Silicon	27.3
Aluminum	8.4
Iron	6.2
Calcium	4.7
Other	7.8

Source: N.Y. Times Almanac.

13. In a recent survey, 3 in 10 people indicated that they are likely to leave their jobs when the economy improves. Of those surveyed, 34% indicated that they would make a career change, 29% want a new job in the same industry, 21% are going to start a business, and 16% are going to retire. Make a pie chart and a Pareto chart for the data. Which chart do you think better represents the data?

Source: National Survey Institute.

14. State which graph (Pareto chart, time series graph, or pie graph) would most appropriately represent the given situation.

 a. The number of students enrolled at a local college for each year during the last five years.

 b. The budget for the student activities department at a certain college for each year during the last five years.

 c. The means of transportation the students use to get to school.

 d. The percentage of votes each of the four candidates received in the last election.

 e. The record temperatures of a city for the last 30 years.

 f. The frequency of each type of crime committed in a city during the year.

15. The age at the swearing-in ceremony of each Canadian prime minister is shown. Construct a stem and leaf plot and analyze the data.

52	74	60	39	65
51	54	66	55	46
70	57	61	45	
47	46	66	46	
69	47	48	59	

Source: www.canadainfolink.ca.

16. The National Insurance Crime Bureau reported that these data represent the number of registered vehicles per car stolen for 35 selected cities in the United States. For example, in Miami, one automobile is stolen for every 38 registered vehicles in the city. Construct a stem and leaf plot for the data and analyze the distribution. (The data have been rounded to the nearest whole number.)

38	53	53	56	69	89	94
41	58	68	66	69	89	52
50	70	83	81	80	90	74
50	70	83	59	75	78	73
92	84	87	84	85	84	89

Source: *USA TODAY.*

17. The growth (in centimetres) of two varieties of plant after 20 days is shown in this table. Construct a back-to-back stem and leaf plot for the data, and compare the distributions.

Variety 1				Variety 2			
20	12	39	38	18	45	62	59
41	43	51	52	53	25	13	57
59	55	53	59	42	55	56	38
50	58	35	38	41	36	50	62
23	32	43	53	45	55		

18. The data shown represent the percentage of unemployed males and females in 1995 for a sample of countries of the world. Using the whole numbers as stems and the decimals as leaves, construct a back-to-back stem and leaf plot and compare the distributions of the two groups.

Females					Males				
8.0	3.7	8.6	5.0	7.0	8.8	1.9	5.6	4.6	1.5
3.3	8.6	3.2	8.8	6.8	2.2	5.6	3.1	5.9	6.6
9.2	5.9	7.2	4.6	5.6	9.8	8.7	6.0	5.2	5.6
5.3	7.7	8.0	8.7	0.5	4.4	9.6	6.6	6.0	0.3
6.5	3.4	3.0	9.4		4.6	3.1	4.1	7.7	

Source: *N.Y. Times Almanac.*

19. These data represent the numbers of cities served on nonstop flights by Southwest Airlines's largest airports. Construct a stem and leaf plot.

38	41	25	32	13
19	18	28	14	29

Source: Southwest Airlines.

Extending the Concepts

20. The number of successful space launches by the United States and Japan for the years 1993–1997 is shown here. Construct a compound time series graph for the data. What comparison can be made regarding the launches?

Year	1993	1994	1995	1996	1997
United States	29	27	24	32	37
Japan	1	4	2	1	2

Source: *The World Almanac and Book of Facts.*

21. Meat production for veal and lamb for the years 1960–2000 is shown here. (Data are in millions of pounds.) Construct a compound time series graph for the data. What comparison can be made regarding meat production?

Year	1960	1970	1980	1990	2000
Veal	1109	588	400	327	225
Lamb	769	551	318	358	234

Source: *The World Almanac and Book of Facts.*

22. The top ten airlines with the most aircraft are listed. Represent these data with an appropriate graph.

American	714	Continental	364
United	603	Southwest	327
Delta	600	British Airways	268
Northwest	424	American Eagle	245
U.S. Airways	384	Lufthansa (Ger.)	233

Source: *Top 10 of Everything.*

23. The top prize-winning countries for Nobel Prizes in Physiology or Medicine are listed here. Represent the data with an appropriate graph.

United States	80	Denmark	5
United Kingdom	24	Austria	4
Germany	16	Belgium	4
Sweden	8	Italy	3
France	7	Australia	3
Switzerland	6		

Source: *Top 10 of Everything.*

Source: Cartoon by Bradford Veley, Marquette, Michigan. Used with permission.

24. The graph shows the increase in the price of a litre of milk. Why might the increase appear to be larger than it really is?

25. The graph shows the projected boom (in millions) in the number of births. Cite several reasons why the graph might be misleading.

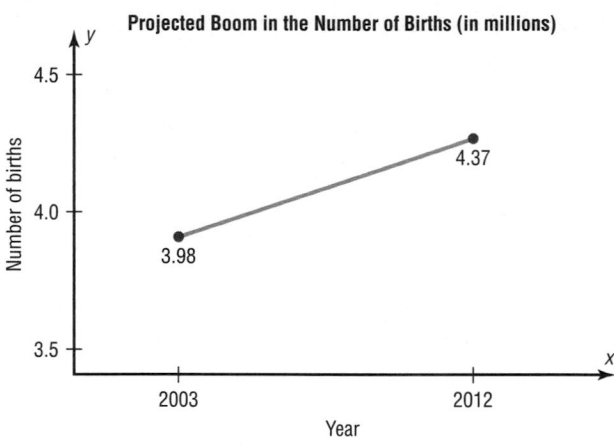

| 2–5 | **Summary** |

When data are collected, they are called raw data. Since very little knowledge can be obtained from raw data, they must be organized in some meaningful way. A frequency distribution using classes is the solution. Once a frequency distribution is constructed, the representation of the data by graphs is a simple task. The most commonly used graphs in research statistics are the histogram, frequency polygon, and ogive. Other graphs, such as the Pareto chart, time series graph, and pie graph, can also be used. Some of these graphs are seen frequently in newspapers, magazines, and various statistical reports.

Finally, a stem and leaf plot uses part of the data values as stems and part of the data values as leaves. This graph has the advantages of a frequency distribution and a histogram.

For step-by-step guidance on the use of technology for this chapter, visit the Online Learning Centre at www.mcgrawhill.ca/olc/bluman. Summary procedures for Minitab, SPSS, Excel, and TI-83 Plus or TI-84 Plus can also be found in Appendix E.

Important Terms

categorical frequency distribution 32

class 31

class boundaries 33

class midpoint 34

class width 33

cumulative frequency 45

frequency 31

frequency distribution 31

frequency polygon 43

grouped frequency distribution 33

histogram 42

lower class limit 33

ogive 45

open-ended distribution 35

Pareto chart 53

pie graph 56

raw data 31

relative frequency graph 46

stem and leaf plot 61

time series graph 55

ungrouped frequency distribution 37

upper class limit 33

Important Formulas

Formula for the percentage of values in each class:

$$\% = \frac{f}{n} \cdot 100\%$$

where

f = frequency of the class

n = total number of values

Formula for the range:

$$R = \text{highest value} - \text{lowest value}$$

Formula for the class width:

$$\text{Class width} = \text{upper boundary} - \text{lower boundary}$$

Formula for the class midpoint:

$$X_m = \frac{\text{lower boundary} + \text{upper boundary}}{2}$$

or

$$X_m = \frac{\text{lower limit} + \text{upper limit}}{2}$$

Formula for the degrees for each section of a pie graph:

$$\text{Degrees} = \frac{f}{n} \cdot 360°$$

Review Exercises

● ● ●

1. The Brunswick Research Organization surveyed 50 randomly selected individuals and asked them the primary way they received the daily news. Their choices were via newspaper (N), television (T), radio (R), or Internet (I). Construct a categorical frequency distribution for the data and interpret the results. The data in this exercise will be used for Exercise 2 in this section.

N	N	T	T	T	I	R	R	I	T
I	N	R	R	I	N	N	N	I	T
I	R	T	T	T	T	N	R	R	I
R	R	I	N	T	R	T	I	I	T
T	I	N	T	T	I	R	N	R	T

2. Construct a pie graph for the data in Exercise 1, and analyze the results.

3. A sporting goods store kept a record of sales of five items for one randomly selected hour during a recent sale. Construct a frequency distribution for the data (B = baseballs, G = golf balls, T = tennis balls, S = soccer balls, F = footballs). (The data for this exercise will be used for Exercise 4 in this section.)

F	B	B	B	G	T	F
G	G	F	S	G	T	
F	T	T	T	S	T	
F	S	S	G	S	B	

4. Draw a pie graph for the data in Exercise 3 showing the sales of each item, and analyze the results.

5. The blood urea nitrogen (BUN) count of 20 randomly selected patients is given here in milligrams per decilitre (mg/dl). Construct an ungrouped frequency distribution for the data. (The data for this exercise will be used for Exercise 6.)

17	18	13	14
12	17	11	20
13	18	19	17
14	16	17	12
16	15	19	22

6. Construct a histogram, frequency polygon, and ogive for the data in Exercise 5 in this section, and analyze the results.

7. The data show the estimated added cost per vehicle use due to bad roads. Construct a frequency distribution using 6 classes. (The data for this exercise will be used for Exercises 8 and 11 in this section.)

165	186	122	172	140	153	208	169
156	114	113	135	131	125	177	136
136	127	112	188	171	179	152	155
116	90	187	136	159	97	141	85
91	170	111	147	165	163	159	150

Source: Federal Highway Administration.

8. Construct a histogram, frequency polygon, and ogive for the data in Exercise 7 in this section, and analyze the results.

9. The data shown (in millions of dollars) are the values of the 30 National Football League franchises. Construct a frequency distribution for the data using 8 classes. (The data for this exercise will be used for Exercises 10 and 12 in this section.)

170	191	171	235	173	187	181	191
200	218	243	200	182	320	184	239
186	199	186	210	209	240	204	193
211	186	197	204	188	242		

Source: Pittsburgh Post-Gazette.

10. Construct a histogram, frequency polygon, and ogive for the data in Exercise 9 in this section, and analyze the results.

11. Construct a histogram, frequency polygon, and ogive by using relative frequencies for the data in Exercise 7 in this section.

12. Construct a histogram, frequency polygon, and ogive by using relative frequencies for the data in Exercise 9 in this section.

13. Construct a Pareto chart for the number of homicides reported for the following cities.

City	Number of homicides
Winnipeg	34
Edmonton	34
Vancouver	56
Calgary	20
Toronto	94
Montréal	63

Source: Statistics Canada.

14. Construct a Pareto chart for the number of trial-ready civil action and equity cases decided in less than six months for the selected counties in southwestern Pennsylvania.

County	Number of cases
Westmoreland	427
Washington	298
Green	151
Fayette	106
Somerset	87

Source: Pittsburgh Tribune-Review.

15. The given data represent the federal minimum hourly wage in the years shown. Draw a time series graph to represent the data and analyze the results.

Year	Wage
1960	$1.00
1965	1.25
1970	1.60
1975	2.10
1980	3.10
1985	3.35
1990	3.80
1995	4.25
2000	5.15
2005	5.15

Source: The World Almanac and Book of Facts.

16. Oil prices have escalated in recent years. The data below indicates the inflation adjusted average world oil price per barrel over a 20-year period. Draw a time series graph to represent the data and analyze the results.

Year	Price per barrel (US$)
1991	$29.19
1992	$27.00
1993	$22.83
1994	$20.79
1995	$21.64
1996	$25.66
1997	$22.86
1998	$14.38
1999	$19.52
2000	$31.29
2001	$25.57
2002	$24.94
2003	$29.63
2004	$39.21
2005	$50.38
2006	$71.93

Source: InflationData.com.

17. The data shows the number of consumer bankruptcies in Ontario and Quebec in select years between 1987 and 2004. Construct two time series graphs and compare the results.

	Quebec	Ontario
1987	7,770	8,232
1997	28,039	33,548
2003	26,341	38,531
2004	26,840	39,341

Source: Office of the Superintendent of Bankruptcy Canada.

18. In a study of 100 women, the numbers shown here indicate the major reason why each woman surveyed worked outside the home. Construct a pie graph for the data and analyze the results.

Reason	Number of women
To support self/family	62
For extra money	18
For something different to do	12
Other	8

19. A survey asked if people would like to spend the rest of their careers with their present employers. The results are shown. Construct a pie graph for the data and analyze the results.

Answer	Number of people
Yes	660
No	260
Undecided	80

20. The number of visitors to the Railroad Museum during 24 randomly selected hours is shown here. Construct a stem and leaf plot for the data.

67	62	38	73	34	43	72	35
53	55	58	63	47	42	51	62
32	29	47	62	29	38	36	41

21. The data set shown here represents the number of hours that 25 part-time employees worked at the Sea Side Amusement Park during a randomly selected week in June. Construct a stem and leaf plot for the data and summarize the results.

16	25	18	39	25	17	29	14	37
22	18	12	23	32	35	24	26	
20	19	25	26	38	38	33	29	

22. A special aptitude test is given to job applicants. The data shown here represent the scores of 30 applicants. Construct a stem and leaf plot for the data and summarize the results.

204	210	227	218	254
256	238	242	253	227
251	243	233	251	241
237	247	211	222	231
218	212	217	227	209
260	230	228	242	200

Data Analysis

• • •

A Data Bank is found in Appendix D, or on the World Wide Web by following links from www.mcgrawhill. ca/olc/bluman

1. From the Data Bank located in Appendix D, choose one of the following variables: age, weight, cholesterol level, systolic pressure, IQ, or sodium level. Select at least 30 values. For these values, construct a grouped frequency distribution. Draw a histogram, frequency polygon, and ogive for the distribution. Describe briefly the shape of the distribution.

2. From the Data Bank, choose one of the following variables: educational level, smoking status, or exercise. Select at least 20 values. Construct an ungrouped frequency distribution for the data. For the distribution, draw a Pareto chart and describe briefly the nature of the chart.

Statistics Today

How Serious Are Hospital Infections?–Revisited

The data presented in numerical form do not convey an easy-to-interpret conclusion; however, when data are presented in graphical form, readers can see the visual impact of the numbers. In this case, a Pareto chart shows that hospital infection death rates caused by multiple infections are the most common, followed by pneumonia. The pie graph also shows that urinary tract infections occur with the highest frequency.

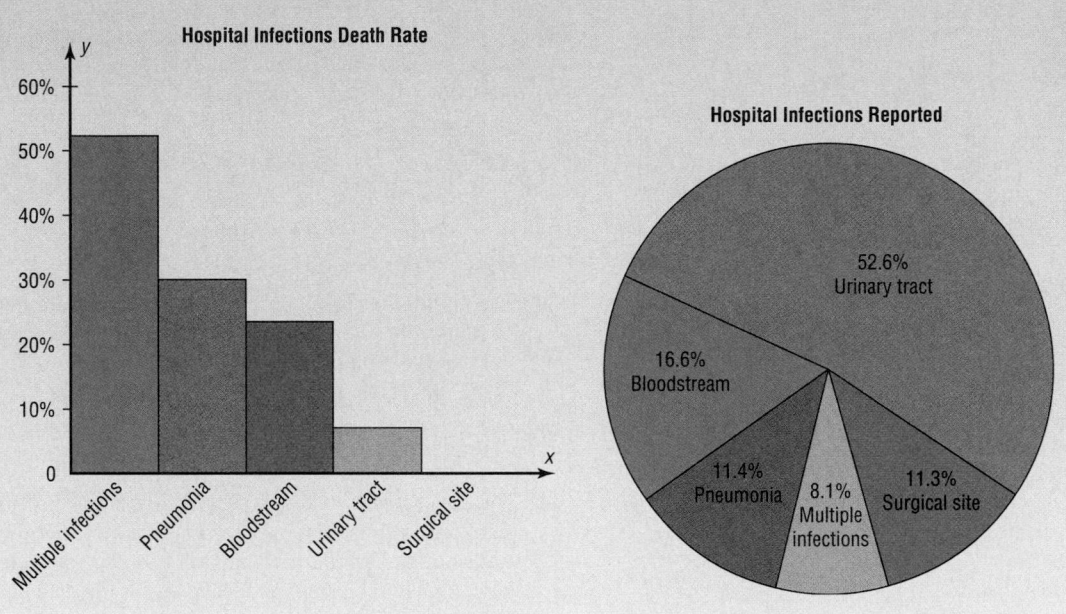

Sources: Canadian Union of Public Employees; Pennsylvania Hospitals Research Brief.

3. From the Data Bank, select at least 30 subjects and construct a categorical distribution for their marital status. Draw a pie graph and describe briefly the findings.

4. Using the data from Data Set IV in Appendix D, construct a frequency distribution and draw a histogram. Describe briefly the shape of the distribution of the tallest buildings in New York City.

5. Using the data from Data Set XI in Appendix D, construct a frequency distribution and draw a frequency polygon. Describe briefly the shape of the distribution for the number of pages in statistics books.

6. Using the data from Data Set IX in Appendix D, divide the United States into four regions, as follows:

Northeast	CT ME MA NH NJ NY PA RI VT
Midwest	IL IN IA KS MI MN MS NE ND OH SD WI
South	AL AR DE DC FL GA KY LA MD NC OK SC TN TX VA WV
West	AK AZ CA CO HI ID MT NV NM OR UT WA WY

Find the total population for each region, and draw a Pareto chart and a pie graph for the data. Analyze the results. Explain which chart might be a better representation for the data.

7. Using the data from Data Set I in Appendix D, make a stem and leaf plot for the record low temperatures in the United States. Describe the nature of the plot.

Chapter Quiz

● ● ●

Determine whether each statement is true or false. If the statement is false, explain why.

1. In the construction of a frequency distribution, it is a good idea to have overlapping class limits, such as 10–20, 20–30, 30–40.

2. Histograms can be drawn by using vertical or horizontal bars.

3. It is not important to keep the width of each class the same in a frequency distribution.

4. Frequency distributions can aid the researcher in drawing charts and graphs.

5. The type of graph used to represent data is determined by the type of data collected and by the researcher's purpose.

6. In construction of a frequency polygon, the class limits are used for the x axis.

7. Data collected over a period of time can be graphed by using a pie graph.

Select the best answer.

8. What is another name for the ogive?

   a. Histogram
   b. Frequency polygon
   c. Cumulative frequency graph
   d. Pareto chart

9. What are the boundaries for 8.6–8.8?

   a. 8–9
   b. 8.5–8.9
   c. 8.55–8.85
   d. 8.65–8.75

10. What graph should be used to show the relationship between the parts and the whole?

   a. Histogram
   b. Pie graph
   c. Pareto chart
   d. Ogive

11. Except for rounding errors, relative frequencies should add up to what sum?

   a. 0
   b. 1
   c. 50
   d. 100

Complete these statements with the best answers.

12. The three types of frequency distributions are _____, _____, and _____.

13. In a frequency distribution, the number of classes should be between _____ and _____.

14. Data such as blood types (A, B, AB, O) can be organized into a(n) _____ frequency distribution.

15. Data collected over a period of time can be graphed using a(n) _____ graph.

16. A statistical device used in exploratory data analysis that is a combination of a frequency distribution and a histogram is called a(n) _____.

17. On a Pareto chart, the frequencies should be represented on the _____ axis.

18. A questionnaire on housing arrangements showed this information obtained from 25 respondents. Construct a frequency distribution for the data (H = house, A = apartment, M = mobile home, C = condominium).

H	C	H	M	H	A	C	A	M
C	M	C	A	M	A	C	C	M
C	C	H	A	H	H	M		

19. Construct a pie graph for the data in Exercise 18.

20. When 30 randomly selected customers left a convenience store, each was asked the number of items he or she purchased. Construct an ungrouped frequency distribution for the data.

2	9	4	3	6
6	2	8	6	5
7	5	3	8	6
6	2	3	2	4
6	9	9	8	9
4	2	1	7	4

21. Construct a histogram, a frequency polygon, and an ogive for the data in Exercise 20.

22. For a recent year, the number of murders in 25 selected cities is shown. Construct a frequency distribution using 9 classes, and analyze the nature of the data in terms of shape, extreme values, etc. (The information in this exercise will be used for Exercise 23 in this section.

248	348	74	514	597
270	71	226	41	39
366	73	241	46	34
149	68	73	63	65
109	598	278	69	27

Source: *Pittsburgh Tribune Review.*

23. Construct a histogram, frequency polygon, and ogive for the data in Exercise 22. Analyze the histogram.

24. Construct a Pareto chart for the number of tonnes (in millions) of trash recycled per year by Americans based on an Environmental Protection Agency study.

Type	Amount
Paper	320.0
Iron/steel	292.0
Aluminum	276.0
Yard waste	242.4
Glass	196.0
Plastics	41.6

Source: *USA TODAY.*

25. The data show the number of fatal trespasser casualties on railroad property in the United States. Draw a time series graph and explain any trend.

Year	1998	1999	2000	2001
Number	536	463	511	540

Source: *Federal Railroad Administration.*

26. The number of visitors to the Historic Museum for
25 randomly selected hours is shown. Construct a
stem and leaf plot for the data.

15	53	48	19	38
86	63	98	79	38
62	89	67	39	26
28	35	54	88	76
31	47	53	41	68

Critical Thinking Challenges

1. The chart shows Canada's greenhouse tomato
production by leading province. Can you see anything
misleading about the graph as drawn?

Source: Statistics Canada—Food and Vegetable Production.

Source: Adapted from Statistics Canada website, www.statcan.ca/cgi-bin/downpub/listpub.cgi?catno=22-003-XIB2006001. Accessed, March 19, 2007.

2. Shown are various statistics about the Great Lakes.
Using appropriate graphs (your choice) and summary
statements, write a report analyzing the data.

	Superior	Michigan	Huron	Erie	Ontario
Length (miles)	350	307	206	241	193
Breadth (miles)	160	118	183	57	53
Depth (feet)	1,330	923	750	210	802
Volume (cubic miles)	2,900	1,180	850	116	393
Area (square miles)	31,700	22,300	23,000	9,910	7,550
Shoreline (U.S., miles)	863	1,400	580	431	300

Source: *The World Almanac and Book of Facts.*

3. A compound time series graph is shown for the
percentage of sales of CDs, cassettes, and vinyl records.
Using the graph, answer these questions.

a. In what year did cassette sales match CD sales?

b. In what year did cassette sales account for 50% of
the sales?

c. What was the percentage difference in sales between
CDs and cassettes for the year 1996?

d. In what year did CDs account for 30% of the sales?

e. What was the change in percentage of sales for
cassettes from 1987 to 2000?

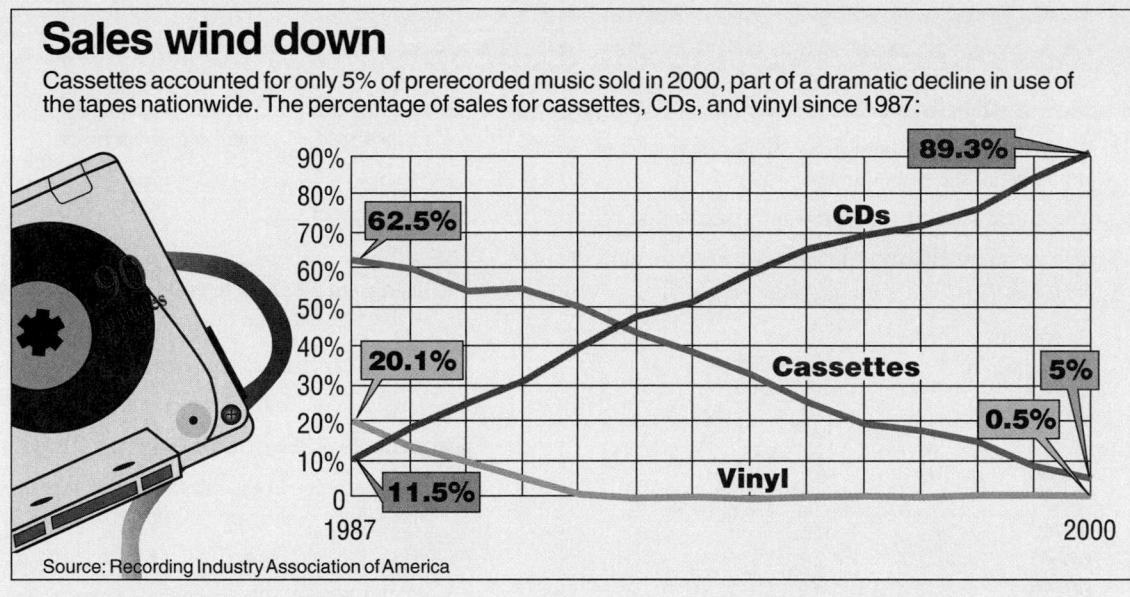

Sales wind down

Cassettes accounted for only 5% of prerecorded music sold in 2000, part of a dramatic decline in use of the tapes nationwide. The percentage of sales for cassettes, CDs, and vinyl since 1987:

Source: Recording Industry Association of America

Source: Copyright 2001, *USA TODAY.* Reprinted with permission.

Data Projects ●●●

Where appropriate, use Minitab, SPSS, the TI-83 Plus, the TI-84 Plus, Excel, or a computer program of your choice to complete the following exercises.

1. Select a categorical (nominal) variable, such as the colours of cars in the school's parking lot or the major fields of the students in statistics class, and collect data on this variable.

   a. State the purpose of the project.
   b. Define the population.
   c. State how the sample was selected.
   d. Show the raw data.
   e. Construct a frequency distribution for the variable.
   f. Draw some appropriate graphs (pie, Pareto, etc.) for the data.
   g. Analyze the results.

2. Using an almanac, select a variable that varies over a period of several years (e.g., silver production), and draw a time series graph for the data. Write a short paragraph interpreting the findings.

3. Select a variable (interval or ratio) and collect at least 30 values. For example, you may ask the students in your class how many hours they study per week or how old they are.

   a. State the purpose of the project.
   b. Define the population.
   c. State how the sample was selected.
   d. Show the raw data.
   e. Construct a frequency distribution for the data.
   f. Draw a histogram, frequency polygon, and ogive for the data.
   g. Analyze the results.

You may use these websites to obtain raw data:

Visit the data sets at the book's website found at www.mcgrawhill.ca/olc/bluman http://lib.stat.cmu.edu/DASL www.statcan.ca

Answers to Applying the Concepts

Section 2–2 Prime Minister Ages at Swearing-In

1. The data were obtained from the population of all prime ministers at the time this text was written.

2. The oldest swearing-in age was 74 years old.

3. The youngest swearing-in age was 39 years old.

4. Answers will vary. One possible answer is

Age at Swearing-In	Frequency
36–40	1
41–45	1
46–50	6
51–55	4
56–60	3
61–65	2
66–70	4
71–75	1

5. Answers will vary. For the frequency distribution given in Exercise 4, there is a peak for the 46–50 class.

6. Answers will vary. Two possible outliers are indicated in class 36–40 (age 39) and class 71–75 (age 74) from raw data.

7. Answers will vary. Data appears to be bimodal with peaks around the 46–55 and 66–70 age groups.

Section 2–3 Selling Real Estate

1. A histogram of the data gives price ranges and the counts of homes in each price range. We can also talk about how the data are distributed by looking at a histogram.

2. A frequency polygon shows increases or decreases in the number of home prices around values.

3. A cumulative frequency polygon shows the number of homes sold at or below a given price.

4. The house that sold for $321,550 is an extreme value in this data set.

5. Answers will vary. One possible answer is that the histogram displays the outlier well since there is a gap in the prices of the homes sold.

6. The distribution of the data is skewed to the right.

Section 2–4 Trends in Cancer Deaths

1. The variables in the graph are the year, cause of death, and rate of death per 100,000 women.

2. The cause of death is qualitative, while the year and death rates are quantitative.

3. Year is a discrete variable, and death rate is continuous. Since cause of death is qualitative, it is neither discrete nor continuous.

4. A line graph was used to display the data.

5. No, a Pareto chart could not be used to display the data, since we can only have one quantitative variable and one categorical variable in a Pareto chart.

6. We cannot use a pie chart for the same reasons as given for the Pareto chart.

7. A Pareto chart is typically used to show a categorical variable listed from the highest-frequency category to the category with the lowest frequency.

8. A time series chart is used to see trends in the data. It can also be used for forecasting and predicting.

CHAPTER **3** Data Description

Objectives

After completing this chapter, you should be able to

1. Summarize data using measures of central tendency, such as the mean, median, mode, and midrange.

2. Describe data using measures of variation, such as the range, variance, and standard deviation.

3. Identify the position of a data value in a data set, using various measures of position, such as percentiles, deciles, and quartiles.

4. Use the techniques of exploratory data analysis, including boxplots and five-number summaries, to discover various aspects of data.

Outline

3–1 Introduction

3–2 Measures of Central Tendency

3–3 Measures of Variation

3–4 Measures of Position

3–5 Exploratory Data Analysis

3–6 Summary

Statistics Today

Do You Live as Well as Other Canadians?

The United Nations ranked Canada fifth in the world on its Human Development Index for 2005, ahead of the United States and Japan but trailing Norway and Australia. Unfortunately this reputation for outstanding living conditions merely represents the well-being of the average Canadian. Regional disparities abound. One measure of quality of life is economic well-being. In 2005, the average Canadian income per capita was $42,464. How did your province compare to this average? See Statistics Today—Revisited, page 137, at the end of the chapter.

This chapter will show you how to obtain and interpret descriptive statistics such as measures of average, measures of variation, and measures of position.

3–1   Introduction

Chapter 2 showed how one can gain useful information from raw data by organizing them into a frequency distribution and then presenting the data by using various graphs. This chapter shows the statistical methods that can be used to summarize data. The most familiar of these methods is the finding of averages.

For example, an average NHL hockey player earned $1.46 million dollars in the 2005–06 season[1] or Canadian university student graduates, in 2002, had an average debt of $18,900.[2] By 2010, the life expectancy of Canadian males will average 79.0 years whereas it is expected that females, on average, will live to 83.1 years.[3]

Canadian nationalist writer and humourist Pierre Berton, once described a typical Canadian as "*someone who knows how to make love in a canoe without tipping it.*"

Are you an average Canadian? Statistics Canada and market researchers collect descriptive statistics from all facets of Canadian life. Here are some findings of the typical Canadian.

Canadian brides marry at an average age of 31.7 years and their grooms at 34.3 years.
Typical Canadian households spend $121.20 on food each week.
Average Canadians eat 27.1 kg of red meat, 13.5 kg of poultry, and 13 dozen eggs per year.[4]
Canadians consume 63.2 litres of milk, 160.1 litres of coffee or tea, and 65.8 litres of beer per capita each year.[5]
Doctor visits by Canadians average 4.5 per year.
The average Canadian browses the Internet for 75 minutes every day.

I̶nteresting Fact

A person has on average 1460 dreams in one year.

---

[1]http://proicehockey.about.com/od/collectivebargainingfaq/f/nhl_salaries.htm;
http://www.thehockeynews.com/en/newsroom/news.asp?idNews=20062.
[2]http://www.millenniumscholarships.ca/images/PressReleases/oct292002.pdf.
[3]Office of the Superintendent of Financial Institutions Canada—Population Projections 2005;
http://www.osfi-bsif.gc.ca/app/DocRepository/1/eng/oca/studies/popcdn_e.pdf.
[4]Adapted from Statistics Canada publication *Food Statistics,* Catalogue 21-020, 2004, vol. 4, no. 1, released May 26, 2005, pages 6 and 7 and www.statcan.ca/bsolc/english/bsolc?catno=21-020-X.
[5]Adapted from Statistics Canada publication *The Daily,* Catalogue 11-001, released May 26, 2005, www.statcan.ca/Daily/English/050526/d050526c.htm.

In these examples, the word *average* is ambiguous, since several different methods can be used to obtain an average. Loosely stated, the average means the centre of the distribution or the most typical case. Measures of average are also called *measures of central tendency* and include the *mean, median, mode,* and *midrange.*

Knowing the average of a data set is not enough to describe the data set entirely. Even though a shoe store owner knows that the average size of a man's shoe is size 10, she would not be in business very long if she ordered only size 10 shoes.

As this example shows, in addition to knowing the average, one must know how the data values are dispersed. That is, do the data values cluster around the mean, or are they spread more evenly throughout the distribution? The measures that determine the spread of the data values are called *measures of variation* or *measures of dispersion.* These measures include the *range, variance,* and *standard deviation.*

Finally, another set of measures is necessary to describe data. These measures are called *measures of position.* They tell where a specific data value falls within the data set or its relative position in comparison with other data values. Common position measures are *percentiles, deciles, quartiles,* and standard scores or *z* scores. These measures are used extensively in psychology and education. Sometimes they are referred to as *norms.*

The measures of central tendency, variation, and position explained in this chapter are part of what is called *traditional statistics.*

Section 3–5 shows the techniques of what is called *exploratory data analysis.* These techniques include the *boxplot* and the *five-number summary.* They can be used to explore data to see what they show (as opposed to the traditional techniques, which are used to confirm conjectures about the data).

3–2   Measures of Central Tendency

Objective

Summarize data using measures of central tendency, such as the mean, median, mode, and midrange.

Historical Note

In 1796, Adolphe Quetelet investigated the characteristics (heights, weights, etc.) of French conscripts to determine the "average man." Florence Nightingale was so influenced by Quetelet's work that she began collecting and analyzing medical records in the military hospitals during the Crimean War. Based on her work, hospitals began keeping accurate records on their patients.

Chapter 1 stated that statisticians use samples taken from populations; however, when populations are small, it is not necessary to use samples since the entire population can be used to gain information. For example, suppose an insurance manager wanted to know the average weekly sales of all the company's representatives. If the company employed a large number of salespeople, say, nationwide, he would have to use a sample and make an inference to the entire sales force. But if the company had only a few salespeople, say, only 87 agents, he would be able to use all representatives' sales for a randomly chosen week and thus use the entire population.

Measures found by using all the data values in the population are called *parameters.* Measures obtained by using the data values from samples are called *statistics;* hence, the average of the sales from a sample of representatives is called a *statistic,* and the average of sales obtained from the entire population is called a *parameter.*

A **statistic** is a characteristic or measure obtained by using the data values from a sample.

A **parameter** is a characteristic or measure obtained by using all the data values from a specific population.

These concepts as well as the symbols used to represent them will be explained in detail in this chapter.

General Rounding Rule   In statistics the basic rounding rule is that when computations are done in the calculation, rounding should not be done until the final answer is calculated. When rounding is done in the intermediate steps, it tends to increase the difference between that answer and the exact one. But in the textbook and solutions manual, it is not practical to show long decimals in the intermediate calculations; hence, the values in the examples are carried out to enough places (usually three or four) to obtain the same answer that a calculator would give after rounding on the last step. Detailed examples to follow will illustrate proper rounding techniques.

The Mean

The *mean,* also known as the *arithmetic average,* is found by adding the values of the data and dividing by the total number of values. For example, the mean of 3, 2, 6, 5, and 4 is found by adding $3 + 2 + 6 + 5 + 4 = 20$ and dividing by 5; hence, the mean of the data is $20 \div 5 = 4$. The values of the data are represented by X's. In this data set, $X_1 = 3$, $X_2 = 2$, $X_3 = 6$, $X_4 = 5$, and $X_5 = 4$. To show a sum of the total X values, the symbol Σ (the capital Greek letter sigma) is used, and ΣX means to find the sum of the X values in the data set. The summation notation is explained in Appendix A.

The **mean** is the sum of the values, divided by the total number of values. The symbol $\overline{X}$ represents the sample mean.

$$\overline{X} = \frac{X_1 + X_2 + X_3 + \cdots + X_n}{n} = \frac{\Sigma X}{n}$$

where n represents the total number of values in the sample.

For a population, the Greek letter μ(mu) is used for the mean.

$$\mu = \frac{X_1 + X_2 + X_3 + \cdots + X_N}{N} = \frac{\Sigma X}{N}$$

where N represents the total number of values in the population.

In statistics, Greek letters are often used to denote parameters, and Roman letters are often used to denote statistics. Assume that the data are obtained from samples unless otherwise specified.

Example 3–1

The data represents the number of days off per year for a sample of individuals selected from nine different countries. Find the mean.

> 20, 26, 40, 36, 23, 42, 35, 24, 30

Source: World Tourism Organization.

Solution

$$\bar{X} = \frac{\Sigma X}{n} = \frac{20 + 26 + 40 + 36 + 23 + 42 + 35 + 24 + 30}{9}$$

$$= \frac{276}{9} = 30.7 \text{ days (rounded)}$$

Hence, the mean of the number of days off is 30.7 days.

Example 3–2

The data depicts the annual chocolate sales (in billions of dollars) for a sample of seven countries in the world. Find the mean.

> 2.0, 4.9, 6.5, 2.1, 5.1, 3.2, 16.6

Source: Euromonitor.

Solution

$$\bar{X} = \frac{\Sigma X}{n} = \frac{2.0 + 4.9 + 6.5 + 2.1 + 5.1 + 3.2 + 16.6}{7}$$

$$= \frac{40.4}{7} = \$5.77 \text{ billion (rounded)}$$

The mean for the sample is \$5.77 billion.

The mean, in most cases, is not an actual data value.

Rounding Rule for the Mean The mean should be rounded to one more decimal place than occurs in the raw data. For example, if the raw data are given in whole numbers, the mean should be rounded to the nearest tenth. If the data are given in tenths, the mean should be rounded to the nearest hundredth, and so on.

The procedure for finding the mean for grouped data uses the midpoints of the classes. This procedure is shown next.

Example 3–3

Using the frequency distribution for Example 2–7, find the mean. The data represent the number of kilometres run during one week for a sample of 20 runners.

Solution

The procedure for finding the mean for grouped data is given here.

Step 1 Make a table as shown.

A Class	B Frequency (f)	C Midpoint (X_m)	D $f \cdot X_m$
5.5–10.5	1		
10.5–15.5	2		
15.5–20.5	3		
20.5–25.5	5		
25.5–30.5	4		
30.5–35.5	3		
35.5–40.5	2		
	$n = 20$		

Step 2 Find the midpoints of each class and enter them in column C.

$$X_m = \frac{5.5 + 10.5}{2} = 8 \qquad \frac{10.5 + 15.5}{2} = 13 \qquad \text{etc.}$$

Step 3 For each class, multiply the frequency by the midpoint, as shown, and place the product in column D.

$$1 \cdot 8 = 8 \qquad 2 \cdot 13 = 26 \qquad \text{etc.}$$

The completed table is shown here.

A Class	B Frequency (f)	C Midpoint (X_m)	D $f \cdot X_m$
5.5–10.5	1	8	8
10.5–15.5	2	13	26
15.5–20.5	3	18	54
20.5–25.5	5	23	115
25.5–30.5	4	28	112
30.5–35.5	3	33	99
35.5–40.5	2	38	76
	$n = 20$		$\Sigma f \cdot X_m = 490$

Step 4 Find the sum of column D.

Step 5 Divide the sum by n to get the mean.

$$\overline{X} = \frac{\Sigma f \cdot X_m}{n} = \frac{490}{20} = 24.5 \text{ kilometres}$$

The procedure for finding the mean for grouped data assumes that the mean of all the raw data values in each class is equal to the midpoint of the class. In reality, this is not true, since the average of the raw data values in each class usually will not be exactly equal to the midpoint. However, using this procedure will give an acceptable approximation of the mean, since some values fall above the midpoint and other values fall below the midpoint for each class, and the midpoint represents an estimate of all values in the class.

The steps for finding the mean for grouped data are summarized in the next Procedure Table.

Procedure Table

Finding the Mean for Grouped Data

Step 1   Make a table as shown.

A	B	C	D
Class	Frequency (f)	Midpoint (X_m)	$f \cdot X_m$

Step 2   Find the midpoints of each class and place them in column C.

Step 3   Multiply the frequency by the midpoint for each class, and place the product in column D.

Step 4   Find the sum of column D.

Step 5   Divide the sum obtained in column D by the sum of the frequencies obtained in column B.

The formula for the mean is

$$\overline{X} = \frac{\Sigma f \cdot X_m}{n}$$

(Note: The symbols $\Sigma f \cdot X_m$ mean to find the sum of the product of the frequency (f) and the midpoint (X_m) for each class.)

Speaking of
Statistics

All things are not equal! Only wealthy Canadian families can afford to purchase a house in parts of Canada. This Snapshot illustrates the average house prices in select Canadian cities in May 2007. Which type of average (mean, median, mode) do you think was used?

Snapshot

Where can you afford to live ?

Victoria $560,574
Edmonton $357,839
Saskatoon $233,917
Ottawa $276,379
Quebec City $165,958
Saint John $137,535
Halifax $219,705
Canada's National Average $314,258

Source: CREA—Canadian Real Estate Association (May 2007).

The Median

An article recently reported that the median income for college and university professors was $81,104. This measure of central tendency means that one-half of all the professors surveyed earned more than $81,104, and one-half earned less than $81,104.[6]

The *median* is the halfway point in a data set. Before one can find this point, the data must be arranged in order. When the data set is ordered, it is called a **data array.** The median either will be a specific value in the data set or will fall between two values, as shown in Examples 3–4 and 3–5.

> The **median** is the midpoint of the data array. The symbol for the median is MD.

Steps in computing the median of a data array

Step 1   Arrange the data in order.

Step 2   Select the middle point.

Example 3–4

Whistler, British Columbia, will host the downhill ski events in the 2010 Winter Olympic Games. This data represents pre-Olympic hotel rates (per night) in select hotels. Find the median.

$$\$134, \$149, \$179, \$330, \$170, \$208, \$170, \$99, \$159$$

Source: www.expedia.com.

Solution

Step 1   Arrange the data in order.

99, 134, 149, 159, 170, 170, 179, 208, 330

Step 2   Select the middle value

99, 134, 149, 159, 170, 170, 179, 208, 330
↑
Median

Hence, the median hotel price is $170.

Example 3–4 had an odd number of values in the data set; hence, the median was an actual data value. When there are an even number of values in the data set, the median will fall between two given values, as illustrated in Example 3–5.

Example 3–5

The number of residential home sales per month in Calgary over a 12-month period is listed below. Find the median.

1877, 2408, 3060, 3497, 3389, 3550, 3388, 2586, 2516, 2180, 2122, 2394

Source: Calgary Real Estate Board.

---

[6]University of Toronto Faculty Association Comparative Study.

Solution

Sort the sales data in ascending order.

1877, 2122, 2180, 2394, 2408, 2516, 2586, 3060, 3388, 3389, 3497, 3550

↑

Median

Since the middle point falls halfway between 2516 and 2586, find the median *MD* by adding the middle two values and dividing by 2.

$$MD = \frac{2516 + 2586}{2} = 2551$$

The median number of residential home sales in Calgary over the 12-month period is 2551.

The Mode

The third measure of average is called the *mode.* The mode is the value that occurs most often in the data set. It is sometimes said to be the most typical case.

> The value that occurs most often in a data set is called the **mode.**

A data set that has only one value that occurs with the greatest frequency is said to be **unimodal.**

If a data set has two values that occur with the same greatest frequency, both values are considered to be the mode and the data set is said to be **bimodal.** If a data set has more than two values that occur with the same greatest frequency, each value is used as the mode, and the data set is said to be **multimodal.** When no data value occurs more than once, the data set is said to have *no mode.* A data set can have more than one mode or no mode at all. These situations will be shown in some of the examples that follow.

Example 3–6

The following data represent the duration (in days) of United States Space Shuttle voyages for the years 1992–1994. Find the mode.

8, 9, 9, 14, 8, 8, 10, 7, 6, 9, 7, 8, 10, 14, 11, 8, 14, 11

Source: The Universal Almanac.

Solution

It is helpful to arrange the data in order, although it is not necessary.

6, 7, 7, 8, 8, 8, 8, 8, 9, 9, 9, 10, 10, 11, 11, 14, 14, 14

Since 8-day voyages occurred five times—a frequency larger than any other number—the mode for the data set is 8.

Example 3–7

The data represents number of sales in the past month for salespersons at a local car dealership.

$$11, 3, 6, 2, 8, 1, 9, 13, 5$$

Solution

Since each value occurs only once, there is no mode.

   Note: Do not say that the mode is zero. That would be incorrect, because in some data, such as temperature, zero can be an actual value.

Example 3–8

The data shows the number of licensed nuclear reactors in the United States for a recent 15-year period. Find the mode.

Source: The World Almanac and Book of Facts.

104	104	104	104	104
107	109	109	109	110
109	111	112	111	109

Solution

Since the values 104 and 109 both occur five times, the modes are 104 and 109. The data set is said to be bimodal.

The mode for grouped data is the modal class. The **modal class** is the class with the largest frequency.

Example 3–9

Find the modal class for the frequency distribution of kilometres that 20 runners ran in one week, used in Example 2–7.

Class	Frequency
5.5–10.5	1
10.5–15.5	2
15.5–20.5	3
20.5–25.5	5 ← Modal class
25.5–30.5	4
30.5–35.5	3
35.5–40.5	2

Solution

The modal class is 20.5–25.5, since it has the largest frequency. Sometimes the midpoint of the class is used rather than the boundaries; hence, the mode could also be given as 23 kilometres per week.

   The mode is the only measure of central tendency that can be used in finding the most typical case when the data are nominal or categorical.

Example 3–10

A survey showed this distribution for the number of students enrolled in each field. Find the mode.

Business	1425
Liberal arts	878
Computer science	632
Education	471
General studies	95

Solution

Since the category with the highest frequency is business, the most typical case is a business major.

An extremely high or extremely low data value in a data set can have a striking effect on the mean of the data set. These extreme values are called *outliers*. This is one reason why when analyzing a frequency distribution, you should be aware of any of these values. For the data set shown in Example 3–11, the mean, median, and mode can be quite different because of extreme values. A method for identifying outliers is given in Section 3–4.

Example 3–11

A small company consists of the owner, the manager, the salesperson, and two technicians, all of whose annual salaries are listed here. (Assume that this is the entire population.)

Staff	Salary
Owner	$50,000
Manager	20,000
Salesperson	12,000
Technician	9,000
Technician	9,000

Find the mean, median, and mode.

Solution

$$\mu = \frac{\Sigma X}{N} = \frac{50,000 + 20,000 + 12,000 + 9000 + 9000}{5} = \$20,000$$

Hence, the mean is $20,000, the median is $12,000, and the mode is $9000.

In Example 3–11, the mean is much higher than the median or the mode. This is so because the extremely high salary of the owner tends to raise the value of the mean. In this and similar situations, the median should be used as the measure of central tendency.

The Midrange

The *midrange* is a rough estimate of the middle. It is found by adding the lowest and highest values in the data set and dividing by 2. It is a very rough estimate of the average and can be affected by one extremely high or low value.

> The **midrange** is defined as the sum of the lowest and highest values in the data set, divided by 2. The symbol MR is used for the midrange.
>
> $$MR = \frac{\text{lowest value} + \text{highest value}}{2}$$

Example 3–12

Luncheon sales, rounded to the nearest dollar, at a Montreal deli over a one-week period were as follows.

$230 $390 $377 $410 $383 $398 $265

Solution

$$MR = \frac{\$230 + \$410}{2} = \frac{\$640}{2} = \$320$$

Hence, the midrange is $320.

If the data set contains one extremely large value or one extremely small value, a higher or lower midrange value will result and may not be a typical description of the middle.

Example 3–13

Assume that the deli luncheon sales for the following week were affected by a major storm. Listed below, rounded to the nearest dollar, are the deli's luncheon sales.

$255 $425 $333 $395 $361 $328 $45

Solution

$$MR = \frac{\$425 + \$45}{2} = \frac{\$470}{2} = \$235$$

Hence, the midrange is $235. The value $235 is not typical of the average luncheon sales at the deli as the outlier value $45 is not typical of the sales.

In statistics, several measures can be used for an average. The most common measures are the mean, median, mode, and midrange. Each has its own specific purpose and use. Exercises 39 through 41 show examples of other averages, such as the harmonic mean, the geometric mean, and the quadratic mean. Their applications are limited to specific areas, as shown in the exercises.

The Weighted Mean

Sometimes, one must find the mean of a data set in which not all values are equally represented. Consider the case of finding the average cost of a litre of gasoline for three taxis. Suppose the drivers buy gasoline at three different service stations at a cost of $0.99, $1.07, and $1.21 per litre. One might try to find the average by using the formula

$$\overline{X} = \frac{\Sigma X}{n}$$

$$= \frac{0.99 + 1.07 + 1.21}{3} = \frac{3.27}{3} = \$1.09$$

But not all drivers purchased the same number of litres. Hence, to find the true average cost per litre, one must take into consideration the number of litres each driver purchased.

The type of mean that considers an additional factor is called the *weighted mean,* and it is used when the values are not all equally represented.

Find the **weighted mean** of a variable X by multiplying each value by its corresponding weight and dividing the sum of the products by the sum of the weights.

$$\overline{X} = \frac{w_1 X_1 + w_2 X_2 + \cdots + w_n X_n}{w_1 + w_2 + \cdots + w_n} = \frac{\Sigma w X}{\Sigma w}$$

where $w_1, w_2, \ldots, w_n$ are the weights and $X_1, X_2, \ldots, X_n$ are the values.

Example 3–14 shows how the weighted mean is used to compute a grade point average. Since courses vary in their credit value, the number of credits must be used as weights.

Example 3–14

A student received an A in English Composition I (3 credits), a C in Introduction to Psychology (3 credits), a B in Biology I (4 credits), and a D in Physical Education (2 credits). Assuming A = 4 grade points, B = 3 grade points, C = 2 grade points, D = 1 grade point, and F = 0 grade points, find the student's grade point average.

Solution

Course	Credits (w)	Grade (X)
English Composition I	3	A (4 points)
Introduction to Psychology	3	C (2 points)
Biology I	4	B (3 points)
Physical Education	2	D (1 point)

$$\overline{X} = \frac{\Sigma w X}{\Sigma w} = \frac{3 \cdot 4 + 3 \cdot 2 + 4 \cdot 3 + 2 \cdot 1}{3 + 3 + 4 + 2} = \frac{32}{12} = 2.7$$

The grade point average is 2.7.

Table 3–1 summarizes the measures of central tendency.

Table 3–1	Summary of Measures of Central Tendency	
Measure	**Definition**	**Symbol(s)**
Mean	Sum of values, divided by total number of values	$\mu, \overline{X}$
Median	Middle point in data set that has been ordered	MD
Mode	Most frequent data value	None
Midrange	Lowest value plus highest value, divided by 2	MR

Researchers and statisticians must know which measure of central tendency is being used and when to use each measure of central tendency. The properties and uses of the four measures of central tendency are summarized next.

Properties and Uses of Central Tendency

The Mean
1. One computes the mean by using all the values of the data.
2. The mean usually varies less than the median or mode when samples are taken from the same population and all three measures are computed for these samples.
3. The mean is used in computing other statistics, such as the variance.
4. The mean for the data set is unique and not necessarily one of the data values.
5. The mean cannot be computed for the data in a frequency distribution that has an open-ended class.
6. The mean is affected by unusual and extreme high or low values, called outliers, and may not be the appropriate average to use in these situations.

The Median
1. The median is used when one must find the centre or middle value of a data set.
2. The median is used when one must determine whether the data values fall into the upper half or lower half of the distribution.
3. The median is used for an open-ended distribution.
4. The median is affected less than the mean by extremely high or extremely low values.

The Mode
1. The mode is used when the most typical case is desired.
2. The mode is the easiest average to compute.
3. The mode can be used when the data are nominal, such as religious preference, gender, or political affiliation.
4. The mode is not always unique. A data set can have more than one mode, or the mode may not exist for a data set.

The Midrange
1. The midrange is easy to compute.
2. The midrange gives the midpoint.
3. The midrange is affected by extremely high or low values in a data set.

Distribution Shapes

In the previous chapter, data was organized into classes in tables and graphed. These data organization and presentation methods are essential to understanding the structure of a data set.

Frequency distributions can assume many shapes. The three most important shapes are positively skewed, symmetric, and negatively skewed. Figure 3–1 shows histograms of each.

In a **positively skewed** or **right-skewed distribution,** the majority of the data values fall to the left of the mean and cluster at the lower end of the distribution; the "tail" is to the right. Typically, the mean is to the right of the median, and the mode is to the left of the median.

For example, if an instructor gave an examination and most of the students did poorly, their scores would tend to cluster on the left side of the distribution. A few high scores would constitute the tail of the distribution, which would be on the right side. Another example of a positively skewed distribution is the incomes of the population of Canada. Most of the incomes cluster about the low end of the distribution; those with high incomes are in the minority and are in the tail at the right of the distribution.

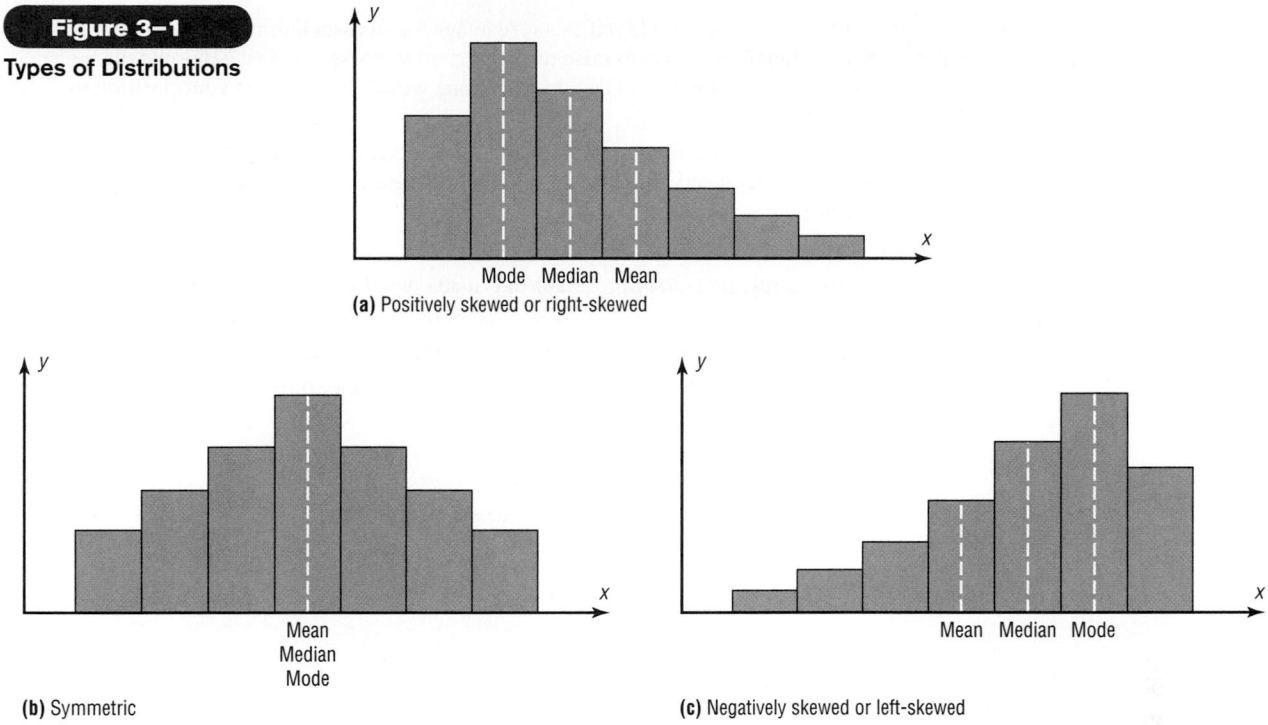

Figure 3–1

Types of Distributions

(a) Positively skewed or right-skewed

Mode Median Mean

(b) Symmetric

Mean
Median
Mode

(c) Negatively skewed or left-skewed

Mean Median Mode

In a **symmetric distribution,** the data values are evenly distributed on both sides of the mean. In addition, when the distribution is unimodal, the mean, median, and mode are the same and are at the centre of the distribution. Examples of symmetric distributions are IQ scores and heights of adult males.

When the majority of the data values fall to the right of the mean and cluster at the upper end of the distribution, with the tail to the left, the distribution is said to be **negatively skewed** or **left-skewed.** Typically, the mean is to the left of the median, and the mode is to the right of the median. As an example, a negatively skewed distribution results if the majority of students score very high on an instructor's examination. These scores will tend to cluster to the right of the distribution.

When a distribution is extremely skewed, the value of the mean will be pulled toward the tail, but the majority of the data values will be greater than the mean or less than the mean (depending on which way the data are skewed); hence, the median rather than the mean is a more appropriate measure of central tendency. An extremely skewed distribution can also affect other statistics.

A measure of skewness for a distribution is discussed in Exercise 48 in Section 3–3.

Applying the Concepts 3–2

Professor Salaries

The following data represent professor salaries (in dollars) from a selection of Canadian universities.

98,243	88,444	151,884	94,280	100,487	99,832
103,311	90,120	87,362	91,231	88,444	93,521

Source: Adapted from Statistics Canada, excerpts from salaries and salary scales of full-time teaching staff at Canadian universities, 2001–2002; www.statcan.ca/bsolc/english/bsolc?catno=81-595-M2004013, February 28, 2007.

1. First, assume that you are employed as a researcher for an association of university administrators and do not wish to raise tuition fees to increase salaries. Compute the mean, median, midrange, and mode and decide which one would best support your position to not raise salaries.

2. Second, assume you work for a university faculty association and want to provide the rationale for a faculty salary increase. Use the best measure of central tendency to support your position.

3. Explain how outliers can be used to support one or the other position.

4. If the salaries represented every professor in Canada, would the averages be parameters or statistics?

5. Which measure of central tendency can be misleading when a data set contains outliers?

6. When one is comparing the measures of central tendency, does the distribution display any skewness? Explain.

See page 142 for the answers.

Exercises 3–2

For Exercises 1 through 8, find (a) the mean, (b) the median, (c) the mode, and (d) the midrange.

1. The average undergraduate grade point average (GPA) for the 25 top-ranked medical schools is listed below.

3.80	3.77	3.70	3.74	3.70
3.86	3.76	3.68	3.67	3.57
3.83	3.70	3.80	3.74	3.67
3.78	3.74	3.73	3.65	3.66
3.75	3.64	3.78	3.73	3.64

   Source: *U.S. News & World Report Best Graduate Schools.*

2. The heights (in meters) of 20 of the world's tallest waterfalls are shown here. (*Note: The height of Niagara Falls is 50.9 meters!*)

979	948	914	900	860	850	840	836	820	818
792	788	773	771	762	755	751	739	725	720

   Source: World Waterfall Database.

3. The following data are the number of burglaries reported for a 12-month period in select Calgary communities. Which measure of average might be the best in this case? Explain your answer.

13	8	22	73	13	2	24	7	13	4	33
7	4	3	6	8	4	16	8	17	9	72

   Source: Calgary Police Service.

4. For a recent year, the number of suspensions in a sample of public schools in Beaver County was 67, 12, 11, 92, and 13. The number of suspensions in a sample of public schools in Butler County was 56, 12, 18, and 21. Do you think that there is a difference in the averages?
   Source: U.S. Department of Education.

5. A researcher claims that each year, there are an average of 300 victims of identity theft in major cities. Twelve were randomly selected, and the number of victims of identity theft in each city is shown. Can you conclude that the researcher was correct?

574	229	663	372	102	88
117	239	465	136	189	75

6. For a recent year, the worth (in billions of dollars) of a sample of the 10 wealthiest people under the age of 60 is shown:

   14, 12, 48, 20, 18, 18, 12.6, 10.4, 7.3, 5.3

   The worth of a sample of 10 of the wealthiest people age 60 and over is shown:

   41.0, 13.7, 10.0, 18.0, 11.3, 7.6, 7, 18, 20, 60

   Based on the averages, can you conclude that those 60 years old and over have a higher net worth?
   Source: *Forbes* magazine.

7. Twelve major earthquakes had Richter magnitudes shown here.

   7.0, 6.2, 7.7, 8.0, 6.4, 6.2,
   7.2, 5.4, 6.4, 6.5, 7.2, 5.4

   Which would you consider the best measure of average?
   Source: *The Universal Almanac.*

8. The data shown are the total compensation (in millions of dollars) for the 50 top-paid CEOs for a recent year. Compare the averages, and state which one you think is the best measure.

17.5	18.0	36.8	31.7	31.7
17.3	24.3	47.7	38.5	17.0
23.7	16.5	25.1	17.4	18.0
37.6	19.7	21.4	28.6	21.6
19.3	20.0	16.9	25.2	19.8
25.0	17.2	20.4	20.1	29.1
19.1	25.2	23.2	25.9	24.0
41.7	24.0	16.8	26.8	31.4
16.9	17.2	24.1	35.2	19.1
22.9	18.2	25.4	35.4	25.5

Source: *USA TODAY.*

9. Find the (*a*) mean, (*b*) median, (*c*) mode, and (*d*) midrange for the data in Exercise 17 in Section 2–2. Is the distribution symmetric or skewed? Use the individual data values.

10. Find the (*a*) mean, (*b*) median, (*c*) mode, and (*d*) midrange for the distances of the home runs for McGwire and Sosa, using the data in Exercise 18 in Section 2–2.

    Compare the means. Decide if the means are approximately equal or if one of the players is hitting longer home runs. Use the individual data values.

11. These data represent the number of traffic fatalities for two specific years for 27 selected American states. Find the (*a*) mean, (*b*) median, (*c*) mode, and (*d*) midrange for each data set. Are the four measures of average for fatalities for year 1 the same as those for year 2? (The data in this exercise will be used in Exercise 15 in Section 3–3.)

Year 1			Year 2		
1113	1488	868	1100	260	205
1031	262	1109	970	1430	300
4192	1586	215	4040	460	350
645	527	254	620	480	485
121	442	313	125	405	85
2805	444	485	2805	690	1430
900	653	170	1555	1160	70
74	1480	69	180	3360	325
158	3181	326	875	705	145

Source: *USA TODAY.*

For Exercises 12 through 21, find the (*a*) mean and (*b*) modal class.

12. For 108 randomly selected college students, this exam score frequency distribution was obtained. (The data in this exercise will be used in Exercise 18 in Section 3–3.)

Class limits	Frequency
90–98	6
99–107	22
108–116	43
117–125	28
126–134	9

13. The final golf scores for The Players Championship in 2006 were

Score	Frequency
280–283	5
284–287	13
288–291	16
292–295	20
296–299	13
300–303	4
304–307	2

Source: PGA.com.

14. Thirty-five different vehicle manufacturers are indicated in *Canada's Fuel Consumption Guide, 2006*. The following distribution indicates the most fuel efficient vehicle reported from each manufacturer. Data shown indicates highway fuel consumption in L/100 km. (This data will be used in Exercise 20 in Section 3–3.)

Class boundaries	Frequency
3.5–6.5	5
6.5–9.5	15
9.5–12.5	8
12.5–15.5	4
15.5–18.5	0
18.5–21.5	2
21.5–24.5	1

Source: Natural Resources Canada—*Fuel Consumption Guide, 2006.*

15. The data show the number of murders in 25 selected cities in a given U.S. state.

Number	Frequency
34–96	13
97–159	2
160–222	0
223–285	5
286–348	1
349–411	1
412–474	0
475–537	1
538–600	2

Do you think that the mean is the best measure of average for these data? Explain your answer. (The information in the exercise will be used in Exercise 21 in Section 3–3.)

16. Find the mean and modal class for the two frequency distributions in Exercises 8 and 18 in Section 2–3. Are the "average" reactions the same? Explain your answer.

17. Eighty randomly selected lightbulbs were tested to determine their lifetimes (in hours). This frequency distribution was obtained. (The data in this exercise will be used in Exercise 23 in Section 3–3.)

Class boundaries	Frequency
52.5–63.5	6
63.5–74.5	12
74.5–85.5	25
85.5–96.5	18
96.5–107.5	14
107.5–118.5	5

18. These data represent the net worth (in millions of dollars) of 45 national corporations.

Class limits	Frequency
10–20	2
21–31	8
32–42	15
43–53	7
54–64	10
65–75	3

19. The cost per load (in cents) of 35 laundry detergents tested by a consumer organization is shown. (The data in this exercise will be used for Exercise 19 in Section 3–3.)

Class limits	Frequency
13–19	2
20–26	7
27–33	12
34–40	5
41–47	6
48–54	1
55–61	0
62–68	2

20. This frequency distribution represents the commission earned (in dollars) by 100 salespeople employed at several branches of a large chain store.

Class limits	Frequency
150–158	5
159–167	16
168–176	20
177–185	21
186–194	20
195–203	15
204–212	3

21. This frequency distribution represents the data obtained from a sample of 75 copying machine service technicians. The values represent the days between service calls for various copying machines.

Class boundaries	Frequency
15.5–18.5	14
18.5–21.5	12
21.5–24.5	18
24.5–27.5	10
27.5–30.5	15
30.5–33.5	6

22. Find the mean and modal class for the data in Exercise 12 in Section 2–2.

23. Find the mean and modal class for the data in Exercise 13 in Section 2–2.

24. Find the mean and modal class for the data in Exercise 14 in Section 2–2.

25. Find the mean and modal class for the data in Exercise 15 in Section 2–2.

26. Find the weighted mean price of three models of automobiles sold. The number and price of each model sold are shown in this list.

Model	Number	Price
A	8	$10,000
B	10	12,000
C	12	8,000

27. Using the weighted mean, find the average number of grams of fat per ounce of meat or fish that a person would consume over a 5-day period if he ate these:

Meat or fish	Fat (g/oz)
3 oz fried shrimp	3.33
3 oz veal cutlet (broiled)	3.00
2 oz roast beef (lean)	2.50
2.5 oz fried chicken drumstick	4.40
4 oz tuna (canned in oil)	1.75

Source: *The World Almanac and Book of Facts.*

28. A recent survey of a new diet cola reported the following percentages of people who liked the taste. Find the weighted mean of the percentages.

Area	% Favoured	Number surveyed
1	40	1000
2	30	3000
3	50	800

29. The costs of three models of helicopters are shown here. Find the weighted mean of the costs of the models.

Model	Number sold	Cost
Sunscraper	9	$427,000
Skycoaster	6	365,000
High-flyer	12	725,000

30. An instructor grades exams, 20%; term paper, 30%; final exam, 50%. A student had grades of 83, 72, and 90, respectively, for exams, term paper, and final exam. Find the student's final average. Use the weighted mean.

31. Another instructor gives four 1-hour exams and one final exam, which counts as two 1-hour exams. Find a student's grade if she received 62, 83, 97, and 90 on the 1-hour exams and 82 on the final exam.

32. For these situations, state which measure of central tendency—mean, median, or mode—should be used.

a. The most typical case is desired.

b. The distribution is open-ended.

c. There is an extreme value in the data set.

d. The data are categorical.

e. Further statistical computations will be needed.

f. The values are to be divided into two approximately equal groups, one group containing the larger values and one containing the smaller values.

33. Describe which measure of central tendency—mean, median, or mode—was probably used in each situation.

a. One-half of the factory workers make more than $5.37 per hour, and one-half make less than $5.37 per hour.

b. The average number of children per family in the Plaza Heights Complex is 1.8.

c. Most people prefer red convertibles over any other colour.

d. The average person cuts the lawn once a week.

e. The most common fear today is fear of speaking in public.

f. The average age of college and university professors is 42.3 years.

34. What types of symbols are used to represent sample statistics? Give an example. What types of symbols are used to represent population parameters? Give an example.

35. A local fast-food company claims that the average salary of its employees is $13.23 per hour. An employee states that most employees make minimum wage. If both are being truthful, how could both be correct?

Extending the Concepts

36. If the mean of five values is 64, find the sum of the values.

37. If the mean of five values is 8.2 and four of the values are 6, 10, 7, and 12, find the fifth value.

38. Find the mean of 10, 20, 30, 40, and 50.

a. Add 10 to each value and find the mean.

b. Subtract 10 from each value and find the mean.

c. Multiply each value by 10 and find the mean.

d. Divide each value by 10 and find the mean.

e. Make a general statement about each situation.

39. The *harmonic mean* (HM) is defined as the number of values, divided by the sum of the reciprocals of each value. The formula is

$$HM = \frac{n}{\Sigma(1/X)}$$

For example, the harmonic mean of 1, 4, 5, and 2 is

$$HM = \frac{4}{1/1 + 1/4 + 1/5 + 1/2} = 2.05$$

This mean is useful for finding the average speed. Suppose a person drove 180 kilometres at 60 kilometres per hour and returned, driving 80 kilometres per hour. The average speed is not 70 kilometres per hour, which is found by adding 60 and 80 and dividing by 2. The average speed is found as shown.

Since

Time = distance ÷ rate

then

$$Time\ 1 = \frac{180}{60} = 3.0 \text{ hours to the destination}$$

$$Time\ 2 = \frac{180}{80} = 2.25 \text{ hours to make the return trip}$$

Hence, the total time is 5.25 hours, and the total kilometres driven are 360. Now, the average speed is

$$Rate = \frac{distance}{time} = \frac{360}{5.25} = 68.57 \text{ kilometres per hour (rounded)}$$

This value can be found by using the harmonic mean formula

$$HM = \frac{2}{1/60 + 1/80} = 68.57 \text{ (rounded)}$$

a. A salesperson drives 300 kilometres round trip at 60 kilometres per hour going to Ottawa and 50 kilometres per hour returning home. Find the average kilometres per hour.

b. A bus driver drives 450 kilometres to Vancouver at 90 kilometres per hour and returns, driving 100 kilometres per hour. Find the average speed.

c. A carpenter buys $500 worth of nails at $25 per kilogram and $500 worth of nails at $5 per kilogram. Find the average cost of 1 kilogram of nails.

40. The *geometric mean* (GM) is defined as the *n*th root of the product of *n* values. The formula is

$$GM = \sqrt[n]{(X_1)(X_2)(X_3)\cdots(X_n)}$$

The geometric mean of 4 and 16 is

$$GM = \sqrt{(4)(16)} = \sqrt{64} = 8$$

The geometric mean of 1, 3, and 9 is

$$GM = \sqrt[3]{(1)(3)(9)} = \sqrt[3]{27} = 3$$

The geometric mean is useful in finding the average of percentages, ratios, indexes, or growth rates. For example, if a person receives a 20% raise after one year of service and a 10% raise after the second year of service, the average percentage raise per year is not 15 but 14.89%, as shown.

$$GM = \sqrt{(1.2)(1.1)} = 1.1489$$

or

$$GM = \sqrt{(120)(110)} = 114.89\%$$

His salary is 120% at the end of the first year and 110% at the end of the second year. This is equivalent to an average of 14.89%, since 114.89% − 100% = 14.89%.

This answer can also be shown by assuming that the person makes $10,000 to start and receives two raises of 20% and 10%.

Raise 1 = 10,000 · 20% = $2000
Raise 2 = 12,000 · 10% = $1200

His total salary raise is $3200. This total is equivalent to

$10,000 · 14.89% = $1489.00
$11,489 · 14.89% = 1710.71
                  ‾‾‾‾‾‾‾‾‾‾
                  $3199.71 ≈ $3200

Find the geometric mean of each of these.

a. The growth rates of the Living Life Insurance Corporation for the past 3 years were 35, 24, and 18%.

b. A person received these percentage raises in salary over a 4-year period: 8, 6, 4, and 5%.

c. A stock increased each year for 5 years at these percentages: 10, 8, 12, 9, and 3%.

d. The price increases, in percentages, for the cost of food in a specific geographic region for the past 3 years were 1, 3, and 5.5%.

41. A useful mean in the physical sciences (such as voltage) is the *quadratic mean* (QM), which is found by taking the square root of the average of the squares of each value. The formula is

$$QM = \sqrt{\frac{\Sigma X^2}{n}}$$

The quadratic mean of 3, 5, 6, and 10 is

$$QM = \sqrt{\frac{3^2 + 5^2 + 6^2 + 10^2}{4}}$$
$$= \sqrt{42.5} = 6.52$$

Find the quadratic mean of 8, 6, 3, 5, and 4.

42. An approximate median can be found for data that have been grouped into a frequency distribution. First it is necessary to find the median class. This is the class that contains the median value. That is the $n/2$ data value. Then it is assumed that the data values are evenly distributed throughout the median class. The formula is

$$MD = \frac{(n/2) - \text{cf}}{f}(w) + L_m$$

where

n = sum of frequencies
cf = cumulative frequency of class immediately preceding the median class
w = width of median class
f = frequency of median class
L_m = lower boundary of median class

Using this formula, find the median for data in the frequency distribution of Exercise 15.

3–3   Measures of Variation

In statistics, to describe the data set accurately, statisticians must know more than the measures of central tendency. Consider Example 3–15.

Example 3–15

Objective ❷

Describe data using measures of variation, such as the range, variance, and standard deviation.

A testing lab wishes to test two experimental brands of outdoor paint to see how long each will last before fading. The testing lab makes six 3.78 L pails of each paint to test. Since different chemical agents are added to each group and only six cans are involved, these two groups constitute two small populations. The results (in months) are shown. Find the mean and median of each group.

Brand A	Brand B
10	35
60	45
50	30
30	35
40	40
20	25

Solution

The mean for brand A is

$$\mu = \frac{\Sigma X}{N} = \frac{210}{6} = 35 \text{ months}$$

The mean for brand B is

$$\mu = \frac{\Sigma X}{N} = \frac{210}{6} = 35 \text{ months}$$

The median for brand A is

$$MD = \frac{30 + 40}{2} = 35 \text{ months}$$

The median for brand B is

$$MD = \frac{35 + 35}{2} = 35 \text{ months}$$

Since both the means and the medians are equal in Example 3–15, one might conclude that both brands of paint last equally well. However, when the data sets are examined graphically, a somewhat different conclusion might be drawn. See Figure 3–2.

Figure 3–2

Examining Data Sets Graphically

Variation of paint (in months)

(a) Brand A

Variation of paint (in months)

(b) Brand B

As Figure 3–2 shows, even though both the means and medians are the same for each brand, the spread, or variation, is quite different. Figure 3–2 shows that brand B performs more consistently; it is less variable. For the spread or variability of a data set, three measures are commonly used: *range, variance,* and *standard deviation.* Each measure will be discussed in this section.

Range

The range is the simplest of the three measures.

> The **range** is the highest value minus the lowest value. The symbol R is used for the range.
>
> $$R = \text{highest value} - \text{lowest value}$$

Example 3–16	Find the ranges for the paints in Example 3–15.

Solution

For brand A, the range is

$$R = 60 - 10 = 50 \text{ months}$$

For brand B, the range is

$$R = 45 - 25 = 20 \text{ months}$$

Make sure the range is given as a single number.

The range for brand A shows that 50 months separate the largest data value from the smallest data value. For brand B, 20 months separate the largest data value from the smallest data value, which is less than one-half of brand A's range.

One extremely high or one extremely low data value can affect the range markedly, as shown in Example 3–17.

Example 3–17	The salaries for the staff of the XYZ Manufacturing Co. are shown here. Find the range.

Staff	Salary
Owner	$100,000
Manager	40,000
Sales representative	30,000
Workers	25,000
	15,000
	18,000

Solution

The range is $R = \$100,000 - \$15,000 = \$85,000$.

Since the owner's salary is included in the data for Example 3–17, the range is a large number. To have a more meaningful statistic to measure the variability, statisticians use measures called the *variance* and *standard deviation*.

Population Variance and Standard Deviation

Before the variance and standard deviation are defined formally, the computational procedure will be shown, since the definition is derived from the procedure.

Rounding Rule for the Standard Deviation   The rounding rule for the standard deviation is the same as that for the mean. The final answer should be rounded to one more decimal place than that of the original data.

Example 3–18   Find the variance and standard deviation for the data set for brand A paint in Example 3–15.

10, 60, 50, 30, 40, 20

Solution

Step 1   Find the mean for the data.

$$\mu = \frac{\Sigma X}{N} = \frac{10 + 60 + 50 + 30 + 40 + 20}{6} = \frac{210}{6} = 35$$

Step 2   Subtract the mean from each data value.

$$10 - 35 = -25 \qquad 50 - 35 = +15 \qquad 40 - 35 = +5$$
$$60 - 35 = +25 \qquad 30 - 35 = -5 \qquad 20 - 35 = -15$$

Step 3   Square each result.

$$(-25)^2 = 625 \qquad (+15)^2 = 225 \qquad (+5)^2 = 25$$
$$(+25)^2 = 625 \qquad (-5)^2 = 25 \qquad (-15)^2 = 225$$

Step 4   Find the sum of the squares.

$$625 + 625 + 225 + 25 + 25 + 225 = 1750$$

Step 5   Divide the sum by N to get the variance.
Variance = $1750 \div 6 = 291.7$ (rounded)

Step 6   Take the square root of the variance to get the standard deviation. Hence, the standard deviation equals $\sqrt{291.7}$, or approximately 17.1. It is helpful to make a table.

A Values (X)	B $X - \mu$	C $(X - \mu)^2$
10	-25	625
60	$+25$	625
50	$+15$	225
30	-5	25
40	$+5$	25
20	-15	225
		1750

Column A contains the raw data X. Column B contains the differences $X - \mu$ obtained in step 2. Column C contains the squares of the differences obtained in step 3.

The preceding computational procedure reveals several things. First, the square root of the variance gives the standard deviation; and vice versa, squaring the standard deviation gives the variance. Second, the variance is actually the average of the square of the distance that each value is from the mean. Therefore, if the values are near the mean, the variance will be small. In contrast, if the values are far from the mean, the variance will be large.

One might wonder why the squared distances are used instead of the actual distances. One reason is that the sum of the distances will always be zero. To verify this result for a specific case, add the values in column B of the table in Example 3–18. When each value is squared, the negative signs are eliminated.

Finally, why is it necessary to take the square root? The reason is that since the distances were squared, the units of the resultant numbers are the squares of the units of the original raw data. Finding the square root of the variance puts the standard deviation in the same units as the raw data.

When you are finding the square root, always use its positive or principal value, since the variance and standard deviation of a data set can never be negative.

The **variance** is the average of the squares of the distance each value is from the mean. The symbol for the population variance is σ^2 (σ is the Greek lowercase letter sigma). The formula for the population variance is

$$\sigma^2 = \frac{\Sigma(X - \mu)^2}{N}$$

where
  X = individual value
  μ = population mean
  N = population size

The **standard deviation** is the square root of the variance. The symbol for the population standard deviation is σ.
  The corresponding formula for the population standard deviation is

$$\sigma = \sqrt{\sigma^2} = \sqrt{\frac{\Sigma(X - \mu)^2}{N}}$$

Example 3–19

Find the variance and standard deviation for brand B paint data in Example 3–15. The months were

35, 45, 30, 35, 40, 25

Solution

Step 1 Find the mean.

$$\mu = \frac{\Sigma X}{N} = \frac{35 + 45 + 30 + 35 + 40 + 25}{6} = \frac{210}{6} = 35$$

Step 2 Subtract the mean from each value, and place the result in column B of the table.

Step 3 Square each result and place the squares in column C of the table.

A X	B $X - \mu$	C $(X - \mu)^2$
35	0	0
45	10	100
30	−5	25
35	0	0
40	5	25
25	−10	100

Each person receives on average 598 pieces of mail per year.

Step 4 Find the sum of the squares in column C.

$$\Sigma(X - \mu)^2 = 0 + 100 + 25 + 0 + 25 + 100 = 250$$

Step 5 Divide the sum by N to get the variance.

$$\sigma^2 = \frac{\Sigma(X - \mu)^2}{N} = \frac{250}{6} = 41.7$$

Step 6 Take the square root to get the standard deviation.

$$\sigma = \sqrt{\frac{\Sigma(X - \mu)^2}{N}} = \sqrt{41.7} = 6.5 \text{ (rounded)}$$

Hence, the standard deviation is 6.5.

Since the standard deviation of brand A is 17.1 (see Example 3–18) and the standard deviation of brand B is 6.5, the data are more variable for brand A. *In summary, when the means are equal, the larger the variance or standard deviation is, the more variable the data are.*

Sample Variance and Standard Deviation

When computing the variance for a sample, one might expect the following expression to be used:

$$\frac{\Sigma(X - \overline{X})^2}{n}$$

where $\overline{X}$ is the sample mean and n is the sample size. *This formula is not usually used, however, since in most cases the purpose of calculating the statistic is to estimate the corresponding parameter.* For example, the sample mean $\overline{X}$ is used to estimate the population mean μ. The expression

$$\frac{\Sigma(X - \overline{X})^2}{n}$$

does not give the best estimate of the population variance because when the population is large and the sample is small (usually less than 30), the variance computed by this formula usually underestimates the population variance resulting in a biased estimate. Therefore, instead of dividing by n, find the variance of the sample by dividing by $n - 1$, giving a slightly larger value and an *unbiased* estimate of the population variance.

The formula for the sample variance, denoted by s^2, is

$$s^2 = \frac{\Sigma(X - \overline{X})^2}{n - 1}$$

where
$\overline{X}$ = sample mean
n = sample size

To find the standard deviation of a sample, one must take the square root of the sample variance, which was found by using the preceding formula.

Formula for the Sample Standard Deviation

The standard deviation of a sample (denoted by s) is

$$s = \sqrt{s^2} = \sqrt{\frac{\Sigma(X - \overline{X})^2}{n - 1}}$$

where

X = individual value
$\overline{X}$ = sample mean
n = sample size

Shortcut formulas for computing the variance and standard deviation are presented next and will be used in the remainder of the chapter and in the exercises. These formulas are mathematically equivalent to the preceding formulas and do not involve using the mean. They save time when repeated subtracting and squaring occur in the original formulas. They are also more accurate when the mean has been rounded.

Shortcut or Computational Formulas for s^2 and s

The shortcut formulas for computing the variance and standard deviation for data obtained from samples are as follows.

Variance	Standard deviation
$s^2 = \dfrac{\Sigma X^2 - [(\Sigma X)^2/n]}{n - 1}$	$s = \sqrt{\dfrac{\Sigma X^2 - [(\Sigma X)^2/n]}{n - 1}}$

Examples 3–20 and 3–21 explain how to use the shortcut formulas.

Example 3–20

Find the sample variance and standard deviation for the amount of European auto sales for a sample of 6 years shown. The data are in millions of dollars.

11.2, 11.9, 12.0, 12.8, 13.4, 14.3

Source: USA TODAY.

Solution

Step 1   Find the sum of the values.

$$\Sigma X = 11.2 + 11.9 + 12.0 + 12.8 + 13.4 + 14.3 = 75.6$$

Step 2   Square each value and find the sum.

$$\Sigma X^2 = 11.2^2 + 11.9^2 + 12.0^2 + 12.8^2 + 13.4^2 + 14.3^2 = 958.94$$

Step 3   Substitute in the formulas and solve.

$$s^2 = \frac{\Sigma X^2 - [(\Sigma X)^2/n]}{n - 1} = \frac{958.94 - [(75.6)^2/6]}{5}$$

$$= 1.28$$

The variance of the sample is 1.28.

$$s = \sqrt{1.28} = 1.13$$

Hence, the sample standard deviation is 1.13.

Note that ΣX^2 is not the same as $(\Sigma X)^2$. The notation ΣX^2 means to square the values first, then sum; $(\Sigma X)^2$ means to sum the values first, then square the sum.

Variance and Standard Deviation for Grouped Data

The procedure for finding the variance and standard deviation for grouped data is similar to that for finding the mean for grouped data, and it uses the midpoints of each class.

Example 3–21

Find the variance and the standard deviation for the frequency distribution of the data in Example 2–7. The data represent the number of kilometres that 20 runners ran during one week.

Class	Frequency	Midpoint
5.5–10.5	1	8
10.5–15.5	2	13
15.5–20.5	3	18
20.5–25.5	5	23
25.5–30.5	4	28
30.5–35.5	3	33
35.5–40.5	2	38

Solution

Step 1 Make a table as shown, and find the midpoint of each class.

A Class	B Frequency (f)	C Midpoint (X_m)	D $f \cdot X_m$	E $f \cdot X^2_m$
5.5–10.5	1	8		
10.5–15.5	2	13		
15.5–20.5	3	18		
20.5–25.5	5	23		
25.5–30.5	4	28		
30.5–35.5	3	33		
35.5–40.5	2	38		

Step 2 Multiply the frequency by the midpoint for each class, and place the products in column D.

$$1 \cdot 8 = 8 \qquad 2 \cdot 13 = 26 \qquad \ldots \qquad 2 \cdot 38 = 76$$

Step 3 Multiply the frequency by the square of the midpoint, and place the products in column E.

$$1 \cdot 8^2 = 64 \qquad 2 \cdot 13^2 = 338 \qquad \ldots \qquad 2 \cdot 38^2 = 2888$$

Step 4 Find the sums of columns B, D, and E. The sum of column B is n, the sum of column D is $\Sigma f \cdot X_m$, and the sum of column E is $\Sigma f \cdot X_m^2$. The completed table is shown.

A	B	C	D	E
Class	Frequency	Midpoint	$f \cdot X_m$	$f \cdot X_m^2$
5.5–10.5	1	8	8	64
10.5–15.5	2	13	26	338
15.5–20.5	3	18	54	972
20.5–25.5	5	23	115	2,645
25.5–30.5	4	28	112	3,136
30.5–35.5	3	33	99	3,267
35.5–40.5	2	38	76	2,888
	$n = 20$		$\Sigma f \cdot X_m = 490$	$\Sigma f \cdot X_m^2 = 13{,}310$

Step 5 Substitute in the formula and solve for s^2 to get the variance.

$$s^2 = \frac{\Sigma f \cdot X_m^2 - [(\Sigma f \cdot X_m)^2 / n]}{n - 1}$$

$$= \frac{13{,}310 - [(490)^2 / 20]}{20 - 1} = 68.7$$

Step 6 Take the square root to get the standard deviation.

$$s = \sqrt{68.7} = 8.3$$

Be sure to use the number found in the sum of column B (i.e., the sum of the frequencies) for n. Do not use the number of classes.

The steps for finding the variance and standard deviation for grouped data are summarized in this Procedure Table.

Procedure Table

Finding the Sample Variance and Standard Deviation for Grouped Data

Step 1 Make a table as shown, and find the midpoint of each class.

A	B	C	D	E
Class	Frequency	Midpoint	$f \cdot X_m$	$f \cdot X_m^2$

Step 2 Multiply the frequency by the midpoint for each class, and place the products in column D.

Step 3 Multiply the frequency by the square of the midpoint, and place the products in column E.

Step 4 Find the sums of columns B, D, and E. (The sum of column B is n. The sum of column D is $\Sigma f \cdot X_m$. The sum of column E is $\Sigma f \cdot X_m^2$.)

Step 5 Substitute in the formula and solve to get the variance.

$$s^2 = \frac{\Sigma f \cdot X_m^2 - [(\Sigma f \cdot X_m)^2 / n]}{n - 1}$$

Step 6 Take the square root to get the standard deviation.

The three measures of variation are summarized in Table 3–2.

Unusual Stat

The average number of times that a man cries in a month is 1.4.

Table 3–2	Summary of Measures of Variation	
Measure	**Definition**	**Symbol(s)**
Range	Distance between highest value and lowest value	R
Variance	Average of the squares of the distance that each value is from the mean	σ^2, s^2
Standard deviation	Square root of the variance	σ, s

Uses of the Variance and Standard Deviation

1. As previously stated, variances and standard deviations can be used to determine the spread of the data. If the variance or standard deviation is large, the data are more dispersed. This information is useful in comparing two (or more) data sets to determine which is more (most) variable.

2. The measures of variance and standard deviation are used to determine the consistency of a variable. For example, in the manufacture of fittings, such as nuts and bolts, the variation in the diameters must be small, or the parts will not fit together.

3. The variance and standard deviation are used to determine the number of data values that fall within a specified interval in a distribution. For example, Chebyshev's theorem (explained later) shows that, for any distribution, at least 75% of the data values will fall within 2 standard deviations of the mean.

4. Finally, the variance and standard deviation are used quite often in inferential statistics. These uses will be shown in later chapters of this textbook.

Coefficient of Variation

Whenever two samples have the same units of measure, the variance and standard deviation for each can be compared directly. For example, suppose an automobile dealer wanted to compare the standard deviation of kilometres driven for the cars she received as trade-ins on new cars. She found that for a specific year, the standard deviation for Buicks was 679 kilometres and the standard deviation for Cadillacs was 563 kilometres. She could say that the variation in kilometres was greater in the Buicks. But what if a manager wanted to compare the standard deviations of two different variables, such as the number of sales per salesperson over a three-month period and the commissions made by these salespeople?

A statistic that allows one to compare standard deviations when the units are different, as in this example, is called the *coefficient of variation*.

The **coefficient of variation,** denoted by CVar, is the standard deviation divided by the mean. The result is expressed as a percentage.

For samples,   For populations,

$$\text{CVar} = \frac{s}{\overline{X}} \cdot 100\% \qquad \text{CVar} = \frac{\sigma}{\mu} \cdot 100\%$$

Example 3–22

The mean of the number of sales of cars over a 3-month period is 87, and the standard deviation is 5. The mean of the commissions is $5225, and the standard deviation is $773. Compare the variations of the two.

Solution

The coefficients of variation are

$$\text{CVar} = \frac{s}{\overline{X}} = \frac{5}{87} \cdot 100\% = 5.7\% \qquad \text{sales}$$

$$\text{CVar} = \frac{773}{5225} \cdot 100\% = 14.8\% \qquad \text{commissions}$$

Since the coefficient of variation is larger for commissions, the commissions are more variable than the sales.

Example 3–23

The mean for the number of pages of a sample of women's fitness magazines is 132, with a variance of 23; the mean for the number of advertisements of a sample of women's fitness magazines is 182, with a variance of 62. Compare the variations.

Solution

The coefficients of variation are

$$\text{CVar} = \frac{\sqrt{23}}{132} \cdot 100\% = 3.6\% \qquad \text{pages}$$

$$\text{CVar} = \frac{\sqrt{62}}{182} \cdot 100\% = 4.3\% \qquad \text{advertisements}$$

The number of advertisements is more variable than the number of pages since the coefficient of variation is larger for advertisements.

Range Rule of Thumb

The range can be used to approximate the standard deviation. The approximation is called the **range rule of thumb.**

The Range Rule of Thumb

A rough estimate of the standard deviation is

$$s \approx \frac{\text{range}}{4}$$

In other words, if the range is divided by 4, an approximate value for the standard deviation is obtained. For example, the standard deviation for the data set 5, 8, 8, 9, 10, 12, and 13 is 2.7, and the range is $13 - 5 = 8$. The range rule of thumb is $s \approx 2$. The range rule of thumb in this case underestimates the standard deviation somewhat; however, it is in the ballpark.

A note of caution should be mentioned here. The range rule of thumb is only an *approximation* and should be used when the distribution of data values is unimodal and roughly symmetric.

The range rule of thumb can be used to estimate the largest and smallest data values of a data set. The smallest data value will be approximately 2 standard deviations below the mean, and the largest data value will be approximately 2 standard deviations above the mean of the data set. The mean for the previous data set is 9.3; hence,

$$\text{Smallest data value} = \overline{X} - 2s = 9.3 - 2(2.8) = 3.7$$

$$\text{Largest data value} = \overline{X} + 2s = 9.3 + 2(2.8) = 14.9$$

Notice that the smallest data value was 5, and the largest data value was 13. Again, these are rough approximations. For many data sets, almost all data values will fall within 2 standard deviations of the mean. Better approximations can be obtained by using Chebyshev's theorem and the empirical rule. These are explained next.

Chebyshev's Theorem

As stated previously, the variance and standard deviation of a variable can be used to determine the spread, or dispersion, of a variable. That is, the larger the variance or standard deviation, the more the data values are dispersed. For example, if two variables measured in the same units have the same mean, say, 70, and variable 1 has a standard deviation of 1.5 while variable 2 has a standard deviation of 10, then the data for variable 2 will be more spread out than the data for variable 1. *Chebyshev's theorem,* developed by the Russian mathematician Pafnuty L. Chebyshev (1821–1894), specifies the proportions of the spread in terms of the standard deviation.

> **Chebyshev's theorem** The proportion of values from a data set that will fall within k standard deviations of the mean will be at least $1 - 1/k^2$, where k is a number greater than 1 (k is not necessarily an integer).

This theorem states that at least three-fourths, or 75%, of the data values will fall within 2 standard deviations of the mean of the data set. This result is found by substituting $k = 2$ in the expression.

$$1 - \frac{1}{k^2} \quad \text{or} \quad 1 - \frac{1}{2^2} = 1 - \frac{1}{4} = \frac{3}{4} = 75\%$$

For the example in which variable 1 has a mean of 70 and a standard deviation of 1.5, at least three-fourths, or 75%, of the data values fall between 67 and 73. These values are found by adding 2 standard deviations to the mean and subtracting 2 standard deviations from the mean, as shown:

$$70 + 2(1.5) = 70 + 3 = 73$$

and

$$70 - 2(1.5) = 70 - 3 = 67$$

For variable 2, at least three-fourths, or 75%, of the data values fall between 50 and 90. Again, these values are found by adding and subtracting, respectively, 2 standard deviations to and from the mean.

$$70 + 2(10) = 70 + 20 = 90$$

and

$$70 - 2(10) = 70 - 20 = 50$$

Furthermore, the theorem states that at least eight-ninths, or 88.89%, of the data values will fall within 3 standard deviations of the mean. This result is found by letting $k = 3$ and substituting in the expression.

$$1 - \frac{1}{k^2} \quad \text{or} \quad 1 - \frac{1}{3^2} = 1 - \frac{1}{9} = \frac{8}{9} = 88.89\% \text{ (rounded)}$$

For variable 1, at least eight-ninths, or approximately 88.89%, of the data values fall between 65.5 and 74.5, since

$$70 + 3(1.5) = 70 + 4.5 = 74.5$$

and

$$70 - 3(1.5) = 70 - 4.5 = 65.5$$

For variable 2, at least eight-ninths, or approximately 88.89%, of the data values fall between 40 and 100.

This theorem can be applied to any distribution regardless of its shape (see Figure 3–3). Examples 3–24 and 3–25 illustrate the application of Chebyshev's theorem.

Figure 3–3

Chebyshev's Theorem

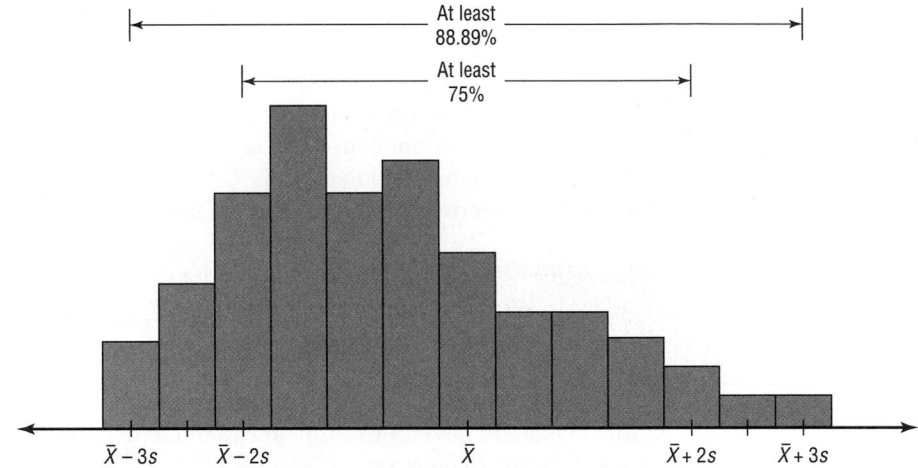

Example 3–24

The mean price of houses in a certain neighbourhood is $50,000, and the standard deviation is $10,000. Find the price range for which at least 75% of the houses will sell.

Solution

Chebyshev's theorem states that three-fourths, or 75%, of the data values will fall within 2 standard deviations of the mean. Thus,

$$\$50{,}000 + 2(\$10{,}000) = \$50{,}000 + \$20{,}000 = \$70{,}000$$

and

$$\$50{,}000 - 2(\$10{,}000) = \$50{,}000 - \$20{,}000 = \$30{,}000$$

Hence, at least 75% of all homes sold in the area will have a price range from $30,000 to $70,000.

Chebyshev's theorem can be used to find the minimum percentage of data values that will fall between any two given values. The procedure is shown in Example 3–25.

Example 3–25

A survey of local companies found that the mean amount of travel allowance for executives was $0.25 per kilometre. The standard deviation was $0.02. Using Chebyshev's theorem, find the minimum percentage of the data values that will fall between $0.20 and $0.30.

Solution

Step 1 Subtract the mean from the larger value.

$$\$0.30 - \$0.25 = \$0.05$$

Step 2 Divide the difference by the standard deviation to get k.

$$k = \frac{0.05}{0.02} = 2.5$$

Step 3 Use Chebyshev's theorem to find the percentage.

$$1 - \frac{1}{k^2} = 1 - \frac{1}{2.5^2} = 1 - \frac{1}{6.25} = 1 - 0.16 = 0.84 \qquad \text{or} \qquad 84\%$$

Hence, at least 84% of the data values will fall between $0.20 and $0.30.

The Empirical (Normal) Rule

Chebyshev's theorem applies to any distribution regardless of its shape. However, when a distribution is *bell-shaped* (or what is called *normal*), the following statements, which make up the **empirical rule,** are true.

Approximately 68% of the data values will fall within 1 standard deviation of the mean.

Approximately 95% of the data values will fall within 2 standard deviations of the mean.

Approximately 99.7% of the data values will fall within 3 standard deviations of the mean.

For example, suppose that the scores on a national achievement exam have a mean of 480 and a standard deviation of 90. If these scores are normally distributed, then approximately 68% will fall between 390 and 570 (480 + 90 = 570 and 480 − 90 = 390). Approximately 95% of the scores will fall between 300 and 660 (480 + 2 · 90 = 660 and 480 − 2 · 90 = 300). Approximately 99.7% will fall between 210 and 750 (480 + 3 · 90 = 750 and 480 − 3 · 90 = 210). See Figure 3–4. (The empirical rule is explained in greater detail in Chapter 7.)

Figure 3–4

The Empirical Rule

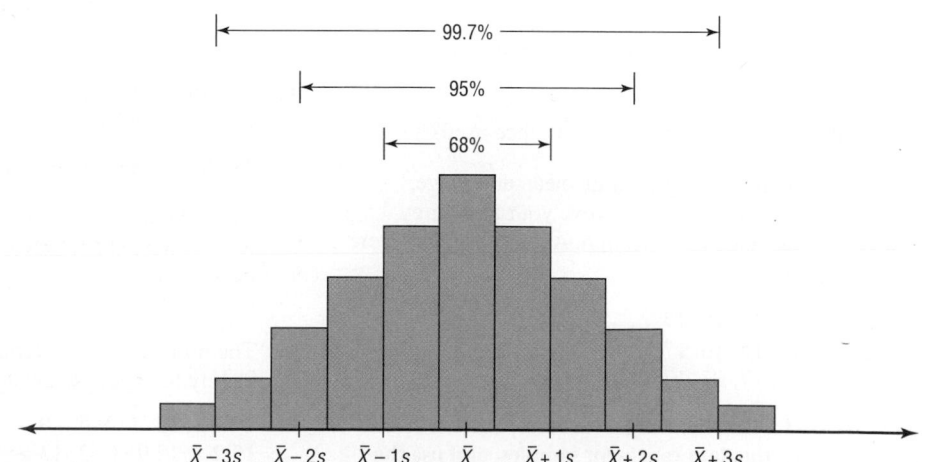

Applying the Concepts 3–3

Blood Pressure

The table lists means and standard deviations. The mean is the number before the plus/minus, and the standard deviation is the number after the plus/minus. The results are from a study attempting to find the average blood pressure of older adults. Use the results to answer the questions.

	Normotensive		Hypertensive	
	Men **($n = 1200$)**	**Women** **($n = 1400$)**	**Men** **($n = 1100$)**	**Women** **($n = 1300$)**
Age	55 ± 10	55 ± 10	60 ± 10	64 ± 10
Blood pressure (mm Hg)				
Systolic	123 ± 9	121 ± 11	153 ± 17	156 ± 20
Diastolic	78 ± 7	76 ± 7	91 ± 10	88 ± 10

1. Apply Chebyshev's theorem to the systolic blood pressure of normotensive men. At least how many of the men in the study fall within 1 standard deviation of the mean?

2. At least how many of those men in the study fall within 2 standard deviations of the mean?

Assume that blood pressure is normally distributed among older adults. Answer the following questions, using the empirical rule instead of Chebyshev's theorem.

3. Give ranges for the diastolic blood pressure (normotensive and hypertensive) of older women.

4. Do the normotensive, male, systolic blood pressure ranges overlap with the hypertensive, male, systolic, blood pressure ranges?

See page 142 for the answers.

Exercises 3–3

1. What is the relationship between the variance and the standard deviation?

2. Why might the range *not* be the best estimate of variability?

3. What are the symbols used to represent the population variance and standard deviation?

4. What are the symbols used to represent the sample variance and standard deviation?

5. Why is the unbiased estimator of variance used?

6. The three data sets have the same mean and range, but is the variation the same? Prove your answer by computing the standard deviation. Assume the data were obtained from samples.

   a. 5, 7, 9, 11, 13, 15, 17
   b. 5, 6, 7, 11, 15, 16, 17
   c. 5, 5, 5, 11, 17, 17, 17

For Exercises 7–13, find the range, variance, and standard deviation. Assume the data represent samples, and use the shortcut formula for the unbiased estimator to compute the variance and standard deviation.

7. The number of incidents where police were needed for a sample of 10 schools in Allegheny County is 7, 37, 3, 8, 48, 11, 6, 0, 10, 3. Are the data consistent or do they vary? Explain your answer.

   Source: U.S. Department of Education.

8. The following data represents the cost of one cigarette (in cents), out of a carton of 200, in each of Canada's provinces and territories.

   38, 40, 42, 36, 42, 40, 34, 39, 32, 42, 43, 37, 35

   Use the range rule of thumb to estimate the standard deviation. Compare the estimate to the actual standard deviation.

   Source: Smoking and Health Action Foundation.

9. The normal morning temperatures (in degrees Celsius) in July for selected Canadian cities are as follows.

   10.7   12.7   9.5   9.4   11.9   11.7   13.4   14.2   15.1
   13.2   12.9   13.2   13.6   10.5   7.6   12   3.7   15.4

The typical monthly precipitation (in millimetres) in July for these same cities is listed here.

17.6   36.1   69.9   101 58.9   58.0 72.0 76.6 88.1
85.6   118.5   84.5   96.8   81.6 121.2 58.2   35.2   39.3

Which data set is more variable?

Source: Environment Canada.

10. The total land area (rounded to 1000 square kilometres or 1000 km^2) for the five largest Canadian provinces is listed here.

QC   1,365,128   AB   642,317
BC   925,186   SK   591,670
ON   917,741

The total land area (rounded to 1000 square kilometres or 1000 km^2) for the five smallest Canadian provinces is listed here.

MB   553,556   NS   53,338
NL   373,872   PE   5,660
NB   71,450

Which data set is more variable?

Source: Natural Resources Canada, The Atlas of Canada.

11. Shown here are the numbers of stories in the 11 tallest buildings in Hong Kong, People's Republic of China.

88, 78, 72, 73, 80, 62, 75, 59, 75, 72, 52

Shown here are the numbers of stories in the 11 tallest buildings in New York City, United States.

102, 77, 66, 70, 59, 72, 69, 75, 60, 48, 60

Which data set is more variable?

Source: www.emporis.com.

12. The following data are the prices per litre of premium gasoline in Canadian dollars in seven foreign countries.

$1.85, $1.76, $1.69, $1.64, $1.59, $1.34, $0.98, $0.70

Do you think the standard deviation of these data is representative of the population standard deviation of gasoline prices in all foreign countries? Explain your answer.

Source: Reuters News Service.

13. The number of weeks on *The New York Times* Best Sellers list for hardcover fiction is

1, 4, 2, 2, 3, 18, 5, 5, 10, 4, 3, 6, 2, 2, 22

Use the range rule of thumb to estimate the standard deviation. Compare the estimate to the actual standard deviation.

Source: The New York Times Book Review.

14. Find the range, variance, and standard deviation for the distances of the home runs for McGwire and Sosa, using the data in Exercise 18 in Section 2–2. Compare the ranges and standard deviations. Decide which is more variable or if the variability is about the same. (Use individual data.)

15. Find the range, variance, and standard deviation for each data set in Exercise 11 of Section 3–2. Based on the results, which data set is more variable?

16. The United States Federal Highway Administration reported the number of deficient bridges in each state. Find the range, variance, and standard deviation.

15,458	1,055	5,008	3,598	8,984
1,337	4,132	10,618	17,361	6,081
6,482	25,090	12,681	16,286	18,832
12,470	17,842	16,601	4,587	47,196
23,205	25,213	23,017	27,768	2,686
7,768	25,825	4,962	22,704	2,694
4,131	13,144	15,582	7,279	12,613
810	13,350	1,208	22,242	7,477
10,902	2,343	2,333	2,979	6,578
14,318	4,773	6,252	734	13,220

Source: *USA TODAY.*

17. Find the range, variance, and standard deviation for the data in Exercise 17 of Section 2–2.

For Exercises 18 through 27, find the variance and standard deviation.

18. For 108 randomly selected college students, this exam score frequency distribution was obtained.

Class limits	Frequency
90–98	6
99–107	22
108–116	43
117–125	28
126–134	9

19. The costs per load (in cents) of 35 laundry detergents tested by a consumer organization are shown here.

Class limits	Frequency
13–19	2
20–26	7
27–33	12
34–40	5
41–47	6
48–54	1
55–61	0
62–68	2

20. Thirty-five automobiles were tested for fuel efficiency (in L/100 km). This frequency distribution was obtained.

Class limits	Frequency
9.0–10.9	6
11.0–12.9	8
13.0–14.9	10
15.0–16.9	11
17.0–18.9	9
19.0–20.9	1

21. The data show the number of murders in 25 selected U.S. cities.

Class limits	Frequency
34–96	13
97–159	2
160–222	0
223–285	5
286–348	1
349–411	1
412–474	0
475–537	1
538–600	2

22. In a study of reaction times to a specific stimulus, a psychologist recorded these data (in seconds).

Class limits	Frequency
2.1–2.7	12
2.8–3.4	13
3.5–4.1	7
4.2–4.8	5
4.9–5.5	2
5.6–6.2	1

23. Eighty randomly selected lightbulbs were tested to determine their lifetimes (in hours). This frequency distribution was obtained.

Class boundaries	Frequency
52.5–63.5	6
63.5–74.5	12
74.5–85.5	25
85.5–96.5	18
96.5–107.5	14
107.5–118.5	5

24. The data represent the murder rate per 100,000 individuals in a sample of selected cities in the United States.

Class	Frequency
5–11	8
12–18	5
19–25	7
26–32	1
33–39	1
40–46	3

Source: FBI and U.S. Census Bureau.

25. Eighty randomly selected batteries were tested to determine their lifetimes (in hours). The following frequency distribution was obtained.

Class boundaries	Frequency
62.5–73.5	5
73.5–84.5	14
84.5–95.5	18
95.5–106.5	25
106.5–117.5	12
117.5–128.5	6

Can it be concluded that the lifetimes of these brands of batteries are consistent?

26. Find the variance and standard deviation for the two distributions in Exercise 8 in Section 2–3 and Exercise 18 in Section 2–3. Compare the variation of the data sets. Decide if one data set is more variable than the other.

27. This frequency distribution represents the data obtained from a sample of word processor repairers. The values are the days between service calls on 80 machines.

Class boundaries	Frequency
25.5–28.5	5
28.5–31.5	9
31.5–34.5	32
34.5–37.5	20
37.5–40.5	12
40.5–43.5	2

28. The average score of the students in one calculus class is 110, with a standard deviation of 5; the average score of students in a statistics class is 106, with a standard deviation of 4. Which class is more variable in terms of scores?

29. The data shows the lengths (in metres) of suspension bridges in the eastern part of North America and western part of North America. Compare the variability of the two samples, using the coefficient of variation.

East: 1298, 1067, 375, 655, 610, 533
West: 1250, 853, 704, 472, 457, 368

Source: *World Almanac and Book of Facts.*

30. The average score on an English final examination was 85, with a standard deviation of 5; the average score on a history final exam was 110, with a standard deviation of 8. Which class was more variable?

31. The average age of the accountants at Three Rivers Corp. is 26 years, with a standard deviation of 6 years; the average salary of the accountants is $31,000, with a standard deviation of $4000. Compare the variations of age and income.

32. Using Chebyshev's theorem, solve these problems for a distribution with a mean of 80 and a standard deviation of 10.
   a. At least what percentage of values will fall between 60 and 100?
   b. At least what percentage of values will fall between 65 and 95?

33. The mean of a distribution is 20 and the standard deviation is 2. Use Chebyshev's theorem.
   a. At least what percentage of the values will fall between 10 and 30?
   b. At least what percentage of the values will fall between 12 and 28?

34. In a distribution of 200 values, the mean is 50 and the standard deviation is 5. Use Chebyshev's theorem.
a. At least how many values will fall between 30 and 70?
b. At most how many values will be less than 40 or more than 60?

35. A sample of the hourly wages of employees who work in restaurants in a large city has a mean of $5.02 and a standard deviation of $0.09. Using Chebyshev's theorem, find the range in which at least 75% of the data values will fall.

36. A sample of the labour costs per hour to assemble a certain product has a mean of $2.60 and a standard deviation of $0.15. Using Chebyshev's theorem, find the range in which at least 88.89% of the data will lie.

37. A survey of a number of the leading brands of cereal shows that the mean content of potassium per serving is 95 milligrams, and the standard deviation is 2 milligrams. Find the range in which at least 88.89% of the data will fall. Use Chebyshev's theorem.

38. The average score on a special test of knowledge of wood refinishing has a mean of 53 and a standard deviation of 6. Using Chebyshev's theorem, find the range of values in which at least 75% of the scores will lie.

39. The average of the number of trials it took a sample of mice to learn to traverse a maze was 12. The standard deviation was 3. Using Chebyshev's theorem, find the minimum percentage of data values that will fall in the range of 4 to 20 trials.

40. The average cost of a certain type of grass seed is $4.00 per box. The standard deviation is $0.10. Using Chebyshev's theorem, find the minimum percentage of data values that will fall in the range of $3.82 to $4.18.

41. The average yearly per capita consumption of fresh fruit in Canada is 68.8 kilograms. Suppose that the distribution of fruit amounts consumed is bell-shaped with a standard deviation equal to 3.1 kilograms. What percentage of Canadians would you expect to consume more than 75 kilograms of fresh fruit per year?

Source: Statistics Canada.

42. The average full-time faculty member in a post-secondary degree-granting institution works an average of 53 hours per week.
a. If we assume the standard deviation is 2.8 hours, what percentage of faculty members work more than 58.6 hours a week?
b. If we assume a bell-shaped distribution, what percentage of faculty members work more than 58.6 hours a week?

Source: National Center for Education Statistics.

Extending the Concepts

43. For this data set, find the mean and standard deviation of the variable. The data represent the serum cholesterol levels of 30 individuals. Count the number of data values that fall within 2 standard deviations of the mean. Compare this with the number obtained from Chebyshev's theorem. Comment on the answer.

211	240	255	219	204
200	212	193	187	205
256	203	210	221	249
231	212	236	204	187
201	247	206	187	200
237	227	221	192	196

44. For this data set, find the mean and standard deviation of the variable. The data represent the ages of 30 customers who ordered a product advertised on television. Count the number of data values that fall within 2 standard deviations of the mean. Compare this with the number obtained from Chebyshev's theorem. Comment on the answer.

42	44	62	35	20
30	56	20	23	41
55	22	31	27	66
21	18	24	42	25
32	50	31	26	36
39	40	18	36	22

45. Using Chebyshev's theorem, complete the table to find the minimum percentage of data values that fall within k standard deviations of the mean.

k	1.5	2	2.5	3	3.5
Percent					

46. Use this data set: 10, 20, 30, 40, 50.
a. Find the standard deviation.
b. Add 5 to each value, and then find the standard deviation.
c. Subtract 5 from each value and find the standard deviation.
d. Multiply each value by 5 and find the standard deviation.
e. Divide each value by 5 and find the standard deviation.
f. Generalize the results of parts *b* through *e*.
g. Compare these results with those in Exercise 38.

47. The mean deviation is found by using this formula:

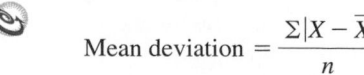

$$\text{Mean deviation} = \frac{\Sigma |X - \overline{X}|}{n}$$

where
$$X = \text{value}$$
$$\overline{X} = \text{mean}$$
$$n = \text{number of values}$$
$$|\ | = \text{absolute value}$$

Find the mean deviation for these data.

5, 9, 10, 11, 11, 12, 15, 18, 20, 22

48. A measure to determine the skewness of a distribution is called the *Pearson coefficient of skewness*. The formula is

$$\text{Skewness} = \frac{3(\overline{X} - \text{MD})}{s}$$

The values of the coefficient usually range from -3 to $+3$. When the distribution is symmetric, the coefficient is zero; when the distribution is positively skewed, it is positive; and when the distribution is negatively skewed, it is negative.

Using the formula, find the coefficient of skewness for each distribution, and describe the shape of the distribution.

a. Mean = 10, median = 8, standard deviation = 3.

b. Mean = 42, median = 45, standard deviation = 4.

c. Mean = 18.6, median = 18.6, standard deviation = 1.5.

d. Mean = 98, median = 97.6, standard deviation = 4.

49. All values of a data set must be within $s\sqrt{n-1}$ of the mean. If a person collected 25 data values that had a mean of 50 and a standard deviation of 3 and you saw that one data value was 67, what would you conclude?

3–4   Measures of Position

In addition to measures of central tendency and measures of variation, there are measures of position or location. These measures include standard scores, percentiles, deciles, and quartiles. They are used to locate the relative position of a data value in the data set. For example, if a value is located at the 80th percentile, it means that 80% of the values fall below it in the distribution and 20% of the values fall above it. The *median* is the value that corresponds to the 50th percentile, since one-half of the values fall below it and one-half of the values fall above it. This section discusses these measures of position.

Standard Scores

There is an old saying, "You can't compare apples and oranges." But with the use of statistics, it can be done to some extent. Suppose that a student scored 90 on a music test and 45 on an English exam. Direct comparison of raw scores is impossible, since the exams might not be equivalent in terms of number of questions, value of each question, and so on. However, a comparison of both scores' position relative to their respective evaluations' average score and dispersion can be made. This comparison uses the mean and standard deviation and is called a standard score or *z* score. (We also use *z* scores in later chapters.)

A *z* **score** or **standard score** for a value is obtained by subtracting the mean from the value and dividing the result by the standard deviation. The symbol for a standard score is *z*. The formula is

$$z = \frac{\text{value} - \text{mean}}{\text{standard deviation}}$$

For samples, the formula is

$$z = \frac{X - \overline{X}}{s}$$

For populations, the formula is

$$z = \frac{X - \mu}{\sigma}$$

The *z* score represents the number of standard deviations that a data value falls above or below the mean.

For the purpose of this book, it will be assumed that when we find z scores, the data were obtained from samples.

Example 3–26

A student scored 65 on a calculus test that had a mean of 50 and a standard deviation of 10; she scored 30 on a history test with a mean of 25 and a standard deviation of 5. Compare her relative positions on the two tests.

Solution

First, find the z scores. For calculus the z score is

$$z = \frac{X - \overline{X}}{s} = \frac{65 - 50}{10} = 1.5$$

For history the z score is

$$z = \frac{30 - 25}{5} = 1.0$$

Since the z score for calculus is larger, her relative position in the calculus class is higher than her relative position in the history class.

Interesting Fact

The average number of faces that a person learns to recognize and remember during his or her lifetime is 10,000.

Note that if the z score is positive, the score is above the mean. If the z score is 0, the score is the same as the mean. And if the z score is negative, the score is below the mean.

Example 3–27

Find the z score for each test, and state which is higher.

Test A	$X = 38$	$\overline{X} = 40$	$s = 5$
Test B	$X = 94$	$\overline{X} = 100$	$s = 10$

Solution

For test A,

$$z = \frac{X - \overline{X}}{s} = \frac{38 - 40}{5} = -0.4$$

For test B,

$$z = \frac{94 - 100}{10} = -0.6$$

The score for test A is relatively higher than the score for test B.

When all data for a variable are transformed into z scores, the resulting distribution will have a mean of 0 and a standard deviation of 1. A z score, then, is actually the number of standard deviations each value is from the mean for a specific distribution. In Example 3–26, the calculus score of 65 was actually 1.5 standard deviations above the mean of 50. This will be explained in greater detail in Chapter 7.

Percentiles

Percentiles are position measures used in educational and health-related fields to indicate the position of an individual in a group.

Percentiles divide a data set into 100 equal parts in which the pth percentile is a value that at most p% of the observations in the data set are less than this value and the remainder are greater.

In many situations, the graphs and tables showing the percentiles for various measures such as test scores, heights, or weights have already been completed. Table 3–3 shows the percentile ranks for scaled scores on the Test of English as a Foreign Language. If a student had a scaled score of 58 for section 1 (listening and comprehension), that student would have a percentile rank of 81. Hence, that student did better than 81% of the students who took section 1 of the exam.

Table 3–3	Percentile Ranks and Scaled Scores on the Test of English as a Foreign Language*				
Scaled score	Section 1: Listening comprehension	Section 2: Structure and written expression	Section 3: Vocabulary and reading comprehension	Total scaled score	Percentile rank
68	99	98			
66	98	96	98	660	99
64	96	94	96	640	97
62	92	90	93	620	94
60	87	84	88	600	89
→58	81	76	81	580	82
56	73	68	72	560	73
54	64	58	61	540	62
52	54	48	50	520	50
50	42	38	40	500	39
48	32	29	30	480	29
46	22	21	23	460	20
44	14	15	16	440	13
42	9	10	11	420	9
40	5	7	8	400	5
38	3	4	5	380	3
36	2	3	3	360	1
34	1	2	2	340	1
32		1	1	320	
30		1	1	300	
Mean	51.5	52.2	51.4	517	Mean
S.D.	7.1	7.9	7.5	68	S.D.

*Based on the total group of 1,178,193 examinees tested from July 1989 through June 1991.
Source: Reprinted by permission of Educational Testing Service, the copyright owner.

Figure 3–5 shows percentiles in graphical form of weights of girls from ages 2 to 18. To find the percentile rank of an 11-year-old who weighs 82 pounds (37.2 kg) start at the 82-pound (37.2 kg) weight on the left axis and move horizontally to the right. Find 11 on the horizontal axis and move up vertically. The two lines meet at the

Figure 3–5

Weights of Girls by Age and Percentile Rankings

Source: Distributed by Mead Johnson Nutritional Division. Reprinted with permission.

50th percentile curved line; hence, an 11-year-old girl who weighs 82 pounds (37.2 kg) is in the 50th percentile for her age group. If the lines do not meet exactly on one of the curved percentile lines, then the percentile rank must be approximated.

Percentiles are also used to compare an individual's test score with the national norm. For example, tests such as the United States National Educational Development Test (NEDT) are taken by students in Grade 9 or 10. A student's scores are compared with those of other students locally and nationally by using percentile ranks. A similar test for elementary school students is called the California Achievement Test.

Percentiles are not the same as percentages. That is, if a student gets 72 correct answers out of a possible 100, she obtains a percentage score of 72. There is no indication of her position with respect to the rest of the class. She could have scored the highest, the lowest, or somewhere in between. On the other hand, if a raw score of 72 corresponds to the 64th percentile, then she did better than 64% of the students in her class.

Percentiles are symbolized by

$$P_0, P_1, P_2, P_3, \ldots, P_{99}, P_{100}$$

and divide the distribution into 100 groups.

Percentile graphs can be constructed as shown in Example 3–28. Percentile graphs use the same values as the cumulative relative frequency graphs described in Section 2–3, except that the proportions have been converted to percents.

| Example 3–28 | The frequency distribution for the systolic blood pressure readings (in millimetres of mercury, mm Hg) of 200 randomly selected college students is shown here. Construct a percentile graph. |

A Class boundaries	B Frequency	C Cumulative frequency	D Cumulative percent
89.5–104.5	24		
104.5–119.5	62		
119.5–134.5	72		
134.5–149.5	26		
149.5–164.5	12		
164.5–179.5	4		
	200		

Solution

Step 1 Find the cumulative frequencies and place them in column C.

Step 2 Find the cumulative percentages and place them in column D. To do this step, use the formula

$$\text{Cumulative \%} = \frac{\text{cumulative frequency}}{n} \cdot 100\%$$

For the first class,

$$\text{Cumulative \%} = \frac{24}{200} \cdot 100\% = 12\%$$

The completed table is shown here.

A Class boundaries	B Frequency	C Cumulative frequency	D Cumulative percent
89.5–104.5	24	24	12
104.5–119.5	62	86	43
119.5–134.5	72	158	79
134.5–149.5	26	184	92
149.5–164.5	12	196	98
164.5–179.5	4	200	100
	200		

Figure 3–6

Percentile Graph for
Example 3–28

Step 3 Graph the data, using class boundaries for the x axis and the percentages for the y axis, as shown in Figure 3–6.

Once a percentile graph has been constructed, one can find the approximate corresponding percentile ranks for given blood pressure values and find approximate blood pressure values for given percentile ranks.

For example, to find the percentile rank of a blood pressure reading of 130, find 130 on the x axis of Figure 3–6, and draw a vertical line to the graph. Then move horizontally to the value on the y axis. Note that a blood pressure of 130 corresponds to approximately the 70th percentile.

If the value that corresponds to the 40th percentile is desired, start on the y axis at 40 and draw a horizontal line to the graph. Then draw a vertical line to the x axis and read the value. In Figure 3–6, the 40th percentile corresponds to a value of approximately 118. Thus, if a person has a blood pressure of 118, he or she is at the 40th percentile.

Finding values and the corresponding percentile ranks by using a graph yields only approximate answers. Several mathematical methods exist for computing percentiles for data. These methods can be used to find the approximate percentile rank of a data value or to find a data value corresponding to a given percentile. When the data set is large (100 or more), these methods yield better results. Examples 3–29 through 3–32 show these methods.

Percentile Formula

The percentile corresponding to a given value X is computed by using the following formula:

$$\text{Percentile} = \frac{(\text{number of values below } X) + 0.5}{\text{total number of values}} \cdot 100\%$$

Example 3–29

A teacher gives a 20-point test to 10 students. The scores are shown here. Find the percentile rank of a score of 12.

18, 15, 12, 6, 8, 2, 3, 5, 20, 10

Solution

Arrange the data in order from lowest to highest.

2, 3, 5, 6, 8, 10, 12, 15, 18, 20

Then substitute into the formula.

$$\text{Percentile} = \frac{(\text{number of values below } X) + 0.5}{\text{total number of values}} \cdot 100\%$$

Since there are six values below a score of 12, the solution is

$$\text{Percentile} = \frac{6 + 0.5}{10} \cdot 100\% = 65\text{th percentile}$$

Thus, a student whose score was 12 did better than 65% of the class.

Note: One assumes that a score of 12 in Example 3–29, for instance, means theoretically any value between 11.5 and 12.5.

Example 3–30

Using the data in Example 3–29, find the percentile rank for a score of 6.

Solution

There are three values below 6. Thus

$$\text{Percentile} = \frac{3 + 0.5}{10} \cdot 100\% = 35\text{th percentile}$$

A student who scored 6 did better than 35% of the class.

Examples 3–31 and 3–32 show a procedure for finding a value corresponding to a given percentile.

Example 3–31

Using the scores in Example 3–29, find the value corresponding to the 25th percentile.

Solution

Step 1 Arrange the data in order from lowest to highest.

2, 3, 5, 6, 8, 10, 12, 15, 18, 20

Step 2 Compute

$$c = \frac{n \cdot p}{100}$$

where
n = total number of values
p = percentile

Thus,

$$c = \frac{10 \cdot 25}{100} = 2.5$$

Step 3   If c is not a whole number, round it up to the next whole number; in this case, $c = 3$. (If c is a whole number, see Example 3–32.) Start at the lowest value and count over to the third value, which is 5. Hence, the value 5 corresponds to the 25th percentile.

Example 3–32

Using the data set in Example 3–29, find the value that corresponds to the 60th percentile.

Solution

Step 1   Arrange the data in order from smallest to largest.

2, 3, 5, 6, 8, 10, 12, 15, 18, 20

Step 2   Substitute in the formula.

$$c = \frac{n \cdot p}{100} = \frac{10 \cdot 60}{100} = 6$$

Step 3   If c is a whole number, use the value halfway between the c and $c + 1$ values when counting up from the lowest value—in this case, the 6th and 7th values.

2, 3, 5, 6, 8, 10, 12, 15, 18, 20

                     ↗   ↖
     6th value   7th value

The value halfway between 10 and 12 is 11. Find it by adding the two values and dividing by 2.

$$\frac{10 + 12}{2} = 11$$

Hence, 11 corresponds to the 60th percentile. Anyone scoring 11 would have done better than 60% of the class.

The steps for finding a value corresponding to a given percentile are summarized in this Procedure Table.

Procedure Table

Finding a Data Value Corresponding to a Given Percentile

Step 1   Arrange the data in order from lowest to highest.

Step 2   Substitute into the formula

$$c = \frac{n \cdot p}{100}$$

where
    n = total number of values
    p = percentile

Step 3A   If c is not a whole number, round up to the next whole number. Starting at the lowest value, count over to the number that corresponds to the rounded-up value.

Step 3B   If c is a whole number, use the value halfway between the cth and $(c + 1)$st values when counting up from the lowest value.

Quartiles and Deciles

Quartiles divide the distribution into four groups, separated by Q_1, Q_2, Q_3.

Note that Q_1 is the same as the 25th percentile; Q_2 is the same as the 50th percentile, or the median; Q_3 corresponds to the 75th percentile, as shown:

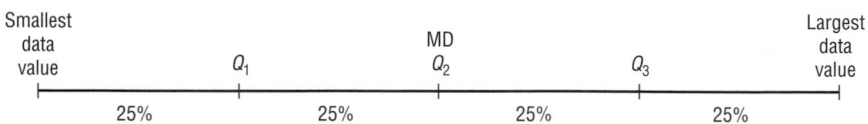

Quartiles can be computed by using the formula given for computing percentiles on page 120. For Q_1 use $p = 25$. For Q_2 use $p = 50$. For Q_3 use $p = 75$. However, an easier method for finding quartiles is found in this Procedure Table.

Procedure Table

Finding Data Values Corresponding to Q_1, Q_2, and Q_3

Step 1   Arrange the data in order from lowest to highest.

Step 2   Find the median of the data values. This is the value for Q_2.

Step 3   Find the median of the data values that fall below Q_2. This is the value for Q_1.

Step 4   Find the median of the data values that fall above Q_2. This is the value for Q_3.

Example 3–33 shows how to find the values of Q_1, Q_2, and Q_3.

Example 3–33

Find Q_1, Q_2, and Q_3 for the data set 15, 13, 6, 5, 12, 50, 22, 18.

Solution

Step 1   Arrange the data in order.

5, 6, 12, 13, 15, 18, 22, 50

Step 2   Find the median (Q_2).

5, 6, 12, 13, 15, 18, 22, 50
$$\uparrow$$
MD

$$MD = \frac{13 + 15}{2} = 14$$

Step 3   Find the median of the data values less than 14.

5, 6, 12, 13
$$\uparrow$$
Q_1

$$Q_1 = \frac{6 + 12}{2} = 9$$

So Q_1 is 9.

Step 4   Find the median of the data values greater than 14.

15, 18, 22, 50
↑
Q_3

$$Q_3 = \frac{18 + 22}{2} = 20$$

Here Q_3 is 20. Hence, $Q_1 = 9$, $Q_2 = 14$, and $Q_3 = 20$.

In addition to dividing the data set into four groups, quartiles can be used as a rough measurement of variability. The **interquartile range (IQR)** is defined as the difference between Q_1 and Q_3 and is the range of the middle 50% of the data.

The interquartile range is used to identify outliers, and it is also used as a measure of variability in exploratory data analysis, as shown in Section 3–5.

Deciles divide the distribution into 10 groups, as shown. They are denoted by D_1, D_2, etc.

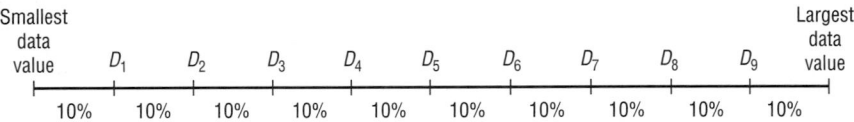

Note that D_1 corresponds to P_{10}; D_2 corresponds to P_{20}; etc. Deciles can be found by using the formulas given for percentiles. Taken altogether then, these are the relationships among percentiles, deciles, and quartiles.

Deciles are denoted by $D_1, D_2, D_3, \ldots, D_9$, and they correspond to $P_{10}, P_{20}, P_{30}, \ldots, P_{90}$.

Quartiles are denoted by Q_1, Q_2, Q_3 and they correspond to P_{25}, P_{50}, P_{75}.

The median is the same as P_{50} or Q_2 or D_5.

The position measures are summarized in Table 3–4.

Table 3–4	Summary of Position Measures	
Measure	**Definition**	**Symbol(s)**
Standard score or z score	Number of standard deviations that a data value is above or below the mean	z
Percentile	Position in hundredths that a data value holds in the distribution	P_n
Decile	Position in tenths that a data value holds in the distribution	D_n
Quartile	Position in fourths that a data value holds in the distribution	Q_n

Outliers

A data set should be checked for extremely high or extremely low values. These values are called *outliers*.

An **outlier** is an extremely high or an extremely low data value when compared with the rest of the data values.

An outlier can strongly affect the mean and standard deviation of a variable. For example, suppose a researcher mistakenly recorded an extremely high data value. This value would then make the mean and standard deviation of the variable much larger than they really were. Outliers can have an effect on other statistics as well.

There are several ways to check a data set for outliers. One method is shown in this Procedure Table.

Procedure Table

Procedure for Identifying Outliers

Step 1   Arrange the data in order and find Q_1 and Q_3.

Step 2   Find the interquartile range: IQR $= Q_3 - Q_1$.

Step 3   Multiply the IQR by 1.5.

Step 4   Subtract the value obtained in step 3 from Q_1 and add the value to Q_3.

Step 5   Check the data set for any data value that is smaller than $Q_1 - 1.5$(IQR) or larger than $Q_3 + 1.5$(IQR).

This procedure is shown in Example 3–34.

Example 3–34   Check the following data set for outliers.

5, 6, 12, 13, 15, 18, 22, 50

Solution

The data value 50 is extremely suspect. These are the steps in checking for an outlier.

Step 1   Find Q_1 and Q_3. This was done in Example 3–33; Q_1 is 9 and Q_3 is 20.

Step 2   Find the interquartile range (IQR), which is $Q_3 - Q_1$.

IQR $= Q_3 - Q_1 = 20 - 9 = 11$

Step 3   Multiply this value by 1.5.

$1.5(11) = 16.5$

Step 4   Subtract the value obtained in step 3 from Q_1, and add the value obtained in step 3 to Q_3.

$9 - 16.5 = -7.5$ and $20 + 16.5 = 36.5$

Step 5   Check the data set for any data values that fall outside the interval from -7.5 to 36.5. The value 50 is outside this interval; hence, it can be considered an outlier.

There are several reasons why outliers may occur. First, the data value may have resulted from a measurement or observational error. Perhaps the researcher measured the variable incorrectly. Second, the data value may have resulted from a recording error. That is, it may have been written or typed incorrectly. Third, the data value may have been obtained from a subject that is not in the defined population. For example, suppose test scores were obtained from a Grade 7 class, but a student in that class was actually in Grade 6 and had special permission to attend the class. This student might have scored extremely low on that particular exam on that day. Fourth, the data value might be a legitimate value that occurred by chance (although the probability is extremely small).

There are no hard-and-fast rules on what to do with outliers, nor is there complete agreement among statisticians on ways to identify them. Obviously, if they occurred as a result of an error, an attempt should be made to correct the error or else the data value should be omitted entirely. When they occur naturally by chance, the statistician must make a decision about whether to include them in the data set.

When a distribution is normal or bell-shaped, data values that are beyond 3 standard deviations of the mean can be considered suspected outliers.

Applying the Concepts 3–4

Determining Dosages

In an attempt to determine necessary dosages of a new drug (HDL) used to control sepsis, assume you administer varying amounts of HDL to 40 mice. You create four groups and label them *low dosage, moderate dosage, large dosage,* and *very large dosage.* The dosages also vary within each group. After the mice are injected with the HDL and the sepsis bacteria, the time until the onset of sepsis is recorded. Your job as a statistician is to effectively communicate the results of the study.

1. Which measures of position could be used to help describe the data results?
2. If 40% of the rats in the top quartile survived after the injection, how many mice would that be?
3. What information can be given from using percentiles?
4. What information can be given from using quartiles?
5. What information can be given from using standard scores?

See page 142 for the answers.

Exercises 3–4

1. What is a z score?

2. Define *percentile rank.*

3. What is the difference between a percentage and a percentile?

4. Define *quartile.*

5. What is the relationship between quartiles and percentiles?

6. What is a decile?

7. How are deciles related to percentiles?

8. To which percentile, quartile, and decile does the median correspond?

9. If the mean value of major league teams is $127 million and the standard deviation is $9 million, find the corresponding z score for each team's value.

   a. 136   d. 113.5
   b. 109   e. 133
   c. 104.5

10. The reaction time to a stimulus for a certain test has a mean of 2.5 seconds and a standard deviation of 0.3 second. Find the corresponding z score for each reaction time.

    a. 2.7   d. 3.1
    b. 3.9   e. 2.2
    c. 2.8

11. A final examination for a psychology course has a mean of 84 and a standard deviation of 4. Find the corresponding z score for each raw score.

    a. 87   d. 76
    b. 79   e. 82
    c. 93

12. An aptitude test has a mean of 220 and a standard deviation of 10. Find the corresponding z score for each exam score.

    a. 200   d. 212
    b. 232   e. 225
    c. 218

13. Which of the following exam scores has a better relative position?

    a. A score of 42 on an exam with $\overline{X} = 39$ and $s = 4$.

    b. A score of 76 on an exam with $\overline{X} = 71$ and $s = 3$.

14. A student scores 60 on a mathematics test that has a mean of 54 and a standard deviation of 3, and she scores 80 on a history test with a mean of 75 and a standard deviation of 2. On which test did she perform better?

15. Which score indicates the highest relative position?

    a. A score of 3.2 on a test with $\overline{X} = 4.6$ and $s = 1.5$.

    b. A score of 630 on a test with $\overline{X} = 800$ and $s = 200$.

    c. A score of 43 on a test with $\overline{X} = 50$ and $s = 5$.

16. This distribution represents the data for weights of Grade 5 boys. Find the approximate weights corresponding to each percentile given by constructing a percentile graph.

Weight (kilograms)	Frequency
23.5–25.0	9
25.0–26.5	12
26.5–28.0	17
28.0–29.5	22
29.5–31.0	15

    a. 25th   c. 80th

    b. 60th   d. 95th

17. For the data in Exercise 16, find the approximate percentile ranks of the following weights.

    a. 26 kilograms

    b. 28 kilograms

    c. 29 kilograms

    d. 25 kilograms

18. (ans) The data shown represent the scores on a national achievement test for a group of Grade 10 students. Find the approximate percentile ranks of these scores by constructing a percentile graph.

    a. 220

    b. 245

    c. 276

    d. 280

    e. 300

Score	Frequency
196.5–217.5	5
217.5–238.5	17
238.5–259.5	22
259.5–280.5	48
280.5–301.5	22
301.5–322.5	6

19. For the data in Exercise 18, find the approximate scores that correspond to these percentiles.

    a. 15th   d. 65th

    b. 29th   e. 80th

    c. 43rd

20. (ans) The airborne speeds in kilometres per hour of 21 aircrafts are shown. Find the approximate values that correspond to the given percentiles by constructing a percentile graph.

Speed (km/h)	Frequency
588–621	4
622–655	2
656–689	3
690–723	2
724–757	1
758–791	2
792–825	3
826–859	4
	$\overline{21}$

    a. 9th   d. 60th

    b. 20th   e. 75th

    c. 45th

Source: *The World Almanac and Book of Facts.*

21. Using the data in Exercise 20, find the approximate percentile ranks of the following kilometres per hour (km/h).

    a. 571 km/h   d. 736 km/h

    b. 604 km/h   e. 802 km/h

    c. 670 km/h

22. Find the percentile ranks of each weight in the data set. The weights are in kilograms.

    78, 82, 86, 88, 92, 97

23. In Exercise 22, what value corresponds to the 30th percentile?

24. Find the percentile rank for each test score in the data set.

    12, 28, 35, 42, 47, 49, 50

25. In Exercise 24, what value corresponds to the 60th percentile?

26. Find the percentile rank for each value in the data set. The data represent the values in billions of dollars of the damage of 10 hurricanes.

    1.1, 1.7, 1.9, 2.1, 2.2, 2.5, 3.3, 6.2, 6.8, 20.3

    Source: Insurance Services Office.

27. What value in Exercise 26 corresponds to the 40th percentile?

28. Find the percentile rank for each test score in the data set.

    5, 12, 15, 16, 20, 21

29. What test score in Exercise 28 corresponds to the 33rd percentile?

30. Using the procedure shown in Example 3–34, check each data set for outliers.

  a. 16, 18, 22, 19, 3, 21, 17, 20
  b. 24, 32, 54, 31, 16, 18, 19, 14, 17, 20
  c. 321, 343, 350, 327, 200
  d. 88, 72, 97, 84, 86, 85, 100
  e. 145, 119, 122, 118, 125, 116
  f. 14, 16, 27, 18, 13, 19, 36, 15, 20

31. Another measure of average is called the *midquartile;* it is the numerical value halfway between Q_1 and Q_3, and the formula is

$$\text{Midquartile} = \frac{Q_1 + Q_3}{2}$$

Using this formula and other formulas, find Q_1, Q_2, Q_3, the midquartile, and the interquartile range for each data set.

  a. 5, 12, 16, 25, 32, 38
  b. 53, 62, 78, 94, 96, 99, 103

3–5   Exploratory Data Analysis

Objective 4

Use the techniques of exploratory data analysis, including boxplots and five-number summaries, to discover various aspects of data.

In traditional statistics, data are organized by using a frequency distribution. From this distribution various graphs such as the histogram, frequency polygon, and ogive can be constructed to determine the shape or nature of the distribution. In addition, various statistics such as the mean and standard deviation can be computed to summarize the data.

The purpose of traditional analysis is to confirm various conjectures about the nature of the data. For example, from a carefully designed study, a researcher might want to know if the proportion of Canadians who are exercising today has increased from ten years ago. This study would contain various assumptions about the population, various definitions such as of exercise, and so on.

In **exploratory data analysis (EDA),** data can be organized using a *stem and leaf plot.* (See Chapter 2.) The measure of central tendency used in EDA is the *median.* The measure of variation used in EDA is the *interquartile range* ($Q_3 - Q_1$). In EDA the data are represented graphically using a **boxplot** (sometimes called a box-and-whisker plot). The purpose of exploratory data analysis is to examine data in order to identify patterns, trends, or relationships. These observations can be simple descriptions such as central measures or dispersions that help in making decisions or suggest further actions. Exploratory data analysis was developed by John Tukey and presented in his book *Exploratory Data Analysis* (Addison-Wesley, 1977).

The Five-Number Summary and Boxplots

A boxplot can be used to graphically represent the data set. These plots involve five specific values:

  1. The lowest value of the data set (i.e., minimum)
  2. Q_1
  3. The median
  4. Q_3
  5. The highest value of the data set (i.e., maximum)

These values are called a **five-number summary** of the data set.

> A **boxplot** is a graph of a data set obtained by drawing a horizontal line from the minimum data value to Q_1, drawing a horizontal line from Q_3 to the maximum data value, and drawing a box whose vertical sides pass through Q_1 and Q_3 with a vertical line inside the box passing through the median or Q_2.

Example 3–35 A stockbroker recorded the number of clients she saw each day over an 11-day period. The data are shown. Construct a boxplot for the data.

$$33, 38, 43, 30, 29, 40, 51, 27, 42, 23, 31$$

Solution

Step 1 Arrange the data in order.

$$23, 27, 29, 30, 31, 33, 38, 40, 42, 43, 51$$

Step 2 Find the median.

$$23, 27, 29, 30, 31, 33, 38, 40, 42, 43, 51$$

Median

Step 3 Find Q_1.

$$23, 27, 29, 30, 31$$

Q_1

Step 4 Find Q_3.

$$38, 40, 42, 43, 51$$

Q_3

Step 5 Draw a scale for the data on the x axis.

Step 6 Locate the lowest value, Q_1, the median, Q_3, and the highest value on the scale.

Step 7 Draw a box around Q_1 and Q_3, draw a vertical line through the median, and connect the upper and lower values, as shown in Figure 3–7.

Figure 3–7

Boxplot for
Example 3–35

The box in Figure 3–7 represents the middle 50% of the data, and the lines represent the lower and upper ends of the data.

Information Obtained from a Boxplot

1. *a.* If the median is near the centre of the box, the distribution is approximately symmetric.

   b. If the median falls to the left of the centre of the box, the distribution is positively skewed.

   c. If the median falls to the right of the centre, the distribution is negatively skewed.

2. *a.* If the lines are about the same length, the distribution is approximately symmetric.
    b. If the right line is larger than the left line, the distribution is positively skewed.
    c. If the left line is larger than the right line, the distribution is negatively skewed.

The boxplot in Figure 3–7 indicates that the distribution is slightly positively skewed.
    If the boxplots for two or more data sets are graphed on the same axis, the distributions can be compared. To compare the averages, use the location of the medians. To compare the variability, use the interquartile range, i.e., the length of the boxes. Example 3–36 shows this procedure.

Example 3–36

A dietitian is interested in comparing the sodium content of real cheese with the sodium content of a cheese substitute. The data for two random samples are shown. Compare the distributions, using boxplots.

Real cheese				Cheese substitute			
310	420	45	40	270	180	250	290
220	240	180	90	130	260	340	310

Source: The Complete Book of Food Counts.

Solution

Step 1 Find Q_1, MD, and Q_3 for the real cheese data.

40   45   90   180   220   240   310   420

↑   ↑   ↑

Q_1 MD Q_3

$$Q_1 = \frac{45 + 90}{2} = 67.5 \qquad MD = \frac{180 + 220}{2} = 200$$

$$Q_3 = \frac{240 + 310}{2} = 275$$

Step 2 Find Q_1, MD, and Q_3 for the cheese substitute data.

130   180   250   260   270   290   310   340

↑   ↑   ↑

Q_1 MD Q_3

$$Q_1 = \frac{180 + 250}{2} = 215 \qquad MD = \frac{260 + 270}{2} = 265$$

$$Q_3 = \frac{290 + 310}{2} = 300$$

Step 3 Draw the boxplots for each distribution on the same graph. See Figure 3–8.

Step 4 Compare the plots. It is quite apparent that the distribution for the cheese substitute data has a higher median than the median for the distribution for the real cheese data. The variation or spread for the distribution of the real cheese data is larger than the variation for the distribution of the cheese substitute data.

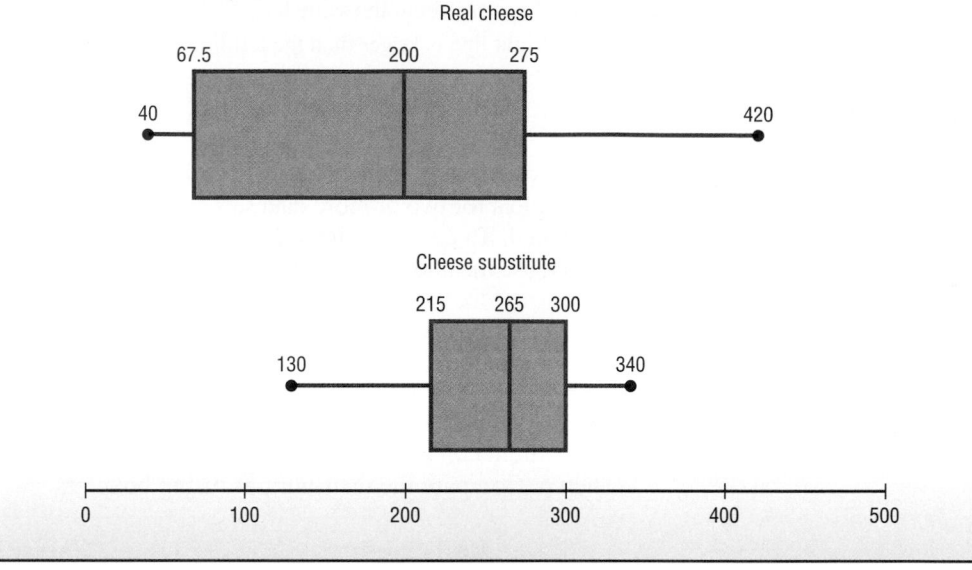

Figure 3–8

Boxplots for
Example 3–36

In exploratory data analysis, *hinges* are used instead of quartiles to construct box-plots. When the data set consists of an even number of values, hinges are the same as quartiles. Hinges for a data set with an odd number of values differ somewhat from quartiles. However, since most calculators and computer programs use quartiles, they will be used in this textbook.

Another important point to remember is that the summary statistics (median and interquartile range) used in exploratory data analysis are said to be *resistant statistics*. A **resistant statistic** is relatively less affected by outliers than a *nonresistant statistic*. The mean and standard deviation are nonresistant statistics. Sometimes when a distribution is skewed or contains outliers, the median and interquartile range may more accurately summarize the data than the mean and standard deviation, since the mean and standard deviation are more affected in this case.

Table 3–5 compares the traditional versus the exploratory data analysis approach.

Table 3–5	Traditional versus EDA Techniques	
Traditional		**Exploratory data analysis**
Frequency distribution		Stem and leaf plot
Histogram		Boxplot
Mean		Median
Standard deviation		Interquartile range

Applying the Concepts 3–5

The Noisy Workplace

Assume you work for CCOHS (Canadian Centre for Occupational Health and Safety) and have complaints about noise levels from some of the workers at a provincial power plant. You charge the power plant with taking decibel readings at six different areas of the plant at different times of the day and week. The results of the data collection are listed. Use boxplots to initially explore the data and make recommendations about which plant areas workers must be provided with protective ear wear. The safe hearing level is at approximately 120 decibels.

Area 1	Area 2	Area 3	Area 4	Area 5	Area 6
30	64	100	25	59	67
12	99	59	15	63	80
35	87	78	30	81	99
65	59	97	20	110	49
24	23	84	61	65	67
59	16	64	56	112	56
68	94	53	34	132	80
57	78	59	22	145	125
100	57	89	24	163	100
61	32	88	21	120	93
32	52	94	32	84	56
45	78	66	52	99	45
92	59	57	14	105	80
56	55	62	10	68	34
44	55	64	33	75	21

See page 142 for the answers.

Exercises 3–5

For Exercises 1–6, identify the five-number summary and find the interquartile range.

1. 8, 12, 32, 6, 27, 19, 54

2. 19, 16, 48, 22, 7

3. 362, 589, 437, 316, 192, 188

4. 147, 243, 156, 632, 543, 303

5. 14.6, 19.8, 16.3, 15.5, 18.2

6. 9.7, 4.6, 2.2, 3.7, 6.2, 9.4, 3.8

For Exercises 7–10, use each boxplot to identify the maximum value, minimum value, median, first quartile, third quartile, and interquartile range.

7.

8.

9.

10.

11. Shown here are the sizes of the police forces in Canada's 10 largest cities in 2005 (the numbers represent hundreds). Construct a boxplot for the data and comment on the shape of the distribution.

89.4, 64.9, 16.0, 12.0, 12.4, 16.3, 31.7, 3.6, 10.0, 5.8

Source: Statistics Canada.

12. Construct a boxplot for the number of bills passed by the Canadian parliament for the past 8 completed sessions. Comment on the shape of the distribution.

46, 21, 28, 47, 25, 58, 50, 82

Source: Parliament of Canada.

13. Construct a boxplot for the following average number of vacation days in selected countries.

42	37	35
34	28	26
13	25	25

Source: World Tourism Organization.

14. Shown here is the number of new theatre productions that appeared on NYC's Broadway for the past several years. Construct a boxplot for the data and comment on the shape of the distribution.

30	28	33	29	37	39
35	37	37	38	34	

Source: The League of American Theaters and Producers Inc.

15. These data represent the average rainfall (in millimetres) for select Canadian cities in April. Construct a boxplot and comment on the skewness of the data.

41.9	75.4	25.1	21.8	20.4	25.7
35.9	64.0	69.0	74.8	75.5	83.4
124.4	81.6	110.4	28.4	10.3	8.3

Source: Environment Canada.

16. These data represent the volumes in cubic metres of the largest dams in the United States and South America. Construct a boxplot of the data for each region and compare the distributions.

United States	South America
96,049	238,189
70,339	209,508
59,641	81,000
50,843	77,995
48,052	43,000
40,089	35,600
38,228	

Source: *New York Times.*

17. A 4-month record for the number of tornadoes in 1999–2001 is given here.

a. Which month has the highest mean number of tornadoes for this 3-year period?

b. Which year has the highest mean number of tornadoes for this 4-month period?

c. Construct three boxplots and compare the distributions.

	2001	2000	1999
April	135	136	177
May	241	241	311
June	248	135	289
July	120	148	102

Source: National Weather Service, Storm Prediction Center.

Extending the Concepts

18. A *modified boxplot* can be drawn by placing a box around Q_1 and Q_3 and then extending the whiskers to the largest and/or smallest values within 1.5 times the interquartile range (i.e., $Q_3 - Q_1$). *Mild outliers* are values between 1.5 (IQR) and 3 (IQR). *Extreme outliers* are data values beyond 3 (IQR).

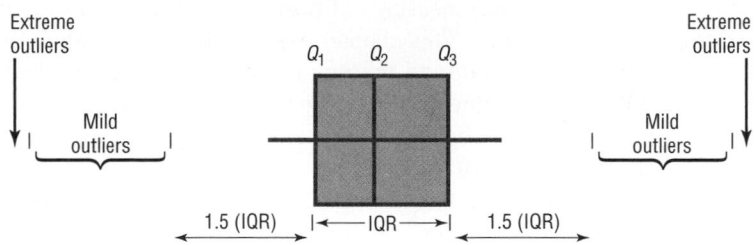

For the data shown here, draw a modified boxplot and identify any mild or extreme outliers. The data represent the number of unhealthful smog days for a specific year for the highest 10 locations.

97	39	43	66	91
43	54	42	53	39

Source: U.S. Public Interest Research Group and Clean Air Network.

3–6   Summary

This chapter explains the basic ways to summarize data. These include measures of central tendency, measures of variation or dispersion, and measures of position. The three most commonly used measures of central tendency are the mean, median, and mode. The midrange is also used occasionally to represent an average. The three most commonly used measurements of variation are the range, variance, and standard deviation.

The most common measures of position are percentiles, quartiles, deciles, and standard scores or z scores. This chapter explains how data values are distributed according to Chebyshev's theorem and the empirical rule. The coefficient of variation is used to describe the standard deviation in relationship to the mean. These methods are commonly called traditional statistical methods and are primarily used to confirm various conjectures about the nature of the data.

Other methods, such as the boxplot and five-number summaries, are part of exploratory data analysis; they are used to examine data to see what they reveal.

After learning the techniques presented in Chapter 2 and this chapter, you will have a substantial knowledge of descriptive statistics. That is, you will be able to collect, organize, summarize, and present data.

For step-by-step guidance on the use of technology for this chapter, visit the Online Learning Centre at www.mcgrawhill.ca/olc/bluman. Summary procedures for Minitab, SPSS, Excel, and TI-83 Plus or TI-84 Plus can also be found in Appendix E.

Important Terms   ● ● ●

bimodal 85	five-number summary 127	negatively skewed or left-skewed distribution 91	range rule of thumb 106
boxplot 127			resistant statistic 130
Chebyshev's theorem 107	interquartile range 123	outlier 123	standard deviation 100
coefficient of variation 105	mean 80	parameter 80	statistic 80
data array 84	median 84	percentile 116	symmetric distribution 91
decile 123	midrange 88	positively skewed or right-skewed distribution 90	unimodal 85
empirical rule 109	modal class 86		variance 100
exploratory data analysis 127	mode 85	quartile 122	weighted mean 89
	multimodal 85	range 98	z score or standard score 114

Important Formulas   ● ● ●

Formula for the mean for individual data:

$$\overline{X} = \frac{\Sigma X}{n} \text{ (sample data)} \quad \mu = \frac{\Sigma X}{N} \text{ (population data)}$$

Formula for the mean for grouped data:

$$\overline{X} = \frac{\Sigma f \cdot X_m}{n}$$

Formula for the weighted mean:

$$\overline{X} = \frac{\Sigma wX}{\Sigma w}$$

Formula for the midrange:

$$\text{MR} = \frac{\text{lowest value} + \text{highest value}}{2}$$

Formula for the range:

$$R = \text{highest value} - \text{lowest value}$$

Formula for the variance for population data:

$$\sigma^2 = \frac{\Sigma(X - \mu)^2}{N}$$

Formula for the variance for sample data (shortcut formula for the unbiased estimator):

$$s^2 = \frac{\Sigma X^2 - [(\Sigma X)^2/n]}{n-1}$$

Formula for the variance for grouped data:

$$s^2 = \frac{\Sigma f \cdot X_m^2 - [(\Sigma f \cdot X_m)^2/n]}{n-1}$$

Formula for the standard deviation for population data:

$$\sigma = \sqrt{\frac{\Sigma(X-\mu)^2}{N}}$$

Formula for the standard deviation for sample data (shortcut formula):

$$s = \sqrt{\frac{\Sigma X^2 - [(\Sigma X)^2/n]}{n-1}}$$

Formula for the standard deviation for grouped data:

$$s = \sqrt{\frac{\Sigma f \cdot X_m^2 - [(\Sigma f \cdot X_m)^2/n]}{n-1}}$$

Formula for the coefficient of variation:

$$\text{CVar} = \frac{s}{\overline{X}} \cdot 100\% \qquad \text{or} \qquad \text{CVar} = \frac{\sigma}{\mu} \cdot 100\%$$

Range rule of thumb:

$$s \approx \frac{\text{range}}{4}$$

Expression for Chebyshev's theorem: The proportion of values from a data set that will fall within k standard deviations of the mean will be at least

$$1 - \frac{1}{k^2}$$

where k is a number greater than 1.

Formula for the z score (standard score):

$$z = \frac{X-\mu}{\sigma} \qquad \text{or} \qquad z = \frac{X-\overline{X}}{s}$$

Formula for the cumulative percentage:

$$\text{Cumulative \%} = \frac{\text{cumulative frequency}}{n} \cdot 100\%$$

Formula for the percentile rank of a value X:

$$\text{Percentile} = \frac{(\text{number of values below } X + 0.5)}{\text{total number of values}} \cdot 100\%$$

Formula for finding a value corresponding to a given percentile:

$$c = \frac{n \cdot p}{100}$$

Formula for interquartile range:

$$\text{IQR} = Q_3 - Q_1$$

Review Exercises

1. The following data represents the reported number of hours of radio listening per week for each of Canada's provinces for young adults in the 18 to 24 age group.

12.9	19.0	13.5	13.4	14.6
15.7	17.4	19.4	18.3	13.3

Source: Statistics Canada.

Find each of these.
a. Mean
b. Median
c. Mode
d. Midrange
e. Range
f. Variance
g. Standard deviation

2. These data represent the area in square kilometres of major islands in the Caribbean Sea and the Mediterranean Sea.

Caribbean Sea			Mediterranean Sea	
280	2,398	1,129	4,991	3,654
194	259	8,648	593	246
13,939	443	300	8,259	1,399
5,957	751	4,828	9,251	24,089
430	1,779	153	223	25,708
110,862	10,992	347		
76,117				

Source: The World Almanac and Book of Facts.

Find each of the following descriptive measures.
a. Mean
b. Median
c. Mode
d. Midrange
e. Range
f. Variance
g. Standard deviation

3. Twelve batteries were tested to see how many hours they would last. The frequency distribution is shown here.

Hours	Frequency
1–3	1
4–6	4
7–9	5
10–12	1
13–15	1

Find each of these.
a. Mean
b. Modal class
c. Variance
d. Standard deviation

4. The following data represent the number of seconds it took 20 students to find information from the Internet on a personal computer.

Class	Frequency
34–38	4
39–43	6
44–48	3
49–53	4
54–58	3

Find each of these.

a. Mean
b. Modal class
c. Variance
d. Standard deviation

5. Shown here is a frequency distribution for the extreme tidal ranges (high tide to low tide) at selected locations in Canada. (Note: Canada's Bay of Fundy has the greatest tidal range in the world at 16.1 metres.)

Tidal Change (m)	Frequency
0–2.95	4
2.95–5.95	7
5.95–8.95	5
8.95–11.95	1
11.95–14.95	1
14.95–17.95	1

Source: The Atlas of Canada.

Find each of the following.

a. Mean
b. Modal class
c. Variance
d. Standard deviation

6. The following distribution illustrates the fuel cost per year to operate various pickup trucks in Canada. *Note: The data assumes a fuel price of 70¢/litre and 20,000 kilometres driving distance.*

Fuel Cost ($/Year)	Frequency
1200–1499	9
1500–1799	48
1800–2099	47
2100–2399	8
2400–2699	0
2700–2999	3
3000–3299	1
3300–3599	1
	117

Source: Natural Resources Canada—*Fuel Consumption Guide 2005.*

Find the following descriptive measures.

a. Mean
b. Modal class
c. Variance
d. Standard deviation

7. In a dental survey of Grade 3 students, this distribution was obtained for the number of cavities found. Find the average number of cavities for the class. Use the weighted mean.

Number of students	Number of cavities
12	0
8	1
5	2
5	3

8. An investor calculated these percentages of each of three stock investments with payoffs as shown. Find the average payoff. Use the weighted mean.

Stock	Percent	Payoff
A	30	$10,000
B	50	3,000
C	20	1,000

9. In an advertisement, a transmission service centre stated that the average years of service of its employees were 13. The distribution is shown here. Using the weighted mean, calculate the correct average.

Number of employees	Years of service
8	3
1	6
1	30

10. If the average number of textbooks in professors' offices is 16, the standard deviation is 5, and the average age of the professors is 43, with a standard deviation of 8, which data set is more variable?

11. A survey of bookstores showed that the average number of magazines carried is 56, with a standard deviation of 12. The same survey showed that the average length of time each store had been in business was 6 years, with a standard deviation of 2.5 years. Which is more variable, the number of magazines or the number of years?

12. The number of previous jobs held by each of six applicants is shown here.

2, 4, 5, 6, 8, 9

a. Find the percentile for each value.
b. What value corresponds to the 30th percentile?
c. Construct a boxplot and comment on the nature of the distribution.

13. The salaries (in millions of dollars) for 29 NFL teams for the 1999–2000 season are given in this frequency distribution.

Class limits	Frequency
39.9–42.8	2
42.9–45.8	2
45.9–48.8	5
48.9–51.8	5
51.9–54.8	12
54.9–57.8	3

Source: www.NFL.com.

a. Construct a percentile graph.

b. Find the values that correspond to the 35th, 65th, and 85th percentiles.

c. Find the percentile of values 44, 48, and 54.

14. Check each data set for outliers.

  a. 506, 511, 517, 514, 400, 521

    b. 3, 7, 9, 6, 8, 10, 14, 16, 20, 12

    c. 14, 18, 27, 26, 19, 13, 5, 25

    d. 112, 157, 192, 116, 153, 129, 131

15. A survey of car rental agencies shows that the average cost of a car rental is $0.32 per kilometre. The standard deviation is $0.03. Using Chebyshev's theorem, find the range in which at least 75% of the data values will fall.

16. The average cost of a certain type of seed per hectare is $42. The standard deviation is $3. Using Chebyshev's theorem, find the range in which at least 88.89% of the data values will fall.

17. The average labour charge for automobile mechanics is $54 per hour. The standard deviation is $4. Find the minimum percentage of data values that will fall within the range of $48 to $60. Use Chebyshev's theorem.

18. For a certain type of job, it costs a company an average of $231 to train an employee to perform the task. The standard deviation is $5. Find the minimum percentage of data values that will fall in the range of $219 to $243. Use Chebyshev's theorem.

19. The average delivery charge for a refrigerator is $32. The standard deviation is $4. Find the minimum percentage of data values that will fall in the range of $20 to $44. Use Chebyshev's theorem.

20. Which of these exam grades has a better relative position?

    a. A grade of 82 on a test with $X = 85$ and $s = 6$.

    b. A grade of 56 on a test with $X = 60$ and $s = 5$.

21. The data shown here represent the number of hours that 12 part-time employees at a toy store worked during the weeks before and after Christmas. Construct two boxplots and compare the distributions.

Before	38	16	18	24	12	30	35	32	31	30	24	35
After	26	15	12	18	24	32	14	18	16	18	22	12

22. A lifestyles study indicated that 11.4 million Canadians, or 47% of the adult population, commute to work on weekdays. The average commute time was 62 minutes. If the standard deviation was 11 minutes, within what limits would you expect approximately 68% of adult commuters times to fall? Assume the distribution is approximately bell-shaped.

Source: The Fraser Institute.

Statistics Today

Do You Live as Well as Other Canadians?—Revisited

The nominal gross domestic product (GDP) per capita or average income for all Canadians was $42,464 but provincial disparity exists. Provincial comparative average GDP for 2005 is listed here.

Alberta	$66,397
Ontario	$42,933
Saskatchewan	$42,743
Newfoundland and Labrador	$41,707
New Brunswick	$41,548
British Columbia	$39,556
Quebec	$36,201
Manitoba	$35,634
Nova Scotia	$33,529
Prince Edward Island	$30,015

Source: Statistics Canada/Haver Analytics

By making comparison using averages, you can see that Alberta leads the country in economic well-being, well above the Canada average and at least 50% higher than all other provinces.

Source: Adapted from Statistics Canada publication *Provincial Economic Accounts, Annual Estimates—Tables and Analytical Document,* Catalogue 13-213 and CANSIM Tables 384-0001, 384-0002, and 051-0001.

Data Analysis

● ● ●

A Data Bank is found in Appendix D, or on the World Wide Web by following links from www.mcgrawhill. ca/olc/bluman

1. From the Data Bank, choose one of the following variables: age, weight, cholesterol level, systolic pressure, IQ, or sodium level. Select at least 30 values, and find the mean, median, mode, and midrange. State which measurement of central tendency best describes the average and why.

2. Find the range, variance, and standard deviation for the data selected in Exercise 1.

3. From the Data Bank, choose 10 values from any variable, construct a boxplot, and interpret the results.

4. Randomly select 10 values from the number of suspensions in the local school districts in southwestern Pennsylvania in Data Set V in Appendix D. Find the mean, median, mode, range, variance, and standard deviation of the number of suspensions by using the Pearson coefficient of skewness.

5. Using the data from Data Set VII in Appendix D, find the mean, median, mode, range, variance, and standard deviation of the acreage owned by the municipalities. Comment on the skewness of the data, using the Pearson coefficient of skewness.

Chapter Quiz

● ● ●

Determine whether each statement is true or false. If the statement is false, explain why.

1. When the mean is computed for individual data, all values in the data set are used.

2. The mean cannot be found for grouped data when there is an open class.

3. A single, extremely large value can affect the median more than the mean.

4. One-half of all the data values will fall above the mode, and one-half will fall below the mode.

5. In a data set, the mode will always be unique.

6. The range and midrange are both measures of variation.

7. One disadvantage of the median is that it is not unique.

8. The mode and midrange are both measures of variation.

9. If a person's score on an exam corresponds to the 75th percentile, then that person obtained 75 correct answers out of 100 questions.

Select the best answer.

10. What is the value of the mode when all values in the data set are different?

 a. 0
 b. 1
 c. There is no mode.
 d. It cannot be determined unless the data values are given.

11. When data are categorized as, for example, places of residence (rural, suburban, urban), the most appropriate measure of central tendency is the

 a. Mean
 b. Median
 c. Mode
 d. Midrange

12. P_{50} corresponds to

 a. Q_2
 b. D_5
 c. IQR
 d. Midrange

13. Which is not part of the five-number summary?

 a. Q_1 and Q_3
 b. The mean
 c. The median
 d. The smallest and the largest data values

14. A statistic that tells the number of standard deviations a data value is above or below the mean is called

 a. A quartile
 b. A percentile
 c. A coefficient of variation
 d. A z score

15. When a distribution is bell-shaped, approximately what percentage of data values will fall within 1 standard deviation of the mean?

 a. 50%
 b. 68%
 c. 95%
 d. 99.7%

Complete these statements with the best answer.

16. A measure obtained from sample data is called a(n) _____.

17. Generally, Greek letters are used to represent _____, and Roman letters are used to represent _____.

18. The positive square root of the variance is called the _____.

19. The symbol for the population standard deviation is _____.

20. When the sum of the lowest data value and the highest data value is divided by 2, the measure is called _____.

21. If the mode is to the left of the median and the mean is to the right of the median, then typically the distribution is _____ skewed.

22. An extremely high or extremely low data value is called a(n) _____.

23. This data highlights the fuel consumption (L/100 km) of the 10 least fuel efficient cars with Canadian sales.

24.7 23.2 22.9 22.9 22.9 22.7 22.4 22.1 22.0 20.8

Source: Natural Resources Canada—*Fuel Consumption Guide* 2006.

a. Mean
b. Median
c. Mode
d. Midrange
e. Range
f. Variance
g. Standard deviation

24. The distribution of the number of errors that 10 students made on a typing test is shown.

Errors	Frequency
0–2	1
3–5	3
6–8	4
9–11	1
12–14	1

Find each of these.

a. Mean
b. Modal class
c. Variance
d. Standard deviation

25. Shown here is a frequency distribution for the number of select Canadian cities with October precipitation (millimetres) in the indicated intervals.

Precipitation (mm)	Frequency
0.5–25.5	5
25.5–50.5	3
50.5–75.5	3
75.5–100.5	3
100.5–125.5	2
125.5–150.5	1
150.5–175.5	1

Source: Environment Canada.

Find each of the descriptive measures.

a. Mean
b. Modal class
c. Variance
d. Standard deviation

26. A survey of 36 selected recording companies showed these numbers of days that it took to receive a shipment from the day it was ordered.

Days	Frequency
1–3	6
4–6	8
7–9	10
10–12	7
13–15	0
16–18	5

Find each of these.

a. Mean
b. Modal class
c. Variance
d. Standard deviation

27. In a survey of Grade 3 students, this distribution was obtained for the number of "best friends" each had.

Number of students	Number of best friends
8	1
6	2
5	3
3	0

Find the average number of best friends for the class. Use the weighted mean.

28. In an advertisement, a retail store stated that its employees averaged 9 years of service. The distribution is shown here.

Number of employees	Years of service
8	2
2	6
3	10

Using the weighted mean, calculate the correct average.

29. The average number of newspapers for sale in an airport newsstand is 12, and the standard deviation is 4. The average age of the pilots is 37 years, with a standard deviation of 6 years. Which data set is more variable?

30. A survey of grocery stores showed that the average number of brands of toothpaste carried was 16, with a standard deviation of 5. The same survey showed the average length of time each store was in business was 7 years, with a standard deviation of 1.6 years. Which is more variable, the number of brands or the number of years?

31. A student scored 76 on a general science test where the class mean and standard deviation were 82 and 8, respectively; he also scored 53 on a psychology test where the class mean and standard deviation were 58 and 3, respectively. In which class was his relative position higher?

32. Which score has the highest relative position?

a. $X = 12$ $\overline{X} = 10$ $s = 4$
b. $X = 170$ $\overline{X} = 120$ $s = 32$
c. $X = 180$ $\overline{X} = 60$ $s = 8$

33. The number of square metres (in 1000s) of 10 of the largest shopping malls in the world is shown below.

660, 557, 353, 297, 297, 279, 260, 232, 223, 214

a. Find the percentile rank for each value.
b. What value corresponds to the 40th percentile?
c. Construct a boxplot and comment on the nature of the distribution.

Source: East Connecticut State University—Shopping Mall Studies.

34. On a philosophy comprehensive exam, this distribution was obtained from 25 students.

Score	Frequency
40.5–45.5	3
45.5–50.5	8
50.5–55.5	10
55.5–60.5	3
60.5–65.5	1

 a. Construct a percentile graph.
 b. Find the values that correspond to the 22nd, 78th, and 99th percentiles.
 c. Find the percentiles of the values 52, 43, and 64.

35. The first column of these data represents the prebuy gas price (in US$ per gallon) of a rental car, and the second column represents the price charged if the car is returned without refilling the gas tank for a selected car rental company. Draw two boxplots for the data and compare the distributions.

Prebuy cost	No prebuy cost
$1.55	$3.80
1.54	3.99
1.62	3.99
1.65	3.85
1.72	3.99
1.63	3.95
1.65	3.94
1.72	4.19
1.45	3.84
1.52	3.94

Source: USA TODAY.

36. The average national SAT score is 1019. If we assume a bell-shaped distribution and a standard deviation equal to 110, what percentage of scores would you expect to fall above 1129? Above 799?

Source: N.Y. Times Almanac, 2002.

Critical Thinking Challenges

1. Averages give us information to help us to see where we stand and enable us to make comparisons. Here is a study on the average cost of a wedding. What type of average—mean, median, mode, or midrange—might have been used for each category?

OTHER PEOPLE'S MONEY

Question: What is the hottest wedding month. **Answer:** It's a tie. September now ranks as high as June in U.S. nuptials. The average attendance is 186 guests. And what kind of tabs are people running up for these affairs? Well, the next time a bride is throwing a bouquet, single women might want to . . . duck!

Reception	**$7246**
Rings	**4042**
Photos/videography	**1263**
Bridal gown	**790**
Flowers	**775**
Music	**745**
Invitations	**374**
Mother of the bride's dress	**198**
Other (veil, limo, fees, etc.)	**3441**
Average cost of a wedding	**$18,874**

Stats: Bride's 2000 State of the Union Report.

Source: Reprinted with permission from the September 2001 *Reader's Digest.* Copyright © 2001 by The Reader's Digest Assn., Inc.

2. This article states that the average yearly cost of smoking a pack of cigarettes a day is $1190. Find the average cost of a pack of cigarettes in your area, and compute the cost per day for one year. Compare your answer with the one in the article.

Save Your Cigarette Money
Bank on your health

On the face of it, it's an easy calculation—you spend so many dollars a day on cigarettes, there are 365 days in a year, a few clicks on the calculator and you can work out how much smoking will cost you in your lifetime. But money doesn't stay the same over time; the price of cigarettes goes up, and so does the cost of living. And your life expectancy doesn't decrease a year for every year you live—the longer you live, the older the age you'll probably live to. So what seems a simple calculation becomes a little trickier—and the numbers can be more than you would expect.

If you smoked a pack a day, your annual savings if you quit smoking could be $3276. Visit the following website to calculate the cost of cigarettes. http://www.quit4life.com/calc_e.asp.

Source: Health Canada.

3. The table shows the median ages of Canadian males and females by province and territory based on data from the 2001 Census. Explain why the median is used instead of the mean.

	Median Age	
Name	**Males**	**Females**
Canada	36.8	38.4
Newfoundland and Labrador	37.9	38.8
Prince Edward Island	36.8	38.5
Nova Scotia	38.0	39.5
New Brunswick	37.7	39.4
Quebec	37.8	39.8
Ontario	36.4	38.0
Manitoba	35.8	37.8
Saskatchewan	35.8	37.6
Alberta	34.4	35.6
British Columbia	37.8	39.0
Yukon Territory	36.4	35.8
Northwest Territories	30.4	29.8
Nunavut	22.3	21.9

Source: Adapted from Statistics Canada website, www.statcan.ca/bsolc/english/bsolc?catno=97F0024X2001001. Accessed March 19, 2007.

Data Projects

● ● ●

Where appropriate, use Minitab, SPSS, the TI-83 Plus, the TI-84 Plus, Excel, or a computer program of your choice to complete the following exercises.

1. Select a variable and collect about 10 values for two groups. (For example, you may want to ask 10 men how many cups of coffee they drink per day and 10 women the same question.)
   a. Define the variable.
   b. Define the populations.
   c. Describe how the samples were selected.

d. Write a paragraph describing the similarities and differences between the two groups, using appropriate descriptive statistics such as means, standard deviations, and so on.

2. Collect data consisting of at least 30 values.

   a. State the purpose of the project.
   b. Define the population.
   c. State how the sample was selected.

d. Using appropriate descriptive statistics, write a paragraph summarizing the data.

You may use the following websites to obtain raw data:

Visit the data sets at the book's website found at www.mcgrawhill.ca/olc/bluman
http://lib.stat.cmu.edu/DASL
http://www.statcan.ca

Answers to Applying the Concepts

● ● ●

Solution 3–2 Professor Salaries

1. The sample mean is $98,929.92, the sample median is $93,900.50, the sample midrange is $119,623, and the sample mode is $88,444. If you work for the administrators and do not want to increase salaries, you would say that the average salary is $119,623.

2. If you work for the faculty association and want a salary increase for professors, the sample mode of $88,444 is the best indicator of low salaries followed by the sample median of $93,900.50.

3. The outlier is $151,884. With outlier removed, the sample mean is $94,115.91, the sample median is $93,521, the sample midrange is $95,336.50, and the sample mode is $88,444. The outlier greatly affected the mean, allowing the administrators to report an average salary that is not representative of the "typical" faculty salary.

4. If the salaries represented every professor at all universities in Canada, the averages would be parameters, since we would have data from the entire population.

5. The mean can be misleading in the presence of outliers, since it is greatly affected by these extreme values.

6. Since the mean is greater than both the median and the mode, the distribution is typically skewed to the right (positively skewed). A sketch of the histogram verifies this distribution shape.

Section 3–3 Blood Pressure

1. Chebyshev's theorem does not work for scores within 1 standard deviation of the mean.

2. At least 75% (900) of the normotensive men will fall in the interval 105–141 mm Hg.

3. About 95% (1330) of the normotensive women have diastolic blood pressures between 62 and 90 mm Hg. About 95% (1235) of the hypertensive women have diastolic blood pressures between 68 and 108 mm Hg.

4. About 95% (1140) of the normotensive men have systolic blood pressures between 105 and 141 mm Hg.

About 95% (1045) of the hypertensive men have systolic blood pressures between 119 and 187 mm Hg. These two ranges do overlap.

Section 3–4 Determining Dosages

1. The quartiles could be used to describe the data results.

2. Since there are 10 mice in the upper quartile, this would mean that 4 of them survived.

3. The percentiles would give us the position of a single mouse with respect to all other mice.

4. The quartiles divide the data into four groups of equal size.

5. Standard scores would give us the position of a single mouse with respect to the mean time until the onset of sepsis.

Section 3–5 The Noisy Workplace

Boxplot of Noise Level Versus Area

From this boxplot, we see that about 25% of the readings in area 5 are above the safe hearing level of 120 decibels. Those workers in area 5 should definitely have protective ear wear. One of the readings in area 6 is above the safe hearing level. It might be a good idea to provide protective ear wear to those workers in area 6 as well. Areas 1–4 appear to be "safe" with respect to hearing level, with area 4 being the safest.

CHAPTER 4

Probability and Counting Rules

Objectives

After completing this chapter, you should be able to

1. Determine sample spaces and find the probability of an event, using classical probability or empirical probability.

2. Find the probability of compound events, using the addition rules.

3. Find the probability of compound events, using the multiplication rules.

4. Find the conditional probability of an event.

5. Find the total number of outcomes in a sequence of events, using the fundamental counting rule.

6. Find the number of ways that *r* objects can be selected from *n* objects, using the permutation rule.

7. Find the number of ways that *r* objects can be selected from *n* objects without regard to order, using the combination rule.

8. Find the probability of an event, using the counting rules.

Outline

4–1 **Introduction**

4–2 **Sample Spaces and Probability**

4–3 **The Addition Rules for Probability**

4–4 **The Multiplication Rules and Conditional Probability**

4–5 **Counting Rules**

4–6 **Probability and Counting Rules (Optional)**

4–7 **Summary**

Statistics Today

Would You Bet Your Life?

Humans not only bet money when they gamble, but also bet their lives by engaging in unhealthy activities such as smoking, drinking, using drugs, and exceeding the speed limit when driving. Many people don't care about the risks involved in these activities since they do not understand the concepts of probability. On the other hand, people may fear activities that involve little risk to health or life because these activities have been sensationalized by the press and media.

In his book *Probabilities in Everyday Life* (Ivy Books, p. 191), John D. McGervey states

When people have been asked to estimate the frequency of death from various causes, the most overestimated categories are those involving pregnancy, tornadoes, floods, fire, and homicide. The most underestimated categories include deaths from diseases such as diabetes, strokes, tuberculosis, asthma, and stomach cancer (although cancer in general is overestimated).

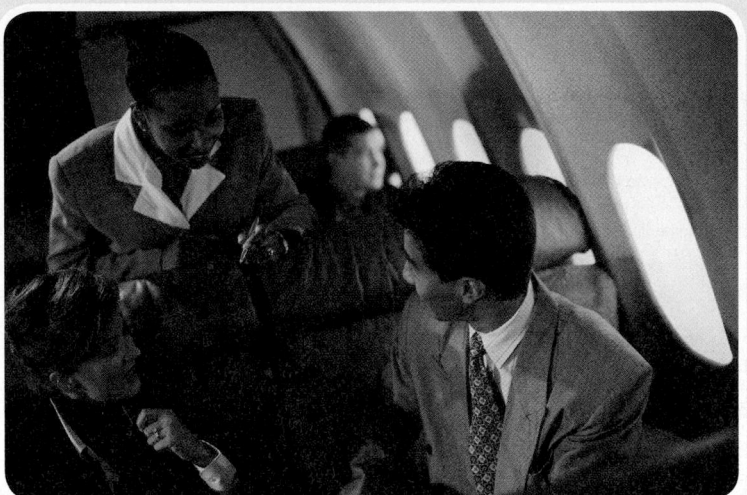

The question then is, Would you feel safer if you flew across Canada on a commercial airline or if you drove? How much greater is the risk of one way to travel over the other? See Statistics Today—Revisited, page 199, at the end of the chapter for the answer.

In this chapter, you will learn about probability—its meaning, how it is computed, and how to evaluate it in terms of the likelihood of an event actually happening.

4–1 Introduction

A cynical person once said, "The only two sure things are death and taxes." This philosophy no doubt arose because so much in people's lives is affected by chance. From the time a person awakes until he or she goes to bed, that person makes decisions regarding the possible events that are governed at least in part by chance. For example, should I carry an umbrella to work today? Will my car battery last until spring? Should I accept that new job?

Probability as a general concept can be defined as the chance of an event occurring. Many people are familiar with probability from observing or playing games of chance, such as card games, slot machines, or lotteries. In addition to being used in games of chance, probability theory is used in the fields of insurance, investments, weather forecasting, and in various other areas. Finally, as stated in Chapter 1, probability is the basis of inferential statistics. For example, predictions are based on probability, and hypotheses are tested by using probability.

The basic concepts of probability are explained in this chapter. These concepts include *probability experiments, sample spaces,* the *addition* and *multiplication rules,* and the *probabilities of complementary events.* Also in this chapter, you will learn the rule for counting, the differences between permutations and combinations, and how to figure out how many different combinations for specific situations exist. Finally, Section 4–6 explains how the counting rules and the probability rules can be used together to solve a wide variety of problems.

4–2   Sample Spaces and Probability

The theory of probability grew out of the study of various games of chance using coins, dice, and cards. Since these devices lend themselves well to the application of concepts of probability, they will be used in this chapter as examples. This section begins by explaining some basic concepts of probability. Then the types of probability and probability rules are discussed.

Basic Concepts

Processes such as flipping a coin, rolling a die, or drawing a card from a deck are called *probability experiments.*

Objective

Determine sample spaces and find the probability of an event, using classical probability or empirical probability.

A **probability experiment** is a chance process that leads to well-defined results called outcomes.

An **outcome** is the result of a single trial of a probability experiment.

A trial means flipping a coin once, rolling one die once, or the like. When a coin is tossed, there are two possible outcomes: head or tail. (*Note:* We exclude the possibility of a coin landing on its edge.) In the roll of a single die, there are six possible outcomes: 1, 2, 3, 4, 5, or 6. In any experiment, the set of all possible outcomes is called the *sample space.*

A **sample space** is the set of all possible outcomes of a probability experiment.

Some sample spaces for various probability experiments are shown here.

Experiment	Sample space
Toss one coin	Head, tail
Roll a die	1, 2, 3, 4, 5, 6
Answer a true/false question	True, false
Toss two coins	Head-head, tail-tail, head-tail, tail-head

It is important to realize that when two coins are tossed, there are *four* possible outcomes, as shown in the fourth experiment above. Both coins could fall heads up. Both coins could fall tails up. Coin 1 could fall heads up and coin 2 tails up. Or coin 1 could fall tails up and coin 2 heads up. Heads and tails will be abbreviated as H and T throughout this chapter.

Example 4–1

Find the sample space for rolling two dice.

Solution

Since each die can land in six different ways, and two dice are rolled, the sample space can be presented by a rectangular array, as shown in Figure 4–1. The sample space is the list of pairs of numbers in the chart.

Figure 4–1

Sample Space for Rolling Two Dice (Example 4–1)

Die 1	Die 2					
	1	2	3	4	5	6
1	(1, 1)	(1, 2)	(1, 3)	(1, 4)	(1, 5)	(1, 6)
2	(2, 1)	(2, 2)	(2, 3)	(2, 4)	(2, 5)	(2, 6)
3	(3, 1)	(3, 2)	(3, 3)	(3, 4)	(3, 5)	(3, 6)
4	(4, 1)	(4, 2)	(4, 3)	(4, 4)	(4, 5)	(4, 6)
5	(5, 1)	(5, 2)	(5, 3)	(5, 4)	(5, 5)	(5, 6)
6	(6, 1)	(6, 2)	(6, 3)	(6, 4)	(6, 5)	(6, 6)

Example 4–2

Find the sample space for drawing one card from an ordinary deck of cards.

Solution

Since there are 4 suits (hearts, clubs, diamonds, and spades) and 13 cards for each suit (ace, numbers 2 through 10, jack, queen, king), there are 52 outcomes in the sample space. See Figure 4–2.

Figure 4–2

Sample Space for Drawing a Card (Example 4–2)

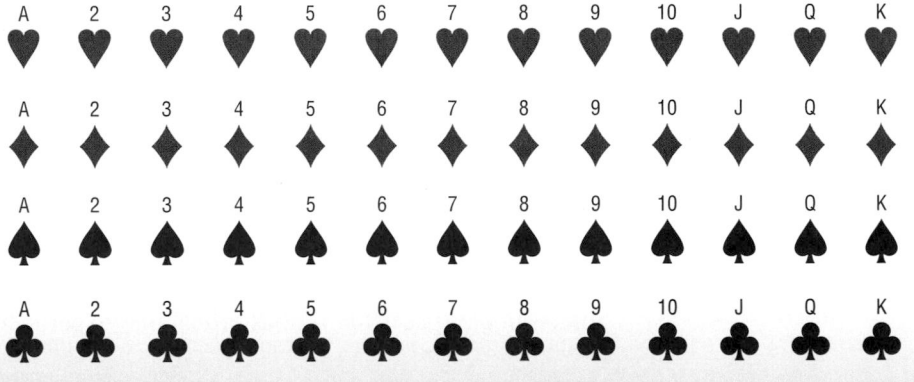

Example 4–3

Find the sample space for the gender of the children if a family has three children. Use B for boy and G for girl.

Solution

There are two genders, male and female, and each child could be either gender. Hence, there are eight possibilities, as shown here.

BBB   BBG   BGB   GBB   GGG   GGB   GBG   BGG

In Examples 4–1 through 4–3, the sample spaces were found by observation and reasoning; however, another way to find all possible outcomes of a probability experiment is to use a *tree diagram*.

> A **tree diagram** is a schematic with branches emanating from a starting point showing all possible outcomes of a probability experiment.

Example 4–4

Use a tree diagram to find the sample space for the gender of three children in a family, as in Example 4–3.

Solution

Since there are two possibilities (boy or girl) for the first child, draw two branches from a starting point and label one B and the other G. Then if the first child is a boy, there are two possibilities for the second child (boy or girl), so draw two branches from B and label one B and the other G. Do the same if the first child is a girl. Follow the same procedure for the third child. The completed tree diagram is shown in Figure 4–3. To find the outcomes for the sample space, trace through all the possible branches, beginning at the starting point for each one.

Figure 4–3

Tree Diagram for Example 4–4

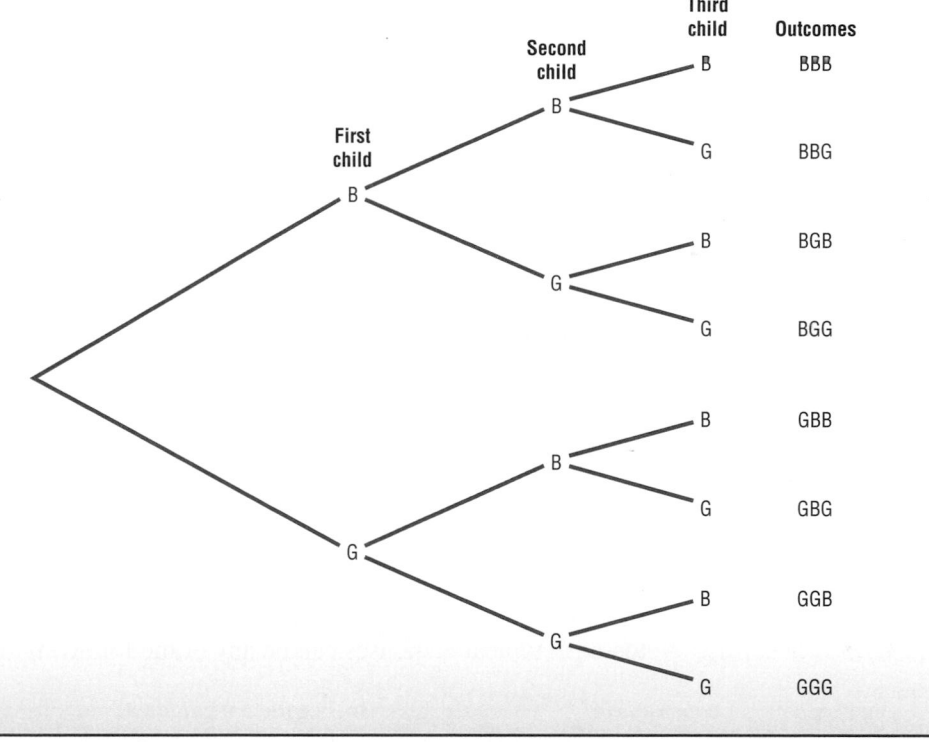

An outcome was defined previously as the result of a single trial of a probability experiment. In many problems, one must find the probability of two or more outcomes. For this reason, it is necessary to distinguish between an outcome and an event.

> An **event** consists of a set of outcomes of a probability experiment.

ℋistorical Note

During the mid-1600s, a professional gambler named Chevalier de Méré made a considerable amount of money on a gambling game. He would bet unsuspecting patrons that in four rolls of a die, he could get at least one 6. He was so successful at the game that some people refused to play. He decided that a new game was necessary to continue his winnings. By reasoning, he figured he could roll at least one double 6 in 24 rolls of two dice, but his reasoning was incorrect and he lost systematically. Unable to figure out why, he contacted a mathematician named Blaise Pascal (1623–1662) to find out why.

Pascal became interested and began studying probability theory. He corresponded with a French government official, Pierre de Fermat (1601–1665), whose hobby was mathematics. Together the two formulated the beginnings of probability theory.

An event can be one outcome or more than one outcome. For example, if a die is rolled and a 6 shows, this result is called an *outcome,* since it is a result of a single trial. An event with one outcome is called a **simple event.** The event of getting an odd number when a die is rolled is called a **compound event,** since it consists of three outcomes or three simple events. In general, a compound event consists of two or more outcomes or simple events.

There are three basic interpretations of probability:

1. Classical probability
2. Empirical or relative frequency probability
3. Subjective probability

Classical Probability

Classical probability uses sample spaces to determine the numerical probability that an event will happen. One does not actually have to perform the experiment to determine that probability. Classical probability is so named because it was the first type of probability studied formally by mathematicians in the seventeenth and eighteenth centuries.

Classical probability assumes that all outcomes in the sample space are equally likely to occur. For example, when a single die is rolled, each outcome has the same probability of occurring. Since there are six outcomes, each outcome has a probability of $\frac{1}{6}$. When a card is selected from an ordinary deck of 52 cards, one assumes that the deck has been shuffled, and each card has the same probability of being selected. In this case, it is $\frac{1}{52}$.

Equally likely events are events that have the same probability of occurring.

Formula for Classical Probability

The probability of any event E is

$$\frac{\text{Number of outcomes in } E}{\text{Total number of outcomes in the sample space}}$$

This probability is denoted by

$$P(E) = \frac{n(E)}{n(S)}$$

This probability is called *classical probability,* and it uses the sample space *S.*

Probabilities can be expressed as fractions, decimals, or—where appropriate—percentages. If one asks, "What is the probability of getting a head when a coin is tossed?" typical responses can be any of the following three.

"One-half."

"Point five."

"Fifty percent."[1]

These answers are all equivalent. In most cases, the answers to examples and exercises given in this chapter are expressed as fractions or decimals, but percentages are used where appropriate.

---

[1]Strictly speaking, a percent is not a probability. However, in everyday language, probabilities are often expressed as percents (i.e., there is a 60% chance of rain tomorrow). For this reason, some probabilities will be expressed as percents throughout this book.

Rounding Rule for Probabilities Probabilities should be expressed as reduced fractions or rounded to two or three decimal places. When the probability of an event is an extremely small decimal, it is permissible to round the decimal to the first nonzero digit after the point. For example, 0.0000587 would be 0.00006. When obtaining probabilities from one of the tables in Appendix C, use the number of decimal places given in the table. If decimals are converted to percentages to express probabilities, move the decimal point two places to the right and add a percent sign.

Example 4–5	For a card drawn from an ordinary deck, find the probability of getting a queen.

Solution

Since there are 52 cards in a deck and there are 4 queens, $P(\text{queen}) = \frac{4}{52} = \frac{1}{13}$.

Example 4–6	If a family has three children, find the probability that all the children are girls.

Solution

The sample space for the gender of children for a family that has three children is BBB, BBG, BGB, GBB, GGG, GGB, GBG, and BGG (see Examples 4–3 and 4–4). Since there is one way in eight possibilities for all three children to be girls,

$$P(\text{GGG}) = \frac{1}{8}$$

Historical Note

Ancient Greeks and Romans made crude dice from animal bones, various stones, minerals, and ivory. When the dice were tested, some were found to be quite accurate and fair.

In probability theory, it is important to understand the meaning of the words *and* and *or*. For example, if you were asked to find the probability of getting a queen *and* a heart when you are drawing a single card from a deck, you would be looking for the queen of hearts. Here the word *and* means "at the same time." The word *or* has two meanings. For example, if you were asked to find the probability of selecting a queen *or* a heart when one card is selected from a deck, you would be looking for one of the 4 queens or one of the 13 hearts. In this case, the queen of hearts would be included in both cases and counted twice. So there would be $4 + 13 - 1 = 16$ possibilities.

On the other hand, if you were asked to find the probability of getting a queen *or* a king, you would be looking for one of the 4 queens or one of the 4 kings. In this case, there would be $4 + 4 = 8$ possibilities. In the first case, both events can occur at the same time; we say that this is an example of the *inclusive or*. In the second case, both events cannot occur at the same time, and we say that this is an example of the *exclusive or*.

Example 4–7	A card is drawn from an ordinary deck. Find these probabilities.

  a. Of getting a jack

  b. Of getting the 6 of clubs (i.e., a 6 and a club)

  c. Of getting a 3 or a diamond

  d. Of getting a 3 or a 6

Solution

  a. Refer to the sample space in Figure 4–2. There are 4 jacks so there are 4 outcomes in event E and 52 possible outcomes in the sample space. Hence,

$$P(\text{jack}) = \frac{4}{52} = \frac{1}{13}$$

b. Since there is only one 6 of clubs in event E, the probability of getting a 6 of clubs is

$$P(6 \text{ of clubs}) = \tfrac{1}{52}$$

c. There are four 3s and 13 diamonds, but the 3 of diamonds is counted twice in this listing. Hence, there are 16 possibilities of drawing a 3 or a diamond, so

$$P(3 \text{ or diamond}) = \tfrac{16}{52} = \tfrac{4}{13}$$

This is an example of the inclusive or.

d. Since there are four 3s and four 6s,

$$P(3 \text{ or } 6) = \tfrac{8}{52} = \tfrac{2}{13}$$

This is an example of the exclusive or.

There are four basic probability rules. These rules are helpful in solving probability problems, in understanding the nature of probability, and in deciding if your answers to the problems are correct.

Probability Rule 1

The probability of any event E is a number (either a fraction or decimal) between and including 0 and 1. This is denoted by $0 \le P(E) \le 1$.

Rule 1 states that probabilities cannot be negative or greater than 1.

Probability Rule 2

If an event E cannot occur (i.e., the event contains no members in the sample space), its probability is 0.

Example 4–8

When a single die is rolled, find the probability of getting a 9.

Solution

Since the sample space is 1, 2, 3, 4, 5, and 6, it is impossible to get a 9. Hence, the probability is $P(9) = \tfrac{0}{6} = 0$.

Probability Rule 3

If an event E is certain, then the probability of E is 1.

In other words, if $P(E) = 1$, then the event E is certain to occur. This rule is illustrated in Example 4–9.

Example 4–9   When a single die is rolled, what is the probability of getting a number less than 7?

Solution

Since all outcomes—1, 2, 3, 4, 5, and 6—are less than 7, the probability is

$$P(\text{number less than } 7) = \tfrac{6}{6} = 1$$

The event of getting a number less than 7 is certain.

In other words, probability values range from 0 to 1. When the probability of an event is close to 0, its occurrence is highly unlikely. When the probability of an event is near 0.5, there is about a 50–50 chance that the event will occur; and when the probability of an event is close to 1, the event is highly likely to occur.

Probability Rule 4

The sum of the probabilities of all the outcomes in the sample space is 1.

For example, in the roll of a fair die, each outcome in the sample space has a probability of $\tfrac{1}{6}$. Hence, the sum of the probabilities of the outcomes is as shown.

Outcome	1	2	3	4	5	6
Probability	$\tfrac{1}{6}$	$\tfrac{1}{6}$	$\tfrac{1}{6}$	$\tfrac{1}{6}$	$\tfrac{1}{6}$	$\tfrac{1}{6}$
Sum	$\tfrac{1}{6}$ +	$\tfrac{1}{6}$ +	$\tfrac{1}{6}$ +	$\tfrac{1}{6}$ +	$\tfrac{1}{6}$ +	$\tfrac{1}{6} = \tfrac{6}{6} = 1$

Complementary Events

Another important concept in probability theory is that of *complementary events*. When a die is rolled, for instance, the sample space consists of the outcomes 1, 2, 3, 4, 5, and 6. The event E of getting odd numbers consists of the outcomes 1, 3, and 5. The event of not getting an odd number is called the *complement* of event E, and it consists of the outcomes 2, 4, and 6.

The **complement of an event** E is the set of outcomes in the sample space that are not included in the outcomes of event E. The complement of E is denoted by $\bar{E}$ (read "E bar").

Example 4–10 further illustrates the concept of complementary events.

Example 4–10   Find the complement of each event.

    a. Rolling a die and getting a 4

    b. Selecting a letter of the alphabet and getting a vowel

    c. Selecting a month and getting a month that begins with a J

    d. Selecting a day of the week and getting a weekday

Solution

a. Getting a 1, 2, 3, 5, or 6

b. Getting a consonant (assume *y* is a consonant)

c. Getting February, March, April, May, August, September, October, November, or December

d. Getting Saturday or Sunday

The outcomes of an event and the outcomes of the complement make up the entire sample space. For example, if two coins are tossed, the sample space is HH, HT, TH, and TT. The complement of "getting all heads" is not "getting all tails," since the event "all heads" is HH, and the complement of HH is HT, TH, and TT. Hence, the complement of the event "all heads" is the event "getting at least one tail."

Since the event and its complement make up the entire sample space, it follows that the sum of the probability of the event and the probability of its complement will equal 1. That is, $P(E) + P(\overline{E}) = 1$. In Example 4–10, let E = all heads, or HH, and let $\overline{E}$ = at least one tail, or HT, TH, TT. Then $P(E) = \frac{1}{4}$ and $P(\overline{E}) = \frac{3}{4}$; hence, $P(E) + P(\overline{E}) = \frac{1}{4} + \frac{3}{4} = 1$.

The rule for complementary events can be stated algebraically in three ways.

Rule for Complementary Events

$$P(\overline{E}) = 1 - P(E) \quad \text{or} \quad P(E) = 1 - P(\overline{E}) \quad \text{or} \quad P(E) + P(\overline{E}) = 1$$

Stated in words, the rule is: *If the probability of an event or the probability of its complement is known, then the other can be found by subtracting the probability from 1.* This rule is important in probability theory because at times the best solution to a problem is to find the probability of the complement of an event and then subtract from 1 to get the probability of the event itself.

Example 4–11

If the probability that a person lives in an industrialized country of the world is $\frac{1}{5}$, find the probability that a person does not live in an industrialized country.

Source: Harper's Index.

Solution

P(not living in an industrialized country) $= 1 - P$(living in an industrialized country)

$$= 1 - \tfrac{1}{5} = \tfrac{4}{5}$$

Probabilities can be represented pictorially by **Venn diagrams.** Figure 4–4(a) shows the probability of a simple event E. The area inside the circle represents the probability of event E, that is, $P(E)$. The area inside the rectangle represents the probability of all the events in the sample space $P(S)$.

The Venn diagram that represents the probability of the complement of an event $P(\overline{E})$ is shown in Figure 4–4(b). In this case, $P(\overline{E}) = 1 - P(E)$, which is the area inside the rectangle but outside the circle representing $P(E)$. Recall that $P(S) = 1$ and $P(E) = 1 - P(\overline{E})$, The reasoning is that $P(E)$ is represented by the area of the circle and $P(\overline{E})$ is the probability of the events that are outside the circle.

Figure 4–4

Venn Diagram for
the Probability and
Complement

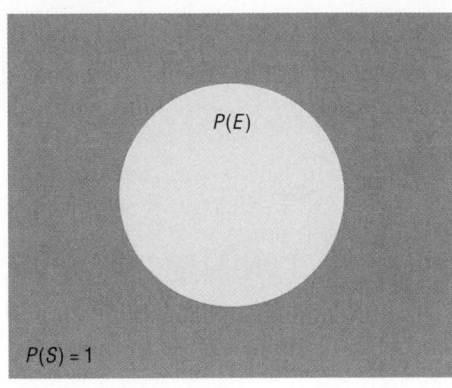

$P(E)$

$P(S) = 1$

(a) Simple probability

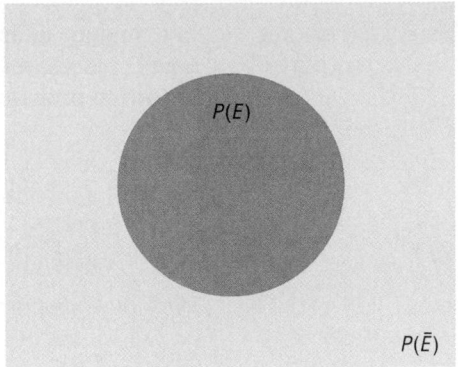

$P(E)$

$P(\bar{E})$

(b) $P(\bar{E}) = 1 - P(E)$

Empirical Probability

The difference between classical and **empirical probability** is that classical probability assumes that certain outcomes are equally likely (such as the outcomes when a die is rolled), while empirical probability relies on actual experience to determine the likelihood of outcomes. In empirical probability, one might actually roll a given die 6000 times, observe the various frequencies, and use these frequencies to determine the probability of an outcome. Suppose, for example, that a researcher asked 25 people if they liked the taste of a new soft drink. The responses were classified as "yes," "no," or "undecided." The results were categorized in a frequency distribution, as shown.

Response	Frequency
Yes	15
No	8
Undecided	2
	Total 25

Probabilities now can be compared for various categories. For example, the probability of selecting a person who liked the taste is $\frac{15}{25}$, or $\frac{3}{5}$, since 15 out of 25 people in the survey answered yes.

Formula for Empirical Probability

Given a frequency distribution, the probability of an event being in a given class is

$$P(E) = \frac{\text{frequency for the class}}{\text{total frequencies in the distribution}} = \frac{f}{n}$$

This probability is called *empirical probability* and is based on observation.

Example 4–12

In the soft drink survey just described, find the probability that a randomly sampled person responded no.

Solution

$$P(E) = \frac{f}{n} = \frac{8}{25}$$

Note: This is the same relative frequency explained in Chapter 2.

Example 4–13

In a random sample of 50 people, 21 had type O blood, 22 had type A blood, 5 had type B blood, and 2 had type AB blood. Set up a frequency distribution and find the following probabilities.

  a. A person has type O blood.

  b. A person has type A or type B blood.

  c. A person has neither type A nor type O blood.

  d. A person does not have type AB blood.

Source: The American Red Cross.

Solution

Type	Frequency
A	22
B	5
AB	2
O	21
	Total 50

a. $P(\text{O}) = \dfrac{f}{n} = \dfrac{21}{50}$

b. $P(\text{A or B}) = \dfrac{22}{50} + \dfrac{5}{50} = \dfrac{27}{50}$

   (Add the frequencies of the two classes.)

c. $P(\text{neither A nor O}) = \dfrac{5}{50} + \dfrac{2}{50} = \dfrac{7}{50}$

   (Neither A nor O means that a person has either type B or type AB blood.)

d. $P(\text{not AB}) = 1 - P(\text{AB}) = 1 - \dfrac{2}{50} = \dfrac{48}{50} = \dfrac{24}{25}$

   (Find the probability of not AB by subtracting the probability of type AB from 1.)

Example 4–14

Hospital records indicated that maternity patients stayed in the hospital for the number of days shown in the distribution.

Number of days stayed	Frequency
3	15
4	32
5	56
6	19
7	5
	127

Find the probabilities that a randomly sampled patient stayed:

  a. exactly 5 days.   *c.* at most 4 days.

  b. less than 6 days.   *d.* at least 5 days.

Solution

a. $P(5) = \dfrac{56}{127}$

b. $P(\text{less than 6 days}) = \dfrac{15}{127} + \dfrac{32}{127} + \dfrac{56}{127} = \dfrac{103}{127}$

(Less than 6 days means 3, 4, or 5 days.)

c. $P(\text{at most 4 days}) = \dfrac{15}{127} + \dfrac{32}{127} = \dfrac{47}{127}$

(At most 4 days means 3 or 4 days.)

d. $P(\text{at least 5 days}) = \dfrac{56}{127} + \dfrac{19}{127} + \dfrac{5}{127} = \dfrac{80}{127}$

(At least 5 days means 5, 6, or 7 days.)

Empirical probabilities can also be found by using a relative frequency distribution, as shown in Section 2–3.

For example, the relative frequency distribution of the soft drink data shown before is

Response	Frequency	Relative frequency
Yes	15	0.60
No	8	0.32
Undecided	2	0.08
	25	1.00

Hence, the probability that a person responded no is 0.32, which is equal to $\frac{8}{25}$.

Law of Large Numbers

When a coin is tossed one time, it is common knowledge that the probability of getting a head is $\frac{1}{2}$. But what happens when the coin is tossed 50 times? Will it come up heads 25 times? Not all the time. One should expect about 25 heads if the coin is fair. But due to chance variation, 25 heads will not occur most of the time.

If the empirical probability of getting a head is computed by using a small number of trials, it is usually not exactly $\frac{1}{2}$. However, as the number of trials increases, the empirical probability of getting a head will approach the theoretical probability of $\frac{1}{2}$, if in fact the coin is fair (i.e., balanced). This phenomenon is an example of the **law of large numbers.**

One should be careful to not think that the number of heads and number of tails tend to "even out." As the number of trials increases, the proportion of heads to the total number of trials will approach $\frac{1}{2}$. This law holds for any type of gambling game—tossing dice, playing roulette, and so on.

It should be pointed out that the probabilities that the proportions steadily approach may or may not agree with those theorized in the classical model. If not, it can have important implications, such as "the die is not fair." Pit bosses in Las Vegas watch for empirical trends that do not agree with classical theories, and they will sometimes take a set of dice out of play if observed frequencies are too far out of line with classical expected frequencies.

Subjective Probability

The third type of probability is called *subjective probability.* **Subjective probability** uses a probability value based on an educated guess or estimate, employing opinions and inexact information.

In subjective probability, a person or group makes an educated guess at the chance that an event will occur. This guess is based on the person's experience and evaluation of a solution. For example, a sportswriter may say that there is a 70% probability that the Toronto Blue Jays will win the pennant next year. A physician might say that, on the basis of her diagnosis, there is a 30% chance the patient will need an operation. A seismologist might say there is an 80% probability that an earthquake will occur in a certain area. These are only a few examples of how subjective probability is used in everyday life.

All three types of probability (classical, empirical, and subjective) are used to solve a variety of problems in business, engineering, and other fields.

Probability and Risk Taking

An area in which people fail to understand probability is risk taking. Actually, people fear situations or events that have a relatively small probability of happening rather than those events that have a greater likelihood of occurring. For example, many people think that the crime rate is increasing every year. However, a published report from the Canadian Centre for Justice Statistics indicates that nationally both property and violent crimes have been steadily decreasing since their peak in 1992.[2]

In his book *How Risk Affects Your Everyday Life*, author James Walsh states, "Today most media coverage of risk to health and well-being focuses on shock and outrage." Shock and outrage make good stories and can scare us about the wrong dangers. For example, the author states that if a person is 20% overweight, the loss of life expectancy is 900 days (about three years), but loss of life expectancy from exposure to radiation emitted by nuclear power plants is 0.02 day. As you can see, being overweight is much more of a threat than being exposed to radioactive emission.

Many people gamble daily with their lives, for example, by using tobacco, drinking and driving, and riding motorcycles. When people are asked to estimate the probabilities or frequencies of death from various causes, they tend to overestimate causes such as accidents, fires, and floods and to underestimate the probabilities of death from diseases (other than cancer), strokes, etc. For example, most people think that their chances of dying of a heart attack are 1 in 20, when in fact they are almost 1 in 3; the chances of dying by pesticide poisoning are 1 in 200,000 (*True Odds* by James Walsh). The reason people think this way is that the news media sensationalize deaths resulting from catastrophic events and rarely mention deaths from disease.

When you are dealing with life-threatening catastrophes such as hurricanes, floods, automobile accidents, or smoking, it is important to get the facts. That is, get the actual numbers from accredited statistical agencies or reliable statistical studies, and then compute the probabilities and make decisions based on your knowledge of probability and statistics.

In summary, then, when you make a decision or plan a course of action based on probability, make sure that you understand the true probability of the event occurring. Also, find out how the information was obtained (i.e., from a reliable source). Weigh the cost of the action and decide if it is worth it. Finally, look for other alternatives or courses of action with less risk involved.

Applying the Concepts 4–2

Tossing a Coin

Assume you are at a carnival and decide to play one of the games. You spot a table where a person is flipping a coin, and since you have an understanding of basic probability, you believe that the odds of winning are in your favour. When you get to the table, you find out

[2]Adapted from Statistics Canada, "Table: Uniform Crime Reporting Survey, CCJS," *Juristat,* Crime statistics in Canada, 2004, Catalogue 85-002, Vol. 25, no. 5, page 5.

that all you have to do is guess which side of the coin will be facing up after it is tossed. You are assured that the coin is fair, meaning that each of the two sides has an equally likely chance of occurring. You think back about what you learned in your statistics class about probability before you decide what to bet on. Answer the following questions about the coin-tossing game.

1. What is the sample space?

2. What are the possible outcomes?

3. What does the classical approach to probability say about computing probabilities for this type of problem?

You decide to bet on heads, believing that it has a 50% chance of coming up. A friend of yours, who had been playing the game for awhile before you got there, tells you that heads has come up the last 9 times in a row. You remember the law of large numbers.

4. What is the law of large numbers, and does it change your thoughts about what will occur on the next toss?

5. What does the empirical approach to probability say about this problem, and could you use it to solve this problem?

6. Can subjective probabilities be used to help solve this problem? Explain.

7. Assume you could win $1 million if you could guess what the results of the next toss will be. What would you bet on? Why?

See page 203 for the answers.

Exercises 4–2

1. What is a probability experiment?

2. Define *sample space*.

3. What is the difference between an outcome and an event?

4. What are equally likely events?

5. What is the range of the values of the probability of an event?

6. When an event is certain to occur, what is its probability?

7. If an event cannot happen, what value is assigned to its probability?

8. What is the sum of the probabilities of all the outcomes in a sample space?

9. If the probability that it will rain tomorrow is 0.20, what is the probability that it won't rain tomorrow? Would you recommend taking an umbrella?

10. A probability experiment is conducted. Which of these cannot be considered a probability of an outcome?

   a. $\frac{1}{3}$ *d.* -0.59 *g.* 1

   b. $-\frac{1}{5}$ *e.* 0   *h.* 33%

   c. 0.80   *f.* 1.45   *i.* 112%

11. Classify each statement as an example of classical probability, empirical probability, or subjective probability.

   a. The probability that a person will watch the 6 o'clock evening news is 0.15.

   b. The probability of winning at Chuck-a-Luck, a three-dice game, is $\frac{75}{216}$.

   c. The probability that a bus will be in an accident on a specific run is about 6%.

   d. The probability of getting a royal flush when five cards are selected at random is $\frac{1}{649,740}$.

   e. The probability that a student will get a C or better in a statistics course is about 70%.

   f. The probability that a new fast-food restaurant will be a success in Regina is 35%.

   g. The probability that interest rates will rise in the next 6 months is 0.50.

12. (ans) If a die is rolled one time, find these probabilities.

   a. Of getting a 4

   b. Of getting an even number

   c. Of getting a number greater than 4

   d. Of getting a number less than 7

   e. Of getting a number greater than 0

f.   Of getting a number greater than 3 or an odd number

g.   Of getting a number greater than 3 and an odd number

13. If two dice are rolled one time, find the probability of getting these results.

a.   A sum of 6

b.   Doubles

c.   A sum of 7 or 11

d.   A sum greater than 9

e.   A sum less than or equal to 4

14. (ans) If one card is drawn from a deck, find the probability of getting these results.

a.   An ace

b.   A diamond

c.   An ace of diamonds

d.   A 4 or a 6

e.   A 4 or a club

f.   A 6 or a spade

g.   A heart or a club

h.   A red queen

i.   A red card or a 7

j.   A black card and a 10

15. A shopping mall has set up a promotion as follows. With any mall purchase, the customer gets to spin the wheel shown here. If the number 1 comes up, the customer wins $10. If the number 2 comes up, the customer wins $5, and if the number 3 or 4 comes up, the customer wins a discount coupon. Find the following probabilities.

a.   The customer wins $10.

b.   The customer wins money.

c.   The customer wins a coupon.

16. Choose one of Canada's 13 provinces or territories at random.

a.   What is the probability that it begins with an N?

b.   What is the probability that it doesn't begin with a vowel? (Note: Assume that "Y" is a vowel.)

17. In a college class of 250 graduating seniors, 50 have jobs waiting, 10 are going to medical school, 20 are going to law school, and 80 are going to various other kinds of graduate schools. Select one graduate at random.

a.   What is the probability that the student is going to graduate school?

b.   What is the probability that the student is going to medical school?

c.   What is the probability that the student will have to start paying back her deferred student loans after 6 months (i.e., does not continue in school)?

18. Seventy-six percent of Canadians of voting age support a national firearms registry. Choose one Canadian voter at random. What is the probability that the selected voter will be opposed to the firearms registry?

Source: The Gallup Poll Organization.

19. In the 2001 Census, Statistics Canada reported that 37% of Canadian families had no children living at home, 27% had one child, 25% had two children, and 11% had three or more children living at home. If a family is selected at random, find the probability that living at home included

a.   Either one or two children

b.   More than one child

c.   Less than three children

d.   Based on the answers to parts *a*, *b*, and *c*, which is most likely to occur?

Source: Statistics Canada.

20. In a recent year, of the 1,184,000 bachelor's degrees conferred, 233,000 were in the field of business, 125,000 were in the social sciences, and 106,000 were in education. If one degree is selected at random, find the following probabilities.

a.   The degree was awarded in education.

b.   The degree was not awarded in business.

Source: National Center for Education Statistics.

21. A couple has three children. Find each probability.

a.   All boys

b.   All girls or all boys

c.   Exactly two boys or two girls

d.   At least one child of each gender

22. In the game of craps using two dice, a person wins on the first roll if a 7 or an 11 is rolled. Find the probability of winning on the first roll.

23. In a game of craps, a player loses on the roll if a 2, 3, or 12 is tossed on the first roll. Find the probability of losing on the first roll.

24. The Association of Workers' Compensation Boards of Canada (AWCBC) publishes statistics on worker injuries. In 2004, the AWCBC reported workplace fatalities by province as follows.

NL	23	ON	365
PEI	1	MB	14
NS	41	SK	30
NB	12	AB	124
QC	176	BC	136

If one workplace fatality is selected at random, what is the probability that the worker was

a. From Ontario (ON)

b. From an Atlantic province (NL or PEI or NS or NB)

c. Not from a Prairie province (MB or SK or AB)

Source: Association of Workers' Compensation Boards of Canada.

25. A roulette wheel has 38 spaces numbered 1 through 36, 0, and 00. Find the probability of getting these results.

a. An odd number (Do not count 0 or 00 as odd.)

b. A number greater than 27

c. A space that contains the digit 0

d. Based on the answers to parts *a*, *b*, and *c*, which is most likely to occur? Explain why.

26. The following data represents the federal prison sentences for Canadian males convicted of various criminal offences in a recent year.

Sentence	Number
Under three years	1848
Three to six years	1548
Six to ten years	341
Ten years or more	96
Life or indeterminate	155
	3988

Source: Correctional Services Canada.

If one male prisoner is selected at random, find the probability that the sentence was

a. Under three years

b. Between three and ten years

c. At least ten years (including life or indeterminate)

27. A CBS News/*New York Times* poll found that of 764 adults surveyed nationwide, 34% felt the United States government was spending too much on space exploration, compared to 19% who felt that the government was spending too little and 35% felt that spending was just right. The remaining responded, "don't know," or had no answer. If one of the respondents is selected at random, what is the probability that the person felt that government spending on space exploration was the right amount or too little?

Source: www.pollingreport.com.

28. A recent *Reader's Digest* survey indicated that 85% of Canadian teens said "it was absolutely essential" to treat "all people equally, regardless of race or ethnic background." If a Canadian teen is selected at random, find the probability that the teen disagrees with this viewpoint on equality of treatment.

Source: www.readersdigest.ca.

29. Roll two dice and multiply the numbers together.

a. Write out the sample space.

b. What is the probability that the product is a multiple of 6?

c. What is the probability that the product is less than 10?

30. The Canadian government's Department of Finance publishes a pamphlet entitled *Where Your Tax Dollar Goes*. A 2005 publication breaks down the tax burden as follows:

45.2% from personal income tax

15.0% from goods and services tax (GST)

15.1% from corporate income tax

8.7% from employment insurance premiums

8.4% from other taxes

7.5% from other revenues

If a revenue source is selected at random, what is the probability that it does not come from either personal income tax or corporate income tax?

Source: Finance Canada.

31. A box contains one of each coin: 1¢, 5¢, 10¢, and 25¢. A coin is selected at random, and it is not replaced; then a second coin is selected at random. Draw a tree diagram and determine the sample space.

32. Draw a tree diagram and determine the sample space for tossing four coins.

33. Four balls numbered 1 through 4 are placed in a box. A ball is selected at random, and its number is noted; then it is replaced. A second ball is selected at random, and its number is noted. Draw a tree diagram and determine the sample space.

34. Kimberly decides to have a computer custom-made. She can select one option from each category.

Megabytes	Processor	Monitor
512	Intel	CRT
1024	AMD	LCD
2048		

Draw a tree diagram for all possible types of computers she can select.

35. Betty and Claire play a tennis tournament consisting of three games. Draw a tree diagram for all possible outcomes of the tournament.

36. A coin is tossed; if it falls heads up, it is tossed again. If it falls tails up, a die is rolled. Draw a tree diagram and determine the outcomes.

Extending the Concepts

37. The distribution of ages of CEOs is as follows:

Age	Frequency
21–30	1
31–40	8
41–50	27
51–60	29
61–70	24
71–up	11

Source: Information based on *USA TODAY* Snapshot.

If a CEO is selected at random, find the probability that his or her age is

a. Between 31 and 40

b. Under 31

c. Over 30 and under 51

d. Under 31 or over 60

38. A person flipped a coin 100 times and obtained 73 heads. Can the person conclude that the coin was unbalanced?

39. A medical doctor stated that with a certain treatment, a patient has a 50% chance of recovering without surgery. That is, "Either he will get well or he won't get well." Comment on this statement.

40. The wheel spinner shown here is spun twice. Find the sample space, and then determine the probability of the following events.

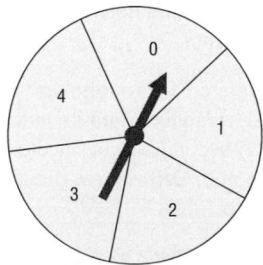

a. An odd number on the first spin and an even number on the second spin (*Note:* 0 is considered even.)

b. A sum greater than 4

c. Even numbers on both spins

d. A sum that is odd

e. The same number on both spins

41. Toss three coins 128 times and record the number of heads (0, 1, 2, or 3); then record your results with the theoretical probabilities. Compute the empirical probabilities of each.

42. Toss two coins 100 times and record the number of heads (0, 1, 2). Compute the probabilities of each outcome, and compare these probabilities with the theoretical results.

43. Odds are used in gambling games to make them fair. For example, if a person rolled a die and won every time he or she rolled a 6, then the person would win on average once every 6 times. So that the game is fair, the odds of 5 to 1 are given. This means that if the person bet $1 and won, he or she could win $5. On average, the player would win $5 once in 6 rolls and lose $1 on the other 5 rolls—hence the term *fair game*.

In most gambling games, the odds given are not fair. For example, if the odds of winning are really 20 to 1, the house might offer 15 to 1 in order to make a profit.

Odds can be expressed as a fraction or as a ratio, such as $\frac{5}{1}$, 5:1, or 5 to 1. Odds are computed in favour of the event or against the event. The formulas for odds are

$$\text{Odds in favour} = \frac{P(E)}{1 - P(E)}$$

$$\text{Odds against} = \frac{P(\overline{E})}{1 - P(\overline{E})}$$

In the die example,

$$\text{Odds in favour of a 6} = \frac{\frac{1}{6}}{\frac{5}{6}} = \frac{1}{5} \text{ or } 1{:}5$$

$$\text{Odds against a 6} = \frac{\frac{5}{6}}{\frac{1}{6}} = \frac{5}{1} \text{ or } 5{:}1$$

Find the odds in favour of and against each event.

a. Rolling a die and getting a 2

b. Rolling a die and getting an even number

c. Drawing a card from a deck and getting a spade

d. Drawing a card and getting a red card

e. Drawing a card and getting a queen

f. Tossing two coins and getting two tails

g. Tossing two coins and getting one tail

4–3   The Addition Rules for Probability

Objective

Find the probability of compound events, using the addition rules.

Many problems involve finding the probability of two or more events. For example, at a large political gathering, one might wish to know, for a person selected at random, the probability that the person is a female or is a Conservative. In this case, there are three possibilities to consider:

1. The person is a female.
2. The person is a Conservative.
3. The person is both a female and a Conservative.

Consider another example. At the same gathering there are Conservatives, Liberals, and New Democrats. If a person is selected at random, what is the probability that the person is a Liberal or a New Democrat? In this case, there are only two possibilities:

1. The person is a Liberal.
2. The person is a New Democrat.

The difference between the two examples is that in the first case, the person selected can be a female and a Conservative at the same time. In the second case, the person selected cannot be both a Liberal and a New Democrat at the same time. In the second case, the two events are said to be *mutually exclusive;* in the first case, they are not mutually exclusive.

> Two events are **mutually exclusive events** if they cannot occur at the same time (i.e., they have no outcomes in common).

In another situation, the events of getting a 4 and getting a 6 when a single card is drawn from a deck are mutually exclusive events, since a single card cannot be both a 4 and a 6. On the other hand, the events of getting a 4 and getting a heart on a single draw are not mutually exclusive, since one can select the 4 of hearts when drawing a single card from an ordinary deck.

The first book on probability, *The Book of Chance and Games,* was written by Jerome Cardan (1501–1576). Cardan was an astrologer, philosopher, physician, mathematician, and gambler. This book contained techniques on how to cheat and how to catch others at cheating.

Example 4–15

Determine which events are mutually exclusive and which are not, when a single die is rolled.

 a. Getting an odd number and getting an even number
 b. Getting a 3 and getting an odd number
 c. Getting an odd number and getting a number less than 4
 d. Getting a number greater than 4 and getting a number less than 4

Solution

 a. The events are mutually exclusive, since the first event can be 1, 3, or 5 and the second event can be 2, 4, or 6.
 b. The events are not mutually exclusive, since the first event is a 3 and the second can be 1, 3, or 5. Hence, 3 is contained in both events.
 c. The events are not mutually exclusive, since the first event can be 1, 3, or 5 and the second can be 1, 2, or 3. Hence, 1 and 3 are contained in both events.
 d. The events are mutually exclusive, since the first event can be 5 or 6 and the second event can be 1, 2, or 3.

Example 4–16   Determine which events are mutually exclusive and which are not, when a single card is drawn from a deck.

      a. Getting a 7 and getting a jack

      b. Getting a club and getting a king

      c. Getting a face card and getting an ace

      d. Getting a face card and getting a spade

Solution

Only the events in parts *a* and *c* are mutually exclusive.

The probability of two or more events can be determined by the *addition rules*. The first addition rule is used when the events are mutually exclusive.

Addition Rule 1

When two events A and B are mutually exclusive, the probability that A or B will occur is

$$P(A \text{ or } B) = P(A) + P(B)$$

Example 4–17   A box contains 3 glazed doughnuts, 4 jelly doughnuts, and 5 chocolate doughnuts. If a person selects a doughnut at random, find the probability that it is either a glazed doughnut or a chocolate doughnut.

Solution

Since the box contains 3 glazed doughnuts, 5 chocolate doughnuts, and a total of 12 doughnuts, $P(\text{glazed or chocolate}) = P(\text{glazed}) + P(\text{chocolate}) = \frac{3}{12} + \frac{5}{12} = \frac{8}{12} = \frac{2}{3}$. The events are mutually exclusive.

Example 4–18   At a political rally, there are 20 Conservatives, 13 Liberals, and 6 New Democrats. If a person is selected at random, find the probability that person is either a Liberal or a New Democrat.

Solution

$$P(\text{Liberal or New Democrat}) = P(\text{Liberal}) + P(\text{New Democrat})$$
$$= \tfrac{13}{39} + \tfrac{6}{39} = \tfrac{19}{39}$$

Example 4–19   A day of the week is selected at random. Find the probability that it is a weekend day.

Solution

$$P(\text{Saturday or Sunday}) = P(\text{Saturday}) + P(\text{Sunday}) = \tfrac{1}{7} + \tfrac{1}{7} = \tfrac{2}{7}$$

When two events are not mutually exclusive, then the probability of the common elements of the two events must be subtracted from the combined probabilities. Refer to the Venn diagram, Figure 4–5(b) on page 164. This technique is illustrated in Example 4–20.

Example 4–20

A single card is drawn from a deck. Find the probability that it is a king or a club.

Solution

Since the king of clubs means a king and a club, it has been counted twice—once as a king and once as a club; therefore, one of the outcomes must be subtracted, as shown.

$$P(\text{king or club}) = P(\text{king}) + P(\text{club}) - P(\text{king of clubs})$$
$$= \tfrac{4}{52} + \tfrac{13}{52} - \tfrac{1}{52} = \tfrac{16}{52} = \tfrac{4}{13}$$

When events are not mutually exclusive, addition rule 2 can be used to find the probability of the events.

Addition Rule 2

If A and B are *not* mutually exclusive, then

$$P(A \text{ or } B) = P(A) + P(B) - P(A \text{ and } B)$$

Note: This rule can also be used when the events are mutually exclusive, since $P(A \text{ and } B)$ will always equal 0. However, it is important to make a distinction between the two situations.

Example 4–21

In a hospital unit there are 8 nurses and 5 physicians; 7 nurses and 3 physicians are females. If a staff person is randomly selected, find the probability that the subject is a nurse or a male.

Solution

The sample space is shown here.

Staff	Females	Males	Total
Nurses	7	1	8
Physicians	3	2	5
Total	10	3	13

The probability is

$$P(\text{nurse or male}) = P(\text{nurse}) + P(\text{male}) - P(\text{male nurse})$$
$$= \tfrac{8}{13} + \tfrac{3}{13} - \tfrac{1}{13} = \tfrac{10}{13}$$

Example 4–22

On New Year's Eve, the probability of a person driving while intoxicated is 0.32, the probability of a person having a driving accident is 0.09, and the probability of a person having a driving accident while intoxicated is 0.06. What is the probability of a person driving while intoxicated or having a driving accident?

Solution

$$P(\text{intoxicated or accident}) = P(\text{intoxicated}) + P(\text{accident})$$
$$- P(\text{intoxicated and accident})$$
$$= 0.32 + 0.09 - 0.06 = 0.35$$

In summary, then, when the two events are mutually exclusive, use addition rule 1. When the events are not mutually exclusive, use addition rule 2.

The probability rules can be extended to three or more events. For three mutually exclusive events A, B, and C,

$$P(A \text{ or } B \text{ or } C) = P(A) + P(B) + P(C)$$

For three events that are *not* mutually exclusive,

$$P(A \text{ or } B \text{ or } C) = P(A) + P(B) + P(C) - P(A \text{ and } B) - P(A \text{ and } C)$$
$$- P(B \text{ and } C) + P(A \text{ and } B \text{ and } C)$$

See Exercises 23, 24, and 25 in this section.

Figure 4–5(a) shows a Venn diagram that represents two mutually exclusive events A and B. In this case, $P(A \text{ or } B) = P(A) + P(B)$, since these events are mutually exclusive and do not overlap. In other words, the probability of occurrence of event A or event B is the sum of the areas of the two circles.

Figure 4–5(b) represents the probability of two events that are *not* mutually exclusive. In this case, $P(A \text{ or } B) = P(A) + P(B) - P(A \text{ and } B)$. The area in the intersection or overlapping part of both circles corresponds to $P(A \text{ and } B)$; and when the area of circle A is added to the area of circle B, the overlapping part is counted twice. It must therefore be subtracted once to get the correct area or probability.

Figure 4–5

Venn Diagrams for the Addition Rules

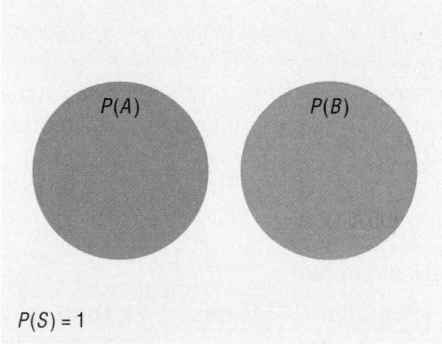

$P(S) = 1$

(a) Mutually exclusive events
$P(A \text{ or } B) = P(A) + P(B)$

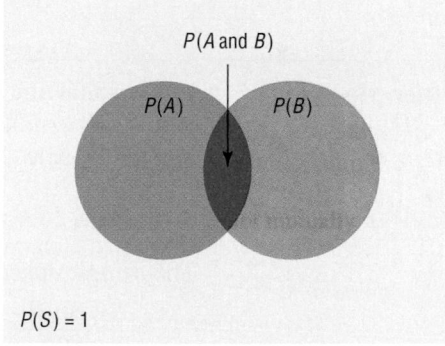

$P(S) = 1$

(b) Non-mutually exclusive events
$P(A \text{ or } B) = P(A) + P(B) - P(A \text{ and } B)$

Note: Venn diagrams were developed by mathematician John Venn (1834–1923) and are used in set theory and symbolic logic. They have been adapted to probability theory also. In set theory, the symbol $\cup$ represents the *union* of two sets, and $A \cup B$ corresponds to A or B. The symbol $\cap$ represents the *intersection* of two sets, and $A \cap B$ corresponds to A and B. Venn diagrams show only a general picture of the probability rules and do not portray all situations, such as $P(A) = 0$, accurately.

Applying the Concepts 4–3

Which Pain Reliever Is Best?

Assume that following an injury you received from playing your favourite sport, you obtain and read information on new pain medications. In that information you read of a study that was conducted to test the side effects of two new pain medications. Use the following table to answer the questions and decide which, if any, of the two new pain medications you will use.

Side effect	Number of side effects in 12-week clinical trial		
	Placebo $n = 192$	**Drug A** $n = 186$	**Drug B** $n = 188$
Upper respiratory congestion	10	32	19
Sinus headache	11	25	32
Stomach ache	2	46	12
Neurological headache	34	55	72
Cough	22	18	31
Lower respiratory congestion	2	5	1

1. How many subjects were in the study?
2. How long was the study?
3. What were the variables under study?
4. What type of variables are they, and what level of measurement are they on?
5. Are the numbers in the table exact figures?
6. What is the probability that a randomly selected person was receiving a placebo?
7. What is the probability that a person was receiving a placebo or drug A? Are these mutually exclusive events? What is the complement to this event?
8. What is the probability that a randomly selected person was receiving a placebo or experienced a neurological headache?
9. What is the probability that a randomly selected person was not receiving a placebo or experienced a sinus headache?

See page 203 for the answers.

Exercises 4–3

1. Define mutually exclusive events, and give an example of two events that are mutually exclusive and two events that are not mutually exclusive.

2. Determine whether these events are mutually exclusive.

    a. Roll a die: Get an even number, and get a number less than 3.

    b. Roll a die: Get a prime number (2, 3, 5), and get an odd number.

    c. Roll a die: Get a number greater than 3, and get a number less than 3.

    d. Select a student in your class: The student has blond hair, and the student has blue eyes.

    e. Select a student in your college or university: The student is in second year, and the student is a business major.

    f. Select any course: It is a calculus course, and it is an English course.

    g. Select a registered voter: The voter is a Conservative, and the voter is a Liberal.

3. An automobile dealer decides to select a month for its annual sale. Find the probability that it will be September or October. Assume all months have an equal probability of being selected. Compute the probability of selecting September or October, using days, and compare the answers.

4. At a community swimming pool there are 2 managers, 8 lifeguards, 3 concession stand clerks, and 2 maintenance people. If a person is selected at random, find the probability that the person is either a lifeguard or a manager.

5. At a convention there are 7 mathematics instructors, 5 computer science instructors, 3 statistics instructors,

and 4 science instructors. If an instructor is selected, find the probability of getting a science instructor or a math instructor.

6. A media rental store rented the following number of movie titles in each of these categories: 170 horror, 230 drama, 120 mystery, 310 romance, and 150 comedy. If a person selects a movie to rent, find the probability that it is a romance or a comedy. Is this event likely or unlikely to occur? Explain your answer.

7. A recent study of 200 nurses found that of 125 female nurses, 56 had bachelor's degrees; and of 75 male nurses, 34 had bachelor's degrees. If a nurse is selected at random, find the probability that the nurse is

  a. A female nurse with a bachelor's degree
  b. A male nurse
  c. A male nurse with a bachelor's degree
  d. Based on your answers to parts *a*, *b*, and *c*, explain which is most likely to occur. Explain why.

8. The probability that a student owns a car is 0.65, and the probability that a student owns a computer is 0.82. If the probability that a student owns both is 0.55, what is the probability that a given student owns neither a car nor a computer?

9. At a particular school with 200 male students, 58 play football, 40 play basketball, and 8 play both. What is the probability that a randomly selected male student plays neither sport?

10. A single card is drawn from a deck. Find the probability of selecting the following.

  a. A 4 or a diamond
  b. A club or a diamond
  c. A jack or a black card

11. In a statistics class there are 18 juniors and 10 seniors; 6 of the seniors are females, and 12 of the juniors are males. If a student is selected at random, find the probability of selecting the following.

  a. A junior or a female
  b. A senior or a female
  c. A junior or a senior

12. At a used-book sale, 100 books are adult books and 160 are children's books. Of the adult books, 70 are nonfiction while 60 of the children's books are nonfiction. If a book is selected at random, find the probability that it is

  a. Fiction
  b. Not a children's nonfiction book
  c. An adult book or a children's nonfiction book

13. The Bargain Auto Mall has these cars in stock.

	SUV	Compact	Mid-sized
Foreign	20	50	20
Domestic	65	100	45

If a car is selected at random, find the probability that it is

  a. Domestic
  b. Foreign and mid-sized
  c. Domestic or an SUV

14. The number of North American endangered species for several groups are listed here.

	Mammals	Birds	Reptiles	Amphibians
Canada	18	21	3	1
United States	41	79	27	53

If one endangered species is selected at random, find the probability that it is

  a. Found in Canada and is a bird
  b. Is a reptile or found in the United States
  c. Warm-blooded

Source: IUCN—The World Conservation Union.

15. A grocery store employs cashiers, stock clerks, and deli personnel. The distribution of employees according to marital status is shown here.

Marital status	Cashiers	Stock clerks	Deli personnel
Married	8	12	3
Not married	5	15	2

If an employee is selected at random, find these probabilities.

  a. The employee is a stock clerk or married.
  b. The employee is not married.
  c. The employee is a cashier or is not married.

16. In a certain geographic region, newspapers are classified as being published daily morning, daily evening, and weekly. Some have a comics section and others do not. The distribution is shown here.

Have comics section	Morning	Evening	Weekly
Yes	2	3	1
No	3	4	2

If a newspaper is selected at random, find these probabilities.

  a. The newspaper is a weekly publication.
  b. The newspaper is a daily morning publication or has comics.
  c. The newspaper is published weekly or does not have comics.

17. Three cable channels (6, 8, and 10) have quiz shows, comedies, and dramas. The number of each is shown here.

Type of show	Channel 6	Channel 8	Channel 10
Quiz show	5	2	1
Comedy	3	2	8
Drama	4	4	2

If a show is selected at random, find these probabilities.

a. The show is a quiz show, or it is shown on channel 8.

b. The show is a drama or a comedy.

c. The show is shown on channel 10, or it is a drama.

18. A local postal carrier distributes first-class letters, advertisements, and magazines. For a certain day, she distributed the following numbers of each type of item.

Delivered to	First-class letters	Ads	Magazines
Home	325	406	203
Business	732	1021	97

If an item of mail is selected at random, find these probabilities.

a. The item went to a home.

b. The item was an ad, or it went to a business.

c. The item was a first-class letter, or it went to a home.

19. The frequency distribution shown here illustrates the number of medical tests conducted on 30 randomly selected emergency patients.

Number of tests performed	Number of patients
0	12
1	8
2	2
3	3
4 or more	5

If a patient is selected at random, find these probabilities.

a. The patient has had exactly 2 tests done.

b. The patient has had at least 2 tests done.

c. The patient has had at most 3 tests done.

d. The patient has had 3 or fewer tests done.

e. The patient has had 1 or 2 tests done.

20. This distribution represents the length of time a patient spends in a hospital.

Days	Frequency
0–3	2
4–7	15
8–11	8
12–15	6
16+	9

If a patient is randomly selected, find these probabilities.

a. The patient spends 3 days or fewer in the hospital.

b. The patient spends fewer than 8 days in the hospital.

c. The patient spends 16 or more days in the hospital.

d. The patient spends a maximum of 11 days in the hospital.

21. A sales representative who visits customers at home finds she sells 0, 1, 2, 3, or 4 items according to the following frequency distribution.

Items sold	Frequency
0	8
1	10
2	3
3	2
4	1

Find the probability that she sells the following.

a. Exactly 1 item

b. More than 2 items

c. At least 1 item

d. At most 3 items

22. A recent study of 300 patients found that of 100 alcoholic patients, 87 had elevated cholesterol levels, and of 200 nonalcoholic patients, 43 had elevated cholesterol levels. If a patient is selected at random, find the probability that the patient is the following.

a. An alcoholic with elevated cholesterol level

b. A nonalcoholic

c. A nonalcoholic with nonelevated cholesterol level

23. If one card is drawn from an ordinary deck of cards, find the probability of getting the following.

a. A king or a queen or a jack

b. A club or a heart or a spade

c. A king or a queen or a diamond

d. An ace or a diamond or a heart

e. A 9 or a 10 or a spade or a club

24. Two dice are rolled. Find the probability of getting

a. A sum of 5, 6, or 7

b. Doubles or a sum of 6 or 8

c. A sum greater than 8 or less than 3

d. Based on the answers to parts a, b, and c, which is least likely to occur? Explain why.

25. An urn contains 6 red balls, 2 green balls, 1 blue ball, and 1 white ball. If a ball is drawn, find the probability of getting a red or a white ball.

26. Three dice are rolled. Find the probability of getting

a. Triples

b. A sum of 5

Extending the Concepts

27. The probability that a customer selects a pizza with mushrooms or pepperoni is 0.43, and the probability that the customer selects only mushrooms is 0.32. If the probability that he or she selects only pepperoni is 0.17, find the probability of the customer selecting both items.

28. In building new homes, a contractor finds that the probability of a home buyer selecting a two-car garage is 0.70 and of selecting a one-car garage is 0.20. Find the probability that the buyer will select no garage. The builder does not build houses with three-car or more garages.

29. In Exercise 28, find the probability that the buyer will not want a two-car garage.

30. Suppose that $P(A) = 0.42$, $P(B) = 0.38$, and $P(A \cup B) = 0.70$. Are A and B mutually exclusive? Explain.

LAFF-A-DAY

ROSS INSURANCE

"I know you haven't had an accident in thirteen years. We're raising your rates because you're about due one."

Source: Reprinted with special permission of King Features Syndicate.

4–4 The Multiplication Rules and Conditional Probability

Section 4–3 showed that the addition rules are used to compute probabilities for mutually exclusive and non-mutually exclusive events. This section introduces the multiplication rules.

Objective ③

Find the probability of compound events, using the multiplication rules.

The Multiplication Rules

The *multiplication rules* can be used to find the probability of two or more events that occur in sequence. For example, if a coin is tossed and then a die is rolled, one can find the probability of getting a head on the coin *and* a 4 on the die. These two events are said to be *independent* since the outcome of the first event (tossing a coin) does not affect the probability outcome of the second event (rolling a die).

Two events A and B are **independent events** if the fact that A occurs does not affect the probability of B occurring.

Here are other examples of independent events:

Rolling a die and getting a 6, and then rolling a second die and getting a 3.

Drawing a card from a deck and getting a queen, replacing it, and drawing a second card and getting a queen.

To find the probability of two independent events that occur in sequence, one must find the probability of each event occurring separately and then multiply the answers. For example, if a coin is tossed twice, the probability of getting two heads is $\frac{1}{2} \cdot \frac{1}{2} = \frac{1}{4}$. This result can be verified by looking at the sample space HH, HT, TH, TT. Then $P(\text{HH}) = \frac{1}{4}$.

Multiplication Rule 1

When two events are independent, the probability of both occurring is

$$P(A \text{ and } B) = P(A) \cdot P(B)$$

Example 4–23

A coin is flipped and a die is rolled. Find the probability of getting a head on the coin and a 4 on the die.

Solution

$$P(\text{head and } 4) = P(\text{head}) \cdot P(4) = \frac{1}{2} \cdot \frac{1}{6} = \frac{1}{12}$$

Note that the sample space for the coin is H, T; and for the die it is 1, 2, 3, 4, 5, 6.

The problem in Example 4–23 can also be solved by using the sample space

H1   H2   H3   H4   H5   H6   T1   T2   T3   T4   T5   T6

The solution is $\frac{1}{12}$, since there is only one way to get the head-4 outcome.

Example 4–24

A card is drawn from a deck and replaced; then a second card is drawn. Find the probability of getting a queen and then an ace.

Solution

The probability of getting a queen is $\frac{4}{52}$, and since the card is replaced, the probability of getting an ace is $\frac{4}{52}$ Hence, the probability of getting a queen and an ace is

$$P(\text{queen and ace}) = P(\text{queen}) \cdot P(\text{ace}) = \frac{4}{52} \cdot \frac{4}{52} = \frac{16}{2704} = \frac{1}{169}$$

Example 4–25

An urn contains 3 red balls, 2 green balls, and 5 white balls. A ball is selected and its colour noted. Then it is replaced. A second ball is selected and its colour noted. Find the probability of each of these.

    a. Selecting 2 green balls

    b. Selecting 1 green ball and then 1 white ball

    c. Selecting 1 red ball and then 1 green ball

Solution

    a. $P(\text{green and green}) = P(\text{green}) \cdot P(\text{green}) = \dfrac{2}{10} \cdot \dfrac{2}{10} = \dfrac{4}{100} = \dfrac{1}{25}$

    b. $P(\text{green and white}) = P(\text{green}) \cdot P(\text{white}) = \dfrac{2}{10} \cdot \dfrac{5}{10} = \dfrac{10}{100} = \dfrac{1}{10}$

    c. $P(\text{red and green}) = P(\text{red}) \cdot P(\text{green}) = \dfrac{3}{10} \cdot \dfrac{2}{10} = \dfrac{6}{100} = \dfrac{3}{50}$

Multiplication rule 1 can be extended to three or more independent events by using the formula

$$P(A \text{ and } B \text{ and } C \text{ and } \cdots \text{ and } K) = P(A) \cdot P(B) \cdot P(C) \cdots P(K)$$

When a small sample is selected from a large population and the subjects are not replaced, the probability of the event occurring changes so slightly that for the most part, it is considered to remain the same. Examples 4–26 and 4–27 illustrate this concept.

Example 4–26

A Statistics Canada health report found that adult Canadians 18 or older experienced five or more sources of stress with time pressure particularly common. The report indicated that 44% of Canadians reported they were trying to do too many things at once. If three adult Canadians are selected, find the probability that all three will suffer stress due to time pressure.

Source: Adapted from Statistics Canada, Excerpt of Health Reports: stress and chronic conditions, excess weight, and arthritis, www.statcan.ca/Daily/English/040121/d040121b.htm. February 28, 2007.

Solution

Let S denote stress. Then

$$P(S \text{ and } S \text{ and } S) = P(S) \cdot P(S) \cdot P(S)$$
$$= (0.44)(0.44)(0.44) \approx 0.085$$

Example 4–27

Approximately 9% of men have a type of colour blindness that prevents them from distinguishing between red and green. If 3 men are selected at random, find the probability that all of them will have this type of red-green colour blindness.

Source: *USA TODAY.*

Solution

Let C denote red-green colour blindness. Then

$$P(C \text{ and } C \text{ and } C) = P(C) \cdot P(C) \cdot P(C)$$
$$= (0.09)(0.09)(0.09)$$
$$= 0.000729$$

Hence, the rounded probability is 0.0007.

In Examples 4–23 through 4–27, the events were independent of one another, since the occurrence of the first event in no way affected the outcome of the second event. On the other hand, when the occurrence of the first event changes the probability of the occurrence of the second event, the two events are said to be *dependent*. For example, suppose a card is drawn from a deck and *not* replaced, and then a second card is drawn. What is the probability of selecting an ace on the first card and a king on the second card?

Before an answer to the question can be given, one must realize that the events are dependent. The probability of selecting an ace on the first draw is $\frac{4}{52}$. If that card is *not* replaced, the probability of selecting a king on the second card after selecting an ace on the first draw is $\frac{4}{51}$, since there are 4 kings and 51 cards remaining. The outcome of the first draw has affected the outcome of the second draw.

Dependent events are formally defined now.

> When the outcome or occurrence of the first event affects the outcome or occurrence of the second event in such a way that the probability is changed, the events are said to be **dependent events.**

Here are some examples of dependent events:

Drawing a card from a deck, not replacing it, and then drawing a second card.

Selecting a ball from an urn, not replacing it, and then selecting a second ball.

Being a lifeguard and getting a suntan.

Having high grades and getting a scholarship.

Parking in a no-parking zone and getting a parking ticket.

To find probabilities when events are dependent, use the multiplication rule with a modification in notation. For the problem just discussed, the probability of getting an ace on the first draw is $\frac{4}{52}$, and the probability of getting a king on the second draw is $\frac{4}{51}$. By the multiplication rule, the probability of both events occurring is

$$\frac{4}{52} \cdot \frac{4}{51} = \frac{16}{2652} = \frac{4}{663}$$

The event of getting a king on the second draw *given* that an ace was drawn the first time is called a *conditional probability*.

The **conditional probability** of an event B in relationship to an event A is the probability that event B occurs after event A has already occurred. The notation for conditional probability is $P(B|A)$. This notation does not mean that B is divided by A; rather, it means the probability that event B occurs given that event A has already occurred. In the card example, $P(B|A)$ is the probability that the second card is a king given that the first card is an ace, and it is equal to $\frac{4}{51}$ since the first card was *not* replaced.

Multiplication Rule 2

When two events are dependent, the probability of both occurring is

$$P(A \text{ and } B) = P(A) \cdot P(B|A)$$

Example 4–28	A person owns a collection of 30 CDs, of which 5 are country music. If 2 CDs are selected at random, find the probability that both are country music.

Solution

Since the events are dependent,

$$P(C_1 \text{ and } C_2) = P(C_1) \cdot P(C_2|C_1) = \frac{5}{30} \cdot \frac{4}{29} = \frac{20}{870} = \frac{2}{87}$$

Example 4–29	The World Wide Insurance Company found that 53% of the residents of a city had homeowner's insurance (H) with the company. Of these clients, 27% also had automobile insurance (A) with the company. If a resident is selected at random, find the probability that the resident has both homeowner's and automobile insurance with the World Wide Insurance Company.

Solution

$$P(\text{H and A}) = P(\text{H}) \cdot P(\text{A}|\text{H}) = (0.53)(0.27) = 0.1431$$

This multiplication rule can be extended to three or more events, as shown in Example 4–30.

Example 4–30	Three cards are drawn from an ordinary deck and not replaced. Find the probability of these.

    a. Getting 3 jacks

    b. Getting an ace, a king, and a queen in order

    c. Getting a club, a spade, and a heart in order

    d. Getting 3 clubs

Solution

$a.$ $P(3 \text{ jacks}) = \dfrac{4}{52} \cdot \dfrac{3}{51} \cdot \dfrac{2}{50} = \dfrac{24}{132{,}600} = \dfrac{1}{5525}$

$b.$ $P(\text{ace and king and queen}) = \dfrac{4}{52} \cdot \dfrac{4}{51} \cdot \dfrac{4}{50} = \dfrac{64}{132{,}600} = \dfrac{8}{16{,}575}$

$c.$ $P(\text{club and spade and heart}) = \dfrac{13}{52} \cdot \dfrac{13}{51} \cdot \dfrac{13}{50} = \dfrac{2197}{132{,}600} = \dfrac{169}{10{,}200}$

$d.$ $P(3 \text{ clubs}) = \dfrac{13}{52} \cdot \dfrac{12}{51} \cdot \dfrac{11}{50} = \dfrac{1716}{132{,}600} = \dfrac{11}{850}$

Tree diagrams can be used as an aid to finding the solution to probability problems when the events are sequential. Example 4–31 illustrates the use of tree diagrams.

Example 4–31	Box 1 contains 2 red balls and 1 blue ball. Box 2 contains 3 blue balls and 1 red ball. A coin is tossed. If it falls heads up, box 1 is selected and a ball is drawn. If it falls tails up, box 2 is selected and a ball is drawn. Find the probability of selecting a red ball.

Solution

With the use of a tree diagram, the sample space can be determined as shown in Figure 4–6. First, assign probabilities to each branch. Next, using the multiplication rule, multiply the probabilities for each branch.

    Finally, use the addition rule, since a red ball can be obtained from box 1 or box 2.

$$P(\text{red}) = \tfrac{2}{6} + \tfrac{1}{8} = \tfrac{8}{24} + \tfrac{3}{24} = \tfrac{11}{24}$$

(*Note:* The sum of all final probabilities will always be equal to 1.)

Tree Diagram for
Example 4–31

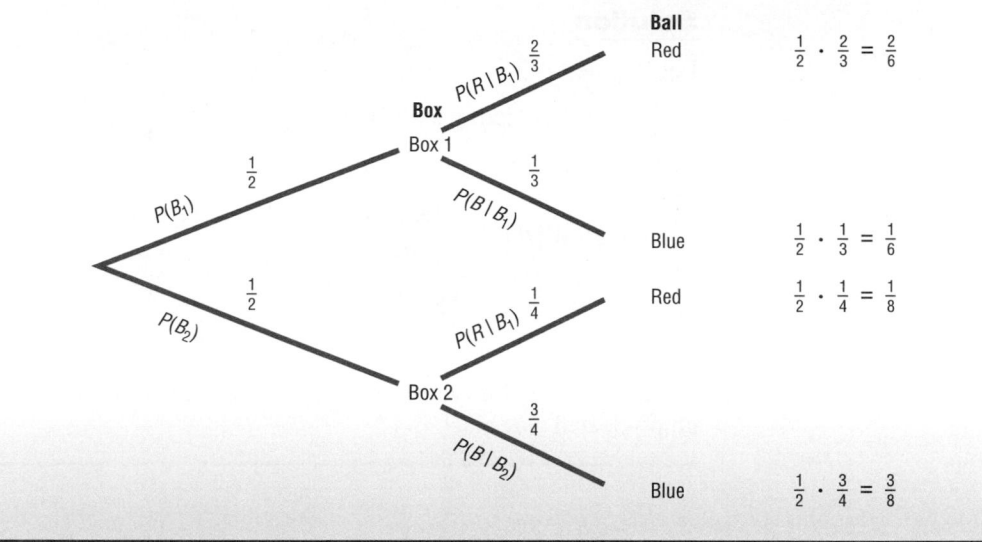

Tree diagrams can be used when the events are independent or dependent, and they can also be used for sequences of three or more events.

Conditional Probability

Objective ④

Find the conditional
probability of an event.

The conditional probability of an event B in relationship to an event A was defined as the probability that event B occurs after event A has already occurred.

The conditional probability of an event can be found by dividing both sides of the equation for multiplication rule 2 by $P(A)$, as shown:

$$P(A \text{ and } B) = P(A) \cdot P(B|A)$$

$$\frac{P(A \text{ and } B)}{P(A)} = \frac{\cancel{P(A)} \cdot P(B|A)}{\cancel{P(A)}}$$

$$\frac{P(A \text{ and } B)}{P(A)} = P(B|A)$$

Formula for Conditional Probability

The probability that the second event B occurs given that the first event A has occurred can be found by dividing the probability that both events occurred by the probability that the first event has occurred. The $P(A)$ cannot equal 0. The formula is

$$P(B|A) = \frac{P(A \text{ and } B)}{P(A)}$$

Examples 4–32, 4–33, and 4–34 illustrate the use of this rule.

Example 4–32

A box contains black chips and white chips. A person selects two chips without replacement. If the probability of selecting a black chip *and* a white chip is $\frac{15}{56}$, and the probability of selecting a black chip on the first draw is $\frac{3}{8}$, find the probability of selecting the white chip on the second draw, *given* that the first chip selected was a black chip.

Solution

Let

$$B = \text{selecting a black chip} \qquad W = \text{selecting a white chip}$$

Then

$$P(W|B) = \frac{P(B \text{ and } W)}{P(B)} = \frac{\frac{15}{56}}{\frac{3}{8}}$$

$$= \frac{15}{56} \div \frac{3}{8} = \frac{15}{56} \cdot \frac{8}{3} = \frac{\overset{5}{\cancel{15}}}{\underset{7}{\cancel{56}}} \cdot \frac{\overset{1}{\cancel{8}}}{\underset{1}{\cancel{3}}} = \frac{5}{7}$$

Hence, the probability of selecting a white chip on the second draw given that the first chip selected was black is $\frac{5}{7}$.

Example 4–33

The probability that Sam parks in a no-parking zone *and* gets a parking ticket is 0.06, and the probability that Sam cannot find a legal parking space and has to park in the no-parking zone is 0.20. On Tuesday, Sam arrives at school and has to park in a no-parking zone. Find the probability that he will get a parking ticket.

Solution

Let

$$N = \text{parking in a no-parking zone} \qquad T = \text{getting a ticket}$$

Then

$$P(T|N) = \frac{P(N \text{ and } T)}{P(N)} = \frac{0.06}{0.20} = 0.30$$

Hence, Sam has a 0.30 probability of getting a parking ticket, given that he parked in a no-parking zone.

The conditional probability of events occurring can also be computed when the data are given in table form, as shown in Example 4–34.

Example 4–34

A recent survey asked 100 people if they thought women in the armed forces should be permitted to participate in combat. The results of the survey are shown.

Gender	Yes	No	Total
Male	32	18	50
Female	8	42	50
Total	40	60	100

Find these probabilities.

a. The respondent answered yes, given that the respondent was a female.

b. The respondent was a male, given that the respondent answered no.

Solution

Let

M = respondent was a male Y = respondent answered yes
F = respondent was a female N = respondent answered no

a. The problem is to find $P(Y|F)$. The rule states

$$P(Y|F) = \frac{P(F \text{ and } Y)}{P(F)}$$

The probability $P(F \text{ and } Y)$ is the number of females who responded yes, divided by the total number of respondents:

$$P(F \text{ and } Y) = \frac{8}{100}$$

The probability $P(F)$ is the probability of selecting a female:

$$P(F) = \frac{50}{100}$$

Then

$$P(Y|F) = \frac{P(F \text{ and } Y)}{P(F)} = \frac{8/100}{50/100}$$

$$= \frac{8}{100} \div \frac{50}{100} = \frac{\overset{4}{\cancel{8}}}{\cancel{100}} \cdot \frac{\overset{1}{\cancel{100}}}{\underset{25}{\cancel{50}}} = \frac{4}{25}$$

b. The problem is to find $P(M|N)$.

$$P(M|N) = \frac{P(N \text{ and } M)}{P(N)} = \frac{18/100}{60/100}$$

$$= \frac{18}{100} \div \frac{60}{100} = \frac{\overset{3}{\cancel{18}}}{\underset{1}{\cancel{100}}} \cdot \frac{\overset{1}{\cancel{100}}}{\underset{10}{\cancel{60}}} = \frac{3}{10}$$

The Venn diagram for conditional probability is shown in Figure 4–7. In this case,

$$P(B|A) = \frac{P(A \text{ and } B)}{P(A)}$$

Figure 4–7

**Venn Diagram for
Conditional Probability**

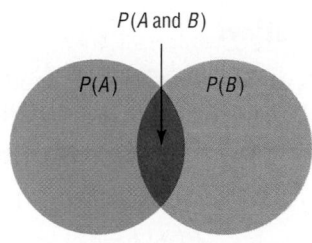

$P(A \text{ and } B)$

$P(A)$ $P(B)$

$P(S)$

$$P(B|A) = \frac{P(A \text{ and } B)}{P(A)}$$

which is represented by the area in the intersection or overlapping part of the circles A and B, divided by the area of circle A. The reasoning here is that if one assumes A has occurred, then A becomes the sample space for the next calculation and is the denominator of the probability fraction $\dfrac{P(A \text{ and } B)}{P(A)}$. The numerator $P(A \text{ and } B)$ represents the probability of the part of B that is contained in A. Hence, $P(A \text{ and } B)$ becomes the numerator of the probability fraction $\dfrac{P(A \text{ and } B)}{P(A)}$. Imposing a condition reduces the sample space.

Probabilities for "At Least"

The multiplication rules can be used with the complementary event rule (Section 4–2) to simplify solving probability problems involving "at least." Examples 4–35, 4–36, and 4–37 illustrate how this is done.

Example 4–35

A game is played by drawing four cards from an ordinary deck and replacing each card after it is drawn. Find the probability of winning if at least one ace is drawn.

Solution

It is much easier to find the probability that no aces are drawn (i.e., losing) and then subtract that value from 1 than to find the solution directly, because that would involve finding the probability of getting one ace, two aces, three aces, and four aces and then adding the results.

Let E = at least one ace is drawn and $\overline{E}$ = no aces drawn. Then

$$P(\overline{E}) = \frac{48}{52} \cdot \frac{48}{52} \cdot \frac{48}{52} \cdot \frac{48}{52}$$

$$= \frac{12}{13} \cdot \frac{12}{13} \cdot \frac{12}{13} \cdot \frac{12}{13} = \frac{20{,}736}{28{,}561}$$

Hence,

$$P(E) = 1 - P(\overline{E})$$

$$P(\text{winning}) = 1 - P(\text{losing}) = 1 - \frac{20{,}736}{28{,}561} = \frac{7{,}825}{28{,}561} \approx 0.27$$

or a hand with at least one ace will win about 27% of the time.

Example 4–36

A coin is tossed 5 times. Find the probability of getting at least one tail.

Solution

It is easier to find the probability of the complement of the event, which is "all heads," and then subtract the probability from 1 to get the probability of at least one tail.

$$P(E) = 1 - P(\overline{E})$$

$$P(\text{at least 1 tail}) = 1 - P(\text{all heads})$$

$$P(\text{all heads}) = (\tfrac{1}{2})^5 = \tfrac{1}{32}$$

Hence,

$$P(\text{at least 1 tail}) = 1 - \tfrac{1}{32} = \tfrac{31}{32}$$

Example 4–37

The Canadian Association of Food Banks publishes a national report on hunger in Canada. A 2004 survey indicated that 38% of Canadian food bank recipients are from Ontario. If 4 Canadian food bank recipients are randomly selected, find the probability that at least one is from Ontario.

Source: The Canadian Association of Food Banks.

Solution

Let E = at least one Ontario food bank recipient and $\overline{E}$ = no Ontario food bank recipients.

Then

$$P(E) = 0.38 \quad \text{and} \quad P(\overline{E}) = 1 - 0.38 = 0.62$$

P(no Ontario food bank recipients) $= (0.62)(0.62)(0.62)(0.62) \approx 0.148$; hence,

P(at least one Ontario food bank recipient) $= 1 - 0.148 = 0.852$.

Similar methods can be used for problems involving "at most."

Applying the Concepts 4–4

Guilty or Innocent?

In July 1964, an elderly woman was mugged in Costa Mesa, California. In the vicinity of the crime a tall, bearded man sat waiting in a yellow car. Shortly after the crime was committed, a young, tall woman, wearing her blond hair in a ponytail, was seen running from the scene of the crime and getting into the car, which sped off. The police broadcast a description of the suspected muggers. Soon afterward, a couple fitting the description was arrested. Although the evidence in the case was largely circumstantial, the two people arrested were nonetheless convicted of the crime. The prosecutor based his entire case on basic probability theory, showing the unlikelihood of another couple being in that area while having all the same characteristics that the elderly woman described. The following probabilities were used.

Characteristic	Assumed probability
Drives yellow car	1 out of 12
Man over 6 feet tall	1 out of 10
Man wearing tennis shoes	1 out of 4
Man with beard	1 out of 11
Woman with blond hair	1 out of 3
Woman with hair in a ponytail	1 out of 13
Woman over 6 feet tall	1 out of 100

1. Compute the probability of another couple being in that area with the same characteristics.

2. Would you use the addition or multiplication rule? Why?

3. Are the characteristics independent or dependent?

4. How are the computations affected by the assumption of independence or dependence?

5. Should any court case be based solely on probabilities?

6. Would you convict the couple who was arrested even if there were no eyewitnesses?

7. Comment on why in today's justice system no person can be convicted solely on the results of probabilities.

8. In actuality, aren't most court cases based on uncalculated probabilities?

See page 203 for the answers.

Exercises 4–4

1. State which events are independent and which are dependent.

   a. Tossing a coin and drawing a card from a deck

   b. Drawing a ball from an urn, not replacing it, and then drawing a second ball

   c. Getting a raise in salary and purchasing a new car

   d. Driving on ice and having an accident

   e. Having a large shoe size and having a high IQ

   f. A father being left-handed and a daughter being left-handed

   g. Smoking excessively and having lung cancer

   h. Eating an excessive amount of ice cream and smoking an excessive amount of cigarettes

2. If 37% of high school students said that they exercise regularly, find the probability that 5 randomly selected high school students will say that they exercise regularly. Would you consider this event likely or unlikely to occur? Explain your answer.

3. If 84% of all people who do aerobics are women, find the probability that if 2 people who do aerobics are randomly selected, both are women. Would you consider this event likely or unlikely to occur? Explain your answer.

4. Transport Canada reports that 87.1% of Canadian drivers and passengers buckle up for safety. If 4 people are selected at random, find the probability that they all used a seat belt while driving.

   Source: Transport Canada.

5. Statistics Canada reports that 24.1% of clerical and administrative roles are performed by men. If 3 women are randomly selected, find the probability that they all perform clerical and administrative duties. Would you consider this event likely or unlikely to occur? Explain your answer.

   Source: Statistics Canada.

6. If 18% of Canada's federal prison inmates are Aboriginal, find the probability that 2 randomly selected federal prison inmates are Aboriginal.

   Source: Statistics Canada.

7. At a local university 54.3% of incoming first-year students have computers. If 3 students are selected at random, find the following probabilities.

   a. None have computers.

   b. At least one has a computer.

   c. All have computers.

8. If 2 cards are selected from a standard deck of 52 cards without replacement, find these probabilities.

   a. Both are spades.

   b. Both are the same suit.

   c. Both are kings.

9. Of 714 players in the National Hockey League (NHL), 383 or 53.6% are Canadian citizens. If 3 NHL players are randomly selected, what is the probability that all are Canadian citizens?

   Source: NHL.com.

10. A *Reader's Digest* survey reported that one-half of Canadian teens favoured the death penalty for persons convicted of murder. If 3 Canadian teens are randomly selected, find the probability that all 3 teens favour the death penalty for convicted murderers.

    Source: www.readersdigest.ca.

11. Of fans who own sports league-licensed apparel, 31% have National Football League (NFL) apparel. If 3 of these fans are selected at random, what is the probability that all have NFL apparel?

    Source: ESPN Chilton Sports Poll.

12. A flashlight has 6 batteries, 2 of which are defective. If 2 are selected at random without replacement, find the probability that both are defective.

13. According to the Campaign 2000—End Child Poverty in Canada website, 16% of Ontario children live in poverty. If 4 Ontario children are randomly selected, what is the probability that none of the children live in poverty?

    Source: www.campaign2000.ca.

14. Alberta ranks first among Canada's provinces with 39% of Alberta households owning firearms. If 3 Alberta households are randomly selected, what is the probability that none of the households own a firearm?

    Source: Alberta Centre for Injury Control & Research.

15. In a department store there are 120 customers, 90 of whom will buy at least one item. If 5 customers are selected at random, one by one, find the probability that all will buy at least one item.

16. Three cards are drawn from a deck *without* replacement. Find these probabilities.

    a. All are jacks.

    b. All are clubs.

    c. All are red cards.

17. In a scientific study there are 8 guinea pigs, 5 of which are pregnant. If 3 are selected at random without replacement, find the probability that all are pregnant.

18. In Exercise 17, find the probability that none are pregnant.

19. In a civic organization, there are 38 members; 15 are men and 23 are women. If 3 members are selected to plan the Canada Day parade, find the probability that all 3 are women. Would you consider this event likely or unlikely to occur? Explain your answer.

20. In Exercise 19, find the probability that all 3 members are men.

21. A manufacturer makes two models of an item: model I, which accounts for 80% of unit sales, and model II, which accounts for 20% of unit sales. Because of defects, the manufacturer has to replace (or exchange) 10% of its model I and 18% of its model II. If a model is selected at random, find the probability that it will be defective.

22. An automobile manufacturer has three factories, A, B, and C. They produce 50, 30, and 20%, respectively, of a specific model of car. Thirty percent of the cars produced in factory A are white, 40% of those produced in factory B are white, and 25% produced in factory C are white. If an automobile produced by the company is selected at random, find the probability that it is white.

23. An insurance company classifies drivers as low-risk, medium-risk, and high-risk. Of those insured, 60% are low-risk, 30% are medium-risk, and 10% are high-risk. After a study, the company finds that during a one-year period, 1% of the low-risk drivers had an accident, 5% of the medium-risk drivers had an accident, and 9% of the high-risk drivers had an accident. If a driver is selected at random, find the probability that the driver will have had an accident during the year.

24. In a certain geographic location, 25% of the wage earners have a college or university degree and 75% do not. Of those who have a college or university degree, 5% earn more than $100,000 a year. Of those who do not have a college or university degree, 2% earn more than $100,000 a year. If a wage earner is selected at random, find the probability that she or he earns more than $100,000 a year.

25. Urn 1 contains 5 red balls and 3 black balls. Urn 2 contains 3 red balls and 1 black ball. Urn 3 contains 4 red balls and 2 black balls. If an urn is selected at random and a ball is drawn, find the probability it will be red.

26. For a recent year, 0.99 of the incarcerated population is adults and 0.07 is female. If an incarcerated person is selected at random, find the probability that the person is a female given that she is an adult.

Source: U.S. Bureau of Justice.

27. In a certain city, the probability that an automobile will be stolen and found within one week is 0.0009. The probability that an automobile will be stolen is 0.0015. Find the probability that a stolen automobile will be found within one week.

28. A circuit to run a model railroad has 8 switches. Two are defective. If a person selects 2 switches at random and tests them, find the probability that the second one is defective, given that the first one is defective.

29. At the Avonlea Country Club, 73% of the members play bridge and swim, and 82% play bridge. If a member is selected at random, find the probability that the member swims, given that the member plays bridge.

30. At a large university, the probability that a student takes calculus and is on the dean's list is 0.042. The probability that a student is on the dean's list is 0.21. Find the probability that the student is taking calculus, given that he or she is on the dean's list.

31. In Rolling Acres Housing Plan, 42% of the houses have a deck and a garage; 60% have a deck. Find the probability that a home has a garage, given that it has a deck.

32. In a pizza restaurant, 95% of the customers order pizza. If 65% of the customers order pizza and a salad, find the probability that a customer who orders pizza will also order a salad.

33. At an exclusive country club, 68% of the members play bridge and drink champagne, and 83% play bridge. If a member is selected at random, find the probability that the member drinks champagne, given that he or she plays bridge.

34. Eighty students in a school cafeteria were asked if they favoured a ban on smoking in the cafeteria. The results of the survey are shown in the table.

Class	Favour	Oppose	No opinion
First Year	15	27	8
Second Year	23	5	2

If a student is selected at random, find these probabilities.

a. Given that the student is in first year, he or she opposes the ban.

b. Given that the student favours the ban, the student in second year.

35. The following table represents patents granted and/or registered in Canada for a specific year organized by product output (type) and nationality of applicant.

	Patents	Trademarks	Copyrights
Canada	1,461	14,273	6,862
Foreign	12,092	15,507	788
	13,553	29,780	7,650

Select one product output at random.

a. What is the probability that it was granted to a Canadian, given that it was a patent product type?

b. What is the probability that it was a copyright product type, given that it was registered to a foreign applicant?

Source: Canadian Intellectual Property Office.

36. The medal distribution from the 2006 Winter Olympic Games is shown in the table.

	Gold	Silver	Bronze
Germany	11	12	6
United States	9	9	7
Austria	9	7	7
Russia	8	6	8
Canada	7	10	7
Other	40	40	49

Choose one medal winner at random.

a. Find the probability that the winner won the gold medal, given that the winner was from Canada.

b. Find the probability that the winner was from Canada, given that the medal was gold.

c. Are the events "medal winner from Canada" and "gold medal won" independent? Explain.

Source: www.torino2006.org.

37. Statistics Canada reports that 71% of marriages occur on a Saturday. If 5 Canadian marriages were randomly selected, find the probability that

a. None of the marriages occurred on a Saturday.

b. At least one of the marriages occurred on a Saturday.

Source: Statistics Canada.

38. Transport Canada reports that 7.4% of road fatalities involve motorcyclists. If 3 road fatality reports are randomly selected, what is the probability that

a. All involve a motorcyclist?

b. None involve a motorcyclist?

c. At least 1 involves a motorcyclist?

Source: Transport Canada.

39. Seventy-six percent of toddlers get their recommended immunizations. Suppose that 6 toddlers are selected at random. What is the probability that at least one has not received the recommended immunizations?

Source: U.S. Federal Interagency Forum on Child and Family Statistics.

40. A lot of portable radios contains 15 good radios and 3 defective ones. If 2 are selected and tested, find the probability that at least one will be defective.

41. Statistics Canada reports that 17.2% of Canadians have a university degree. Suppose that 5 Canadians are randomly selected. What is the probability that at least one of the selected has a university degree?

Source: Statistics Canada.

42. Of Ph.D. students, 60% have paid assistantships. If 3 students are selected at random, find the probabilities.

a. All have assistantships.

b. None have assistantships.

c. At least one has an assistantship.

Source: U.S. Department of Education/*Chronicle of Higher Education.*

43. If 4 cards are drawn from a deck of 52 and not replaced, find the probability of getting at least one club.

44. At a local clinic there are 8 men, 5 women, and 3 children in the waiting room. If 3 patients are randomly selected, find the probability that there is at least one child among them.

45. It has been found that 6% of all automobiles on the road have defective brakes. If 5 automobiles are stopped and checked by the state police, find the probability that at least one will have defective brakes.

46. A medication is 75% effective against a bacterial infection. Find the probability that if 12 people take the medication, at least one person's infection will not improve.

47. A coin is tossed 5 times; find the probability of getting at least one tail. Would you consider this event likely to happen? Explain your answer.

48. If 3 letters of the alphabet are selected at random, find the probability of getting at least one letter x. Letters can be used more than once. Would you consider this event likely to happen? Explain your answer.

49. A die is rolled 7 times. Find the probability of getting at least one 3. Would you consider this event likely to occur? Explain your answer.

50. At a teachers' conference, there were 4 English teachers, 3 mathematics teachers, and 5 science teachers. If 4 teachers are selected for a committee, find the probability that at least one is a science teacher.

51. If a die is rolled 3 times, find the probability of getting at least one even number.

52. In a large vase, there are 8 roses, 5 daisies, 12 lilies, and 9 orchids. If 4 flowers are selected at random, find the probability that at least one of the flowers is a rose. Would you consider this event likely to occur? Explain your answer.

Extending the Concepts

53. Let *A* and *B* be two mutually exclusive events. Are *A* and *B* independent events? Explain your answer.

54. The Bargain Auto Mall has the following cars in stock.

	SUV	Compact	Mid-sized
Foreign	20	50	20
Domestic	65	100	45

Are the events "compact" and "domestic" independent? Explain.

55. An admissions director knows that the probability a student will enroll after a campus visit is 0.55, or $P(E) = 0.55$. While students are on campus visits, interviews with professors are arranged. The admissions director computes these conditional probabilities for students enrolling after visiting three professors, DW, LP, and MH.

$$P(E|DW) = 0.95 \qquad P(E|LP) = 0.55 \qquad P(E|MH) = 0.15$$

Is there something wrong with the numbers? Explain.

56. Event *A* is the event that a person remembers a certain product commercial. Event *B* is the event that a person buys the product. If $P(B) = 0.35$, comment on each of these conditional probabilities if you were vice president for sales.

a. $P(B|A) = 0.20$
b. $P(B|A) = 0.35$
c. $P(B|A) = 0.55$

4–5 Counting Rules

Many times one wishes to know the number of all possible outcomes for a sequence of events. To determine this number, three rules can be used: the *fundamental counting rule,* the *permutation rule,* and the *combination rule.* These rules are explained here, and they will be used in Section 4–6 to find probabilities of events.

The first rule is called the **fundamental counting rule.**

The Fundamental Counting Rule

Objective ⑤

Find the total number of outcomes in a sequence of events, using the fundamental counting rule.

Fundamental Counting Rule

In a sequence of *n* events in which the first one has k_1 possibilities and the second event has k_2 and the third has k_3, and so forth, the total number of possibilities of the sequence will be

$$k_1 \cdot k_2 \cdot k_3 \cdots k_n$$

Note: In this case *and* means to multiply.

Examples 4–38 through 4–41 illustrate the fundamental counting rule.

Example 4–38

A coin is tossed and a die is rolled. Find the number of outcomes for the sequence of events.

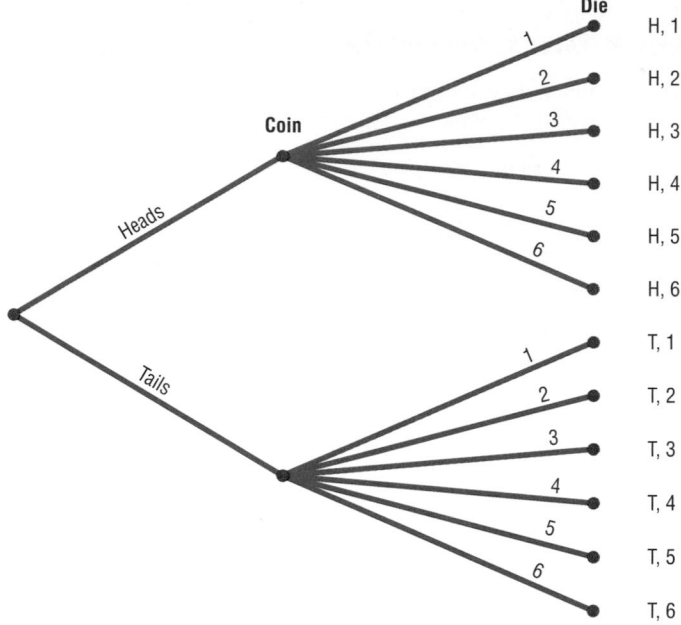

Figure 4–8

Complete Tree Diagram
for Example 4–38

Interesting Fact

Possible games of
chess: 25×10^{115}

Solution

Since the coin can land either heads up or tails up and since the die can land with any one of six numbers showing face up, there are $2 \cdot 6 = 12$ possibilities. A tree diagram can also be drawn for the sequence of events. See Figure 4–8.

Example 4–39

A paint manufacturer wishes to manufacture several different paints. The categories include

Colour	Red, blue, white, black, green, brown, yellow
Type	Latex, oil
Texture	Flat, semigloss, high gloss
Use	Outdoor, indoor

How many different kinds of paint can be made if a person can select one colour, one type, one texture, and one use?

Solution

A person can choose one colour and one type and one texture and one use. Since there are 7 colour choices, 2 type choices, 3 texture choices, and 2 use choices, the total number of possible different paints is

Colour		Type		Texture		Use	
7	·	2	·	3	·	2	= 84

Example 4–40

There are four blood types, A, B, AB, and O, Blood can also be Rh+ and Rh−. Finally, a blood donor can be classified as either male or female. How many different ways can a donor have his or her blood labelled?

Figure 4–9

Complete Tree Diagram for Example 4-40

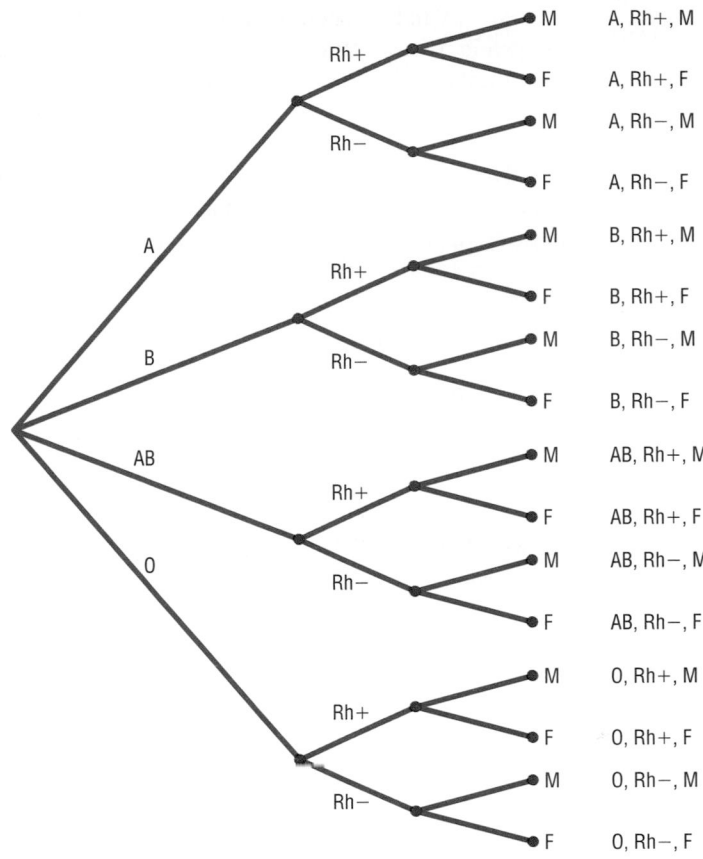

		M	A, Rh+, M
	Rh+	F	A, Rh+, F
	Rh−	M	A, Rh−, M
		F	A, Rh−, F
A		M	B, Rh+, M
	Rh+	F	B, Rh+, F
B	Rh−	M	B, Rh−, M
		F	B, Rh−, F
AB		M	AB, Rh+, M
	Rh+	F	AB, Rh+, F
0	Rh−	M	AB, Rh−, M
		F	AB, Rh−, F
		M	0, Rh+, M
	Rh+	F	0, Rh+, F
	Rh−	M	0, Rh−, M
		F	0, Rh−, F

Solution

Since there are 4 possibilities for blood type, 2 possibilities for Rh factor, and 2 possibilities for the gender of the donor, there are $4 \cdot 2 \cdot 2$, or 16, different classification categories, as shown.

Blood type		**Rh**		**Gender**	
4	$\cdot$	2	$\cdot$	2	= 16

A tree diagram for the events is shown in Figure 4–9.

When determining the number of different possibilities of a sequence of events, one must know whether repetitions are permissible.

Example 4–41

The digits 0, 1, 2, 3, and 4 are to be used in a four-digit ID card. How many different cards are possible if repetitions are permitted?

Solution

Since there are 4 spaces to fill and 5 choices for each space, the solution is

$$5 \cdot 5 \cdot 5 \cdot 5 = 5^4 = 625$$

Now, what if repetitions are not permitted? For Example 4–41, the first digit can be chosen in 5 ways. But the second digit can be chosen in only 4 ways, since there are only four digits left, etc. Thus, the solution is

$$5 \cdot 4 \cdot 3 \cdot 2 = 120$$

The same situation occurs when one is drawing balls from an urn or cards from a deck. If the ball or card is replaced before the next one is selected, then repetitions are permitted, since the same one can be selected again. But if the selected ball or card is not replaced, then repetitions are not permitted, since the same ball or card cannot be selected the second time.

These examples illustrate the fundamental counting rule. In summary: *If repetitions are permitted, then the numbers stay the same going from left to right. If repetitions are not permitted, then the numbers decrease by 1 for each place left to right.*

Two other rules that can be used to determine the total number of possibilities of a sequence of events are the permutation rule and the combination rule.

Factorial Notation

Historical Note

In 1808 Christian Kramp first used the factorial notation.

These rules use *factorial notation*. The factorial notation uses the exclamation point.

$$5! = 5 \cdot 4 \cdot 3 \cdot 2 \cdot 1$$
$$9! = 9 \cdot 8 \cdot 7 \cdot 6 \cdot 5 \cdot 4 \cdot 3 \cdot 2 \cdot 1$$

To use the formulas in the permutation and combination rules, a special definition of $0!$ is needed. $0! = 1$.

Factorial Formulas

For any counting n

$$n! = n(n - 1)(n - 2) \cdots 1$$
$$0! = 1$$

Permutations

A **permutation** is an arrangement of n objects in a specific order.

Examples 4–42 and 4–43 illustrate permutations.

Example 4–42

Suppose a business owner has a choice of five locations in which to establish her business. She decides to rank each location according to certain criteria, such as price of the store and parking facilities. How many different ways can she rank the five locations?

Solution

There are

$$5! = 5 \cdot 4 \cdot 3 \cdot 2 \cdot 1 = 120$$

different possible rankings. The reason is that she has 5 choices for the first location, 4 choices for the second location, 3 choices for the third location, etc.

In Example 4–42 all objects were used up. But what happens when not all objects are used up? The answer to this question is given in Example 4–43.

Example 4–43

Suppose the business owner in Example 4–42 wishes to rank only the top three of the five locations. How many different ways can she rank them?

Solution

Using the fundamental counting rule, she can select any one of the five for first choice, then any one of the remaining four locations for her second choice, and finally, any one of the remaining locations for her third choice, as shown.

First choice		Second choice		Third choice
$\boxed{5}$	$\cdot$	$\boxed{4}$	$\cdot$	$\boxed{3}$ $= 60$

The solutions in Examples 4–42 and 4–43 are permutations.

Objective 6

Find the number of ways that r objects can be selected from n objects, using the permutation rule.

Permutation Rule

The arrangement of n objects in a specific order using r objects at a time is called a *permutation of n objects taking r objects at a time*. It is written as $_nP_r$, and the formula is

$$_nP_r = \frac{n!}{(n - r)!}$$

The notation $_nP_r$ is used for permutations.

$$_6P_4 \text{ means } \frac{6!}{(6 - 4)!} \qquad \text{or} \qquad \frac{6!}{2!} = \frac{6 \cdot 5 \cdot 4 \cdot 3 \cdot \cancel{2} \cdot \cancel{1}}{\cancel{2} \cdot \cancel{1}} = 360$$

Although Examples 4–42 and 4–43 were solved by the multiplication rule, they can now be solved by the permutation rule.

In Example 4–42, five locations were taken and then arranged in order; hence,

$$_5P_5 = \frac{5!}{(5 - 5)!} = \frac{5!}{0!} = \frac{5 \cdot 4 \cdot 3 \cdot 2 \cdot 1}{1} = 120$$

(Recall that $0! = 1$.)

In Example 4–43, three locations were selected from five locations, so $n = 5$ and $r = 3$; hence

$$_5P_3 = \frac{5!}{(5 - 3)!} = \frac{5!}{2!} = \frac{5 \cdot 4 \cdot 3 \cdot \cancel{2} \cdot \cancel{1}}{\cancel{2} \cdot \cancel{1}} = 60$$

Examples 4–44 and 4–45 illustrate the permutation rule.

Example 4–44

A television news director wishes to use 3 news stories on an evening show. One story will be the lead story, one will be the second story, and the last will be a closing story. If the director has a total of 8 stories to choose from, how many possible ways can the program be set up?

Solution

Since order is important, the solution is

$$_8P_3 = \frac{8!}{(8-3)!} = \frac{8!}{5!} = 336$$

Hence, there would be 336 ways to set up the program.

Example 4–45

How many different ways can a chairperson and an assistant chairperson be selected for a research project if there are 7 scientists available?

Solution

$$_7P_2 = \frac{7!}{(7-2)!} = \frac{7!}{5!} = 42$$

Combinations

Suppose a dress designer wishes to select two colours of material to design a new dress, and she has on hand four colours. How many different possibilities can there be in this situation?

Objective ⑦

Find the number of ways that *r* objects can be selected from *n* objects without regard to order, using the combination rule.

This type of problem differs from previous ones in that the order of selection is not important. That is, if the designer selects yellow and red, this selection is the same as the selection red and yellow. This type of selection is called a *combination*. The difference between a permutation and a combination is that in a combination, the order or arrangement of the objects is not important; by contrast, order *is* important in a permutation. Example 4–46 illustrates this difference.

A selection of distinct objects without regard to order is called a **combination.**

Example 4–46

Given the letters A, B, C, and D, list the permutations and combinations for selecting two letters.

Solution

The permutations are

AB	BA	CA	DA
AC	BC	CB	DB
AD	BD	CD	DC

In permutations, AB is different from BA. But in combinations, AB is the same as BA since the order of the objects does not matter in combinations. Therefore, if duplicates are removed from a list of permutations, what is left is a list of combinations, as shown.

AB	B̶A̶	C̶A̶	D̶A̶
AC	BC	C̶B̶	D̶B̶
AD	BD	CD	D̶C̶

Hence the combinations of A, B, C, and D are AB, AC, AD, BC, BD, and CD. (Alternatively, BA could be listed and AB crossed out, etc.) The combinations have been listed alphabetically for convenience, but this is not a requirement.

Combinations are used when the order or arrangement is not important, as in the selecting process. Suppose a committee of 5 students is to be selected from 25 students. The 5 selected students represent a combination, since it does not matter who is selected first, second, etc.

Combination Rule

The number of combinations of r objects selected from n objects is denoted by $_nC_r$ and is given by the formula

$$_nC_r = \frac{n!}{(n-r)!r!}$$

Example 4–47

How many combinations of 4 objects are there, taken 2 at a time?

Solution

Since this is a combination problem, the answer is

$$_4C_2 = \frac{4!}{(4-2)!2!} = \frac{4!}{2!2!} = \frac{\overset{2}{\cancel{4}} \cdot 3 \cdot \cancel{2!}}{\cancel{2} \cdot 1 \cdot \cancel{2!}} = 6$$

This is the same result shown in Example 4–46.

Notice that the expression for $_nC_r$ is

$$\frac{n!}{(n-r)!r!}$$

which is the formula for permutations with $r!$ in the denominator. In other words,

$$_nC_r = \frac{_nP_r}{r!}$$

This $r!$ divides out the duplicates from the number of permutations, as shown in Example 4–46. For each 2 letters, there are 2 permutations but only one combination. Hence, dividing the number of permutations by $r!$ eliminates the duplicates. This result can be verified for other values of n and r. Note: $_nC_n = 1$.

Example 4–48

A bicycle shop owner has 12 mountain bicycles in the showroom. The owner wishes to select 5 of them to display at a bicycle show. How many different ways can a group of 5 be selected?

Solution

$$_{12}C_5 = \frac{12!}{(12-5)!5!} = \frac{12!}{7!5!} = \frac{12 \cdot 11 \cdot \overset{2}{\cancel{10}} \cdot \overset{3}{\cancel{9}} \cdot \overset{2}{\cancel{8}} \cdot \cancel{7!}}{\cancel{7!} \cdot \cancel{5} \cdot \cancel{4} \cdot \cancel{3} \cdot \cancel{2} \cdot 1} = 792$$

Example 4–49

In a club there are 7 women and 5 men. A committee of 3 women and 2 men is to be chosen. How many different possibilities are there?

Solution

Here, one must select 3 women from 7 women, which can be done in $_7C_3$, or 35, ways. Next, 2 men must be selected from 5 men, which can be done in $_5C_2$, or 10, ways. Finally, by the fundamental counting rule, the total number of different ways is $35 \cdot 10 = 350$, since one is choosing both men and women. Using the formula gives

$$_7C_3 \cdot {}_5C_2 = \frac{7!}{(7-3)!3!} \cdot \frac{5!}{(5-2)!2!} = 350$$

Table 4–1 Summarizes the counting rules.

Table 4–1	Summary counting rules	
Rule	**Definition**	**Formula**
Fundamental counting rule	The number of ways a sequence of n events can occur if the first event can occur in k_1 ways, the second event can occur in k_2 ways, etc.	$k_1 \cdot k_2 \cdot k_3 \cdots k_n$
Permutation rule	The number of permutations of n objects taking r objects at a time (order is important)	$_nP_r = \dfrac{n!}{(n-r)!}$
Combination rule	The number of combinations of r objects taken from n objects (order is not important)	$_nC_r = \dfrac{n!}{(n-r)!r!}$

Applying the Concepts 4–5

Garage Door Openers

Garage door openers originally had a series of 4 on/off switches so that homeowners could personalize the frequencies that opened their garage doors. If all garage door openers were set at the same frequency, anyone with a garage door opener could open anyone else's garage door.

1. Use a tree diagram to show how many different positions 4 consecutive on/off switches could be in.

After garage door openers became more popular, another set of 4 on/off switches was added to the systems.

2. Find a pattern of how many different positions are possible with the addition of each on/off switch.

3. How many different positions are possible with 8 consecutive on/off switches?

4. Is it reasonable to assume, if you owned a garage door opener with 8 switches, that someone could use his/her garage door opener to open your garage door by trying all the different possible positions?

In 1989 it was reported that the ignition keys for 1988 Dodge Caravans were made from a single blank that had 5 cuts on it. Each cut was made at one out of 5 possible levels. In 1988, assume there was 420,000 Dodge Caravans sold in Canada.

5. How many different possible keys can be made from the same key blank?

6. How many different 1988 Dodge Caravans could any one key start?

Look at the ignition key for your car and count the number of cuts on it. Assume that the cuts are made at one of five possible levels. Most car companies use one key blank for all their makes and models of cars.

7. Conjecture how many cars your car company sold over recent years, and then figure out how many other cars your car key could start. What would you do to decrease the odds of someone being able to open another vehicle with his or her key?

See page 204 for the answers.

Exercises 4–5

1. How many 5-digit United States numeric postal (zip) codes are possible if the same 5 digits can be repeated? If the 5 digits cannot be repeated?

2. How many ways can a baseball manager arrange a batting order of 9 players?

3. How many different ways can 7 different video game cartridges be arranged on a shelf?

4. How many different ways can 6 radio commercials be played during a one-hour radio program?

5. A store manager wishes to display 8 different brands of shampoo in a row. How many ways can this be done?

6. There are 8 different statistics books, 6 different geometry books, and 3 different trigonometry books. A student must select one book of each type. How many different ways can this be done?

7. At a local cheerleaders' camp, 5 routines must be practiced. A routine may not be repeated. In how many different orders can these 5 routines be presented?

8. Assume a radio station must have 4 call letters for identification. If the call letters for a radio station must begin with C or V, how many different call letters can be made if repetitions are not allowed? If repetitions are allowed?

9. How many different 3-digit identification tags can be made if the digits can be used more than once? If the first digit must be a 5 and repetitions are not permitted?

10. How many different ways can 9 trophies be arranged on a shelf?

11. If a baseball manager has 5 pitchers and 2 catchers, how many different possible pitcher-catcher combinations can he field?

12. There are 2 major roads from city X to city Y and 4 major roads from city Y to city Z. How many different trips can be made from city X to city Z passing through city Y?

13. Evaluate each of these.

   a. $8!$ e. $_7P_5$ i. $_5C_5$
   b. $10!$ f. $_{12}P_4$ j. $_6P_2$
   c. $0!$ g. $_5P_3$
   d. $1!$ h. $_6P_0$

14. The County Assessment Bureau decides to reassess homes in 8 different areas. How many different ways can this be accomplished?

15. How many different 4-colour code stripes can be made on a sports car if each code consists of the colours green, red, blue, and white? All colours are used only once.

16. An inspector must select 3 tests to perform in a certain order on a manufactured part. He has a choice of 7 tests. How many ways can he perform 3 different tests?

17. Anderson Research Co. decides to test-market a product in 6 areas. How many different ways can 3 areas be selected in a certain order for the first test?

18. How many different ways can a city health department inspector visit 5 restaurants in a city with 10 restaurants?

19. How many different 4-letter permutations can be formed from the letters in the word *decagon*?

20. In a board of directors composed of 8 people, how many ways can 1 chief executive officer, 1 director, and 1 treasurer be selected?

21. How many different ID cards can be made if there are 6 digits on a card and no digit can be used more than once?

22. How many different ways can 5 Public Service announcements be run during 1 hour of time?

23. How many different ways can 4 tickets be selected from 50 tickets if each ticket wins a different prize?

24. How many different ways can a researcher select 5 rats from 20 rats and assign each to a different test?

25. How many different signals can be made by using at least 3 distinct flags if there are 5 different flags from which to select?

26. An investigative agency has 7 cases and 5 agents. How many different ways can the cases be assigned if only 1 case is assigned to each agent?

27. **(ans)** Evaluate each expression.

   a. $_5C_2$ d. $_6C_2$ g. $_3C_3$ j. $_4C_3$
   b. $_8C_3$ e. $_6C_4$ h. $_9C_7$
   c. $_7C_4$ f. $_3C_0$ i. $_{12}P_2$

28. How many ways can 3 cards be selected from a standard deck of 52 cards, disregarding the order of selection?

29. How many ways are there to select 3 bracelets from a box of 10 bracelets, disregarding the order of selection?

30. How many ways can 4 baseball players and 3 basketball players be selected from 12 baseball players and 9 basketball players?

31. How many ways can a committee of 4 people be selected from a group of 10 people?

32. If a person can select 3 presents from 10 presents under a Christmas tree, how many different combinations are there?

33. How many different tests can be made from a test bank of 20 questions if the test consists of 5 questions?

34. The general manager of a fast-food restaurant chain must select 6 restaurants from 11 for a promotional program. How many different possible ways can this selection be done?

35. How many different ways can a theatrical group select 2 musicals and 3 dramas from 11 musicals and 8 dramas to be presented during the year?

36. In a train yard there are 4 tank cars, 12 boxcars, and 7 flatcars. How many ways can a train be made up consisting of 2 tank cars, 5 boxcars, and 3 flatcars? (In this case, order is not important.)

37. There are 7 women and 5 men in a department. How many ways can a committee of 4 people be selected? How many ways can this committee be selected if there must be 2 men and 2 women on the committee? How many ways can this committee be selected if there must be at least 2 women on the committee?

38. Wake Up cereal comes in 2 types, crispy and crunchy. If a researcher has 10 boxes of each, how many ways can she select 3 boxes of each for a quality control test?

39. How many ways can a dinner patron select 3 appetizers and 2 vegetables if there are 6 appetizers and 5 vegetables on the menu?

40. How many ways can a jury of 6 women and 6 men be selected from 10 women and 12 men?

41. How many ways can a foursome of 2 men and 2 women be selected from 10 men and 12 women in a golf club?

42. A U.S. state narcotics bureau must form a 5-member investigative team. If it has 25 agents from which to choose, how many different possible teams can be formed?

43. How many different ways can an instructor select 2 textbooks from a possible 17?

44. The U.S Environmental Protection Agency must investigate 9 mills for complaints of air pollution. How many different ways can a representative select 5 of these to investigate this week?

45. How many ways can a person select 7 television commercials from 11 television commercials?

46. How many ways can a person select 8 videotapes from 10 tapes?

47. A buyer decides to stock 8 different posters. How many ways can she select these 8 if there are 20 from which to choose?

48. An advertising manager decides to have an ad campaign in which 8 special calculators will be hidden at various locations in a shopping mall. If she has 17 locations from which to pick, how many different possible combinations can she choose?

Extending the Concepts

49. How many different ways can a person select one or more coins if she has 2 nickels, 1 dime, and 1 quarter?

50. In a barnyard there is an assortment of chickens and cows. Counting heads, one gets 15; counting legs, one gets 46. How many of each are there?

51. How many different ways can five people—A, B, C, D, and E—sit in a row at a movie theatre if (*a*) A and B must sit together; (*b*) C must sit to the right of, but not necessarily next to, B; (*c*) D and E will not sit next to each other?

52. Using combinations, calculate the number of each poker hand in a deck of cards. (A poker hand consists of 5 cards dealt in any order.)

  a. Royal flush
  b. Straight flush
  c. Four of a kind
  d. Full house

4–6   Probability and Counting Rules (Optional)

Objective

Find the probability of an event, using the counting rules.

The counting rules can be combined with the probability rules in this chapter to solve many types of probability problems. By using the fundamental counting rule, the permutation rules, and the combination rule, one can compute the probability of outcomes of many experiments, such as getting a full house when 5 cards are dealt or selecting a committee of 3 women and 2 men from a club consisting of 10 women and 10 men.

Example 4–50   Find the probability of getting 4 aces when 5 cards are drawn from an ordinary deck of cards.

Solution

There are $_{52}C_5$ ways to draw 5 cards from a deck. There is only one way to get 4 aces (i.e., $_4C_4$), but there are 48 possibilities to get the fifth card. Therefore, there are 48 ways to get 4 aces and 1 other card. Hence,

$$P(4 \text{ aces}) = \frac{_4C_4 \cdot 48}{_{52}C_5} = \frac{1 \cdot 48}{2{,}598{,}960} = \frac{48}{2{,}598{,}960} = \frac{1}{54{,}145}$$

Example 4–51   A box contains 24 transistors, 4 of which are defective. If 4 are sold at random, find the following probabilities.

    a. Exactly 2 are defective.   *c.* All are defective.

    b. None is defective.   *d.* At least 1 is defective.

Solution

There are $_{24}C_4$ ways to sell 4 transistors, so the denominator in each case will be 10,626.

    a. Two defective transistors can be selected as $_4C_2$ and 2 nondefective ones as $_{20}C_2$. Hence,

$$P(\text{exactly 2 defectives}) = \frac{_4C_2 \cdot _{20}C_2}{_{24}C_4} = \frac{1{,}140}{10{,}626} = \frac{190}{1{,}771}$$

    b. The number of ways to choose no defectives is $_{20}C_4$. Hence,

$$P(\text{no defectives}) = \frac{_{20}C_4}{_{24}C_4} = \frac{4{,}845}{10{,}626} = \frac{1{,}615}{3{,}542}$$

    c. The number of ways to choose 4 defectives from 4 is $_4C_4$, or 1. Hence,

$$P(\text{all defectives}) = \frac{1}{_{24}C_4} = \frac{1}{10{,}626}$$

    d. To find the probability of at least 1 defective transistor, find the probability that there are no defective transistors, and then subtract that probability from 1.

$$P(\text{at least 1 defective}) = 1 - P(\text{no defectives})$$

$$= 1 - \frac{_{20}C_4}{_{24}C_4} = 1 - \frac{1{,}615}{3{,}542} = \frac{1{,}927}{3{,}542}$$

Example 4–52   A store has 6 *TV Graphic* magazines and 8 *Newstime* magazines on the counter. If two customers purchased a magazine, find the probability that one of each magazine was purchased.

Solution

$$P(1 \text{ } TV \text{ } Graphic \text{ and } 1 \text{ } Newstime) = \frac{_6C_1 \cdot _8C_1}{_{14}C_2} = \frac{6 \cdot 8}{91} = \frac{48}{91}$$

Example 4–53

A combination lock consists of the 26 letters of the alphabet. If a 3-letter combination is needed, find the probability that the combination will consist of the letters ABC in that order. The same letter can be used more than once. (*Note:* A combination lock is really a permutation lock.)

Solution

Since repetitions are permitted, there are $26 \cdot 26 \cdot 26 = 17{,}576$ different possible combinations. And since there is only one ABC combination, the probability is $P(\text{ABC}) = 1/26^3 = 1/17{,}576$.

Example 4–54

There are 8 married couples in a tennis club. If 1 man and 1 woman are selected at random to plan the summer tournament, find the probability that they are married to each other.

Solution

Since there are 8 ways to select the man and 8 ways to select the woman, there are $8 \cdot 8$, or 64, ways to select 1 man and 1 woman. Since there are 8 married couples, the solution is $\frac{8}{64} = \frac{1}{8}$.

As indicated at the beginning of this section, the counting rules and the probability rules can be used to solve a large variety of probability problems found in business, gambling, economics, biology, and other fields.

Applying the Concepts 4–6

Counting Rules and Probability

One of the biggest problems for students when doing probability problems is to decide which formula or formulas to use. Another problem is to decide whether two events are independent or dependent. Use the following problem to help develop a better understanding of these concepts.

Assume you are given a 5-question multiple-choice quiz. Each question has 5 possible answers: A, B, C, D, and E.

1. How many events are there?
2. Are the events independent or dependent?
3. If you guess at each question, what is the probability that you get all of them correct?
4. What is the probability that a person would guess answer A for each question?

Assume that you are given a test in which you are to match the correct answers in the right column with the questions in the left column. You can use each answer only once.

5. How many events are there?
6. Are the events independent or dependent?
7. What is the probability of getting them all correct if you are guessing?
8. What is the difference between the two problems?

See page 204 for the answers.

Speaking of

Statistics

Probabilities can be used to assess the danger of a situation. For example, the chances of dying from a shark attack are 1 in 100 million while the chances of dying from a heart attack are 1 in 400. Hence, we are at greater risk from dying of heart disease. Using the probabilities in the table, explain why we should be more afraid of smoking or a bad diet than of walking across a street.

How much danger are Americans really in?

Americans are 71,500 times more likely to die in a car crash this year than to be killed by anthrax. Indeed, Americans are 8,300 times more likely to get killed walking across the street, says risk expert Fred Kilbourne, a member of the board of Conference of Consulting Actuaries.[1] He calculates an American's chance of dying this year from any cause—from anthrax to drowning—is 1 in 130.

Based on deaths in the USA, these are each American's risk

Motor vehicle accidents	1 in 7,000
Being shot by a gun	1 in 10,000
Falling down	1 in 20,000
Poison	1 in 40,000
Walking across the street	1 in 60,000
Drowning	1 in 75,000
House fire	1 in 100,000
Bicycle accident	1 in 500,000
Commercial plane crash	1 in 1 million
Lightning strike	1 in 3 million
Shark attack	1 in 100 million
Roller coaster accident	1 in 300 million
Anthrax	**1 in 500 million**

Kilbourne says the major killers are not accidents but illness and disease.

The risk of death per person per year in the USA for:

Heart disease	1 in 400
Cancer	1 in 600
Stroke	1 in 2,000
Flu and pneumonia	1 in 3,000

1 – Kilbourne cautions that actuarial assessments, the predictive numbers used by the insurance industry, are based on "the assumption that the future will look reasonably like the past. We may not be able to make that assumption on every issue right now."

Source: Copyright 2001, *USA TODAY.* Reprinted with permission.

Exercises 4–6

1. Find the probability of getting 2 face cards (king, queen, or jack) when 2 cards are drawn from a deck without replacement.

2. A parent–teacher committee consisting of 4 people is to be formed from 20 parents and 5 teachers. Find the probability that the committee will consist of these people. (Assume that the selection will be random.)

   a. All teachers

   b. 2 teachers and 2 parents

   c. All parents

   d. 1 teacher and 3 parents

3. In a company there are 7 executives: 4 women and 3 men. Three are selected to attend a management seminar. Find these probabilities.

   a. All 3 selected will be women.

   b. All 3 selected will be men.

   c. 2 men and 1 woman will be selected.

   d. 1 man and 2 women will be selected.

4. The composition of Canada's senate based on party affiliation as of July 2007 is

61 Liberals   27 Conservatives   17 Others

A new committee is being formed to study ways to benefit the arts in education. If 3 Senators are selected at random to head the committee, what is the probability that they will all be Liberals? What is the probability that they will all be Conservatives? What is the probability that their will be one from each designated party affiliation, including Other parties? Note: *Conservative senators include Progressive Conservatives.*

Source: The Senate of Canada.

5. Since each jurisdiction joined Canada's confederation, there have been 255 elected provincial and territorial premiers, as of 2007, as shown.

Alberta	13	Nunavut	1
British Columbia	34	Ontario	24
Manitoba	21	Prince Edward Island	32
New Brunswick	31	Quebec	34
Nova Scotia	26	Saskatchewan	14
Newfoundland/ Labrador	9	Yukon	7
Northwest Territories	9		

Suppose that 4 premiers are chosen at random to be the subject of a documentary. Find the probability that

a. All 4 hail from British Columbia.

b. 2 are from the Northwest Territories and 2 are from the Yukon.

Source: canadainfolink.com.

6. A package contains 12 LCD panels, 3 of which had defective pixels. If 4 LCD panels are selected, find the probability of getting

a. No defective LCD panels

b. 1 defective LCD panel

c. 3 defective LCD panels

7. If 50 tickets are sold and 2 prizes are to be awarded, find the probability that one person will win 2 prizes if that person buys 2 tickets.

8. Find the probability of getting a full house (3 cards of one denomination and 2 of another) when 5 cards are dealt from an ordinary deck.

9. A committee of 4 people is to be formed from 6 doctors and 8 dentists. Find the probability that the committee will consist of

a. All dentists

b. 2 dentists and 2 doctors

c. All doctors

d. 3 doctors and 1 dentist

e. 1 doctor and 3 dentists

10. An insurance sales representative selects 3 policies to review. The group of policies she can select from contains 8 life policies, 5 automobile policies, and 2 homeowner policies. Find the probability of selecting

a. All life policies

b. Both homeowner policies

c. All automobile policies

d. 1 of each policy

e. 2 life policies and 1 automobile policy

11. A drawer contains 11 identical red socks and 8 identical black socks. Suppose that you choose 2 socks at random in the dark

a. What is the probability that you get a pair of red socks?

b. What is the probability that you get a pair of black socks?

c. What is the probability that you get 2 unmatched socks?

d. Where did the other red sock go?

12. Find the probability of selecting 3 science books and 4 math books from 8 science books and 9 math books. The books are selected at random.

13. When 3 dice are rolled, find the probability of getting a sum of 7.

14. Find the probability of randomly selecting 2 mathematics books and 3 physics books from a box containing 4 mathematics books and 8 physics books.

15. Find the probability that if 5 different-sized washers are arranged in a row, they will be arranged in order of size.

16. Using the information in Exercise 52 in Section 4–5, find the probability of each poker hand.

a. Royal flush

b. Straight flush

c. 4 of a kind

4–7   # Summary

In this chapter, the basic concepts and rules of probability are explained. The three types of probability are classical, empirical, and subjective. Classical probability uses sample spaces. Empirical probability uses frequency distributions and is based on observation. In subjective probability, the researcher makes an educated guess about the chance of an event occurring.

A probability event consists of one or more outcomes of a probability experiment. Two events are said to be mutually exclusive if they cannot occur at the same time. Events can also be classified as independent or dependent. If events are independent, whether or not the first event occurs does not affect the probability of the next event occurring. If the probability of the second event occurring is changed by the occurrence of the first event, then the events are dependent. The complement of an event is the set of outcomes in the sample space that are not included in the outcomes of the event itself. Complementary events are mutually exclusive.

Probability problems can be solved by using the addition rules, the multiplication rules, and the complementary event rules.

Finally, the fundamental counting rule, the permutation rule, and the combination rule can be used to determine the number of outcomes of events; then these numbers can be used to determine the probabilities of events.

For step-by-step guidance on the use of technology for this chapter, visit the Online Learning Centre at www.mcgrawhill.ca/olc/bluman. Summary procedures for Minitab, SPSS, Excel, and TI-83 Plus or TI-84 Plus can also be found in Appendix E.

Important Terms   ● ● ●

classical probability 148

combination 186

complement of an event 151

compound event 148

conditional probability 171

dependent events 171

empirical probability 153

equally likely events 148

event 147

fundamental counting rule 181

independent events 168

law of large numbers 155

mutually exclusive events 161

outcome 145

permutation 184

probability 144

probability experiment 145

sample space 145

simple event 148

subjective probability 155

tree diagram 147

Venn diagrams 152

Important Formulas   ● ● ●

Formula for classical probability:

$$P(E) = \frac{\text{number of outcomes in } E}{\text{total number of outcomes in sample space}} = \frac{n(E)}{n(S)}$$

Formula for empirical probability:

$$P(E) = \frac{\text{frequency for class}}{\text{total frequencies in distribution}} = \frac{f}{n}$$

Addition rule 1, for two mutually exclusive events:

$$P(A \text{ or } B) = P(A) + P(B)$$

Addition rule 2, for events that are not mutually exclusive:

$$P(A \text{ or } B) = P(A) + P(B) - P(A \text{ and } B)$$

Multiplication rule 1, for independent events:

$$P(A \text{ and } B) = P(A) \cdot P(B)$$

Multiplication rule 2, for dependent events:

$$P(A \text{ and } B) = P(A) \cdot P(B|A)$$

Formula for conditional probability:

$$P(B|A) = \frac{P(A \text{ and } B)}{P(A)}$$

Formula for complementary events:

$$P(\overline{E}) = 1 - P(E) \quad \text{or} \quad P(E) = 1 - P(\overline{E})$$

$$\text{or} \quad P(E) + P(\overline{E}) = 1$$

Fundamental counting rule: In a sequence of n events in which the first one has k_1 possibilities, the second event has k_2 possibilities, the third has k_3 possibilities, etc., the total number possibilities of the sequence will be

$$k_1 \cdot k_2 \cdot k_3 \cdots k_n$$

Permutation rule: The number of permutations of n objects taking r objects at a time when order is important is

$$_nP_r = \frac{n!}{(n - r)!}$$

Combination rule: The number of combinations of r objects selected from n objects when order is not important is

$$_nC_r = \frac{n!}{(n - r)!r!}$$

Review Exercises

1. When a die is rolled, find the probability of getting a
   a. 5
   b. 6
   c. Number less than 5

2. When a card is selected from a deck, find the probability of getting
   a. A club
   b. A face card or a heart
   c. A 6 and a spade
   d. A king
   e. A red card

3. In a survey conducted at a local restaurant during breakfast hours, 20 people preferred orange juice, 16 preferred grapefruit juice, and 9 preferred apple juice with breakfast. If a person is selected at random, find the probability that she or he prefers grapefruit juice.

4. If a die is rolled one time, find these probabilities.
   a. Getting a 5
   b. Getting an odd number
   c. Getting a number less than 3

5. A recent survey indicated that in a town of 1500 households, 850 had cordless telephones. If a household is randomly selected, find the probability that it has a cordless telephone.

6. During a sale at a men's store, 16 white sweaters, 3 red sweaters, 9 blue sweaters, and 7 yellow sweaters were purchased. If a customer is selected at random, find the probability that he bought
   a. A blue sweater
   b. A yellow or a white sweater
   c. A red, a blue, or a yellow sweater
   d. A sweater that was not white

7. At a swimwear store, the managers found that 16 women bought white bathing suits, 4 bought red suits, 3 bought blue suits, and 7 bought yellow suits. If a

customer is selected at random, find the probability that she bought
   a. A blue suit
   b. A yellow or a red suit
   c. A white or a yellow or a blue suit
   d. A suit that was not red

8. When two dice are rolled, find the probability of getting
   a. A sum of 5 or 6
   b. A sum greater than 9
   c. A sum less than 4 or greater than 9
   d. A sum that is divisible by 4
   e. A sum of 14
   f. A sum less than 13

9. The probability that a person owns a car is 0.80, that a person owns a boat is 0.30, and that a person owns both a car and a boat is 0.12. Find the probability that a person owns either a boat or a car.

10. There is a 0.39 probability that John will purchase a new car, a 0.73 probability that Mary will purchase a new car, and a 0.36 probability that both will purchase a new car. Find the probability that neither will purchase a new car.

11. A CTV Newsnet poll indicates that 36% of Canadians believe that authorities are exaggerating the level of risk of the avian flu in order to encourage people to take precautions. If 5 Canadians are randomly selected, find the probability that all 5 feel the avian flu risk is exaggerated.
    Source: CTV Newsnet, March 2005.

12. A study entitled "Canadians, Public Libraries and the Information Highway" examined Canadians' usage of public libraries. On a basic level, 63% of survey respondents reported having a public library card. Find the probability that 5 randomly selected Canadians have a public library card.
    Source: Canadian Library Association.

13. Three cards are drawn from an ordinary deck *without replacement*. Find the probability of getting

    a. All black cards

    b. All spades

    c. All queens

14. A coin is tossed and a card is drawn from a deck. Find the probability of getting

    a. A head and a 6

    b. A tail and a red card

    c. A head and a club

15. A box of candy contains 6 chocolate-covered cherries, 3 peppermints, 2 caramels, and 2 strawberry creams. If a piece of candy is selected, find the probability of getting a caramel or a peppermint.

16. A manufacturing company has three factories: X, Y, and Z. The daily output of each is shown here.

Product	Factory X	Factory Y	Factory Z
TVs	18	32	15
Stereos	6	20	13

If one item is selected at random, find these probabilities.

    a. It was manufactured at factory X or is a stereo.

    b. It was manufactured at factory Y or factory Z.

    c. It is a TV or was manufactured at factory Z.

17. A vaccine has a 90% probability of being effective in preventing a certain disease. The probability of getting the disease if a person is not vaccinated is 50%. In a certain geographic region, 25% of the people get vaccinated. If a person is selected at random, find the probability that he or she will contract the disease.

18. A manufacturer makes three models of a television set, models A, B, and C. A store sells 40% of model A sets, 40% of model B sets, and 20% of model C sets. Of model A sets, 3% have stereo sound; of model B sets, 7% have stereo sound; and of model C sets, 9% have stereo sound. If a set is sold at random, find the probability that it has stereo sound.

19. The probability that Sue will live on campus and buy a new car is 0.37. If the probability that she will live on campus is 0.73, find the probability that she will buy a new car, given that she lives on campus.

20. The probability that a customer will buy a television set and buy an extended warranty is 0.03. If the probability that a customer will purchase a television set is 0.11, find the probability that the customer will also purchase the extended warranty.

21. Of the members of the Blue River Health Club, 43% have a lifetime membership and exercise regularly (three or more times a week). If 75% of the club members exercise regularly, find the probability that a randomly selected member is a life member, given that he or she exercises regularly.

22. The probability that it snows and the bus arrives late is 0.023. José hears the weather forecast, and there is a 40% chance of snow tomorrow. Find the probability that the bus will be late, given that it snows.

23. At a large factory, the employees were surveyed and classified according to their level of education and whether they smoked. The data are shown in the table.

| | Educational level | | |
Smoking habit	Not high school graduate	High school graduate	College/ university graduate
Smoke	6	14	19
Do not smoke	18	7	25

If an employee is selected at random, find these probabilities.

    a. The employee smokes, given that he or she graduated from college or university.

    b. Given that the employee did not graduate from high school, he or she is a smoker.

24. A survey found that 77% of bike riders sometimes ride without a helmet. If 4 bike riders are randomly selected, find the probability that at least one of the riders does not wear a helmet all the time.

Source: USA TODAY.

25. A coin is tossed 5 times. Find the probability of getting at least one tail.

26. Health Canada reports that an estimated 2.7 million or 8.2% of Canadians suffer from asthma, a chronic lung disease. If 5 Canadians are randomly selected, find the probability that at least one has asthma.

Source: Health Canada.

27. Most Canadian provincial automobile licence plates contain 6 digits—3 letters followed by 3 numbers. How many different licence plates can be made if repetitions are allowed? If repetitions are not allowed? If repetitions are allowed in the letters but not the digits?

28. How many different arrangements of the letters in the word *bread* can be made?

29. How many ways can 3 outfielders and 4 infielders be chosen from 5 outfielders and 7 infielders?

30. How many different ways can 8 computer operators be seated in a row?

31. How many ways can a student select 2 electives from a possible choice of 10 electives?

32. There are 6 Conservative, 5 Liberal, and 4 New Democrat MPs who have volunteered to serve on a House of Commons committee. If the committee must contain 3 Conservatives, 2 Liberals, and 1 New Democrat, how many ways can the committee be selected?

33. How many different computer passwords are possible if each consists of 4 symbols and if the first one must be a letter and the other 3 must be digits?

34. A new employee has a choice of 5 health care plans, 3 retirement plans, and 2 different expense accounts. If a person selects one of each option, how many different options does he or she have?

35. There are 12 students who wish to enroll in a particular course. There are only 4 seats left in the classroom. How many different ways can 4 students be selected to attend the class?

36. A candy store allows customers to select 3 different candies to be packaged and mailed. If there are 13 varieties available, how many possible selections can be made?

37. If a student can select 5 novels from a reading list of 20 for a course in literature, how many different possible ways can this selection be done?

38. If a student can select one of 3 language courses, one of 5 mathematics courses, and one of 4 history courses, how many different schedules can be made?

39. New Ontario licence plates are being issued in the form of ABCD-123—4 letters followed by 3 digits. How many such licence plates are possible? If the plates are issued at random, what is the probability of the issuing of licence plate LUCK-777?

40. A newspaper advertises 5 different movies, 3 plays, and 2 baseball games for the weekend. If a couple selects 3 activities, find the probability that they attend 2 plays and 1 movie.

41. In an office there are 3 secretaries, 4 accountants, and 2 receptionists. If a committee of 3 is to be formed, find the probability that one of each will be selected.

42. For a survey, a subject can be classified as follows:

Gender: male or female

Marital status: single, married, widowed, divorced

Occupation: administration, faculty, staff

Draw a tree diagram for the different ways a person can be classified.

Statistics Today

Would You Bet Your Life?–Revisited

In his book *Probabilities in Everyday Life*, John D. McGervey states that the chance of being killed on any given commercial airline flight is almost 1 in 1 million and that the chance of being killed during a transcontinental auto trip is about 1 in 8000. The corresponding probabilities are $1/1,000,000 = 0.000001$ as compared to $1/8000 = 0.000125$. Since the second number is 125 times greater than the first number, you have a much higher risk driving than flying across Canada.

Chapter Quiz

Determine whether each statement is true or false. If the statement is false, explain why.

1. Subjective probability has little use in the real world.

2. Classical probability uses a frequency distribution to compute probabilities.

3. In classical probability, all outcomes in the sample space are equally likely.

4. When two events are not mutually exclusive, $P(A \text{ or } B) = P(A) + P(B)$.

5. If two events are dependent, they must have the same probability of occurring.

6. An event and its complement can occur at the same time.

7. The arrangement ABC is the same as BAC for combinations.

8. When objects are arranged in a specific order, the arrangement is called a combination.

Select the best answer.

9. The probability that an event happens is 0.42. What is the probability that the event won't happen?

a. −0.42   c. 0
b. 0.58   d. 1

10. When a meteorologist says that there is a 30% chance of showers, what type of probability is the person using?

a. Classical   c. Relative
b. Empirical   d. Subjective

11. The sample space for tossing 3 coins consists of how many outcomes?

a. 2   c. 6
b. 4   d. 8

12. The complement of guessing 5 correct answers on a 5-question true/false exam is

a. Guessing 5 incorrect answers
b. Guessing at least 1 incorrect answer
c. Guessing at least 1 correct answer
d. Guessing no incorrect answers

13. When two dice are rolled, the sample space consists of how many events?

a. 6
b. 12
c. 36
d. 54

14. What is $_nP_0$?

a. 0
b. 1
c. n
d. It cannot be determined.

15. What is the number of permutations of 6 different objects taken all together?

a. 0
b. 1
c. 36
d. 720

16. What is 0!?

a. 0
b. 1
c. Undefined
d. 10

17. What is $_nC_n$?

a. 0
b. 1
c. n
d. It cannot be determined.

Complete the following statements with the best answer.

18. The set of all possible outcomes of a probability experiment is called the _____.

19. The probability of an event can be any number between and including _____ and _____.

20. If an event cannot occur, its probability is _____.

21. The sum of the probabilities of the events in the sample space is _____.

22. When two events cannot occur at the same time, they are said to be _____.

23. When a card is drawn, find the probability of getting

a. A jack
b. A 4
c. A card less than 6 (an ace is considered above 6)

24. When a card is drawn from a deck, find the probability of getting

a. A diamond
b. A 5 or a heart
c. A 5 and a heart
d. A king
e. A red card

25. At a men's clothing store, 12 men purchased blue golf sweaters, 8 purchased green sweaters, 4 purchased grey sweaters, and 7 bought black sweaters. If a customer is selected at random, find the probability that he purchased

a. A blue sweater
b. A green or grey sweater
c. A green or black or blue sweater
d. A sweater that was not black

26. When 2 dice are rolled, find the probability of getting

a. A sum of 6 or 7
b. A sum greater than 8
c. A sum less than 3 or greater than 8
d. A sum that is divisible by 3
e. A sum of 16
f. A sum less than 11

27. The probability that a person owns a microwave oven is 0.75, that a person owns a compact disk player is 0.25, and that a person owns both a microwave and a CD player is 0.16. Find the probability that a person owns either a microwave or a CD player, but not both.

28. Of the physics graduates of a university, 30% received a starting salary of $30,000 or more. If 5 of the graduates are selected at random, find the probability that all had a starting salary of $30,000 or more.

29. Five cards are drawn from an ordinary deck *without* replacement. Find the probability of getting

a. All red cards
b. All diamonds
c. All aces

30. The probability that Samantha will be accepted by the college or university of her choice and obtain a scholarship is 0.35. If the probability that she is accepted by the college or university is 0.65, find the probability that she will obtain a scholarship given that she is accepted by the college or university.

31. The probability that a customer will buy a car and an extended warranty is 0.16. If the probability that a customer will purchase a car is 0.30, find the probability that the customer will also purchase the extended warranty.

32. Of the members of the Spring Lake Bowling Lanes, 57% have a lifetime membership and bowl regularly (three or more times a week). If 70% of the club members bowl regularly, find the probability that a randomly selected member is a lifetime member, given that he or she bowls regularly.

33. The probability that Mike has to work overtime and it rains is 0.028. Mike hears the weather forecast, and there is a 50% chance of rain. Find the probability that he will have to work overtime, given that it rains.

34. At a large factory, the employees were surveyed and classified according to their level of education and whether they attend a sports event at least once a month. The data are shown in the table.

| | Educational level | | |
| | Two-year | Four-year |
Sports event	**High school graduate**	**college degree**	**college degree**
Attend	16	20	24
Do not attend	12	19	25

If an employee is selected at random, find the probability that

a. The employee attends sports events regularly, given that he or she graduated from college (2- or 4-year degree)

b. Given that the employee is a high school graduate, he or she does not attend sports events regularly

35. In a certain high-risk group, the chances of a person having suffered a heart attack are 55%. If 6 people are chosen, find the probability that at least 1 will have had a heart attack.

36. A single die is rolled 4 times. Find the probability of getting at least one 5.

37. If 85% of all people have brown eyes and 6 people are selected at random, find the probability that at least 1 of them has brown eyes.

38. How many ways can 5 sopranos and 4 altos be selected from 7 sopranos and 9 altos?

39. How many different ways can 8 speakers be seated on a stage?

40. A soda machine servicer must restock and collect money from 15 machines, each one at a different location. How many ways can she select 4 machines to service in 1 day?

41. One company's ID cards consist of 5 letters followed by 2 digits. How many cards can be made if repetitions are allowed? If repetitions are not allowed?

42. How many different arrangements of the letters in the word *number* can be made?

43. A physics test consists of 25 true/false questions. How many different possible answer keys can be made?

44. How many different ways can 5 cellular telephones be selected from 8 cellular phones?

45. On a lunch counter, there are 3 oranges, 5 apples, and 2 bananas. If 3 pieces of fruit are selected, find the probability that 1 orange, 1 apple, and 1 banana are selected.

46. A cruise director schedules 4 different movies, 2 bridge games, and 3 tennis games for a 2-day period. If a couple selects 3 activities, find the probability that they attend 2 movies and 1 tennis game.

47. At a sorority meeting, there are 6 third-year students, 4 second-year students, and 2 first-year students. If a committee of 3 is to be formed, find the probability that 1 of each will be selected.

48. For a banquet, a committee can select beef, pork, chicken, or veal; baked potatoes or mashed potatoes; and peas or green beans for a vegetable. Draw a tree diagram for all possible choices of a meat, a potato, and a vegetable.

Critical Thinking Challenges

● ● ●

1. Consider this problem: A con man has 3 coins. One coin has been specially made and has a head on each side. A second coin has been specially made, and on each side it has a tail. Finally, a third coin has a head and a tail on it. All coins are of the same denomination. The con man places the 3 coins in his pocket, selects one, and shows you one side. It is heads. He is willing to bet you even money that it is the two-headed coin. His reasoning is that it can't be the two-tailed coin since a head is showing; therefore, there is a 50–50 chance of it being the two-headed coin. Would you take the bet? (*Hint:* See Exercise 1 in Data Projects.)

2. Chevalier de Méré won money when he bet unsuspecting patrons that in 4 rolls of 1 die, he could get at least one 6, but he lost money when he bet that in

24 rolls of 2 dice, he could get at least a double 6. Using the probability rules, find the probability of each event and explain why he won the majority of the time on the first game but lost the majority of the time when playing the second game. (*Hint:* Find the probabilities of losing each game and subtract from 1.)

3. How many people do you think need to be in a room so that 2 people will have the same birthday (month and day)? You might think it is 366. This would, of course, guarantee it (excluding leap year), but how many people would need to be in a room so that there would be a 90% probability that 2 people would be born on the same day? What about a 50% probability?

Actually, the number is much smaller than you may think. For example, if you have 50 people in a room, the probability that 2 people will have the same birthday is 97%. If you have 23 people in a room, there is a 50% probability that 2 people were born on the same day!

The problem can be solved by using the probability rules. It must be assumed that all birthdays are equally likely, but this assumption will have little effect on the answers. The way to find the answer is by using the complementary event rule as P (2 people having the same birthday) $= 1 - P$ (all have different birthdays).

For example, suppose there were 3 people in the room. The probability that each had a different birthday would be

$$\frac{365}{365} \cdot \frac{364}{365} \cdot \frac{363}{365} = \frac{_{365}P_3}{365^3} = 0.992$$

Hence, the probability that at least 2 of the 3 people will have the same birthday will be

$$1 - 0.992 = 0.008$$

Hence, for k people, the formula is

P(at least 2 people have the same birthday)

$$= 1 - \frac{_{365}P_k}{365^k}$$

Using your calculator, complete the table and verify that for at least a 50% chance of 2 people having the same birthday, 23 or more people will be needed.

Number of people	Probability that at least 2 have the same birthday
1	0.000
2	0.003
5	0.027
10	
15	
20	
21	
22	
23	

4. We know that if the probability of an event happening is 100%, then the event is a certainty. Can it be concluded that if there is a 50% chance of contracting a communicable disease through contact with an infected person, there would be a 100% chance of contracting the disease if 2 contacts were made with the infected person? Explain your answer.

Data Projects

● ● ●

1. Make a set of 3 cards—one with a red star on both sides, one with a black star on both sides, and one with a black star on one side and a red star on the other side. With a partner, play the game described on page 201 in the first Critical Thinking Challenge 100 times, and record the results of how many times you win and how many times your partner wins. (*Note:* Do not change options during the 100 trials.)

   a. Do you think the game is fair (i.e., does one person win approximately 50% of the time)?
   b. If you think the game is unfair, explain what the probabilities might be and why.

2. Take a coin and tape a small weight (e.g., part of a paper clip) to one side. Flip the coin 100 times and record the results. Do you think you have changed the probabilities of the results of flipping the coin? Explain.

3. This game is called *Diet Fractions*. Roll 2 dice and use the numbers to make a fraction less than or equal to 1. Player A wins if the fraction cannot be reduced; otherwise, player B wins.

   a. Play the game 100 times and record the results.

   b. Decide if the game is fair or not. Explain why or why not.
   c. Using the sample space for 2 dice, compute the probabilities of winning for player A and for player B. Do these agree with the results obtained in part *a*?

Source: George W. Bright, John G. Harvey, and Margariete Montague Wheeler, "Fair Games, Unfair Games." Chapter 8, *Teaching Statistics and Probability.* NCTM 1981 Yearbook. Reston, Va.: The National Council of Teachers of Mathematics, Inc., 1981, p. 49. Used with permission.

4. Often when playing gambling games or collecting items in cereal boxes, one wonders how long will it be before one achieves a success. For example, suppose there are 6 different types of toys with 1 toy packaged at random in a cereal box. If a person wanted a certain toy, about how many boxes would that person have to buy on average before obtaining that particular toy? Of course, there is a possibility that the particular toy would be in the first box opened or that the person might never obtain the particular toy. These are the extremes.

   a. To find out, simulate the experiment using dice. Start rolling dice until a particular number, say, 3, is obtained, and keep track of how many rolls are necessary. Repeat 100 times. Then find the average.

b. You may decide to use another number, such as 10 different items. In this case, use 10 playing cards (ace through 10 of diamonds), select a particular card (say, an ace), shuffle the deck each time, deal the cards, and count how many cards are turned over before the ace is obtained. Repeat 100 times, then find the average.

c. Summarize the findings for both experiments.

Answers to Applying the Concepts ●●●

Section 4–2 Tossing a Coin

1. The sample space is the listing of all possible outcomes of the coin toss.

2. The possible outcomes are heads or tails.

3. Classical probability says that a fair coin has a 50–50 chance of coming up heads or tails.

4. The law of large numbers says that as you increase the number of trials, the overall results will approach the theoretical probability. However, since the coin has no "memory," it still has a 50–50 chance of coming up heads or tails on the next toss. Knowing what has already happened should not change your opinion on what will happen on the next toss.

5. The empirical approach to probability is based on running an experiment and looking at the results. You cannot do that at this time.

6. Subjective probabilities could be used if you believe the coin is biased.

7. Answers will vary; however, they should address that a fair coin has a 50–50 chance of coming up heads or tails on the next flip.

Section 4–3 Which Pain Reliever Is Best?

1. There were $192 + 186 + 188 = 566$ subjects in the study.

2. The study lasted for 12 weeks.

3. The variables are the type of pain reliever and the side effects.

4. Both variables are qualitative and nominal.

5. The numbers in the table are exact figures.

6. The probability that a randomly selected person was receiving a placebo is $192/566 = 0.3392$ (about 34%).

7. The probability that a randomly selected person was receiving a placebo or drug A is $(192 + 186)/566 = 378/566 = 0.6678$ (about 67%). These are mutually exclusive events. The complement is that a randomly selected person was receiving drug B.

8. The probability that a randomly selected person was receiving a placebo or experienced a neurological headache is $(192 + 55 + 72)/566 = 319/566 = 0.5636$ (about 56%).

9. The probability that a randomly selected person was not receiving a placebo or experienced a sinus headache is $(186 + 188)/566 + 11/566 = 385/566 = 0.6802$ (about 68%).

Section 4–4 Guilty or Innocent?

1. The probability of another couple with the same characteristics being in that area is $\frac{1}{12} \cdot \frac{1}{10} \cdot \frac{1}{4} \cdot \frac{1}{11} \cdot \frac{1}{3} \cdot \frac{1}{13} \cdot \frac{1}{100} = \frac{1}{20,592,000}$, assuming the characteristics are independent of one another.

2. You would use the multiplication rule, since we are looking for the probability of multiple events happening together.

3. We do not know if the characteristics are dependent or independent, but we assumed independence for the calculation in question 1.

4. The probabilities would change if there were dependence among two or more events.

5. Answers will vary. One possible answer is that probabilities can be used to explain how unlikely it is to have a set of events occur at the same time (in this case, how unlikely it is to have another couple with the same characteristics in that area).

6. Answers will vary. One possible answer is that if the only eyewitness was the woman who was mugged and the probabilities are accurate, it seems very unlikely that a couple matching these characteristics would be in that area at that time. This might cause you to convict the couple.

7. Answers will vary. One possible answer is that our probabilities are theoretical and serve a purpose when appropriate, but that court cases are based on much more than impersonal chance.

8. Answers will vary. One possible answer is that juries decide whether or not to convict a defendant if they find evidence "beyond a reasonable doubt" that the person is guilty. In probability terms, this means that if the defendant was actually innocent, then the chance of seeing the events that occurred are so unlikely as to have occurred by chance. Therefore, the jury concludes that the defendant is guilty.

Section 4–5 Garage Door Openers

1. Four on/off switches lead to 16 different settings.

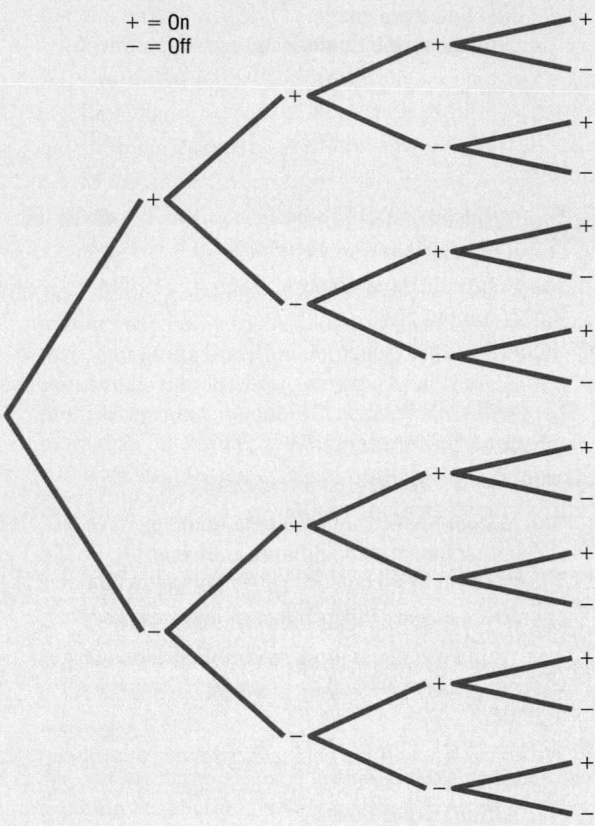

+ = On
− = Off

2. With 5 on/off switches, there are $2^5 = 32$ different settings. With 6 on/off switches, there are $2^6 = 64$ different settings. In general, if there are k on/off switches, there are 2^k different settings.

3. With 8 consecutive on/off switches, there are $2^8 = 256$ different settings.

4. It is less likely for someone to be able to open your garage door if you have 8 on/off settings (probability about 0.4%) than if you have 4 on/off switches (probability about 6.0%). Having 8 on/off switches in the opener seems pretty safe.

5. Each key blank could be made into $5^5 = 3,125$ possible keys.

6. If there were 420,000 Dodge Caravans sold in Canada, then any one key could start about $420,000/3,125 = 134.4$, or about 134, different Caravans.

7. Answers will vary.

Section 4–6 Counting Rules and Probability

1. There are five different events: each multiple-choice question is an event.

2. These events are independent.

3. If you guess on 1 question, the probability of getting it correct is 0.20. Thus, if you guess on all 5 questions, the probability of getting all of them correct is $(0.20)^5 = 0.00032$.

4. The probability that a person would guess answer A for a question is 0.20, so the probability that a person would guess answer A for each question is $(0.20)^5 = 0.00032$.

5. There are five different events: each matching question is an event.

6. These are dependent events.

7. The probability of getting them all correct if you are guessing is $\frac{1}{5} \cdot \frac{1}{4} \cdot \frac{1}{3} \cdot \frac{1}{2} \cdot \frac{1}{1} = \frac{1}{120} = 0.0083$.

8. The difference between the two problems is that we are sampling without replacement in the second problem, so the denominator changes in the event probabilities.

5 Discrete Probability Distributions

Objectives

After completing this chapter, you should be able to

1. Construct a probability distribution for a random variable.

2. Find the mean, variance, standard deviation, and expected value for a discrete random variable.

3. Find the exact probability for X successes in n trials of a binomial experiment.

4. Find the mean, variance, and standard deviation for the variable of a binomial distribution.

5. Find probabilities for outcomes of variables, using the Poisson, hypergeometric, and multinomial distributions.

Outline

5–1 Introduction

5–2 Probability Distributions

5–3 Mean, Variance, Standard Deviation, and Expectation

5–4 The Binomial Distribution

5–5 Other Types of Distributions (Optional)

5–6 Summary

Statistics Today

Is Pooling Worthwhile?

Blood samples are used to screen people for certain diseases. When the disease is rare, health-care workers sometimes combine or pool the blood samples of a group of individuals into one batch and then test it. If the test result of the batch is negative, no further testing is needed since none of the individuals in the group has the disease. However, if the test result of the batch is positive, each individual in the group must be tested.

Consider this hypothetical example: Suppose the probability of a person having the disease is 0.05, and a pooled sample of 15 individuals is tested. What is the probability that no further testing will be needed for the individuals in the sample? The answer to this question can be found by using what is called the *binomial distribution*. See Statistics Today— Revisited, page 243, at the end of the chapter.

This chapter explains probability distributions in general and a specific, often used distribution called the binomial distribution. The Poisson, hypergeometric, and multinomial distributions are also explained.

5–1   Introduction

Many decisions in business, insurance, and other real-life situations are made by assigning probabilities to all possible outcomes pertaining to the situation and then evaluating the results. For example, a saleswoman can compute the probability that she will make 0, 1, 2, or 3 or more sales in a single day. An insurance company might be able to assign probabilities to the number of vehicles a family owns. A self-employed speaker might be able to compute the probabilities for giving 0, 1, 2, 3, or 4 or more speeches each week. Once these probabilities are assigned, statistics such as the mean, variance, and standard deviation can be computed for these events. With these statistics, various decisions can be made. The saleswoman will be able to compute the average number of sales she makes per week, and if she is working on commission, she will be able to approximate her weekly income over a period of time, say, monthly. The public speaker will be able to plan ahead and approximate his average income and expenses. The insurance company can use its information to design special computer forms and programs to accommodate its customers' future needs.

This chapter explains the concepts and applications of what is called a *probability distribution*. In addition, special probability distributions, such as the *binomial, multinomial, Poisson,* and *hypergeometric* distributions, are explained.

5–2   Probability Distributions

Objective

Construct a probability distribution for a random variable.

Before probability distribution is defined formally, the definition of a variable is reviewed. In Chapter 1, a *variable* was defined as a characteristic or attribute that can assume different values. Various letters of the alphabet, such as X, Y, or Z, are used to represent variables. Since the variables in this chapter form a probability distribution, they are called *random variables.*

For example, if a die is rolled, a letter such as X can be used to represent the outcomes. Then the value that X can assume is 1, 2, 3, 4, 5, or 6, corresponding to the outcomes of rolling a single die. If two coins are tossed, a letter, say Y, can be used to represent the number of heads, in this case 0, 1, or 2. As another example, if the temperature at 8:00 A.M. is 6°C and at noon it is 12°C, then the values T that the temperature assumes are said to be random, since they are due to varying atmospheric conditions at the time the temperature was taken.

> A **random variable** is a function that assigns a unique numerical value, determined by chance, to each outcome of an experiment.

Also recall from Chapter 1 that one can classify variables as discrete or continuous by observing the values the variable can assume. If a variable can assume only a specific number of values, such as the outcomes for the roll of a die or the outcomes for the toss of a coin, then the variable is called a *discrete variable.*

Discrete variables have a finite number of possible values or an infinite number of values that can be counted. The word *counted* means that they can be enumerated using the numbers 1, 2, 3, etc. For example, the number of joggers in Riverview Park each day and the number of phone calls received after a TV commercial airs are examples of discrete variables, since they can be counted.

Variables that can assume all values in the interval between any two given values are called *continuous variables.* For example, if the temperature goes from 17°C to 26°C in a 24-hour period, it has passed through every possible number from 17°C to 26°C. *Continuous random variables are obtained from data that can be measured rather than counted.* Continuous random variables can assume an infinite number of values and can be decimal and fractional values. On a continuous scale, a person's weight might be exactly 83.201 kilograms if a scale could measure weight to the thousandths place; however, on a digital scale that measures only to tenths of kilograms, the weight would be 83.2 kilograms. Examples of continuous variables are heights, weights, temperatures, and time. In this chapter only discrete random variables are used; Chapter 6 explains continuous random variables.

The procedure shown here for constructing a probability distribution for a discrete random variable uses the probability experiment of tossing three coins. Recall that when three coins are tossed, the sample space is represented as TTT, TTH, THT, HTT, HHT, HTH, THH, HHH; and if X is the random variable for the number of heads, then X assumes the value 0, 1, 2, or 3.

Probabilities for the values of X can be determined as follows:

No heads	One head			Two heads			Three heads
TTT	TTH	THT	HTT	HHT	HTH	THH	HHH
$\frac{1}{8}$	$\frac{1}{8}$	$\frac{1}{8}$	$\frac{1}{8}$	$\frac{1}{8}$	$\frac{1}{8}$	$\frac{1}{8}$	$\frac{1}{8}$
$\frac{1}{8}$	$\frac{3}{8}$			$\frac{3}{8}$			$\frac{1}{8}$

Hence, the probability of getting no heads is $\frac{1}{8}$, one head is $\frac{3}{8}$, two heads is $\frac{3}{8}$, and three heads is $\frac{1}{8}$. From these values, a probability distribution can be constructed by listing the outcomes and assigning the probability of each outcome, as shown here.

Number of heads X	0	1	2	3
Probability $P(X)$	$\frac{1}{8}$	$\frac{3}{8}$	$\frac{3}{8}$	$\frac{1}{8}$

> A **discrete probability distribution** consists of the values a random variable can assume and the corresponding probabilities of the values.

Discrete probability distributions can be shown by using a graph or a table. Probability distributions can also be represented by a formula. See Exercises 31–36 at the end of this section for examples.

Probability examples in this section utilize discrete data procedures whereas Chapter 6 makes use of methods for solving problems relating to continuous data.

Example 5–1

Construct a probability distribution for rolling a single die.

Solution

Since the sample space is 1, 2, 3, 4, 5, 6 and each outcome has a probability of $\frac{1}{6}$, the distribution is as shown.

Outcome X	1	2	3	4	5	6
Probability $P(X)$	$\frac{1}{6}$	$\frac{1}{6}$	$\frac{1}{6}$	$\frac{1}{6}$	$\frac{1}{6}$	$\frac{1}{6}$

Probability distributions can be shown graphically by representing the values of X on the x axis and the probabilities $P(X)$ on the y axis.

Example 5–2

Represent graphically the probability distribution for the sample space for tossing three coins.

Number of heads X	0	1	2	3
Probability $P(X)$	$\frac{1}{8}$	$\frac{3}{8}$	$\frac{3}{8}$	$\frac{1}{8}$

Solution

The values that X assumes are located on the x axis, and the values for $P(X)$ are located on the y axis. The graph is shown in Figure 5–1.

Figure 5–1

Probability Distribution for Example 5–2

Note that for visual appearances, it is not necessary to start with 0 at the origin.

Examples 5–1 and 5–2 are illustrations of *theoretical* probability distributions. One did not need to actually perform the experiments to compute the probabilities. In contrast, to construct actual probability distributions, one must observe the variable over a period of time. They are empirical, as shown in Example 5–3.

Example 5–3

During the summer months, a rental agency keeps track of the number of chainsaws it rents each day during a period of 90 days. The number of saws rented per day is represented by the variable X. The results are shown here. Compute the probability $P(X)$ for each X, and construct a probability distribution and graph for the data.

X	Number of days
0	45
1	30
2	15
	Total 90

Solution

The probability $P(X)$ can be computed for each X by dividing the number of days that X saws were rented by total days.

For 0 saws: $\frac{45}{90} = 0.50$

For 1 saw: $\frac{30}{90} \approx 0.33$

For 2 saws: $\frac{15}{90} \approx 0.17$

The distribution is shown here.

Number of saws rented X	0	1	2
Probability $P(X)$	0.50	0.33	0.17

The graph is shown in Figure 5–2.

Figure 5–2

Probability Distribution for Example 5–3

Speaking of

Statistics

Coins, Births, and Other Random (?) Events

Examples of random events such as tossing coins are used in almost all books on probability. But is flipping a coin really a random event?

Tossing coins dates back to ancient Roman times when the coins usually consisted of the Emperor's head on one side (i.e., heads) and another icon such as a ship on the other side redundant. Tossing coins was used in both fortune telling and ancient Roman games.

A Chinese form of divination called the *I-Ching* (pronounced E-Ching) is thought to be at least 4000 years old. It consists of 64 hexagrams made up of six horizontal lines. Each line is either broken or unbroken, representing the yin and the yang. These 64 hexagrams are supposed to represent all possible situations in life. To consult the I-Ching, a question is asked and then three coins are tossed six times. The way the coins fall, either heads up or heads down, determines whether the line is broken (yin) or unbroken (yang). Once the hexagon is determined, its meaning is consulted and interpreted to get the answer to the question. (*Note:* Another method used to determine the hexagon employs yarrow sticks.)

In the 16th century, a mathematician named Abraham DeMoivre used the outcomes of tossing coins to study what later became known as the normal distribution; however, his work at that time was not widely known.

Mathematicians usually consider the outcomes of a coin toss a random event. That is, each probability of getting a head is $\frac{1}{2}$, and the probability of getting a tail is $\frac{1}{2}$. Also, it is not possible to predict with 100% certainty which outcome will occur. But new studies question this theory. During World War II a South African mathematician named John Kerrich tossed a coin 10,000 times while he was interned in a German prison camp. Unfortunately, the results of his experiment were never recorded, so we don't know the number of heads that occurred.

Several studies have shown that when a coin-tossing device is used, the probability that a coin will land on the same side on which it is placed on the coin-tossing device is about 51%. It would take about 10,000 tosses to become aware of this bias. Furthermore, researchers showed that when a coin is spun on its edge, the coin would fall tails up about 80% of the time since there is more metal on the heads side of a coin. This makes the coin slightly heavier on the heads side than on the tails side.

Another assumption commonly made in probability theory is that the number of male births is equal to the number of female births and that the probability of a boy being born is $\frac{1}{2}$ and the probability of a girl being born is $\frac{1}{2}$. We know this is not exactly true.

In the later 1700s, a French mathematician named Pierre Simon Laplace attempted to prove that more males than females are born. He used records from 1745 to 1770 in Paris and showed that the percentage of females born was about 49%. Although these percentages vary somewhat from location to location, further surveys show they are generally true worldwide. Even though there are discrepancies, we generally consider the outcomes to be 50–50 since these discrepancies are relatively small.

Based on this article, would you consider the coin toss at the beginning of a football game fair?

Two Requirements for a Probability Distribution

1. The sum of the probabilities of all the events in the sample space must equal 1; that is, $\Sigma P(X) = 1$.

2. The probability of each event in the sample space must be between or equal to 0 and 1. That is, $0 \leq P(X) \leq 1$.

The first requirement states that the sum of the probabilities of all the events must be equal to 1. This sum cannot be less than 1 or greater than 1 since the sample space includes *all* possible outcomes of the probability experiment. The second requirement states that the probability of any individual event must be a value from 0 to 1. The reason (as stated in Chapter 4) is that the range of the probability of any individual value can be 0, 1, or any value between 0 and 1. A probability cannot be a negative number or greater than 1.

Example 5–4

Determine whether each distribution is a probability distribution.

a.

X	0	5	10	15	20
P(X)	$\frac{1}{5}$	$\frac{1}{5}$	$\frac{1}{5}$	$\frac{1}{5}$	$\frac{1}{5}$

c.

X	1	2	3	4
P(X)	$\frac{1}{4}$	$\frac{1}{8}$	$\frac{1}{16}$	$\frac{9}{16}$

b.

X	0	2	4	6
P(X)	-1.0	1.5	0.3	0.2

d.

X	2	3	7
P(X)	0.5	0.3	0.4

Solution

a. Yes, it is a probability distribution.

b. No, it is not a probability distribution, since $P(X)$ cannot be 1.5 or -1.0.

c. Yes, it is a probability distribution.

d. No, it is not, since $\Sigma P(X) = 1.2$.

Many variables in business, education, engineering, and other areas can be analyzed by using probability distributions. Section 5–3 shows methods for finding the mean and standard deviation for a probability distribution.

Applying the Concepts 5–2

Dropping College/University Courses

Use the following table to answer the questions.

Reason for Dropping a College/University Course	Frequency	Percentage
Too difficult	45	
Illness	40	
Change in work schedule	20	
Change of major	14	
Family-related problems	9	
Money	7	
Miscellaneous	6	
No meaningful reason	3	

1. What is the variable under study? Is it a random variable?
2. How many people were in the study?
3. Complete the table.
4. From the information given, what is the probability that a student will drop a class because of illness? Money? Change of major?
5. Would you consider the information in the table to be a probability distribution?
6. Are the categories mutually exclusive?
7. Are the categories independent?
8. Are the categories exhaustive?
9. Are the two requirements for a discrete probability distribution met?

See page 246 for the answers.

Exercises 5–2

1. Define and give three examples of a random variable.

2. Explain the difference between a discrete and a continuous random variable.

3. Give three examples of a discrete random variable.

4. Give three examples of a continuous random variable.

5. What is a probability distribution? Give an example.

For Exercises 6 through 11, determine whether the distribution represents a probability distribution. If it does not, state why.

6.
X	1	6	11	16	21
P(X)	$\frac{1}{7}$	$\frac{1}{7}$	$\frac{3}{7}$	$\frac{2}{7}$	$\frac{1}{7}$

7.
X	3	6	8	12
P(X)	0.3	0.5	0.7	−0.8

8.
X	3	6	8
P(X)	−0.3	0.6	0.7

9.
X	1	2	3	4	5
P(X)	$\frac{3}{10}$	$\frac{1}{10}$	$\frac{1}{10}$	$\frac{2}{10}$	$\frac{3}{10}$

10.
X	20	30	40	50
P(X)	1.1	0.2	0.9	0.3

11.
X	5	10	15
P(X)	1.2	0.3	0.5

For Exercises 12 through 18, state whether the variable is discrete or continuous.

12. The speed of a jet airplane

13. The number of cheeseburgers a fast-food restaurant serves each day

14. The number of people who play the national Lotto 6/49 lottery each day

15. The weight of a Siberian tiger

16. The time it takes to complete a marathon

17. The number of mathematics majors in your school

18. The blood pressures of all patients admitted to a hospital on a specific day

For Exercises 19 through 26, construct a probability distribution for the data and draw a graph for the distribution.

19. The probabilities that a patient will have 0, 1, 2, or 3 medical tests performed on entering a hospital are $\frac{6}{15}$, $\frac{5}{15}$, $\frac{3}{15}$, and $\frac{1}{15}$, respectively.

20. The probabilities of a return on an investment of $1000, $2000, and $3000 are $\frac{1}{2}$, $\frac{1}{4}$, and $\frac{1}{4}$, respectively.

21. The probabilities of a machine manufacturing 0, 1, 2, 3, 4, or 5 defective parts in one day are 0.75, 0.17, 0.04, 0.025, 0.01, and 0.005, respectively.

22. The probabilities that a customer will purchase 0, 1, 2, or 3 books are 0.45, 0.30, 0.15, and 0.10, respectively.

23. A die is loaded in such a way that the probabilities of getting 1, 2, 3, 4, 5, and 6 are $\frac{1}{2}$, $\frac{1}{6}$, $\frac{1}{12}$, $\frac{1}{12}$, $\frac{1}{12}$, and $\frac{1}{12}$, respectively.

24. The probabilities that a customer selects 1, 2, 3, 4, and 5 items at a convenience store are 0.32, 0.12, 0.23, 0.18, and 0.15, respectively.

25. The probabilities that a surgeon operates on 3, 4, 5, 6, or 7 patients in any one day are 0.15, 0.20, 0.25, 0.20, and 0.20, respectively.

26. Three patients are given a headache relief tablet. The probabilities for 0, 1, 2, or 3 successes are 0.18, 0.52, 0.21, and 0.09, respectively.

27. A box contains two $5 bills, three $10 bills, one $20 bill, and three $50 bills. Construct a probability distribution for the data.

28. Construct a probability distribution for a family of 3 children. Let X represent the number of boys.

29. Construct a probability distribution for drawing a card from a deck of 40 cards consisting of 10 cards numbered 1, 10 cards numbered 2, 15 cards numbered 3, and 5 cards numbered 4.

30. Using the sample space for tossing 2 dice, construct a probability distribution for the sums 2 through 12.

Extending the Concepts

A probability distribution can be written in formula notation such as $P(X) = 1/X$, where $X = 2, 3, 6$. The distribution is shown as follows:

X	2	3	6
$P(X)$	$\frac{1}{2}$	$\frac{1}{3}$	$\frac{1}{6}$

For Exercises 31 through 36, write the distribution for the formula and determine whether it is a probability distribution.

31. $P(X) = X/6$ for $X = 1, 2, 3$

32. $P(X) = X$ for $X = 0.2, 0.3, 0.5$

33. $P(X) = X/6$ for $X = 3, 4, 7$

34. $P(X) = X + 0.1$ for $X = 0.1, 0.02, 0.04$

35. $P(X) = X/7$ for $X = 1, 2, 4$

36. $P(X) = X/(X + 2)$ for $X = 0, 1, 2$

5–3 Mean, Variance, Standard Deviation, and Expectation

Objective ②

Find the mean, variance, standard deviation, and expected value for a discrete random variable.

The mean, variance, and standard deviation for a probability distribution are computed differently from the mean, variance, and standard deviation for samples. This section explains how these measures—as well as a new measure called the *expectation*—are calculated for probability distributions.

Mean

In Chapter 3, the mean for a sample or population was computed by adding the values and dividing by the total number of values, as shown in the formulas

$$\overline{X} = \frac{\Sigma X}{n} \qquad \mu = \frac{\Sigma X}{N}$$

But how would one compute the mean of the number of spots that show on top when a die is rolled? One could try rolling the die, say, 10 times, recording the number of spots, and finding the mean; however, this answer would only approximate the true mean. What about 50 rolls or 100 rolls? Actually, the more times the die is rolled, the better the approximation. One might ask, then, How many times must the die be rolled to get the exact answer? *It must be rolled an infinite number of times.* Since this task is impossible, the previous formulas cannot be used because the denominators would be infinity. Hence, a new method of computing the mean is necessary. This method gives the exact theoretical value of the mean as if it were possible to roll the die an infinite number of times.

Before the formula is stated, an example will be used to explain the concept. Suppose two coins are tossed repeatedly, and the number of heads that occurred is recorded. What will be the mean of the number of heads? The sample space is

HH, HT, TH, TT

Historical Note

A professor, Augustin Louis Cauchy (1789–1857), wrote a book on probability. While he was teaching at the Military School of Paris, one of his students was Napoleon Bonaparte.

and each outcome has a probability of $\frac{1}{4}$. Now, in the long run, one would *expect* two heads (HH) to occur approximately $\frac{1}{4}$ of the time, one head to occur approximately $\frac{1}{2}$ of the time (HT or TH), and no heads (TT) to occur approximately $\frac{1}{4}$ of the time. Hence, on average, one would expect the number of heads to be

$$\tfrac{1}{4} \cdot 2 + \tfrac{1}{2} \cdot 1 + \tfrac{1}{4} \cdot 0 = 1$$

That is, if it were possible to toss the coins many times or an infinite number of times, the *average* of the number of heads would be 1.

Hence, to find the mean for a probability distribution, one must multiply each possible outcome by its corresponding probability and find the sum of the products.

Formula for the Mean of a Probability Distribution

The mean of a random variable with a discrete probability distribution is

$$\mu = X_1 \cdot P(X_1) + X_2 \cdot P(X_2) + X_3 \cdot P(X_3) + \cdots + X_n \cdot P(X_n)$$
$$= \Sigma X \cdot P(X)$$

where $X_1, X_2, X_3, \ldots, X_n$ are the outcomes and $P(X_1), P(X_2), P(X_3), \ldots, P(X_n)$ are the corresponding probabilities.

Note: $\Sigma X \cdot P(X)$ means to sum the products.

Rounding Rule for the Mean, Variance, and Standard Deviation for a Probability Distribution

The rounding rule for the mean, variance, and standard deviation for variables of a probability distribution is this: The mean, variance, and standard deviation should be rounded to one more decimal place than the outcome X. When fractions are used, they should be reduced to lowest terms.

Examples 5–5 through 5–8 illustrate the use of the formula.

Example 5–5

Find the mean of the number of spots that appear when a die is tossed.

Solution

In the toss of a die, the mean can be computed thus.

Outcome X	1	2	3	4	5	6
Probability $P(X)$	$\frac{1}{6}$	$\frac{1}{6}$	$\frac{1}{6}$	$\frac{1}{6}$	$\frac{1}{6}$	$\frac{1}{6}$

$$\mu = \Sigma X \cdot P(X) = 1 \cdot \tfrac{1}{6} + 2 \cdot \tfrac{1}{6} + 3 \cdot \tfrac{1}{6} + 4 \cdot \tfrac{1}{6} + 5 \cdot \tfrac{1}{6} + 6 \cdot \tfrac{1}{6}$$
$$= \tfrac{21}{6} = 3\tfrac{1}{2} \text{ or } 3.5$$

That is, when a die is tossed many times, the theoretical mean will be 3.5. Note that even though the die cannot show a 3.5, the theoretical average is 3.5.

The reason why this formula gives the theoretical mean is that in the long run, each outcome would occur approximately $\frac{1}{6}$ of the time. Hence, multiplying the outcome by its corresponding probability and finding the sum would yield the theoretical mean. In other words, outcome 1 would occur approximately $\frac{1}{6}$ of the time, outcome 2 would occur approximately $\frac{1}{6}$ of the time, etc.

Example 5–6

In a family with 2 children, find the mean of the number of children who will be girls.

Solution

The probability distribution is as follows:

Number of girls X	0	1	2
Probability $P(X)$	$\frac{1}{4}$	$\frac{1}{2}$	$\frac{1}{4}$

Hence, the mean is

$$\mu = \Sigma X \cdot P(X) = 0 \cdot \tfrac{1}{4} + 1 \cdot \tfrac{1}{2} + 2 \cdot \tfrac{1}{4} = 1$$

Example 5–7

If 3 coins are tossed, find the mean of the number of heads that occur. (See the table preceding Example 5–1.)

Solution

The probability distribution is

Number of heads X	0	1	2	3
Probability $P(X)$	$\frac{1}{8}$	$\frac{3}{8}$	$\frac{3}{8}$	$\frac{1}{8}$

The mean is

$$\mu = \Sigma X \cdot P(X) = 0 \cdot \tfrac{1}{8} + 1 \cdot \tfrac{3}{8} + 2 \cdot \tfrac{3}{8} + 3 \cdot \tfrac{1}{8} = \tfrac{12}{8} = 1\tfrac{1}{2} \text{ or } 1.5$$

The value 1.5 cannot occur as an outcome. Nevertheless, it is the long-run or theoretical average.

Example 5–8

The probability distribution shown represents the number of trips of 5 nights or more that Canadian adults take per year. (That is, 6% do not take any trips lasting 5 nights or more, 70% take one trip lasting 5 nights or more per year, etc.) Find the mean.

Number of trips X	0	1	2	3	4
Probability $P(X)$	0.06	0.70	0.20	0.03	0.01

Solution

$$\begin{aligned}
\mu &= \Sigma X \cdot P(X) \\
&= (0)(0.06) + (1)(0.70) + (2)(0.20) + (3)(0.03) + (4)(0.01) \\
&= 0 + 0.70 + 0.40 + 0.09 + 0.04 \\
&= 1.23 \approx 1.2
\end{aligned}$$

Hence, the mean of the number of trips lasting 5 nights or more per year taken by Canadian adults is 1.2.

In 1892, the Canadian
Criminal Code
declared a complete
ban on all gambling
activities.

Variance and Standard Deviation

For a probability distribution, the mean of the random variable describes the measure of the so-called long-run or theoretical average, but it does not tell anything about the spread of the distribution. Recall from Chapter 3 that in order to measure this spread or variability, statisticians use the variance and standard deviation. These formulas were used:

$$\sigma^2 = \frac{\Sigma(X - \mu)^2}{N} \qquad \text{or} \qquad \sigma = \sqrt{\frac{\Sigma(X - \mu)^2}{N}}$$

These formulas cannot be used for a random variable of a probability distribution since N is infinite, so the variance and standard deviation must be computed differently.

To find the variance for the random variable of a probability distribution, subtract the theoretical mean of the random variable from each outcome and square the difference. Then multiply each difference by its corresponding probability and add the products. The formula is

$$\sigma^2 = \Sigma[(X - \mu)^2 \cdot P(X)]$$

Finding the variance by using this formula is somewhat tedious. So for simplified computations, a shortcut formula can be used. This formula is algebraically equivalent to the longer one and is used in the examples that follow.

Formula for the Variance of a Probability Distribution

Find the variance of a probability distribution by multiplying the square of each outcome by its corresponding probability, summing those products, and subtracting the square of the mean. The formula for the variance of a probability distribution is

$$\sigma^2 = \Sigma[X^2 \cdot P(X)] - \mu^2$$

The standard deviation of a probability distribution is

$$\sigma = \sqrt{\sigma^2} \qquad \text{or} \qquad \sqrt{\Sigma[X^2 \cdot P(X)] - \mu^2}$$

Remember that the variance and standard deviation cannot be negative.

Example 5–9

Compute the variance and standard deviation for the probability distribution in Example 5–5.

Solution

Recall that the mean is $\mu = 3.5$, as computed in Example 5–5. Square each outcome and multiply by the corresponding probability, sum those products, and then subtract the square of the mean.

$$\sigma^2 = \left(1^2 \cdot \tfrac{1}{6} + 2^2 \cdot \tfrac{1}{6} + 3^2 \cdot \tfrac{1}{6} + 4^2 \cdot \tfrac{1}{6} + 5^2 \cdot \tfrac{1}{6} + 6^2 \cdot \tfrac{1}{6}\right) - (3.5)^2 \approx 2.9$$

To get the standard deviation, find the square root of the variance.

$$\sigma = \sqrt{2.9} \approx 1.7$$

Example 5–10	Five balls numbered 0, 2, 4, 6, and 8 are placed in a bag. After the balls are mixed, one is selected, its number is noted, and then it is replaced. If this experiment is repeated many times, find the variance and standard deviation of the numbers on the balls.

Solution

Let X be the number on each ball. The probability distribution is

Number on ball X	0	2	4	6	8
Probability $P(X)$	$\frac{1}{5}$	$\frac{1}{5}$	$\frac{1}{5}$	$\frac{1}{5}$	$\frac{1}{5}$

Historical Note

In 1657 a Dutch mathematician, Christian Huygens, wrote a treatise on the Pascal-Fermat correspondence and introduced the idea of *mathematical expectation*.

The mean is

$$\mu = \Sigma X \cdot P(X) = 0 \cdot \tfrac{1}{5} + 2 \cdot \tfrac{1}{5} + 4 \cdot \tfrac{1}{5} + 6 \cdot \tfrac{1}{5} + 8 \cdot \tfrac{1}{5} = 4.0$$

The variance is

$$\begin{aligned}
\sigma^2 &= \Sigma[X^2 \cdot P(X)] - \mu^2 \\
&= [0^2 \cdot (\tfrac{1}{5}) + 2^2 \cdot (\tfrac{1}{5}) + 4^2 \cdot (\tfrac{1}{5}) + 6^2 \cdot (\tfrac{1}{5}) + 8^2 \cdot (\tfrac{1}{5})] - 4^2 \\
&= [0 + \tfrac{4}{5} + \tfrac{16}{5} + \tfrac{36}{5} + \tfrac{64}{5}] - 16 \\
&= \tfrac{120}{5} - 16 \\
&= 24 - 16 = 8
\end{aligned}$$

The standard deviation is $\sigma = \sqrt{8} \approx 2.8$.

The mean, variance, and standard deviation can also be found by using vertical columns, as shown [0.2 is used for $P(X)$ since $\frac{1}{5} = 0.2$].

X	$P(X)$	$X \cdot P(X)$	$X^2 \cdot P(X)$
0	0.2	0	0
2	0.2	0.4	0.8
4	0.2	0.8	3.2
6	0.2	1.2	7.2
8	0.2	1.6	12.8
		$\Sigma X \cdot P(X) = 4.0$	$\Sigma X^2 \cdot P(X) = 24.0$

Find the mean by summing the $X \cdot P(X)$ column and the variance by summing the $X^2 \cdot P(X)$ column and subtracting the square of the mean:

$$\sigma^2 = 24 - 4^2 = 8 \qquad \text{and} \qquad \sigma = \sqrt{8} \approx 2.8$$

Example 5–11	A talk radio station has 4 telephone lines. If the host is unable to talk (i.e., during a commercial) or is talking to a person, the other callers are placed on hold. When all lines are in use, others who are trying to call in get a busy signal. The probability that 0, 1, 2, 3, or 4 people will get through is shown in the distribution. Find the variance and standard deviation for the distribution.

X	0	1	2	3	4
$P(X)$	0.18	0.34	0.23	0.21	0.04

Should the station have considered getting more phone lines installed?

Solution

The mean is

$$\mu = \Sigma X \cdot P(X)$$
$$= 0 \cdot (0.18) + 1 \cdot (0.34) + 2 \cdot (0.23) + 3 \cdot (0.21) + 4 \cdot (0.04)$$
$$= 1.6 \text{ (rounded)}$$

The variance is

$$\sigma^2 = \Sigma [X^2 \cdot P(X)] - \mu^2$$
$$= [0^2 \cdot (0.18) + 1^2 \cdot (0.34) + 2^2 \cdot (0.23) + 3^2 \cdot (0.21) + 4^2 \cdot (0.04)] - 1.6^2$$
$$= [0 + 0.34 + 0.92 + 1.89 + 0.64] - 2.56$$
$$= 3.79 - 2.56 = 1.23$$
$$= 1.2 \text{ (rounded)}$$

The standard deviation is $\sigma = \sqrt{\sigma^2}$, or $\sigma = \sqrt{1.2} = 1.1$ (rounded)

No. The mean number of people calling at any one time is 1.6. Since the standard deviation is 1.1, most callers would be accommodated by having 4 phone lines because $\mu + 2\sigma$ would be $1.6 + 2(1.1) = 1.6 + 2.2 = 3.8$. Very few callers would get a busy signal since at least 75% of the callers would either get through or be put on hold. (See Chebyshev's theorem in Section 3–3.)

Expectation

Another concept related to the mean for a probability distribution is the concept of expected value or expectation. Expected value is used in various types of games of chance, in insurance, and in other areas, such as decision theory.

The **expected value** of a discrete random variable of a probability distribution is the theoretical average of the variable. The formula is

$$\mu = E(X) = \Sigma X \cdot P(X)$$

The symbol $E(X)$ is used for the expected value.

The formula for the expected value is the same as the formula for the theoretical mean. The expected value, then, is the theoretical mean of the probability distribution. That is, $E(X) = \mu$.

When expected value problems involve money, it is customary to round the answer to the nearest cent.

Example 5–12

One thousand tickets are sold at $1 each for a colour television valued at $350. What is the expected value of the gain if a person purchases one ticket?

Solution

The problem can be set up as follows:

	Win	Lose
Gain X	$349	−$1
Probability $P(X)$	$\dfrac{1}{1000}$	$\dfrac{999}{1000}$

Two things should be noted. First, for a win, the net gain is $349, since the person does not get the cost of the ticket ($1) back. Second, for a loss, the gain is represented by a negative number, in this case −$1. The solution, then, is

$$E(X) = \$349 \cdot \frac{1}{1000} + (-\$1) \cdot \frac{999}{1000} = -\$0.65$$

Expected value problems of this type can also be solved by finding the overall gain (i.e., the value of the prize won or the amount of money won, not considering the cost of the ticket for the prize or the cost to play the game) and subtracting the cost of the tickets or the cost to play the game, as shown:

$$E(X) = \$350 \cdot \frac{1}{1000} - \$1 = -\$0.65$$

Here, the overall gain ($350) must be used.

Note that the expectation is −$0.65. This does not mean that a person loses $0.65, since the person can only win a television set valued at $350 or lose $1 on the ticket. What this expectation means is that the average of the losses is $0.65 for each of the 1000 ticket holders. Here is another way of looking at this situation: If a person purchased one ticket each week over a long time, the average loss would be $0.65 per ticket, since theoretically, on average, that person would win the set once for each 1000 tickets purchased.

Example 5–13

One thousand tickets are sold at $1 each for 4 prizes of $100, $50, $25, and $10. After each prize drawing, the winning ticket is then returned to the pool of tickets. What is the expected value if a person purchases 2 tickets?

Gain X	$98	$48	$23	$8	−$2
Probability $P(X)$	$\frac{2}{1000}$	$\frac{2}{1000}$	$\frac{2}{1000}$	$\frac{2}{1000}$	$\frac{992}{1000}$

Solution

$$E(X) = \$98 \cdot \frac{2}{1000} + \$48 \cdot \frac{2}{1000} + \$23 \cdot \frac{2}{1000} + \$8 \cdot \frac{2}{1000} + (-\$2) \cdot \frac{992}{1000}$$

$$= -\$1.63$$

An alternate solution is

$$E(X) = \$100 \cdot \frac{2}{1000} + \$50 \cdot \frac{2}{1000} + \$25 \cdot \frac{2}{1000} + \$10 \cdot \frac{2}{1000} - \$2$$

$$= -\$1.63$$

Example 5–14

A financial advisor suggests that his client select one of two types of bonds in which to invest $5000. Bond X pays a return of 4% and has a default rate of 2%. Bond Y has a $2\frac{1}{2}$% return and a default rate of 1%. Find the expected rate of return and decide which bond would be a better investment. When the bond defaults, the investor loses all the investment.

Solution

The return on bond X is $\$5000 \cdot 4\% = \$200$. The expected return then is

$$E(X) = \$200(0.98) - \$5000(0.02) = \$96$$

The return on bond Y is $\$5000 \cdot 2\frac{1}{2}\% = \$125$. The expected return then is

$$E(X) = \$125(0.99) - \$5000(0.01) = \$73.75$$

Hence, bond X would be a better investment since the expected return is higher.

In gambling games, if the expected value of the game is zero, the game is said to be fair. If the expected value of a game is positive, then the game is in favour of the player. That is, the player has a better-than-even chance of winning. If the expected value of the game is negative, then the game is said to be in favour of the house. That is, in the long run, the players will lose money.

In their book *The Complete Idiot's Guide to Gambling Like a Pro* (Alpha Books, 2002), authors Stanford Wong and Susan Spector give the expectations for various gambling games. The expected earnings game from a $100 bet Keno is $73, Roulette is $94.70, and Baccarat is $98.80. That means that the house wins $27 on Keno, $5.30 on Roulette, and $1.20 on Baccarat for every $100 bet. The bottom line here is that if you gamble long enough, sooner or later you will end up losing money.

Applying the Concepts 5–3

Expected Value

On March 28, 1979, the nuclear generating facility at Three Mile Island, Pennsylvania, began discharging radiation into the atmosphere. People exposed to even low levels of radiation can experience health problems ranging from very mild to severe, even causing death. A local newspaper reported that 11 babies were born with kidney problems in the three-county area surrounding the Three Mile Island nuclear power plant. The expected value for that problem in infants in that area was 3. Answer the following questions.

1. What does *expected value* mean?

2. Would you expect the exact value of 3 all the time?

3. If a news reporter stated that the number of cases of kidney problems in newborns was nearly four times as much as was usually expected, do you think pregnant mothers living in that area would be overly concerned?

4. Is it unlikely that 11 occurred by chance?

5. Are there any other statistics that could better inform the public?

6. Assume that 3 out of 2500 babies were born with kidney problems in that three-county area the year before the accident. Also assume that 11 out of 2500 babies were born with kidney problems in that three-county area the year after the accident. What is the real percent of increase in that abnormality?

7. Do you think that pregnant mothers living in that area should be overly concerned after looking at the results in terms of rates?

See page 246 for the answers.

Exercises 5–3

1. From past experience, a company has found that in cartons of transistors, 92% contain no defective transistors, 3% contain one defective transistor, 3% contain two defective transistors, and 2% contain three defective transistors. Find the mean, variance, and standard deviation for the defective transistors. About how many extra transistors per day would the company need to replace the defective ones if it used 10 cartons per day?

2. The number of suits sold per day at a retail store is shown in the table, with the corresponding probabilities. Find the mean, variance, and standard deviation of the distribution.

Number of suits sold X	19	20	21	22	23
Probability $P(X)$	0.2	0.2	0.3	0.2	0.1

If the manager of the retail store wants to be sure that he has enough suits for the next 5 days, how many should the manager purchase?

3. A bank vice president feels that each savings account customer has, on average, three credit cards. The following distribution represents the number of credit cards people own. Find the mean, variance, and standard deviation. Is the vice president correct?

Number of cards X	0	1	2	3	4
Probability $P(X)$	0.18	0.44	0.27	0.08	0.03

4. The number of refrigerators sold per day at a local appliance store is shown in the table, along with the corresponding probabilities. Find the mean, variance, and standard deviation.

Number of refrigerators sold X	0	1	2	3	4
Probability $P(X)$	0.1	0.2	0.3	0.2	0.2

5. A public speaker computes the probabilities for the number of speeches she gives each week. Compute the mean, variance, and standard deviation of the distribution shown.

Number of speeches X	0	1	2	3	4	5
Probability $P(X)$	0.06	0.42	0.22	0.12	0.15	0.03

If she receives $100 per speech, about how much will she earn per week?

6. A recent survey by an insurance company showed the following probabilities for the number of bedrooms in each insured home. Find the mean, variance, and standard deviation for the distribution.

Number of bedrooms X	2	3	4	5
Probability $P(X)$	0.3	0.4	0.2	0.1

7. A concerned parents group determined the number of commercials shown in each of 5 children's programs over a period of time. Find the mean, variance, and standard deviation for the distribution shown.

Number of commercials X	5	6	7	8	9
Probability $P(X)$	0.2	0.25	0.38	0.10	0.07

8. A study conducted by a TV station showed the number of televisions per household and the corresponding probabilities for each. Find the mean, variance, and standard deviation.

Number of televisions X	1	2	3	4
Probability $P(X)$	0.32	0.51	0.12	0.05

If you were taking a survey on the programs that were watched on television, how many program diaries would you send to each household in the survey?

9. The following distribution shows the number of students enrolled in CPR classes offered by the local fire department. Find the mean, variance, and standard deviation for the distribution.

Number of students X	12	13	14	15	16
Probability $P(X)$	0.15	0.20	0.38	0.18	0.09

10. A pizza shop owner determines the number of pizzas that are delivered each day. Find the mean, variance, and standard deviation for the distribution shown. If the manager stated that 45 pizzas were delivered on one day, do you think that this is a believable claim?

Number of deliveries X	35	36	37	38	39
Probability $P(X)$	0.1	0.2	0.3	0.3	0.1

11. An insurance company insures a person's antique coin collection worth $20,000 for an annual premium of $300. If the company figures that the probability of the collection being stolen is 0.002, what will be the company's expected profit?

12. A landscape contractor bids on jobs where he can make $3000 profit. The probabilities of getting 1, 2, 3, or 4 jobs per month are shown.

Number of jobs	1	2	3	4
Probability	0.2	0.3	0.4	0.1

Find the contractor's expected profit per month.

13. If a person rolls doubles when he tosses two dice, he wins $5. For the game to be fair, how much should the person pay to play the game?

14. If a player rolls two dice and gets a sum of 2 or 12, she wins $20. If the person gets a 7, she wins $5. The cost to play the game is $3. Find the expectation of the game.

15. A lottery offers one $1000 prize, one $500 prize, and five $100 prizes. One thousand tickets are sold at $3 each. Find the expectation if a person buys one ticket.

16. In Exercise 15, find the expectation if a person buys two tickets. Assume that the player's ticket is replaced after each draw and that the same ticket can win more than one prize.

17. For a daily lottery, a person selects a three-digit number. If the person plays for $1, she can win $500. Find the expectation. In the same daily lottery, if a person boxes a number, she will win $80. Find the expectation if the number 123 is played for $1 and boxed. (When a number is "boxed," it can win when the digits occur in any order.)

18. A 35-year-old woman purchases a $100,000 term life insurance policy for an annual payment of $360. Based on a period life table, the probability that she will survive the year is 0.999057. Find the expected value of the policy for the insurance company.

19. A person decides to invest $50,000 in a gas well. Based on history, the probabilities of the outcomes are as follows.

Outcome	$P(X)$
$80,000 (Highly successful)	0.2
$40,000 (Moderately successful)	0.7
−$50,000 (Dry well)	0.1

Find the expected value of the investment. Would you consider this a good investment?

Extending the Concepts

20. Construct a probability distribution for the sum shown on the faces when two dice are rolled. Find the mean, variance, and standard deviation of the distribution.

21. When one die is rolled, the expected value of the number of spots is 3.5. In Exercise 20, the mean number of spots was found for rolling two dice. What is the mean number of spots if three dice are rolled?

22. The formula for finding the variance for a probability distribution is

$$\sigma^2 = \Sigma[(X - \mu)^2 \cdot P(X)]$$

Verify algebraically that this formula gives the same result as the shortcut formula shown in this section.

23. Roll a die 100 times. Compute the mean and standard deviation. How does the result compare with the theoretical results of Example 5–5?

24. Roll two dice 100 times and find the mean, variance, and standard deviation of the sum of the spots. Compare the result with the theoretical results obtained in Exercise 20.

25. Conduct a survey of the number of extracurricular activities your classmates are enrolled in. Construct a probability distribution and find the mean, variance, and standard deviation.

26. In a recent promotional campaign, a company offered these prizes and the corresponding probabilities. Find the expected value of winning. The tickets are free.

Number of prizes	Amount	Probability
1	$100,000	$\frac{1}{1,000,000}$
2	10,000	$\frac{1}{50,000}$
5	1,000	$\frac{1}{10,000}$
10	100	$\frac{1}{1000}$

If the winner has to mail in the winning ticket to claim the prize, what will be the expectation if the cost of the stamp is considered? Use the current cost of a stamp for a first-class letter.

This study shows that a part of the brain reacts to the impact of losing, and it might explain why people tend to increase their bets after losing when gambling. Explain how this type of split decision making may influence fighter pilots, firefighters, or police officers, as the article states.

THE GAMBLER'S FALLACY
WHY WE EXPECT TO STRIKE IT RICH AFTER A LOSING STREAK

A GAMBLER USUALLY WAGERS more after taking a loss, in the misguided belief that a run of bad luck increases the probability of a win. We tend to cling to the misconception that past events can skew future odds. "On some level, you're thinking, 'If I just lost, it's going to even out.' The extent to which you're disturbed by a loss seems to go along with risky behaviour," says University of Michigan psychologist William Gehring, Ph.D., co-author of a new study linking dicey decision-making to neurological activity originating in the medial frontal cortex, long thought to be an area of the brain used in error detection.

Because people are so driven to up the ante after a loss, Gehring believes that the medial frontal cortex unconsciously influences future decisions based on the impact of the loss, in addition to registering the loss itself.

Gehring drew this conclusion by asking 12 subjects fitted with electrode caps to choose either the number 5 or 25, with the larger number representing the riskier bet.

On any given round, both numbers could amount to a loss, both could amount to a gain or the results could split, one number signifying a loss, the other a gain.

The medial frontal cortex responded to the outcome of a gamble within a quarter of a second, registering sharp electrical impulses only after a loss. Gehring points out that if the medial frontal cortex simply detected errors it would have reacted after participants chose the lesser of two possible gains. In other words, choosing "5" during a round in which both numbers paid off and betting on "25" would have yielded a larger profit.

After the study appeared in *Science*, Gehring received several emails from stock traders likening the "gambler's fallacy" to impulsive trading decisions made directly after off-loading a losing security. Researchers speculate that such risky, split-second decision-making could extend to fighter pilots, firefighters, and police officers—professions in which rapid-fire decisions are crucial and frequent.

—*Dan Schulman*

Source: *Psychology Today*, August 2002, p. 22. Used with permission.

5–4   The Binomial Distribution

Objective ❸

Find the exact probability for *X* successes in *n* trials of a binomial experiment.

Many types of probability problems have only two outcomes or can be reduced to two outcomes. For example, when a coin is tossed, it can land heads or tails. When a baby is born, it will be either male or female. In a basketball game, a team either wins or loses. A true/false item can be answered in only two ways, true or false. Other situations can be reduced to two outcomes. For example, a medical treatment can be classified as effective or ineffective, depending on the results. A person can be classified as having normal or abnormal blood pressure, depending on the measure of the blood pressure gauge. A multiple-choice question, even though there are four or five answer choices, can be classified as correct or incorrect. Situations like these are called *binomial experiments*.

In 1653, Blaise Pascal
created a triangle
of numbers called
Pascal's triangle that
can be used in the
binomial distribution.

A **binomial experiment** is a probability experiment that satisfies the following four requirements:

1. There must be a fixed number of trials.
2. Each trial can have only two outcomes or outcomes that can be reduced to two outcomes. These outcomes can be considered as either success or failure.
3. The outcomes of each trial must be independent of each other.
4. The probability of a success must remain the same for each trial.

A binomial experiment and its results give rise to a special probability distribution called the *binomial distribution*.

The **binomial distribution** is a discrete probability distribution of the number of successes in a series of n independent trials with each trial having two possible outcomes and a constant probability of success.

In binomial experiments, the outcomes are usually classified as successes or failures. For example, the correct answer to a multiple-choice item can be classified as a success, but any of the other choices would be incorrect and hence classified as a failure. The notation that is commonly used for binomial experiments and the binomial distribution is defined now.

Notation for the Binomial Distribution

$P(S)$ The symbol for the probability of success

$P(F)$ The symbol for the probability of failure

p The numerical probability of a success

q The numerical probability of a failure

$$P(S) = p \qquad \text{and} \qquad P(F) = 1 - p = q$$

n The number of trials

X The number of successes in n trials

Note that $0 \leq X \leq n$ and $X = 0, 1, 2, 3, \ldots, n$

The probability of a success in a binomial experiment can be computed with this formula.

Binomial Probability Formula

In a binomial experiment, the probability of exactly X successes in n trials is

$$P(X) = \frac{n!}{(n - X)!X!} \cdot p^X \cdot q^{n-X}$$

An explanation of why the formula works is given following Example 5–15.

Example 5–15

A coin is tossed 3 times. Find the probability of getting exactly 2 heads.

Solution

This problem can be solved by looking at the sample space. There are 3 ways to get 2 heads.

     HHH, <u>HHT, HTH, THH,</u> TTH, THT, HTT, TTT

The answer is $\frac{3}{8}$, or 0.375.

Looking at the problem in Example 5–15 from the standpoint of a binomial experiment, one can show that it meets the four requirements.

1. There are a fixed number of trials (three).

2. There are only two outcomes for each trial, heads or tails.

3. The outcomes are independent of one another (the outcome of one toss in no way affects the outcome of another toss).

4. The probability of a success (heads) is $\frac{1}{2}$ in each case.

In this case, $n = 3$, $X = 2$, $p = \frac{1}{2}$, and $q = \frac{1}{2}$. Hence, substituting in the formula gives

$$P(2 \text{ heads}) = \frac{3!}{(3 - 2)!2!} \cdot \left(\frac{1}{2}\right)^2 \left(\frac{1}{2}\right)^1 = \frac{3}{8} = 0.375$$

which is the same answer obtained by using the sample space.

The same example can be used to explain the formula. First, note that there are three ways to get exactly two heads and one tail from a possible eight ways. They are HHT, HTH, and THH. In this case, then, the number of ways of obtaining two heads from three coin tosses is $_3C_2$, or 3, as shown in Chapter 4. In general, the number of ways to get X successes from n trials without regard to order is

$$_nC_X = \frac{n!}{(n - X)!X!}$$

This is the first part of the binomial formula. (Some calculators can be used for this.)

Next, each success has a probability of $\frac{1}{2}$ and can occur twice. Likewise, each failure has a probability of $\frac{1}{2}$ and can occur once, giving the $(\frac{1}{2})^2(\frac{1}{2})^1$ part of the formula. To generalize, then, each success has a probability of p and can occur X times, and each failure has a probability of q and can occur $n - X$ times. Putting it all together yields the binomial probability formula.

Example 5–16

A publication entitled "Statistical Report on the Health of Canadians" indicated that 3 out of 5 Canadians aged 12 years and over visited a physician one or more times in the past year. If 10 Canadians aged 12+ years are randomly selected, find the probability that exactly 3 people visited a physician at least once last year.

Source: Public Health Agency of Canada.

Solution

In this case, $n = 10$, $X = 3$, $p = 3/5$, and $q = 2/5$. Hence,

$$P(3) = \frac{10!}{(10 - 3)!3!}\left(\frac{3}{5}\right)^3\left(\frac{2}{5}\right)^7 \approx 0.042$$

Source: Statistics Canada.

Example 5–17

A recent study on youth and the labour market reports that the employment rate for young Canadians aged 15 to 24 was 86.6%. If 5 Canadian youths are selected at random, find the probability that at least 3 of them are employed.

Source: Statistics Canada.

Solution

To find the probability that at least 3 youths are employed, it is necessary to find the individual probabilities for 3, 4, or 5, and then add them to get the total probability.

$$P(3) = \frac{5!}{(5 - 3)!3!}(0.866)^3(0.134)^2 \approx 0.117$$

$$P(4) = \frac{5!}{(5 - 4)!4!}(0.866)^4(0.134)^1 \approx 0.377$$

$$P(5) = \frac{5!}{(5 - 5)!5!}(0.866)^5(0.134)^0 \approx 0.487$$

Hence,

P(at least 3 youths are employed)

$= 0.117 + 0.377 + 0.487 = 0.981$

Source: Adapted from Statistics Canada publication *The Daily*, Catalogue 11-001, November 23, 2005, and also available from Statistics Canada website www.statcan.ca/Daily/English/051123/d051123b.htm. February 28, 2007.

Computing probabilities by using the binomial probability formula can be quite tedious at times, so tables have been developed for selected values of n and p. Table B in Appendix C gives the probabilities for individual events. Example 5–18 shows how to use Table B to compute probabilities for binomial experiments.

Example 5–18

Solve the problem in Example 5–15 by using Table B in Appendix C.

Solution

Since $n = 3$, $X = 2$, and $p = 0.5$, the value 0.375 is found as shown in Figure 5–3.

Figure 5–3

Using Table B for
Example 5–18

Example 5–19

Results of a study on fear of crime finds that 22% of young Canadians (15 to 24 years old) feel worried when home alone at night. If a random sample of 20 young Canadians is selected, find these probabilities by using the binomial table.

 a. There are exactly 5 people in the sample who are worried when home alone at night.

 b. There are at most 3 people in the sample who are worried when home alone at night.

 c. There are at least 3 people in the sample who are worried when home alone at night.

Source: Statistics Canada.

Solution

 a. $n = 20$, $p = 0.22$, and $X = 5$. From the table, one gets 0.192

 b. $n = 20$ and $p = 0.22$, "At most 3 people" means 0, or 1, or 2, or 3.

   Hence, the solution is

$$P(0) + P(1) + P(2) + P(3) = 0.007 + 0.039 + 0.105 + 0.178$$
$$= 0.329$$

 c. $n = 20$ and $p = 0.22$. "At least 3 people" means 3, 4, 5, . . . , 20. This problem can best be solved by finding $P(0) + P(1) + P(2)$ and subtracting from 1.

$$P(0) + P(1) + P(2) = 0.007 + 0.039 + 0.105 = 0.151$$
$$1 - 0.151 = 0.849$$

Source: Adapted from Statistics Canada publication *A Profile of Criminal Victimization: Results of the 1999 General Social Survey,* Catalogue 85-553, Release date: August 8, 2001, page 54 and also available on Statistics Canada website www.statcan.ca/english/ freepub/85-553-XIE/0019985-553-XIE.pdf. February 28, 2007.

Example 5–20

Transport Canada reports that in a recent year 40% of fatally injured drivers tested had been drinking based on tests of blood alcohol content. If a random sample of 15 driver traffic fatalities is selected, find the probability that at least 12 involved a driver who had been drinking.

Source: Transport Canada.

Solution

Now, $n = 15$, $p = 0.40$, and $X = \{12, 13, 14, 15\}$. From Table B in Appendix C, $P(12) = 0.002$. Since $P(13)$, $P(14)$, and $P(15)$ are not indicated in the table, use the rounded value 0.000 as the respective probabilities are less than 0.0005. Hence the probability of at least 12 is 0.002 or 0.2%.

Source: www.tc.gc.ca/roadsafety/tp/tp3322/2004/page6.htm. Reprinted with the permission of the Minister of Public Works and Government Services Canada, 2007.

Objective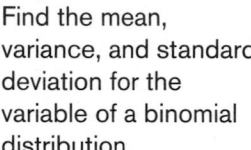

Find the mean, variance, and standard deviation for the variable of a binomial distribution.

Remember that in the use of the binomial distribution, the outcomes must be independent. For example, in the selection of components from a batch to be tested, each component must be replaced before the next one is selected. Otherwise, the outcomes are not independent. However, a dilemma arises because there is a chance that the same component could be selected again. This situation can be avoided by not replacing the component and using a distribution called the hypergeometric distribution to calculate the probabilities. The hypergeometric distribution is presented later in this chapter. Note that when the population is large and the sample is small, the binomial probabilities can be shown to be nearly the same as the corresponding hypergeometric probabilities.

Mean, Variance, and Standard Deviation for the Binomial Distribution

The mean, variance, and standard deviation of a variable that has the *binomial distribution* can be found by using the following formulas.

$$\text{Mean } \mu = n \cdot p \qquad \text{Variance } \sigma^2 = n \cdot p \cdot q \qquad \text{Standard deviation } \sigma = \sqrt{n \cdot p \cdot q}$$

These formulas are algebraically equivalent to the formulas for the mean, variance, and standard deviation of the variables for probability distributions, but because they are for variables of the binomial distribution, they have been simplified by using algebra. The algebraic derivation is omitted here, but their equivalence is shown in Example 5–21.

Example 5–21

A coin is tossed 4 times. Find the mean, variance, and standard deviation of the number of heads that will be obtained.

Solution

With the formulas for the binomial distribution and $n = 4$, $p = \frac{1}{2}$, and $q = \frac{1}{2}$, the results are

$$\mu = n \cdot p = 4 \cdot \tfrac{1}{2} = 2$$
$$\sigma^2 = n \cdot p \cdot q = 4 \cdot \tfrac{1}{2} \cdot \tfrac{1}{2} = 1$$
$$\sigma = \sqrt{1} = 1$$

From Example 5–21, when four coins are tossed many, many times, the average of the number of heads that appear is 2, and the standard deviation of the number of heads is 1. Note that these are theoretical values.

As stated previously, this problem can be solved by using the formulas for expected value. The distribution is shown.

No. of heads X	0	1	2	3	4
Probability $P(X)$	$\frac{1}{16}$	$\frac{4}{16}$	$\frac{6}{16}$	$\frac{4}{16}$	$\frac{1}{16}$

$$\mu = E(X) = \Sigma X \cdot P(X) = 0 \cdot \tfrac{1}{16} + 1 \cdot \tfrac{4}{16} + 2 \cdot \tfrac{6}{16} + 3 \cdot \tfrac{4}{16} + 4 \cdot \tfrac{1}{16} = \tfrac{32}{16} = 2$$

$$\sigma^2 = \Sigma X^2 \cdot P(X) - \mu^2$$

$$= 0^2 \cdot \tfrac{1}{16} + 1^2 \cdot \tfrac{4}{16} + 2^2 \cdot \tfrac{6}{16} + 3^2 \cdot \tfrac{4}{16} + 4^2 \cdot \tfrac{1}{16} - 2^2 = \tfrac{80}{16} - 4 = 1$$

$$\sigma = \sqrt{1} = 1$$

Hence, the simplified binomial formulas give the same results.

Example 5–22

A die is rolled 480 times. Find the mean, variance, and standard deviation of the number of 2s that will be rolled.

Solution

This is a binomial situation, where getting a 2 is a success and not getting a 2 is a failure; hence, $n = 480$, $p = \frac{1}{6}$, and $q = \frac{5}{6}$.

$$\mu = n \cdot p = 480 \cdot \tfrac{1}{6} = 80$$

$$\sigma^2 = n \cdot p \cdot q = 480 \cdot \left(\tfrac{1}{6}\right)\left(\tfrac{5}{6}\right) \approx 66.7$$

$$\sigma = \sqrt{n \cdot p \cdot q} = \sqrt{66.7} \approx 8.2$$

On average, there will be eighty 2s. The standard deviation is 8.2.

Example 5–23

A Statistics Canada publication reported that 3% of Canadian mothers experience multiple births, primarily twins. If a random sample of 5000 births is taken, find the mean, variance, and standard deviation of the number of mothers delivering twins or more.

Source: Statistics Canada.

Solution

This is a binomial situation, since a birth can result in multiple births or not multiple births (i.e., two outcomes),

$$\mu = n \cdot p = (5000)(0.03) = 150$$

$$\sigma^2 = n \cdot p \cdot q = (5000)(0.03)(0.97) = 145.5$$

$$\sigma = \sqrt{n \cdot p \cdot q} = \sqrt{145.5} \approx 12.1$$

For the sample, the average number of multiple births is 150, the variance is 145.5, or 146, and the standard deviation is 12.1 or 12 (if rounded).

Source: Adapted from Statistics Canada publication *Births, 2003*, Catalogue 84F0210X, Release date: July 12, 2005, also available on Statistics Canada website www.statcan.ca/english/freepub/84F0210XIE/84F0210XIE2003000.pdf. February 28, 2007.

Applying the Concepts 5–4

Unsanitary Restaurants

Health officials routinely check sanitary conditions of restaurants. Assume you visit a popular tourist spot and read in the newspaper that in 3 out of every 7 restaurants checked, there were unsatisfactory health conditions found. Assuming you are planning to eat out 10 times while you are there on vacation, answer the following questions.

1. How likely is it that you will eat at 3 restaurants with unsanitary conditions?

2. How likely is it that you will eat at 4 or 5 restaurants with unsanitary conditions?

3. Explain how you would compute the probability of eating in at least 1 restaurant with unsanitary conditions. Could you use the complement to solve this problem?

4. What is the most likely number to occur in this experiment?

5. How variable will the data be around the most likely number?

6. Is this a binomial distribution?

7. If it is a binomial distribution, does that mean that the likelihood of a success is always 50% since there are only two possible outcomes?

Check your answers by using the following computer-generated table.

Mean = 4.3   **Std. dev. = 1.56557**

X	P(X)	Cum. Prob.
0	0.00362	0.00362
1	0.02731	0.03093
2	0.09272	0.12365
3	0.18651	0.31016
4	0.24623	0.55639
5	0.22291	0.77930
6	0.14013	0.91943
7	0.06041	0.97983
8	0.01709	0.99692
9	0.00286	0.99979
10	0.00022	1.00000

See page 246 for the answers.

Exercises 5–4

1. Which of the following are binomial experiments or can be reduced to binomial experiments?

   a. Surveying 100 people to determine if they like Sudsy Soap

   b. Tossing a coin 100 times to see how many heads occur

   c. Drawing a card with replacement from a deck and getting a heart

   d. Asking 1000 people which brand of cigarettes they smoke

   e. Testing 4 different brands of aspirin to see which brands are effective

   f. Testing one brand of aspirin by using 10 people to determine whether it is effective

   g. Asking 100 people if they smoke

   h. Checking 1000 applicants to see whether they were admitted to White Oak College

   i. Surveying 300 prisoners to see how many different crimes they were convicted of

   j. Surveying 300 prisoners to see whether this is their first offence

2. **(ans)** Compute the probability of X successes, using Table B in Appendix C.

   a. $n = 2, p = 0.30, X = 1$ b. $n = 4, p = 0.60, X = 3$

   c. $n = 5, p = 0.10, X = 0$ d. $n = 10, p = 0.40, X = 4$

   e. $n = 12, p = 0.90, X = 2$ f. $n = 15, p = 0.80, X = 12$

   g. $n = 17, p = 0.05, X = 0$ h. $n = 20, p = 0.50, X = 10$

   i. $n = 16, p = 0.20, X = 3$

3. Compute the probability of X successes, using the binomial formula.

    a. $n = 6, X = 3, p = 0.03$
    b. $n = 4, X = 2, p = 0.18$
    c. $n = 5, X = 3, p = 0.63$
    d. $n = 9, X = 0, p = 0.42$
    e. $n = 10, X = 5, p = 0.37$

For Exercises 4 through 13, assume all variables are binomial. (*Note:* If values are not found in Table B of Appendix C, use the binomial formula.)

4. A burglar alarm system has 6 fail-safe components. The probability of each failing is 0.05. Find these probabilities.

    a. Exactly 3 will fail.
    b. Fewer than 2 will fail.
    c. None will fail.
    d. Compare the answers for parts *a*, *b*, and *c*, and explain why the results are reasonable.

5. A student takes a 20-question, true/false exam and guesses on each question. Find the probability of passing if the lowest passing grade is 15 correct out of 20. Would you consider this event likely to occur? Explain your answer.

6. A student takes a 20-question, multiple-choice exam with 5 choices for each question and guesses on each question. Find the probability of guessing at least 15 out of 20 correctly. Would you consider this event likely or unlikely to occur? Explain your answer.

7. In a survey, 30% of the people interviewed said that they bought most of their books during the last 3 months of the year (October, November, December). If 9 people are selected at random, find the probability that exactly 3 of these people bought most of their books during October, November, and December.

    Source: USA Snapshot, *USA TODAY.*

8. In a Gallup Survey, 90% of the people interviewed were unaware that maintaining a healthy weight could reduce the risk of stroke. If 15 people are selected at random, find the probability that at least 9 are unaware that maintaining a proper weight could reduce the risk of stroke.

    Source: USA Snapshot, *USA TODAY.*

9. In a survey, 3 of 4 students said the courts show "too much concern" for criminals. Find the probability that at most 3 out of 7 randomly selected students will agree with this statement.

    Source: *Harper's Index.*

10. *Juristat,* a Statistics Canada publication concerning Canada's criminal justice system, recently reported that 31.9% of Aboriginal people have been involved in some form of violent victimization. If 10 Aboriginals were selected at random, find the probability that at least 5 have been victimized.

    Source: Statistics Canada.

11. The Environics Research Group conducted a poll for the Department of Fisheries and Oceans (DFO) on Canadian attitudes towards the East Coast seal hunt. A majority, 53%, of informed respondents offered conditional supported for the seal hunt. If a random sample of 5 Canadians were given the same arguments for and against the seal hunt, find these probabilities.

    a. Exactly 2 respondents will support the seal hunt.
    b. At most 3 respondents will support the seal hunt.
    c. At least 2 respondents will support the seal hunt.
    d. Fewer than 3 respondents will support the seal hunt.

    Source: Fisheries and Oceans Canada.

12. Find these probabilities for a sample of 20 teenagers if 70% of them had compact disc players by the age of 16.

    a. At least 14 had CD players
    b. Exactly 9 had CD players
    c. More than 17 had CD players
    d. Which event, *a*, *b*, or *c*, is most likely to occur? Explain why.

13. If 80% of the people in a community have Internet access from their homes, find these probabilities for a sample of 10 people.

    a. At most 6 have Internet access.
    b. Exactly 6 have Internet access.
    c. At least 6 have Internet access.
    d. Which event, *a*, *b*, or *c*, is most likely to occur? Explain why.

14. Find the mean, variance, and standard deviation for each of the values of n and p when the conditions for the binomial distribution are met.

    a. $n = 100, p = 0.75$
    b. $n = 300, p = 0.3$
    c. $n = 20, p = 0.5$
    d. $n = 10, p = 0.8$
    e. $n = 1000, p = 0.1$
    f. $n = 500, p = 0.25$
    g. $n = 50, p = \frac{2}{5}$
    h. $n = 36, p = \frac{1}{6}$

15. The 2001 Census of Canada indicated that 1% of adult Canadians have achieved either their doctorate (Ph.D. or M.D.) designation. If 800 adult Canadians are selected at random, find the mean, variance, and standard deviation of the number who have doctorates.

    Source: Statistics Canada.

16. Find the mean, variance, and standard deviation for the number of heads when 20 coins are tossed.

17. If 3% of calculators are defective, find the mean, variance, and standard deviation of a lot of 300 calculators.

18. It has been reported that 83% of federal government employees use email. If a sample of 200 federal government employees is selected, find the mean, variance, and standard deviation of the number who use email.

    Source: *USA TODAY.*

19. The average Canadian teen views 14.1 hours of TV per week, with approximately 8% of their week devoted to TV. If 1000 Canadian teens are randomly selected, find the mean, variance, and standard deviation of the number of teens who watch TV each week.

Source: Statistics Canada.

20. In a restaurant, a study found that 42% of all patrons smoked. If the seating capacity of the restaurant is 80 people, find the mean, variance, and standard deviation of the number of smokers. About how many seats should be available for smoking customers?

21. A survey found that 25% of pet owners had their pets bathed professionally rather than do it themselves. If 18 pet owners are randomly selected, find the probability that exactly 5 people have their pets bathed professionally.

Source: USA Snapshot, *USA TODAY.*

22. The proportion of Canadian households that rely only on cellphones for communications instead of landline phones is estimated at 4.8% by a recent Statistics Canada residential telephone service survey. If 15 Canadian households are randomly selected, find the probability that exactly 2 use only cellphones at home.

Source: Statistics Canada.

23. A TD Bank-sponsored Ipsos Reid survey reported that 35% of Canada's urban dwelling adults are likely to consider purchasing a condominium as their primary residence. If 10 urbanites are randomly selected, find the probability that at 3 of the adults are likely to consider a condominium purchase.

Source: Ipos Reid Survey.

24. In a survey, 58% of American adults said they had never heard of the Internet. If 20 American adults are selected at random, find the probability that exactly 12 will say they have never heard of the Internet.

Source: *Harper's Index.*

25. In the past year, 13% of businesses have eliminated jobs. If 5 businesses are selected at random, find the probability that at least 3 have eliminated jobs during the last year.

Source: *USA TODAY.*

26. Of graduating high school students, 14% said that their generation will be remembered for their social concerns. If 7 graduating students are selected at random, find the probability that either 2 or 3 will agree with that statement.

Source: *USA TODAY.*

27. The Canadian Centre for Justice Statistics reported that 7% of Canada's youth, aged 12 to 17, were charged with criminal code offences (excluding traffic). If 13 Canadian youths are randomly selected, find the probability that 2 have been charged with a criminal code offence.

Source: Statistics Canada.

Extending the Concepts

28. The graph shown here represents the probability distribution for the number of girls in a family of 3 children. From this graph, construct a probability distribution.

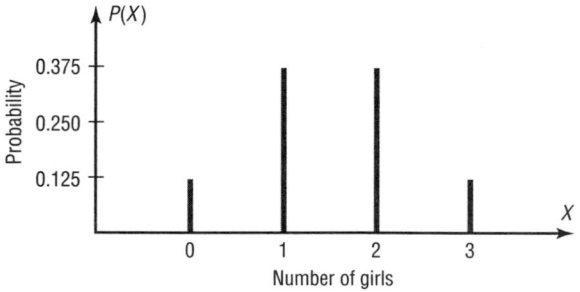

29. Construct a binomial distribution graph for the number of defective computer chips in a lot of four if $p = 0.3$.

5–5   Other Types of Distributions (Optional)

In addition to the binomial distribution, other types of distributions are used in statistics. Three of the most commonly used distributions are the multinomial distribution, the Poisson distribution, and the hypergeometric distribution. They are described next.

Objective 5

Find probabilities for outcomes of variables, using the Poisson, hypergeometric, and multinomial distributions.

The Multinomial Distribution

Recall that in order for an experiment to be binomial, two outcomes are required for each trial. But if each trial in an experiment has more than two outcomes, a distribution called the **multinomial distribution** must be used. For example, a survey might require the responses of "approve," "disapprove," or "no opinion." In another situation, a person may have a choice of one of five activities for Friday night, such as a movie, dinner, baseball game, play, or party. Since these situations have more than two possible outcomes for each trial, the binomial distribution cannot be used to compute probabilities.

The multinomial distribution can be used for such situations if the probabilities for each trial remain constant and the outcomes are independent for a fixed number of trials. The events must also be mutually exclusive.

Formula for the Multinomial Distribution

If X consists of events $E_1, E_2, \ldots, E_k$, which have corresponding probabilities $p_1, p_2, \ldots, p_k$ of occurring, and X_1 is the number of times E_1 will occur, X_2 is the number of times E_2 will occur, etc., then the probability that X will occur is

$$P(X) = \frac{n!}{X_1! \cdot X_2! \cdots X_k!} \cdot p_1^{X_1} \cdot p_2^{X_2} \cdots p_k^{X_k}$$

where $X_1 + X_2 + \cdots + X_k = n$ and $p_1 + p_2 + \cdots + p_k = 1$.

Example 5–24

In a large city, 50% of the people choose a movie, 30% choose dinner and a play, and 20% choose shopping as a leisure activity. If a sample of 5 people is randomly selected, find the probability that 3 are planning to go to a movie, one to a play, and one to a shopping mall.

Solution

We know that $n = 5$, $X_1 = 3$, $X_2 = 1$, $X_3 = 1$, $p_1 = 0.50$, $p_2 = 0.30$, and $p_3 = 0.20$. Substituting in the formula gives

$$P(X) = \frac{5!}{3! \cdot 1! \cdot 1!} \cdot (0.50)^3 (0.30)^1 (0.20)^1 = 0.15$$

Again, note that the multinomial distribution can be used even though replacement is not done, provided that the sample is small in comparison with the population.

Example 5–25

In a music store, a manager found that the probabilities that a person buys 0, 1, or 2 or more CDs are 0.3, 0.6, and 0.1, respectively. If six customers enter the store, find the probability that one won't buy any CDs, three will buy 1 CD, and two will buy 2 or more CDs.

Solution

It is given that $n = 6$, $X_1 = 1$, $X_2 = 3$, $X_3 = 2$, $p_1 = 0.3$, $p_2 = 0.6$, and $p_3 = 0.1$. Then

$$P(X) = \frac{6!}{1! 3! 2!} \cdot (0.3)^1 (0.6)^3 (0.1)^2$$

$$= 60 \cdot (0.3)(0.216)(0.01) = 0.03888$$

Example 5–26

A box contains 4 white balls, 3 red balls, and 3 blue balls. A ball is selected at random, and its colour is written down. It is replaced each time. Find the probability that if 5 balls are selected, 2 are white, 2 are red, and 1 is blue.

Solution

We know that $n = 5$, $X_1 = 2$, $X_2 = 2$, $X_3 = 1$; $p_1 = \frac{4}{10}$, $p_2 = \frac{3}{10}$, and $p_3 = \frac{3}{10}$; hence,

$$P(X) = \frac{5!}{2!2!1!} \cdot \left(\frac{4}{10}\right)^2 \left(\frac{3}{10}\right)^2 \left(\frac{3}{10}\right)^1 = \frac{81}{625}$$

Historical Note

Simeon D. Poisson (1781–1840) formulated the distribution that bears his name. It appears only once in his writings and is only one page long. Mathematicians paid little attention to it until 1907, when a statistician named W. S. Gosset found real applications for it.

Thus, the multinomial distribution is similar to the binomial distribution but has the advantage of allowing one to compute probabilities when there are more than two outcomes for each trial in the experiment. That is, the multinomial distribution is a general distribution, and the binomial distribution is a special case of the multinomial distribution.

The Poisson Distribution

A discrete probability distribution that is useful when n is large and p is small and when the independent variables occur over a period of time is called the **Poisson distribution.** In addition to being used for the stated conditions (i.e., n is large, p is small, and the variables occur over a period of time), the Poisson distribution can be used when a density of items is distributed over a given area or volume, such as the number of plants growing per hectare or the number of defects in a given length of videotape.

Formula for the Poisson Distribution

The probability of X occurrences in an interval of time, volume, area, etc., for a variable where λ (Greek letter lambda) is the mean number of occurrences per unit (time, volume, area, etc.) is

$$P(X; \lambda) = \frac{e^{-\lambda}\lambda^X}{X!} \qquad \text{where } X = 0, 1, 2, \ldots$$

The letter e is a constant approximately equal to 2.7183.

Round the answers to four decimal places.

Example 5–27

If there are 200 typographical errors randomly distributed in a 500-page manuscript, find the probability that a given page contains exactly 3 errors.

Solution

First, find the mean number λ of errors. Since there are 200 errors distributed over 500 pages, each page has an average of

$$\lambda = \frac{200}{500} = \frac{2}{5} = 0.4$$

or 0.4 error per page. Since $X = 3$, substituting into the formula yields

$$P(X; \lambda) = \frac{e^{-\lambda}\lambda^X}{X!} = \frac{(2.7183)^{-0.4}(0.4)^3}{3!} \approx 0.0072$$

Thus, there is less than a 1% probability that any given page will contain exactly 3 errors.

Since the mathematics involved in computing Poisson probabilities is somewhat complicated, tables have been compiled for these probabilities. Table C in Appendix C gives P for various values for λ and X.

In Example 5–27, where X is 3 and λ is 0.4, the table gives the value 0.0072 for the probability. See Figure 5–4.

Figure 5–4

Using Table C in Appendix C

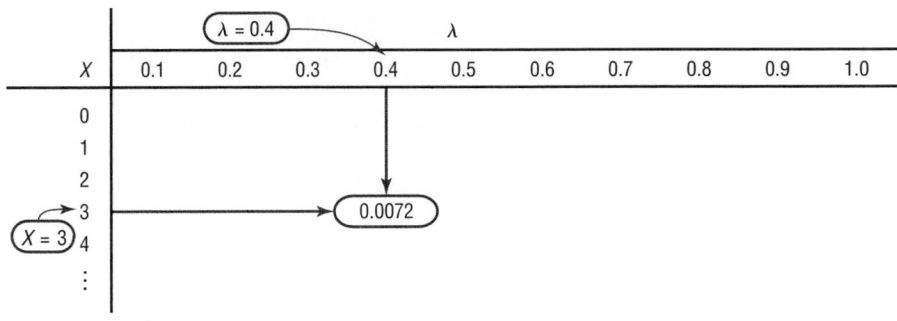

Example 5–28

A sales firm receives, on the average, 3 calls per hour on its toll-free number. For any given hour, find the probability that it will receive the following.

   a. At most 3 calls   *b.* At least 3 calls   *c.* 5 or more calls

Solution

a. "At most 3 calls" means 0, 1, 2, or 3 calls. Hence,

$$P(0; 3) + P(1; 3) + P(2; 3) + P(3; 3)$$
$$= 0.0498 + 0.1494 + 0.2240 + 0.2240$$
$$= 0.6472$$

b. "At least 3 calls" means 3 or more calls. It is easier to find the probability of 0, 1, and 2 calls and then subtract this answer from 1 to get the probability of at least 3 calls.

$$P(0; 3) + P(1; 3) + P(2; 3) = 0.0498 + 0.1494 + 0.2240 = 0.4232$$

and

$$1 - 0.4232 = 0.5768$$

c. For the probability of 5 or more calls, it is easier to find the probability of getting 0, 1, 2, 3, or 4 calls and subtract this answer from 1. Hence,

$$P(0; 3) + P(1; 3) + P(2; 3) + P(3; 3) + P(4; 3)$$
$$= 0.0498 + 0.1494 + 0.2240 + 0.2240 + 0.1680$$
$$= 0.8152$$

and

$$1 - 0.8152 = 0.1848$$

Thus, for the events described, the part *a* event is most likely to occur and the part *c* event is least likely to occur.

The Poisson distribution can also be used to approximate the binomial distribution when the expected value $\lambda = n \cdot p$ is less than 5, as shown in Example 5–29. (The same is true when $n \cdot q < 5$.)

Example 5–29

If approximately 2% of the people in a room of 200 people are left-handed, find the probability that exactly 5 people there are left-handed.

Solution

Since $\lambda = n \cdot p$, then $\lambda = (200)(0.02) = 4$. Hence,

$$P(X; \lambda) = \frac{(2.7183)^{-4}(4)^5}{5!} \approx 0.1563$$

which is verified by the formula $_{200}C_5(0.02)^5(0.98)^{195} \approx 0.1579$. The difference between the two answers is based on the fact that the Poisson distribution is an approximation and rounding has been used.

The Hypergeometric Distribution

When sampling is done *without* replacement, the binomial distribution does not give exact probabilities, since the trials are not independent. The smaller the size of the population, the less accurate the binomial probabilities will be.

For example, suppose a committee of four people is to be selected from seven women and five men. What is the probability that the committee will consist of three women and one man?

To solve this problem, one must find the number of ways a committee of three women and one man can be selected from seven women and five men. This answer can be found by using combinations; it is

$$_7C_3 \cdot {_5C_1} = 35 \cdot 5 = 175$$

Next, find the total number of ways a committee of four people can be selected from 12 people. Again, by the use of combinations, the answer is

$$_{12}C_4 = 495$$

Finally, the probability of getting a committee of three women and one man from seven women and five men is

$$P(X) = \frac{175}{495} = \frac{35}{99}$$

The results of the problem can be generalized by using a special probability distribution called the hypergeometric distribution. The **hypergeometric distribution** is a distribution of a variable that has two outcomes when sampling is done without replacement.

The probabilities for the hypergeometric distribution can be calculated by using the formula given next.

Formula for the Hypergeometric Distribution

Given a population with only two types of objects (females and males, defective and nondefective, successes or failures, etc.), such that there are a items of one kind and b items of another kind and $a + b$ equals the total population, the probability $P(X)$ of selecting without replacement a sample of size n with X items of type a and $n - X$ items of type b is

$$P(X) = \frac{_aC_X \cdot {_bC_{n-X}}}{_{a+b}C_n}$$

The basis of the formula is that there are $_aC_X$ ways of selecting the first type of items, $_bC_{n-X}$ ways of selecting the second type of items, and $_{a+b}C_n$ ways of selecting n items from the entire population.

Example 5–30

Ten people apply for a job as assistant manager of a restaurant. Five have completed college and 5 have not. If the manager selects 3 applicants at random, find the probability that all 3 are college graduates.

Solution

Assigning the values to the variables gives

$$a = 5 \text{ college graduates} \qquad n = 3$$
$$b = 5 \text{ nongraduates} \qquad X = 3$$

and $n - X = 0$. Substituting in the formula gives

$$P(X) = \frac{_5C_3 \cdot {_5C_0}}{_{10}C_3} = \frac{10}{120} = \frac{1}{12}$$

Example 5–31

A recent study found that 4 out of 9 houses were underinsured. If 5 houses are selected from the 9 houses, find the probability that exactly 2 are underinsured.

Solution

In this problem

$$a = 4 \qquad b = 5 \qquad n = 5 \qquad X = 2 \qquad n - X = 3$$

Then

$$P(X) = \frac{_4C_2 \cdot {_5C_3}}{_9C_5} = \frac{60}{126} = \frac{10}{21}$$

In many situations where objects are manufactured and shipped to a company, the company selects a few items and tests them to see whether they are satisfactory or defective. If a certain percentage is defective, the company then can refuse the whole shipment. This procedure saves the time and cost of testing every single item. To make the judgment about whether to accept or reject the whole shipment based on a small sample of tests, the company must know the probability of getting a specific number of defective items. To calculate the probability, the company uses the hypergeometric distribution.

Example 5–32

A lot of 12 compressor tanks is checked to see whether there are any defective tanks. Three tanks are checked for leaks. If 1 or more of the 3 is defective, the lot is rejected. Find the probability that the lot will be rejected if there are actually 3 defective tanks in the lot.

Solution

Since the lot is rejected if at least 1 tank is found to be defective, it is necessary to find the probability that none are defective and subtract this probability from 1.

Here, $a = 3$, $b = 9$, $n = 3$, $X = 0$; so

$$P(X) = \frac{{}_3C_0 \cdot {}_9C_3}{{}_{12}C_3} = \frac{1 \cdot 84}{220} = 0.38$$

Hence,

$$P(\text{at least one defective}) = 1 - P(\text{no defectives}) = 1 - 0.38 = 0.62$$

There is a 0.62, or 62%, probability that the lot will be rejected when 3 of the 12 tanks are defective.

A summary of the discrete distributions used in this chapter is shown in Table 5–1.

Table 5–1	Summary of Discrete Distributions

1. Binomial distribution

$$P(X) = \frac{n!}{(n - X)!X!} \cdot p^X \cdot q^{n-X}$$

$$\mu = n \cdot p \qquad \sigma = \sqrt{n \cdot p \cdot q}$$

Used when there are only two independent outcomes for a fixed number of independent trials and the probability for each success remains the same for each trial.

2. Multinomial distribution

$$P(X) = \frac{n!}{X_1! \cdot X_2! \cdots X_k!} \cdot p_1^{X_1} \cdot p_2^{X_2} \cdots p_k^{X_k}$$

where

$$X_1 + X_2 + \cdots + X_k = n \text{ and } p_1 + p_2 + \cdots + p_k = 1$$

Used when the distribution has more than two outcomes, the probabilities for each trial remain constant, outcomes are independent, and there are a fixed number of trials.

3. Poisson distribution

$$P(X; \lambda) = \frac{e^{-\lambda}\lambda^X}{X!} \qquad \text{where } X = 0, 1, 2, \ldots$$

Used when n is large and p is small, the independent variable occurs over a period of time, or a density of items is distributed over a given area or volume.

4. Hypergeometric distribution

$$P(X) = \frac{{}_aC_X \cdot {}_bC_{n-X}}{{}_{a+b}C_n}$$

Used when there are two outcomes and sampling is done without replacement.

Applying the Concepts 5–5

Rockets and Targets

During the latter days of World War II, the Germans developed flying rocket bombs. These bombs were used to attack London. Allied military intelligence didn't know whether these bombs were fired at random or had a sophisticated aiming device. To determine the answer, they used the Poisson distribution.

To assess the accuracy of these bombs, London was divided into 576 square regions. Each region was $\frac{1}{4}$ square kilometre in area. They then compared the number of actual hits with the theoretical number of hits by using the Poisson distribution. If the values in both distributions were close, then they would conclude that the rockets were fired at random. The actual distribution is as follows:

Hits	0	1	2	3	4	5
Regions	229	211	93	35	7	1

1. Using the Poisson distribution, find the theoretical values for each number of hits. In this case, the number of bombs was 535, and the number of regions was 576. So

$$\mu = \frac{535}{576} \approx 0.929$$

For 3 hits,

$$P(X) = \frac{\mu^X \cdot e^{-\mu}}{X!}$$

$$= \frac{(0.929)^3(2.7183)^{-0.929}}{3!} \approx 0.0528$$

Hence the number of hits is $(0.0528)(576) = 30.4128$.

Complete the table for the other number of hits.

Hits	0	1	2	3	4	5
Regions				30.4		

2. Write a brief statement comparing the two distributions.

3. Based on your answer to question 2, can you conclude that the rockets were fired at random?

See page 246 for the answer.

Exercises 5–5

1. Use the multinomial formula and find the probabilities for each.

   a. $n = 6, X_1 = 3, X_2 = 2, X_3 = 1, p_1 = 0.5, p_2 = 0.3, p_3 = 0.2$

   b. $n = 5, X_1 = 1, X_2 = 2, X_3 = 2, p_1 = 0.3, p_2 = 0.6, p_3 = 0.1$

   c. $n = 4, X_1 = 1, X_2 = 1, X_3 = 2, p_1 = 0.8, p_2 = 0.1, p_3 = 0.1$

   d. $n = 3, X_1 = 1, X_2 = 1, X_3 = 1, p_1 = 0.5, p_2 = 0.3, p_3 = 0.2$

   e. $n = 5, X_1 = 1, X_2 = 3, X_3 = 1, p_1 = 0.7, p_2 = 0.2, p_3 = 0.1$

2. The probabilities that a textbook page will have 0, 1, 2, or 3 typographical errors are 0.79, 0.12, 0.07, and 0.02, respectively. If eight pages are randomly selected, find the probability that four will contain no errors, two will contain 1 error, one will contain 2 errors, and one will contain 3 errors.

3. The probabilities are 0.25, 0.40, and 0.35 that an 18-wheel truck will have 0 violations, 1 violation, or 2 or more violations when it is given a safety inspection. If eight trucks are inspected, find the probability that three will have 0 violations, two will have 1 violation, and three will have 2 or more violations.

4. When a customer enters a pharmacy, the probabilities that he or she will have 0, 1, 2, or 3 prescriptions filled are 0.60, 0.25, 0.10, and 0.05, respectively. For a sample of six people who enter the pharmacy, find the probability that two will have 0 prescriptions, two will have 1 prescription, one will have 2 prescriptions, and one will have 3 prescriptions.

5. A die is rolled 4 times. Find the probability of two 1s, one 2, and one 3.

6. According to Mendel's theory, if tall and colourful plants are crossed with short and colourless plants, the corresponding probabilities are $\frac{9}{16}, \frac{3}{16}, \frac{3}{16}$, and $\frac{1}{16}$ for tall and colourful, tall and colourless, short and colourful, and short and colourless, respectively. If eight plants are selected, find the probability that one will be tall and colourful, three will be tall and colourless, three will be short and colourful, and one will be short and colourless.

7. Find each probability $P(X; \lambda)$, using Table C in Appendix C.

   a. $P(5; 4)$
   b. $P(2; 4)$
   c. $P(6; 3)$
   d. $P(10; 7)$
   e. $P(9; 8)$

8. If 2% of the batteries manufactured by a company are defective, find the probability that in a case of 144 batteries, there are 3 defective ones.

9. A recent study of robberies for a certain geographic region showed an average of one robbery per 20,000 people. In a city of 80,000 people, find the probability of the following.

   a. No robberies
   b. One robbery
   c. Two robberies
   d. Three or more robberies

10. In a 400-page manuscript, there are 200 randomly distributed misprints. If a page is selected, find the probability that it has one misprint.

11. A telephone soliciting company obtains an average of 5 orders per 1000 solicitations. If the company reaches 250 potential customers, find the probability of obtaining at least 2 orders.

12. A mail-order company receives an average of 5 orders per 500 solicitations. If it sends out 100 advertisements, find the probability of receiving at least 2 orders.

13. A videotape has an average of 1 defect every 300 metres. Find the probability of at least 1 defect in 900 metres.

14. If 3% of all cars fail the emissions inspection, find the probability that in a sample of 90 cars, 3 will fail. Use the Poisson approximation.

15. The average number of phone inquiries per day at the poison control centre is 4. Find the probability it will receive 5 calls on a given day. Use the Poisson approximation.

16. In a batch of 2000 calculators, there are, on average, 8 defective ones. If a random sample of 150 is selected, find the probability of 5 defective ones.

17. In a camping club of 18 members, 9 prefer hoods and 9 prefer hats and earmuffs. On a recent winter outing attended by 6 members, find the probability that exactly 3 members wore earmuffs and hats.

18. A bookstore owner examines 5 books from each lot of 25 to check for missing pages. If he finds at least 2 books with missing pages, the entire lot is returned. If, indeed, there are 5 books with missing pages, find the probability that the lot will be returned.

19. Shirts are packed at random in two sizes, regular and extra large. Four shirts are selected from a box of 24 and checked for size. If there are 15 regular shirts in the box, find the probability that all 4 will be regular size.

20. A shipment of 24 computer keyboards is rejected if 4 are checked for defects and at least 1 is found to be defective. Find the probability that the shipment will be returned if there are actually 6 defective keyboards.

21. A shipment of 24 electric typewriters is rejected if 3 are checked for defects and at least 1 is found to be defective. Find the probability that the shipment will be returned if there are actually 6 typewriters that are defective.

5-6   Summary

Many variables have special probability distributions. This chapter presented several of the most common probability distributions, including the binomial distribution, the multinomial distribution, the Poisson distribution, and the hypergeometric distribution.

The binomial distribution is used when there are only two outcomes for an experiment, there are a fixed number of trials, the probability is the same for each trial, and the outcomes are independent of one another. The multinomial distribution is an extension of the binomial distribution and is used when there are three or more outcomes for an experiment. The hypergeometric distribution is used when sampling is done without replacement. Finally, the Poisson distribution is used in special cases when independent events occur over a period of time, area, or volume.

A probability distribution can be graphed, and the mean, variance, and standard deviation can be found. The mathematical expectation can also be calculated for a probability distribution. Expectation is used in insurance and games of chance.

For step-by-step guidance on the use of technology for this chapter, visit the Online Learning Centre at www.mcgrawhill.ca/olc/bluman. Summary procedures for Minitab, SPSS, Excel, and TI-83 Plus or TI-84 Plus can also be found in Appendix E.

Important Terms   ● ● ●

binomial distribution   224

binomial experiment   224

discrete probability distribution   208

expected value   218

hypergeometric distribution   236

multinomial distribution   233

Poisson distribution   234

random variable   207

Important Formulas   ● ● ●

Formula for the mean of a probability distribution:

$$\mu = \Sigma X \cdot P(X)$$

Formulas for the variance and standard deviation of a probability distribution:

$$\sigma^2 = \Sigma[X^2 \cdot P(X)] - \mu^2$$
$$\sigma = \sqrt{\Sigma[X^2 \cdot P(X)] - \mu^2}$$

Formula for expected value:

$$E(X) = \Sigma X \cdot P(X)$$

Binomial probability formula:

$$P(X) = \frac{n!}{(n - X)!X!} \cdot p^X \cdot q^{n - X}$$

Formula for the mean of the binomial distribution:

$$\mu = n \cdot p$$

Formulas for the variance and standard deviation of the binomial distribution:

$$\sigma^2 = n \cdot p \cdot q \qquad \sigma = \sqrt{n \cdot p \cdot q}$$

Formula for the multinomial distribution:

$$P(X) = \frac{n!}{X_1! \cdot X_2! \cdots X_k!} \cdot p_1^{X_1} \cdot p_2^{X_2} \cdots p_k^{X_k}$$

Formula for the Poisson distribution:

$$P(X; \lambda) = \frac{e^{-\lambda}\lambda^x}{X!} \quad \text{where } X = 0, 1, 2, \cdots$$

Formula for the hypergeometric distribution:

$$P(X) = \frac{{}_aC_X \cdot {}_bC_{n-X}}{{}_{a+b}C_n}$$

Review Exercises

●●●

For Exercises 1 through 3, determine whether the distribution represents a probability distribution. If it does not, state why.

1.
X	1	2	3	4	5
P(X)	$\frac{1}{10}$	$\frac{3}{10}$	$\frac{1}{10}$	$\frac{2}{10}$	$\frac{3}{10}$

2.
X	10	20	30
P(X)	0.1	0.4	0.3

3.
X	8	12	16	20
P(X)	$\frac{5}{6}$	$\frac{1}{12}$	$\frac{1}{12}$	$\frac{1}{12}$

4. The number of emergency calls a local police department receives per 24-hour period is distributed as shown here. Construct a graph for the data.

Number of calls X	10	11	12	13	14
Probability P(X)	0.02	0.12	0.40	0.31	0.15

5. A study was conducted to determine the number of radios each household has. The data are shown here. Draw a graph for the data.

Number of radios	0	1	2	3	4
Probability P(X)	0.05	0.30	0.45	0.12	0.08

6. A box contains 5 pennies, 3 dimes, 1 quarter, and 1 loonie. Construct a probability distribution and draw a graph for the data.

7. At Tyler's Tie Shop, Tyler found the probabilities that a customer will buy 0, 1, 2, 3, or 4 ties, as shown. Construct a graph for the distribution.

Number of ties X	0	1	2	3	4
Probability P(X)	0.30	0.50	0.10	0.08	0.02

8. A bank has a drive-through service. The number of customers arriving during a 15-minute period is distributed as shown. Find the mean, variance, and standard deviation for the distribution.

Number of customers X	0	1	2	3	4
Probability P(X)	0.12	0.20	0.31	0.25	0.12

9. At a small community museum, the number of visitors per hour during the day has the distribution shown here. Find the mean, variance, and standard deviation for the data.

Number of visitors X	13	14	15	16	17
Probability P(X)	0.12	0.15	0.29	0.25	0.19

10. During a recent paint sale at Corner Hardware, the number of cans of paint purchased was distributed as shown. Find the mean, variance, and standard deviation of the distribution.

Number of cans X	1	2	3	4	5
Probability P(X)	0.42	0.27	0.15	0.10	0.06

11. The number of inquiries received per day for a university catalogue is distributed as shown. Find the mean, variance, and standard deviation for the data.

Number of inquiries X	22	23	24	25	26	27
Probability P(X)	0.08	0.19	0.36	0.25	0.07	0.05

12. A producer plans an outdoor regatta for May 3. The cost of the regatta is $8000. This includes advertising, security, printing tickets, entertainment, etc. The producer plans to make $15,000 profit if all goes well. However, if it rains, the regatta would have to be cancelled. According to the weather report, the probability of rain is 0.3. Find the producer's expected profit.

13. A person selects a card from a deck. If it is a red card, he wins $1. If it is a black card between or including 2 and 10, he wins $5. If it is a black face card, he wins $10; and if it is a black ace, he wins $100. Find the expectation of the game. How much should a person bet if the game is to be fair?

14. If 30% of all commuters ride the train to work, find the probability that if 10 workers are selected, 5 will ride the train.

15. If 90% of all people between the ages of 30 and 50 drive a car, find these probabilities for a sample of 20 people in that age group.

    a. Exactly 20 drive a car.
    b. At least 15 drive a car.
    c. At most 15 drive a car.

16. If 10% of the people who are given a certain drug experience dizziness, find these probabilities for a sample of 15 people who take the drug.

    a. At least 2 people will become dizzy.
    b. Exactly 3 people will become dizzy.
    c. At most 4 people will become dizzy.

17. If 75% of nursing students are able to pass a drug calculation test, find the mean, variance, and standard deviation of the number of students who pass the test in a sample of 180 nursing students.

18. A club has 225 members. If there is a 70% attendance rate per meeting, find the mean, variance, and standard

deviation of the number of people who will be present at each meeting.

19. Amnesty International reports that 69% of Canadians moderately or strongly support the return of the death penalty, abolished by parliament in 1976. If 7 Canadians are selected at random, what is the probability that at least 3 will support the return of capital punishment?

    Source: www.amnesty.ca.

20. A Statistics Canada article on home heating and the environment estimates that 50% of Canadian households rely on natural gas heating, 33% use electricity, 13% heat with oil furnaces, and about 4% use wood burning heaters. If a random sample of 500 Canadian households was selected, find the mean, variance, and standard deviation for each category of heating fuel.

    Source: Statistics Canada.

21. Health Canada reports that 1 in 5 Canadians, aged 15 years of age and older, smoke cigarettes. If a random sample of 20 Canadians aged 15 years and older is selected, find the probability that exactly 5 are current smokers.

    Source: Health Canada.

22. One out of four Americans over age 55 has eaten pizza for breakfast. If a sample of 10 Americans over age 55 is selected at random, find the probability that at most 3 have eaten pizza for breakfast.

    Source: Harper's Index.

23. **(Opt.)** The probabilities that a person will make 0, 1, 2, and 3 errors on an insurance claim are 0.70, 0.20, 0.08, and 0.02, respectively. If 20 claims are selected, find the probability that 12 will contain no errors, 4 will contain 1 error, 3 will contain 2 errors, and 1 will contain 3 errors.

24. **(Opt.)** Before a DVD player leaves the factory, it is given a quality control check. The probabilities that a DVD player contains 0, 1, or 2 defects are 0.90, 0.06,

and 0.04, respectively. In a sample of 12 players, find the probability that 8 have 0 defects, 3 have 1 defect, and 1 has 2 defects.

25. **(Opt.)** In a Christmas display, the probability that all lights are the same colour is 0.50; that 2 colours are used is 0.40; and that 3 or more colours are used is 0.10. If a sample of 10 displays is selected, find the probability that 5 have only 1 colour of light, 3 have 2 colours, and 2 have 3 or more colours.

26. **(Opt.)** If 4% of the population carries a certain genetic trait, find the probability that in a sample of 100 people, there are exactly 8 people who have the trait. Assume the distribution is approximately Poisson.

27. **(Opt.)** Computer Help Hot Line receives, on the average, 6 calls per hour asking for assistance. The distribution is Poisson. For any randomly selected hour, find the probability that the company will receive

    a. At least 6 calls.
    b. 4 or more calls.
    c. At most 5 calls.

28. **(Opt.)** The number of boating accidents on Lake Emilie follows a Poisson distribution. The probability of an accident is 0.003. If there are 1000 boats on the lake during a summer month, find the probability that there will be 6 accidents.

29. **(Opt.)** If 5 cards are drawn from a deck, find the probability that 2 will be hearts.

30. **(Opt.)** Of the 50 automobiles in a used-car lot, 10 are white. If 5 automobiles are selected to be sold at an auction, find the probability that exactly 2 will be white.

31. **(Opt.)** A board of directors consists of 7 men and 5 women. If a slate of 3 officers is selected, find these probabilities.

    a. Exactly 2 are men.
    b. All 3 are women.
    c. Exactly 2 are women.

Is Pooling Worthwhile?–Revisited

Statistics Today

In the case of the pooled sample, the probability that only one test will be needed can be determined by using the binomial distribution. The question being asked is: In a sample of 15 individuals, what is the probability that no individual will have the disease? Hence, $n = 15$, $p = 0.05$, and $X = 0$. From Table B in Appendix C, the probability is 0.463, or 46% of the time, only one test will be needed. For screening purposes, then, pooling samples in this case would save considerable time, money, and effort as opposed to testing every individual in the population.

Chapter Quiz

● ● ●

Determine whether each statement is true or false. If the statement is false, explain why.

1. The expected value of a random variable can be thought of as a long-run average.

2. The number of courses a student is taking this semester is an example of a continuous random variable.

3. When the multinomial distribution is used, the outcomes must be dependent.

4. A binomial experiment has a fixed number of trials.

Complete these statements with the best answer.

5. Random variable values are determined by _____.

6. The mean for a binomial variable can be found by using the formula _____.

7. One requirement for a probability distribution is that the sum of all the events in the sample space must equal _____.

Select the best answer.

8. What is the sum of the probabilities of all outcomes in a probability distribution?

   a. 0
   b. $\frac{1}{2}$
   c. 1
   d. It cannot be determined.

9. How many outcomes are there in a binomial experiment?

   a. 0
   b. 1
   c. 2
   d. It varies.

10. The number of plants growing in a specific area can be approximated by what distribution?

    a. Binomial
    b. Multinomial
    c. Hypergeometric
    d. Poisson

For questions 11 through 14, determine if the distribution represents a probability distribution. If not, state why.

11.

X	1	2	3	4	5
P(X)	$\frac{1}{7}$	$\frac{2}{7}$	$\frac{2}{7}$	$\frac{3}{7}$	$\frac{2}{7}$

12.

X	3	6	9	12	15
P(X)	0.3	0.5	0.1	0.08	0.02

13.

X	50	75	100
P(X)	0.5	0.2	0.3

14.

X	4	8	12	16
P(X)	$\frac{1}{6}$	$\frac{3}{12}$	$\frac{1}{2}$	$\frac{1}{12}$

15. The number of fire calls the Conestoga Valley Fire Company receives per day is distributed as follows:

Number X	5	6	7	8	9
Probability P(X)	0.28	0.32	0.09	0.21	0.10

Construct a graph for the data.

16. A study was conducted to determine the number of telephones each household has. The data are shown here.

Number of telephones	0	1	2	3	4
Frequency	2	30	48	13	7

Construct a probability distribution and draw a graph for the data.

17. During a recent CD sale at Matt's Music Store, the number of CDs customers purchased was distributed as follows:

Number X	0	1	2	3	4
Probability P(X)	0.10	0.23	0.31	0.27	0.09

Find the mean, variance, and standard deviation of the distribution.

18. The number of calls received per day at a crisis hot line is distributed as follows:

Number X	30	31	32	33	34
Probability P(X)	0.05	0.21	0.38	0.25	0.11

Find the mean, variance, and standard deviation of the distribution.

19. There are 6 playing cards placed face down in a box. They are the 4 of diamonds, the 5 of hearts, the 2 of clubs, the 10 of spades, the 3 of diamonds, and the 7 of hearts. A person selects a card. Find the expected value of the draw.

20. A person selects a card from an ordinary deck of cards. If it is a black card, she wins $2. If it is a red card between or including 3 and 7, she wins $10. If it is a red face card, she wins $25; and if it is a black jack, she wins an extra $100. Find the expectation of the game.

21. If 40% of all commuters ride to work in carpools, find the probability that if 8 workers are selected, 5 will ride in carpools.

22. If 60% of all women are employed outside the home, find the probability that in a sample of 20 women,

    a. Exactly 15 are employed.
    b. At least 10 are employed.
    c. At most 5 are not employed outside the home.

23. If 80% of the applicants are able to pass a driver's proficiency road test, find the mean, variance, and standard deviation of the number of people who pass the test in a sample of 300 applicants.

24. A history class has 75 members. If there is a 12% absentee rate per class meeting, find the mean, variance, and standard deviation of the number of students who will be absent from each class.

25. The probability that a person will make 0, 1, 2, or 3 errors on his or her income tax return is 0.50, 0.30, 0.15, and 0.05, respectively. If 30 claims are selected, find the probability that 15 will contain zero errors, 8 will contain one error, 5 will contain two errors, and 2 will contain three errors.

26. Before a television set leaves the factory, it is given a quality control check. The probability that a television contains zero, one, or two defects is 0.88, 0.08, and 0.04, respectively. In a sample of 16 televisions, find the probability that 9 will have no defects, 4 will have one defect, and 3 will have two defects.

27. Among the teams in a bowling league, the probability that the uniforms are all one colour is 0.45, that two colours are used is 0.35, and that three or more colours are used is 0.20. If a sample of 12 uniforms is selected, find the probability that 5 contain only one colour, 4 contain two colours, and 3 contain three or more colours.

28. If 8% of the population of trees are elm trees, find the probability that in a sample of 100 trees, there are exactly 6 elm trees. Assume the distribution is approximately Poisson.

29. Sports Scores Hot Line receives, on the average, 8 calls per hour requesting the latest sports scores. The distribution is Poisson in nature. For any randomly selected hour, find the probability that the company will receive

    a. At least 8 calls.
    b. 3 or more calls.
    c. At most 7 calls.

30. There are 48 raincoats for sale at a local men's clothing store. Twelve are black. If 6 raincoats are selected to be marked down, find the probability that exactly 3 will be black.

31. A youth group has 8 boys and 6 girls. If a slate of 4 officers is selected, find the probability that exactly

    a. 3 are girls.
    b. 2 are girls.
    c. 4 are boys.

Critical Thinking Challenges

1. The Ontario Lottery Corporation sells Pick-4, a game of chance, in which 4 numbers are selected from a field of 0 to 9, with replacement. The top prize is awarded if the 4 digits on the ticket match the 4 digits randomly selected, in the same order. If one ticket is purchased, find the probability of winning the top prize.

    Source: Ontario Lottery Corporation.

2. In the Pick-4 game, a $1 ticket will earn a top prize of $5000 if the 4 digits on the ticket match the winning selection in the order drawn. What is the expected value of winning? Is it worth it?

    Source: Ontario Lottery Corporation.

3. If you play the same 4 numbers in the Pick-4 daily game, in how many years and days would you expect your first win, assuming that you have average luck?

    Source: Ontario Lottery Corporation.

4. In the game Chuck-a-Luck, three dice are rolled. A player bets a certain amount (say $1.00) on a number from 1 to 6. If the number appears on one die, the person wins $1.00. If it appears on two dice, the person wins $2.00, and if it appears on all three dice, the person wins $3.00. What are the chances of winning $1.00? $2.00? $3.00?

5. What is the expected value of the game of Chuck-a-Luck if a player bets $1.00 on one number?

Data Projects

Probability Distributions   Roll three dice 100 times, recording the sum of the spots on the faces as you roll. Then find the average of the spots. How close is this to the theoretical average? Refer to Exercise 21 on page 222.

Answers to Applying the Concepts ● ● ●

Section 5–2 Dropping College/University Courses

1. The random variable under study is the reason for dropping a college/university course.

2. There were a total of 144 people in the study.

3. The complete table is as follows:

Reason for dropping a college/university course	Frequency	Percentage
Too difficult	45	31.25
Illness	40	27.78
Change in work schedule	20	13.89
Change of major	14	9.72
Family-related problems	9	6.25
Money	7	4.86
Miscellaneous	6	4.17
No meaningful reason	3	2.08

4. The probability that a student will drop a class because of illness is about 28%. The probability that a student will drop a class because of money is about 5%. The probability that a student will drop a class because of a change of major is about 10%.

5. The information is not itself a probability distribution, but it can be used as one.

6. The categories are not necessarily mutually exclusive, but we treated them as such in computing the probabilities.

7. The categories are not independent.

8. The categories are exhaustive.

9. Since all the probabilities are between 0 and 1, inclusive, and the probabilities sum to 1, the requirements for a discrete probability distribution are met.

Section 5–3 Expected Value

1. The expected value is the mean in a discrete probability distribution.

2. We would expect variation from the expected value of 3.

3. Answers will vary. One possible answer is that pregnant mothers in that area might be overly concerned upon hearing that the number of cases of kidney problems in newborns was nearly 4 times what was usually expected. Other mothers (particularly those who had taken a statistics course!) might ask for more information about the claim.

4. Answers will vary. One possible answer is that it does seem unlikely to have 11 newborns with kidney problems when we expect only 3 newborns to have kidney problems.

5. The public might better be informed by percentages or rates (e.g., rate per 1000 newborns).

6. The increase of eight babies born with kidney problems represents a 0.32% increase (less than $\frac{1}{2}$ of 1%).

7. Answers will vary. One possible answer is that the percentage increase does not seem to be something to be overly concerned about.

Section 5–4 Unsanitary Restaurants

1. The probability of eating at 3 restaurants with unsanitary conditions out of the 10 restaurants is 0.18651.

2. The probability of eating at 4 or 5 restaurants with unsanitary conditions out of the 10 restaurants is 0.24623 + 0.22291 = 0.46914.

3. To find this probability, you could add the probabilities for eating at 1, 2, … , 10 unsanitary restaurants. An easier way to compute the probability is to subtract the probability of eating at no unsanitary restaurants from 1 (using the complement rule).

4. The highest probability for this distribution is 4, but the expected number of unsanitary restaurants that you would eat at is $10 \cdot \frac{3}{7} = 4.3$.

5. The standard deviation for this distribution is
$$\sqrt{10\left(\tfrac{3}{7}\right)\left(\tfrac{4}{7}\right)} = 1.56.$$

6. This is a binomial distribution. We have two possible outcomes: "success" is eating in an unsanitary restaurant; "failure" is eating in a sanitary restaurant. The probability that one restaurant is unsanitary is independent of the probability that any other restaurant is unsanitary. The probability that a restaurant is unsanitary remains constant at $\frac{3}{7}$. And we are looking at the number of unsanitary restaurants that we eat at out of 10 "trials."

7. The likelihood of success will vary from situation to situation. Just because we have two possible outcomes, this does not mean that each outcome occurs with probability 0.50.

Section 5–5 Rockets and Targets

1. The theoretical values for the number of hits are

Hits	0	1	2	3	4	5
Regions	227.5	211.3	98.2	30.4	7.1	1.3

2. The actual values are very close to the theoretical values.

3. Since the actual values are close to the theoretical values, it does appear that the rockets were fired at random.

CHAPTER 6

The Normal Distribution

Objectives

After completing this chapter, you should be able to

1. Identify distributions as symmetric or skewed.

2. Identify the properties of a normal distribution.

3. Find the area under the standard normal distribution, given various z scores.

4. Find probabilities for a normally distributed variable by transforming it into a standard normal variable.

5. Find specific data values for given percentages, using the standard normal distribution.

6. Use the central limit theorem to solve problems involving sample means for large samples.

7. Use the normal approximation to compute probabilities for a binomial variable.

Outline

6–1   Introduction

6–2   Properties of a Normal Distribution

6–3   The Standard Normal Distribution

6–4   Applications of the Normal Distribution

6–5   The Central Limit Theorem

6–6   The Normal Approximation to the Binomial Distribution

6–7   Summary

Statistics Today

What Is Normal?

Medical researchers have determined so-called normal intervals for a person's blood pressure, cholesterol, triglycerides, and the like. For example, the normal range of systolic blood pressure is 110 to 140. The normal interval for a person's triglycerides is from 30 to 200 milligrams per decilitre (mg/dl). By measuring these variables, a physician can determine if a patient's vital statistics are within the normal interval or if some type of treatment is needed to correct a condition and avoid future illnesses. The question then is, How does one determine the so-called normal intervals? See Statistics Today—Revisited, page 289, at the end of the chapter.

In this chapter, you will learn how researchers determine normal intervals for specific medical tests by using a normal distribution. You will see how the same methods are used to determine the lifetimes of batteries, the strength of ropes, and many other traits.

6–1   Introduction

Random variables can be either discrete or continuous. Discrete variables and their distributions were explained in Chapter 5. Recall that a discrete variable cannot assume all values between any two given values of the variables. On the other hand, a continuous variable can assume all values between any two given values of the variables. Examples of continuous variables are the heights of adult men, body temperatures of rats, and cholesterol levels of adults. Many continuous variables, such as the examples just mentioned, have distributions that are bell-shaped, and these are called *approximately normally distributed variables*. For example, if a researcher selects a random sample of 100 adult women, measures their heights, and constructs a histogram, the researcher gets a graph similar to the one shown in Figure 6–1(a). Now, if the researcher increases the sample size and decreases the width of the classes, the histograms will look like the ones shown in Figure 6–1(b) and (c). Finally, if it were possible to measure exactly the heights of all adult females in Canada and plot them, the histogram would very closely approximate a continuous curve referred to as the *normal distribution curve,* shown in Figure 6–1(d). This distribution is also known as a *bell curve* or a *Gaussian distribution,* named for the German mathematician Carl Friedrich Gauss (1777–1855), who derived its equation.

No variable fits a normal distribution perfectly, since a normal distribution is a theoretical distribution. However, a normal distribution can be used to describe many variables, because the deviations from a normal distribution are very small. This concept will be explained further in Section 6–2.

When the data values are evenly distributed about the mean, a distribution is said to be a **symmetric distribution.** (A normal distribution is symmetric.) Figure 6–2(a) shows

Figure 6–1

Histograms for the
Distribution of Heights
of Adult Women

(a) Random sample of 100 women

(b) Sample size increased and class width decreased

(c) Sample size increased and class width
decreased further

(d) Normal distribution for the population

Figure 6–2

Normal and Skewed
Distributions

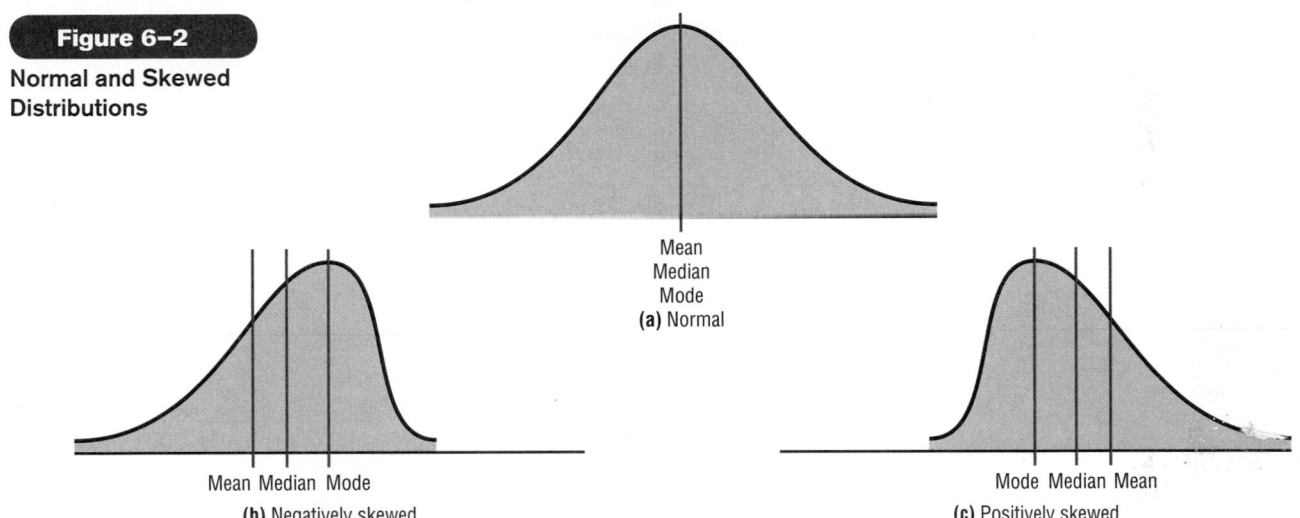

Mean
Median
Mode
(a) Normal

Mean Median Mode
(b) Negatively skewed

Mode Median Mean
(c) Positively skewed

Objective

Identify distributions
as symmetric or
skewed.

a symmetric distribution. When the majority of the data values fall to the left or right of
the mean, the distribution is said to be *skewed*. When the majority of the data values fall
to the right of the mean, the distribution is said to be a **negatively or left-skewed distribution**. Typically the mean is to the left of the median, and the mean and the median are
to the left of the mode. See Figure 6–2(b). When the majority of the data values fall to the
left of the mean, a distribution is said to be a **positively or right-skewed distribution**.
Generally the mean falls to the right of the median, and both the mean and the median
fall to the right of the mode. See Figure 6–2(c).

The "tail" of the curve indicates the direction of skewness (right is positive, left negative). These distributions can be compared with the ones shown in Figure 3–1 on page 91.
Both types follow the same principles.

This chapter will present the properties of a normal distribution and discuss its applications. Then a very important fact about a normal distribution called the *central limit
theorem* will be explained. Finally, the chapter will explain how a normal distribution
curve can be used as an approximation to other distributions, such as the binomial distribution. Since a binomial distribution is a discrete distribution, a correction for continuity
may be employed when a normal distribution is used for its approximation.

6-2   Properties of a Normal Distribution

Objective

Identify the properties of a normal distribution.

The *normal distribution curve* can be used to study many variables that are approximately normal. The equation to generate a normal, bell-shaped, curve is derived using mathematical methods beyond the scope of an introductory statistics text. In applied statistics, tables or technology will be used to solve specific problems instead of equations.

The area under the normal curve is most important in determining statistical probabilities for continuous random variables located on the x axis. The height of the normal curve is not relevant for calculating probabilities using tables or technology. Subsequently the y axis is often omitted in the illustration of the normal curve.

The shape and position of a normal distribution curve depend on two parameters, the *mean* and *standard deviation*. This results in unique distributions for each normally distributed random variable. Figure 6–3(a) shows two normal distributions with the same mean but different standard deviations. The larger the standard deviation, the more dispersed, or spread out, the distribution is. Figure 6–3(b) shows two normal distributions with the same standard deviation but different means. These curves have the same shapes but are located at different positions on the x axis. Figure 6–3(c) shows two normal distributions with different means and different standard deviations affecting both position and shape.

A **normal distribution** is a continuous, symmetric, bell-shaped distribution of a variable.

The properties of a normal distribution, including those mentioned in the definition, are explained next.

Summary of the Properties of the Normal Distribution

1. A normal distribution is bell-shaped with the two tails continuing indefinitely in both directions never touching the x axis.
2. The normal curve is symmetric about the centre—mean, median, and mode.
3. The total area under the normal distribution curve is equal to 1. That is 100% of all continuous random variables fall under the normal curve.

Figure 6–3

Shapes of Normal Distributions

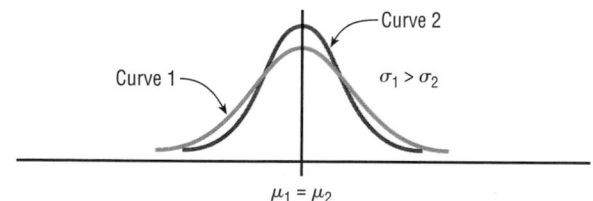

(a) Same means but different standard deviations

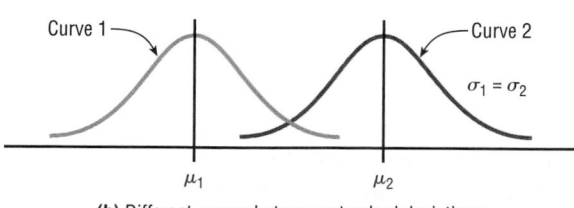

(b) Different means but same standard deviations

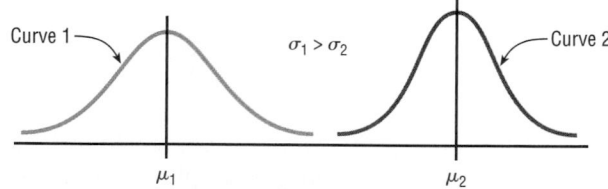

(c) Different means and different standard deviations

Empirical Rule and Areas Under the Normal Curve

Section 3–3 discussed the *empirical rule* for bell-shaped data distributions. Using empirical rule methods and normal distribution properties, areas under the normal curve within 1, 2, and 3 standard deviations (σ) of the population mean (μ), can be determined. Refer to Figure 6–4.

Figure 6–4

Areas Under a Normal Distribution Curve

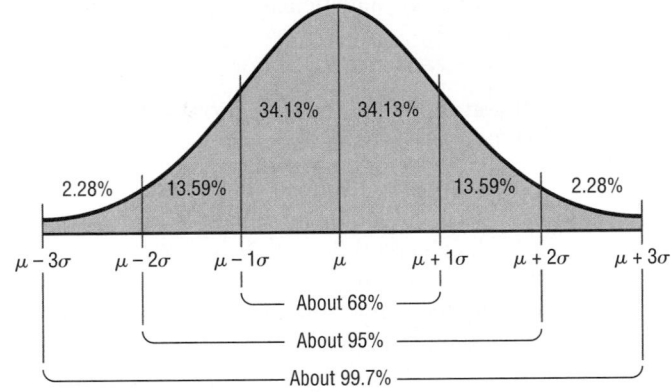

The following example will illustrate the relationship between the population mean and standard deviation and a normally distributed continuous random variable.

Example 6–1

Assume that cellphone battery life is normally distributed with a mean of 4.5 hours and a standard deviation of 1.2 hours. Determine the life of the cellphone batteries within 0, ± 1, ± 2, and ± 3 standard deviations of the mean. Sketch, then interpret your answer.

Solution

Given $\mu = 4.50$ hours and $\sigma = 1.25$ hours. Refer to Figure 6–4.

$$\mu - 3\sigma = 4.50 - 3(1.25) = 0.75$$
$$\mu - 2\sigma = 4.50 - 2(1.25) = 2.00$$
$$\mu - 1\sigma = 4.50 - 1(1.25) = 3.75$$
$$\mu - 0\sigma = 4.50 - 0(1.25) = 4.50$$
$$\mu + 1\sigma = 4.50 + 1(1.25) = 5.75$$
$$\mu + 2\sigma = 4.50 + 2(1.25) = 7.00$$
$$\mu + 3\sigma = 4.50 + 3(1.25) = 8.25$$

The X values that correspond to $-3, -2, -1, 0, +1, +2, +3$ standard deviations from the mean are illustrated in Figure 6–5.

Figure 6–5

Normal Distribution Curve ($\mu = 4.50$, $\sigma = 1.25$)

Referring to Figure 6–4 about 68% of the cellphone batteries will last between 3.25 and 5.75 hours, about 95% will last between 2.00 and 7.00 hours and about 99.7% will last between 0.75 and 8.25 hours. These percentages also represent the probabilities that the cellphones will last in the range indicated.

6-3 The Standard Normal Distribution

Objective

Find the area under the standard normal distribution, given various z scores.

Since each normally distributed variable has its own mean and standard deviation, as stated earlier, the shape and location of these curves will vary. In practical applications, then, one would require a table of areas under the curve for each variable. To simplify this situation, statisticians use the *standard normal distribution*.

> The **standard normal distribution** is a normal distribution with a mean of 0 and a standard deviation of 1.

The standard normal distribution as shown in Figure 6–5 should be compared with the areas under the normal distribution curve in Figure 6–4. The values under the curve indicate the proportion of area in each section. For example, the area between the mean and 1 standard deviation above the mean is about 0.3413, or 34.13%. In other words, if continuous data is normally distributed there is a probability of 0.3413 that a data value will fall between the mean and 1 standard deviation above the mean.

Formula for Standard Score

The *standard score* indicates the number of standard deviations that a data value is located above (positive z score) or below (negative z score) the mean. To convert a continuous random variable X to a standard score z, use the following formula.

$$z = \frac{X - \mu}{\sigma}$$

z = standard score
X = continuous random variable or X value
μ = population mean
σ = population standard deviation

Example 6–2

A student scored 85 on a statistics test with a test mean of 67 and a standard deviation of 9. Assuming that the test is normally distributed, convert the test score to a standard score. Interpret.

Solution

Given $X = 85$, $\mu = 67$, $\sigma = 9$, substitute into the standard score formula.

$$z = \frac{X - \mu}{\sigma} = \frac{85 - 67}{9} = 2.0$$

The student score of 85 is 2.0 standard deviations above the mean of 67. Also, approximately 47.72% (34.13% + 13.59%) of all scores fall between the mean of 67 and the score of 85. Another interpretation would be the probability that a student scores between 67 and 85 on the statistics test is 0.4772.

A few practical applications of the standard normal distribution method include:

- Locating the cutoff point for admission into a graduate program of study
- Determining the percentage of women who weigh between 50 and 60 kilograms
- Finding the probability that a cellphone battery will last longer than 4.5 hours

Figure 6–6

Figure 6–6

Standard Normal
Distribution

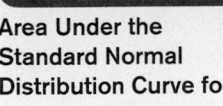

Bell-shaped
distributions occurred
quite often in early
coin-tossing and die-
rolling experiments.

The next section will focus on procedures to find percentages and probabilities for continuous random variables using standard score tables and areas under the normal distribution curve. Additional applications of the normal distribution using X values will be shown in Section 6–4.

Finding Areas Under the Standard Normal Distribution Curve

For the solution of problems using the standard normal distribution, the following procedure will provide a useful guideline.

Step 1 Sketch and label the normal curve shading the desired area.

Step 2 Look up the cumulative area to the left of each z score in the sketch using Table E–1—Negative z Scores and Table E–2—Positive z Scores in Appendix C.

Step 3 If necessary, perform the appropriate operation to obtain the desired area.

Rounding Areas

Tables E–1 and E–2 display the z scores rounded to one decimal place and the probabilities rounded to four decimal places. If converting area to a percentage, round to two decimal places.

Example 6–3

Find the area under the standard normal distribution curve to the left of $z = 1.25$.

Solution

Sketch the curve and represent the area as shown in Figure 6–7.

Figure 6–7

Area Under the
Standard Normal
Distribution Curve for
Example 6–3

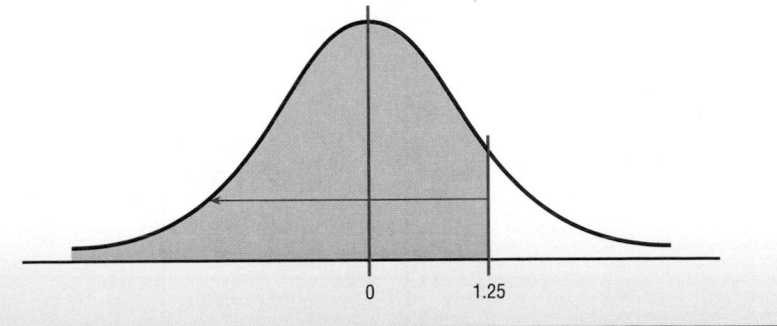

Refer to Table E–2—Positive z Scores in Appendix C, which refers to the cumulative area to the **left** of the z score. Look under the column labelled z to $z = 1.2$ and look to the right of the row labelled z to $z = 0.05$. Read to the right of $z = 1.2$ and below $z = 0.05$ and locate where they intersect, .8944, which represents the cumulative area to the **left** of $z = 1.25$. Refer to Figure 6–8. Therefore, the desired area is 0.8944, or 89.44%.

Figure 6–8

Using Table E–2
in Appendix C for
Example 6–3

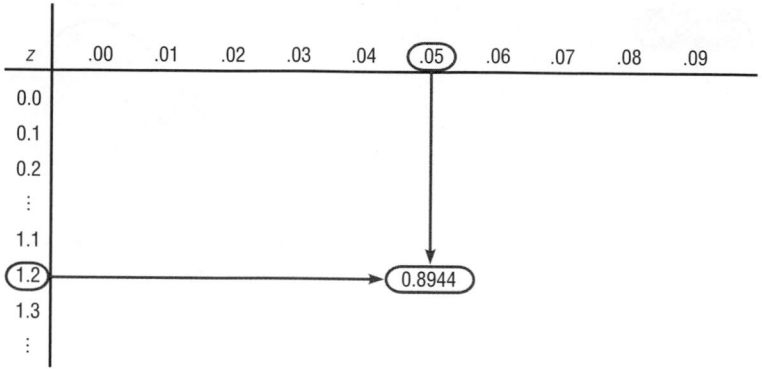

Example 6–4

Find the area under the standard normal distribution curve to the right of $z = -2.33$.

Solution

Sketch the curve and represent the area as shown in Figure 6–9.

Figure 6–9

Area Under the
Standard Normal
Distribution Curve for
Example 6–4

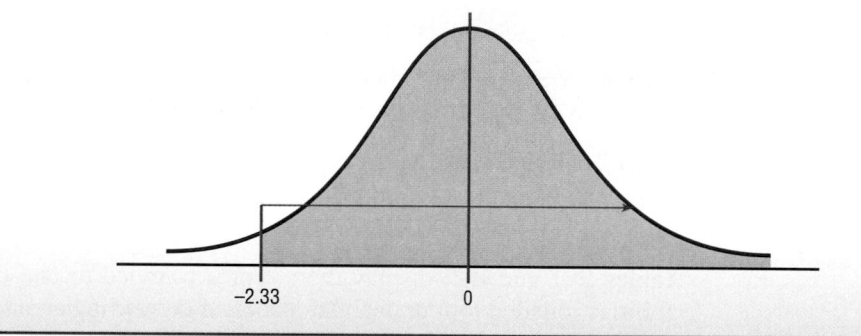

Refer to Table E–1—Negative z Scores in Appendix C, which refers to the cumulative area to the **left** of the z score. Look under the column labelled z to $z = -2.3$ and look to the right of the row labelled z to $z = 0.03$. Read to the right of $z = -2.3$ and below $z = 0.03$ and locate where they intersect, 0.0099, which represents the cumulative area to the **left** of $z = -2.33$. Refer to Figure 6–10.

Since the area desired is to the **right** of $z = -2.33$ and the total area under the normal curve is 1.0, subtract 1.000 from 0.0099 to obtain 0.9901. Therefore the area to the right of $z = -2.33$ is 0.9901, or 99.01%.

Figure 6–10

Using Table E–1
in Appendix C for
Example 6–4

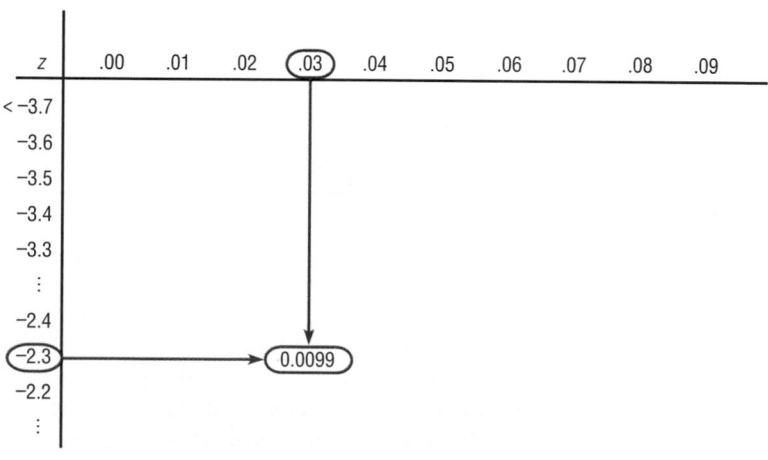

Example 6–5	Find the area under the normal curve between $z = -0.67$ and $z = 1.96$.

Solution

Sketch the curve and shade the desired area as shown in Figure 6–11.

Figure 6–11
Area Under the Standard Normal Distribution Curve for Example 6–5

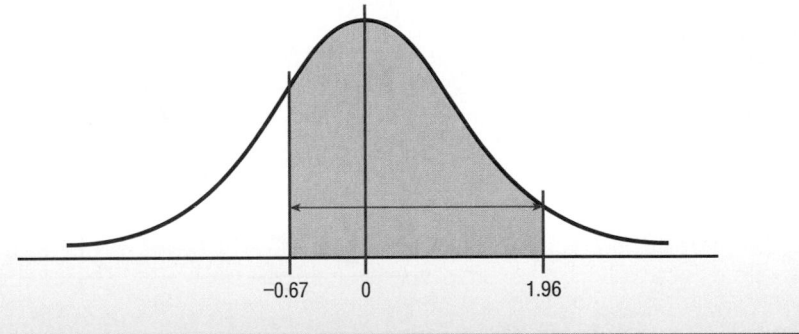

Refer to Table E–1—Negative z Scores in Appendix C. The cumulative area to the **left** of $z = -0.67$ is .2514. Refer to Table E–2—Positive z Scores in Appendix C. The cumulative area to the **left** of $z = 1.96$ is .9750.

Since the area desired is **between** $z = -0.67$ and $z = 1.96$, subtract the cumulative area to the left of $z = 1.96$ (0.9750) from the cumulative area to the left of $z = -0.67$ (0.2514) to obtain 0.7236. Therefore the area between $z = -0.67$ and $z = 1.96$ is 0.7236, or 72.36%.

A Normal Distribution Curve as a Probability Distribution Curve

A normal distribution curve can be used as a probability distribution curve for normally distributed variables. Recall that a normal distribution is a *continuous distribution*, as opposed to a discrete probability distribution, as explained in Chapter 5. The fact that it is continuous means that there are no gaps in the curve. In other words, for every z score on the x axis, there is a corresponding height, or frequency, value.

The area under the standard normal distribution curve can also be thought of as a probability. That is, if it were possible to select any z score at random, the probability of choosing one, say, between 0 and 2.00 would be the same as the area under the curve between 0 and 2.00. In this case, the area is 0.4772. Therefore, the probability of randomly selecting any z score between 0 and 2.00 is 0.4772. The problems involving probability are solved in the same manner as the previous examples involving areas in this section. Referring to Example 6–5, the area under the curve between $z = -0.67$ and $z = 1.96$ is 0.7236 can be written as the probability of randomly selecting a score between $z = -0.67$ and $z = 1.96$ is 0.7236.

Probability Notation

Problems involving continuous probability distributions are written using the following format.

$P(z > a)$ refers to the probability that a z score is greater than a.

$P(z < a)$ refers to the probability that a z score is less than a.

$P(a < z < b)$ refers to the probability the z score is between a and b.

Note: In continuous distributions, the probability of any exact z score is 0 since the area would be represented by a vertical line above the value. In theory, vertical lines have no area. Therefore, $P(a \leq z \leq b) = P(a < z < b)$.

Example 6–6

Find the probability of randomly selecting a value with a z score that is between $z = 0.44$ and $z = 1.22$.

Solution

Sketch the curve and shade the desired area as shown in Figure 6–12.

Figure 6–12

Area Under the Standard Normal Distribution Curve for Example 6–6

Refer to Table E–2—Positive z Scores in Appendix C. Since the area desired is **between** $z = 0.44$ and $z = 1.22$, subtract the cumulative area to the **left** of $z = 1.22$ (0.8888) from the cumulative area to the **left** of $z = 0.44$ (0.6700) to obtain 0.2138.

Using probability notation, $P(0.44 < z < 1.22) = 0.2138$ or 21.38% of all values fall between 0.44 and 1.22 standard deviations above the mean.

Finding z Scores When Given Areas

Some statistical applications involve finding z scores when the area under the standard normal distribution curve is given. The procedure involves working from inside Table E–1—Negative z Scores (cumulative areas to the left from 0.001 to 0.5000) or Table E–2—Positive z Scores (cumulative areas to the left from 0.5000 to 0.9999) in Appendix C. Locate the desired area or the area **closest to** the desired area then read the corresponding z score on the outside margins that intersect with this area. Refer to Example 6–7.

Example 6–7

Find the z score that corresponds to a cumulative area to the left of 0.7500.

Solution

Sketch the curve and shade the desired area as shown in Figure 6–13.

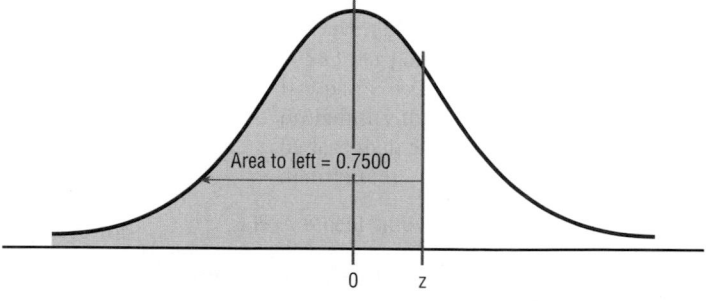

Area to left = 0.7500

Refer to Table E–2—Positive z Scores in Appendix C as the cumulative areas to the left range from 0.5000 to 0.9999 and the desired area (0.7500) is in this range. Locate the area inside the table **closest to** 0.7500 (0.7486). Read out to the z scores in the margin above and to the left of 0.7486. The z score that intersects with 0.7486 is $z = 0.67$. Refer to Figure 6–13.

Figure 6–13

Using Table E–2 in Appendix C for Example 6–7

Note: If the desired area is **exactly** halfway between two areas in the table, find the average of the z scores that correspond to the areas below and above the desired area. For example, the area 0.9500 is **exactly** halfway between 0.9495 and 0.9505, which correspond to z scores of $z = 1.64$ and $z = 1.65$, respectively. Therefore, the average of these two z scores is $z = 1.645$. Also 0.9950 is equidistant from 0.9949 ($z = 2.57$) and 0.9951 ($z = 2.58$), therefore the average of $z = 2.575$ will be used. In a similar manner use z scores for 0.0500 ($z = -1.645$) and 0.0050 ($z = -2.575$). Refer to Table E-1 and E-2 in Appendix C.

Area and Probability Relationship

The rationale for using an area under a continuous curve to determine a probability can be understood by considering the example of a watch that is powered by a battery. When the battery goes dead, what is the probability that the minute hand will stop somewhere between the numbers 2 and 5 on the face of the watch? In this case, the values of the variable constitute a continuous variable since the hour hand can stop anywhere on the dial's face between 0 and 12 (one revolution of the minute hand). Hence, the sample space can be considered to be 12 units long, and the distance between the numbers 2 and 5 is $5 - 2$, or 3 units. Hence, the probability that the minute hand stops on a number between 2 and 5 is $\frac{3}{12} = \frac{1}{4}$. See Figure 6–14(a).

Figure 6–14

The Relationship Between Area and Probability

$P = \frac{3}{12} = \frac{1}{4}$

(a) Clock

Area $= 3 \cdot \frac{1}{12} = \frac{3}{12} = \frac{1}{4}$

(b) Rectangle

The problem could also be solved by using a graph of a continuous variable. Let us assume that since the watch can stop anytime at random, the values where the minute hand would land are spread evenly over the range of 0 through 12. The graph would then consist of a *continuous uniform distribution* with a range of 12 units. Now if we require the area under the curve to be 1 (like the area under the standard normal distribution), the height of the rectangle formed by the curve and the x axis would need to be $\frac{1}{12}$. The reason is that the area of a rectangle is equal to the base times the height. If the base is 12 units long, then the height would have to be $\frac{1}{12}$ since $12 \cdot \frac{1}{12} = 1$.

The area of the rectangle with a base from 2 through 5 would be $3 \cdot \frac{1}{12}$, or $\frac{1}{4}$. See Figure 6–14(b). Notice that the area of the small rectangle is the same as the probability found previously. Hence the area of this rectangle corresponds to the probability of this event. The same reasoning can be applied to the standard normal distribution curve shown in Example 6–6.

Finding the area under the standard normal distribution curve is the first step in solving a wide variety of practical applications in which the variables are normally distributed. Some of these applications will be presented in Section 6–4.

Applying the Concepts 6–3

Assessing Normality

Many times in statistics it is necessary to see if a distribution of data values is approximately normally distributed. There are special techniques that can be used. One technique is to draw a histogram for the data and see if it is approximately bell-shaped. (*Note:* It does not have to be exactly symmetric to be bell-shaped.)

The numbers of branches of the 50 top libraries are shown.

67	84	80	77	97	59	62	37	33	42
36	54	18	12	19	33	49	24	25	22
24	29	9	21	21	22	24	31	17	21
13	19	19	22	22	30	41	22	18	20
26	33	14	14	16	22	26	10	16	24

Source: *The World Almanac and Book of Facts.*

1. Construct a frequency distribution for the data.
2. Construct a histogram for the data.
3. Describe the shape of the histogram.
4. Based on your answer to question 3, do you feel that the distribution is approximately normal?

In addition to the histogram, distributions that are approximately normal have about 68% of the values fall within 1 standard deviation of the mean, about 95% of the data values fall within 2 standard deviations of the mean, and almost 100% of the data values fall within 3 standard deviations of the mean. (See Figure 6–4.)

5. Find the mean and standard deviation for the data.
6. What percent of the data values fall within 1 standard deviation of the mean?
7. What percent of the data values fall within 2 standard deviations of the mean?
8. What percent of data values fall within 3 standard deviations of the mean?
9. How do your answers to questions 6, 7, and 8 compare to 68, 95, and 100%, respectively?
10. Does your answer help support the conclusion you reached in question 4? Explain.

(More techniques for assessing normality are explained in Section 6–4.)
See page 293 for the answers.

Exercises 6–3

1. What are the characteristics of a normal distribution?

2. Why is the standard normal distribution important in statistical analysis?

3. What is the total area under the standard normal distribution curve?

4. What percentage of the area falls below the mean? Above the mean?

5. About what percentage of the area under the normal distribution curve falls within 1 standard deviation above and below the mean? 2 standard deviations? 3 standard deviations?

For Exercises 6 through 25, find the area under the standard normal distribution curve.

6. Between $z = 0$ and $z = 1.66$

7. Between $z = 0$ and $z = 0.75$

8. Between $z = 0$ and $z = -0.35$

9. Between $z = 0$ and $z = -2.07$

10. To the right of $z = 1.10$

11. To the right of $z = 0.23$

12. To the left of $z = -0.48$

13. To the left of $z = -1.43$

14. Between $z = 1.23$ and $z = 1.90$

15. Between $z = 0.79$ and $z = 1.28$

16. Between $z = -0.96$ and $z = -0.36$

17. Between $z = -1.56$ and $z = -1.83$

18. Between $z = 0.24$ and $z = -1.12$

19. Between $z = 2.47$ and $z = -1.03$

20. To the left of $z = 1.31$

21. To the left of $z = 2.11$

22. To the right of $z = -1.92$

23. To the right of $z = -0.15$

24. To the left of $z = -2.15$ and to the right of $z = 1.62$

25. To the right of $z = 1.92$ and to the left of $z = -0.44$

In Exercises 26 through 39, find probabilities for each, using the standard normal distribution.

26. $P(0 < z < 1.69)$

27. $P(0 < z < 0.67)$

28. $P(-1.23 < z < 0)$

29. $P(-1.57 < z < 0)$

30. $P(z > 1.16)$

31. $P(z > 2.83)$

32. $P(z < -1.77)$

33. $P(z < -1.21)$

34. $P(-0.05 < z < 1.10)$

35. $P(-2.46 < z < 1.74)$

36. $P(1.12 < z < 1.43)$

37. $P(1.46 < z < 2.97)$

38. $P(z > -1.39)$

39. $P(z < 1.42)$

For Exercises 40 through 45, find the z score that corresponds to the given area.

40.

41.

42.

43.

44.

0.9671

45.

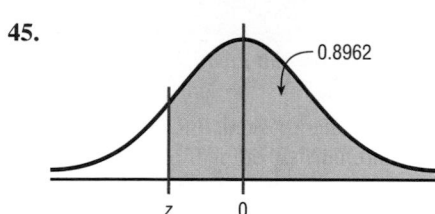

0.8962

46. Find the z score to the right of the mean so that

    a. 53.98% of the area under the distribution curve lies to the left of it.

    b. 71.90% of the area under the distribution curve lies to the left of it.

    c. 96.78% of the area under the distribution curve lies to the left of it.

47. Find the z score to the left of the mean so that

    a. 98.87% of the area under the distribution curve lies to the right of it.

    b. 82.12% of the area under the distribution curve lies to the right of it.

    c. 60.64% of the area under the distribution curve lies to the right of it.

48. Find two z scores so that 44% of the middle area is bounded by them.

49. Find two z scores, one positive and one negative, so that the areas in the two tails total the following values.

    a. 5%

    b. 10%

    c. 1%

Extending the Concepts

50. In the standard normal distribution, find the values of z for the 75th, 80th, and 92nd percentiles.

51. Find $P(-1 < z < 1)$, $P(-2 < z < 2)$, and $P(-3 < z < 3)$. How do these values compare with the empirical rule?

52. Find z_0 such that $P(z > z_0) = 0.1234$.

53. Find z_0 such that $P(-1.2 < z < z_0) = 0.8671$.

54. Find z_0 such that $P(z_0 < z < 2.5) = 0.7672$.

55. Find z_0 such that the area between z_0 and $z = -0.5$ is 0.2345 (two answers).

56. Find z_0 such that $P(-z_0 < z < z_0) = 0.86$.

57. The mathematical equation for the standard normal distribution is

$$y = \frac{e^{-(X-\mu)^2/(2\sigma^2)}}{\sigma\sqrt{2\pi}}$$

    Where $\pi \approx 3.14$, $e \approx 2.718$
    μ = population mean
    σ = population standard deviation

    Given $\mu = 0$ and $\sigma = 1$, solve for $X = \{-2, -1.5, -1, -0.5, 0, 0.5, 1, 1.5, 2.0\}$.

58. Use the results in exercise 57 to graph the standard normal distribution.

   6–4   ## Applications of the Normal Distribution

Objective ④

Find probabilities for a normally distributed variable by transforming it into a standard normal variable.

The standard normal distribution curve can be used to solve a wide variety of practical problems. The only requirement is that the variable be normally or approximately normally distributed. There are several mathematical tests to determine whether a variable is normally distributed. See the Critical Thinking Challenges on page 291. For all the problems presented in this chapter, one can assume that the variable is normally or approximately normally distributed.

    To solve problems using the standard normal distribution, the continuous random variable X must be converted to a standard score z, a quantity without units derived by subtracting the population mean μ from the X value and then dividing the difference by the population standard deviation σ. This is the same formula previously presented in Sections 3–4 and 6–3.

$$z = \frac{X - \mu}{\sigma}$$

After X values have been converted, procedures learned in Section 6–3 using Tables E–1 and E–2—Standard Normal z Distribution Cumulative Areas in Appendix C can be used to solve problems involving proportion, percentage, and probability.

For example, suppose that the scores for a standardized test are normally distributed, have a mean of 100, and have a standard deviation of 15. When the scores are transformed to z scores, the two distributions coincide, as shown in Figure 6–15. (Recall that the z distribution has a mean of 0 and a standard deviation of 1.)

Figure 6–15

Test Scores and Their Corresponding z Values

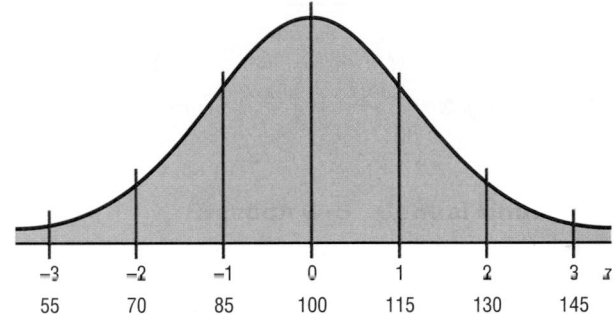

To solve the application problems in this section, transform the values of the variable to z scores and then find the areas under the standard normal distribution, as explained in Section 6–3.

Example 6–8

The mean time Canadians, with computers and an Internet connection, spend online is 34 hours per month with a standard deviation of 4.5 hours. Assuming the data is normally distributed; find the percentage of Canadians who spend less than 40 hours online per month.

Source: Comscore Media Matrix, Canada, Demographic Profile Report, October 2004.

Solution

Step 1   Sketch the curve and represent the area, as shown in Figure 6–16.

Figure 6–16

Area Under a Normal Curve for Example 6–8

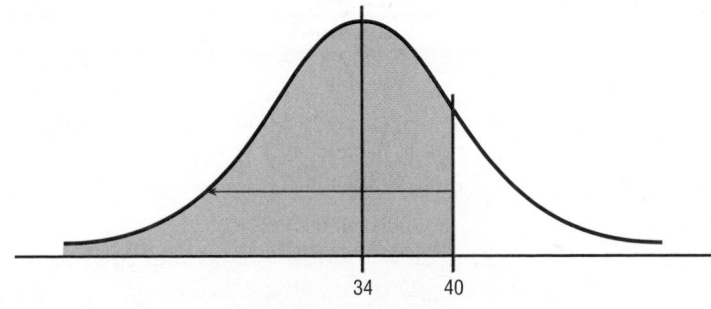

Step 2 Find the z score for $X = 40$.

$$z = \frac{X - \mu}{\sigma} = \frac{40 - 34}{4.5} = 1.33$$

Hence, 40 is 1.33 standard deviations above the mean of 34, as shown for the z distribution in Figure 6–17.

Figure 6–17

Area and z Values for Example 6–8

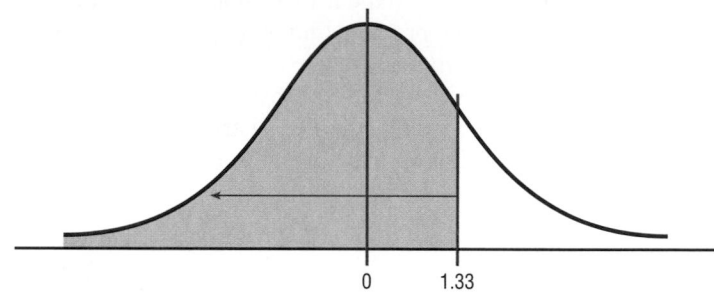

0   1.33

Step 3 Find the area by using Table E–2—Positive z Scores. The cumulative area to the left of $z = 1.33$ is 0.9082.

Therefore, 90.82% of Canadians spend less than 40 hours per month online.

Example 6–9

Each month, a Canadian household generates an average of 13 kilograms of newspaper for garbage or recycling. Assume the data is normally distributed with a standard deviation of 1 kilogram. If a household is selected at random, find the probability of its generating

 a. Between 12 and 15 kilograms per month.

 b. More than 13.7 kilograms per month.

Assume the variable is approximately normally distributed.

Solution a

Step 1 Sketch the figure and represent the area. See Figure 6–18.

Figure 6–18

Area Under a Normal Curve for Part *a* of Example 6–9

Historical Note

Astronomers in the late 1700s and the 1800s used the principles underlying the normal distribution to correct measurement errors that occurred in charting the positions of the planets.

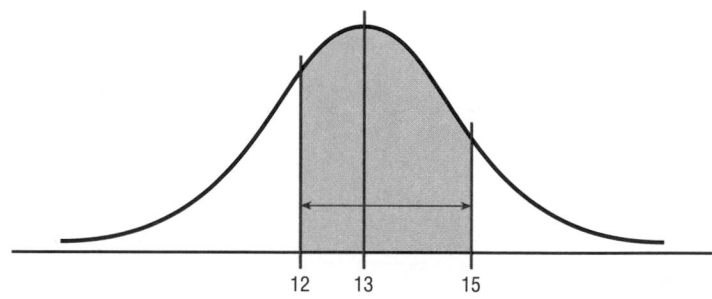

12   13   15

Step 2 Convert $X = 12$ and $X = 15$ to z scores.

$$z_1 = \frac{X - \mu}{\sigma} = \frac{12 - 13}{1} = -1$$

$$z_2 = \frac{X - \mu}{\sigma} = \frac{15 - 13}{1} = 2$$

Step 3   Find the desired area. Refer to Table E–1—Negative z Scores in Appendix C. The cumulative area to the left of $z = -1.0$ is 0.1587. Refer to Table E–2—Positive z Scores in Appendix C. The cumulative area to the left of $z = 2.0$ is 0.9772. Subtract the cumulative area to the left of $z = 2.0$ (0.9772) from the cumulative area to the left of $z = 1.0$ (0.1587) to obtain the desired area 0.8185. Refer to Figure 6–19.

Figure 6–19

Area and z Values for Part a of Example 6–9

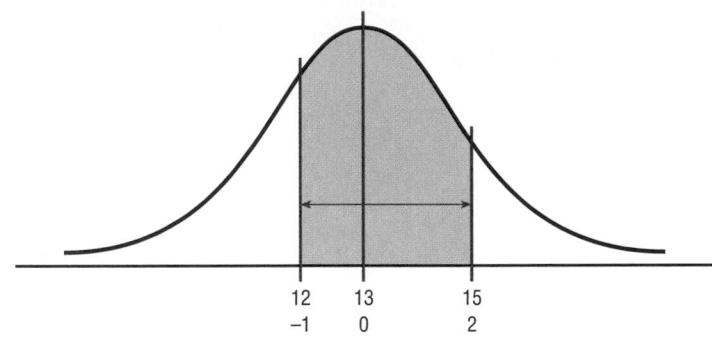

Hence, the probability that a randomly selected household generates between 12 and 15 kilograms of newspapers per month is 81.85%.

Solution b

Step 1   Sketch the figure and represent the area. See Figure 6–20.

Figure 6–20

Area Under a Normal Curve for Part b of Example 6–9

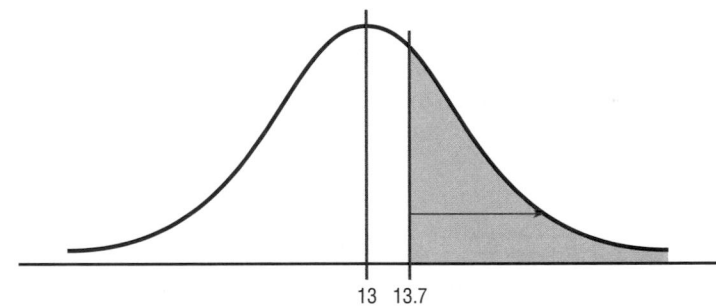

Step 2   Convert $X = 13.7$ to a z score.

$$z = \frac{X - \mu}{\sigma} = \frac{13.7 - 13}{1} = 0.7$$

Step 3   Find the desired area. Refer to Table E–2—Positive z Scores in Appendix C. The cumulative area to the left of $z = 0.7$ is 0.7580. Since the total area under the normal curve is 1.0, subtract this area 1.000 from the cumulative area to the left of $z = 0.7$ (0.7580) to obtain the desired area 0.2420.

Hence the probability that a randomly selected household will accumulate more than 13.7 kilograms of newspapers is 0.2420, or 24.2%.

A normal distribution can also be used to answer questions of "How many?" This application is shown in Example 6–10.

Example 6–10

The Canadian Association of Emergency Physicians collates data for emergency medical services (EMS) response times for 911 calls. The average time to respond to an emergency call was 13 minutes. Assume that the variable is normally distributed with a standard deviation of 3.2 minutes. If 50 emergency 911 calls are randomly selected, approximately how many calls would you expect the response time to be less than 10 minutes?

Source: Canadian Association of Emergency Physicians.

Solution

Step 1 Draw a figure and represent the area as shown in Figure 6–21.

Figure 6–21

Area Under a Normal Curve for Example 6–10

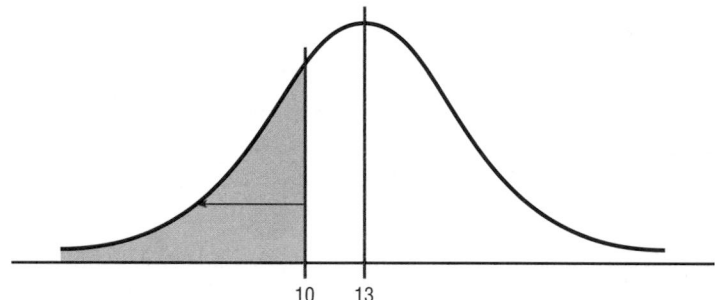

Step 2 Find the z score for $X = 10$.

$$z = \frac{X - \mu}{\sigma} = \frac{10 - 13}{3.2} = -0.94$$

Step 3 Find the desired area. Refer to Table E–1—Negative z Scores in Appendix C. The cumulative area to the left of $z = -0.94$ is 0.1736.

Step 4 To find out how many emergency calls will be responded to in less than 10 minutes, multiply the sample size 50 by 0.1736 to obtain 8.68. Hence, 8.68 or approximately 9 of the emergency calls will have a response time of less than 10 minutes.

Note: For problems using percentages, be sure to change the percentage to a decimal before multiplying. Also, round the answer to the nearest whole number, since it is not possible to have 8.68 calls.

Finding Data Values Given Specific Probabilities

A normal distribution can also be used to find the specific data values for given percentages. This X value represents the desired cutoff point separating the specified area from the remainder of the curve. Simply determine the z score that corresponds to the area to the **left** of the X value using Table E–1 or Table E–2 as previously illustrated. Substitute the z score and the given mean (μ) and standard deviation (σ) into the standard score formula and solve for X.

To simplify the calculation, the standard score formula $z = \dfrac{X - \mu}{\sigma}$ has been rearranged and can be used to solve for X.

$$X = z \cdot \sigma + \mu$$

This application is shown in Example 6–11.

Example 6–11

Objective ⑤

Find specific data values for given percentages, using the standard normal distribution.

To qualify for a police academy, candidates must score in the top 10% on a general abilities test. The test has a mean of 200 and a standard deviation of 20. Find the lowest possible score to qualify. Assume the test scores are normally distributed.

Solution

Since the test scores are normally distributed, the test value X that cuts off the upper 10% of the area under a normal distribution curve is desired. This area is shown in Figure 6–22.

Figure 6–22

Area Under a Normal Curve for Example 6–11

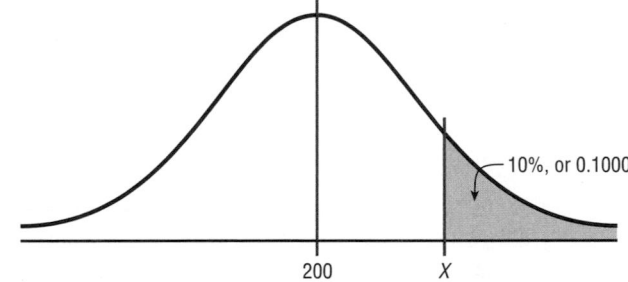

Work backward to solve this problem.

Step 1 Subtract 0.1000 from the total area under the normal curve, 1.000 to obtain 0.9000.

Step 2 Find the z score from Table E–2—Positive z Scores in Appendix C that corresponds to the cumulative area to the left **closest to** the desired area 0.9000. The **closest** value to 0.9000 is 0.8997, which corresponds to a z score of 1.28. Refer to Figure 6–23.

Figure 6–23

Finding the z Score from Table E–2— Positive z Scores in Appendix C

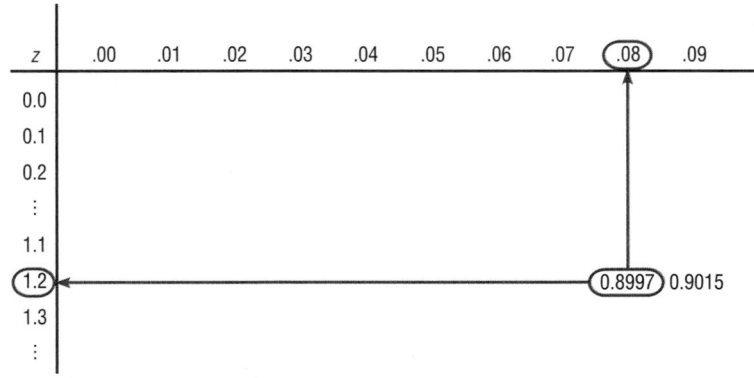

Interesting Fact

The average CEO reaches the Canadian average annual earnings by 9:46 a.m. on January 2.

Step 3 Substitute in the rearranged standard score formula.

$$X = z \cdot \sigma + \mu$$
$$X = (1.28)(20) + 200$$
$$X = 225.6$$
$$X = 226 \text{ (rounded)}$$

A score of 226 should be used as a cutoff. Anybody scoring 226 or higher qualifies.

Example 6–12

For a medical study, a researcher wishes to select people in the middle 60% of the population based on blood pressure. If the mean systolic blood pressure is 120 and the standard deviation is 8, find the upper and lower readings that would qualify people to participate in the study.

Solution

Assume that blood pressure readings are normally distributed; then cutoff points are as shown in Figure 6–24.

Figure 6–24

Area Under a Curve for Example 6–12

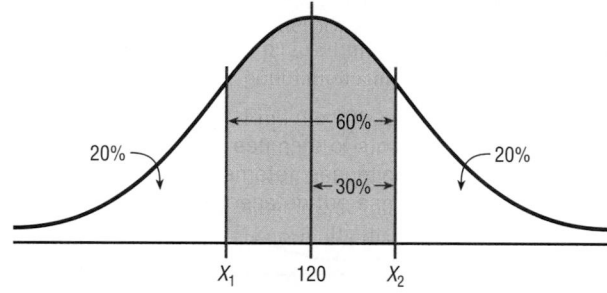

The two X values enclosing the middle 60% of the population have cumulative areas of 20% and 80% to the left, respectively. The z score that corresponds to X_1 with a cumulative area to the left closest to 0.2000 (.2005) is $z = -0.84$. The z score that corresponds to X_2 with a cumulative area to the left closest to 0.8000 (.7995) is $z = 0.84$.

Substitute into the standard score formula rearranged for X.

$$X_1 = z \cdot \sigma + \mu = (-0.84)(8) + 120 = 113.28$$
$$X_2 = z \cdot \sigma + \mu = (0.84)(8) + 120 = 126.72$$

Therefore, the middle 60% of the population will have blood pressure readings of between 113.28 and 126.72, or $113.28 < X < 126.72$.

As shown in this section, a normal distribution is a useful tool in answering many questions about variables that are normally or approximately normally distributed.

Normality Assumption

The key assumption made when determining probabilities for continuous random variables is that the data is drawn randomly from a population that approximates a normal distribution. Methods will be learned in later chapters that will allow normal distribution tables to be used for non-normal populations. Other methods will assume normality without providing proof. Statistical methods have been developed to test if a population is normal. The simplest test of normality, if data is available, is to plot the data frequencies and construct a histogram. If the histogram is bell-shaped then the data is considered normally distributed. If the data is uniform, skewed, or not bell-shaped, then the data are not normally distributed.

There are several other methods used by statisticians to check for normality, most beyond the scope of an introductory statistics text. A method using normal probability graph paper is shown in the Critical Thinking Challenges section, page 291, at the end of the chapter, and the chi-square goodness-of-fit test shown in Chapter 11. Other tests used to test for normality include the Pearson's index PI of skewness, Kolmogorov-Smikirov test, the Lilliefoers test, and with technology, the Normal Quantile Plot. An explanation of these tests can be found in advanced textbooks.

Applying the Concepts 6–4

Smart People

Assume you are thinking about starting a Mensa chapter in your hometown of Visiala, California, which has a population of about 10,000 people. You need to know how many people would qualify for Mensa, which requires an IQ of at least 130. You realize that IQ is normally distributed with a mean of 100 and a standard deviation of 15. Complete the following.

1. Find the approximate number of people in Visiala that are eligible for Mensa.
2. Is it reasonable to continue your quest for a Mensa chapter in Visiala?
3. How would you proceed to find out how many of the eligible people would actually join the new chapter? Be specific about your methods of gathering data.
4. What would be the minimum IQ score needed if you wanted to start an Ultra-Mensa club that included only the top 1% of IQ scores?

See page 293 for the answers.

Exercises 6–4

1. The average admission charge for a movie is $5.39. If the distribution of admission charges is normal with a standard deviation of $0.79, what is the probability that a randomly selected admission charge is less than $3.00?

   Source: *N.Y. Times Almanac.*

2. The average salary for university faculty at the beginning of the millennium was $76,284. Use a standard deviation of $12,247 and assume that university salaries are normally distributed. What is the probability that a randomly selected faculty member earns these salaries?

   a. Between $70,000 and $80,000.
   b. Less than $50,000.

   Source: Statistics Canada.

3. The average number of male inmates in Canada's provincial and federal prison system, over a 12-year period, was 100,809 with a standard deviation of 15,488. Assume that prison inmate numbers are normally distributed. Find the probability that in a randomly selected year the inmate population is

   a. Greater than 110,000.
   b. Between 80,000 and 90,000.

   Source: Correctional Service, Canada.

4. The SAT Reasoning Test, formerly the Scholastic Aptitude Test, is used by colleges and universities in the United States to aid in the selection of incoming national and international students. If the average score is 1019 and the scores are normally distributed with $\sigma = 90$, what is the 90th percentile score? What is the probability that a randomly selected score exceeds 1200?

   Source: *N.Y. Times Almanac.*

5. The average number of calories in a 50-gram chocolate bar is 225. Suppose that the distribution of calories is approximately normal with $\sigma = 10$. Find the probability that a randomly selected chocolate bar will have

   a. Between 200 and 220 calories.
   b. Less than 200 calories.

   Source: *The Doctor's Pocket Calorie, Fat, and Carbohydrate Counter.*

6. The average age of CEOs is 56 years. Assume the variable is normally distributed. If the standard deviation is 4 years, find the probability that the age of a randomly selected CEO will be in the following range.

   a. Between 53 and 59 years old
   b. Between 58 and 63 years old
   c. Between 50 and 55 years old

   Source: Michael D. Shook and Robert L. Shook, *The Book of Odds.*

7. The average salary for a Queens College full professor is $85,900. If the average salaries are normally distributed with a standard deviation of $11,000, find these probabilities.

   a. The professor makes more than $90,000.
   b. The professor makes more than $75,000.

   Source: AAUP, *Chronicle of Higher Education.*

8. Full-time Ph.D. students receive an average of $12,837 per year. If the average salaries are normally distributed with a standard deviation of $1500, find these probabilities.

   a. The student makes more than $15,000.
   b. The student makes between $13,000 and $14,000.

   Source: U.S. Education Dept., *Chronicle of Higher Education.*

9. A survey found that people keep their microwave ovens an average of 3.2 years. The standard deviation is 0.56 year. If a person decides to buy a new microwave oven, find the probability that he or she has owned the old oven for the following amount of time. Assume the variable is normally distributed.

   a. Less than 1.5 years
   b. Between 2 and 3 years
   c. More than 3.2 years
   d. What percent of microwave ovens would be replaced if a warranty of 18 months were given?

10. The average commute to work (one way) is 25.5 minutes according to the 2000 Census. If we assume that commuting times are normally distributed with a standard deviation of 6.1 minutes, what is the probability that a randomly selected commuter spends more than 30 minutes a day commuting one way?

    Source: *N.Y. Times Almanac.*

11. The average credit card debt for college seniors is $3262. If the debt is normally distributed with a standard deviation of $1100, find these probabilities.

    a. That the senior owes at least $1000
    b. That the senior owes more than $4000
    c. That the senior owes between $3000 and $4000

    Source: *USA TODAY.*

12. The average time a person spends at the Barefoot Landing Seaquarium is 96 minutes. The standard deviation is 17 minutes. Assume the variable is normally distributed. If a visitor is selected at random, find the probability that he or she will spend the following time at the seaquarium.

    a. At least 120 minutes
    b. At most 80 minutes
    c. Suggest a time for a bus to return to pick up a group of tourists.

13. The average time for a mail carrier to cover his or her route is 380 minutes, and the standard deviation is 16 minutes. If one of these trips is selected at random, find the probability that the carrier will have the following route time. Assume the variable is normally distributed.

    a. At least 350 minutes
    b. At most 395 minutes
    c. How might a mail carrier estimate a range for the time he or she will spend en route?

14. British Columbia's Lake Osoyoos is Canada's warmest lake with mean summer water temperatures of 24°C. Assume the summer temperatures are normally distributed with a standard deviation of 1.9°C. For a randomly selected summer day, find the probability that the water temperature will be as follows.

    a. Above 26°C.
    b. Below 27.5°C.
    c. Between 21°C and 23°C.
    d. If the lake temperature were above 27.5°C, would you consider the water warm?

    Source: www.olwgs.org.

15. The average waiting time to be seated for dinner at a popular restaurant is 23.5 minutes, with a standard deviation of 3.6 minutes. Assume the variable is normally distributed. When a patron arrives at the restaurant for dinner, find the probability that the patron will have to wait the following time.

    a. Between 15 and 22 minutes
    b. Less than 18 minutes or more than 25 minutes
    c. Is it likely that a person will be seated in less than 15 minutes?

16. A local medical research association proposes to sponsor a footrace. The average time it takes to run the course is 45.8 minutes with a standard deviation of 3.6 minutes. If the association decides to include only the top 25% of the racers, what should be the cutoff time in the tryout run? Assume the variable is normally distributed. Would a person who runs the course in 40 minutes qualify?

17. A marine sales dealer finds that the average price of a previously owned boat is $6492. He decides to sell boats that will appeal to the middle 66% of the market in terms of price. Find the maximum and minimum prices of the boats the dealer will sell. The standard deviation is $1025, and the variable is normally distributed. Would a boat priced at $5550 be sold in this store?

18. The Fraser Institute reports that British Columbia ranks first in Canada for charitable donations with the average taxpayer claiming a charitable donation of $1194. Suppose that the distribution of contributions is normal with a standard deviation of $149. Find the limits for the middle 50% of contributions.

    Source: The Fraser Institute.

19. A contractor decided to build homes that will include the middle 80% of the market. If the average size of homes built is 1810 square feet, find the maximum and minimum sizes of the homes the contractor should build. Assume that the standard deviation is 92 square feet and the variable is normally distributed.

    Source: Michael D. Shook and Robert L. Shook, *The Book of Odds.*

20. If the average price of a new home is $145,500, find the maximum and minimum prices of the houses that a contractor will build to include the middle 80% of the market. Assume that the standard deviation of prices is $1500 and the variable is normally distributed.

    Source: Michael D. Shook and Robert L. Shook, *The Book of Odds.*

21. The average price of a personal computer (PC) is $949. If the computer prices are approximately normally distributed and $\sigma = \$100$, what is the probability that a randomly selected PC costs more than $1200? The least expensive 10% of personal computers cost less than what amount?

    Source: *N.Y. Times Almanac.*

22. To help students improve their reading, a school district decides to implement a reading program. It is to be administered to the bottom 5% of the students in the district, based on the scores on a reading achievement exam. If the average score for the students in the district is 122.6, find the cutoff score that will make a student eligible for the program. The standard deviation is 18. Assume the variable is normally distributed.

23. An automobile dealer finds that the average price of a previously owned vehicle is $8256. He decides to sell cars that will appeal to the middle 60% of the market in terms of price. Find the maximum and minimum prices of the cars the dealer will sell. The standard deviation is $1150, and the variable is normally distributed.

24. The average age of Amtrak passenger train cars is 19.4 years. If the distribution of ages is normal and 20% of the cars are older than 22.8 years, find the standard deviation.

    Source: *N.Y. Times Almanac.*

25. The average length of a hospital stay is 5.9 days. If we assume a normal distribution and a standard deviation of 1.7 days, 15% of hospital stays are less than how many days? Twenty-five percent of hospital stays are longer than how many days?

    Source: *N.Y. Times Almanac.*

26. A mandatory competency test for second-year high school students has a normal distribution with a mean of 400 and a standard deviation of 100.

    a. The top 3% of students receive $500. What is the minimum score you would need to receive this award?

    b. The bottom 1.5% of students must go to summer school. What is the minimum score you would need to stay out of this group?

27. An advertising company plans to market a product to low-income families. A study states that for a particular area, the average income per family is $24,596 and the standard deviation is $6256. If the company plans to target the bottom 18% of the families based on income, find the cutoff income. Assume the variable is normally distributed.

28. If a one-person household spends an average of $40 per week on groceries, find the maximum and minimum dollar amounts spent per week for the middle 50% of one-person households. Assume that the standard deviation is $5 and the variable is normally distributed.

    Source: Michael D. Shook and Robert L. Shook, *The Book of Odds.*

29. The mean lifetime of a wristwatch is 25 months, with a standard deviation of 5 months. If the distribution is normal, for how many months should a guarantee be made if the manufacturer does not want to exchange more than 10% of the watches? Assume the variable is normally distributed.

30. To qualify for security officers' training, recruits are tested for stress tolerance. The scores are normally distributed, with a mean of 62 and a standard deviation of 8. If only the top 15% of recruits are selected, find the cutoff score.

31. In the distributions shown, state the mean and standard deviation for each. *Hint:* See Figures 6–4 and 6–6. Also the vertical lines are 1 standard deviation apart.

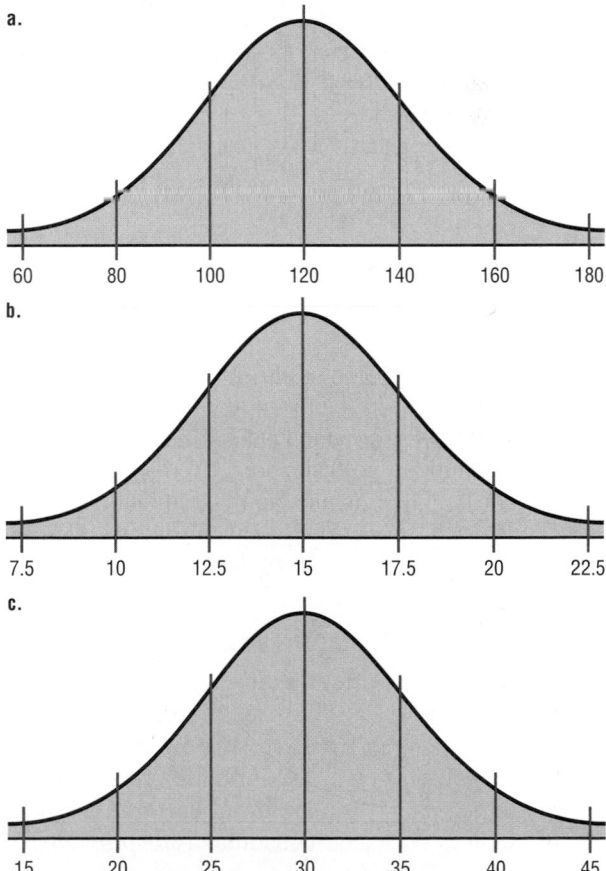

32. Suppose that the mathematics SAT scores for high school seniors for a specific year have a mean of 456 and a standard deviation of 100 and are approximately normally distributed. If a subgroup of these high school seniors, those who are in the National Honour Society, is selected, would you expect the distribution of scores to have the same mean and standard deviation? Explain your answer.

33. Given a data set, how could you decide if the distribution of the data was approximately normal?

34. If a distribution of raw scores were plotted and then the scores were transformed to z scores, would the shape of the distribution change? Explain your answer.

35. In a normal distribution, find σ when $\mu = 110$ and 2.87% of the area lies to the right of 112.

36. In a normal distribution, find μ when σ is 6 and 3.75% of the area lies to the left of 85.

37. In a certain normal distribution, 1.25% of the area lies to the left of 42, and 1.25% of the area lies to the right of 48. Find μ and σ.

38. An instructor gives a 100-point examination in which the grades are normally distributed. The mean is 60 and the standard deviation is 10. If there are 5% A's and 5% F's, 15% B's and 15% D's, and 60% C's, find the scores that divide the distribution into those categories.

39. The data shown represent the number of outdoor drive-in movies in the United States for a 14-year period. Check for normality.

2084	1497	1014	910	899	870	837	859
848	826	815	750	637	737		

Source: National Association of Theater Owners.

40. The data shown represent the cigarette tax (in cents) for 30 randomly selected American states. Check for normality.

3	58	5	65	17	48	52	75	21	76	58	36
100	111	34	41	23	44	33	50	13	18	7	12
20	24	66	28	28	31						

Source: Commerce Clearing House.

41. The data shown represent the box office total revenue (in millions of dollars) for a randomly selected sample of the top-grossing films in 2001. Check for normality.

294	241	130	144	113	70	97	94	91	202	74	79
71	67	67	56	180	199	165	114	60	56	53	51

Source: *USA TODAY.*

42. The data shown represent the number of runs made each year during Major League Baseball Hall-of-Famer Bill Mazeroski's career. Check for normality.

30	59	69	50	58	71	55	43	66	52	56	62
36	13	29	17	3							

Source: *Greensburg Tribune Review.*

6–5   The Central Limit Theorem

Objective

Use the central limit theorem to solve problems involving sample means for large samples.

In addition to knowing how individual data values vary about the mean for a population, statisticians are interested in knowing how the means of samples of the same size taken from the same population vary about the population mean.

Distribution of Sample Means

Suppose a researcher selects a sample of 30 adult males and finds the mean of the measure of the triglyceride levels for the sample subjects to be 187 milligrams/decilitre. Then suppose a second sample is selected, and the mean of that sample is found to be 192 milligrams/decilitre. Continue the process for 100 samples. What happens then is that the mean becomes a random variable, and the sample means 187, 192, 184, . . . , 196 constitute a *sampling distribution of sample means*.

> A **sampling distribution of sample means** is a distribution using the means computed from all possible random samples of a specific size taken from a population.

If the samples are randomly selected with replacement, the sample means, for the most part, will be somewhat different from the population mean μ. These differences are caused by sampling error.

> **Sampling error** is the difference between the sample measure and the corresponding population measure due to the fact that the sample is not a perfect representation of the population.

When all possible samples of a specific size are selected with replacement from a population, the distribution of the sample means for a variable has two important properties, which are explained next.

Properties of the Distribution of Sample Means

1. The mean of the sample means will be the same as the population mean.
2. The standard deviation of the sample means will be smaller than the standard deviation of the population, and it will be equal to the population standard deviation divided by the square root of the sample size.

The following example illustrates these two properties. Suppose a professor gave an 8-point quiz to a small class of four students. The results of the quiz were 2, 6, 4, and 8. For the sake of discussion, assume that the four students constitute the population. The mean of the population is

$$\mu = \frac{2 + 6 + 4 + 8}{4} = 5$$

The standard deviation of the population is

$$\sigma = \sqrt{\frac{(2 - 5)^2 + (6 - 5)^2 + (4 - 5)^2 + (8 - 5)^2}{4}} = 2.236$$

The graph of the original distribution is shown in Figure 6–25. This is called a *uniform distribution*.

Figure 6–25

Distribution of Quiz Scores

Now, if all samples of size 2 are taken with replacement and the mean of each sample is found, the distribution is as shown.

Sample	Mean	Sample	Mean
2, 2	2	6, 2	4
2, 4	3	6, 4	5
2, 6	4	6, 6	6
2, 8	5	6, 8	7
4, 2	3	8, 2	5
4, 4	4	8, 4	6
4, 6	5	8, 6	7
4, 8	6	8, 8	8

A frequency distribution of sample means is as follows.

$\overline{X}$	f
2	1
3	2
4	3
5	4
6	3
7	2
8	1

For the data from the example just discussed, Figure 6–26 shows the graph of the sample means. The histogram appears to be approximately normal.

The mean of the sample means, denoted by $\mu_{\overline{X}}$, is

$$\mu_{\overline{X}} = \frac{2 + 3 + \cdots + 8}{16} = \frac{80}{16} = 5$$

which is the same as the population mean. Hence,

$$\mu_{\overline{X}} = \mu$$

The standard deviation of sample means, denoted by $\sigma_{\overline{X}}$, is

$$\sigma_{\overline{X}} = \sqrt{\frac{(2 - 5)^2 + (3 - 5)^2 + \cdots + (8 - 5)^2}{16}} = 1.581$$

which is the same as the population standard deviation, divided by $\sqrt{2}$:

$$\sigma_{\overline{X}} = \frac{2.236}{\sqrt{2}} = 1.581$$

(*Note:* Rounding rules were not used here in order to show that the answers coincide.)

In summary, if all possible samples of size n are taken with replacement from the same population, the mean of the sample means, denoted by $\mu_{\overline{X}}$, equals the population mean μ; and the standard deviation of the sample means, denoted by $\sigma_{\overline{X}}$, equals $\sigma/\sqrt{n}$. The standard deviation of the sample means is called the **standard error of the mean.** Hence,

$$\sigma_{\overline{X}} = \frac{\sigma}{\sqrt{n}}$$

A third property of the sampling distribution of sample means pertains to the shape of the distribution and is explained by the **central limit theorem.**

Figure 6–26

Distribution of Sample Means

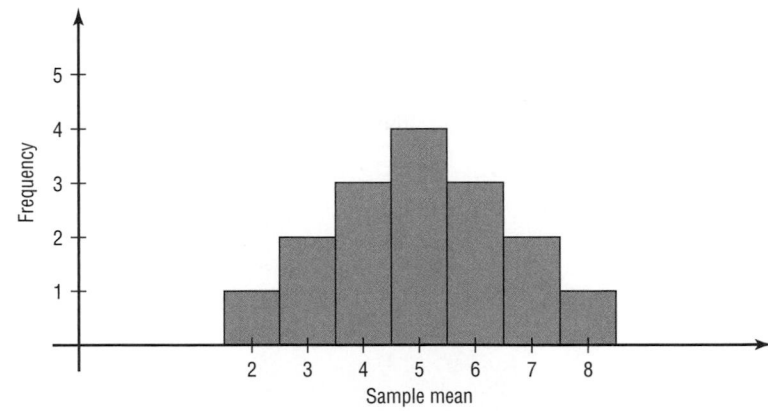

The Central Limit Theorem

As the sample size n increases without limit, the shape of the distribution of the sample means taken with replacement from a population with mean μ and standard deviation σ will approach a normal distribution. As previously shown, this distribution will have a mean μ and a standard deviation $\sigma/\sqrt{n}$.

If the sample size is sufficiently large, the central limit theorem can be used to answer questions about sample means in the same manner that a normal distribution can be used to answer questions about individual values. The only difference is that a new formula must be used for the z scores. It is

$$z = \frac{\overline{X} - \mu}{\sigma/\sqrt{n}}$$

Notice that $\overline{X}$ is the sample mean, and the denominator must be adjusted since means are being used instead of individual data values. The denominator is the standard deviation of the sample means.

If a large number of samples of a given size are selected from a normally distributed population, or if a large number of samples of a given size that is greater than or equal to 30 are selected from a population that is not normally distributed, and the sample means are computed, then the distribution of sample means will look like the one shown in Figure 6–27. Their percentages indicate the areas of the regions.

Figure 6–27

Distribution of Sample Means for Large Number of Samples

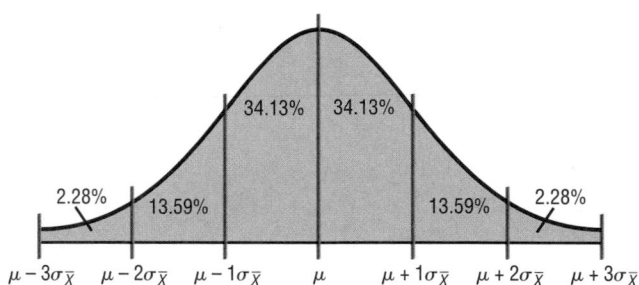

It's important to remember two things when you use the central limit theorem:

1. When the original variable is normally distributed, the distribution of the sample means will be normally distributed, for any sample size n.

2. When the distribution of the original variable might not be normal, a sample size of 30 or more is needed to use a normal distribution to approximate the distribution of the sample means. The larger the sample, the better the approximation will be.

Examples 6–13 through 6–15 show how the standard normal distribution can be used to answer questions about sample means.

Example 6–13

A. C. Neilsen reported that children between the ages of 2 and 5 watch an average of 25 hours of television per week. Assume the variable is normally distributed and the standard deviation is 3 hours. If 20 children between the ages of 2 and 5 are randomly selected, find the probability that the mean of the number of hours they watch television will be greater than 26.3 hours.

Source: Michael D. Shook and Robert L. Shook, *The Book of Odds.*

Solution

Since the variable is approximately normally distributed, the distribution of sample means will be approximately normal, with a mean of 25. The standard deviation of the sample means is

$$\sigma_{\overline{X}} = \frac{\sigma}{\sqrt{n}} = \frac{3}{\sqrt{20}} = 0.671$$

The distribution of the means is shown in Figure 6–28, with the appropriate area shaded.

Figure 6–28

Distribution of
the Means for
Example 6–13

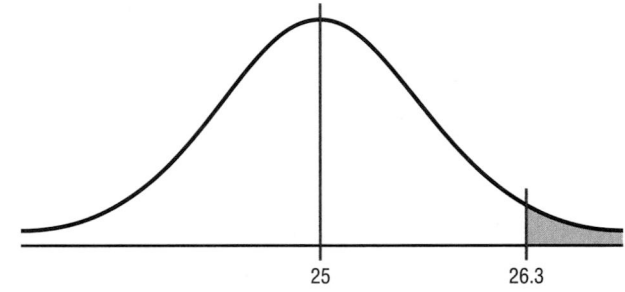

The z score is

$$z = \frac{\overline{X} - \mu}{\sigma/\sqrt{n}} = \frac{26.3 - 25}{3/\sqrt{20}} = \frac{1.3}{0.671} = 1.94$$

The cumulative area to the left for $z = 1.94$ is 0.9738. Since the desired area is to the right of $z = 1.94$, subtract 0.9738 from the total area under the curve, 1.000. Hence, $1.000 - 0.9738 = 0.0262$, or 2.62%.

One can conclude that the probability of obtaining a sample mean larger than 26.3 hours is 2.62% [i.e., $P(\overline{X} > 26.3) = 2.62\%$].

Example 6–14

The average age of light-duty vehicles in Canada is 8.5 years, or 102 months. Assume a standard deviation of 16 months. If a random sample of 36 vehicles is selected, find the probability that the mean of their age is between 96 and 106 months

Source: DesRosiers Automotive Consultants Inc.

Solution

Since the sample is 30 or larger, the normality assumption is not necessary. The desired area is shown in Figure 6–29.

Figure 6–29

Area Under a
Normal Curve for
Example 6–14

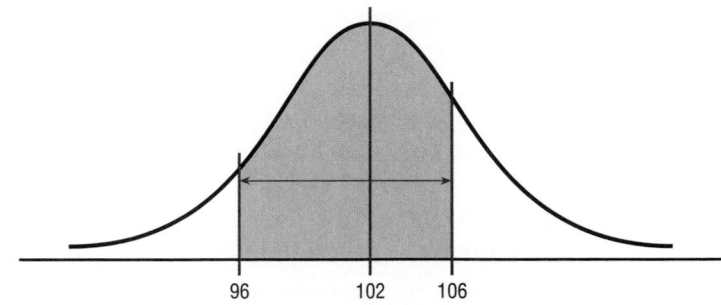

Convert $\overline{X}_1 = 96$ and $\overline{X}_2 = 106$ to z scores.

$$z_1 = \frac{\overline{X}_1 - \mu}{\frac{\sigma}{\sqrt{n}}} = \frac{96 - 102}{\frac{16}{\sqrt{36}}} = -2.25$$

$$z_2 = \frac{\overline{X}_2 - \mu}{\frac{\sigma}{\sqrt{n}}} = \frac{106 - 102}{\frac{16}{\sqrt{36}}} = 1.5$$

The cumulative area to the left of $z_1 = -2.25$ is 0.0122. The cumulative area to the left of $z_2 = 1.5$ is 0.9332. Hence, the desired area is $0.9332 - 0.0122 = 0.9210$, or 92.1%.

Hence, the probability of obtaining a sample mean between 96 and 106 months is 92.1%; that is, $P(96 < \overline{X} < 106) = 92.1\%$.

Example 6–15

The average annual Canadian consumption of red meat is 62.9 kilograms per person. Assume a standard deviation of 7 kilograms and an approximately normal distribution.

    a. Find the probability that a person selected at random consumes less than 65 kilograms per year.

    b. If a sample of 40 individuals is selected, find the probability that the mean of the sample will be less than 65 kilograms per year.

Source: Adapted from Statistics Canada publications *Food Consumption in Canada* (Part 1), Catalogue 32–229 and *Food Consumption in Canada* (Part 2), Catalogue 32–230.

Solution

    a. Since the question asks about an individual person, the formula $z = (X - \mu)/\sigma$ is used. The distribution is shown in Figure 6–30.

Figure 6–30

Area Under a Normal Curve for Part *a* of Example 6–15

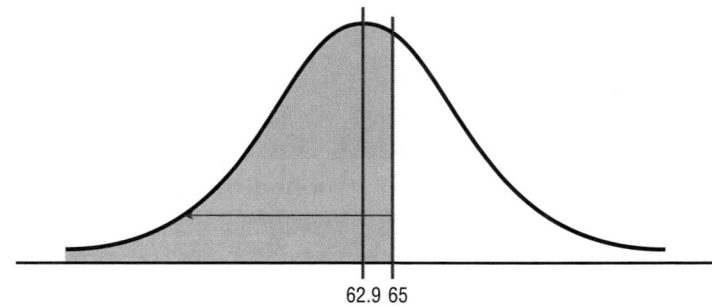

62.9 65
Distribution of individual data values for the population

Convert the X value to a z score.

$$z = \frac{X - \mu}{\sigma} = \frac{65 - 62.9}{7} = 0.3$$

The desired area is the cumulative area to the left of $z = 0.3$, which is 0.6179.

        Hence, the probability of selecting a Canadian who consumes less than 65 kilograms of red meat per year is 0.6179, or 61.79%; that is, $P(X < 65) = 0.6179$.

    b. Since the question concerns the mean of a sample with size 40, the formula $z = (\overline{X} - \mu)/(\sigma\sqrt{n})$ is used. The distribution is shown in Figure 6–31.

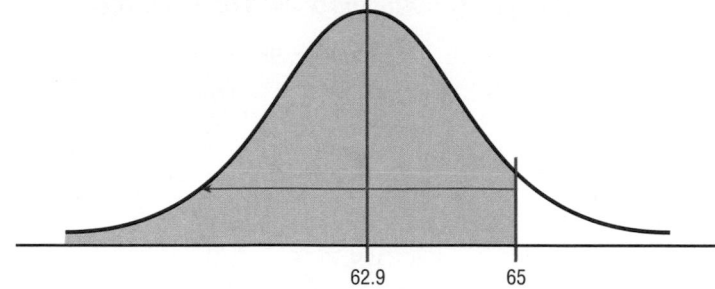

Figure 6–31

Area Under a Normal
Curve for Part *b* of
Example 6–15

62.9   65

Distribution of means for all samples of size 40 from the population

Convert the $\overline{X}$ value to a z score.

$$z = \frac{\overline{X} - \mu}{\frac{\sigma}{\sqrt{n}}} = \frac{65 - 62.9}{\frac{7}{\sqrt{40}}} = 1.90$$

The desired area is the cumulative area to the left of $z = 1.90$, which is 0.9713.

Hence, the probability that the mean of a sample of 40 Canadians who consume less than 65 kilograms of red meat per year is 0.9713, or 97.13%; that is, $P(\overline{X} < 65) = 0.9713$.

Comparing the two probabilities, one can see that the probability of selecting an individual who consumes less than 65 kilograms of red meat per year is 61.79%, but the probability of selecting 40 people with a mean consumption of red meat that is less than 65 kilograms per year is 97.13%. This rather large difference is due to the fact that the distribution of sample means is much less variable than the distribution of individual data values. (*Note:* An individual person is the equivalent of saying $n = 1$.)

Finite Population Correction Factor (Optional)

The formula for the standard error of the mean $\sigma/\sqrt{n}$ is accurate when the samples are drawn with replacement or are drawn without replacement from a very large or infinite population. Since sampling with replacement is for the most part unrealistic, a *correction factor* is necessary for computing the standard error of the mean for samples drawn without replacement from a finite population. Compute the correction factor by using the expression

$$\sqrt{\frac{N - n}{N - 1}}$$

where N is the population size and n is the sample size.

This correction factor is necessary if relatively large samples are taken from a small population, because the sample mean will then more accurately estimate the population mean and there will be less error in the estimation. Therefore, the standard error of the mean must be multiplied by the correction factor to adjust for large samples taken from a small population. That is,

$$\sigma_{\overline{X}} = \frac{\sigma}{\sqrt{n}} \cdot \sqrt{\frac{N - n}{N - 1}}$$

Finally, the formula for the z score becomes

$$z = \frac{\overline{X} - \mu}{\frac{\sigma}{\sqrt{n}} \cdot \sqrt{\frac{N-n}{N-1}}}$$

When the population is large and the sample is small, the correction factor is generally not used, since it will be very close to 1.00.

The formulas and their uses are summarized in Table 6–1.

Table 6–1	Summary of Formulas and Their Uses
Formula	**Use**
1. $z = \dfrac{\overline{X} - \mu}{\sigma}$	Used to gain information about an individual data value when the variable is normally distributed.
2. $z = \dfrac{\overline{X} - \mu}{\sigma/\sqrt{n}}$	Used to gain information when applying the central limit theorem about a sample mean when the variable is normally distributed or when the sample size is 30 or more.

Applying the Concepts 6–5

Central Limit Theorem

Twenty students from a statistics class each collected a random sample of times on how long it took students to get to class from their homes. All the sample sizes were 30. The resulting means are listed.

Student	Mean	Std. Dev.	Student	Mean	Std. Dev.
1	22	3.7	11	27	1.4
2	31	4.6	12	24	2.2
3	18	2.4	13	14	3.1
4	27	1.9	14	29	2.4
5	20	3.0	15	37	2.8
6	17	2.8	16	23	2.7
7	26	1.9	17	26	1.8
8	34	4.2	18	21	2.0
9	23	2.6	19	30	2.2
10	29	2.1	20	29	2.8

1. The students noticed that everyone had different answers. If you randomly sample over and over from any population, with the same sample size, will the results ever be the same?

2. The students wondered whose results were right. How can they find out what the population mean and standard deviation are?

3. Input the means into the computer and check to see if the distribution is normal.

4. Check the mean and standard deviation of the means. How do these values compare to the students' individual scores?

5. Is the distribution of the means a sampling distribution?

6. Check the sampling error for students 3, 7, and 14.

7. Compare the standard deviation of the sample of the 20 means. Is that equal to the standard deviation from student 3 divided by the square of the sample size? How about for student 7, or 14?

See page 293 for the answers.

Exercises 6–5

1. If samples of a specific size are selected from a population and the means are computed, what is this distribution of means called?

2. Why do most of the sample means differ somewhat from the population mean? What is this difference called?

3. What is the mean of the sample means?

4. What is the standard deviation of the sample means called? What is the formula for this standard deviation?

5. What does the central limit theorem say about the shape of the distribution of sample means?

6. What formula is used to gain information about an individual data value when the variable is normally distributed?

7. What formula is used to gain information about a sample mean when the variable is normally distributed or when the sample size is 30 or more?

For Exercises 8 through 25, assume that the sample is taken from a large population and the correction factor can be ignored.

8. The waste management industry reports that Canadian individuals dispose of an average of 760 kilograms of non-hazardous material in a given year. Assume a standard deviation of 90 kilograms. Find the probability that the mean of a sample of 55 Canadians will be between 750 and 775 kilograms.

   Source: Statistics Canada—Waste Management Industry Survey.

9. The average yearly cost per household of owning a dog is $186.80. Suppose that we randomly select 50 households that own a dog. What is the probability that the sample mean for these 50 households is less than $175.00? Assume $\sigma = \$32$.

   Source: N.Y. Times Almanac.

10. In 2006, experienced teachers in Alberta earned an average annual salary of $80,402. Assume that the salary distribution is normal with a standard deviation of $9500.

    a. What is the probability that a randomly selected experienced teacher in Alberta earned less than $78,000 per annum?

    b. In a random sample of 100 experienced Alberta teacher salaries, what is the probability that the sample mean is less than $78,000?

    Source: Alberta Learning.

11. The mean weight of 15-year-old males is 64.4 kilograms, and the standard deviation is 5.6 kilograms. If a random sample of thirty-six 15-year-old males is selected, find the probability that the mean of the sample will be greater than 65.5 kilograms. Assume the variable is normally

distributed. Based on your answer, would you consider the group overweight?

12. In 2006, the average starting salary for new Alberta teachers with 4 years of education was $47,373. Assume a normal distribution with $\sigma = \$8,750$.

    a. What is the probability that a randomly selected new teacher's salary is greater than $50,000?

    b. What is the probability that the mean for a random sample of 80 new teachers is greater than $50,000?

    Source: Alberta Learning.

13. Canadian households spend an average of $124 per week on food in either stores or restaurants. Assume a standard deviation of $11 per week. If a sample of 40 households is randomly selected, find the probability that the mean of the sample is less than $120.

    Source: Statistics Canada.

14. The national U.S. average SAT score is 1019. Suppose that nothing is known about the shape of the distribution and that the standard deviation is 100. If a random sample of 200 scores were selected and the sample mean were calculated to be 1050, would you be surprised? Explain.

    Source: N.Y. Times Almanac.

15. The average number of milligrams (mg) of sodium in a certain brand of low-salt microwave frozen dinners is 660 mg, and the standard deviation is 35 mg. Assume the variable is normally distributed.

    a. If a single dinner is selected, find the probability that the sodium content will be more than 670 mg.

    b. If a sample of 10 dinners is selected, find the probability that the mean of the sample will be larger than 670 mg.

    c. Why is the probability for part a greater than that for part b?

16. The average age of chemical engineers is 37 years with a standard deviation of 4 years. If an engineering firm employs 25 chemical engineers, find the probability that the average age of the group is greater than 38.2 years old. If this is the case, would it be safe to assume that the engineers in this group are generally much older than average?

17. Health Canada reports that the average adult drinks 1.5 litres of water daily, including water used in drinks such as coffee, tea, and juice. Assume a normally distributed variable with a standard deviation of 0.3 litres per day. If 15 Canadian adults are selected at random, find the probability that the sample mean of daily water consumption will be between 1.3 and 1.6 litres.

    Source: Health Canada.

18. The average public elementary school has 458 students. Assume the standard deviation is 97. If a random sample of 36 public elementary schools is selected, find the probability that the number of students enrolled is between 450 and 465.

19. *The Globe and Mail* reported that the average annual Canadian out-of-pocket expense on vision care was $1701 per household. If the standard deviation is $205, find the probability that the sample mean of 50 household vision care expenditures randomly selected will be between $1650 and $1750.

Source: www.theglobeandmail.com.

20. A report by Statistics Canada indicates that the average Canadian university undergraduate tuition was $4172 per year. Assume that tuitions are normally distributed with a standard deviation of $525.

  a. Find the probability that a randomly selected undergraduate student pays less than $4000 per year for tuition.

  b. Find the probability that, for a randomly selected sample of 25 undergraduate students, the mean tuition paid is less than $4000.

  c. Why is the probability for part *b* higher than the probability for part *a*?

Source: Statistics Canada.

21. The average time it takes a group of adults to complete a certain achievement test is 46.2 minutes. The standard deviation is 8 minutes. Assume the variable is normally distributed.

  a. Find the probability that a randomly selected adult will complete the test in less than 43 minutes.

  b. Find the probability that, if 50 randomly selected adults take the test, the mean time it takes the group to complete the test will be less than 43 minutes.

  c. Does it seem reasonable that an adult would finish the test in less than 43 minutes? Explain.

  d. Does it seem reasonable that the mean of the 50 adults could be less than 43 minutes?

22. Assume that the mean systolic blood pressure of normal adults is 120 millimetres of mercury (mm Hg) and the standard deviation is 5.6. Assume the variable is normally distributed.

  a. If an individual is selected, find the probability that the individual's pressure will be between 120 and 121.8 mm Hg.

  b. If a sample of 30 adults is randomly selected, find the probability that the sample mean will be between 120 and 121.8 mm Hg.

  c. Why is the answer to part *a* so much smaller than the answer to part *b*?

23. The average cholesterol content of a certain brand of eggs is 215 milligrams, and the standard deviation is 15 milligrams. Assume the variable is normally distributed.

  a. If a single egg is selected, find the probability that the cholesterol content will be greater than 220 milligrams.

  b. If a sample of 25 eggs is selected, find the probability that the mean of the sample will be larger than 220 milligrams.

Source: *Living Fit.*

24. At a large publishing company, the mean age of proofreaders is 36.2 years, and the standard deviation is 3.7 years. Assume the variable is normally distributed.

  a. If a proofreader from the company is randomly selected, find the probability that his or her age will be between 36 and 37.5 years.

  b. If a random sample of 15 proofreaders is selected, find the probability that the mean age of the proofreaders in the sample will be between 36 and 37.5 years.

25. Statistics Canada reports the per capita (average) annual consumption of eggs in Canada was 15.5 dozen, or 186 eggs. Assume the standard deviation of egg consumption is 18 eggs. If 35 Canadian consumers are selected, find the probability that the mean number of eggs consumed is between 180 and 190.

Source: Statistics Canada.

Extending the Concepts

For Exercises 26 and 27, check to see whether the correction factor should be used. If so, be sure to include it in the calculations.

26. In a study of the life expectancy of 500 people in a certain geographic region, the mean age at death was 72.0 years, and the standard deviation was 5.3 years. If a sample of 50 people from this region is selected, find the probability that the mean life expectancy will be less than 70 years.

27. A study of 800 homeowners in a certain area showed that the average value of the homes was $82,000, and the standard deviation was $5000. If 50 homes are for sale, find the probability that the mean of the values of these homes is greater than $83,500.

28. The average breaking strength of a certain brand of steel cable is 907 kilograms, with a standard deviation of 45 kilograms. A sample of 20 cables is selected and tested. Find the sample mean that will cut off the upper

95% of all samples of size 20 taken from the population. Assume the variable is normally distributed.

29. The standard deviation of a variable is 15. If a sample of 100 individuals is selected, compute the standard error of the mean. What size sample is necessary to double the standard error of the mean?

30. In Exercise 29, what size sample is needed to cut the standard error of the mean in half?

6–6   The Normal Approximation to the Binomial Distribution

A normal distribution is often used to solve problems that involve the binomial distribution since, when n is large (say, 100), the calculations are too difficult to do by hand using the binomial distribution. Recall from Chapter 5 that a binomial distribution has the following characteristics:

1. There must be a fixed number of trials.

2. The outcome of each trial must be independent.

3. Each experiment can have only two outcomes or outcomes that can be reduced to two outcomes.

4. The probability of a success must remain the same for each trial.

Also, recall that a binomial distribution is determined by n (the number of trials) and p (the probability of a success). When p is approximately 0.5, and as n increases, the shape of the binomial distribution becomes similar to that of a normal distribution. The larger n is and the closer p is to 0.5, the more similar the shape of the binomial distribution is to that of a normal distribution.

Objective

Use the normal approximation to compute probabilities for a binomial variable.

But when p is close to 0 or 1 and n is relatively small, a normal approximation is inaccurate. As a rule of thumb, statisticians generally agree that a normal approximation should be used only when $n \cdot p$ and $n \cdot q$ are both greater than or equal to 5. (*Note:* $q = 1 - p$.) For example, if p is 0.3 and n is 10, then $np = (10)(0.3) = 3$, and a normal distribution should not be used as an approximation. On the other hand, if $p = 0.5$ and $n = 10$, then $np = (10)(0.5) = 5$ and $nq = (10)(0.5) = 5$, and a normal distribution can be used as an approximation. See Figure 6–32.

In addition to the previous condition of $np \geq 5$ and $nq \geq 5$, a correction for continuity may be used in the normal approximation.

> A **correction for continuity** is a correction employed when a continuous distribution is used to approximate a discrete distribution.

The continuity correction means that for any specific value of X, say 8, the boundaries of X in the binomial distribution (in this case, 7.5 to 8.5) must be used. (See Section 1–3.) Hence, when one employs a normal distribution to approximate the binomial, the boundaries of any specific value X must be used as they are shown in the binomial distribution. For example, for $P(X = 8)$, the correction is $P(7.5 < X < 8.5)$. For $P(X \leq 7)$, the correction is $P(X < 7.5)$. For $P(X \geq 3)$, the correction is $P(X > 2.5)$.

Students sometimes have difficulty deciding whether to add 0.5 or subtract 0.5 from the data value for the correction factor. Table 6–2 summarizes the different situations.

The formulas for the mean and standard deviation for the binomial distribution are necessary for calculations. They are

$$\mu = n \cdot p \qquad \text{and} \qquad \sigma = \sqrt{n \cdot p \cdot q}$$

Figure 6-32

Comparison of the
Binomial Distribution
and a Normal
Distribution

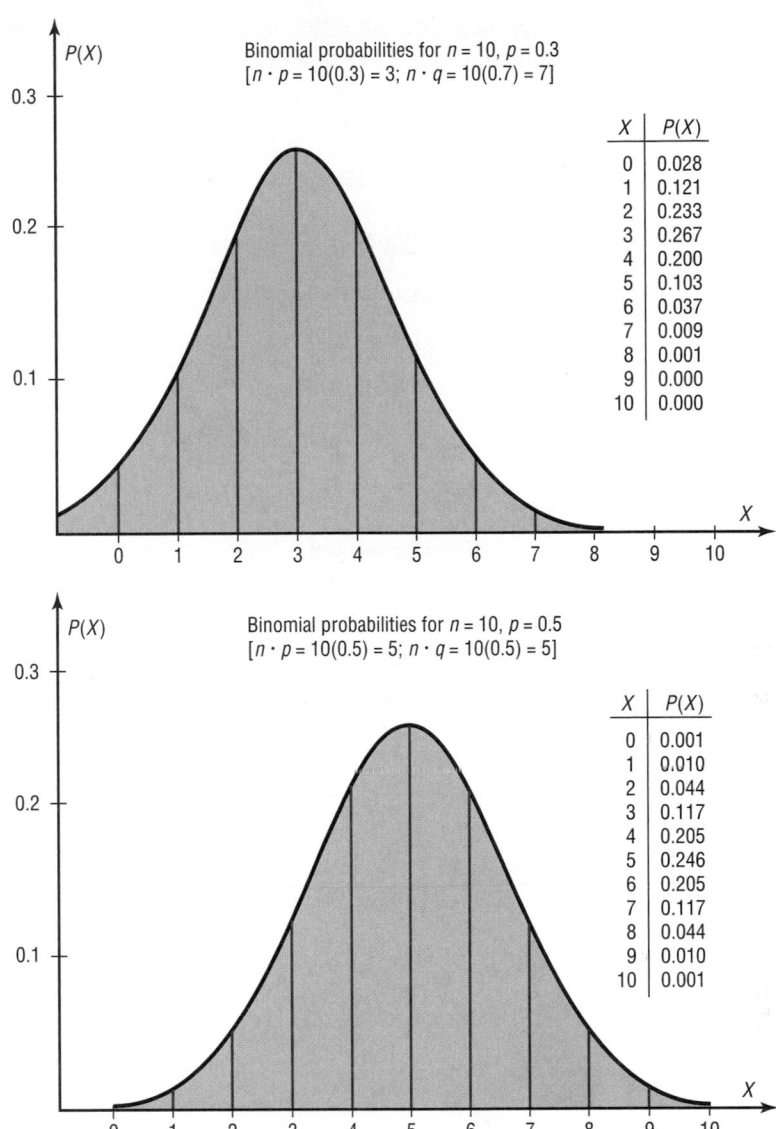

Table 6-2   **Summary of the Normal Approximation to the Binomial Distribution**

Binomial	Normal
When finding:	Use:
1. $P(X = a)$	$P(a - 0.5 < X < a + 0.5)$
2. $P(X \geq a)$	$P(X > a - 0.5)$
3. $P(X > a)$	$P(X > a + 0.5)$
4. $P(X \leq a)$	$P(X < a + 0.5)$
5. $P(X < a)$	$P(X < a - 0.5)$

For all cases, $\mu = n \cdot p$, $\sigma = \sqrt{n \cdot p \cdot q}$, $n \cdot p \geq 5$, and $n \cdot q \geq 5$.

The steps for using the normal distribution to approximate the binomial distribution are shown in this Procedure Table.

Procedure Table

Procedure for the Normal Approximation to the Binomial Distribution

Step 1 Check to see whether the normal approximation can be used.

Step 2 Find the mean μ and the standard deviation σ.

Step 3 Write the problem in probability notation, using X.

Step 4 Rewrite the problem by using the continuity correction factor, and show the corresponding area under the normal distribution.

Step 5 Find the corresponding z scores.

Step 6 Find the solution.

Example 6–16

A marketing study reported that 26% of Canadian drivers surveyed talk on cellphones while driving. If 300 drivers are selected at random, find the probability that exactly 90 have talked on their cellphones while driving.

Source: Leger Marketing.

Solution

Step 1 Here, $p = 0.26$, $q = 0.74$, and $n = 300$.

$$np = (300)(0.26) = 78 \qquad nq = (300)(0.74) = 222$$

Since $np \geq 5$ and $nq \geq 5$, the normal distribution can be used.

Step 2 Find the mean and standard deviation.

$$\mu = np = (300)(0.26) = 78$$
$$\sigma = \sqrt{npq} = \sqrt{(300)(0.26)(0.74)} = \sqrt{57.72} = 7.6$$

Step 3 Write the problem in probability notation $P(X = 90)$.

Step 4 Rewrite the problem by using the continuity correction factor. See approximation number 1 in Table 6–2; $P(90 - 0.5 < X < 90 + 0.5) = P(89.5 < X < 90.5)$. Show the corresponding area under the normal distribution curve. See Figure 6–33.

Figure 6–33

Area Under a Normal Curve and X Values for Example 6–16

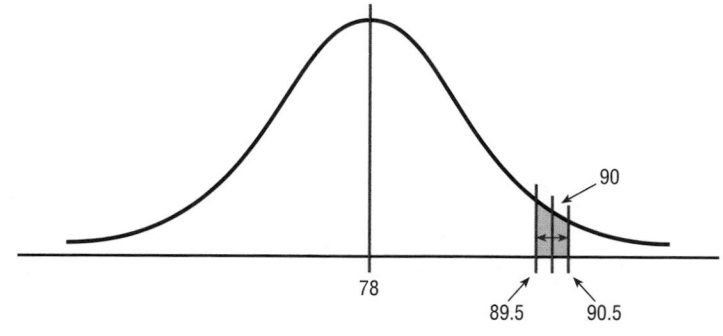

Step 5 Find the corresponding z scores. Since 90 represents any value between $X_1 = 89.5$ and $X_2 = 90.5$, find both z scores.

$$z_1 = \frac{89.5 - 78}{7.6} = 1.51 \qquad z_2 = \frac{90.5 - 78}{7.6} = 1.64$$

Step 6 Find the desired area. The cumulative area to the left of $z = 1.51$ is 0.9345 and the cumulative area to the left of $z = 1.64$ is 0.9495. Hence, the desired area is $0.9495 - 0.9345 = 0.4495 - 0.4245 = 0.015$, or 1.5%.

Therefore, the probability that exactly 90 out of 300 Canadian drivers are talking on their cellphones is 1.5%.

Example 6–17

Of the members of a bowling league, 10% are widowed. If 200 bowling league members are selected at random, find the probability that 10 or more will be widowed.

Solution

Here, $p = 0.10$, $q = 0.90$, and $n = 200$.

Step 1 Since $np = (200)(0.10) = 20$ and $nq = (200)(0.90) = 180$, the normal approximation can be used.

Step 2 $\mu = np = (200)(0.10) = 20$

$$\sigma = \sqrt{npq} = \sqrt{(200)(0.10)(0.90)} = \sqrt{18} = 4.24$$

Step 3 $P(X \geq 10)$.

Step 4 See approximation number 2 in Table 6–2: $P(X > 10 - 0.5) = P(X > 9.5)$. The desired area is shown in Figure 6–34.

Figure 6–34

Area Under a Normal Curve and X Value for Example 6–17

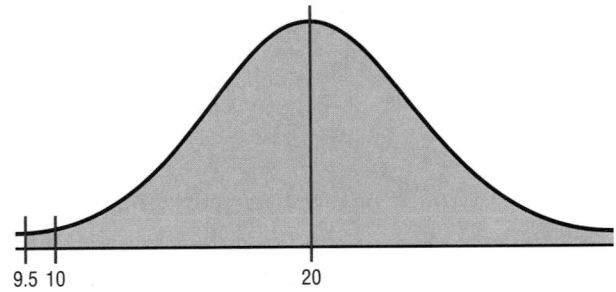

Step 5 Since the problem is to find the probability of 10 or more widowers, a normal distribution graph is as shown in Figure 6–34. Hence the area greater then $X = 9.5$ must be used to get the correct approximation. Convert $X = 9.5$ to a z score.

$$z = \frac{9.5 - 20}{4.24} = -2.48$$

Step 6 Find the desired area. The cumulative area to the left of $z = -2.48$ is 0.0066. Hence, the desired area is $1.000 - 0.0066 = 0.9934$, or 99.34%.

It can be concluded, then, that the probability of 10 or more widowed people in a random sample of 200 bowling league members is 99.34%.

Example 6–18

If a baseball player's batting average is 0.320 (32%), find the probability that the player will get at most 26 hits in 100 times at bat.

Solution

Here, $p = 0.32$, $q = 0.68$, and $n = 100$.

Step 1 Since $np = (100)(0.320) = 32$ and $nq = (100)(0.680) = 68$, the normal distribution can be used to approximate the binomial distribution.

Step 2 $\mu = np = (100)(0.320) = 32$

$\sigma = \sqrt{npq} = \sqrt{(100)(0.32)(0.68)} = \sqrt{21.76} \approx 4.66$

Step 3 $P(X \leq 26)$.

Step 4 See approximation number 4 in Table 6–2: $P(X < 26 + 0.5) = P(X < 26.5)$. The desired area is shown in Figure 6–35.

Figure 6–35

Area Under a
Normal Curve for
Example 6–18

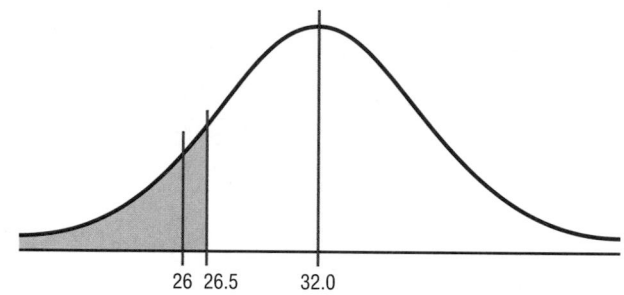

26 26.5   32.0

Step 5 The z score is

$$z = \frac{26.5 - 32}{4.66} = -1.18$$

Step 6 The cumulative area to the left of $z = -1.18$ is 0.1190. Therefore, the desired area is 0.1190, or 11.90%.

Hence the probability that the player will get at most 26 hits is 11.90%.

The closeness of the normal approximation is illustrated in Example 6–19.

Example 6–19

When $n = 10$ and $p = 0.5$, use the binomial distribution table (Table B in Appendix C) to find the probability that $X = 6$. Then use the normal approximation to find the probability that $X = 6$.

Solution

From Table B, for $n = 10$, $p = 0.5$, and $X = 6$, the probability is 0.205.
    For a normal approximation,

$$\mu = np = (10)(0.5) = 5$$
$$\sigma = \sqrt{npq} = \sqrt{(10)(0.5)(0.5)} \approx 1.58$$

Now, $X = 6$ is represented by the boundaries 5.5 and 6.5. So the z scores are

$$z_1 = \frac{6.5 - 5}{1.58} = 0.95 \qquad z_2 = \frac{5.5 - 5}{1.58} = 0.32$$

The corresponding area for 0.95 is 0.3289, and the corresponding area for 0.32 is 0.1255.

The solution is $0.3289 - 0.1255 = 0.2034$, which is very close to the binomial table value of 0.205. The desired area is shown in Figure 6–36.

Figure 6–36

Area Under a
Normal Curve for
Example 6–19

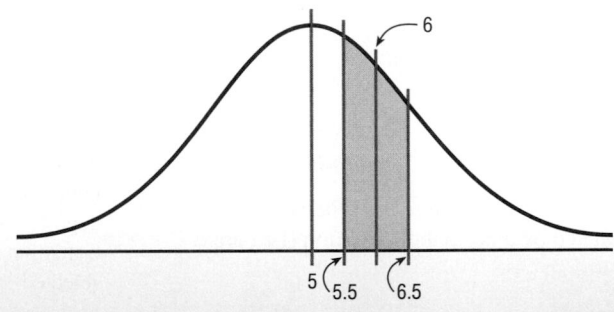

The normal approximation also can be used to approximate other distributions, such as the Poisson distribution (see Table C in Appendix C).

Applying the Concepts 6–6

How Safe Are You?

Assume one of your favourite activities is mountain climbing. When you go mountain climbing, you have several safety devices to keep you from falling. You notice that attached to one of your safety hooks is a reliability rating of 97%. You estimate that throughout the next year you will be using this device about 100 times. Answer the following questions.

1. Does a reliability rating of 97% mean that there is a 97% chance that the device will not fail any of the 100 times?
2. What is the probability of at least one failure?
3. What is the complement of this event?
4. Can this be considered a binomial experiment?
5. Can you use the binomial probability formula? Why or why not?
6. Find the probability of at least two failures.
7. Can you use a normal distribution to accurately approximate the binomial distribution? Explain why or why not.
8. Is correction for continuity needed?
9. How much safer would it be to use a second safety hook independently of the first?

See page 294 for the answers.

Exercises 6–6

1. Explain why a normal distribution can be used as an approximation to a binomial distribution. What conditions must be met to use the normal distribution to approximate the binomial distribution? Why is a correction for continuity necessary?

2. **(ans)** Use the normal approximation to the binomial to find the probabilities for the specific value(s) of X.

   a. $n = 30, p = 0.5, X = 18$
   b. $n = 50, p = 0.8, X = 44$
   c. $n = 100, p = 0.1, X = 12$
   d. $n = 10, p = 0.5, X \geq 7$
   e. $n = 20, p = 0.7, X \leq 12$
   f. $n = 50, p = 0.6, X \leq 40$

3. Check each binomial distribution to see whether it can be approximated by a normal distribution (i.e., are $np \geq 5$ and $nq \geq 5$?).

   a. $n = 20, p = 0.5$
   b. $n = 10, p = 0.6$
   c. $n = 40, p = 0.9$
   d. $n = 50, p = 0.2$
   e. $n = 30, p = 0.8$
   f. $n = 20, p = 0.85$

4. Of all 3- to 5-year-old children, 56% are enrolled in school. If a sample of 500 such children is randomly selected, find the probability that at least 250 will be enrolled in school.

   Source: *Statistical Abstract of the United States.*

5. Two out of 5 adult smokers acquired the habit by age 14. If 400 smokers are randomly selected, find the probability that 170 or more acquired the habit by age 14.

   Source: *Harper's Index.*

6. A theatre owner has found that 5% of patrons do not show up for the performance that they purchased tickets for. If the theatre has 100 seats, find the probability that 6 or more patrons will not show up for the sold-out performance.

7. The percentage of Canadians 15 years and older with at least a high school graduate certificate is 66.8%. In a random sample of 300 Canadians 15 years old and older, what is the probability that more than 200 have at least a high school graduate certificate?

   Source: Statistics Canada.

8. A study "Young Canadians in a Wired World," researched online behaviours of children and youth from Grades 4 to 11. One finding was that 94% of the respondents connect to the Internet from home. If a random sample of 75 young Canadians was taken, find the probability that fewer than 70 will have a home Internet connection.

   Source: Media Awareness Network.

9. Statistics Canada's study on education attainment reports that 61% of Canadian adults aged 25 to 34 years have post-secondary documentation, i.e., university degree, college diploma, or trade credential. If 250 Canadian adults, aged 25 to 34 years, are randomly selected, find the probability that more than 125 have post-secondary documentation.

   Source: Statistics Canada.

10. Women make up 24% of the science and engineering workforce. In a random sample of 400 science and engineering employees, what is the probability that more than 120 are women?

    Source: *Science and Engineering Indicators,* www.nsf.gov.

11. Women comprise 83.3% of all elementary school teachers. In a random sample of 300 elementary school teachers, what is the probability that more than 50 are men?

    Source: *N.Y. Times Almanac.*

12. Canada's labour force consists of 11.9% workers who are self-employed. If 150 workers from across Canada are selected at random, what is the probability that more than 20 workers are self-employed?

    Source: Statistics Canada.

13. The mayor of a small town estimates that 35% of the residents in his town favour the construction of a municipal parking lot. If there are 350 people at a town meeting, find the probability that at least 100 favour construction of the parking lot. Based on your answer, is it likely that 100 or more people would favour the parking lot?

Extending the Concepts

14. Recall that for use of a normal distribution as an approximation to the binomial distribution, the conditions $np \geq 5$ and $nq \geq 5$ must be met. For each given probability, compute the minimum sample size needed for use of the normal approximation.

    a. $p = 0.1$ d. $p = 0.8$
    b. $p = 0.3$ e. $p = 0.9$
    c. $p = 0.5$

6-7   Summary

A normal distribution can be used to describe a variety of variables, such as heights, weights, and temperatures. A normal distribution is bell-shaped, unimodal, symmetric, and continuous; its mean, median, and mode are equal. Since each variable has its own distribution with mean μ and standard deviation σ, mathematicians use the standard normal distribution, which has a mean of 0 and a standard deviation of 1. Other approximately normally distributed variables can be transformed to the standard normal distribution with the formula $z = (X - \mu)/\sigma$.

A normal distribution can also be used to describe a sampling distribution of sample means. These samples must be of the same size and randomly selected with replacement from the population. The means of the samples will differ somewhat from the population mean, since samples are generally not perfect representations of the population from which they came. The mean of the sample means will be equal to the population mean; and the standard deviation of the sample means will be equal to the population standard deviation, divided by the square root of the sample size. The central limit theorem states that as the size of the samples increases, the distribution of sample means will be approximately normal.

A normal distribution can be used to approximate other distributions, such as a binomial distribution. For a normal distribution to be used as an approximation, the conditions $np \geq 5$ and $nq \geq 5$ must be met. Also, a correction for continuity may be used for more accurate results.

For step-by-step guidance on the use of technology for this chapter, visit the Online Learning Centre at www.mcgrawhill.ca/olc/bluman. Summary procedures for Minitab, SPSS, Excel, and TI-83 Plus or TI-84 Plus can also be found in Appendix E.

Important Terms   ● ● ●

central limit theorem 272	normal distribution 250	sampling error 271	symmetric distribution 248
correction for continuity 280	positively or right-skewed distribution 249	standard error of the mean 272	
negatively or left-skewed distribution 249	sampling distribution of sample means 270	standard normal distribution 251	

Important Formulas   ● ● ●

Formula for the z score (or standard score):

$$z = \frac{X - \mu}{\sigma}$$

Formula for finding a specific data value:

$$X = z \cdot \sigma + \mu$$

Formula for the mean of the sample means:

$$\mu_{\overline{X}} = \mu$$

Formula for the standard error of the mean:

$$\sigma_{\overline{X}} = \frac{\sigma}{\sqrt{n}}$$

Formula for the z score for the central limit theorem:

$$z = \frac{\overline{X} - \mu}{\sigma/\sqrt{n}}$$

Formulas for the mean and standard deviation for the binomial distribution:

$$\mu = n \cdot p \qquad \sigma = \sqrt{n \cdot p \cdot q}$$

Review Exercises

1. Find the area under the standard normal distribution curve for each.

   a. Between $z = 0$ and $z = 1.95$
   b. Between $z = 0$ and $z = 0.37$
   c. Between $z = 1.32$ and $z = 1.82$
   d. Between $z = -1.05$ and $z = 2.05$
   e. Between $z = -0.03$ and $z = 0.53$
   f. Between $z = +1.10$ and $z = -1.80$
   g. To the right of $z = 1.99$
   h. To the right of $z = -1.36$
   i. To the left of $z = -2.09$
   j. To the left of $z = 1.68$

2. Using the standard normal distribution, find each probability.

   a. $P(0 < z < 2.07)$
   b. $P(-1.83 < z < 0)$
   c. $P(-1.59 < z < +2.01)$
   d. $P(1.33 < z < 1.88)$
   e. $P(-2.56 < z < 0.37)$
   f. $P(z > 1.66)$
   g. $P(z < -2.03)$
   h. $P(z > -1.19)$
   i. $P(z < 1.93)$
   j. $P(z > -1.77)$

3. The average annual salary of employed Canadians, aged 15 to 24, with less than a high school graduate certificate is $19,476. Assume the variable is normally distributed with a standard deviation of $2050. Find these probabilities for a randomly selected 15- to 24-year-old worker with less than high school completion.

   a. The worker earns more than $19,476.
   b. The worker earns less than $18,000.
   c. If you were offered a job at $18,000, how would you compare your salary with the salaries of the population of 15- to 24-year-olds without a high school graduate certificate?

   Source: Statistics Canada.

4. Canadian medical doctors' average fee-for-service billing to their provincial health-care system is $202,000 per annum. If the billings of medical doctors are normally distributed with a standard deviation of $13,700, find the probability that

   a. An individual medical doctor fee-for-service billing is more than $210,000.
   b. A random sample of 9 medical doctors' fee-for-service billing is more than $210,000.

   Source: Canadian Institute for Health Information.

5. A vehicular fatality inquest in Ontario monitored a section of highway in which the posted speed limit was 80 kilometres per hour (km/h). The report indicated that during the monitored time period the average speed of vehicles in this section of highway was 98 km/h. Assume speeds are normally distributed with a standard deviation of 9.7 km/h. What percentage of vehicles that were monitored exceeded the posted speed limit? If police decided to ticket only motorists exceeding 85 km/h, what percentage of motorists would be ticketed?

   Source: Ontario Legislature—Hansard debates.

6. The national average for a new car loan was 8.28%. If the rate is normally distributed with a standard deviation of 3.5%, find these probabilities.

   a. One can receive a rate less than 9%.
   b. One can receive a rate less than 8%.

   Source: www.bankrate.com/*New York Times*.

7. During a 6-month period the average monthly precipitation in Vancouver was 116.4 millimetres (mm). If the average precipitation is normally distributed with a standard deviation of 32.8 mm, find these probabilities

   a. A randomly selected year will have precipitation greater than 100 mm for the same 6-month period.
   b. Five randomly selected years will have an average precipitation greater than 100 mm for the same 6-month period.

   Source: Environment Canada.

8. The average weight of an airline passenger's suitcase is 20 kilograms (kg). The standard deviation is 0.9 kg. If 15% of the suitcases are overweight, find the maximum weight allowed by the airline. Assume the variable is normally distributed.

9. An educational study to be conducted requires a test score in the middle 40% range. If $\mu = 100$ and $\sigma = 15$, find the highest and lowest acceptable test scores that would enable a candidate to participate in the study. Assume the variable is normally distributed.

10. The average cost of XYZ brand running shoes is $83 per pair, with a standard deviation of $8. If 9 pairs of running shoes are selected, find the probability that the mean cost of a pair of shoes will be less than $80. Assume the variable is normally distributed.

11. A recent study of the life span of portable compact disc players found the average to be 3.7 years with a standard deviation of 0.6 year. If a random sample of 32 people who own CD players is selected, find the probability that the mean lifetime of the sample will be less than 3.4 years. If the mean is less than 3.4 years, would you consider that 3.7 years might be incorrect?

12. The probability of winning on a slot machine is 5%. If a person plays the machine 500 times, find the probability of winning 30 times. Use the normal approximation to the binomial distribution.

13. Census information indicates that 14.1% of the Canadian labour force is employed in a trade-related occupation. If 400 working Canadians are selected at random, find the probability that at least 50 are employed in a trade-related occupation.

    Source: Statistics Canada.

14. In a large university, 30% of first-year students elect to enroll in a personal finance course offered by the university. Find the probability that of 800 randomly selected first-year students, at least 260 have elected to enroll in the course.

15. The age group 20 to 29 represents 13% of Canada's total population. If 150 Canadians are selected at random, find the probability that at least 25 are in their "20s."

    Source: Statistics Canada.

16. The heights (in metres above sea level) of a random sample of the world's active volcanoes are shown here. Check for normality.

4095	1565	3456	3726	2277
2890	3774	2339	1592	1716
1087	2168	1783	1731	3836
1703	2462	2911	2458	819
1600	1936	1400	799	2849
1833	731	1725	654	926

Source: *N.Y. Times Almanac.*

17. A random sample of enrolments in Pennsylvania's private four-year colleges is listed here. Check for normality.

1350	1886	1743	1290	1767
2067	1118	3980	1773	4605
1445	3883	1486	980	1217
3587				

Source: *N.Y. Times Almanac.*

What Is Normal?–Revisited

Statistics Today

Many of the variables measured in medical tests—blood pressure, triglyceride level, etc.—are approximately normally distributed for the majority of the population in the United States. Thus, researchers can find the mean and standard deviation of these variables. Then, using these two measures along with the z values, they can find normal intervals for healthy individuals. For example, 95% of the systolic blood pressures of healthy individuals fall within 2 standard deviations of the mean. If an individual's pressure is outside the determined normal range (either above or below), the physician will look for a possible cause and prescribe treatment if necessary.

Chapter Quiz

Determine whether each statement is true or false. If the statement is false, explain why.

1. The total area under a normal distribution is infinite.

2. The standard normal distribution is a continuous distribution.

3. All variables that are approximately normally distributed can be transformed to standard normal variables.

4. The z score corresponding to a number below the mean is always negative.

5. The area under the standard normal distribution to the left of $z = 0$ is negative.

6. The central limit theorem applies to means of samples selected from different populations.

Select the best answer.

7. The mean of the standard normal distribution is

    a. 0
    b. 1
    c. 100
    d. Variable

8. Approximately what percentage of normally distributed data values will fall within 1 standard deviation above or below the mean?

    a. 68%
    b. 95%
    c. 99.7%
    d. Variable

9. Which is not a property of the standard normal distribution?

   a. It's symmetric about the mean.
   b. It's uniform.
   c. It's bell-shaped.
   d. It's unimodal.

10. When a distribution is positively skewed, the usual relationship of the mean, median, and mode from left to right will be

   a. Mean, median, mode
   b. Mode, median, mean
   c. Median, mode, mean
   d. Mean, mode, median

11. The standard deviation of all possible sample means equals

   a. The population standard deviation.
   b. The population standard deviation divided by the population mean.
   c. The population standard deviation divided by the square root of the sample size.
   d. The square root of the population standard deviation.

Complete the following statements with the best answer.

12. When one is using the standard normal distribution, $P(z < 0) = $ _____.

13. The difference between a sample mean and a population mean is due to _____.

14. The mean of the sample means equals _____.

15. The standard deviation of all possible sample means is called _____.

16. The normal distribution can be used to approximate the binomial distribution when $n \cdot p$ and $n \cdot q$ are both greater than or equal to _____.

17. The correction factor for the central limit theorem should be used when the sample size is greater than _____ the size of the population.

18. Find the area under the standard normal distribution for each.

   a. Between 0 and 1.50
   b. Between 0 and -1.25
   c. Between 1.56 and 1.96
   d. Between -1.20 and -2.25
   e. Between -0.06 and 0.73
   f. Between 1.10 and -1.80
   g. To the right of $z = 1.75$
   h. To the right of $z = -1.28$
   i. To the left of $z = -2.12$
   j. To the left of $z = 1.36$

19. Using the standard normal distribution, find each probability.

   a. $P(0 < z < 2.16)$
   b. $P(-1.87 < z < 0)$
   c. $P(-1.63 < z < 2.17)$
   d. $P(1.72 < z < 1.98)$
   e. $P(-2.17 < z < 0.71)$
   f. $P(z > 1.77)$
   g. $P(z < -2.37)$
   h. $P(z > -1.73)$
   i. $P(z < 2.03)$
   j. $P(z > -1.02)$

20. The average amount of rain per year in St. John's, Newfoundland and Labrador is 69.9 millimetres (mm). The standard deviation is 24.7 mm. Find the probability that next year St. John's will receive the following amount of rainfall. Assume the variable is normally distributed.

   a. At most 65 mm of rain.
   b. At least 80 mm of rain.
   c. Between 60 mm and 75 mm of rain.
   d. How many millimetres of rain would you consider to be an extremely wet year?

   Source: Environment Canada.

21. The average height of adult women in Canada is 163 centimetres (cm). Assume a standard deviation of 6.3 cm and a normally distributed variable. Find the probability that a randomly selected Canadian adult female's height will be

   a. Greater than 170 cm.
   b. Less than 160 cm.
   c. Between 160 cm and 170 cm.
   d. Find the 5th and 95th percentiles of heights.

   Source: Canadian Fitness and Lifestyle Research Institute.

22. Statistics Canada reports that the average Canadian consumes 90.5 litres of coffee per year. Suppose coffee consumption is normally distributed with a standard deviation of 11 litres per year. If a Canadian is randomly selected find the probability that the amount of coffee consumed per year is

   a. Between 80 and 90 litres.
   b. Less than 80 litres.
   c. At least 70 litres.
   d. At most 100 litres.

   Source: Statistics Canada.

23. The average number of years a person takes to complete a graduate degree program is 3. The standard deviation is 4 months. Assume the variable is normally distributed. If an individual enrolls in the program, find the probability that it will take

   a. More than 4 years to complete the program.
   b. Less than 3 years to complete the program.

c. Between 3.8 and 4.5 years to complete the program.

d. Between 2.5 and 3.1 years to complete the program.

24. On the daily run of an express bus, the average number of passengers is 48. The standard deviation is 3. Assume the variable is normally distributed. Find the probability that the bus will have

a. Between 36 and 40 passengers.

b. Fewer than 42 passengers.

c. More than 48 passengers.

d. Between 43 and 47 passengers.

25. The average thickness of books on a library shelf is 8.3 centimetres. The standard deviation is 0.6 centimetre. If 20% of the books are oversized, find the minimum thickness of the oversized books on the library shelf. Assume the variable is normally distributed.

26. Membership in an elite organization requires a test score in the upper 30% range. If $\mu = 115$ and $\sigma = 12$, find the lowest acceptable score that would enable a candidate to apply for membership. Assume the variable is normally distributed.

27. The average repair cost of a microwave oven is $55, with a standard deviation of $8. The costs are normally distributed. If 12 ovens are repaired, find the probability that the mean of the repair bills will be greater than $60.

28. The average electric bill in a residential area is $72 for the month of April. The standard deviation is $6. If the amounts of the electric bills are normally distributed, find the probability that the mean of the bill for 15 residents will be less than $75.

29. A study on insomnia, a sleep disorder, indicates that 14% of Canadians 15 years of age and older are affected. If 50 Canadians, aged 15 years and older, are randomly selected, find the probability that 7 or more suffer from insomnia.

Source: Statistics Canada.

30. If 10% of the people in a certain factory are members of a union, find the probability that, in a sample of 2000, fewer than 180 people are union members.

31. The proportion of Canadian households online remains steady at 73%. In a random sample of 420 households, what is the probability that fewer than 300 are connected online?

Source: TNS Canadian Facts.

32. A Statistics Canada report indicates that 24.5% of the Canadian workforce is employed in sales and services occupations. If 75 Canadian workers are randomly selected, find the probability that at most 20 are employed in this occupation.

Source: Statistics Canada.

33. The number of calories contained in a selection of fast-food sandwiches is shown here. Check for normality.

390	405	580	300	320
540	225	720	470	560
535	660	530	290	440
390	675	530	1010	450
320	460	290	340	610
430	530			

Source: *The Doctor's Pocket Calorie, Fat, and Carbohydrate Counter.*

34. The average GMAT scores for the top-30 ranked U.S. graduate schools of business are listed here. Check for normality.

718	703	703	703	700	690	695	705	690	688
676	681	689	686	691	669	674	652	680	670
651	651	637	662	641	645	645	642	660	636

Source: *U.S. News & World Report Best Graduate Schools.*

Critical Thinking Challenges ● ● ●

Sometimes a researcher must decide whether a variable is normally distributed. There are several ways to do this. One simple but very subjective method uses special graph paper, which is called *normal probability paper.* For the distribution of systolic blood pressure readings given in Chapter 3 of the textbook, the following method can be used:

1. Make a table, as shown.

Boundaries	Frequency	Cumulative frequency	Cumulative percent frequency
89.5–104.5	24		
104.5–119.5	62		
119.5–134.5	72		
134.5–149.5	26		
149.5–164.5	12		
164.5–179.5	4		
	200		

2. Find the cumulative frequencies for each class, and place the results in the third column.

3. Find the cumulative percents for each class by dividing each cumulative frequency by 200 (the total frequencies) and multiplying by 100%. (For the first class, it would be $24/200 \times 100\% = 12\%$.) Place these values in the last column.

4. Using the normal probability paper shown in Table 6–3, label the x axis with the class boundaries as shown and plot the percents.

5. If the points fall approximately in a straight line, it can be concluded that the distribution is normal. Do you feel that this distribution is approximately normal? Explain your answer.

6. To find an approximation of the mean or median, draw a horizontal line from the 50% point on the y axis over to the curve and then a vertical line down to the x axis. Compare this approximation of the mean with the computed mean.

7. To find an approximation of the standard deviation, locate the values on the x axis that correspond to the 16 and 84% values on the y axis. Subtract these two values and divide the result by 2. Compare this approximate standard deviation to the computed standard deviation.

8. Explain why the method used in step 7 works.

Table 6–3	Normal Probability Paper

Data Projects

1. Select a variable (interval or ratio) and collect 30 data values. Some suggestions might include heights of the students in your class, grade point averages of students, running times of feature length movies, etc.

    a. Construct a frequency distribution for the variable.
    b. Use the procedure described in the Critical Thinking Challenge on page 291 to graph the distribution on normal probability paper.

    c. Can you conclude that the data are approximately normally distributed? Explain your answer.

2. Repeat Exercise 1, using all the values from Data Set II in Appendix D.

3. Repeat Exercise 1, using a random sample of 30 values from Data Set III in Appendix D.

Answers to Applying the Concepts

Section 6–3   Assessing Normality

1. Answers will vary. One possible frequency distribution is the following:

Branches	Frequency
0–9	1
10–19	14
20–29	17
30–39	7
40–49	3
50–59	2
60–69	2
70–79	1
80–89	2
90–99	1

2. Answers will vary according to the frequency distribution in question 1. This histogram matches the frequency distribution in question 1.

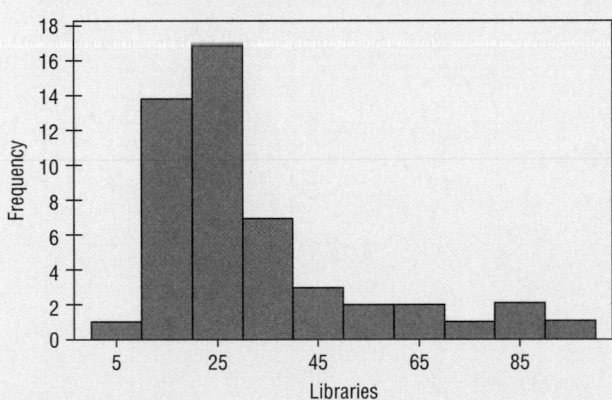

Histogram of Libraries

3. The histogram is unimodal and skewed to the right (positively skewed).

4. The distribution does not appear to be normal.

5. The mean number of branches is $\bar{x} = 31.4$, and the standard deviation is $s = 20.6$.

6. Of the data values, 80% fall within 1 standard deviation of the mean (between 10.8 and 52).

7. Of the data values, 92% fall within 2 standard deviations of the mean (between 0 and 72.6).

8. Of the data values, 98% fall within 3 standard deviations of the mean (between 0 and 93.2).

9. My values in questions 6–8 differ from the 68, 95, and 100% that we would see in a normal distribution.

10. These values support the conclusion that the distribution of the variable is not normal.

Section 6–4   Smart People

1. $z = \frac{130 - 100}{15} = 2$. The area to the right of 2 in the standard normal table is about 0.0228, so I would expect about $10{,}000(0.0228) = 228$ people in Visiala to qualify for Mensa.

2. It does seem reasonable to continue my quest to start a Mensa chapter in Visiala.

3. Answers will vary. One possible answer would be to randomly call telephone numbers (both home and cellphones) in Visiala, ask to speak to an adult, and ask whether the person would be interested in joining Mensa.

4. To have an Ultra-Mensa club, I would need to find the people in Visiala who have IQs that are at least 2.326 standard deviations above average. This means that I would need to recruit those with IQs that are at least 135:

$$2.326 = \frac{x - 100}{15} \Rightarrow x = 100 + 2.326(15) = 134.89$$

Section 6–5   Central Limit Theorem

1. It is very unlikely that we would ever get the same results for any of our random samples. While it is a remote possibility, it is highly unlikely.

2. A good estimate for the population mean would be to find the average of the students' sample means. Similarly, a good estimate for the population standard deviation would be to find the average of the students' sample standard deviations.

3. The distribution appears to be somewhat left (negatively) skewed.

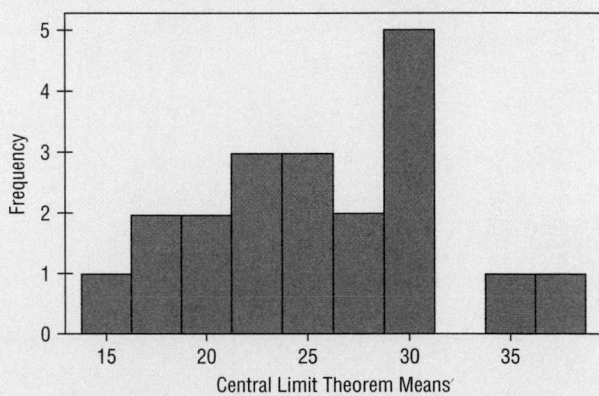

Histogram of Central Limit Theorem Means

4. The mean of the students' means is 25.4, and the standard deviation is 5.8.

5. The distribution of the means is not a sampling distribution, since it represents just 20 of all possible samples of size 30 from the population.

6. The sampling error for student 3 is $18 - 25.4 = -7.4$; the sampling error for student 7 is $26 - 25.4 = +0.6$; the sampling error for student 14 is $29 - 25.4 = +3.6$.

7. The standard deviation for the sample of the 20 means is greater than the standard deviations for each of the individual students. So it is not equal to the standard deviation divided by the square root of the sample size.

Section 6–6   How Safe Are You?

1. A reliability rating of 97% means that, on average, the device will not fail 97% of the time. We do not know how many times it will fail for any particular set of 100 climbs.

2. The probability of at least 1 failure in 100 climbs is $1 - (0.97)^{100} = 1 - 0.0476 = 0.9524$ (about 95%).

3. The complement of the event in question 2 is the event of "no failures in 100 climbs."

4. This can be considered a binomial experiment. We have two outcomes: success and failure. The probability of the equipment working (success) remains constant at 97%. We have 100 independent climbs. And we are counting the number of times the equipment works in these 100 climbs.

5. We could use the binomial probability formula, but it would be very messy computationally.

6. The probability of at least two failures *cannot* be estimated with the normal distribution (see below). So the probability is $1 - [(0.97)^{100} + 100(0.97)^{99}(0.03)] = 1 - 0.1946 = 0.8054$ (about 80.5%).

7. We *should not* use the normal approximation to the binomial since $nq < 10$.

8. If we had used the normal approximation, we would have needed a correction for continuity, since we would have been approximating a discrete distribution with a continuous distribution.

9. Since a second safety hook will be successful or fail independently of the first safety hook, the probability of failure drops from 3% to $(0.03)(0.03) = 0.0009$, or 0.09%.

CHAPTER **7**

Confidence Intervals and Sample Size

Objectives

After completing this chapter, you should be able to

1 Find the confidence interval for the mean when σ is known or $n \geq 30$.

2 Determine the minimum sample size for finding a confidence interval for the mean.

3 Find the confidence interval for the mean when σ is unknown and $n < 30$.

4 Find the confidence interval for a proportion.

5 Determine the minimum sample size for finding a confidence interval for a proportion.

6 Find a confidence interval for a variance and a standard deviation.

Outline

7–1 Introduction

7–2 Confidence Intervals for the Mean (σ Known or $n \geq 30$) and Sample Size

7–3 Confidence Intervals for the Mean (σ Unknown and $n < 30$)

7–4 Confidence Intervals and Sample Size for Proportions

7–5 Confidence Intervals for Variances and Standard Deviations (Optional)

7–6 Summary

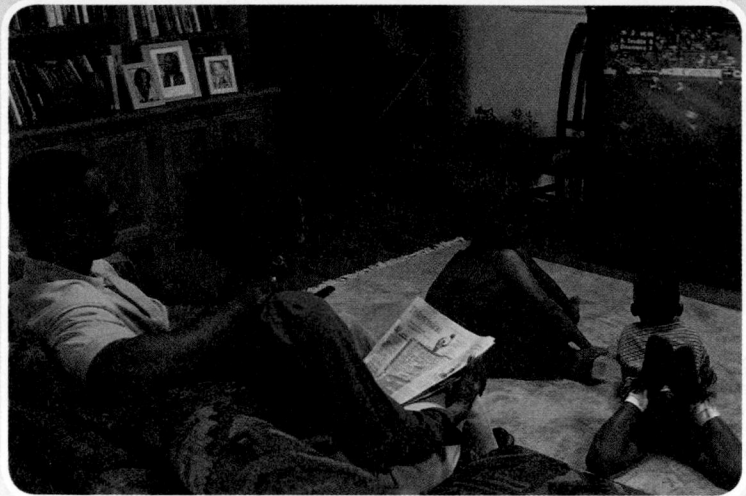

Statistics Today

Would You Change the Channel?

A survey by the Roper Organization found that 45% of the people who were offended by a television program would change the channel, while 15% would turn off their television sets. The survey further stated that the margin of error is 3 percentage points, and 4000 adults were interviewed. Several questions arise:

1. How do these estimates compare with the true population percentages?
2. What is meant by a margin of error of 3 percentage points?
3. Is the sample of 4000 large enough to represent the population of all adults who watch television in Canada?

See Statistics Today—Revisited, page 328, at the end of the chapter for the answers.

After reading this chapter, you will be able to answer these questions, since this chapter explains how statisticians can use statistics to make estimates of parameters.

Source: The Associated Press.

7–1 Introduction

One aspect of inferential statistics is **estimation,** which is the process of estimating the value of a parameter from information obtained from a sample. For example, Statistics Canada and other public as well as private agencies collect economic, societal, and cultural data of the people and resources of the country. Examples of data disseminated through these sources include the following.

> *"The average Canadian male spends $71.73 per week on food compared to female weekly food expenditure of $61.78." (Statistics Canada)*[1]
> *"1 in 5 Canadians list talking on mobile phones as their biggest grievance with other drivers on the road, yet 1 in 4 are guilty of it themselves." (Leger Marketing)*
> *"Television viewing by Canadians averages 21 hours per week." (Statistics Canada)*[2]
> *"44% of Canadian drivers change their own vehicle spark plugs." (DesRosiers Automotive Consultants)*
> *"Cannabis dependence is significantly higher among youth (27%) than adults (5%)." (Canadian Community Epidemiology Network on Drug Use)*

Since the populations from which these values were obtained are large, these values are only *estimates* of the true parameters and are derived from data collected from samples.

The statistical procedures for estimating the population mean, proportion, variance, and standard deviation will be explained in this chapter.

---

[1]Adapted from Statistics Canada publication *Food Expenditure in Canada,* Catalogue 62–554, 2001, Release date: February 21, 2003, page 55.

[2]Adapted from Statistics Canada website http://dissemination.statcan.ca/Daily/English/021202/d021202a.htm. February 28, 2007.

An important question in estimation is that of sample size. How large should the sample be in order to make an accurate estimate? This question is not easy to answer since the size of the sample depends on several factors, such as the accuracy desired and the probability of making a correct estimate. The question of sample size will be explained in this chapter also.

7–2   Confidence Intervals for the Mean (σ Known or $n \geq 30$) and Sample Size

Objective

Find the confidence interval for the mean when σ is known or $n \geq 30$.

Suppose a college president wishes to estimate the average age of students attending classes this semester. The president could select a random sample of 100 students and find the average age of these students, say, 22.3 years. From the sample mean, the president could infer that the average age of all the students is 22.3 years. This type of estimate is called a *point estimate.*

> **A point estimate** is a specific numerical value estimate of a parameter. The best point estimate of the population mean μ is the sample mean $\overline{X}$.

One might ask why other measures of central tendency, such as the median and mode, are not used to estimate the population mean. The reason is that the means of samples vary less than other statistics (such as medians and modes) when many samples are selected from the same population. Therefore, the sample mean is the best estimate of the population mean.

Sample measures (i.e., statistics) are used to estimate population measures (i.e., parameters). These statistics are called **estimators.** As previously stated, the sample mean is a better estimator of the population mean than the sample median or sample mode.

A good estimator should satisfy the three properties described now.

Three Properties of a Good Estimator

1. The estimator should be an **unbiased estimator.** That is, the expected value or the mean of the estimates obtained from samples of a given size is equal to the parameter being estimated.
2. The estimator should be consistent. For a **consistent estimator,** as sample size increases, the value of the estimator approaches the value of the parameter estimated.
3. The estimator should be a **relatively efficient estimator.** That is, of all the statistics that can be used to estimate a parameter, the relatively efficient estimator has the smallest variance.

Confidence Intervals

As stated in Chapter 6, the sample mean will be, for the most part, somewhat different from the population mean due to sampling error. Therefore, one might ask a second question: How good is a point estimate? The answer is that there is no way of knowing how close a particular point estimate is to the population mean.

This answer places some doubt on the accuracy of point estimates. For this reason, statisticians prefer another type of estimate, called an *interval estimate.*

> An **interval estimate** of a parameter is an interval or a range of values used to estimate the parameter. This estimate may or may not contain the value of the parameter being estimated.

In an interval estimate, the parameter is specified as being between two values. For example, an interval estimate for the average age of all students might be $26.9 < \mu < 27.7$, or 27.3 ± 0.4 years.

Either the interval contains the parameter or it does not. A degree of confidence (usually a percent) can be assigned before an interval estimate is made. For instance, one may wish to be 95% confident that the interval contains the true population mean. Another question then arises. Why 95%? Why not 99 or 99.5%?

If one desires to be more confident, such as 99 or 99.5% confident, then the interval must be larger. For example, a 99% confidence interval for the mean age of college students might be $26.7 < \mu < 27.9$, or 27.3 ± 0.6. Hence, a tradeoff occurs. To be more confident that the interval contains the true population mean, one must make the interval wider.

The **confidence level** of an interval estimate of a parameter is the probability that the interval estimate will contain the parameter, assuming that a large number of samples are selected and that the estimation process on the same parameter is repeated.

A **confidence interval** is a specific interval estimate of a parameter determined by using data obtained from a sample and by using the specific confidence level of the estimate.

Intervals constructed in this way are called *confidence intervals*. Three common confidence intervals are used: the 90, the 95, and the 99% confidence intervals.

The algebraic derivation of the formula for determining a confidence interval for a mean will be shown later. A brief intuitive explanation will be given first.

The central limit theorem states that when the sample size is large, approximately 95% of the sample means will fall within ± 1.96 standard errors of the population mean, that is,

$$\mu \pm 1.96 \left(\frac{\sigma}{\sqrt{n}} \right)$$

Now, if a specific sample mean is selected, say, $\overline{X}$, there is a 95% probability that it falls within the range of $\mu \pm 1.96(\sigma/\sqrt{n})$. Likewise, there is a 95% probability that the interval specified by

$$\overline{X} \pm 1.96 \left(\frac{\sigma}{\sqrt{n}} \right)$$

will contain μ, as will be shown later. Stated another way,

$$\overline{X} - 1.96 \left(\frac{\sigma}{\sqrt{n}} \right) < \mu < \overline{X} + 1.96 \left(\frac{\sigma}{\sqrt{n}} \right)$$

Hence, one can be 95% confident that the population mean is contained within that interval when the values of the variable are normally distributed in the population.

For example, in order to target new account advertising, a researcher would like an estimate of the average age and household income of all online stock traders at a confidence level of 95%. Using techniques presented in this chapter, the researcher selects a random sample of new accounts and discovers that on average online stock traders are between 39.5 and 46.5 years old with household incomes between $89,750 and $110,250. With a 95% degree of confidence in the estimates of the true population mean, the researcher will target these demographics for new accounts.

The value used for the 95% confidence interval, 1.96, is obtained from Table E–2 in Appendix C. For a 99% confidence interval, the value 2.575 is used instead of 1.96 in the formula. This value is also obtained from Table E–2 and is based on the standard normal distribution. Since other confidence intervals are used in statistics, the symbol $z_{\alpha/2}$ (read "zed sub alpha over two") is used in the general formula for confidence intervals. The Greek letter α (alpha) represents the total area in both tails of the standard normal distribution curve, and $\alpha/2$ represents the area in each one of the tails. More will be said after Examples 7–1 and 7–2 about finding other values for $z_{\alpha/2}$.

The relationship between α and the confidence level is that the stated confidence level is the percentage equivalent to the decimal value of $1 - \alpha$, and vice versa. When the 95% confidence interval is to be found, $\alpha = 0.05$, since $1 - 0.05 = 0.95$, or 95%. When $\alpha = 0.01$, then $1 - \alpha = 1 - 0.01 = 0.99$, and the 99% confidence interval is being calculated.

Formula for the Confidence Interval of the Mean for a Specific α

$$\overline{X} - z_{\alpha/2}\left(\frac{\sigma}{\sqrt{n}}\right) < \mu < \overline{X} + z_{\alpha/2}\left(\frac{\sigma}{\sqrt{n}}\right)$$

For a 90% confidence interval, $z_{\alpha/2} = 1.645$; for a 95% confidence interval, $z_{\alpha/2} = 1.96$; and for a 99% confidence interval, $z_{\alpha/2} = 2.575$.

The term $z_{\alpha/2}(\sigma/\sqrt{n})$ is called the *margin of error,* also referred to as the *maximum error of estimate.* For a specific value, say, $\alpha = 0.05$, 95% of the sample means will fall within this error value on either side of the population mean, as previously explained. See Figure 7–1.

Figure 7–1

95% Confidence Interval

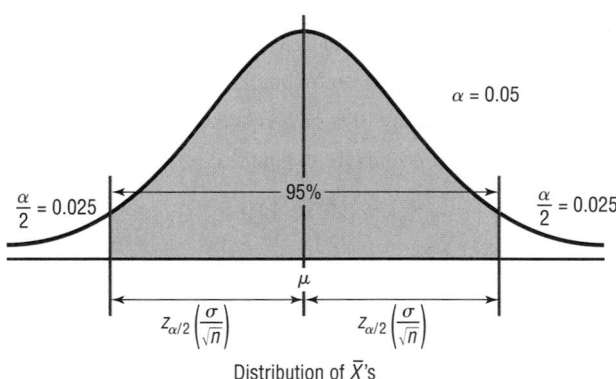

The distribution figure labels: $\alpha = 0.05$; $\frac{\alpha}{2} = 0.025$; 95%; $\frac{\alpha}{2} = 0.025$; μ; $z_{\alpha/2}\left(\frac{\sigma}{\sqrt{n}}\right)$; $z_{\alpha/2}\left(\frac{\sigma}{\sqrt{n}}\right)$; Distribution of $\overline{X}$'s

> The **margin of error** is the maximum likely difference between the point estimate of a parameter and the actual value of the parameter.

A more detailed explanation of the margin of error follows Examples 7–1 and 7–2, which illustrate the computation of confidence intervals.

Rounding Rule for a Confidence Interval for a Mean
When you are computing a confidence interval for a population mean by using *raw data,* round off to one more decimal place than the number of decimal places in the original data. When you

are computing a confidence interval for a population mean by using a sample mean and a standard deviation, round off to the same number of decimal places as given for the mean.

Example 7–1

A researcher wishes to estimate the average amount of money a person spends on lottery tickets each month. A sample of 50 people who play the lottery found the mean to be $19 and the standard deviation to be 6.8. Find the best point estimate of the population mean and the 95% confidence interval of the population mean.

Source: USA TODAY.

Solution

The best point estimate of the mean is $19. For the 95% confidence interval use $z = 1.96$.

$$19 - 1.96\left(\frac{6.8}{\sqrt{50}}\right) < \mu < 19 + 1.96\left(\frac{6.8}{\sqrt{50}}\right)$$

$$19 - 1.9 < \mu < 19 + 1.9$$

$$17.1 < \mu < 20.9$$

or

$$19 \pm 1.9$$

Hence, one can say with 95% confidence the true mean of the population is between $17.10 and $20.90, based on a sample of 50 people who play the lottery.

Example 7–2

A survey of 30 adults found that the mean age of a person's primary vehicle is 5.6 years. Assuming the standard deviation of the population is 0.8 year, find the best point estimate of the population mean and the 99% confidence interval of the population mean.

Source: Based on information in *USA TODAY.*

Solution

The best point estimate of the population mean is 5.6 years.

$$5.6 - 2.575\left(\frac{0.8}{\sqrt{30}}\right) < \mu < 5.6 + 2.575\left(\frac{0.8}{\sqrt{30}}\right)$$

$$5.6 - 0.38 < \mu < 5.6 + 0.38$$

$$5.22 < \mu < 5.98$$

or

$$5.2 < \mu < 6.0 \text{ (rounded)}$$

Hence, one can be 99% confident that the mean age of all primary vehicles is between 5.2 and 6.0 years, based on 30 vehicles.

Another way of looking at a confidence interval is shown in Figure 7–2. According to the central limit theorem, approximately 95% of the sample means fall within 1.96 standard deviations of the population mean if the sample size is 30 or more or if σ is known when n is less than 30 and the population is normally distributed. If it were possible to build a confidence interval about each sample mean, as was done in Examples 7–1 and 7–2

Figure 7–2

95% Confidence Interval for Sample Means

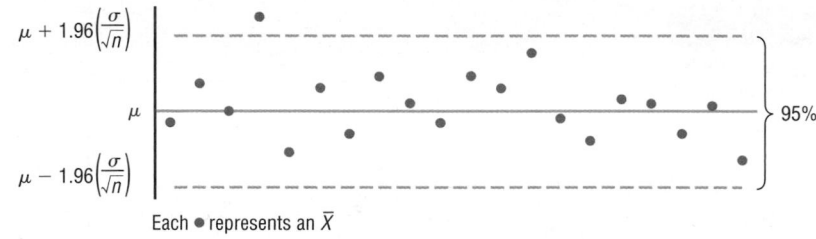

for μ, 95% of these intervals would contain the population mean, as shown in Figure 7–3. Hence, one can be 95% confident that an interval built around a specific sample mean would contain the population mean. If one desires to be 99% confident, the confidence intervals must be enlarged so that 99 out of every 100 intervals contain the population mean.

Figure 7–3

95% Confidence Intervals for Each Sample Mean

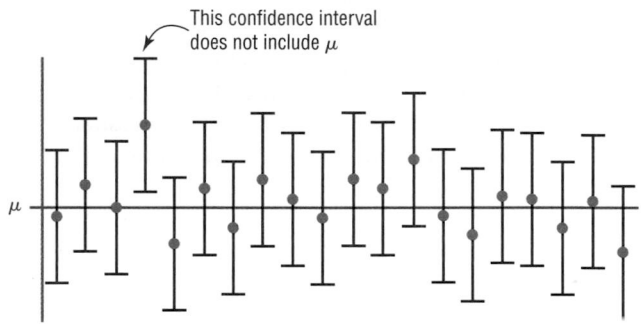

Since other confidence intervals (besides 90, 95, and 99%) are sometimes used in statistics, an explanation of how to find the values for $z_{\alpha/2}$ is necessary. As stated previously, the Greek letter α represents the total of the areas in both tails of the normal distribution. The value for α is found by subtracting the decimal equivalent for the desired confidence level from 1. For example, if one wanted to find the 98% confidence interval, one would change 98% to 0.98 and find $\alpha = 1 - 0.98$, or 0.02. Then $\alpha/2$ is obtained by dividing α by 2. So $\alpha/2$ is 0.02/2, or 0.01. Finally, $z_{0.01}$ is the z value that will give an area of 0.01 in both the left and right tails of the standard normal distribution curve. See Figure 7–4.

Figure 7–4

Finding $\alpha/2$ for a 98% Confidence Interval

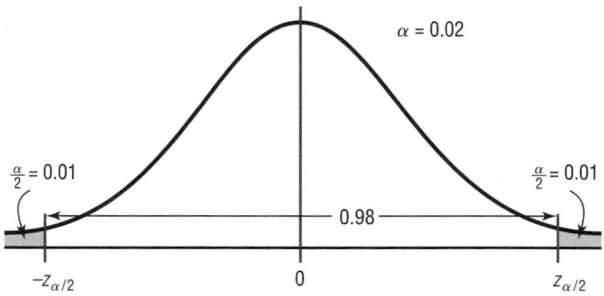

Once $\alpha/2$ is determined, the corresponding $z_{\alpha/2}$ score can be found by using the procedure shown in Section 6–3 "Finding z Scores When Given Areas". In summary, to obtain the $z_{\alpha/2}$ score for a 98% confidence level, subtract 0.9800 from 1.000 to obtain $\alpha = 0.02$, therefore $\alpha/2 = 0.02/2 = 0.01$. In Table E–2—Positive z Scores the area 0.0100 to the right is the cumulative area 0.9900 ($1.0000 - 0.0100$) to the left, where $z = 2.33$. Refer to Figure 7–5.

Figure 7-5

Finding $z_{\alpha/2}$ for a 98%
Confidence Interval

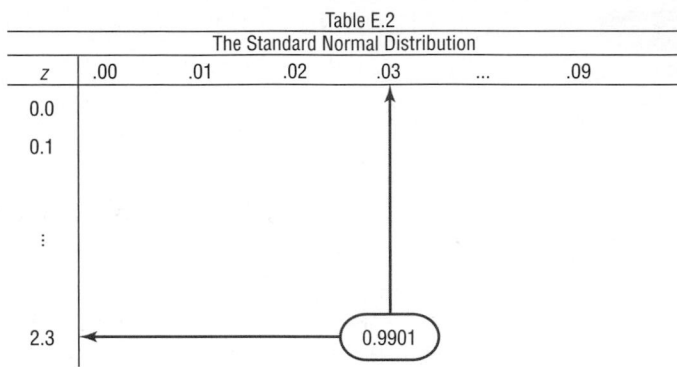

Table E.2
The Standard Normal Distribution

z	.00	.01	.02	.03	...	.09
0.0						
0.1						
⋮						
2.3				0.9901		

For confidence intervals, only the positive z score is used in the formula.

When the original variable is normally distributed and σ is known, the standard normal distribution can be used to find confidence intervals regardless of the size of the sample. When $n \geq 30$, the distribution of means will be approximately normal even if the original distribution of the variable departs from normality. Also, if $n \geq 30$ (some authors use $n > 30$), s can be substituted for σ in the formula for confidence intervals; and the standard normal distribution can be used to find confidence intervals for means, as shown in Example 7–3.

Example 7-3

The following data represent a random sample of 30 house prices (in thousands of dollars) in Calgary. Find the 90% confidence interval estimate of the mean price of all Calgary houses.

318.3	507.5	351.9	292.2	487.7	587.2
373.9	261.5	261.5	350.6	381.0	782.3
508.0	262.8	289.3	360.9	447.7	795.8
437.3	276.2	300.0	441.4	545.0	337.0
450.8	317.5	332.5	634.6	945.3	393.6

Source: Calgary Real Estate Board.

Solution

Step 1 Find the mean and standard deviation for the data. Use the formula shown in Chapter 3 or your calculator. The mean $\overline{X} = 434.38$. The standard deviation $s = 171.25$.

Step 2 Find $\alpha/2$. Since the 90% confidence interval is to be used,
$\alpha = 1 - 0.90 = 0.10$, and

$$\frac{\alpha}{2} = \frac{0.10}{2} = 0.05$$

Step 3 Find $z_{\alpha/2}$. Subtract 0.05 (area in right tail) from 1.0000 to get 0.9500 (cumulative area to the left). The corresponding z value obtained from Table E–2 for 0.9500 is $z = 1.645$, as this score is halfway between $z = 1.64$ (0.9495) and $z = 1.65$ (0.9505).

Step 4 Substitute into the formula

$$\overline{X} - z_{\alpha/2}\left(\frac{s}{\sqrt{n}}\right) < \mu < \overline{X} + z_{\alpha/2}\left(\frac{s}{\sqrt{n}}\right)$$

(Since $n \geq 30$, s is used in place of σ when σ is unknown.)

$$434.38 - 1.645\left(\frac{171.25}{\sqrt{30}}\right) < \mu < 434.38 + 1.645\left(\frac{171.25}{\sqrt{30}}\right)$$

$$434.38 - 51.43 < \mu < 434.38 + 51.43$$

$$382.94 < \mu < 485.81$$

Hence, one can be 90% confident that the population mean of Calgary house prices is between $382,940 and $485,810, based on a sample of 30 house sales.

Comment to Computer and Statistical Calculator Users

This chapter and subsequent chapters include examples using raw data. If you are using computer or calculator programs to find the solutions, the answers you get may vary somewhat from the ones given in the textbook. This is so because computers and calculators do not round the answers in the intermediate steps and can use 12 or more decimal places for computation. Also, they use more exact values than those given in the tables in the back of this book. These discrepancies are part and parcel of statistics.

Objective 2

Determine the minimum sample size for finding a confidence interval for the mean.

Sample Size

Sample size determination is closely related to statistical estimation. Quite often, one asks, How large a sample is necessary to make an accurate estimate? The answer is not simple, since it depends on three things: the maximum error of estimate, the population standard deviation, and the degree of confidence. For example, how close to the true mean does one want to be (2 units, 5 units, etc.), and how confident does one wish to be (90, 95, 99%, etc.)? For the purpose of this chapter, it will be assumed that the population standard deviation of the variable is known or has been estimated from a previous study.

The formula for sample size is derived from the margin of error formula

$$E = z_{\alpha/2}\left(\frac{\sigma}{\sqrt{n}}\right)$$

and this formula is solved for n as follows:

$$E\sqrt{n} = z_{\alpha/2}(\sigma)$$

$$\sqrt{n} = \frac{z_{\alpha/2} \cdot \sigma}{E}$$

Hence, $n = \left(\frac{z_{\alpha/2} \cdot \sigma}{E}\right)^2$

Formula for the Minimum Sample Size Needed for an Interval Estimate of the Population Mean

$$n = \left(\frac{z_{\alpha/2} \cdot \sigma}{E}\right)^2$$

where E is the margin of error. If necessary, round the answer *up* to obtain a whole number. That is, if there is any fraction or decimal portion in the answer, use the next whole number for sample size n.

Example 7–4

The college president asks the statistics teacher to estimate the average age of the students at their college. How large a sample is necessary? The statistics teacher would like to be 99% confident that the estimate should be accurate within 1 year. From a previous study, the standard deviation of the ages is known to be 3 years.

Solution

Since $\alpha = 0.01$ (or $1 - 0.99$), $z_{\alpha/2} = 2.575$, and $E = 1$, substituting in the formula, one gets

$$n = \left(\frac{z_{\alpha/2} \cdot \sigma}{E}\right)^2 = \left[\frac{(2.575)(3)}{1}\right]^2 \approx 59.7$$

which is rounded up to 60. Therefore, to be 99% confident that the estimate is within 1 year of the true mean age, the teacher needs a sample size of at least 60 students. (Always round n up to the next whole number. For example, if $n = 59.2$, round it up to 60.)

Notice that when one is finding the sample size, the size of the population is irrelevant when the population is large or infinite or when sampling is done with replacement. In other cases, an adjustment is made in the formula for computing sample size. This adjustment is beyond the scope of this book.

The formula for determining sample size requires the use of the population standard deviation. What happens when σ is unknown? In this case, an attempt is made to estimate σ. One such way is to use the standard deviation s obtained from a sample taken previously as an estimate for σ. The standard deviation can also be estimated by dividing the range by 4.

Sometimes, interval estimates rather than point estimates are reported. For instance, one may read a statement: "On the basis of a sample of 200 families, the survey estimates that a Canadian family of two spends an average of $84 per week for groceries. One can be 95% confident that this estimate is accurate within $3 of the true mean." This statement means that the 95% confidence interval of the true mean is

$$\$84 - \$3 < \mu < \$84 + \$3$$
$$\$81 < \mu < \$87$$

The algebraic derivation of the formula for a confidence interval is shown next. As explained in Chapter 6, the sampling distribution of the mean is approximately normal when large samples ($n \geq 30$) are taken from a population. Also,

$$z = \frac{\overline{X} - \mu}{\sigma/\sqrt{n}}$$

Furthermore, there is a probability of $1 - \alpha$ that a z will have a value between $-z_{\alpha/2}$ and $+z_{\alpha/2}$. Hence,

$$-z_{\alpha/2} < \frac{\overline{X} - \mu}{\sigma/\sqrt{n}} < z_{\alpha/2}$$

Using algebra, one finds

$$-z_{\alpha/2} \cdot \frac{\sigma}{\sqrt{n}} < \overline{X} - \mu < z_{\alpha/2} \cdot \frac{\sigma}{\sqrt{n}}$$

Subtracting $\overline{X}$ from both sides and from the middle, one gets

$$-\overline{X} - z_{\alpha/2} \cdot \frac{\sigma}{\sqrt{n}} < -\mu < -\overline{X} + z_{\alpha/2} \cdot \frac{\sigma}{\sqrt{n}}$$

Interesting Fact

Canadian households with post-secondary students spend more on tuition fees than food in a year.

Multiplying by -1, one gets

$$\overline{X} + z_{\alpha/2} \cdot \frac{\sigma}{\sqrt{n}} > \mu > \overline{X} - z_{\alpha/2} \cdot \frac{\sigma}{\sqrt{n}}$$

Reversing the inequality, one gets the formula for the confidence interval:

$$\overline{X} - z_{\alpha/2} \cdot \frac{\sigma}{\sqrt{n}} < \mu < \overline{X} + z_{\alpha/2} \cdot \frac{\sigma}{\sqrt{n}}$$

Applying the Concepts 7–2

Making Decisions with Confidence Intervals

Assume you work for Kimberly Clark Corporation, the makers of Kleenex. The job you are presently working on requires you to decide how many Kleenexes are to be put in the new automobile glove compartment boxes. Complete the following.

1. How will you decide on a reasonable number of Kleenexes to put in the boxes?

2. When do people usually need Kleenexes?

3. What type of data collection technique would you use?

4. Assume you found out that from your sample of 85 people, on average about 57 Kleenexes are used throughout the duration of a cold, with a standard deviation of 15. Use a confidence interval to help you decide how many Kleenexes will go in the boxes.

5. Explain how you decided on how many Kleenexes will go in the boxes.

See page 331 for the answers.

Exercises 7–2

1. What is the difference between a point estimate and an interval estimate of a parameter? Which is better? Why?

2. What information is necessary to calculate a confidence interval?

3. What is the margin of error?

4. What is meant by the 95% confidence interval of the mean?

5. What are three properties of a good estimator?

6. What statistic best estimates μ?

7. What is necessary to determine the sample size?

8. When one is determining the sample size for a confidence interval, is the size of the population relevant?

9. Find each.

   a. $z_{\alpha/2}$ for the 99% confidence interval

   b. $z_{\alpha/2}$ for the 98% confidence interval

   c. $z_{\alpha/2}$ for the 95% confidence interval

   d. $z_{\alpha/2}$ for the 90% confidence interval

   e. $z_{\alpha/2}$ for the 94% confidence interval

10. Find the 95% confidence interval for the mean paid attendance at the Major League Baseball All-Star games. A random sample of the paid attendances is shown.

47,596	68,751	5,838
69,831	28,843	53,107
31,391	48,829	50,706
62,892	55,105	63,974
56,674	38,362	51,549
31,938	31,851	56,088
34,906	38,359	72,086
34,009	50,850	43,801
46,127	49,926	54,960
32,785	48,321	49,671

Source: *Time Almanac.*

11. A sample of the reading scores of 35 Grade 5 students has a mean of 82. The standard deviation of the sample is 15.

    a. Find the best point estimate of the mean.
    b. Find the 95% confidence interval of the mean reading scores of all Grade 5 students.
    c. Find the 99% confidence interval of the mean reading scores of all Grade 5 students.
    d. Which interval is larger? Explain why.

12. Find the 90% confidence interval of the population mean for the number of detached house sales in Toronto districts over a one-year period. A random sample of 40 districts is shown.

941	573	2864	739
920	759	889	928
1461	799	667	1991
988	718	1280	1137
1278	921	272	624
546	1106	1019	913
1285	535	1463	1377
910	1208	435	2124
1145	538	855	888
650	1105	455	2306

    Source: Toronto Real Estate Board.

13. A study of 40 English composition professors showed that they spent, on average, 12.6 minutes correcting a student's term paper.

    a. Find the best point estimate of the mean.
    b. Find the 90% confidence interval of the mean time for all composition papers when $\sigma = 2.5$ minutes.
    c. If a professor stated that he spent, on average, 30 minutes correcting a term paper, what would be your reaction?

14. A study of 35 golfers showed that their average score on a particular course was 92. The standard deviation of the sample is 5.

    a. Find the best point estimate of the mean.
    b. Find the 95% confidence interval of the mean score for all golfers.
    c. Find the 95% confidence interval of the mean score if a sample of 60 golfers is used instead of a sample of 35.
    d. Which interval is smaller? Explain why.

15. A survey of individuals who passed the seven exams and obtained the rank of Fellow in the actuarial field finds the average salary to be $150,000. If the standard deviation for the sample of 35 Fellows was

$15,000, construct a 95% confidence interval for all Fellows.

Source: www.BeAnActuary.org.

16. A survey of 30 gas stations randomly selected nationwide on Canada Day 2006 indicate the following prices (cents per litre) of regular gasoline fuel. Estimate the average price per litre of fuel with 90% confidence.

117.8	96.4	99.9	96.9	111.9	110.2
109.9	100.4	109.5	96.6	104.5	114.9
114.9	99.9	108.8	103.2	95.8	110.7
112.9	109.5	109.9	103.2	105.4	122.8
108.2	108.8	104.2	96.9	107.4	114.9

Source: MJ Ervin & Associates.

17. A study of 415 kindergarten students showed that they have seen on average 5000 hours of television. If the sample standard deviation is 900, find the 95% confidence level of the mean for all students. If a parent claimed that his children watched 4000 hours, would the claim be believable?

Source: U.S. Department of Education.

18. A random sample of 76 four-year-olds attending day-care centres showed that the yearly tuition averaged $3648. The standard deviation of the sample was $630, and the sample size was 50. Find the 90% confidence interval of the true mean. If a day-care centre were starting up and wanted to keep tuition low, what would be a reasonable amount to charge?

19. Noise levels at various area urban hospitals were measured in decibels. The mean of the noise levels in 84 corridors was 61.2 decibels, and the standard deviation was 7.9. Find the 95% confidence interval of the true mean.

Source: M. Bayo, A. Garcia, and A. Garcia, "Noise Levels in an Urban Hospital and Workers' Subjective Responses," *Archives of Environmental Health* 50, no. 3, p. 249 (May–June 1995). Reprinted with permission of the Helen Dwight Reid Educational Foundation. Published by Heldref Publications, 1319 Eighteenth St. N.W., Washington, D.C. 20036-1802. Copyright © 1995.

20. The growing seasons for a random sample of 35 United States cities were recorded, yielding a sample mean of 190.7 days and a sample standard deviation of 54.2 days. Estimate the true mean population of the growing season with 95% confidence.

Source: *The Old Farmer's Almanac.*

21. A university dean of students wishes to estimate the average number of hours students spend doing homework per week. The standard deviation from a previous study is 6.2 hours. How large a sample must be selected if he wants to be 99% confident of finding whether the true mean differs from the sample mean by 1.5 hours?

22. In the hospital study cited in Exercise 19, the mean noise level in the 171 ward areas was 58.0 decibels, and the standard deviation was 4.8. Find the 90% confidence interval of the true mean.

Source: M. Bayo, A. Garcia, and A. Garcia, "Noise Levels in an Urban Hospital and Workers' Subjective Responses," *Archives of Environmental Health* 50, no. 3, p. 249 (May–June 1995). Reprinted with permission of the Helen Dwight Reid Educational Foundation. Published by Heldref Publications, 1319 Eighteenth St. N.W., Washington, D.C. 20036-1802. Copyright © 1995.

23. An insurance company is trying to estimate the average number of sick days that full-time food service workers use per year. A pilot study found the standard deviation to be 2.5 days. How large a sample must be selected if the company wants to be 95% confident of getting an interval that contains the true mean with a maximum error of 1 day?

24. A pizza shop owner wishes to find the 95% confidence interval of the true mean cost of a large plain pizza. How large should the sample be if she wishes to be accurate to within $0.15? A previous study showed that the standard deviation of the price was $0.26.

25. A researcher is interested in estimating the average monthly salary of sports reporters in a large city. He wants to be 90% confident that his estimate is correct. If the standard deviation is $1100, how large a sample is needed to get the desired information and to be accurate to within $150?

7–3   Confidence Intervals for the Mean (σ Unknown and $n < 30$)

Objective ③

Find the confidence interval for the mean when σ is unknown and $n < 30$.

When σ is known and the variable is normally distributed or when σ is unknown and $n \geq 30$, the standard normal distribution is used to find confidence intervals for the mean. However, in many situations, the population standard deviation is not known and the sample size is less than 30. In such situations, the standard deviation from the sample can be used in place of the population standard deviation for confidence intervals. But a somewhat different distribution, called the *t* **distribution,** must be used when the sample size is less than 30 and the variable is normally or approximately normally distributed.

Some important characteristics of the *t* distribution are described now.

Historical Note

The *t* distribution was formulated in 1908 by an Irish brewing company employee named W. S. Gosset. Gosset was involved in researching new methods of manufacturing ale. Because brewing company employees were not allowed to publish results, Gosset published his finding using the pseudonym *Student;* hence, the *t* distribution is sometimes called *Student's t distribution.*

Characteristics of the *t* Distribution

The *t* distribution shares some characteristics of the normal distribution and differs from it in others. The *t* distribution is similar to the standard normal distribution in these ways.

1. It is bell-shaped.
2. It is symmetric about the mean.
3. The mean, median, and mode are equal to 0 and are located at the centre of the distribution.
4. The curve never touches the *x* axis.

The *t* distribution differs from the standard normal distribution in the following ways.

1. The variance is greater than 1.
2. The *t* distribution is actually a group of curves with different dispersions and heights based on the concept of *degrees of freedom,* which is related to sample size.
3. As the sample size increases, the *t* distribution approaches the standard normal distribution. See Figure 7–6.

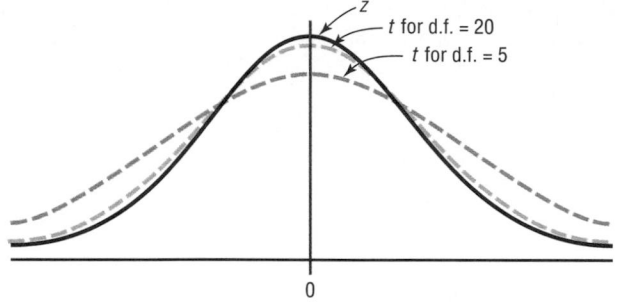

Figure 7–6

The *t* Family of Curves

Many statistical distributions use the concept of degrees of freedom, and the formulas for finding the degrees of freedom vary for different statistical tests. The **degrees of freedom** are the number of values that are free to vary after a sample statistic has been computed, and they tell the researcher which specific curve to use when a distribution consists of a family of curves.

For example, if the mean of 5 values is 10, then 4 of the 5 values are free to vary. But once 4 values are selected, the fifth value must be a specific number to get a sum of 50, since $50 \div 5 = 10$. Hence, the degrees of freedom are $5 - 1 = 4$, and this value tells the researcher which *t* curve to use.

The symbol d.f. will be used for degrees of freedom. The degrees of freedom for a confidence interval for the mean are found by subtracting 1 from the sample size. That is, d.f. $= n - 1$. *Note:* For some statistical tests used later in this book, the degrees of freedom are not equal to $n - 1$.

The formula for finding a confidence interval about the mean by using the *t* distribution is given now.

Formula for a Specific Confidence Interval for the Mean When σ Is Unknown and $n < 30$

$$\overline{X} - t_{\alpha/2}\left(\frac{s}{\sqrt{n}}\right) < \mu < \overline{X} + t_{\alpha/2}\left(\frac{s}{\sqrt{n}}\right)$$

The degrees of freedom are $n - 1$.

The values for $t_{\alpha/2}$ are found in Table F in Appendix C. The top row of Table F, labelled Confidence Intervals, is used to get these values. The other two rows, labelled One tail and Two tails, will be explained in Chapter 8 and should not be used here.

Example 7–5 shows how to find the value in Table F for $t_{\alpha/2}$.

Example 7–5

Find the $t_{\alpha/2}$ value for a 95% confidence interval when the sample size is 22.

Solution

The d.f. $= 22 - 1$, or 21. Find 21 in the left column and 95% in the row labelled Confidence Intervals. The intersection where the two meet gives the value for $t_{\alpha/2}$, which is 2.080. See Figure 7–7.

Figure 7–7

Finding $t_{\alpha/2}$ for Example 7–5

Table F

The t Distribution

	Confidence Intervals	50%	80%	90%	95%	98%	99%
d.f.	One tail α	0.25	0.10	0.05	0.025	0.01	0.005
	Two tails α	0.50	0.20	0.10	0.05	0.02	0.01
1							
2							
3							
⋮							
21					2.080	2.518	2.831
⋮							
$z \propto$		0.674	1.282	1.645	1.960	2.326	2.576

Note: At the bottom of Table F where d.f. $= \infty$, the $z_{\alpha/2}$ values can be found for specific confidence intervals. The reason is that as the degrees of freedom increase, the t distribution approaches the standard normal distribution.

Examples 7–6 and 7–7 show how to find the confidence interval when one is using the t distribution.

Example 7–6

Ten randomly selected automobiles were stopped, and the tread depth of the right tire was measured. The mean was 0.8 centimetres and the standard deviation was 0.2 centimetres. Find the 95% confidence interval of the population mean tread depth. Assume that the variable is approximately normally distributed.

Solution

Since σ is unknown and s must replace it, the t distribution (Table F) must be used for 95% confidence interval. Hence, with 9 degrees of freedom, $t_{\alpha/2} = 2.262$.

The 95% confidence interval of the population mean is found by substituting in the formula

$$\overline{X} - t_{\alpha/2}\left(\frac{s}{\sqrt{n}}\right) < \mu < \overline{X} + t_{\alpha/2}\left(\frac{s}{\sqrt{n}}\right)$$

Hence, $\quad 0.8 - (2.262)\left(\frac{0.2}{\sqrt{10}}\right) < \mu < 0.8 + (2.262)\left(\frac{0.2}{\sqrt{10}}\right)$

$$0.8 - 0.143 < \mu < 0.8 + 0.143$$
$$0.657 < \mu < 0.943$$

Therefore, one can be 95% confident that the population mean tread depth of all right front tires is between 0.657 and 0.943 centimetres based on a sample of 10 tires.

Example 7–7

The data represent a sample of the number of home fires in Canada started by smoking for selected years. Find the 99% confidence interval for the mean number of home fires started by smoking each year. Assume the data is from a normally distributed population.

| 3929 | 3260 | 1019 | 2535 | 3175 |
| 2968 | 3448 | 3790 | 2532 | 4185 |

Source: Council of Canadian Fire Marshals and Fire Commissioners.

Solution

Step 1 Find the mean and standard deviation for the data. Use the formula in Chapter 3 or your calculator. The mean $\overline{X} = 3084.1$. The standard deviation $s = 911.7$.

Step 2 Find $t_{\alpha/2}$ in Table F. Use the 99% confidence interval with d.f. = 9. It is 3.250.

Step 3 Substitute in the formula and solve.

$$\overline{X} - t_{\alpha/2}\left(\frac{s}{\sqrt{n}}\right) < \mu < \overline{X} + t_{\alpha/2}\left(\frac{s}{\sqrt{n}}\right)$$

$$3084.1 - 3.250\left(\frac{911.7}{\sqrt{10}}\right) < \mu < 3084.1 + 3.250\left(\frac{911.7}{\sqrt{10}}\right)$$

$$3084.1 - 3.250\left(\frac{911.7}{\sqrt{10}}\right) < \mu < 3084.1 + 3.250\left(\frac{911.7}{\sqrt{10}}\right)$$

$$3084.1 - 937.0 < \mu < 3084.1 + 937.0$$

$$2147.1 < \mu < 4021.1$$

Step 4 One can be 99% confident that the population mean number of home fires started by smoking each year is between 2147.1 and 4021.1, based on a sample of home fires occurring over a 10-year period.

Students sometimes have difficulty deciding whether to use $z_{\alpha/2}$ or $t_{\alpha/2}$ values when finding confidence intervals for the mean. As stated previously, when σ is known, $z_{\alpha/2}$ values can be used *no matter what the sample size is,* as long as the variable is normally distributed or $n \geq 30$. When σ is unknown and $n \geq 30$, then s can be used in the formula and $z_{\alpha/2}$ values can be used. Finally, when σ is unknown and $n < 30$, s is used in the formula and $t_{\alpha/2}$ values are used, as long as the variable is approximately normally distributed. These rules are summarized in Figure 7–8.

Figure 7–8

When to Use the z or t Distribution

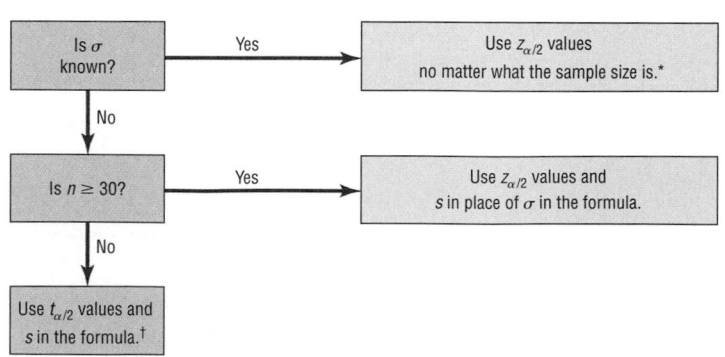

*Variable must be normally distributed when $n < 30$.
†Variable must be approximately normally distributed.

It should be pointed out that some statisticians have a different point of view. They use $z_{\alpha/2}$ values when σ is known and $t_{\alpha/2}$ values when σ is unknown. In these circumstances, a t table that contains t values for sample sizes greater than or equal to 30 would be needed. The procedure shown in Figure 7–8 is the one used throughout this textbook.

Applying the Concepts 7–3

Sport Drink Decision

Assume you get a new job as a coach for a sports team, and one of your first decisions is to choose the sports drink that the team will use during practices and games. You obtain a *Sports Report* magazine so you can use your statistical background to help you make the best decision. The following table lists the most popular sports drinks and some important information about each of them. Answer the following questions about the table.

Drink	Calories	Sodium	Potassium	Cost
Gatorade	60	110	25	$1.29
Powerade	68	77	32	1.19
All Sport	75	55	55	0.89
10-K	63	55	35	0.79
Exceed	69	50	44	1.59
1st Ade	58	58	25	1.09
Hydra Fuel	85	23	50	1.89

1. Would this be considered a small sample?
2. Compute the mean cost per container, and create a 90% confidence interval about that mean. Do all the costs per container fall inside the confidence interval? If not, which ones do not?
3. Are there any you would consider outliers?
4. How many degrees of freedom are there?
5. If cost is a major factor influencing your decision, would you consider cost per container or cost per serving?
6. List which drink you would recommend and why.

See page 331 for the answers.

Exercises 7–3

1. What are the properties of the t distribution?
2. What is meant by *degrees of freedom*?
3. When should the t distribution be used to find a confidence interval for the mean?
4. Find the values for each.

   a. $t_{\alpha/2}$ and $n = 18$ for the 99% confidence interval for the mean

   b. $t_{\alpha/2}$ and $n = 23$ for the 95% confidence interval for the mean

   c. $t_{\alpha/2}$ and $n = 15$ for the 98% confidence interval for the mean

   d. $t_{\alpha/2}$ and $n = 10$ for the 90% confidence interval for the mean

   e. $t_{\alpha/2}$ and $n = 20$ for the 95% confidence interval for the mean

For Exercises 5 through 20, assume that all variables are approximately normally distributed.

5. The average hemoglobin reading for a sample of 20 teachers was 16 grams per 100 millilitres, with a sample standard deviation of 2 grams. Find the 99% confidence interval of the true mean.

6. A random sample of city property taxes for single-family detached homes in 7 Ontario cities was researched for the 2005 taxation year.

   $1928 $2171 $2420 $3239 $2819 $2872 $3006

Find a 98% confidence interval estimate for the average city property tax for all Ontario cities in 2005.

Source: BMA Management Consulting Inc.

7. An American state representative wishes to estimate the mean number of women representatives per state legislature. A random sample of 17 states is selected, and the number of women representatives is shown. Based on the sample, what is the point estimate of the mean? Find the 90% confidence interval of the mean population. (*Note:* The population mean is actually 31.72, or about 32.) Compare this value to the point estimate and the confidence interval. There is something unusual about the data. Describe it and state how it would affect the confidence interval.

5	33	35	37	24
31	16	45	19	13
18	29	15	39	18
58	132			

8. A random sample of the number of barrels (in millions) of oil produced per day by world oil-producing countries is listed here. Estimate the mean oil production with 95% confidence.

3.56   1.90   7.83   2.83   1.91   5.88   2.91   6.08

Source: *N.Y. Times Almanac.*

9. A sample of 6 university wrestlers had an average weight of 125 kilograms (kg) with a standard deviation of 5.5 kg. Find the 90% confidence interval of the true mean weight of all university wrestlers. If a coach claimed that the average weight of the wrestlers on his team was 141 kg, would the claim be believable?

10. The daily salaries of substitute teachers for 8 local school districts is shown. What is the point estimate for the mean? Find the 90% confidence interval of the mean for the salaries of substitute teachers in the region.

60	56	60	55	70	55	60	55

Source: *Pittsburgh Tribune Review.*

11. A recent study of 28 employees of XYZ company showed that the mean of the distance they travelled to work was 23 km. The standard deviation of the sample mean was 3 km. Find the 95% confidence interval of the true mean. If a manager wanted to be sure that most of his employees would not be late, how much time would he suggest they allow for the commute if the average speed were 48 km per hour?

12. A meteorologist who sampled 13 thunderstorms found that the average speed at which they travelled across a certain U.S. state was 24 km per hour. The standard deviation of the sample was 2.7 km per hour. Find the 99% confidence interval of the mean. If a meteorologist wanted to use the highest speed to predict the times it would take storms to travel across the U.S. state in order to issue warnings, what figure would she likely use?

13. A recent study of 25 students showed that they spent an average of $18.53 for gasoline per week. The standard deviation of the sample was $3.00. Find the 95% confidence interval of the true mean.

14. For a group of 10 men subjected to a stress situation, the mean number of heartbeats per minute was 126, and the standard deviation was 4. Find the 95% confidence interval of the true mean.

15. For the stress test described in Exercise 14, six women had an average heart rate of 115 beats per minute. The standard deviation of the sample was 6 beats. Find the 95% confidence interval of the true mean for the women.

16. For a sample of 24 operating rooms taken in the hospital study mentioned in Exercise 19 in Section 7–2, the mean noise level was 41.6 decibels, and the standard deviation was 7.5. Find the 95% confidence interval of the true mean of the noise levels in the operating rooms.

Source: M. Bayo, A. Garcia, and A. Garcia, "Noise Levels in an Urban Hospital and Workers' Subjective Responses," *Archives of Environmental Health* 50, no. 3, p. 249 (May–June 1995). Reprinted with permission of the Helen Dwight Reid Educational Foundation. Published by Heldref Publications, 1319 Eighteenth St. N.W., Washington, D.C. 20036-1802. Copyright © 1995.

17. The number of grams of carbohydrates in a 340-ml (12-oz) serving of a regular soft drink is listed here for a random sample of sodas. Estimate the mean number of carbohydrates in all brands of soda with 95% confidence.

48	37	52	40	43	46	41	38
41	45	45	33	35	52	45	41
30	34	46	40				

Source: *The Doctor's Pocket Calorie, Fat, and Carbohydrate Counter.*

18. For a group of 22 college football players, the mean heart rate after a morning workout session was 86 beats per minute, and the standard deviation was 5. Find the 90% confidence interval of the true mean for all college football players after a workout session. If a coach did not want to work his team beyond its capacity, what would be the maximum value he should use for the mean number of heartbeats per minute?

19. The average yearly income of 28 college instructors was $56,718. The standard deviation was $650. Find the 95% confidence interval of the true mean. If a faculty member wishes to see if he or she is being paid below average, what salary value should he or she use?

20. The number of unhealthy days based on the AQI (Air Quality Index) for a random sample of metropolitan areas is shown. Construct a 98% confidence interval based on the data.

61	12	6	40	27	38	93	5	13	40

Source: *N.Y. Times Almanac.*

Extending the Concepts

21. A *one-sided confidence* interval can be found for a mean by using

$$\mu > \overline{X} - t_\alpha \frac{s}{\sqrt{n}} \qquad \text{or} \qquad \mu < \overline{X} + t_\alpha \frac{s}{\sqrt{n}}$$

where t_α is the value found under the row labelled One tail. Find two one-sided 95% confidence intervals of the population mean for the data shown, and interpret the answers. The data represent the daily revenues in dollars from 20 parking meters in a small municipality.

2.60	1.05	2.45	2.90
1.30	3.10	2.35	2.00
2.40	2.35	2.40	1.95
2.80	2.50	2.10	1.75
1.00	2.75	1.80	1.95

7–4   Confidence Intervals and Sample Size for Proportions

Objective 4

Find the confidence interval for a proportion.

Transport Canada's "National Occupant Restraint Program" surveyed seat belt use among Canadians. Occupants of pickup trucks were least likely to "buckle up" with a rate of 85%. The parameter 85% is called a **proportion.** It means that 17 out of 20 occupants of pickup trucks in Canada wear their seat belts. A proportion represents a part of a whole. It can be expressed as a fraction, decimal, or percentage. In this case, $85\% = 0.85 = 85/100$ or $17/20$. Proportions can also represent probabilities. In this case, if an occupant of a pickup truck is selected at random, the probability that he/she is wearing a seat belt is 0.85. (Source: www. transportcanada.com/roadsafety/tp2436/rs200601/pdf/rs200601es.pdf. Reprinted with the permission of the Minister of Public Works and Government Services Canada, 2007.)

Proportions can be obtained from samples or populations. The following symbols will be used.

Symbols Used in Proportion Notation

$$p = \text{population proportion}$$
$$\hat{p} \ (\text{read ``}p\text{ hat''}) = \text{sample proportion}$$

For a sample proportion,

$$\hat{p} = \frac{X}{n} \qquad \text{and} \qquad \hat{q} = \frac{n - X}{n} \qquad \text{or} \qquad 1 - \hat{p}$$

where X = number of sample units that possess the characteristics of interest and n = sample size.

For example, in a study, 200 people were asked if they were satisfied with their job or profession; 162 said that they were. In this case, $n = 200$, $X = 162$, and $\hat{p} = X/n = 162/200 = 0.81$. It can be said that for this sample, 0.81, or 81%, of those surveyed were satisfied with their job or profession. The sample proportion is $\hat{p} = 0.81$.

The proportion of people who did not respond favourably when asked if they were satisfied with their job or profession constituted $\hat{q}$, where $\hat{q} = (n - X)/n$. For this survey, $\hat{q} = (200 - 162)/200 = 38/200$, or 0.19, or 19%.

When $\hat{p}$ and $\hat{q}$ are given in decimals or fractions, $\hat{p} + \hat{q} = 1$. When $\hat{p}$ and $\hat{q}$ are given in percentages, $\hat{p} + \hat{q} = 100\%$. It follows, then, that $\hat{q} = 1 - \hat{p}$, or $\hat{p} = 1 - \hat{q}$, when $\hat{p}$ and $\hat{q}$ are in decimal or fraction form. For the sample survey on job satisfaction, $\hat{q}$ can also be found by using $\hat{q} = 1 - \hat{p}$, or $1 - 0.81 = 0.19$.

Similar reasoning applies to population proportions; that is, $p = 1 - q$, $q = 1 - p$, and $p + q = 1$, when p and q are expressed in decimal or fraction form. When p and q are expressed as percentages, $p + q = 100\%$, $p = 100\% - q$, and $q = 100\% - p$.

Example 7–8

In a recent survey of 150 vehicles, 54 had air conditioning. Find $\hat{p}$ and $\hat{q}$, where $\hat{p}$ is the proportion of vehicles with air conditioning.

Solution

Since $X = 54$ and $n = 150$,

$$\hat{p} = \frac{X}{n} = \frac{54}{150} = 0.36 = 36\%$$

$$\hat{q} = \frac{n - X}{n} = \frac{150 - 54}{150} = \frac{96}{150} = 0.64 = 64\%$$

One can also find $\hat{q}$ by using the formula $\hat{q} = 1 - \hat{p}$. In this case, $\hat{q} = 1 - 0.36 = 0.64$.

As with means, the statistician, given the sample proportion, tries to estimate the population proportion. Point and interval estimates for a population proportion can be made by using the sample proportion. For a point estimate of p (the population proportion), $\hat{p}$ (the sample proportion) is used. On the basis of the three properties of a good estimator, $\hat{p}$ is unbiased, consistent, and relatively efficient. But as with means, one is not able to decide how good the point estimate of p is. Therefore, statisticians also use an interval estimate for a proportion, and they can assign a probability that the interval will contain the population proportion.

For example, following the election of Stéphane Dion as leader at the Liberal Leadership Convention in December 2006, pollsters published the following results: If an election was held, support for the Liberals would be 37%, Conservatives, 31%, NDP, 14%, Bloc Quebecois, 11%, and Green Party 7% with a margin of error of 3.1%, at a 95% level of confidence. That is, the Liberals would conceivably garner between 33.9% and 40.1%, the Conservatives between 27.9% and 34.1%, and so on. (Source: The Strategic Council for *The Globe and Mail*—CTV.)

The confidence interval for a particular p is based on the sampling distribution of $\hat{p}$. When the sample size n is no more than 5% of the population size, the sampling distribution of $\hat{p}$ is approximately normally distributed with a mean of p and a standard deviation of $\sqrt{\frac{pq}{n}}$, where $q = 1 - p$.

Confidence Intervals

To construct a confidence interval about a proportion, one must use the margin of error, which is

$$E = z_{\alpha/2}\sqrt{\frac{\hat{p}\hat{q}}{n}}$$

Confidence intervals about proportions must meet the criteria that $np \geq 5$ and $nq \geq 5$.

Formula for a Specific Confidence Interval for a Proportion

$$\hat{p} - z_{\alpha/2}\sqrt{\frac{\hat{p}\hat{q}}{n}} < p < \hat{p} + z_{\alpha/2}\sqrt{\frac{\hat{p}\hat{q}}{n}}$$

when np and nq are each greater than or equal to 5.

Rounding Rule for a Confidence Interval for a Proportion   Round off to three decimal places.

Example 7–9

A sample of 500 nursing applications included 60 from men. Find the 90% confidence interval of the true proportion of men who applied to the nursing program.

Solution

Since $\alpha = 1 - 0.90 = 0.10$ and $z_{\alpha/2} = 1.645$, substituting in the formula

$$\hat{p} - z_{\alpha/2}\sqrt{\frac{\hat{p}\hat{q}}{n}} < p < \hat{p} + z_{\alpha/2}\sqrt{\frac{\hat{p}\hat{q}}{n}}$$

when $\hat{p} = 60/500 = 0.12$ and $\hat{q} = 1 - 0.12 = 0.88$, one gets

$$0.12 - 1.645\sqrt{\frac{(0.12)(0.88)}{500}} < p < 0.12 + 1.645\sqrt{\frac{(0.12)(0.88)}{500}}$$

$$0.12 - 0.024 < p < 0.12 + 0.024$$

$$0.096 < p < 0.144$$

or

$$9.6\% < p < 14.4\%$$

Hence, one can be 90% confident that the percentage of applicants who are men is between 9.6 and 14.4%.

When a specific percentage is given, the percentage becomes $\hat{p}$ when it is changed to a decimal. For example, if the problem states that 12% of the applicants were men, then $\hat{p} = 0.12$.

Example 7–10

A survey of 200,000 boat owners found that 12% of the pleasure boats were named *Serenity*. Find the 95% confidence interval of the true proportion of boats named *Serenity*.

Source: USA TODAY Snapshot.

Solution

From the Snapshot, $\hat{p} = 0.12$ (i.e., 12%), and $n = 200,000$. Since $z_{\alpha/2} = 1.96$, substituting in the formula

$$\hat{p} - z_{\alpha/2}\sqrt{\frac{\hat{p}\hat{q}}{n}} < p < \hat{p} + z_{\alpha/2}\sqrt{\frac{\hat{p}\hat{q}}{n}}$$

yields $$0.12 - 1.96\sqrt{\frac{(0.12)(0.88)}{200,000}} < p < 0.12 + 1.96\sqrt{\frac{(0.12)(0.88)}{200,000}}$$

$$0.119 < p < 0.121$$

Hence, one can say with 95% confidence that the true percentage of boats named *Serenity* is between 11.9 and 12.1%.

Sample Size for Proportions

To find the sample size needed to determine a confidence interval about a proportion, use this formula:

Objective ⑤

Determine the minimum sample size for finding a confidence interval for a proportion.

Formula for Minimum Sample Size Needed for Interval Estimate of a Population Proportion

$$n = \hat{p}\hat{q}\left(\frac{z_{\alpha/2}}{E}\right)^2$$

If necessary, round up to obtain a whole number.

This formula can be found by solving the maximum error of estimate value for *n:*

$$E = z_{\alpha/2}\sqrt{\frac{\hat{p}\hat{q}}{n}}$$

There are two situations to consider. First, if some approximation of $\hat{p}$ is known (e.g., from a previous study), that value can be used in the formula.

Second, if no approximation of $\hat{p}$ is known, one should use $\hat{p} = 0.5$. This value will give a sample size sufficiently large to guarantee an accurate prediction, given the confidence interval and the error of estimate. The reason is that when $\hat{p}$ and $\hat{q}$ are each 0.5, the product $\hat{p}\hat{q}$ is at maximum, as shown here.

$\hat{p}$	$\hat{q}$	$\hat{p}\hat{q}$
0.1	0.9	0.09
0.2	0.8	0.16
0.3	0.7	0.21
0.4	0.6	0.24
0.5	**0.5**	**0.25**
0.6	0.4	0.24
0.7	0.3	0.21
0.8	0.2	0.16
0.9	0.1	0.09

Example 7–11

A researcher wishes to estimate with 95% confidence the proportion of Canadians who have a home computer. A previous study shows that 68.7% of those interviewed had a computer at home. The researcher wishes to be accurate within 2% of the true proportion. Find the minimum sample size necessary.

Solution

Since $z_{\alpha/2} = 1.96$, $E = 0.02$, $\hat{p} = 0.687$, and $\hat{q} = 0.313$, then

$$n = \hat{p}\hat{q}\left(\frac{z_{\alpha/2}}{E}\right)^2 = (0.687)(0.313)\left(\frac{1.96}{0.02}\right)^2 = 2065.16$$

which, when rounded up, is 2066 people to interview.

Example 7-12

The same researcher wishes to estimate the proportion of executives who own a mobile phone. She wants to be 90% confident and be accurate within 5% of the true proportion. Find the minimum sample size necessary.

Solution

Since there is no prior knowledge of $\hat{p}$, statisticians assign the values $\hat{p} = 0.5$ and $\hat{q} = 0.5$. The sample size obtained by using these values will be large enough to ensure the specified degree of confidence. Hence,

$$n = \hat{p}\hat{q}\left(\frac{z_{\alpha/2}}{E}\right)^2 = (0.5)(0.5)\left(\frac{1.645}{0.05}\right)^2 = 270.60$$

which, when rounded up, is 271 executives to ask.

In determining the sample size, the size of the population is irrelevant. Only the degree of confidence and the maximum error are necessary to make the determination.

Speaking of
Statistics

Does Success Bring Happiness?

W. C. Fields said, "Start every day off with a smile and get it over with."

Do you think people are happy because they are successful, or are they successful because they are just happy people? A recent survey conducted by *Money* magazine showed that 34% of the people surveyed said that they were happy because they were successful; however, 63% said that they were successful because they were happy individuals. The people surveyed had an average household income of $75,000 or more. The margin of error was ±2.5%. Based on the information in this article, what would be the confidence interval for each percent?

Applying the Concepts 7-4

Contracting Influenza

To answer the questions, use the following table describing the percentage of Americans who reported contracting influenza by gender and race/ethnicity.

Influenza

Characteristic	Percent	(95% CI)
Gender		
Men	48.8	(47.1–50.5%)
Women	51.5	(50.2–52.8%)
Race/ethnicity		
Caucasian	52.2	(51.1–53.3%)
African American	33.1	(29.5–36.7%)
Hispanic	47.6	(40.9–54.3%)
Other	39.7	(30.8–48.5%)
Total	50.4	(49.3–51.5%)

Forty-nine states and the District of Columbia participated in the study. Weighted means were used. The sample size was 19,774. There were 12,774 women and 7000 men.

1. Explain what (95% CI) means.
2. How large is the error for men reporting influenza?
3. What is the sample size?
4. How does sample size affect the size of the confidence interval?
5. Would the confidence intervals be larger or smaller for a 90% CI, using the same data?
6. Where does the 51.5% under influenza for women fit into its associated 95% CI?

See page 331 for the answers.

Exercises 7–4

1. In each case, find $\hat{p}$ and $\hat{q}$.

    a. $n = 80$ and $X = 40$
    b. $n = 200$ and $X = 90$
    c. $n = 130$ and $X = 60$
    d. $n = 60$ and $X = 35$
    e. $n = 95$ and $X = 43$

2. (**ans**) Find $\hat{p}$ and $\hat{q}$ for each percentage. (Use each percentage for $\hat{p}$.)

    a. 15%
    b. 37%
    c. 71%
    d. 51%
    e. 79%

3. A United States Travel Data Centre survey conducted for *Better Homes and Gardens* of 1500 adults found that 39% said that they would take more vacations this year than last year. Find the 95% confidence interval for the true proportion of adults who said that they will travel more this year.
    Source: *USA TODAY.*

4. A study of diabetes in Canada reported that of 4345 people surveyed, 2.7% reported to be diagnosed with diabetes. Find the 90% confidence interval of the population proportion of Canadians with diabetes.
    Source: Campbell's Survey on Well-Being in Canada.

5. The proportion of students in private schools is around 11%. A random sample of 450 students from a wide geographic area indicated that 55 attended private schools. Estimate the true proportion of students attending private schools with 95% confidence. How does your estimate compare to 11%?
    Source: National Center for Education Statistics (www.nces.ed.gov).

6. The Gallup Poll found that 27% of American adults surveyed nationwide said they had personally been in a tornado. How many adults should be surveyed to estimate the true proportion of adults who have been in a tornado with a 95% confidence interval 5% wide?
    Source: www.pollingreport.com.

7. A survey found that out of 200 workers, 168 said they were interrupted three or more times an hour by phone messages, faxes, etc. Find the 90% confidence interval of the population proportion of workers who are interrupted three or more times an hour.
    Source: Based on information from *USA TODAY* Snapshot.

8. A CBS News/*New York Times* poll found that 329 out of 763 adults said they would travel to outer space in their lifetime, given the chance. Estimate the true proportion of adults who would like to travel to outer space with 92% confidence.
    Source: www.pollingreport.com.

9. A study by the University of Michigan found that one in five 13- and 14-year-olds is an occasional

smoker. To see how the smoking rate of the students at a large school district compared to the national rate, the superintendent surveyed two hundred 13- and 14-year-old students and found that 23% said they were sometime smokers. Find the 99% confidence interval of the true proportion, and compare this with the University of Michigan study.

Source: *USA TODAY.*

10. A survey of 50 first-time white-water canoers showed that 23 did not want to repeat the experience. Find the 90% confidence interval of the true proportion of canoers who did not wish to canoe the rapids a second time. If a rafting company wants to distribute brochures for repeat trips, what is the minimum number it should print?

11. A survey of 85 families showed that 36 owned at least one DVD player. Find the 99% confidence interval of the true proportion of families who own at least one DVD player. If another survey in a different location found that the proportion of families who owned at least one DVD player was 0.52, would you consider that the proportion of families in this area was larger than in the area where the original survey was done?

12. In a certain countrywide school district, a survey of 350 students showed that 28% carried their lunches to school. Find the 95% confidence interval of the true proportion of students who carried their lunches to school. If the cafeteria manager wanted to be reasonably sure that all the children who didn't bring their lunches could purchase a lunch, how many lunches should she plan to make each day? Explain your answer.

13. In a Gallup Poll of 1005 individuals, 452 thought they were worse off financially than a year ago. Find the 95% confidence interval for the true proportion of individuals that feel they are worse off financially.

Source: Gallup Poll.

14. In a survey of 1023 Canadian adults, 614 respondents are not concerned about the health threat of avian flu. Find the 95% confidence interval for the true proportion of Canadians who do not feel threatened by the avian flu.

Source: CTV.ca.

15. A medical researcher wishes to determine the percentage of females who take vitamins. He wishes to be 99% confident that the estimate is within 2 percentage points of the true proportion. A recent study of 180 females showed that 25% took vitamins.

   a. How large should the sample size be?
   b. If no estimate of the sample proportion is available, how large should the sample be?

16. A recent study indicated that 29% of the 100 women over age 55 in the study were widows.

   a. How large a sample must one take to be 90% confident that the estimate is within 0.05 of the true proportion of women over age 55 who are widows?
   b. If no estimate of the sample proportion is available, how large should the sample be?

17. A researcher wishes to estimate the proportion of Canadians who are in favour of the Kyoto Protocol's call for the reduction of emissions of greenhouse gases. She wants to be 99% confident that her estimate is within 5% of the true proportion.

   a. How large a sample should be taken if in a prior survey of Canadians, 70% were in favour of the Kyoto Protocol?
   b. If no estimate of the sample proportion is available, how large should the sample be?

18. Obesity is defined as a *body mass index* (BMI) of 3 kg/m^2 or more. A 95% confidence interval for the percentage of U.S. adults aged 20 years and over who were obese was found to be 22.4% to 23.5%. What was the sample size?

Source: National Center for Health Statistics (www.cdc.gov/nchs).

19. How large a sample should be surveyed to estimate the true proportion of college students who do laundry once a week within 3% with 95% confidence?

20. A U.S. federal report indicated that 27% of children ages 2 to 5 years had a good diet—an increase over previous years. How large a sample is needed to estimate the true proportion of children with good diets within 2% with 95% confidence?

Source: Federal Interagency Forum on Child and Family Statistics, *Washington Observer-Reporter.*

Extending the Concepts

21. If a sample of 600 people is selected and the researcher decides to have a maximum error of estimate of 4% on the specific proportion who favour gun control, find the degree of confidence. A recent study showed that 50% were in favour of some form of gun control.

22. In a U.S. study, 68% of 1015 adults said that they believe the Republicans favour the rich. If the margin of error was 3 percentage points, what was the confidence interval used for the proportion?

Source: *USA TODAY.*

7–5   Confidence Intervals for Variances and Standard Deviations (Optional)

Objective 6

Find a confidence interval for a variance and a standard deviation.

The χ^2 distribution with 2 degrees of freedom was formulated by a mathematician named Hershel in 1869 while he was studying the accuracy of shooting arrows at a target. Many other mathematicians have since contributed to its development.

In Sections 7–2 through 7–4, confidence intervals were calculated for means and proportions. This section will explain how to find confidence intervals for variances and standard deviations. In statistics, the variance and standard deviation of a variable are as important as the mean. For example, when products that fit together (such as pipes) are manufactured, it is important to keep the variations of the diameters of the products as small as possible; otherwise, they will not fit together properly and will have to be scrapped. In the manufacture of medicines, the variance and standard deviation of the medication in the pills play an important role in making sure patients receive the proper dosage. For these reasons, confidence intervals for variances and standard deviations are necessary.

To calculate these confidence intervals, a new statistical distribution is needed. It is called the **chi-square distribution.**

The chi-square variable is similar to the t variable in that its distribution is a family of curves based on the number of degrees of freedom. The symbol for chi-square is χ^2 (Greek letter chi, pronounced "ki"). Several of the distributions are shown in Figure 7–9, along with the corresponding degrees of freedom. The chi-square distribution is obtained from the values of $(n-1)s^2/\sigma^2$ when random samples are selected from a normally distributed population whose variance is σ^2.

A chi-square variable cannot be negative, and the distributions are positively skewed. At about 100 degrees of freedom, the chi-square distribution becomes somewhat symmetric. The area under each chi-square distribution is equal to 1.00, or 100%.

Figure 7–9

The Chi-Square Family of Curves

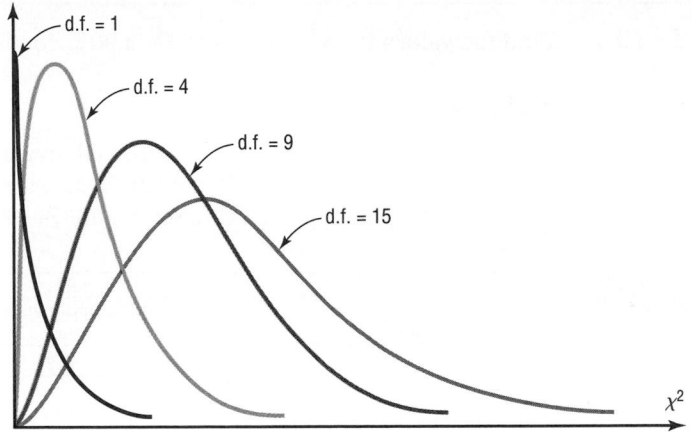

Table G in Appendix C gives the values for the chi-square distribution. These values are used in the denominators of the formulas for confidence intervals. Two different values are used in the formula. One value is found on the left side of the table, and the other is on the right. For example, to find the table values corresponding to the 95% confidence interval, one must first change 95% to a decimal and subtract it from 1 ($1 - 0.95 = 0.05$). Then divide the answer by 2 ($\alpha/2 = 0.05/2 = 0.025$). This is the column on the right side of the table, used to get the values for χ^2_{right}. To get the value for χ^2_{left}, subtract the value of $\alpha/2$ from 1 ($1 - 0.05/2 = 0.975$). Finally, find the appropriate row corresponding to the degrees of freedom $n - 1$. A similar procedure is used to find the values for a 90 or 99% confidence interval.

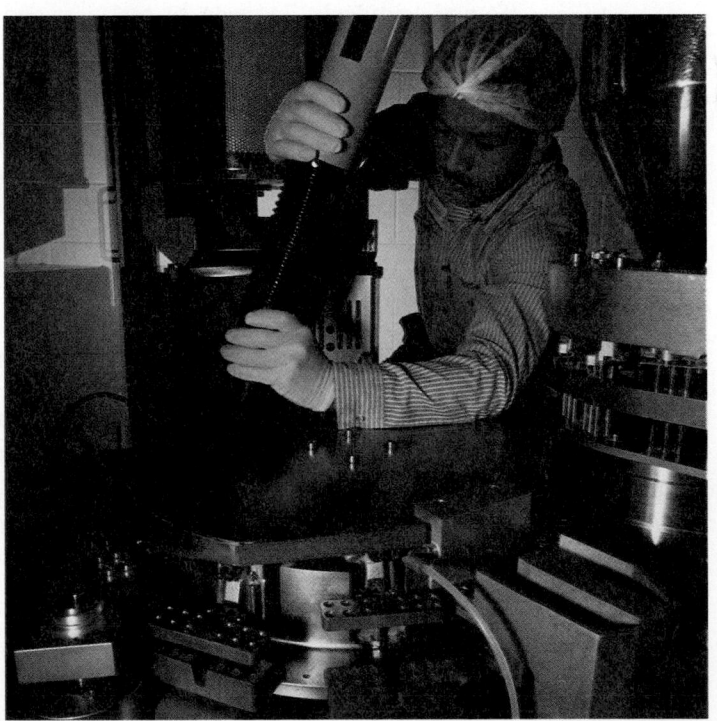

Example 7–13

Find the values for χ^2_{right} and χ^2_{left} for a 90% confidence interval when $n = 25$.

Solution

To find χ^2_{right}, subtract $1 - 0.90 = 0.10$ and divide by 2 to get 0.05.

To find χ^2_{left}, subtract $1 - 0.05$ to get 0.95. Hence, use the 0.95 and 0.05 columns and the row corresponding to 24 d.f. See Figure 7–10.

Figure 7–10

χ^2 **Table for Example 7–13**

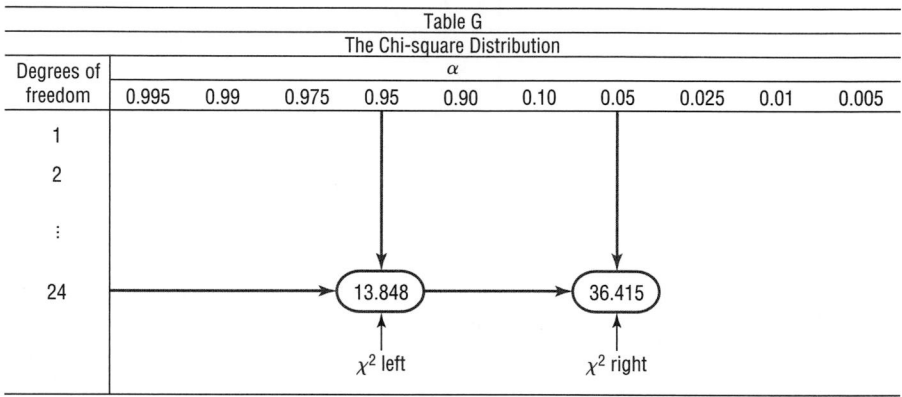

The answers are

$$\chi^2_{\text{right}} = 36.415$$
$$\chi^2_{\text{left}} = 13.848$$

Useful estimates for σ^2 and σ are s^2 and s, respectively.

To find confidence intervals for variances and standard deviations, one must assume that the variable is normally distributed.

The formulas for the confidence intervals are shown here.

Formula for the Confidence Interval for a Variance

$$\frac{(n-1)s^2}{\chi^2_{\text{right}}} < \sigma^2 < \frac{(n-1)s^2}{\chi^2_{\text{left}}}$$

d.f. $= n - 1$

Formula for the Confidence Interval for a Standard Deviation

$$\sqrt{\frac{(n-1)s^2}{\chi^2_{\text{right}}}} < \sigma < \sqrt{\frac{(n-1)s^2}{\chi^2_{\text{left}}}}$$

d.f. $= n - 1$

Recall that s^2 is the symbol for the sample variance and s is the symbol for the sample standard deviation. If the problem gives the sample standard deviation s, be sure to *square* it when you are using the formula. But if the problem gives the sample variance s^2, *do not square it* when using the formula, since the variance is already in square units.

Rounding Rule for a Confidence Interval for a Variance or Standard Deviation When you are computing a confidence interval for a population variance or standard deviation by using raw data, round off to one more decimal place than the number of decimal places in the original data.

When you are computing a confidence interval for a population variance or standard deviation by using a sample variance or standard deviation, round off to the same number of decimal places as given for the sample variance or standard deviation.

Example 7–14 shows how to find a confidence interval for a variance and standard deviation.

Example 7–14

Find the 95% confidence interval for the variance and standard deviation of the nicotine content of cigarettes manufactured if a sample of 20 cigarettes has a standard deviation of 1.6 milligrams.

Solution

Since $\alpha = 0.05$, the two critical values, respectively, for the 0.025 and 0.975 levels for 19 degrees of freedom are 32.852 and 8.907. The 95% confidence interval for the variance is found by substituting in the formula.

$$\frac{(n-1)s^2}{\chi^2_{\text{right}}} < \sigma^2 < \frac{(n-1)s^2}{\chi^2_{\text{left}}}$$

$$\frac{(20-1)(1.6)^2}{32.852} < \sigma^2 < \frac{(20-1)(1.6)^2}{8.907}$$

$$1.5 < \sigma^2 < 5.5$$

Hence, one can be 95% confident that the true variance for the nicotine content is between 1.5 and 5.5.

For the standard deviation, the confidence interval is

$$\sqrt{1.5} < \sigma < \sqrt{5.5}$$

$$1.2 < \sigma < 2.3$$

Hence, one can be 95% confident that the true standard deviation for the nicotine content of all cigarettes manufactured is between 1.2 and 2.3 milligrams based on a sample of 20 cigarettes.

Example 7–15

 Find the 90% confidence interval for the variance and standard deviation for the price in dollars of an adult single-day ski lift ticket. The data represent a selected sample of American ski resorts. Assume the variable is normally distributed.

59	54	53	52	51
39	49	46	49	48

Source: USA TODAY.

Solution

Step 1 Find the variance for the data. Use the formulas in Chapter 3 or your calculator. The variance $s^2 = 28.2$.

Step 2 Find χ^2_{right} and χ^2_{left} from Table G in Appendix C. Since $\alpha = 0.10$, the two critical values are 3.325 and 16.919, using d.f. = 9 and 0.95 and 0.05.

Step 3   Substitute in the formula and solve.

$$\frac{(n-1)s^2}{\chi^2_{\text{right}}} < \sigma^2 < \frac{(n-1)s^2}{\chi^2_{\text{left}}}$$

$$\frac{(10-1)(28.2)}{16.919} < \sigma^2 < \frac{(10-1)(28.2)}{3.325}$$

$$15.0 < \sigma^2 < 76.3$$

For the standard deviation

$$\sqrt{15} < \sigma < \sqrt{76.3}$$
$$3.87 < \sigma < 8.73$$

Hence one can be 90% confident that the standard deviation for the price of all single-day ski lift tickets of the population is between \$3.87 and \$8.73 based on a sample of 10 American ski resorts. (Two decimal places are used since the data are in dollars and cents.)

Note: If you are using the standard deviation instead (as in Example 7–14) of the variance, be sure to square the standard deviation when substituting in the formula.

Applying the Concepts 7–5

Confidence Interval for Standard Deviation

Shown are the ages (in years) of U.S. Presidents at the time of their deaths.

67	90	83	85	73	80	78	79
68	71	53	65	74	64	77	56
66	63	70	49	57	71	67	71
58	60	72	67	57	60	90	63
88	78	46	64	81	93		

1. Do the data represent a population or a sample?
2. Select a random sample of 12 ages and find the variance and standard deviation.
3. Find the 95% confidence interval of the standard deviation.
4. Find the standard deviation of all the data values.
5. Does the confidence interval calculated in question 3 contain the mean?
6. If it does not, give a reason why.
7. What assumption(s) must be considered for constructing the confidence interval in step 3?

See page 331 for the answers.

Exercises 7–5

1. What distribution must be used when computing confidence intervals for variances and standard deviations?

2. What assumption must be made when computing confidence intervals for variances and standard deviations?

3. Using Table G, find the values for χ^2_{left} and χ^2_{right}.
   a. $\alpha = 0.05, n = 12$
   b. $\alpha = 0.10, n = 20$
   c. $\alpha = 0.05, n = 27$
   d. $\alpha = 0.01, n = 6$
   e. $\alpha = 0.10, n = 41$

4. Find the 90% confidence interval for the variance and standard deviation for the lifetime of disposable camera batteries if a sample of 16 disposable camera batteries has a standard deviation of 2.1 months. Assume the variable is normally distributed. Do you feel that the lifetimes of the batteries are relatively consistent?

5. Find the 95% confidence interval for the variance and standard deviation for the time it takes a customer to place a telephone order with a large catalogue company if a sample of 23 telephone orders has a standard deviation of 3.8 minutes. Assume the variable is normally distributed. Do you think that the times are relatively consistent?

6. Find the 99% confidence interval for the variance and standard deviation of the weights of twenty-five 3.78-litre containers of motor oil if a sample of 14 containers has a variance of 3096. The weights are given in grams. Assume the variable is normally distributed.

7. The sugar content (in grams) for a random sample of 113-ml (4-oz) containers of applesauce is shown. Find the 99% confidence interval for the population variance and standard deviation. Assume the variable is normally distributed.

18.6	19.5	20.2	20.4	19.3
21.0	20.3	19.6	20.7	18.9
22.1	19.7	20.8	18.9	20.7
21.6	19.5	20.1	20.3	19.9

8. Find the 90% confidence interval for the variance and standard deviation of the ages of seniors at Oak Park College if a sample of 24 students has a standard deviation of 2.3 years. Assume the variable is normally distributed.

9. The number of calories in a 28-ml (1-oz) serving of various kinds of regular cheese is shown. Estimate the population variance and standard deviation with 90% confidence.

110	45	100	95	110
110	100	110	95	120
130	100	80	105	105
90	110	70	125	108

Source: *The Doctor's Pocket Calorie, Fat, and Carbohydrate Counter.*

10. A random sample of stock prices per share (in dollars) is shown. Find the 90% confidence interval for the variance and standard deviation for the prices. Assume the variable is normally distributed.

26.69	13.88	28.37	12.00
75.37	7.50	47.50	43.00
3.81	53.81	13.62	45.12
6.94	28.25	28.00	60.50
40.25	10.87	46.12	14.75

Source: *Pittsburgh Tribune Review.*

11. A service station advertises that customers will have to wait no more than 30 minutes for an oil change. A sample of 28 oil changes has a standard deviation of 5.2 minutes. Find the 95% confidence interval of the population standard deviation of the time spent waiting for an oil change.

12. Find the 95% confidence interval for the variance and standard deviation of the ounces of coffee that a machine dispenses in 340-ml (12-oz) cups. Assume the variable is normally distributed. The data are given.

12.03 12.10 12.02 11.98 12.00 12.05 11.97 11.99

Extending the Concepts

13. A confidence interval for a standard deviation for large samples taken from a normally distributed population can be approximated by

$$s - z_{\alpha/2}\frac{s}{\sqrt{2n}} < \sigma < s + z_{\alpha/2}\frac{s}{\sqrt{2n}}$$

Find the 95% confidence interval for the population standard deviation of calculator batteries. A sample of 200 calculator batteries has a standard deviation of 18 months.

7–6 Summary

An important aspect of inferential statistics is estimation. Estimations of parameters of populations are accomplished by selecting a random sample from that population and choosing and computing a statistic that is the best estimator of the parameter. A good estimator must be unbiased, consistent, and relatively efficient. The best estimators of μ and p are $\overline{X}$ and $\hat{p}$, respectively. The best estimators of σ^2 and σ are s^2 and s, respectively.

There are two types of estimates of a parameter: point estimates and interval estimates. A point estimate is a specific value. For example, if a researcher wishes to estimate the average length of a certain adult fish, a sample of the fish is selected and measured. The mean of this sample is computed, for example, 3.2 centimetres. From this sample mean, the researcher estimates the population mean to be 3.2 centimetres.

The problem with point estimates is that the accuracy of the estimate cannot be determined. For this reason, statisticians prefer to use the interval estimate. By computing an interval about the sample value, statisticians can be 95 or 99% (or some other percentage) confident that their estimate contains the true parameter. The confidence level is determined by the researcher. The higher the confidence level, the wider the interval of the estimate must be. For example, a 95% confidence interval of the true mean length of a certain species of fish might be

$$3.17 < \mu < 3.23$$

whereas the 99% confidence interval might be

$$3.15 < \mu < 3.25$$

When the confidence interval of the mean is computed, the z scores or t values are used, depending on whether the population standard deviation is known and depending on the size of the sample. If σ is known or $n \geq 30$, the z scores can be used. If σ is not known, the t values must be used when the sample size is less than 30 and the population is normally distributed.

Closely related to computing confidence intervals is the determination of the sample size to make an estimate of the mean. This information is needed to determine the minimum sample size necessary.

1. The degree of confidence must be stated.
2. The population standard deviation must be known or be able to be estimated.
3. The maximum error of estimate must be stated.

Confidence intervals and sample sizes can also be computed for proportions, using the normal distribution; and confidence intervals for variances and standard deviations can be computed, using the chi-square distribution.

For step-by-step guidance on the use of technology for this chapter, visit the Online Learning Centre at www.mcgrawhill.ca/olc/bluman. Summary procedures for Minitab, SPSS, Excel, and TI-83 Plus or TI-84 Plus can also be found in Appendix E.

Important Terms ● ● ●

chi-square distribution 320	degrees of freedom 308	margin of error 299	relatively efficient estimator 297
confidence interval 298	estimation 296		
confidence level 298	estimator 297	point estimate 297	t distribution 307
consistent estimator 297	interval estimate 297	proportion 313	unbiased estimator 297

Important Formulas

Formula for the confidence interval of the mean when σ is known (when $n \geq 30$, s can be used if σ is unknown):

$$\overline{X} - z_{\sigma/2}\left(\frac{\sigma}{\sqrt{n}}\right) < \mu < \overline{X} + z_{\sigma/2}\left(\frac{\sigma}{\sqrt{n}}\right)$$

Formula for the sample size for means:

$$n = \left(\frac{z_{\sigma/2} \cdot \sigma}{E}\right)^2$$

where E is the maximum error.

Formula for the confidence interval of the mean when σ is unknown and $n < 30$:

$$\overline{X} - t_{\sigma/2}\left(\frac{s}{\sqrt{n}}\right) < \mu < \overline{X} + t_{\sigma/2}\left(\frac{s}{\sqrt{n}}\right)$$

Formula for the confidence interval for a proportion:

$$\hat{p} - z_{\sigma/2}\sqrt{\frac{\hat{p}\hat{q}}{n}} < p < \hat{p} + z_{\sigma/2}\sqrt{\frac{\hat{p}\hat{q}}{n}}$$

where $\hat{p} = X/n$ and $\hat{q} = 1 - \hat{p}$.

Formula for the sample size for proportions:

$$n = \hat{p}\hat{q}\left(\frac{z_{\sigma/2}}{E}\right)^2$$

Formula for the confidence interval for a variance:

$$\frac{(n-1)s^2}{\chi^2_{\text{right}}} < \sigma^2 < \frac{(n-1)s^2}{\chi^2_{\text{left}}}$$

Formula for confidence interval for a standard deviation:

$$\sqrt{\frac{(n-1)s^2}{\chi^2_{\text{right}}}} < \sigma < \sqrt{\frac{(n-1)s^2}{\chi^2_{\text{left}}}}$$

Review Exercises

1. A study of 36 marathon runners showed that they could run at an average rate of 12.6 kilometres per hour (km/h). The sample standard deviation is 0.9 km/h. Find a point estimate of the population mean. Find the 90% confidence interval for the mean of all runners. Based on the results, what minimum speed should a runner obtain to qualify to run in a marathon?

2. A survey of 1275 Canadians indicated that 1224 prefer buying products that can be recycled. Find a 95% confidence interval for the true population proportion.

   Source: Sharp Canada.

3. A survey of 1100 hospital admissions reports that the average length of stay for seniors aged 65 and over who are hospitalized for falls is 13 days. Find a point estimate of the population mean. Find the 95% confidence interval of the true mean. Assume the standard deviation was 1.3 days.

   Source: Canadian Institute for Health Information.

4. A sample of 14 districts in Toronto found the following monthly rental payments for a 1-bedroom condominium (in dollars).

1511	1605	2025	1275	1100	1203	1462
1563	1488	1100	1447	1254	1259	1323

   Find a point estimate of the population mean. Find the 95% confidence interval for the population mean.

   Source: Toronto Real Estate Board.

5. For a certain urban area, in a sample of 5 months, an average of 28 mail carriers were bitten by dogs each month. The standard deviation of the sample was 3. Find the 90% confidence interval of the true mean number of mail carriers who are bitten by dogs each month. Assume the variable is normally distributed.

6. A researcher is interested in estimating the average salary of teachers in a large urban school district. She wants to be 95% confident that her estimate is correct. If the standard deviation is $1050, how large a sample is needed to be accurate within $200?

7. A researcher wishes to estimate, within $25, the true average amount of postage a college spends each year. If she wishes to be 90% confident, how large a sample is necessary? The standard deviation is known to be $80.

8. The Friends of Canadian Broadcasting commissioned a poll of 1100 adult Canadians. On the question of Canadian content, 61% of respondents felt that there should be a specified minimum amount of Canadian programming on television. Find the 95% confidence interval of the true proportion of all adults who favour a defined minimum Canadian television content.

   Source: Friends of Canadian Broadcasting.

9. In a recent study of 75 people, 41 said they were dissatisfied with their community's snow removal service. Find the 95% confidence interval of the true proportion of individuals who are dissatisfied with their community's snow removal service. Based on the results, should the supervisor consider making improvements in the snow removal service?

10. In a recent study of 100 people, 85 said that they were dissatisfied with their local elected officials. Find

the 90% confidence interval of the true proportion of individuals who are dissatisfied with their local elected officials.

11. The U.S. federal report in Exercise 10 also stated that 88% of children under age 18 were covered by health insurance in 2000. How large a sample is needed to estimate the true proportion of covered children with 90% confidence with a confidence interval 0.05 wide?

Source: Washington Observer-Reporter.

12. A survey by *Brides* magazine found that 8 out of 10 brides are planning to take the surname of their new husband. How large a sample is needed to estimate the true proportion within 3% with 98% confidence?

Source: Time magazine.

13. The standard deviation of the diameter of 18 baseballs was 0.29 cm. Find the 95% confidence interval of the true standard deviation of the diameters of the baseballs. Do you think the manufacturing process should be checked for inconsistency?

14. A random sample of 22 lawn mowers was selected, and the motors were tested to see how many kilometres per litre of gasoline each one obtained. The variance of the measurements was 2.6. Find the 95% confidence interval of the true variance.

15. A random sample of 15 snowmobiles was selected, and the lifetime (in months) of the batteries was measured. The variance of the sample was 8.6. Find the 90% confidence interval of the true variance.

16. Health Canada does not consider the small quantities of PCBs (Polychlorinated Biphenyls) in fish and seafood to be a health risk. A sample of 28 salmon is measured for PCB contamination. The standard deviation of PCB levels was 10.6 parts per billion (ppb). Find the 95% confidence interval of the standard deviation of the PCB contaminants.

Source: Health Canada Fish & Seafood Survey, 2002.

Statistics Today

Would You Change the Channel?–Revisited

The estimates given in the survey are point estimates. However, since the margin of error is stated to be 3 percentage points, an interval estimate can easily be obtained. For example, if 45% of the people changed the channel, then the confidence interval of the true percentages of people who changed channels would be 42% $< p < 48\%$. The article fails to state whether a 90%, 95%, or some other percentage was used for the confidence interval.

Using the formula given in Section 7–4, a minimum sample size of 1068 would be needed to obtain a 95% confidence interval for p, as shown. Use $\hat{p}$ and $\hat{q}$ as 0.5, since no value is known for $\hat{p}$

$$n = \hat{p}\hat{q}\left(\frac{z_{\alpha/2}}{E}\right)^2$$
$$= (0.5)(0.5)\left(\frac{1.96}{0.03}\right)^2 = 1067.1$$
$$= 1068$$

● ● ●

Data Analysis

A Data Bank is found in Appendix D, or on the World Wide Web by following links from www.mcgrawhill.ca/olc/bluman.

1. From the Data Bank choose a variable, find the mean, and construct the 95 and 99% confidence intervals of the population mean. Use a sample of at least 30 subjects. Find the mean of the population,

and determine whether it falls within the confidence interval.

2. Repeat Exercise 1, using a different variable and a sample of 15.

3. Repeat Exercise 1, using a proportion. For example, construct a confidence interval for the proportion of individuals who did not complete high school.

4. From Data Set III in Appendix D, select a sample of 30 values and construct the 95 and 99% confidence intervals of the mean length in kilometres of major North American rivers. Find the mean of all the values, and determine if the confidence intervals contain the mean.

5. From Data Set VI in Appendix D, select a sample of 20 values and find the 90% confidence interval of the mean of the number of acres. Find the mean of all the values, and determine if the confidence interval contains the mean.

6. Select a random sample of 20 of the record high temperatures found in Data Set I in Appendix D. Find the proportion of temperatures below 44°C. Construct a 95% confidence interval for this proportion. Then find the true proportion of temperatures below 44°C, using all the data. Is the true proportion contained in the confidence interval? Explain.

Chapter Quiz

● ● ●

Determine whether each statement is true or false. If the statement is false, explain why.

1. Interval estimates are preferred over point estimates since a confidence level can be specified.

2. For a specific confidence interval, the larger the sample size, the smaller the maximum error of estimate will be.

3. An estimator is consistent if, as the sample size decreases, the value of the estimator approaches the value of the parameter estimated.

4. To determine the sample size needed to estimate a parameter, one must know the maximum error of estimate.

Select the best answer.

5. When a 99% confidence interval is calculated instead of a 95% confidence interval with n being the same, the maximum error of estimate will be

   a. Smaller.
   b. Larger.
   c. The same.
   d. It cannot be determined.

6. The best point estimate of the population mean is

   a. The sample mean.
   b. The sample median.
   c. The sample mode.
   d. The sample midrange.

7. When the population standard deviation is unknown and the sample size is less than 30, what table value should be used in computing a confidence interval for a mean?

   a. z
   b. t
   c. χ^2
   d. None of the above

Complete the following statements with the best answer.

8. A good estimator should be _____, _____, and _____.

9. The maximum difference between the point estimate of a parameter and the actual value of the parameter is called _____.

10. The statement "The average height of an adult male is 178 centimetres" is an example of a(n) _____ estimate.

11. The three confidence intervals used most often are the _____%, _____%, and _____%.

12. A random sample of 49 shoppers showed that they spend an average of $23.45 per visit at the Saturday Mornings Bookstore. The standard deviation of the sample was $2.80. Find a point estimate of the population mean. Find the 90% confidence interval of the true mean.

13. An irate patient complained that the cost of a doctor's visit was too high. She randomly surveyed 20 other patients and found that the mean amount of money they spent on each doctor's visit was $44.80. The standard deviation of the sample was $3.53. Find a point estimate of the population mean. Find the 95% confidence interval of the population mean. Assume the variable is normally distributed.

14. The average weight of 40 randomly selected minivans is 1882 kilograms with a standard deviation of 218 kilograms. Assuming that minivan weights are normally distributed, find a point estimate of the population mean. Find the 99% confidence interval of the true mean weight of the minivans.

15. In a study of 10 insurance sales representatives from a certain large city, the average age of the group was 48.6 years and the standard deviation was 4.1 years. Assume the variable is normally distributed. Find the 95% confidence interval of the population mean age of all insurance sales representatives in that city.

16. In a hospital, a sample of 8 weeks was selected, and it was found that an average of 438 patients were treated in the emergency room each week. The standard deviation was 16. Find the 99% confidence interval of the true mean. Assume the variable is normally distributed.

17. For a certain urban area, it was found that in a sample of 4 months, an average of 31 burglaries occurred each month. The standard deviation was 4. Assume the variable is normally distributed. Find the 90%

confidence interval of the true mean number of burglaries each month.

18. A university dean wishes to estimate the average number of hours that freshmen study each week. The standard deviation from a previous study is 2.6 hours. How large a sample must be selected if he wants to be 99% confident of finding whether the true mean differs from the sample mean by 0.5 hour?

19. A researcher wishes to estimate within $300 the true average amount of money a county spends on road repairs each year. If she wants to be 90% confident, how large a sample is necessary? The standard deviation is known to be $900.

20. A recent study of 75 workers found that 53 people rode the bus to work each day. Find the 95% confidence interval of the proportion of all workers who rode the bus to work.

21. In a study of 150 accidents that required treatment in an emergency room, 36% involved children under 6 years of age. Find the 90% confidence interval of the true proportion of accidents that involve children under the age of 6.

22. A survey of 90 families showed that 40 owned at least one television set. Find the 95% confidence interval of the true proportion of families who own at least one television set.

23. A nutritionist wishes to determine, within 3%, the true proportion of adults who do not eat any lunch. If he wishes to be 95% confident that his estimate contains the population proportion, how large a sample will be necessary? A previous study found that 15% of the 125 people surveyed said they did not eat lunch.

24. A sample of 25 novels has a standard deviation of 9 pages. Find the 95% confidence interval of the population standard deviation.

25. Find the 90% confidence interval for the variance and standard deviation for the time it takes an inspector to check a truck for safety if a sample of 27 trucks has a standard deviation of 6.8 minutes. Assume the variable is normally distributed.

26. A sample of 20 automobiles has a pollution by-product release standard deviation of 15 ml when 1 litre of gasoline is used. Find the 90% confidence interval of the population standard deviation.

Critical Thinking Challenges ●●●

A confidence interval for a median can be found by using these formulas

$$U = \frac{n+1}{2} + \frac{z_{\alpha/2}\sqrt{n}}{2} \qquad \text{(round up)}$$

$$L = n - U + 1$$

to define positions in the set of ordered data values.

Suppose a data set has 30 values, and one wants to find the 95% confidence interval for the median. Substituting in the formulas, one gets

$$U = \frac{30+1}{2} + \frac{1.96\sqrt{30}}{2} = 21 \qquad \text{(rounded up)}$$

$$L = 30 - 21 + 1 = 10$$

when $n = 30$ and $z_{\alpha/2} = 1.96$.

Arrange the data in order from smallest to largest, and then select the 10th and 21st values of the data array; hence, $X_{10} <$ median $< X_{21}$.

Find the 90% confidence interval for the median for the data in Exercise 12 in Section 7–2.

Data Projects ●●●

Use Minitab, SPSS, the TI-83 Plus, the TI-84 Plus, Excel or a computer program of your choice to complete these exercises.

1. Select several variables, such as the number of points a football team scored in each game of a specific season, the number of passes completed, or the number of yards gained. Using confidence intervals for the mean, determine the 90, 95, and 99% confidence intervals. (Use z or t, whichever is relevant.) Decide which you think is more appropriate. When this is completed, write a summary of your findings by answering the following questions.

   a. What was the purpose of the study?
   b. What was the population?
   c. How was the sample selected?

   d. What were the results obtained by using confidence intervals?
   e. Did you use z or t? Why?

2. Using the same data or different data, construct a confidence interval for a proportion. For example, you might want to find the proportion of passes completed by the quarterback or the proportion of passes that were intercepted. Write a short paragraph summarizing the results.

You may use the following websites to obtain raw data:

Visit the data sets at the book's website found at www.mcgrawhill.ca/olc/bluman
http://lib.stat.cmu.edu/DASL
www.statcan.ca

Answers to Applying the Concepts

••• •

Section 7–2 Making Decisions with Confidence Intervals

1. Answers will vary. One possible answer is to find out the average number of Kleenexes that a group of randomly selected individuals use in a 2-week period.

2. People usually need Kleenexes when they have a cold or when their allergies are acting up.

3. If we want to concentrate on the number of Kleenexes used when people have colds, we select a random sample of people with colds and have them keep a record of how many Kleenexes they use during their colds.

4. Answers may vary. I will use a 95% confidence interval:

$$\bar{x} \pm 1.96\frac{s}{\sqrt{n}} = 57 \pm 1.96\frac{15}{\sqrt{85}} = 57 \pm 3.2$$

I am 95% confident that the interval 53.8–60.2 contains the true mean number of Kleenexes used by people when they have colds. It seems reasonable to put 60 Kleenexes in the new automobile glove compartment boxes.

5. Answers will vary. Since I am 95% confident that the interval contains the true average, any number of Kleenexes between 54 and 60 would be reasonable. Sixty seemed to be the most reasonable answer, since it is close to 2 standard deviations above the sample mean.

Section 7–3 Sport Drink Decision

1. Answers will vary. One possible answer is that this is a small sample since we are only looking at seven popular sport drinks.

2. The mean cost per container is $1.25, with standard deviation of $0.39. The 90% confidence interval is

$$\bar{x} \pm t_{\alpha/2}\frac{s}{\sqrt{n}} = 1.25 \pm 1.943\frac{0.39}{\sqrt{7}} = 1.25 \pm 0.29$$

or $0.96 < \mu < 1.54$.

The 10-K, All Sport, Exceed, and Hydra Fuel all fall outside of the confidence interval.

3. None of the values appear to be outliers.

4. There are $7 - 1 = 6$ degrees of freedom.

5. Cost per serving would impact my decision on purchasing a sport drink, since this would allow me to compare the costs on an equal scale.

6. Answers will vary.

Section 7–4 Contracting Influenza

1. (95% CI) means that these are the 95% confidence intervals constructed from the data.

2. The margin of error for men reporting influenza is $\frac{50.5 - 47.1}{2} = 1.7\%$

3. The total sample size was 19,774.

4. The larger the sample size, the smaller the margin of error (all other things being held constant).

5. A 90% confidence interval would be narrower (smaller) than a 95% confidence interval, since we need to include fewer values in the interval.

6. The 51.5% is the middle of the confidence interval, since it is the point estimate for the confidence interval.

Section 7–5 Confidence Interval for Standard Deviation

1. The data represent a population, since we have the age at death for all deceased U.S. Presidents (at the time of the writing of this book).

2. Answers will vary. One possible sample is 56, 67, 53, 46, 63, 77, 63, 57, 71, 57, 80, 65, which results in a standard deviation of 9.9 years and a variance of 98.0.

3. Answers will vary. The 95% confidence interval for the standard deviation is $\sqrt{\frac{(n-1)s^2}{\chi^2_{\text{right}}}}$ to $\sqrt{\frac{(n-1)s^2}{\chi^2_{\text{left}}}}$. In this case we have $\sqrt{\frac{(12-1)9.9^2}{21.920}} = \sqrt{49.1839} = 7.0$ to $\sqrt{\frac{(12-1)9.9^2}{3.8158}} = \sqrt{282.538} = 16.8$ or 7.0 to 16.8 years.

4. The standard deviation for all the data values is 11.6 years.

5. Answers will vary. Yes, the confidence interval does contain the population standard deviation.

6. Answers will vary.

7. We need to assume that the distribution of ages at death is normal.

CHAPTER 8 Hypothesis Testing

Objectives

After completing this chapter, you should be able to

1. Understand the definitions used in hypothesis testing.

2. State the null and alternative hypotheses.

3. Find critical values for the z test.

4. State the five steps used in hypothesis testing.

5. Test means for large samples, using the z test.

6. Test means for small samples, using the t test.

7. Test proportions, using the z test.

8. Test variances or standard deviations, using the chi-square test.

9. Test hypotheses, using confidence intervals.

10. Explain the relationship between type I and type II errors and the power of a test.

Outline

8–1 Introduction

8–2 Steps in Hypothesis Testing—Traditional Method

8–3 z Test for a Mean

8–4 t Test for a Mean

8–5 z Test for a Proportion

8–6 χ^2 Test for a Variance or Standard Deviation

8–7 Additional Topics Regarding Hypothesis Testing

8–8 Summary

Statistics Today

How Much Better Is Better?

Suppose a provincial Minister of Education reviews test results of the Program for International Student Assessment (PISA), a project of the Organization for Economic Co-operation and Development (OECD).

The OECD average from all countries taking the PISA test was 500. Furthermore, assume a sample of students writing the PISA test in the minister's province scored, on average, 530. Can the provincial minister conclude that the students in his/her province scored higher than the average? At first glance, you might be inclined to say yes, since 530 is higher than 500. But recall that the means of samples vary about the population mean when samples are selected from a specific population. So the question arises, Is there a real difference in the means, or is the difference simply due to chance (i.e., sampling error)? In this chapter, you will learn how to answer that question by using statistics that explain hypothesis testing. See Statistics Today— Revisited, p. 391, for the answer. In this chapter, you will learn how to answer many questions of this type by using statistics that are explained in the theory of hypothesis testing.

Source: Measuring Up: Canadian Results from the OECD PISA Study.

8–1   Introduction

Researchers are interested in answering many types of questions. For example, a scientist might want to know whether the earth is warming up. A physician might want to know whether a new medication will lower a person's blood pressure. An educator might wish to see whether a new teaching technique is better than a traditional one. A retail merchant might want to know whether the public prefers a certain colour in a new line of fashion. Automobile manufacturers are interested in determining whether seat belts will reduce the severity of injuries caused by accidents. These types of questions can be addressed through statistical **hypothesis testing,** which is a decision-making process for evaluating claims about a population. In hypothesis testing, the researcher must define the population under study, state the particular hypotheses that will be investigated, assign an acceptable error level, select a sample from the population, collect the data, perform the calculations required for the statistical test, and reach a conclusion.

Hypotheses concerning parameters such as means and proportions can be investigated. There are two specific statistical tests used for hypotheses concerning means: the *z test* and the *t test.* This chapter will explain in detail the hypothesis-testing procedure along with the z test and the t test. In addition, a hypothesis-testing procedure for testing a single variance or standard deviation using the chi-square distribution is explained in Section 8–6.

The three methods used to test hypotheses are

1. The traditional method
2. The *P*-value method
3. The confidence interval method

The *traditional method* will be explained first. It has been used since the hypothesis-testing method was formulated. A newer method, called the *P-value method,* has become popular with the advent of modern computers and high-powered statistical calculators. It will be explained at the end of Section 8–3. The third method, the *confidence interval method,* is explained in Section 8–7 and illustrates the relationship between hypothesis testing and confidence intervals.

8–2   Steps in Hypothesis Testing—Traditional Method

Every hypothesis-testing situation begins with the statement of a hypothesis.

> A **statistical hypothesis** is a conjecture about a population parameter. This conjecture may or may not be true.

Objective 1

Understand the definitions used in hypothesis testing.

There are two types of statistical hypotheses for each situation: the null hypothesis and the alternative hypothesis.

> The **null hypothesis,** symbolized by H_0, is a statistical hypothesis that states that a parameter is equal to a specific value, or that there is no difference between two parameters.

> The **alternative hypothesis,** symbolized by H_1, is a statistical hypothesis that states a parameter is either less than, not equal to, or greater than a specific value, or states that there is a difference between two parameters.

(*Note:* Although the definitions of null and alternative hypotheses given here use the word *parameter,* these definitions can be extended to include other terms such as *distributions* and *randomness.* This is explained in later chapters.)

As an illustration of how hypotheses should be stated, three different statistical studies will be used as examples.

Situation A   A medical researcher is interested in finding out whether a new medication will have any undesirable side effects. The researcher is particularly concerned with the pulse rate of the patients who take the medication. Will the pulse rate increase, decrease, or remain unchanged after a patient takes the medication?

Objective 2

State the null and alternative hypotheses.

Since the researcher knows that the mean pulse rate for the population under study is 82 beats per minute, the hypotheses for this situation are

$$H_0\colon \mu = 82 \qquad \text{and} \qquad H_1\colon \mu \neq 82$$

The null hypothesis specifies that the mean will remain unchanged, and the alternative hypothesis states that it will be different. This test is called a *two-tailed test* (a term that will be formally defined later in this section), since the possible side effects of the medicine could be to raise or lower the pulse rate.

Situation B   A chemist invents an additive to increase the life of an automobile battery. If the mean lifetime of the automobile battery without the additive is 36 months, then her hypotheses are

$$H_0 : \mu = 36 \quad \text{and} \quad H_1 : \mu > 36$$

In this situation, the chemist is interested only in increasing the lifetime of the batteries, so her alternative hypothesis is that the mean is greater than 36 months. The null hypothesis is that the mean is less than or equal to 36 months. This test is called *right-tailed,* since the interest is in an increase only.

Situation C   A contractor wishes to lower heating bills by using a special type of insulation in houses. If the average of the monthly heating bills is $78, her hypotheses about heating costs with the use of insulation are

$$H_0 : \mu = \$78 \quad \text{and} \quad H_1 : \mu < \$78$$

This test is a *left-tailed test,* since the contractor is interested only in lowering heating costs.

To state hypotheses correctly, researchers must translate the *conjecture* or *claim* from words into mathematical symbols. The basic symbols used are as follows:

| Equal to | = | Not equal to | ≠ |
| Less than | < | Greater than | > |

The null and alternative hypotheses are stated together, and the null hypothesis contains the equals sign, as shown (where k represents a specified number).

Two-tailed test	Right-tailed test	Left-tailed test
$H_0: \mu = k$	$H_0: \mu = k$	$H_0: \mu = k$
$H_1: \mu \neq k$	$H_1: \mu > k$	$H_1: \mu < k$

The formal definitions of the different types of tests are given later in this section.

Example 8–1

State the null and alternative hypotheses for each conjecture.

a. A researcher thinks that if expectant mothers use vitamin pills, the birth weight of the babies will increase. The average birth weight of the population is 3.9 kilograms.

b. An engineer hypothesizes that the mean number of defects can be decreased in a manufacturing process of compact discs by using robots instead of humans for certain tasks. The mean number of defective discs per 1000 is 18.

c. A psychologist feels that playing soft music during a test will change the results of the test. The psychologist is not sure whether the grades will be higher or lower. In the past, the mean of the scores was 73.

Solution

a. $H_0: \mu = 3.9$ and $H_1: \mu > 3.9$
b. $H_0: \mu = 18$ and $H_1: \mu < 18$
c. $H_0: \mu = 73$ and $H_1: \mu \neq 73$

After stating the hypothesis, the researcher designs the study. The researcher selects the correct *statistical test,* chooses an appropriate *level of significance,* and formulates a plan for conducting the study. In situation A, for instance, the researcher will select a sample of patients who will be given the drug. After allowing a suitable time for the drug to be absorbed, the researcher will measure each person's pulse rate.

Recall that when samples of a specific size are selected from a population, the means of these samples will vary about the population mean, and the distribution of the sample means will be approximately normal when the sample size is 30 or more. (See Section 6–5.) So even if the null hypothesis is true, the mean of the pulse rates of the sample of patients will not, in most cases, be exactly equal to the population mean of 82 beats per minute. There are two possibilities. Either the null hypothesis is true, and the difference between the sample mean and the population mean is due to chance; *or* the null hypothesis is false, and the sample came from a population whose mean is not 82 beats per minute but is some other value that is not known. These situations are shown in Figure 8–1.

The farther away the sample mean is from the population mean, the more evidence there would be for rejecting the null hypothesis. The probability that the sample came from a population whose mean is 82 decreases as the distance between the means increases.

If the mean pulse rate of the sample were, say, 83, the researcher would probably conclude that this difference was due to chance and would not reject the null hypothesis. But if the sample mean were, say, 90, then in all likelihood the researcher would conclude that the medication increased the pulse rate of the users and would reject the null hypothesis. The question is, Where does the researcher draw the line? This decision is not made on feelings or intuition; it is made statistically. That is, the difference must be significant and in all likelihood not due to chance. Statistical tests and significance levels are essential to credible decision making.

A **statistical test** uses the data obtained from a sample to make a decision about whether the null hypothesis should be rejected.

The numerical value calculated from the sample data in a statistical test is called the **test statistic.**

Figure 8–1

Situations in Hypothesis Testing

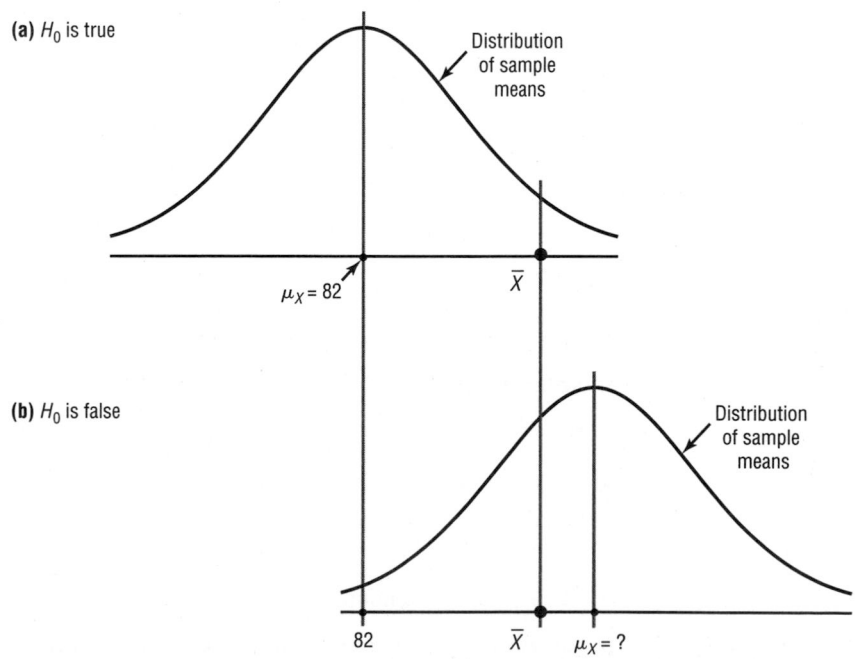

(a) H_0 is true

Distribution of sample means

$\mu_{\bar{X}} = 82$ $\bar{X}$

(b) H_0 is false

Distribution of sample means

82   $\bar{X}$ $\mu_{\bar{X}} = ?$

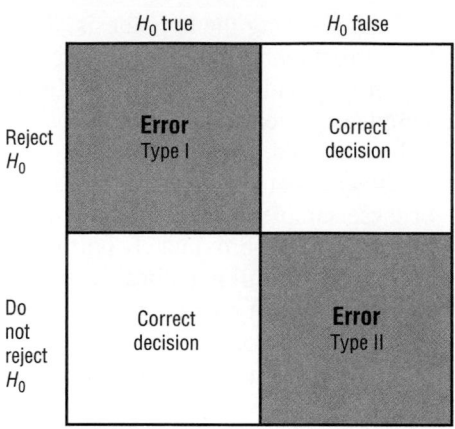

In this type of statistical test, the mean is computed for the data obtained from the sample and is compared with the population mean. Then a decision is made to reject or not reject the null hypothesis on the basis of the value obtained from the statistical test. If the difference is significant, the null hypothesis is rejected. If it is not, then the null hypothesis is not rejected.

In the hypothesis-testing situation, there are four possible outcomes. In reality, the null hypothesis may or may not be true, and a decision is made to reject or not reject it on the basis of the data obtained from a sample. The four possible outcomes are shown in Figure 8–2. Notice that there are two possibilities for a correct decision and two possibilities for an incorrect decision.

If a null hypothesis is true and it is rejected, then a *type I error* is made. In situation A, for instance, the medication might not significantly change the pulse rate of all the users in the population; but it might change the rate, by chance, of the subjects in the sample. In this case, the researcher will reject the null hypothesis when it is really true, thus committing a type I error.

On the other hand, the medication might not change the pulse rate of the subjects in the sample, but when it is given to the general population, it might cause a significant increase or decrease in the pulse rate of users. The researcher, on the basis of the data obtained from the sample, will not reject the null hypothesis, thus committing a *type II error.*

In situation B, the additive might not significantly increase the lifetimes of automobile batteries in the population, but it might increase the lifetimes of the batteries in the sample. In this case, the null hypothesis would be rejected when it was really true. This would be a type I error. On the other hand, the additive might not work on the batteries selected for the sample, but if it were to be used in the general population of batteries, it might significantly increase their lifetimes. The researcher, on the basis of information obtained from the sample, would not reject the null hypothesis, thus committing a type II error.

A **type I error** occurs if one rejects the null hypothesis when it is true.

A **type II error** occurs if one does not reject the null hypothesis when it is false.

The hypothesis-testing situation can be likened to a jury trial. In a jury trial, there are four possible outcomes. The defendant is either guilty or innocent, and he or she will be convicted or acquitted. See Figure 8–3.

Now the hypotheses are

H_0: The defendant is innocent

H_1: The defendant is not innocent (i.e., guilty)

Figure 8–3

Hypothesis Testing and a Jury Trial

H_0: The defendant is innocent.
H_1: The defendant is not innocent.

The results of a trial can be shown as follows:

	H_0 true (innocent)	H_0 false (not innocent)
Reject H_0 (convict)	Type I error 1.	Correct decision 2.
Do not reject H_0 (acquit)	Correct decision 3.	Type II error 4.

Next, the evidence is presented in court by the prosecutor, and based on this evidence, the jury decides the verdict, innocent or guilty.

If the defendant is convicted but he or she did not commit the crime, then a type I error has been committed. See block 1 of Figure 8–3. On the other hand, if the defendant is convicted and he or she has committed the crime, then a correct decision has been made. See block 2.

If the defendant is acquitted and he or she did not commit the crime, a correct decision has been made by the jury. See block 3. However, if the defendant is acquitted and he or she did commit the crime, then a type II error has been made. See block 4.

The decision of the jury does not prove that the defendant did or did not commit the crime. The decision is based on the evidence presented. If the evidence is strong enough, the defendant will be convicted in most cases. If the evidence is weak, the defendant will be acquitted in most cases. Nothing is proved absolutely. Likewise, the decision to reject or not reject the null hypothesis does not prove anything. *The only way to prove anything statistically is to use the entire population,* which, in most cases, is not possible. The decision, then, is made on the basis of probabilities. That is, when there is a large difference between the mean obtained from the sample and the hypothesized mean, the null hypothesis is probably not true. The question is, How large a difference is necessary to reject the null hypothesis? Here is where the level of significance is used.

Unusual Stat

Almost one-quarter of children of Generation X parents (born 1967 to 1976) return home after moving out.

The **level of significance** is the maximum probability of committing a type I error. This probability is symbolized by α (Greek letter **alpha**). That is, P (type I error) $= \alpha$.

The probability of a type II error is symbolized by β, the Greek letter **beta.** That is, P (type II error) $= \beta$. In most hypothesis-testing situations, β cannot easily be computed; however, α and β are related in that decreasing one increases the other.

Statisticians generally agree on using three arbitrary significance levels: the 0.10, 0.05, and 0.01 levels. That is, if the null hypothesis is rejected, the probability of a type I error will be 10, 5, or 1%, depending on which level of significance is used. Here is another way of putting it: When $\alpha = 0.10$, there is a 10% chance of rejecting a true null hypothesis; when $\alpha = 0.05$, there is a 5% chance of rejecting a true null hypothesis; and when $\alpha = 0.01$, there is a 1% chance of rejecting a true null hypothesis.

In a hypothesis-testing situation, the researcher decides what level of significance to use. It does not have to be the 0.10, 0.05, or 0.01 level. It can be any level, depending on the seriousness of the type I error. After a significance level is chosen, a *critical value* is selected from a table for the appropriate test. If a z test is used, for example, the z tables

(Tables E–1 and E–2 in Appendix C) is consulted to find the critical value. The critical value determines the critical and noncritical regions.

> The **critical value** separates the critical region from the noncritical region.
>
> The **critical** or **rejection region** is the range of values of the test statistic that indicates that there is a significant difference and that the null hypothesis should be rejected.
>
> The **noncritical** or **nonrejection region** is the range of values of the test statistic that indicates that the difference was probably due to chance and that the null hypothesis should not be rejected.

The critical value can be on the right side of the mean or on the left side of the mean for a one-tailed test. Its location depends on the inequality sign of the alternative hypothesis. For example, in situation B, where the chemist is interested in increasing the average lifetime of automobile batteries, the alternative hypothesis is H_1: $\mu > 36$. Since the inequality sign is $>$, the null hypothesis will be rejected only when the sample mean is significantly greater than 36. Hence, the critical value must be on the right side of the mean. Therefore, this test is called a right-tailed test.

> A **one-tailed test** indicates that the null hypothesis should be rejected when the test statistic is in the critical region on one side of the mean. A one-tailed test is either a **right-tailed test** or **left-tailed test,** depending on the direction of the inequality of the alternative hypothesis.

Objective 3

Find critical values for the z test.

To obtain the critical value, the researcher must choose an alpha level. In situation B, suppose the researcher chose $\alpha = 0.01$. Then the researcher must find a z score such that 1% of the area falls to the right of the z score and 99% falls to the left of the z score, as shown in Figure 8–4(a).

Next, the researcher must find the value in Table E–2 closest to 0.9900 (0.9901), which corresponds to a z score of 2.33. Therefore the critical z value is 2.33 as shown in Figure 8–4(b).

The critical and noncritical regions and the critical value are shown in Figure 8–5.

Figure 8–4

Finding the Critical Value for $\alpha = 0.01$ (Right-Tailed Test)

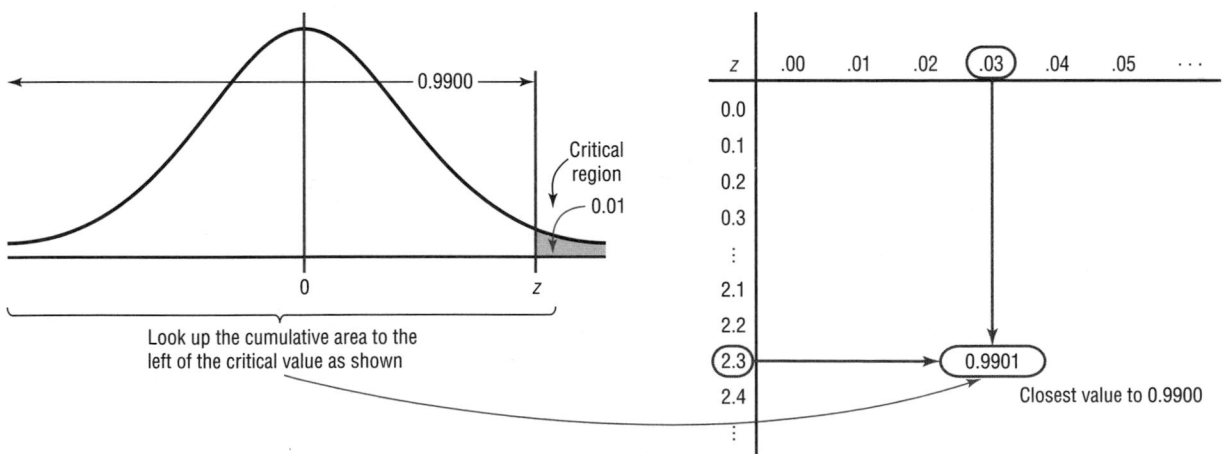

(a) The critical region

(b) The critical value from Table E–2

Figure 8–5

Critical and Noncritical
Regions for $\alpha = 0.01$
(Right-Tailed Test)

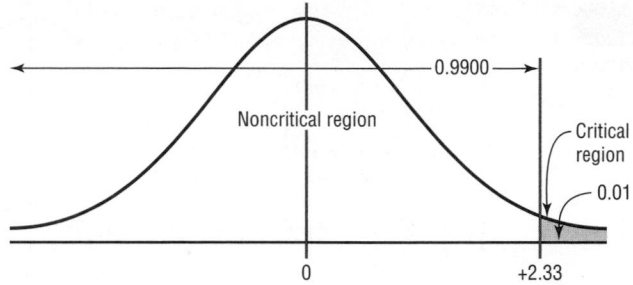

Now, move on to situation C, where the contractor is interested in lowering the heating bills. The alternative hypothesis is H_1: $\mu < \$78$. Hence, the critical value falls to the left of the mean. This test is thus a left-tailed test. At $\alpha = 0.01$, the critical value is -2.33, as shown in Figure 8–6. Refer to Table E–1 in Appendix C.

Figure 8–6

Critical and Noncritical
Regions for $\alpha = 0.01$
(Left-Tailed Test)

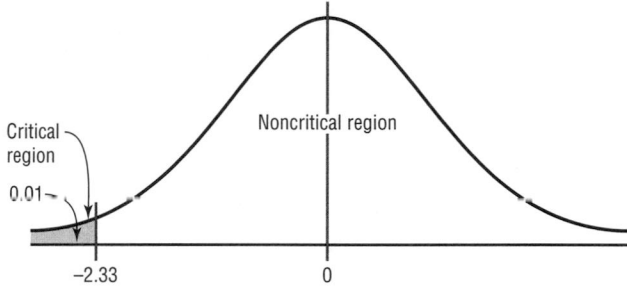

When a researcher conducts a two-tailed test, as in situation A, the null hypothesis can be rejected when there is a significant difference in either direction, above or below the mean.

> In a **two-tailed test**, the null hypothesis should be rejected when the test statistic is in either of the two critical regions.

For a two-tailed test, then, the critical region must be split into two equal parts. If $\alpha = 0.01$, then one-half of the area, or $\alpha/2 = 0.005$, must be to the right of the mean and one-half must be to the left of the mean, as shown in Figure 8–7.

In this case, the area to be found in Table E–1 is 0.0050 (area in left tail is 0.005) with a critical z value of -2.575. The cumulative area to the left in Table E–2 is 0.9950 (area in right tail is 0.005) with a critical z value of $+2.575$, as shown in Figure 8–8.

Figure 8–7

Finding the Critical
Values for $\alpha = 0.01$
(Two-Tailed Test)

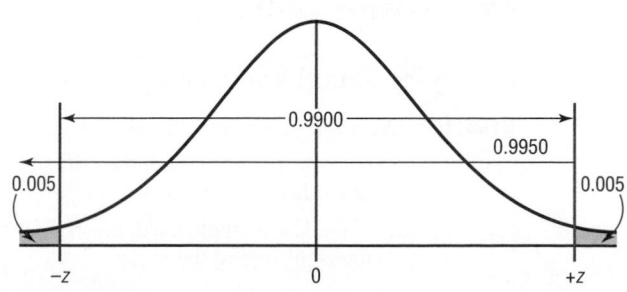

Figure 8–8

Critical and Noncritical Regions for $\alpha = 0.01$ (Two-Tailed Test)

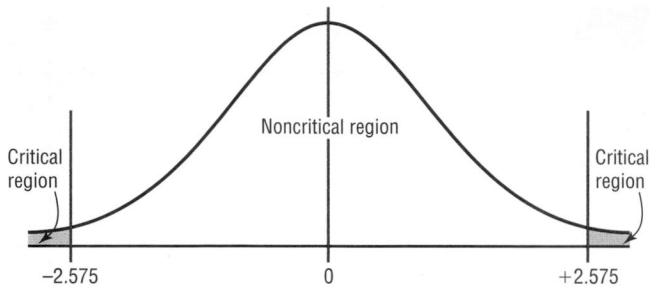

Critical region

Noncritical region

Critical region

−2.575   0   +2.575

Figure 8–9

Summary of Hypothesis Testing and Critical Values

	α	Critical Value
	0.10	−1.28
	0.05	−1.645
	0.01	−2.33

$H_0: \mu = k$
$H_1: \mu < k$

(a) Left-tailed

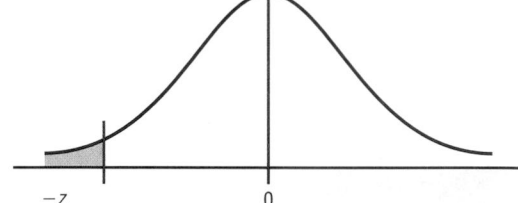

−z   0

	α	Critical Value
	0.10	1.28
	0.05	1.645
	0.01	2.33

$H_0: \mu = k$
$H_1: \mu > k$

(b) Right-tailed

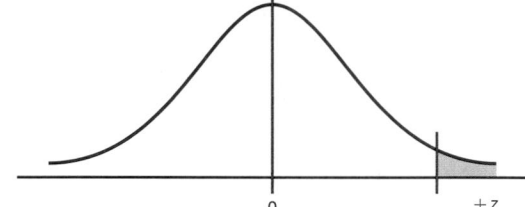

0   +z

	α	$\alpha/2$	Critical Value
	0.10	0.05	±1.645
	0.05	0.025	±1.96
	0.01	0.005	±2.575

$H_0: \mu = k$
$H_1: \mu \neq k$

(c) Two-tailed

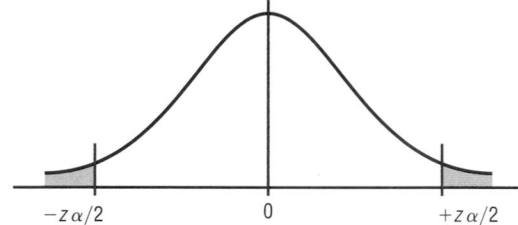

$-z\alpha/2$ 0 $+z\alpha/2$

A similar procedure is used for other values of α.

Figure 8–9 with rejection regions shaded shows the critical value for the three situations discussed in this section for values of $\alpha = 0.10$, $\alpha = 0.05$, and $\alpha = 0.01$. The procedure for finding critical values is outlined next (where k is a specified number).

Procedure Table

Finding the Critical Values for Specific α Values, Using Tables E–1 and E–2

Step 1 Draw the figure and indicate the appropriate area.

    a. If the test is left-tailed, the critical region, with an area equal to a, will be on the left side of the mean.

    b. If the test is right-tailed, the critical region, with an area equal to a, will be on the right side of the mean.

c. If the test is two-tailed, α must be divided by 2; one-half of the area will be to the right of the mean, and one-half will be to the left of the mean.

Step 2   a. For a left-tailed test, look up the area (equivalent to α) in Table E–1—Negative z Scores.

b. For a right-tailed test, look up the area (equivalent to $1 - \alpha$) in Table E–2—Positive z Scores.

c. For a two-tailed test, look up the area (equivalent to $\alpha/2$) in Table E–1—Negative z Scores and look up the area (equivalent to $1 - \alpha/2$) in Table E–2—Positive z Scores.

Step 3   Find the z score that corresponds to the area. This will be the critical value.

Example 8–2

Using Tables E–1 and E–2 in Appendix C, find the critical value(s) for each situation and draw the appropriate figure, showing the critical region.

a. A left-tailed test with $\alpha = 0.10$.

b. A two-tailed test with $\alpha = 0.02$.

c. A right-tailed test with $\alpha = 0.005$.

Solution a

Step 1   Draw the figure and indicate the appropriate area. Since this is a left-tailed test, the area of 0.10 is located in the left tail, as shown in Figure 8–10.

Step 2   Look up the area closest to 0.1000 in Table E–1; in this case 0.1003.

Step 3   Find the z score that corresponds to this area. The z score for 0.1003 is -1.28. Hence, the critical value is -1.28 on the left-tail. See Figure 8–10.

Figure 8–10

Critical Value and Critical Region for part *a* of Example 8–2

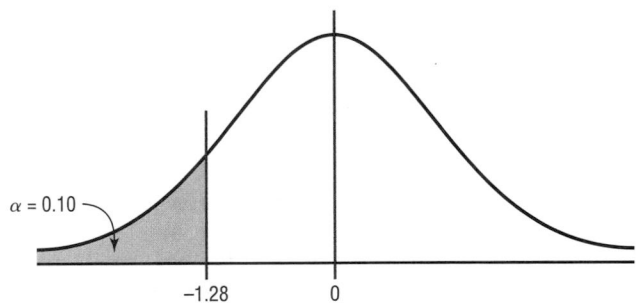

$\alpha = 0.10$

-1.28 0

Solution b

Step 1   Draw the figure and indicate the appropriate area. In this case, there are two areas equivalent to $\alpha/2$, or $0.02/2 = 0.01$.

Step 2   For the left tail, look up the area closest to 0.0100 in Table E–1; in this case 0.0099. For the right tail, look up the area closest to 0.9900 ($1 - 0.01$) in Table E–2; in this case 0.9901.

Step 3   Find the z scores that correspond to each area. The z score for 0.0099 is -2.33 and the z score for 0.9901 is $+2.33$. Hence, the two critical values are -2.33 on the left-tail and $+2.33$ on the right-tail. See Figure 8–11.

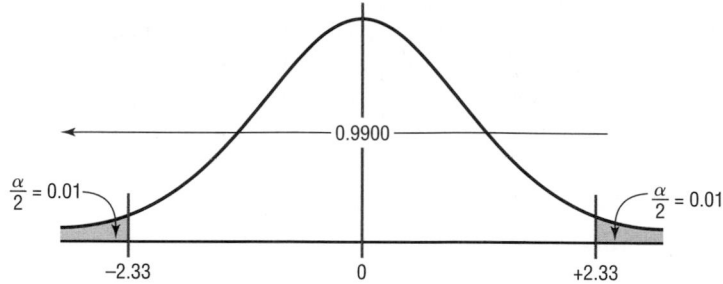

Solution *c*

Step 1   Draw the figure and indicate the appropriate area. Since this is a right-tailed test, the area 0.005 is located in the right tail, as shown in Figure 8–12.

Figure 8–12

Critical Value and
Critical Region for part
c of Example 8–2

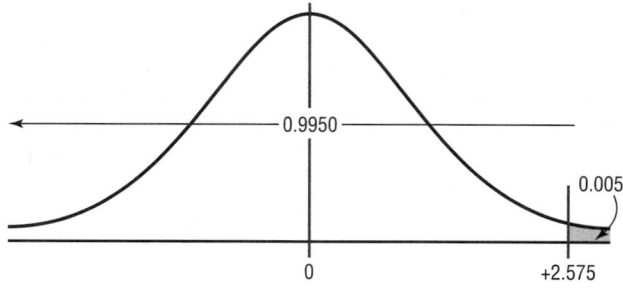

Step 2   Look up the area closest to 0.9950 (1 − 0.005) in Table E–2; in this case equal distance to 0.9949 and 0.9951.

Step 3   Find the *z* score that corresponds to each area. The *z* score for 0.9949 is +2.57 and the *z* score for 0.9951 is +2.58. The average of the two *z* scores is +2.575. Hence, the critical value is +2.575 on the right-tail. See Figure 8–12.

Objective ④

State the five steps
used in hypothesis
testing.

In hypothesis testing, the following steps are recommended.

1. State the hypotheses. Be sure to state both the null and the alternative hypotheses.
2. Design the study. This step includes selecting the correct statistical test, choosing a level of significance, and formulating a plan to carry out the study. The plan should include information such as the definition of the population, the way the sample will be selected, and the methods that will be used to collect the data.
3. Conduct the study and collect the data.
4. Evaluate the data. The data should be tabulated in this step, and the statistical test should be conducted. Finally, decide whether to reject or not reject the null hypothesis.
5. Summarize the results.

For the purposes of this chapter, a simplified version of the hypothesis-testing procedure will be used, since designing the study and collecting the data will be omitted. The steps are summarized in the Procedure Table.

Procedure Table

Solving Hypothesis-Testing Problems (Traditional Method)

Step 1   State the hypotheses and identify the claim.

Step 2   Find the critical value(s) from the appropriate table in Appendix C.

Step 3   Compute the test statistic.

Step 4   Make the decision to reject or not reject the null hypothesis.

Step 5   Summarize the results.

Applying the Concepts 8–2

Eggs and Your Health

The Incredible Edible Egg company recently found that eating eggs does not increase a person's blood serum cholesterol. Five hundred subjects participated in a study that lasted for two years. The participants were randomly assigned to either a no-egg group or a moderate-egg group. The blood serum cholesterol levels were checked at the beginning and at the end of the study. Overall, the groups' levels were not significantly different. The company reminds us that eating eggs is healthy if done in moderation. Many of the previous studies relating eggs and high blood serum cholesterol jumped to improper conclusions.

Using this information, answer these questions.

1. What prompted the study?
2. What is the population under study?
3. Was a sample collected?
4. What was the hypothesis?
5. Was data collected?
6. Were any statistical tests run?
7. What was the conclusion?

See page 394 for the answers.

Exercises 8–2

1. Define *null* and *alternative hypotheses,* and give an example of each.

2. What is meant by a type I error? A type II error? How are they related?

3. What is meant by a statistical test?

4. Explain the difference between a one-tailed and a two-tailed test.

5. What is meant by the critical region? The noncritical region?

6. What symbols are used to represent the null hypothesis and the alternative hypothesis?

7. What symbols are used to represent the probabilities of type I and type II errors?

8. Explain what is meant by a significant difference.

9. When should a one-tailed test be used? A two-tailed test?

10. List the steps in hypothesis testing.

11. In hypothesis testing, why can't the hypothesis be proved true?

12. (ans) Using the *z* table (Table E–2), find the critical value (or values) for each.

    a. $\alpha = 0.05$, two-tailed test

    b. $\alpha = 0.01$, left-tailed test

    c. $\alpha = 0.005$, right-tailed test

    d. $\alpha = 0.01$, right-tailed test

    e. $\alpha = 0.05$, left-tailed test

    f. $\alpha = 0.02$, left-tailed test

    g. $\alpha = 0.05$, right-tailed test

    h. $\alpha = 0.01$, two-tailed test

    i. $\alpha = 0.04$, left-tailed test

    j. $\alpha = 0.02$, right-tailed test

13. For each conjecture, state the null and alternative hypotheses:

    a. The average age of college students is 24.6 years.

    b. The average income of accountants is \$51,497.

    c. The average age of attorneys is greater than 25.4 years.

    d. The average score of 50 high school basketball games is less than 88.

    e. The average pulse rate of male marathon runners is less than 70 beats per minute.

    f. The average cost of a DVD player is \$79.95.

    g. The average weight loss for a sample of people who exercise 30 minutes per day for 6 weeks is 3.7 kilograms.

8–3   *z* Test for a Mean

Objective

Test means for large samples, using the *z* test.

In this chapter, two statistical tests for means will be explained: the *z* test, used to test for the mean of a large sample, and the *t* test, used for the mean of a small sample. This section explains the *z* test, and Section 8–4 explains the *t* test.

    Many hypotheses are tested using a statistical test based on the following general formula:

$$\text{Test statistic} = \frac{(\text{observed value}) - (\text{expected value})}{\text{standard error}}$$

The observed value is the statistic (such as the mean) that is computed from the sample data. The expected value is the parameter (such as the mean) that one would expect to obtain if the null hypothesis were true—in other words, the hypothesized value. The denominator is the standard error of the statistic being tested (in this case, the standard error of the mean).

    The *z* test is defined formally as follows.

> The **z test** is a statistical test for the mean of a population. It can be used when $n \geq 30$, or when the population is normally distributed and σ is known.
>   The formula for the test statistic, *z*, is
>
> $$z = \frac{\overline{X} - \mu}{\sigma/\sqrt{n}}$$
>
> where
> $\overline{X}$ = sample mean
> μ = hypothesized population mean
> σ = population standard deviation
> n = sample size

    For the *z* test, the observed value is the value of the sample mean. The expected value is the value of the population mean, assuming that the null hypothesis is true. The denominator $\sigma/\sqrt{n}$ is the standard error of the mean.

    The formula for the *z* test is the same formula shown in Chapter 6 for the situation where one is using a distribution of sample means. Recall that the central limit theorem allows one to use the standard normal distribution to approximate the distribution of sample means when $n \geq 30$. If σ is unknown, *s* can be used when $n \geq 30$.

As stated in Section 8–2, there are five steps for solving *hypothesis-testing* problems:

Step 1 State the hypotheses and identify the claim.

Step 2 Find the critical value(s).

Step 3 Compute the test statistic.

Step 4 Make the decision to reject or not reject the null hypothesis.

Step 5 Summarize the results.

Example 8–3 illustrates these five steps.

Speaking of
Statistics

This study found that people who used pedometers reported having increased energy, mood improvement, and weight loss. State possible null and alternative hypotheses for the study. What would be a likely population? What is the sample size? Comment on the sample size.

RD HEALTH

Step to It

IT FITS in your hand, costs less than $30, and will make you feel great. Give up? A pedometer. Brenda Rooney, an epidemiologist at Gundersen Lutheran Medical Center in LaCrosse, Wis., gave 500 people pedometers and asked them to take 10,000 steps—about 8 kilometres or five miles—a day. (Office workers typically average about 4000 steps a day.) By the end of eight weeks, 56 percent reported having more energy, 47 percent improved their mood and 50 percent lost weight. The subjects reported that seeing their total step-count motivated them to take more.

— JENNIFER BRAUNSCHWEIGER

Source: Reprinted with permission from the April 2002 *Reader's Digest.* Copyright © 2002 by The Reader's Digest Assn. Inc.

Example 8–3

A researcher reports that the average salary of full professors in Canadian universities is $100,735. A sample of 30 full professors has a mean of $103,746. At $\alpha = 0.05$, test the claim that full professors earn more than $100,735 a year. The standard deviation of the population is $12,499.

Source: Excerpt adapted from Statistics Canada publication *Salaries and Salary Scales of Full-time Teaching Staff at Canadian Universities 2004/2005: Final Report* Catalogue 81-595, No. 48, Released December 5, 2006, page 11.

Solution

Step 1 State the hypothesis and identify the claim.

$$H_0: \mu = \$100{,}735 \quad \text{and} \quad H_1: \mu > \$100{,}735 \ (\text{claim})$$

Step 2 Find the critical value. Since $\alpha = 0.05$ and the test is a right-tailed test, the critical value is $z = +1.645$

Step 3 Compute the test statistic.

$$z = \frac{\overline{X} - \mu}{\sigma/\sqrt{n}} = \frac{\$103{,}746 - \$100{,}735}{\$12{,}499/\sqrt{30}} \approx 1.319$$

Figure 8–13

Summary of the *z* Test of Example 8–3

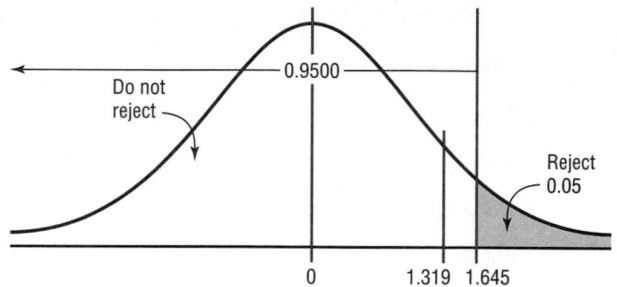

0.9500

Do not reject

Reject 0.05

0   1.319   1.645

Step 4   Make the decision. Since the test statistic, $+1.319$, is less than the critical value, $+1.645$, and is not in the critical region, the decision is to not reject the null hypothesis. This test is summarized in Figure 8–13.

Step 5   Summarize the results. There is not enough evidence to support the claim that full professors earn more on average than \$100,735 a year.

Comment: Even though in Example 8–3 the sample mean, \$103,746, is higher than the hypothesized population mean of \$100,735, it is not *significantly* higher. Hence, the difference may be due to chance. When the null hypothesis is not rejected, there is still a chance of a type II error, i.e., of not rejecting the null hypothesis when it is false.

The probability of a type II error is not easily ascertained. Further explanation about the type II error is given in Section 8–7. For now, it is only necessary to realize that the probability of type II error exists when the decision is not to reject the null hypothesis.

Also note that when the null hypothesis is not rejected, it cannot be accepted as true. There is merely not enough evidence to say that it is false. This guideline may sound a little confusing, but the situation is analogous to a jury trial. The verdict is either guilty or not guilty and is based on the evidence presented. If a person is judged not guilty, it does not mean that the person is proved innocent; it only means that there was not enough evidence to reach the guilty verdict.

Example 8–4

A researcher claims that the average cost of men's athletic shoes is less than \$80. He selects a random sample of 36 pairs of shoes from a catalogue and finds the following costs (in dollars). (The costs have been rounded to the nearest dollar.) Is there enough evidence to support the researcher's claim at $\alpha = 0.10$?

60	70	75	55	80	55
50	40	80	70	50	95
120	90	75	85	80	60
110	65	80	85	85	45
75	60	90	90	60	95
110	85	45	90	70	70

Solution

Step 1   State the hypotheses and identify the claim

$$H_0: \mu \geq \$80 \quad \text{and} \quad H_1: \mu < \$80 \text{ (claim)}$$

Step 2   Find the critical value. Since $\alpha = 0.10$ and the test is a left-tailed test, the critical value is -1.28.

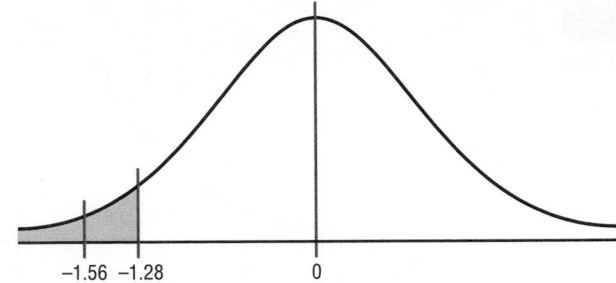

Figure 8–14

Critical Value and Test
Statistic for Example
8–4

-1.56 -1.28   0

Step 3 Compute the test statistic. Since the exercise gives raw data, it is necessary to find the mean and standard deviation of the data. Using the formulas in Chapter 3 or your calculator gives $\overline{X} = 75.0$ and $s = 19.2$. Substitute in the formula

$$z = \frac{\overline{X} - \mu}{s/\sqrt{n}} = \frac{75 - 80}{19.2/\sqrt{36}} \approx -1.56$$

Step 4 Make the decision. Since the test statistic, -1.56, falls in the critical region, the decision is to reject the null hypothesis. See Figure 8–14.

Step 5 Summarize the results. There is enough evidence to support the claim that the average cost of men's athletic shoes is less than $80.

Comment: In Example 8–4, the difference is said to be significant. However, when the null hypothesis is rejected, there is always a chance of a type I error. In this case, the probability of a type I error is at most 0.10, or 10%.

Example 8–5

The Medical Rehabilitation Education Foundation reports that the average cost of rehabilitation for stroke victims is $24,672. To see if the average cost of rehabilitation is different at a particular hospital, a researcher selects a random sample of 35 stroke victims at the hospital and finds that the average cost of their rehabilitation is $25,226. The standard deviation of the population is $3251. At $\alpha = 0.01$, can it be concluded that the average cost of stroke rehabilitation at a particular hospital is different from $24,672?

Source: Snapshot, *USA TODAY.*

Solution

Step 1 State the hypotheses and identify the claim.

$$H_0: \mu = \$24{,}672 \quad \text{and} \quad H_1: \mu \neq \$24{,}672 \text{ (claim)}$$

Step 2 Find the critical values. Since $\alpha = 0.01$ and the test is a two-tailed test, the critical values are $+2.575$ and -2.575.

Step 3 Compute the test statistic.

$$z = \frac{\overline{X} - \mu}{\sigma/\sqrt{n}} = \frac{25{,}226 - 24{,}672}{3251/\sqrt{35}} \approx 1.01$$

Figure 8–15

Critical Values and Test Statistic for Example 8–5

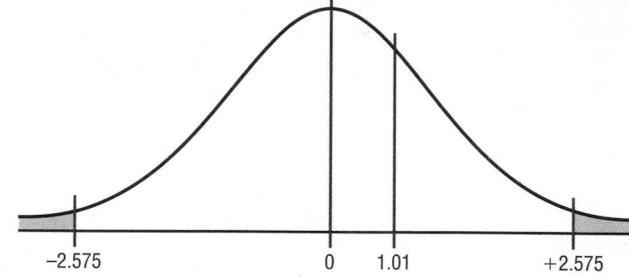

-2.575   0   1.01   +2.575

Step 4 Make the decision. Do not reject the null hypothesis, since the test statistic falls in the noncritical region, as shown in Figure 8–15.

Step 5 Summarize the results. There is not enough evidence to support the claim that the average cost of rehabilitation at the particular hospital is different from $24,672.

As with confidence intervals, the central limit theorem states that when the population standard deviation σ is unknown, the sample standard deviation s can be used in the formula as long as the sample size is 30 or more. The formula to calculate the test statistic for the z test in this case is

$$z = \frac{\overline{X} - \mu}{s/\sqrt{n}}$$

When n is less than 30 and σ is unknown, the t test must be used. The t test will be explained in Section 8–4.

When interpreting the hypothesis test results, it is important to know what claim is being tested, the null hypothesis or the alternative hypothesis. In either case, we would reject the null hypothesis if the test statistic falls in the critical region; otherwise we would fail to reject the null hypothesis. The four possible outcomes and summary statements are shown.

Outcomes of a Hypothesis-Testing Situation

1. Claim is H_o and H_0 is rejected, then there is sufficient evidence to reject the claim.
2. Claim is H_o and H_0 is not rejected, then there is not sufficient evidence to reject the claim.
3. Claim is H_1 and H_0 is rejected, then there is sufficient evidence to support the claim.
4. Claim is H_1 and H_0 is not rejected, then there is not sufficient evidence to support the claim.

For example, suppose a researcher claims that the mean daily maximum temperature of Ottawa in July is 27°C. In this case, the claim would be the null hypothesis, H_0: $\mu = 27$, since the researcher is asserting that the parameter is a specific value. If the null hypothesis is rejected, the conclusion would be that there is enough evidence to reject the claim that the mean maximum temperature of Ottawa in July is 27°C.

On the other hand, suppose the researcher claims that the mean maximum temperature of Ottawa in July is not 27°C. The claim would be the alternative hypothesis H_1: $\mu \neq 27$. Furthermore, suppose that the null hypothesis is not rejected. The conclusion, then, would be that there is not enough evidence to support the claim that the mean maximum temperature of Ottawa in July is not 27°C.

Again, remember that nothing is being proven true or false. The statistician is only stating that there is or is not enough evidence to say that a claim is *probably* true or false. As noted previously, the only way to prove something would be to use the entire population under study, and usually this cannot be done, especially when the population is very large.

P-Value Method for Hypothesis Testing

Statisticians usually test hypotheses at the common α levels of 0.05 or 0.01 and sometimes at 0.10. Recall that the choice of the level depends on the seriousness of the type I error. Besides listing an α value, many computer statistical packages give a P-value for hypothesis tests.

> The **P-value** (or probability value) is the probability that a sample statistic (such as the sample mean) could have been selected from the population(s) being tested (or that a more improbable sample could be selected in the direction of the alternative hypothesis) given the assumption that the null hypothesis is true.

In other words, the P-value is the actual area under the standard normal distribution curve (or other curve, depending on what statistical test is being used) representing the probability of a particular sample statistic or a more extreme sample statistic occurring if the null hypothesis is true.

For example, suppose that a null hypothesis is H_0: $\mu = 50$ and the mean of a sample is $\overline{X} = 52$. If the statistical software displayed a P-value of 0.0356 for a statistical test, then the probability of getting a sample mean of 52 or greater is 0.0356 if the true population mean is 50 (for the given sample size and standard deviation). The relationship between the P-value and the α value can be explained in this manner. For $P = 0.0356$, the null hypothesis would be rejected at $\alpha = 0.05$ but not at $\alpha = 0.01$. See Figure 8–16.

Figure 8–16

Comparison of α Values and P-Values

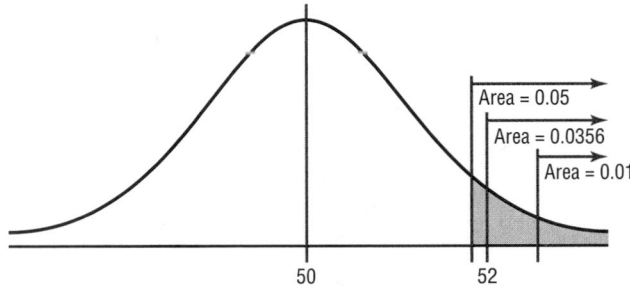

Area = 0.05
Area = 0.0356
Area = 0.01

50   52

When the hypothesis test is two-tailed, the area in one tail must be doubled. For a two-tailed test, if α is 0.05 and the area in one tail is 0.0356, the P-value will be 2(0.0356) = 0.0712. That is, the null hypothesis should not be rejected at $\alpha = 0.05$, since 0.0712 is greater than 0.05. In summary, the null hypothesis is rejected only if the P-value is less than or equal to the significance level (α); otherwise if the P-value is greater than the significance level (α) do not reject the null hypothesis.

The P-value for the z test can be found by using Table E–1 or Table E–2 in Appendix C. First find the cumulative area to the left under the standard normal curve that corresponds to the calculated test statistic or z score.

- For a left-tailed test, H_1:$\mu < k$, the P-value is the cumulative area to the left associated with the z score.
- For a right-tailed test, H_1:$\mu > k$, the P-value is one minus the cumulative area to the left (or cumulative area to the right) associated with the z score.
- For a two-tailed test, H_1:$\mu \neq k$, the P-value is twice the cumulative area to the left if the z score is negative or twice the cumulative area to the right if the z score is positive.

This procedure is shown in Step 3 of Examples 8–6 and 8–7.

The P-value method for testing hypotheses differs from the traditional method somewhat. The steps for the P-value method are summarized next.

Procedure Table

Solving Hypothesis-Testing Problems (*P*-Value Method)

Step 1   State the hypotheses and identify the claim.

Step 2   Compute the test statistic.

Step 3   Find the *P*-value.

Step 4   Make the decision.

Step 5   Summarize the results.

Examples 8–6 and 8–7 show how to use the *P*-value method to test hypotheses.

Example 8–6

A researcher wishes to test the claim that the average age of lifeguards in Ocean City is greater than 24 years. She selects a sample of 36 guards and finds the mean of the sample to be 24.7 years, with a standard deviation of 2 years. Is there evidence to support the claim at $\alpha = 0.05$? Use the *P*-value method.

Solution

Step 1   State the hypotheses and identify the claim.

$$H_0: \mu = 24 \qquad \text{and} \qquad H_1: \mu > 24 \text{ (claim)}$$

Step 2   Compute the test statistic.

$$z = \frac{24.7 - 24}{2/\sqrt{36}} = 2.10$$

Step 3   Find the *P*-value. Since the test statistic (*z* score) in Step 2 is positive, look up the corresponding area in Table E–2 in Appendix C. For $z = 2.10$, the cumulative area to the left is 0.9821. Since the alternative hypothesis indicates a right-tailed test, subtract this area from 1 to obtain the cumulative area to the right.

$$1.0000 - 0.9821 = 0.0179$$

Hence, the *P*-value is 0.0179.

Step 4   Make the decision. Since the *P*-value is less than 0.05, the decision is to reject the null hypothesis. See Figure 8–17.

Figure 8–17

P-Value and α Value for Example 8–6

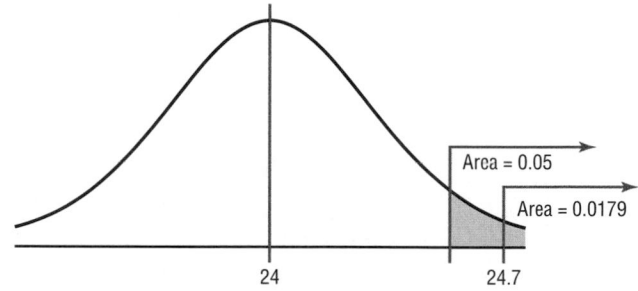

Step 5   Summarize the results. There is enough evidence to support the claim that the average age of lifeguards in Ocean City is greater than 24 years.

Note: Had the researcher chosen $\alpha = 0.01$, the null hypothesis would not have been rejected, since the *P*-value (0.0179) is greater than 0.01.

Example 8–7

A researcher claims that the average wind speed in a certain city is 8 kilometres per hour. A sample of 32 days has an average wind speed of 8.2 kilometres per hour. The standard deviation of the sample is 0.6 kilometre per hour. At $\alpha = 0.05$, is there enough evidence to reject the claim? Use the *P*-value method.

Solution

Step 1 State the hypotheses and identify the claim.

$$H_0\colon \mu = 8 \ (\text{claim}) \qquad \text{and} \qquad H_1\colon \mu \neq 8$$

Step 2 Compute the test statistic.

$$z = \frac{8.2 - 8}{0.6/\sqrt{32}} \approx 1.89$$

Step 3 Find the *P*-value. Since the test statistic (*z* score) in Step 2 is positive, look up the corresponding area in Table E–2 in Appendix C. For $z = 1.89$, the cumulative area to the left is 0.9706. Since the alternative hypothesis indicates a two-tailed test and the *z* score is positive, calculate twice the cumulative area to the right.

$$2(1.0000 - 0.9706) = 2(0.0294) = 0.0588$$

Hence, the *P*-value is 0.0588.

Step 4 Make the decision. The decision is to not reject the null hypothesis, since the *P*-value is greater than 0.05. See Figure 8–18.

Figure 8–18

P-Values and α Values for Example 8–7

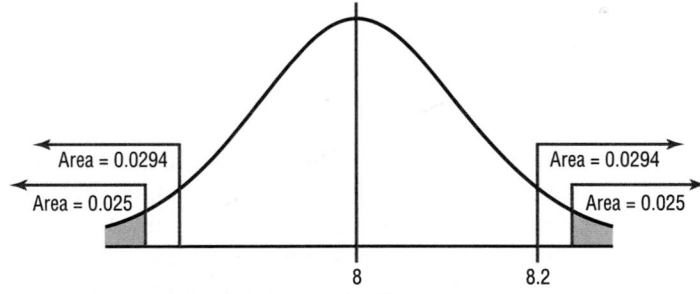

Step 5 Summarize the results. There is not enough evidence to reject the claim that the average wind speed is 8 kilometres per hour.

In Examples 8–6 and 8–7, the *P*-value and the α value were shown on a normal distribution curve to illustrate the relationship between the two values; however, it is not necessary to draw the normal distribution curve to make the decision whether to reject the null hypothesis. One can use the following rule:

Decision Rule When Using a P-Value

If *P*-value $\leq \alpha$, reject the null hypothesis.
If *P*-value $> \alpha$, fail to reject the null hypothesis.

In Example 8–6, P-value $= 0.0179$ and $\alpha = 0.05$. Since P-value $\leq \alpha$, the null hypothesis was rejected. In Example 8–7, P-value $= 0.0588$ and $\alpha = 0.05$. Since P-value $> \alpha$, the null hypothesis was not rejected.

The P-values given on calculators and computers are slightly different from those found with Tables E–1 and E–2. This is due to the fact that z values and the values in Tables E–1 and E–2 have been rounded.

A clear distinction between the α value and the P-value should be made. The α value is chosen by the researcher before the statistical test is conducted. The P-value is computed after the sample mean has been found.

There are two schools of thought on P-values. Some researchers do not choose an α value but report the P-value and allow the reader to decide whether the null hypothesis should be rejected.

In this case, the following guidelines can be used, but be advised that these guidelines are not written in stone, and some statisticians may have other opinions.

Guidelines for *P*-Values

If P-value ≤ 0.01, reject the null hypothesis. The difference is highly significant.

If P-value > 0.01 but P-value ≤ 0.05, reject the null hypothesis. The difference is significant.

If P-value > 0.05 but P-value ≤ 0.10, consider the consequences of type I error before rejecting the null hypothesis.

If P-value > 0.10, do not reject the null hypothesis. The difference is not significant.

Others decide on the α value in advance and use the P-value to make the decision, as shown in Examples 8–6 and 8–7. A note of caution is needed here: If a researcher selects $\alpha = 0.01$ and the P-value is 0.03, the researcher may decide to change the α value from 0.01 to 0.05 so that the null hypothesis will be rejected. This, of course, should not be done. If the α level is selected in advance, it should be used in making the decision.

One additional note on hypothesis testing is that the researcher should distinguish between *statistical significance* and *practical significance*. When the null hypothesis is rejected at a specific significance level, it can be concluded that the difference is probably not due to chance and thus is statistically significant. However, the results may not have any practical significance. For example, suppose that a new fuel additive decreases the litres per 100 kilometres that a car consumes by 0.15 litres for a sample of 1000 automobiles. The results may be statistically significant at the 0.05 level, but it would hardly be worthwhile to market the product for such a small increase. Hence, there is no practical significance to the results. It is up to the researcher to use common sense when interpreting the results of a statistical test.

Applying the Concepts 8–3

Car Thefts

You recently received a job with a company that manufactures an automobile antitheft device. To conduct an advertising campaign for your product, you need to make a claim about the number of automobile thefts per year. Since the population of cities in Canada varies, you decide to use rates per 10,000 people. (The rates are based on the number of people living in the cities.) Your boss said that last year the theft rate was 50 vehicles. You want to see if it has changed. The following are rates per 10,000 people for 36 randomly selected locations in Canada.

37	75	41	18	20	160
78	29	51	57	42	34
115	158	35	34	12	16
49	82	50	83	29	35
30	71	58	51	100	23
58	54	200	44	23	49

Source: Adapted from the Statistics Canada publication *Juristat,* Crime Statistics in Canada, 2005, Catalogue 85-002, Volume 26, No. 4.

Using this information, answer these questions.

1. What are the hypotheses that you would use?
2. Is the sample considered large or small?
3. What assumption must be met before the hypothesis test can be conducted?
4. Which probability distribution would you use?
5. Would you select a one- or two-tailed test? Why?
6. What critical value(s) would you use?
7. Conduct a hypothesis test.
8. What is your decision?
9. What is your conclusion?
10. Write a brief statement summarizing your conclusion.
11. If you lived in a city whose population was about 50,000, how many automobile thefts per year would you expect to occur?

See page 394 for the answers.

Exercises 8–3

For Exercises 1 through 13, perform each of the following steps.

 a. State the hypotheses and identify the claim.
 b. Find the critical value(s).
 c. Compute the test statistic.
 d. Make the decision.
 e. Summarize the results.

Use diagrams to show the critical region (or regions), and use the traditional method of hypothesis testing unless otherwise specified.

1. A survey claims that the average cost of a hotel room in Atlanta is $69.21. To test the claim, a researcher selects a sample of 30 hotel rooms and finds that the average cost is $68.43. The standard deviation of the population is $3.72. At $\alpha = 0.05$, is there enough evidence to reject the claim?

Source: *USA TODAY.*

2. It has been reported that the average credit card debt for university seniors is $3262. The student council at a large university feels that their seniors have a debt much less than this, so it conducts a study of 50 randomly selected seniors and finds that the average debt is $2995 with a sample standard deviation of $1100. With $\alpha = 0.05$, is the student council correct?

Source: *USA TODAY.*

3. A researcher states that the average revenue of the top 1000 Canadian companies is less than $15 billion. A sample of 50 companies is randomly selected, and the revenues (rounded to the nearest billion dollars) are shown. At $\alpha = 0.05$, is there enough evidence to support the researcher's claim?

29	2	32	5	28
24	32	2	26	23
19	27	5	19	4
4	3	10	5	9
8	17	9	18	7
6	10	7	15	5
2	5	21	10	4
22	27	18	1	7
18	2	14	8	18
14	3	1	6	11

Source: *The Globe and Mail Report on Business.*

4. Full-time lecturers receive an average salary of $48,927 according to a report on Canadian university teaching staff salary scales. A dean of medical studies at a university feels that lecturers in her province have a higher salary than the national average. She surveys 44 lecturers selected at random and finds their average salary is $51,607 with a standard deviation of $2500. At $\alpha = 0.05$, are lecturers paid a higher salary in the dean's province?

Source: Statistics Canada.

5. A report in 2006 claimed that the age of Air Canada's commercial airline fleet averaged 9.8 years. An airline executive suggests that the age of Air Canada's fleet was less than the age claimed by the report due to new aircraft purchases. A random sample of 36 aircraft from Air Canada's fleet is selected and the average age of the aircraft is 8.1 years. The standard deviation of the sample is 1.8 years. At $\alpha = 0.01$, can it be concluded that the average age is less than the 2006 report?

Source: www.airfleets.net.

6. The average production of potatoes in Prince Edward Island is 29.1 tonnes per hectare. A new plant food has been developed and is tested on 60 individual plots of land. The mean yield with the new plant food is 30.6 tonnes of potatoes per hectare with a standard deviation of 5.7 tonnes. At $\alpha = 0.05$, can one conclude that the average production has increased?

Source: Statistics Canada.

7. Popular growth charts indicate that the average length of 1-year old toddlers (both genders) is 73.7 centimetres. Thirty toddlers are measured on their first birthday, randomly selected from multiple day-care centres in northern communities. At $\alpha = 0.05$, can it be concluded that the average 1-year old toddler height differs from 73.7 centimetres in these communities?

64	89	76	66	75
76	76	71	74	76
74	69	84	69	74
81	64	67	65	81
72	81	80	75	86
81	71	71	81	75

Source: www.keepkidshealthy.com.

8. At a certain university the mean income of parents of the entering class is reported to be $91,600. The president of another university feels that the parents' income for her entering class is greater than $91,600. She surveys 100 randomly selected families and finds the mean income to be $96,321 with a standard deviation of $9555. With $\alpha = 0.05$, is she correct?

Source: Chronicle of Higher Education.

9. Average undergraduate cost for tuition, fees, room, and board for all institutions last year was $19,410. A random sample of costs this year for 40 institutions of higher learning indicated that the sample mean was $22,098, and the sample standard deviation was $6050. At the 0.01 level of significance, is there sufficient evidence to conclude that the cost of attendance has increased?

Source: N.Y. Times Almanac.

10. A real estate agent claims that the average price of a single family home in British Columbia's capital of Victoria is $475,000. A random sample of 36 homes sold in Victoria is selected, and the prices in dollars are shown. Is there enough evidence to reject the agent's claim at $\alpha = 0.05$?

488,800	399,000	509,000	449,900	599,000	327,500
539,900	479,900	598,000	799,000	469,000	349,500
579,900	485,000	625,000	309,000	439,900	349,900
599,000	499,900	754,900	374,900	379,900	519,000
634,900	529,000	769,500	479,000	379,900	439,900
635,000	533,500	775,000	369,900	364,900	379,000

Source: www.mls.ca.

11. On average Canadians watch 21.4 hours of television per week. A sociologist claims that TV viewers in Quebec differ from the Canadian national average. A random sample of 35 Quebec households during a one week period had a mean of 23.3 hours and a standard deviation of 3.2 hours. Is there sufficient evidence at the 0.01 level of significance that the average weekly television viewing hours for Quebecers differs from the national average of all Canadians?

Source: Statistics Canada.

12. The average salary for public school teachers for a specific year was reported to be $39,385. A random sample of 50 public school teachers had a mean of $41,680 and a standard deviation of $5975. Is there sufficient evidence at the $\alpha = 0.05$ level to conclude that the mean salary differs from $39,385?

Source: N.Y. Times Almanac.

13. To see if young men ages 8 through 17 years spend more or less than the U.S. national average of $24.44 per shopping trip to a local mall, the manager surveyed 33 young men and found the average amount spent per visit was $22.97. The standard deviation of the sample was $3.70. At $\alpha = 0.02$, can it be concluded that the average amount spent at a local mall is not equal to the national average of $24.44?

Source: USA TODAY.

14. What is meant by a P-value?

15. State whether the null hypothesis should be rejected on the basis of the given P-value.

   a. P-value = 0.258, $\alpha = 0.05$, one-tailed test
   b. P-value = 0.0684, $\alpha = 0.10$, two-tailed test
   c. P-value = 0.0153, $\alpha = 0.01$, one-tailed test
   d. P-value = 0.0232, $\alpha = 0.05$, two-tailed test
   e. P-value = 0.002, $\alpha = 0.01$, one-tailed test

16. A researcher claims that the average yearly consumption of bottled water in Canada is equal to 27 litres per capita. In a sample of 50 randomly selected Canadians, the mean yearly consumption of bottled water was 29.3 litres. The standard deviation of the sample was 1.8 litres. Find the P-value for the test. On the basis of the P-value, is the researcher's claim valid?

Source: Statistics Canada.

17. In winter driving conditions, it takes all vehicles longer to stop on snow-covered roads. Travelling at 90 kilometres per hour (km/h), the stopping distance for the average passenger vehicle on loose snow is 213 metres. A tire manufacturer claims that vehicles equipped with their winter tires decrease the stopping distance on snow-covered roads. A sample of 20 vehicles equipped with the manufacturer's tires was tested in winter on a test track. The average stopping distance at a speed of 90 km/h on loose snow was 211.6 metres. Assume a population standard deviation of 2.4 metres. Test the claim that the average stopping distance decreased with the new winter tires. Find the P-value. On the basis of the P-value, should the null hypothesis be rejected at $\alpha = 0.01$? Assume that the variable is normally distributed.

Source: Government of Ontario.

18. A store manager hypothesizes that the average number of pages a person copies on the store's copy machine is less than 40. A sample of 50 customers' orders is selected. At $\alpha = 0.01$, is there enough evidence to support the claim? Use the P-value hypothesis-testing method.

2	2	2	5	32
5	29	8	2	49
21	1	24	72	70
21	85	61	8	42
3	15	27	113	36
37	5	3	58	82
9	2	1	6	9
80	9	51	2	122
21	49	36	43	61
3	17	17	4	1

19. A health researcher read that a 91-kilogram male can burn an average of 546 calories per hour playing tennis. Thirty-six males were randomly selected and tested. The mean of the number of calories burned per hour was 544.8. Test the claim that the average number of calories burned is actually less than 546, and find the P-value. On the basis of the P-value, should the null hypothesis be rejected at $\alpha = 0.01$? The standard deviation of the sample is 3. Can it be concluded that the average number of calories burned is less than originally thought?

20. A special cable has a breaking strength of 363 kilograms. The standard deviation of the population is 5.5 kilograms. A researcher selects a sample of 20 cables and finds that the average breaking strength is 360 kilograms. Can one reject the claim that the breaking strength is 363 kilograms? Find the P-value. Should the null hypothesis be rejected at $\alpha = 0.01$? Assume that the variable is normally distributed.

21. Several years ago the Agriculture Division of Statistics Canada reported that the average size of farms in Canada was 246 hectares (ha). A random sample of 50 farms was selected, and the mean size of the farm was 296 ha. The standard deviation of the sample was 59 ha. Test the claim at $\alpha = 0.05$ that the average farm size is larger today, by using the P-value method. Should the Agriculture Division update its information?

Source: Statistics Canada Census of Agriculture.

22. Ten years ago the average farm size in Ontario was 81 hectares (ha). The standard deviation of the population was 7 ha. A recent study consisting of 22 Ontario farms showed that the average farm size was 83.9 ha. Use the P-value method to test the claim, at $\alpha = 0.10$, that the average farm size has not changed in the past 10 years. Use $\sigma = 7$ ha and assume that the variable is normally distributed.

Source: Statistics Canada.

23. A car manufacturer recommends that new vehicle transmissions be serviced at 48,000 kilometres (km) to maintain proper function. To see whether their customers are adhering to this recommendation, a car dealership selects a random sample of 40 customers and finds that the average distance driven by the serviced automobiles was 48,730 km. The standard deviation of the sample is 2694 km. Using the P-value method, test the claim that the owners are having their transmissions serviced at 48,000 km. Use $\alpha = 0.10$.

24. A motorist claims that the South Boro Police issue an average of 60 speeding tickets per day. These data show the number of speeding tickets issued each day for a period of one month. Assume σ is 13.42. Is there enough evidence to reject the motorist's claim at $\alpha = 0.05$? Use the P-value method.

72	45	36	68	69	71	57	60
83	26	60	72	58	87	48	59
60	56	64	68	42	57	57	
58	63	49	73	75	42	63	

25. A manager states that in his factory, the average number of days per year missed by the employees due to illness is less than the national average of 10. The following data show the number of days missed by 40 employees last year. Is there sufficient evidence to believe the manager's statement at $\alpha = 0.05$? (Use s to estimate σ.) Use the P-value method.

0	6	12	3	3	5	4	1
3	9	6	0	7	6	3	4
7	4	7	1	0	8	12	3
2	5	10	5	15	3	2	5
3	11	8	2	2	4	1	9

Extending the Concepts

26. Suppose a statistician chose to test a hypothesis at $\alpha = 0.01$. The critical value for a right-tailed test is $+2.33$. If the test statistic was 1.97, what would the decision be? What would happen if, after seeing the test statistic, she decided to choose $\alpha = 0.05$? What would the decision be? Explain the contradiction, if there is one.

27. The president of a company states that the average hourly wage of her employees is \$8.65. A sample of 50 employees has the distribution shown. At $\alpha = 0.05$, is the president's statement believable? (Use s to approximate σ.)

Class	Frequency
8.35–8.43	2
8.44–8.52	6
8.53–8.61	12
8.62–8.70	18
8.71–8.79	10
8.80–8.88	2

8–4   *t* Test for a Mean

Objective 6

Test means for small samples, using the *t* test.

When the population standard deviation is unknown and the sample size is less than 30, the *z* test is inappropriate for testing hypotheses involving means. A different test, called the *t test,* is used. The *t* test is used when σ is unknown, $n < 30$, and the distribution of the variable is approximately normal.

As stated in Chapter 7, the *t* distribution is similar to the standard normal distribution in the following ways.

1. It is bell-shaped.
2. It is symmetric about the mean.
3. The mean, median, and mode are equal to 0 and are located at the centre of the distribution.
4. The curve never touches the *x* axis.

The *t* distribution differs from the standard normal distribution in the following ways.

1. The variance is greater than 1.
2. The *t* distribution is a family of curves based on the *degrees of freedom,* which is a number related to sample size. (Recall that the symbol for degrees of freedom is d.f. See Section 7–3 for an explanation of degrees of freedom.)
3. As the sample size increases, the *t* distribution approaches the normal distribution.

The *t* test is defined next.

The **t test** is a statistical test for the mean of a population and is used when the population is normally or approximately normally distributed, σ is unknown, and $n < 30$.
   The formula for the *t* test is

$$t = \frac{\overline{X} - \mu}{s/\sqrt{n}}$$

The degrees of freedom are d.f. $= n - 1$.

The formula for the *t* test is similar to the formula for the *z* test. But since the population standard deviation σ is unknown, the sample standard deviation s is used instead.

The critical values for the *t* test are given in Table F in Appendix C. For a one-tailed test, find the α level by looking at the top row of the table and finding the appropriate column. Find the degrees of freedom by looking down the left-hand column. Notice that degrees of freedom are given for values from 1 through 28. When the degrees of freedom are 29 or more, the row with ∞ (infinity) is used. Note that the values in this row are the same as the values for the *z* distribution, since as the sample size increases, the *t* distribution approaches the *z* distribution. When the sample size is 30 or more, statisticians generally agree that the two distributions can be considered identical, since the difference between their values is relatively small.

Example 8–8

Find the critical *t* value for $\alpha = 0.05$ with d.f. = 16 for a right-tailed *t* test.

Solution

Find the 0.05 column in the top row and 16 in the left-hand column. Where the row and column meet, the appropriate critical value is found; it is $+1.746$. See Figure 8–19.

Figure 8–19

Finding the Critical Value for the *t* Test in Table F (Example 8–8)

Example 8–9

Find the critical *t* value for $\alpha = 0.01$ with d.f. = 22 for a left-tailed test.

Solution

Find the 0.01 column in the row labelled One tail, and find 22 in the left column. The critical value is -2.508 since the test is a one-tailed left test.

Example 8–10

Find the critical values for $\alpha = 0.10$ with d.f. = 18 for a two-tailed *t* test.

Solution

Find the 0.10 column in the row labelled Two tails, and find 18 in the column labelled d.f. The critical values are $+1.734$ and -1.734.

Example 8–11

Find the critical value for $\alpha = 0.05$ with d.f. $= 28$ for a right-tailed t test.

Solution

Find the 0.05 column in the One tail row and 28 in the left column. The critical value is $+1.701$.

When you test hypotheses by using the t test (traditional method), follow the same procedure as for the z test, except use Table F in Appendix C.

Step 1 State the hypotheses and identify the claim.

Step 2 Find the critical value(s) from Table F.

Step 3 Compute the test statistic.

Step 4 Make the decision to reject or not reject the null hypothesis.

Step 5 Summarize the results.

Remember that the t test should be used when the population is approximately normally distributed, the population standard deviation is unknown, and the sample size is less than 30.

Examples 8–12 through 8–14 illustrate the application of the t test.

Example 8–12

A health care recruitment agency claims that the average starting salary for Canada's practical nursing graduates is \$39,500. Suppose a random sample of 10 nursing graduates yields an average salary of \$38,554 and a standard deviation of \$750. At $\alpha = 0.05$, is there enough evidence to reject the recruitment agency's claim? Assume the variable is approximately normally distributed.

Solution

Step 1 $H_0: \mu = \$39,500$ (claim) and $H_1: \mu \neq \$39,500$

Step 2 The critical values are $+2.262$ and -2.262 for $\alpha = 0.05$ (two tails) and d.f. $= 9$.

Step 3 The test statistic is

$$t = \frac{\overline{X} - \mu}{s/\sqrt{n}} = \frac{\$38,554 - \$39,500}{\$750/\sqrt{10}} \approx -3.989$$

Step 4 Reject the null hypothesis, since $-3.989 < -2.262$ as shown in Figure 8–20.

Step 5 There is enough evidence to reject the claim that the starting salary of practical nurses is \$39,500.

Figure 8–20

Summary of the t Test of Example 8–12

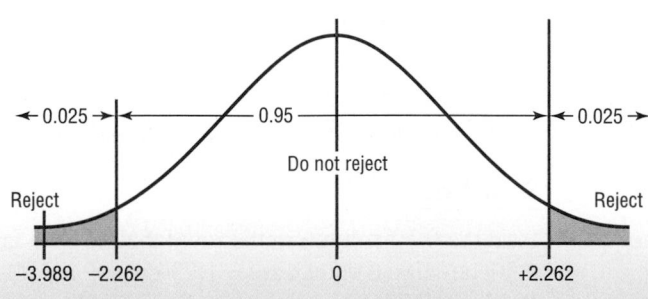

Example 8–13

A union representative claims that the average daily salary for substitute teachers is less than $185 per day in Southern Ontario school districts. A sample of 8 school districts is randomly selected, and the daily salaries (in dollars) are shown. Is there enough evidence to support the union representative's claim at $\alpha = 0.10$? Assume that the population data is normally distributed.

$$185 \quad 179 \quad 185 \quad 173 \quad 198 \quad 171 \quad 185 \quad 172$$

Solution

Step 1 H_0: $\mu = \$185$ and H_1: $\mu < \$185$ (claim)

Step 2 At $\alpha = 0.10$ and d.f. $= 7$, the critical value is -1.415.

Step 3 To compute the test statistic, the mean and standard deviation must be found. Using either the formulas in Chapter 3 or your calculator, $\overline{X} = \$181$ and $s = \$9.15$.

$$t = \frac{\overline{X} - \mu}{s/\sqrt{n}} = \frac{\$181 - \$185}{\$9.15/\sqrt{8}} \approx -1.237$$

Step 4 Do not reject the null hypothesis, since -1.237 falls in the noncritical region. See Figure 8–21.

Figure 8–21

Critical Value and Test Statistic for Example 8–13

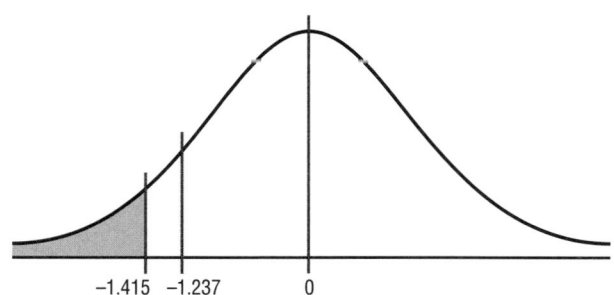

$$-1.415 \quad -1.237 \qquad 0$$

Step 5 There is not enough evidence to support the union's claim that the average salary of substitute teachers in Southern Ontario school districts is less than $185 per day.

The *P*-values for the *t* test can be found by using Table F; however, specific *P*-values for *t* tests cannot be obtained from the table since only selected values of α (for example, 0.01, 0.05) are given. To find specific *P*-values for *t* tests, one would need tables similar to Tables E–1 and E–2 in Appendix C for each degree of freedom. Since this is not practical, only *intervals* can be found for *P*-values. Examples 8–14 to 8–16 show how to use Table F to determine intervals for *P*-values for the *t* test.

Example 8–14

Find the *P*-value when the *t* test statistic is 2.056, the sample size is 11, and the test is right-tailed.

Solution

To get the *P*-value, look across the row with 10 degrees of freedom (d.f. $= n - 1$) in Table F and find the two values that 2.056 falls between. They are 1.812 and 2.228.

Figure 8–22

Finding the *P*-Value for Example 8–14

Confidence intervals	50%	80%	90%	95%	98%	99%
One tail, α	0.25	0.10	(0.05)	(0.025)	0.01	0.005
d.f. Two tails, α	0.50	0.20	0.10	0.05	0.02	0.01
1	1.000	3.078	6.314	12.706	31.821	63.657
2	0.816	1.886	2.920	4.303	6.965	9.925
3	0.765	1.638	2.353	3.182	4.541	5.841
4	0.741	1.533	2.132	2.776	3.747	4.604
5	0.727	1.476	2.015	2.571	3.365	4.032
6	0.718	1.440	1.943	2.447	3.143	3.707
7	0.711	1.415	1.895	2.365	2.998	3.499
8	0.706	1.397	1.860	2.306	2.896	3.355
9	0.703	1.383	1.833	2.262	2.821	3.250
(10)	0.700	1.372	(1.812)	(2.228)	2.764	3.169
11	0.697	1.363	1.796	2.201	2.718	3.106
12	0.695	1.356	1.782	2.179	2.681	3.055
13	0.694	1.350	1.771	2.160	2.650	3.012
14	0.692	1.345	1.761	2.145	2.624	2.977
15	0.691	1.341	1.753	2.131	2.602	2.947
⋮	⋮	⋮	⋮	⋮	⋮	⋮
(z) ∞	0.674	1.282	1.645	1.960	2.326	2.576

*2.056 falls between 1.812 and 2.228.

Since this is a right-tailed test, look up to the row labelled One tail, α and find the two α values corresponding to 1.812 and 2.228. They are 0.05 and 0.025, respectively. See Figure 8–22. Hence, the *P*-value would be contained in the interval $0.025 < P\text{-value} < 0.05$. This means that the *P*-value is between 0.025 and 0.05. If α were 0.05, one would reject the null hypothesis since the *P*-value is less than 0.05. But if α were 0.01, one would not reject the null hypothesis since the *P*-value is greater than 0.01. (Actually, it is greater than 0.025.)

Example 8–15

Find the *P*-value when the *t* test value is 2.983, the sample size is 6, and the test is two-tailed.

Solution

To get the *P*-value, look across the row with d.f. $= 5$ and find the two values that 2.983 falls between. They are 2.571 and 3.365. Then look up to the row labelled Two tails, α to find the corresponding α values.

In this case, they are 0.05 and 0.02. Hence the *P*-value is contained in the interval $0.02 < P\text{-value} < 0.05$. This means that the *P*-value is between 0.02 and 0.05. In this case, if $\alpha = 0.05$, the null hypothesis can be rejected since $P\text{-value} < 0.05$; but if $\alpha = 0.01$, the null hypothesis cannot be rejected since $P\text{-value} > 0.01$ (actually $P\text{-value} > 0.02$).

Note: **Since many students will be using calculators or computer programs that give the specific *P*-value for the *t* test and other tests presented later in this textbook, these specific values, in addition to the intervals, will be given for the answers to the examples and exercises.**

The *P*-value obtained from a calculator for Example 8–14 is 0.033. The *P*-value obtained from a calculator for Example 8–15 is 0.031.

To test hypotheses using the *P*-value method, follow the same steps as explained in Section 8–3. These steps are repeated here.

Step 1   State the hypotheses and identify the claim.

Step 2   Compute the test statistic.

Step 3   Find the *P*-value.

Step 4   Make the decision.

Step 5   Summarize the results.

This method is shown in Example 8–16.

Example 8–16

A physician claims that joggers' maximal volume oxygen uptake is greater than the average of all adults. A sample of 15 joggers has a mean of 40.6 millilitres per kilogram (ml/kg) and a standard deviation of 6 ml/kg. If the average of all adults is 36.7 ml/kg, is there enough evidence to support the physician's claim at $\alpha = 0.05$?

Solution

Step 1   State the hypotheses and identify the claim.

$$H_0: \mu = 36.7 \qquad \text{and} \qquad H_1: \mu > 36.7 \ (\text{claim})$$

Step 2   Compute the test statistic. The test statistic is

$$t = \frac{\overline{X} - \mu}{s/\sqrt{n}} = \frac{40.6 - 36.7}{6/\sqrt{15}} \approx 2.517$$

Step 3   Find the *P*-value. Looking across the row with d.f. = 14 in Table F, one sees that 2.517 falls between 2.145 and 2.624, corresponding to $\alpha = 0.025$ and $\alpha = 0.01$ since this is a right-tailed test. Hence, *P*-value > 0.01 and *P*-value < 0.025 or 0.01 < *P*-value < 0.025. That is, the *P*-value is somewhere between 0.01 and 0.025. (The *P*-value obtained from a calculator is 0.012.)

Step 4   Reject the null hypothesis since *P*-value < 0.05 (that is, *P*-value < α).

Step 5   There is enough evidence to support the claim that the joggers' maximal volume oxygen uptake is greater than 36.7 ml/kg.

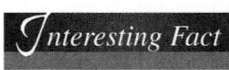

Interesting Fact

Canada has 4000 centenarians, 3400 of whom are women.

Students sometimes have difficulty deciding whether to use the *z* test or *t* test. The rules are the same as those pertaining to confidence intervals.

1. If σ is known, use the *z* test. The variable must be normally distributed if $n < 30$.

2. If σ is unknown but $n \geq 30$, use the *z* test and use *s* in place of σ in the formula.

3. If σ is unknown and $n < 30$, use the *t* test. (The population must be approximately normally distributed.)

These rules are summarized in Figure 8–23.

Speaking of
Statistics

Can Sunshine Relieve Pain?

A study conducted at the University of Pittsburgh showed that hospital patients in rooms with lots of sunlight required less pain medication the day after surgery and during their total stay in the hospital than patients who were in darker rooms.

Patients in the sunny rooms averaged 3.2 milligrams of pain reliever per hour for their total stay as opposed to 4.1 milligrams per hour for those in darker rooms. This study compared two groups of patients. Although no statistical tests were mentioned in the article, what statistical test do you think the researchers used to compare the groups?

Figure 8–23

Using the z or t Test

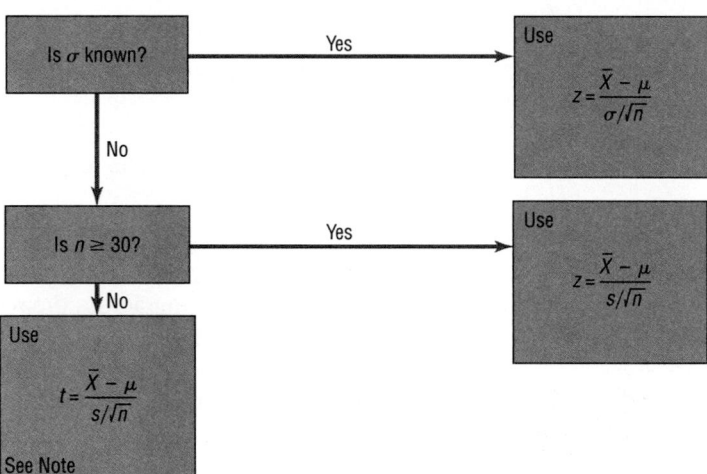

Note: With d.f. = $n - 1$, and the population must be approximately normally distributed.

Applying the Concepts 8–4

How Much Nicotine Is in Those Cigarettes?

A tobacco company claims that its best-selling cigarettes contain at most 40 mg of nicotine. This claim is tested at the 1% significance level by using the results of 15 randomly selected cigarettes. The mean was 42.6 mg and the standard deviation was 3.7 mg. Evidence suggests that nicotine is normally distributed. Information from a computer output of the hypothesis test is listed.

Sample mean = 42.6	P-value = 0.008
Sample standard deviation = 3.7	Significance level = 0.01
Sample size = 15	Test statistic $t = 2.72155$
Degrees of freedom = 14	Critical value $t = 2.62610$

1. What are the degrees of freedom?
2. Is this a large or small sample test?
3. Is this a comparison of one or two samples?
4. Is this a right-tailed, left-tailed, or two-tailed test?
5. From observing the *P*-value, what would you conclude?
6. By comparing the test statistic to the critical value, what would you conclude?
7. Is there a conflict in this output? Explain.
8. What has been proved in this study?

See page 394 for the answers.

Exercises 8–4

1. In what ways is the *t* distribution similar to the standard normal distribution? In what ways is the *t* distribution different from the standard normal distribution?

2. What are the degrees of freedom for the *t* test?

3. Find the critical value (or values) for the *t* test for each.

   a. $n = 10$, $\alpha = 0.05$, right-tailed
   b. $n = 18$, $\alpha = 0.10$, two-tailed
   c. $n = 6$, $\alpha = 0.01$, left-tailed
   d. $n = 9$, $\alpha = 0.025$, right-tailed
   e. $n = 15$, $\alpha = 0.05$, two-tailed
   f. $n = 23$, $\alpha = 0.005$, left-tailed
   g. $n = 28$, $\alpha = 0.01$, two-tailed
   h. $n = 17$, $\alpha = 0.02$, two-tailed

4. **(ans)** Using Table F, find the *P*-value interval for each test value.

   a. $t = 2.321$, $n = 15$, right-tailed
   b. $t = 1.945$, $n = 28$, two-tailed
   c. $t = -1.267$, $n = 8$, left-tailed
   d. $t = 1.562$, $n = 17$, two-tailed
   e. $t = 3.025$, $n = 24$, right-tailed
   f. $t = -1.145$, $n = 5$, left-tailed
   g. $t = 2.179$, $n = 13$, two-tailed
   h. $t = 0.665$, $n = 10$, right-tailed

For Exercises 5 through 18, perform each of the following steps.

   a. State the hypotheses and identify the claim.
   b. Find the critical value(s).
   c. Find the test statistic.
   d. Make the decision.
   e. Summarize the results.

Use the traditional method of hypothesis testing unless otherwise specified.

Assume that the population is approximately normally distributed.

5. The average amount of rainfall during the summer months for the Maritime Provinces is 281.5 millimetres (mm). A researcher selects a random sample of 10 cities in the Maritimes in 2006 and finds that the average amount of rainfall was 265.2 mm. The standard deviation of the sample is 17.4 mm. At $\alpha = 0.05$, can it be concluded that the mean rainfall in 2006 was below 281.5 mm?

   Source: Environment Canada.

6. A government bureaucrat claims that the average area of British Columbia's provincial parks is less than 137.6 square kilometres (km^2). A random sample of five parks is selected, and the area, in km^2, is shown. At $\alpha = 0.01$, is there enough evidence to support the claim?

   | 280 | 32 | 109 | 68 | 155 |

   Source: British Columbia Parks.

7. The average salary of mayors from Canada's cities is reported to be equal to $120,000. To test this claim, 5 Canadian cities are selected and it is found that the average salary is $132,389. Assume the population standard deviation is $12,121. Using $\alpha = 0.05$, test the claim that the reported salary is incorrect.

   Source: *Calgary Herald.*

8. A survey finds that urban Canadians average 62.1 minutes commuting to and from work. A chamber of commerce executive claims that the average commute time in her city is less than the Canadian average commute time and she wants to publicize this. She randomly selects 25 commuters and finds the average commute time is 53.9 minutes with a standard deviation of 12.9 minutes. At $\alpha = 0.10$, test the executive's claim.

   Source: Statistics Canada.

9. An architect designing a new office tower estimates that the average height of Canada's tallest buildings of 30 or more stories is at least 200 metres. A random sample of 10 buildings is selected and the heights in metres are shown. At $\alpha = 0.025$, is there enough evidence to reject the claim.

   | 155 | 195 | 224 | 183 | 167 | 177 | 190 | 263 | 155 | 215 |

   Source: www.architecture.about.com.

10. A report on Toronto's real estate market indicated that a two-bedroom condominium unit's rental rate averaged $1765 per month. A company subsidizing new employee housing selects a random sample of 15 similar rental units and found the average rent was $1924 with a standard deviation of $374. At $\alpha = 0.05$, test the claim that there is no difference in the average rents.

Source: MLS Rental Market Report.

11. The average undergraduate cost for tuition, fees, and room and board for two-year institutions last year was $13,252. The following year, a random sample of 20 two-year institutions had a mean of $15,560 and a standard deviation of $3500. Is there sufficient evidence at the $\alpha = 0.01$ level to conclude that the mean cost has increased?

Source: N.Y. Times Almanac.

12. A large university reports that the mean salary of parents of an entering class is $91,600. To see how this compares to his university, a president surveys 28 randomly selected families and finds that their average income is $88,500. If the standard deviation is $10,000, can the president conclude that there is a difference? At $\alpha = 0.10$, is he correct?

Source: Chronicle of Higher Education.

13. During a recent year the average cost of making a movie was $54.8 million. This year, a random sample of 15 recent action movies had an average production cost of $62.3 million with a variance of $90.25 million. At the 0.05 level of significance, can it be concluded that it costs more than average to produce an action movie?

Source: N.Y. Times Almanac.

14. An average serving of 30-gram cookies contains 150 calories. A random sample of 15 different brands of 30-gram cookies resulted in the following calorie amounts. At the $\alpha = 0.01$ level, is there sufficient evidence that the average calorie content of 30-gram cookies is greater than 150 calories?

140	165	190	200	225	165	195	185
200	140	190	180	185	160	150	

Source: Health Canada.

15. The average running time for current Broadway shows is 2 hours 12 minutes. A producer in another city claims that the length of time of productions in his city is the same. He samples 8 shows and finds the time to be 2 hours 5 minutes with a standard deviation of 11 minutes. Using $\alpha = 0.05$, is the producer correct?

Source: New York Times, Arts and Leisure.

16. In 1999, the *Atlas of Canada* reported that Canadians use an average of 343 litres of water per person per day. To test the hypothesis that this figure may no longer be true, a researcher randomly selects 16 people and found that they used on average 332 litres per day with $s = 14.9$ litres. At $\alpha = 0.05$, is there enough evidence that the *Atlas of Canada* figure may no longer be correct? Use the P-value method.

Source: Environment Canada.

17. A report by the Gallup Poll stated that on average a woman visits her physician 5.8 times a year. A researcher randomly selects 20 women and obtained these data.

3	2	1	3	7	2	9	4	6	6
8	0	5	6	4	2	1	3	4	1

At $\alpha = 0.05$ can it be concluded that the average is still 5.8 visits per year? Use the P-value method.

18. Statistics Canada published a study on *Changes in Job Tenure and Job Stability in Canada*. The study reported that on average workers aged 25 to 34 years worked for 4.3 years before changing jobs. To see if this average is correct, a researcher selected a sample of 8 workers aged 25 to 34 years who completed a job term. The worker job tenures (in years) are listed.

2.1	5.9	7.2	4.3	5.3	11.1	1.5	2.7

At $\alpha = 0.05$ can it be concluded that the mean job tenure for workers aged 25 to 34 years is 4.3 years? Use the P-value method. Give one reason why the respondents might not have given the exact number of years that they have worked.

Source: Statistics Canada.

19. A random sample of stipends of teaching assistants in economics is listed. Is there sufficient evidence at the $\alpha = 0.05$ level to conclude that the average stipend differs from $15,000? The stipends listed (in dollars) are for the academic year.

14,000	18,000	12,000	14,356	13,185
13,419	14,000	11,981	17,604	12,283
16,338	15,000			

Source: Chronicle of Higher Education.

20. The average family size was reported as 3.18. A random sample of families in a particular school district resulted in the following family sizes:

5	4	5	4	4	3	6	4	3	3	5
6	3	3	2	7	4	5	2	2	2	3
5	2									

At $\alpha = 0.05$, does the average family size differ from the national average?

Source: N.Y. Times Almanac.

8–5   *z* Test for a Proportion

Many hypothesis-testing situations involve proportions. Recall from Chapter 7 that a *proportion* is the same as a percentage of the population.

Objective ⑦

Test proportions, using the *z* test.

These data were adapted from the book *What Canadians Think* by Darrell Bricker and John Wright (Doubleday Canada, 2005):

- 33% of Canadians feel that Newfoundlanders have the best sense of humour
- 69% of pet owners allow their pets in bed at night
- 57% of Albertans will barbecue all year round
- 94% of Canadians would put their trust in a firefighter

A hypothesis test involving a population proportion can be considered as a binomial experiment when there are only two outcomes and the probability of a success does not change from trial to trial. Recall from Section 5–4 that the mean is $\mu = np$ and the standard deviation is $\sigma = \sqrt{npq}$ for the binomial distribution.

Since a normal distribution can be used to approximate the binomial distribution when $np \geq 5$ and $nq \geq 5$, the standard normal distribution can be used to test hypotheses for proportions.

Formula for the *z* Test for Proportions

$$z = \frac{\hat{p} - p}{\sqrt{pq/n}}$$

where

$$\hat{p} = \frac{X}{n} \quad \text{(sample proportion)}$$

p = population proportion

$q = 1 - p$

n = sample size

The formula is derived from the normal approximation to the binomial and follows the general formula

$$\text{Test statistic} = \frac{(\text{observed value}) - (\text{expected value})}{\text{standard error}}$$

We obtain $\hat{p}$ from the sample (i.e., observed value), p is the expected value (i.e., hypothesized population proportion), and $\sqrt{pq/n}$ is the standard error.

The formula $z = \dfrac{\hat{p} - p}{\sqrt{pq/n}}$ can be derived from the formula $z = \dfrac{X - \mu}{\sigma}$ by substituting $\mu = np$ and $\sigma = \sqrt{npq}$ and then dividing both numerator and denominator by n. Some algebra is used. See Exercise 23 in this section.

The steps for hypothesis testing are the same as those shown in Section 8–3. Tables E–1 and E–2 are used to find critical values and *P*-values.

Examples 8–17 to 8–19 show the traditional method of hypothesis testing. Example 8–20 shows the *P*-value method.

Sometimes it is necessary to find $\hat{p}$, as shown in Examples 8–17, 8–19, and 8–20, and sometimes $\hat{p}$ is given in the exercise. See Example 8–18.

Example 8–17

A Quebec adult educator estimates that 15% of adults, aged 25 to 34 years, have yet to complete their high school diploma. The educator surveys a random sample of 200 Quebec adults, aged 25 to 34 years, and discovers that 38 have not completed their high school diploma. At $\alpha = 0.05$, is there significant evidence to reject the educator's claim?

Source: Excerpt from *30 Years of Education: Canada's Language Groups,* adapted from Statistics Canada publication *Canadian Social Trends,* Catalogue 11-008, Winter 2003.

Solution

Step 1 State the hypothesis and identify the claim.

$$H_0: p = 0.15 \text{ (claim)} \quad \text{and} \quad H_1: p \neq 0.15$$

Step 2 Find the critical value. Since $\alpha = 0.05$ and the test is a two-tailed test, the critical values are $z = \pm 1.96$.

Step 3 Compute the test statistic. First, it is necessary to find $\hat{p}$.

$$\hat{p} = \frac{X}{n} = \frac{38}{200} = 0.19 \quad \text{and} \quad p = 0.15 \quad \text{and} \quad q = 1 - 0.15 = 0.85$$

Substitute the formula and solve.

$$z = \frac{\hat{p} - p}{\sqrt{pq/n}} = \frac{0.19 - 0.15}{\sqrt{(0.15)(0.85)/200}} \approx 1.584$$

Step 4 Make the decision. Do not reject the null hypothesis, since the test statistic falls outside the critical region, as shown in Figure 8–24.

Figure 8–24

Critical Values and Test Statistic for Example 8–17

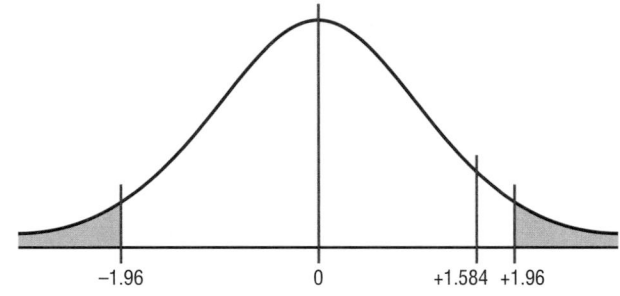

$-1.96 \qquad 0 \qquad +1.584 \ +1.96$

Step 5 Summarize the results. There is not enough evidence to reject the claim that the 15% of Quebec adults, aged 25 to 34 years, have yet to complete their high school diploma.

Example 8–18 A telephone company representative estimates that 40% of its customers have call-waiting service. To test this hypothesis, she selected a sample of 100 customers and found that 37% had call waiting. At $\alpha = 0.01$, is there enough evidence to reject the claim?

Solution

Step 1 State the hypotheses and identify the claim.

$$H_0: p = 0.40 \text{ (claim)} \quad \text{and} \quad H_1: p \neq 0.40$$

Step 2 Find the critical value(s). Since $\alpha = 0.01$ and this test is two-tailed, the critical values are ± 2.575.

Step 3 Compute the test statistic. It is not necessary to find $\hat{p}$ since it is given in the exercise; $\hat{p} = 0.37$. Substitute in the formula and solve.

$$p = 0.40 \quad \text{and} \quad q = 1 - 0.40 = 0.60$$

$$z = \frac{\hat{p} - p}{\sqrt{pq/n}} = \frac{0.37 - 0.40}{\sqrt{(0.40)(0.60)/100}} = -0.612$$

Figure 8–25

Critical Values and Test Statistic for Example 8–18

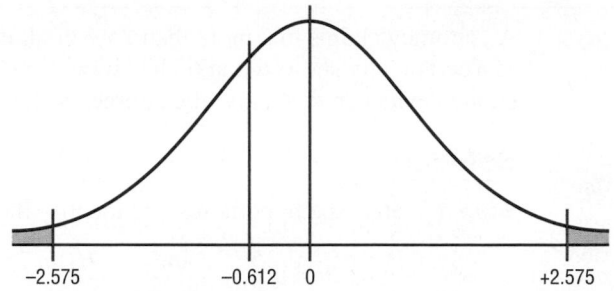

−2.575   −0.612   0   +2.575

Step 4   Make the decision. Do not reject the null hypothesis, since the test statistic falls in the noncritical region, as shown in Figure 8–25.

Step 5   Summarize the results. There is not enough evidence to reject the claim that 40% of the telephone company's customers have call waiting.

Example 8–19

A statistician read that at least 59% of Canada's population opposes the abolishment of the penny (1¢ coin) as was done in Australia and New Zealand. To see if this claim is valid, the statistician selected a random sample of 80 Canadians and found that 41 were opposed to abolishing the penny. At $\alpha = 0.01$, test the claim that at least 59% oppose the penny's abolishment.

Source: Harris Poll.

Solution

Step 1   State the hypothesis and identify the claim. (Note: At least infers $\geq$ and the null hypothesis assumes a state of equality, therefore the alternative is $<$.)

H_0: $p = 0.59$ (claim)   and H_1: $p < 0.59$

Step 2   Find the critical value. Since $\alpha = 0.01$ and the test is left-tailed test, the critical value is −2.33.

Step 3   Compute the test statistic.

$$\hat{p} = \frac{X}{n} = \frac{41}{80} = 0.5125$$

$$p = 0.59 \quad \text{and} \quad q = 1 - 0.59 = 0.41$$

$$z = \frac{\hat{p} - p}{\sqrt{pq/n}} = \frac{0.5125 - 0.59}{\sqrt{(0.59)(0.41)/80}} \approx -1.409$$

Step 4   Do not reject the null hypothesis, since the test statistic does not fall in the critical region, as shown in Figure 8–26.

Figure 8–26

Critical Value and Test Statistic for Example 8–19

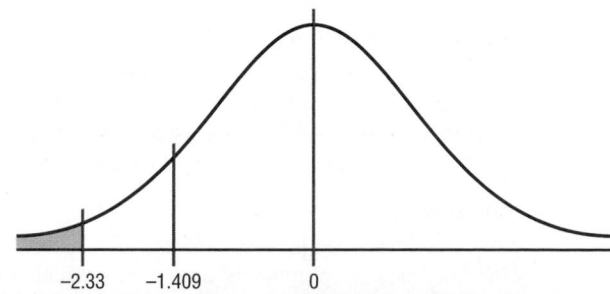

−2.33   −1.409   0

Step 5   There is not enough evidence to reject the claim that at least 59% of the population opposes the abolishment of the penny coin.

Example 8–20

An attorney claims that more than 25% of all lawyers advertise. A sample of 200 lawyers in a certain city showed that 63 had used some form of advertising. At $\alpha = 0.05$, is there enough evidence to support the attorney's claim? Use the P-value method.

Solution

Step 1   State the hypotheses and identify the claim.

$$H_0: p = 0.25 \quad \text{and} \quad H_1: p > 0.25 \text{ (claim)}$$

Step 2   Compute the test statistic.

$$\hat{p} = \frac{X}{n} = \frac{63}{200} = 0.315$$

$$p = 0.25 \quad \text{and} \quad q = 1 - 0.25 = 0.75$$

$$z = \frac{\hat{p} - p}{\sqrt{pq/n}} = \frac{0.315 - 0.25}{\sqrt{(0.25)(0.75)/200}} \approx 2.12$$

Step 3   Find the P-value. The area under the curve for $z = 2.12$ is 0.9830. Subtracting the area from 1.000, one gets $1.000 - 0.983 = 0.0170$. The P-value is 0.0170.

Step 4   Reject the null hypothesis, since $0.0170 < 0.05$ (that is, P-value < 0.05). See Figure 8–27.

Figure 8–27

P-Value and α Value for Example 8–20

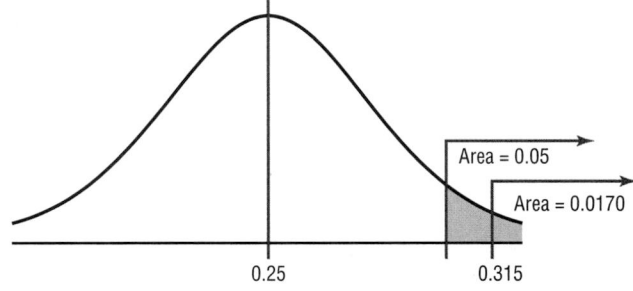

Step 5   There is enough evidence to support the attorney's claim that more than 25% of the lawyers use some form of advertising.

Applying the Concepts 8–5

Quitting Smoking

Assume you are part of a research team that compares products designed to help people quit smoking. The Condor Consumer Products Company would like more specific details about the study to be made available to the scientific community. Review the following and then answer the questions about how you would have conducted the study.

New StopSmoke

No method has been proved more effective. StopSmoke provides significant advantages to all other methods. StopSmoke is simpler to use, and it requires no weaning. StopSmoke is also significantly less expensive than the leading brands. StopSmoke's superiority has been proved in two independent studies.

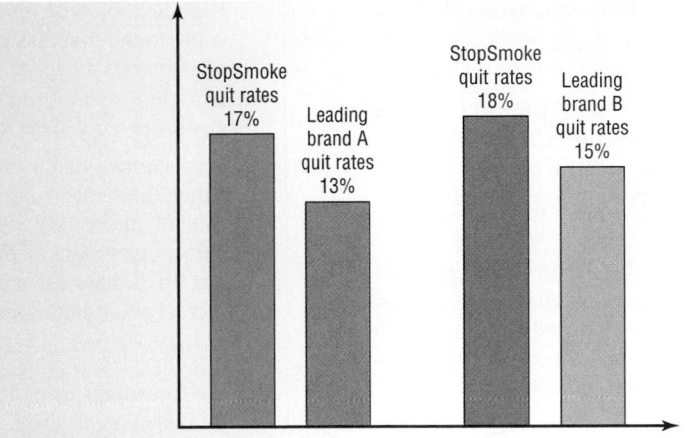

1. What were the statistical hypotheses?
2. What were the null hypotheses?
3. What were the alternative hypotheses?
4. Were any statistical tests run?
5. Were one- or two-tailed tests run?
6. What were the levels of significance?
7. If a type I error was committed, explain what it would have been.
8. If a type II error was committed, explain what it would have been.
9. What did the studies prove?
10. Two statements are made about significance. One states that StopSmoke provides significant advantages, and the other states that StopSmoke is significantly less expensive than other leading brands. Are they referring to statistical significance? What other type of significance is there?

See page 395 for the answers.

Exercises 8–5

1. Give three examples of proportions.

2. Why is a proportion considered a binomial variable?

3. When one is testing hypotheses by using proportions, what are the necessary requirements?

4. What are the mean and the standard deviation of a proportion?

For Exercises 5 through 15, perform each of the following steps.

   a. State the hypotheses and identify the claim.
   b. Find the critical value(s).
   c. Compute the test statistic.
   d. Make the decision.
   e. Summarize the results.

Use the traditional method of hypothesis testing unless otherwise specified.

5. A recent survey found that 64.7% of the population own their homes. In a random sample of 150 heads of households, 92 responded that they owned their homes.

At the 0.01 level of significance, does that indicate a difference from the national proportion?

Source: *N.Y. Times Almanac.*

6. Of families 48.8% have stockholdings. A random sample of 250 families indicated that 142 owned some type of stock. At what level of significance would you conclude that this was a significant difference?

Source: *N.Y. Times Almanac.*

7. It has been reported that 40% of the adult population participate in computer hobbies during their leisure time. A random sample of 180 adults found that 65 engaged in computer hobbies. At $\alpha = 0.01$, is there sufficient evidence to conclude that the proportion differs from 40%?

Source: *N.Y. Times Almanac.*

8. The percentage of physicians who are women is 27.9%. In a survey of physicians employed by a large university health system, 45 of 120 randomly selected physicians were women. Is there sufficient evidence at the 0.05 level of significance to conclude that the proportion

of women physicians at the university health system exceeds 27.9%?

Source: *N.Y. Times Almanac.*

9. A published report indicated that 51.6% of Canadians are mobile communication subscribers. A researcher surveyed 150 Canadians and found that 74 were subscribers. At $\alpha = 0.05$, test the accuracy of the reported claim.

Source: Statistics Canada.

10. Canada Council reported that 35% of adults attended a Canadian performing arts performance in the past year. To test this claim, a researcher surveyed 90 people and found that 40 people had attended a performance in the past year. At $\alpha = 0.05$, test the claim that this figure is correct.

Source: Canada Council.

11. A published report claims that 7.3% of vehicle fatalities involve motorcyclists. An insurance investigator studies 50 randomly selected accidents and finds that 4 fatalities implicated motorcyclists. Using $\alpha = 0.05$, can the report be disproved?

Source: Transport Canada.

12. A report on the website Women's Health Matters claims that 26% of Canadian women exercise regularly as a way to reduce stress. In order to test the claim a random sample of 100 women was taken and 21 indicated that exercise was used to relieve stress. Use $\alpha = 0.10$ and the *P*-value method. Could the results be generalized to all Canadian women?

13. The Canadian Association of Food Banks (CAFB) claims that 13.3% of food bank users have jobs. To test the claim a random sample of 60 patrons at food banks were surveyed and 10 had jobs. Use $\alpha = 0.01$ and the *P*-value method. On the basis of the results, would you agree with CAFB's claim?

Source: CAFB—Hungercount 2004.

14. Statistics Canada reports that 50.1% of homes in Canada were heated by natural gas. A random sample of 200 homes found that 111 were heated by natural gas. Does the evidence support the claim, or has the percentage changed? Use $\alpha = 0.05$ and the *P*-value method.

Source: Statistics Canada.

15. Researchers suspect that 18% of all high school students smoke at least one pack of cigarettes a day. At Wilson

High School, with an enrolment of 300 students, a study found that 50 students smoked at least one pack of cigarettes a day. At $\alpha = 0.05$, test the claim that 18% of all high school students smoke at least one pack of cigarettes a day. Use the *P*-value method.

16. For a certain year a study reports that the percentage of college students using credit cards was 83%. A college dean of student services feels that this is too high for her university, so she randomly selects 50 students and finds that 40 of them use credit cards. At $\alpha = 0.04$, is she correct about her university?

Source: *USA TODAY.*

17. For Canadians using library services, a national survey by Canadian Heritage claims that 44% borrow books. A library director feels that this is not true so he randomly selects 100 borrowers and finds that 59 borrowed library books. Can he show that the Canadian Heritage survey is incorrect? Use $\alpha = 0.05$.

Source: Canadian Heritage—Reading and Buying Books for Pleasure.

18. In a survey of earned doctorates in Canadian universities, 64% of respondents indicated that paid teaching assistantships aided in financing their studies. A university dean feels that this figure is high for her province. A random sample of 50 PhD students finds that 27 have assistantships. At $\alpha = 0.05$, is the dean correct?

Source: Statistics Canada.

19. A gun control advocacy study published research indicating that firearm-related fatalities account for 10% of all injury deaths in the province. Believing this figure to be high, a researcher selects a random sample of 37 injury deaths and discovers that 3 deaths were firearm-related. Is the researcher's claim correct, at $\alpha = 0.05$?

Source: Alberta Centre for Injury Control & Research—Firearm Deaths and Injuries.

20. For a specific survey, the Gallup Poll reported that 45% of individuals felt they were worse off than one year ago. A politician feels that this is too high for her district, so she commissions her own survey and finds that, out of 150 randomly selected citizens, 58 feel they are worse off today than one year ago. At $\alpha = 0.05$, is the politician correct about her district?

Source: Gallup Poll, *USA TODAY.*

Extending the Concepts

When *np* or *nq* is not 5 or more, the binomial table (Table B in Appendix C) must be used to find critical values in hypothesis tests involving proportions.

21. A coin is tossed 9 times and 3 heads appear. Can one conclude that the coin is not balanced? Use $\alpha = 0.10$. [*Hint:* Use the binomial table and find $2P(X \leq 3)$ with $p = 0.5$ and $n = 9$.]

22. In the past, 20% of all airline passengers flew first class. In a sample of 15 passengers, 5 flew first class. At $\alpha = 0.10$, can one conclude that the proportions have changed?

23. Show that $z = \dfrac{\hat{p} - p}{\sqrt{pq/n}}$ can be derived from $z = \dfrac{X - \mu}{\sigma}$ by substituting $\mu = np$ and $\sigma = \sqrt{npq}$ and dividing both numerator and denominator by n.

8–6 χ^2 **Test for a Variance or Standard Deviation**

Objective 8

Test variances or standard deviations, using the chi-square test.

In Chapter 7, the chi-square distribution was used to construct a confidence interval for a single variance or standard deviation. This distribution is also used to test a claim about a single variance or standard deviation.

To find the area under the chi-square distribution, use Table G in Appendix C. There are three cases to consider:

1. Finding the chi-square critical value for a specific α when the hypothesis test is right-tailed.
2. Finding the chi-square critical value for a specific α when the hypothesis test is left-tailed.
3. Finding the chi-square critical values for a specific α when the hypothesis test is two-tailed.

Example 8–21

Find the critical chi-square value for 15 degrees of freedom when $\alpha = 0.05$ and the test is right-tailed.

Solution

The distribution is shown in Figure 8–28.

Figure 8–28

Chi-Square Distribution for Example 8–21

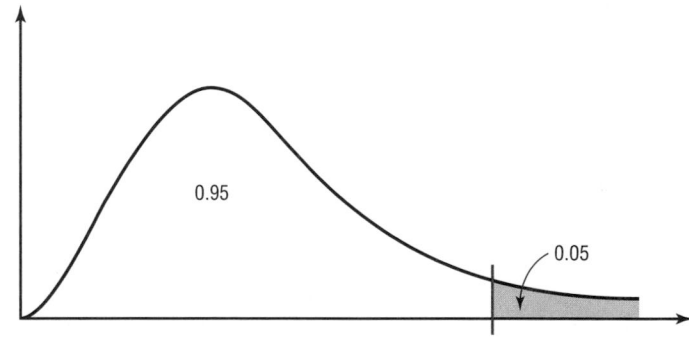

Find the α value at the top of Table G, and find the corresponding degrees of freedom in the left column. The critical value is located where the two columns meet—in this case, 24.996. See Figure 8–29.

Figure 8–29

Locating the Critical Value in Table G for Example 8–21

Example 8–22

Find the critical chi-square value for 10 degrees of freedom when $\alpha = 0.05$ and the test is left-tailed.

Solution

This distribution is shown in Figure 8–30.

Figure 8–30

Chi-Square Distribution for Example 8–22

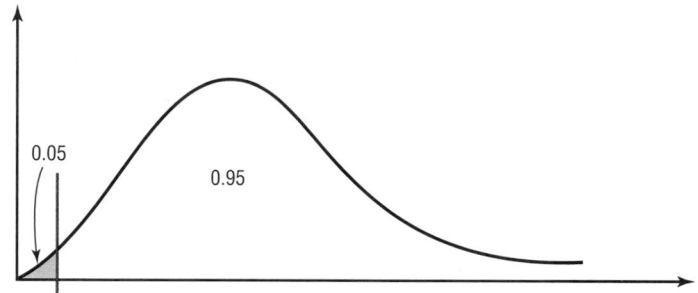

When the test is left-tailed, the α value must be subtracted from 1, that is, $1 - 0.05 = 0.95$. The left side of the table is used, because the chi-square table gives the area to the right of the critical value, and the chi-square statistic cannot be negative. The table is set up so that it gives the values for the area to the right of the critical value. In this case, 95% of the area will be to the right of the value.

For 0.95 and 10 degrees of freedom, the critical value is 3.940. See Figure 8–31.

Figure 8–31

Locating the Critical Value in Table G for Example 8–22

Degrees of freedom	α									
	0.995	0.99	0.975	0.95	0.90	0.10	0.05	0.025	0.01	0.005
1										
2										
⋮										
10				3.940						
⋮										

Example 8–23

Find the critical chi-square values for 22 degrees of freedom when $\alpha = 0.05$ and a two-tailed test is conducted.

Solution

When a two-tailed test is conducted, the area must be split, as shown in Figure 8–32. Note that the area to the right of the larger value is 0.025 (0.05/2), and the area to the right of the smaller value is 0.975 (1.00 − 0.05/2).

Figure 8–32

Chi-Square Distribution for Example 8–23

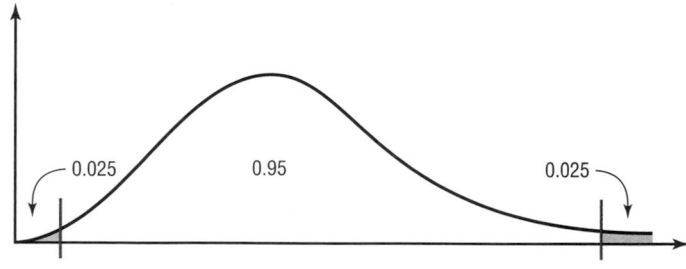

Remember that chi-square values cannot be negative. Hence, one must use α values in the table of 0.025 and 0.975. With 22 degrees of freedom, the critical values are 36.781 and 10.982, respectively.

After the degrees of freedom reach 30, Table G gives values only for multiples of 10 (40, 50, 60, etc.). When the exact degrees of freedom one is seeking are not specified in the table, the closest smaller value should be used. For example, if the given degrees of freedom are 36, use the table value for 30 degrees of freedom. This guideline keeps the type I error equal to or below the α value.

When one is testing a claim about a single variance using the **chi-square test,** there are three possible test situations: right-tailed test, left-tailed test, and two-tailed test.

If a researcher believes the variance of a population to be greater than some specific value, say, 225, then the researcher states the hypotheses as

$$H_0\text{: } \sigma^2 = 225 \qquad \text{and} \qquad H_1\text{: } \sigma^2 > 225$$

and conducts a right-tailed test.

If the researcher believes the variance of a population to be less than 225, then the researcher states the hypotheses as

$$H_0\text{: } \sigma^2 = 225 \qquad \text{and} \qquad H_1\text{: } \sigma^2 < 225$$

and conducts a left-tailed test.

Finally, if a researcher does not wish to specify a direction, he or she states the hypotheses as

$$H_0\text{: } \sigma^2 = 225 \qquad \text{and} \qquad H_1\text{: } \sigma^2 \neq 225$$

and conducts a two-tailed test.

Formula for the Chi-Square Test for a Single Variance

$$\chi^2 = \frac{(n-1)s^2}{\sigma^2}$$

with degrees of freedom equal to $n - 1$ and where

n = sample size
s^2 = sample variance
σ^2 = hypothesized population variance

One might ask, Why is it important to test variances? There are several reasons. First, in any situation where consistency is required, such as in manufacturing, one would like to have the smallest variation possible in the products. For example, when bolts are manufactured, the variation in diameters due to the process must be kept to a minimum, or the nuts will not fit them properly. In education, consistency is required on a test. That is, if the same students take the same test several times, they should get approximately the same grades, and the variance of each of the student's grades should be small. On the other hand, if the test is to be used to judge learning, the overall standard deviation of all the grades should be large so that one can differentiate those who have learned the subject from those who have not learned it.

Three assumptions are made for the chi-square test, as outlined here.

Assumptions for the Chi-Square Test for a Single Variance

1. The sample must be randomly selected from the population.
2. The population must be normally distributed for the variable under study.
3. The observations must be independent of one another.

The traditional method for hypothesis testing follows the same five steps listed earlier. They are repeated here.

Step 1 State the hypotheses and identify the claim.

Step 2 Find the critical value(s).

Step 3 Compute the test statistic.

Step 4 Make the decision.

Step 5 Summarize the results.

Examples 8–24 through 8–26 illustrate the traditional hypothesis-testing procedure for variances.

Example 8–24

An instructor wishes to see whether the variation in scores of the 23 students in her class is less than the variance of the population. The variance of the class is 198. Is there enough evidence to support the claim that the variation of the students is less than the population variance ($\sigma^2 = 225$) at $\alpha = 0.05$? Assume that the scores are normally distributed.

Solution

Step 1 State the hypotheses and identify the claim.

$$H_0: \sigma^2 = 225 \quad \text{and} \quad H_1: \sigma^2 < 225 \ (\text{claim})$$

Step 2 Find the critical value. Since this test is left-tailed and $\alpha = 0.05$, use the value $1 - 0.05 = 0.95$. The degrees of freedom are $n - 1 = 23 - 1 = 22$. Hence, the critical value is 12.338. Note that the critical region is on the left, as shown in Figure 8–33.

Figure 8–33

Critical Value for Example 8–24

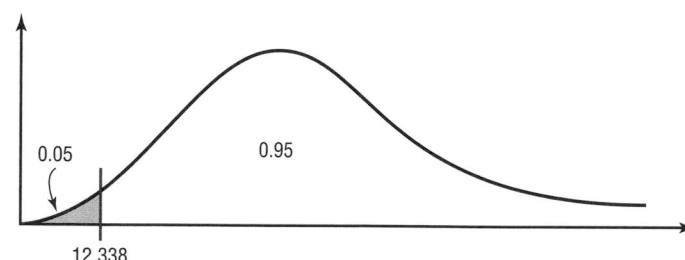

0.05

0.95

12.338

Step 3 Compute the test statistic.

$$\chi^2 = \frac{(n-1)s^2}{\sigma^2} = \frac{(23-1)(198)}{225} = 19.36$$

Step 4 Make the decision. Since the test statistic, 19.36, falls in the noncritical region, as shown in Figure 8–34, the decision is to not reject the null hypothesis.

Figure 8–34

Critical Value and Test Statistic for Example 8–24

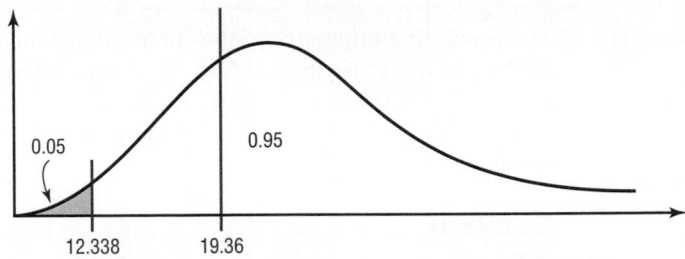

Step 5   Summarize the results. There is not enough evidence to support the claim that the variation in test scores of the instructor's students is less than the variation in scores of the population.

Example 8–25

A hospital administrator believes that the standard deviation of the number of people using outpatient surgery per day is greater than 8. A random sample of 15 days is selected. The data are shown. At $\alpha = 0.10$, is there enough evidence to support the administrator's claim? Assume the variable is normally distributed.

25	30	5	15	18
42	16	9	10	12
12	38	8	14	27

Solution

Step 1   State the hypotheses and identify the claim.

$$H_0: \sigma^2 = 64 \qquad \text{and} \qquad H_1: \sigma^2 > 64 \ (\text{claim})$$

Since the standard deviation is given, it should be squared to get the variance.

Step 2   Find the critical statistic. Since this test is right-tailed with d.f. of $15 - 1 = 14$ and $\alpha = 0.10$, the critical value is 21.064.

Step 3   Compute the test value. Since raw data are given, the standard deviation of the sample must be found by using the formula in Chapter 3 or your calculator. It is $s = 11.2$.

$$\chi^2 = \frac{(n-1)s^2}{\sigma^2} = \frac{(15-1)(11.2)^2}{64} = 27.44$$

Step 4   Make the decision. The decision is to reject the null hypothesis since the test statistic, 27.44, is greater than the critical value, 21.064, and falls in the critical region. See Figure 8–35.

Figure 8–35

Critical Value and Test Statistic for Example 8–25

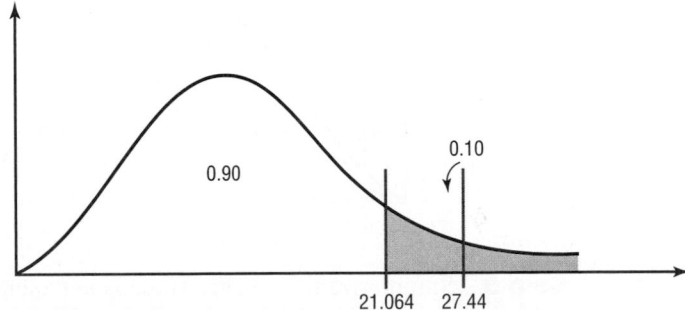

Step 5   Summarize the results. There is enough evidence to support the claim that the standard deviation is greater than 8.

Example 8–26

A cigarette manufacturer wishes to test the claim that the variance of the nicotine content of its cigarettes is 0.644. Nicotine content is measured in milligrams, and assume that it is normally distributed. A sample of 20 cigarettes has a standard deviation of 1.00 milligram. At $\alpha = 0.05$, is there enough evidence to reject the manufacturer's claim?

Solution

Step 1 State the hypotheses and identify the claim.

$$H_0: \sigma^2 = 0.644 \text{ (claim)} \qquad \text{and} \qquad H_1: \sigma^2 \neq 0.644$$

Step 2 Find the critical values. Since this test is a two-tailed test at $\alpha = 0.05$, the critical values for 0.025 and 0.975 must be found. The degrees of freedom are 19; hence, the critical values are 32.852 and 8.907, respectively. The critical or rejection regions are shown in Figure 8–36.

Figure 8–36

Critical Values for Example 8–26

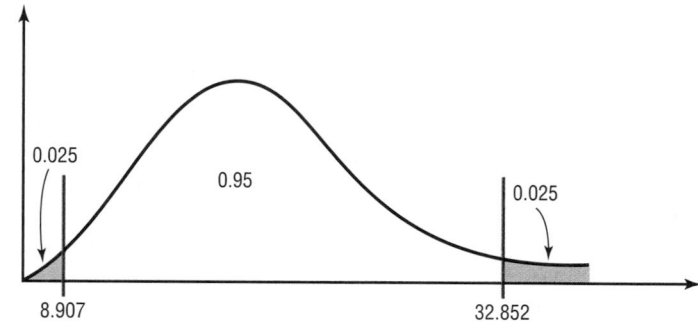

Step 3 Compute the test statistic.

$$\chi^2 = \frac{(n-1)s^2}{\sigma^2} = \frac{(20-1)(1.0)^2}{0.644} \approx 29.503$$

Since the standard deviation s is given in the problem, it must be squared for the formula.

Step 4 Make the decision. Do not reject the null hypothesis, since the test statistic falls between the critical values ($8.907 < 29.503 < 32.852$) and in the noncritical region, as shown in Figure 8–37.

Figure 8–37

Critical Values and Test Statistic for Example 8–26

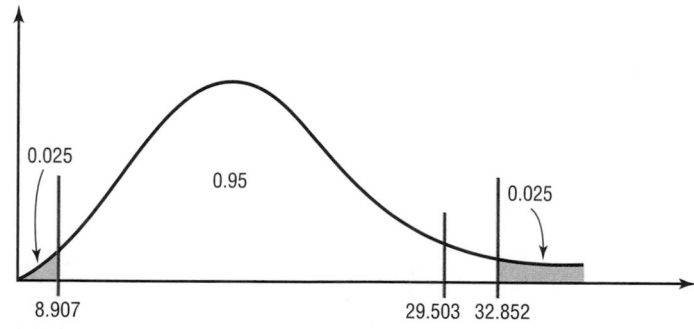

Step 5 Summarize the results. There is not enough evidence to reject the manufacturer's claim that the variance of the nicotine content of the cigarettes is equal to 0.644.

Approximate *P*-values for the chi-square test can be found by using Table G in Appendix C. The procedure is somewhat more complicated than the previous procedures for finding *P*-values for the *z* and *t* tests since the chi-square distribution is not exactly symmetric and χ^2 values cannot be negative. As we did for the *t* test, we will determine an *interval* for the *P*-value based on the table. Examples 8–27 through 8–29 show the procedure.

Example 8–27	Find the *P*-value when $\chi^2 = 19.274$, $n = 8$, and the test is right-tailed.

Solution

To get the *P*-value, look across the row with d.f. = 7 in Table G and find the two values that 19.274 falls between. They are 18.475 and 20.278. Look up to the top row and find the α values corresponding to 18.475 and 20.278. They are 0.01 and 0.005, respectively. See Figure 8–38. Hence the *P*-value is contained in the interval $0.005 < P\text{-value} < 0.01$. (The *P*-value obtained from a calculator is 0.007.)

Figure 8–38

P-Value Interval for Example 8–27

*19.274 falls between 18.475 and 20.278

Example 8–28	Find the *P*-value when $\chi^2 = 3.823$, $n = 13$, and the test is left-tailed.

Solution

To get the *P*-value, look across the row with d.f. = 12 and find the two values that 3.823 falls between. They are 3.571 and 4.404. Look up to the top row and find the values corresponding to 3.571 and 4.404. They are 0.99 and 0.975, respectively. When the χ^2 test value falls on the left side, each of the values must be subtracted from 1 to get the interval that *P*-value falls between.

$$1 - 0.99 = 0.01 \qquad \text{and} \qquad 1 - 0.975 = 0.025$$

Hence the *P*-value falls in the interval

$$0.01 < P\text{-value} < 0.025$$

(The *P*-value obtained from a calculator is 0.014.)

When the χ^2 test is two-tailed, both interval values must be doubled. If a two-tailed test were being used in Example 8–28, then the interval would be $2(0.01) < P\text{-value} < 2(0.025)$, or $0.02 < P\text{-value} < 0.05$.

The *P*-value method for hypothesis testing for a variance or standard deviation follows the same steps shown in the preceding sections.

Step 1   State the hypotheses and identify the claim.

Step 2   Compute the test statistic.

Step 3   Find the *P*-value.

Step 4   Make the decision.

Step 5   Summarize the results.

Example 8–29 shows the *P*-value method for variances or standard deviations.

Example 8–29

A researcher knows from past studies that the standard deviation of the time it takes to inspect a car is 16.8 minutes. A sample of 24 cars is selected and inspected. The standard deviation was 12.5 minutes. At $\alpha = 0.05$, can it be concluded that the standard deviation has changed? Use the *P*-value method.

Solution

Step 1   State the hypotheses and identify the claim.

$$H_0: \sigma = 16.8 \qquad \text{and} \qquad H_1: \sigma \neq 16.8 \text{ (claim)}$$

Step 2   Compute the test statistic.

$$\chi^2 = \frac{(n-1)s^2}{\sigma^2} = \frac{(24-1)(12.5)^2}{(16.8)^2} \approx 12.733$$

Step 3   Find the *P*-value. Using Table G with d.f. = 23, the value 12.733 falls between 11.689 and 13.091, corresponding to 0.975 and 0.95, respectively. Since these values are found on the left side of the distribution, each value must be subtracted from 1. Hence $1 - 0.975 = 0.025$ and $1 - 0.95 = 0.05$. Since this is a two-tailed test, the area must be doubled to obtain the *P*-value interval. Hence $0.05 < P\text{-value} < 0.10$, or somewhere between 0.05 and 0.10. (The *P*-value obtained from a calculator is 0.085.)

Step 4   Make the decision. Since $\alpha = 0.05$ and the *P*-value is between 0.05 and 0.10, the decision is to not reject the null hypothesis since *P*-value $> \alpha$.

Step 5   Summarize the results. There is not enough evidence to support the claim that the standard deviation has changed.

Applying the Concepts 8–6

Testing Fuel Consumption Claims

Assume that you are working for the Office of Consumer Affairs and have recently been getting complaints about the highway fuel consumption of the new Dodge Caravan. DaimlerChrysler Corporation agrees to allow you to select at random 40 of its new Dodge Caravans to test the highway gas consumption. DaimlerChrysler claims that the Caravans consume 9.6 L/100 km. Your results show a mean fuel consumption of 10.1 L/100 km and a standard deviation of 1.5. You support DaimlerChrysler's claim.

Source: Fuel Consumption Guide, 2007, http://oee.nrcan.gc.ca/Publications/transportation/fuel.guide/2007/index.cfm. Reproduced with the permission of the Minister of Public Works and Government Services Canada, courtesy of the Department of Natural Resources Canada, 2007.

1. Show why you support DaimlerChrysler's claim by listing the *P*-value from your output. After more complaints, you decide to test the variability of the L/100 km on the highway. From further questioning of DaimlerChrysler's quality control engineers, you find they are claiming a standard deviation of 0.5.

2. Test the claim about the standard deviation.

3. Write a short summary of your results and any necessary action that DaimlerChrysler must take to remedy customer complaints.

4. State your position about the necessity to perform tests of variability along with tests of the means.

See page 395 for the answers.

Exercises 8–6

1. Using Table G, find the critical value(s) for each, show the critical and noncritical regions, and state the appropriate null and alternative hypotheses. Use $\sigma^2 = 225$.

   a. $\alpha = 0.05, n = 18$, right-tailed

   b. $\alpha = 0.10, n = 23$, left-tailed

   c. $\alpha = 0.05, n = 15$, two-tailed

   d. $\alpha = 0.10, n = 8$, two-tailed

   e. $\alpha = 0.01, n = 17$, right-tailed

   f. $\alpha = 0.025, n = 20$, left-tailed

   g. $\alpha = 0.01, n = 13$, two-tailed

   h. $\alpha = 0.025, n = 29$, left-tailed

2. Using Table G, find the *P*-value interval for each χ^2 test value.

   a. $\chi^2 = 29.321, n = 16$, right-tailed

   b. $\chi^2 = 10.215, n = 25$, left-tailed

   c. $\chi^2 = 24.672, n = 11$, two-tailed

   d. $\chi^2 = 23.722, n = 9$, right-tailed

   e. $\chi^2 = 13.974, n = 28$, two-tailed

   f. $\chi^2 = 10.571, n = 19$, left-tailed

   g. $\chi^2 = 12.144, n = 6$, two-tailed

   h. $\chi^2 = 8.201, n = 23$, two-tailed

For Exercises 3 through 9, assume that the variables are normally or approximately normally distributed. Use the traditional method of hypothesis testing unless otherwise specified.

3. A nutritionist claims that the standard deviation of the number of calories in 15 millilitres of the major brands of pancake syrup is 60. A sample of major brands of syrup is selected, and the number of calories is shown. At $\alpha = 0.10$, can the claim be rejected?

53	210	100	200	100	220
210	100	240	200	100	210
100	210	100	210	100	60

   Source: Based on information from *The Complete Book of Food Counts* by Corrine T. Netzer, Dell Publishers, New York.

4. A researcher claims that the standard deviation of the number of yearly forest fires in Canada is greater than 400. For a 15-year period, the standard deviation of the number of forest fires in Canada is 403. Test the claim at $\alpha = 0.01$. What factor would influence the variation of the number of forest fires that occurred in Canada?

   Source: National Forestry Database Program.

5. Test the claim that the standard deviation of the motor vehicle theft rate per year in Canada is less than 500 if

a sample of 21 years had a standard deviation of 448.9. Theft rates are expressed per 100,000 population. Use $\alpha = 0.05$.

Source: Statistics Canada—*Juristat.*

6. A random sample of weights (in kilograms) of Canadian Football League (CFL) players is listed. At $\alpha = 0.05$, is there sufficient evidence that the variance of all football players in the CFL is less than 500?

90.7	78	104.8	126.6
101.2	79.4	136.1	95.3
78.9	93.0	133.8	122.5
96.2	92.5	136.1	133.8

Source: Canadian Football League.

7. The manager of a large company claims that the standard deviation of the time (in minutes) that it takes a telephone call to be transferred to the correct office in her company is 1.2 minutes or less. A sample of 15 calls is selected, and the calls are timed. The standard deviation of the sample is 1.8 minutes. At $\alpha = 0.01$, test the claim that the standard deviation is less than or equal to 1.2 minutes. Use the *P*-value method.

8. A machine fills 355-millilitre (ml) bottles with soda. For the machine to function properly, the standard deviation must be less than or equal to 0.9 ml. A sample of 8 bottles is selected, and the number of millilitres of soda in each bottle is given. At $\alpha = 0.05$, can we reject the claim that the machine is functioning properly? Use the *P*-value method.

355.8	357.8	355.5	354.3
325.3	356.4	354.0	354.6

9. A random sample of 20 different kinds of doughnuts had the following calorie counts. At $\alpha = 0.01$, is there sufficient evidence to conclude that the standard deviation is greater than 20 calories?

290	320	260	220	300	310	310	270	250	230
270	260	310	200	250	250	270	210	260	300

Source: *The Doctor's Pocket Calorie, Fat, and Carbohydrate Counter.*

10. The highest temperatures (°C) on record for randomly selected days in July in Toronto are listed.

36.7	39.4	37.2	40.6	35.4	35.0	35.6

At $\alpha = 0.05$, is there sufficient evidence to conclude that the standard deviation for high temperatures is less than 2.5°C?

Source: Environment Canada.

11. A researcher claims that the standard deviation of the number of deaths annually from fires in Canada is less than 150. If a sample of 11 randomly selected years had a standard deviation of 147.5, is the claim believable? Use $\alpha = 0.05$.

Source: Council of Canadian Fire Marshals and Fire Commissioners.

12. A survey by the City of Chilliwack in British Columbia indicated that almost one-half of motorists would agree to speeding tickets of vehicles over 5 kilometres per hour (km/h) over the posted 30 km/h. Assume that 5 km/h is claimed to be the standard deviation of driver speeds. A speed watch is established in a 30 km/h zone. The standard deviation of 50 vehicles through the zone is 7 km/h. Test the 5 km/h claim at $\alpha = 0.05$.

Source: City of Chilliwack website.

13. A random sample of home run totals for Major League Baseball's National League Home Run Champions from 1938 to 2001 is shown. At the 0.05 level of significance, is there sufficient evidence to conclude that the variance is greater than 25?

34	47	43	23	36	50	42
44	43	40	39	41	47	45

Source: *N.Y. Times Almanac.*

14. Are some fast-food restaurants healthier than others? The number of grams of fat in a regular serving of French fries for a random sample of restaurants is shown. Is there sufficient evidence to conclude that the standard deviation exceeds 4 grams of fat? Use $\alpha = 0.05$.

15	13	15	22	13	21	10	20
10	17	11	17	15	18	24	18

Source: *The Doctor's Pocket Calorie, Fat, and Carbohydrate Counter.*

8–7   Additional Topics Regarding Hypothesis Testing

In hypothesis testing, there are several other concepts that might be of interest to students in elementary statistics. These topics include the relationship between hypothesis testing and confidence intervals, and some additional information about the type II error.

Objective ⑨

Test hypotheses, using confidence intervals.

Confidence Intervals and Hypothesis Testing

There is a relationship between confidence intervals and two-tailed hypothesis testing. When the null hypothesis is rejected in a hypothesis-testing situation, the confidence interval for the mean using the same level of significance *will not* contain the hypothesized mean. Likewise, when the null hypothesis is not rejected, the confidence interval computed using the same level of significance *will* contain the hypothesized mean. Examples 8–30 and 8–31 show this concept for two-tailed tests.

Example 8–30

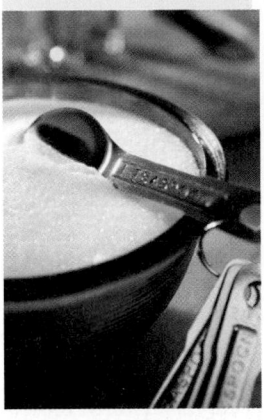

Sugar is packed in 2-kilogram (kg) bags. An inspector suspects the bags may not contain 2 kg. A sample of 50 bags produces a mean of 1.85 kg and a standard deviation of 0.3 kg. Is there enough evidence to conclude that the bags do not contain 2 kg as stated at $\alpha = 0.05$? Also, find the 98% confidence interval of the true mean.

Solution

Now H_0: $\mu = 2$ and H_1: $\mu \neq 2$ (claim). The critical values are $+1.96$ and -1.96. The test statistic is

$$z = \frac{\overline{X} - \mu}{s/\sqrt{n}} = \frac{1.85 - 2}{0.3/\sqrt{50}} \approx -3.54$$

Since $-3.54 < -1.96$, the null hypothesis is rejected. There is enough evidence to support the claim that the bags do not weigh 2 kilograms.

The 95% confidence for the mean is given by

$$\overline{X} - z_{\alpha/2}\frac{s}{\sqrt{n}} < \mu < \overline{X} + z_{\alpha/2}\frac{s}{\sqrt{n}}$$

$$1.85 - 1.96\frac{0.3}{\sqrt{50}} < \mu < 1.85 + 1.96\frac{0.3}{\sqrt{50}}$$

$$1.77 < \mu < 1.93$$

Notice that the 95% confidence interval of μ does *not* contain the hypothesized value $\mu = 2$. As expected, the hypothesis test and the confidence interval are in agreement.

Example 8–31

A researcher claims that adult hogs fed a special diet will have an average weight of 91 kilograms. A sample of 10 hogs has an average weight of 90.2 kilograms and a standard deviation of 1.5 kilograms. At $\alpha = 0.05$, can the claim be rejected? Also, find the 95% confidence interval of the true mean. Assume the population is approximately normally distributed.

Solution

Now H_0: $\mu = 91$ kilograms (claim) and H_1: $\mu \neq 91$ kilograms. The t test must be used since σ is unknown and $n < 30$. The critical values at $\alpha = 0.05$ with 9 degrees of freedom are $+2.262$ and -2.262. The test statistic is

$$t = \frac{\overline{X} - \mu}{s/\sqrt{n}} = \frac{90.2 - 91}{1.5/\sqrt{10}} \approx -1.687$$

Thus, the null hypothesis is not rejected. There is not enough evidence to reject the claim that the weight of the adult hogs is 91 kilograms.

The 95% confidence for the mean is given by

$$\overline{X} - t_{\alpha/2}\frac{s}{\sqrt{n}} < \mu < \overline{X} + t_{\alpha/2}\frac{s}{\sqrt{n}}$$

$$90.2 - (2.262)\left(\frac{1.5}{\sqrt{10}}\right) < \mu < 90.2 + (2.262)\left(\frac{1.5}{\sqrt{10}}\right)$$

$$89.1 < \mu < 91.3$$

The 95% confidence interval does contain the hypothesized mean $\mu = 91$. Again there is agreement between the hypothesis test and the confidence interval.

In summary, then, when the null hypothesis is rejected, the confidence interval computed at the same significance level will not contain the value of the mean that is stated in the null hypothesis. On the other hand, when the null hypothesis is not rejected, the confidence interval computed at the same significance level will contain the value of the mean stated in the null hypothesis. These results are true for other hypothesis-testing situations and are not limited to means tests.

The relationship between confidence intervals and hypothesis testing presented here is valid for two-tailed tests. The relationship between one-tailed hypothesis tests and one-sided or one-tailed confidence intervals is also valid; however, this technique is beyond the scope of this textbook.

Type II Error and the Power of a Test

Recall that in hypothesis testing, there are two possibilities: Either the null hypothesis H_0 is true, or it is false. Furthermore, on the basis of the statistical test, the null hypothesis is either rejected or not rejected. These results give rise to four possibilities, as shown in Figure 8–39. This figure is similar to Figure 8–2.

Objective 10

Explain the relationship between type I and type II errors and the power of a test.

As stated previously, there are two types of errors: type I and type II. A type I error can occur only when the null hypothesis is rejected. By choosing a level of significance, say, 0.05 or 0.01, the researcher can determine the probability of committing a type I error. For example, suppose that the null hypothesis was H_0: $\mu \leq 50$, and it was rejected. At the 0.05 level, the researcher has only a 5% chance of being wrong, i.e., of rejecting a true null hypothesis.

On the other hand, if the null hypothesis is not rejected, then either it is true or a type II error has been committed. A type II error occurs when the null hypothesis is indeed false, but is not rejected. The probability of committing a type II error is denoted as β.

The value of β is not easy to compute. It depends on several things, including the value of α, the size of the sample, the population standard deviation, and the actual difference between the hypothesized value of the parameter being tested and the true parameter. The researcher has control over two of these factors, namely, the selection of α and the size of the sample. The standard deviation of the population is sometimes known or can be estimated. The major problem, then, lies in knowing the actual difference between the hypothesized parameter and the true parameter. If this difference were known, then the value of the parameter would be known; and if the parameter were known, then there would be no need to do any hypothesis testing. Hence, the value of β

Figure 8–39

Possibilities in Hypothesis Testing

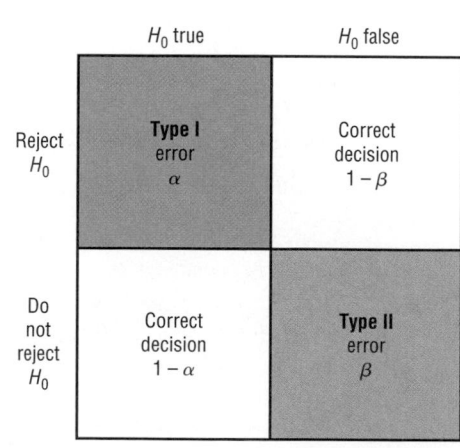

cannot be computed. But this does not mean that it should be ignored. What the researcher usually does is to try to minimize the size of β or to maximize what is called the **power of a test.**

The power of a statistical test measures the sensitivity of the test to detect a real difference in parameters if one actually exists. The power of a test is a probability and, like all probabilities, can have values ranging from 0 to 1. The higher the power, the more sensitive the test is to detecting a real difference between parameters if there is a difference. In other words, the closer the power of a test is to 1, the better the test is for rejecting the null hypothesis if the null hypothesis is, in fact, false.

The power of a test is equal to $1 - \beta$, that is, 1 minus the probability of committing a type II error. The power of the test is shown in the upper right-hand block of Figure 8–39. If somehow it were known that $\beta = 0.04$, then the power of a test would be $1 - 0.04 = 0.96$, or 96%. In this case, the probability of rejecting the null hypothesis when it is false is 96%.

As stated previously, the power of a test depends on the probability of committing a type II error, and since β is not easily computed, the power of a test cannot be easily computed. (See the Critical Thinking Challenge on page 393.)

However, there are some guidelines that can be used when you are conducting a statistical study concerning the power of a test. When you are conducting a statistical study, use the test that has the highest power for the data. There are times when the researcher has a choice of two or more statistical tests to test the hypotheses. The tests with the highest power should be used. It is important, however, to remember that statistical tests have assumptions that need to be considered.

If these assumptions cannot be met, then another test with lower power should be used. The power of a test can be increased by increasing the value of α. For example, instead of using $\alpha = 0.01$, use $\alpha = 0.05$. Recall that as α increases, β decreases. So if β is decreased, then $1 - \beta$ will increase, thus increasing the power of the test.

Another way to increase the power of a test is to select a larger sample size. A larger sample size would make the standard error of the mean smaller and consequently reduce β. (The derivation is omitted.)

These two methods should not be used at the whim of the researcher. Before α can be increased, the researcher must consider the consequences of committing a type I error. If these consequences are more serious than the consequences of committing a type II error, then α should not be increased.

Likewise, there are consequences to increasing the sample size. These consequences might include an increase in the amount of money required to do the study and an increase in the time needed to tabulate the data. When these consequences result, increasing the sample size may not be practical.

There are several other methods a researcher can use to increase the power of a statistical test, but these methods are beyond the scope of this book.

One final comment is necessary. When the researcher fails to reject the null hypothesis, this does not mean that there is not enough evidence to support alternative hypotheses. It may be that the null hypothesis is false, but the statistical test has too low a power to detect the real difference; hence, one can conclude only that in this study, there is not enough evidence to reject the null hypothesis.

The relationship among α, β, and the power of a test can be analyzed in greater detail than the explanation given here. However, it is hoped that this explanation will show the student that there is no magic formula or statistical test that can guarantee foolproof results when a decision is made about the validity of H_0. Whether the decision is to reject H_0 or not to reject H_0, there is in either case a chance of being wrong. The goal, then, is to try to keep the probabilities of type I and type II errors as small as possible.

Applying the Concepts 8–7

Confidence Intervals and Hypothesis Testing

Hypothesis testing and testing claims with confidence intervals are two different approaches that lead to the same conclusion. In the following activities, you will compare and contrast those two approaches.

Assume that you are working for the Office of Consumer Affairs and have recently been getting complaints about the highway fuel consumption of the new Dodge Caravan. DaimlerChrysler Corporation agrees to allow you to random select 40 of its new Dodge Caravan to test the highway gas consumption. DaimlerChrysler claims that the Caravans consume 10.1 L/100 km. Your results show a mean fuel consumption of 9.6 L/100 km with a standard deviation of 2.0 L/100 km. Uncertain whether to generate a confidence interval estimate or run a hypothesis test, you decide to do both at the same time.

1. Draw a normal curve labelling the critical values, critical regions, test statistic, and population mean. List the significance level and the null and alternative hypotheses.

2. Draw a confidence interval directly below the normal distribution, labelling the sample mean, error, and boundary values.

3. Explain which parts from each approach are the same and which parts are different.

4. Draw a picture of a normal curve and confidence interval where the sample and hypothesized means are equal.

5. Draw a picture of a normal curve and confidence interval where the lower boundary of the confidence interval is equal to the hypothesized mean.

6. Draw a picture of a normal curve and confidence interval where the sample mean falls in the left critical region of the normal curve.

See page 395 for the answers.

Exercises 8–7

1. A ski shop manager claims that the average of the sales for her shop is $1800 a day during the winter months. Ten winter days are selected at random, and the mean of the sales is $1830. The standard deviation of the population is $200. Can one reject the claim at $\alpha = 0.05$? Find the 95% confidence interval of the mean. Does the confidence interval interpretation agree with the hypothesis test results? Explain. Assume that the variable is normally distributed.

2. Charter bus records show that in past years, the buses carried an average of 42 people per trip to Niagara Falls. The standard deviation of the population in the past was found to be 8. This year, the average of 10 trips showed a mean of 48 people booked. Can one reject the claim, at $\alpha = 0.10$, that the average is still the same? Find the 90% confidence interval of the mean. Does the confidence interval interpretation agree with the hypothesis-testing results? Explain. Assume that the variable is normally distributed.

3. The sales manager of a rental agency claims that the monthly maintenance fee for a condominium in the Lakewood region is $86. Past surveys showed that the

standard deviation of the population is $6. A sample of 15 owners shows that they pay an average of $84. Test the manager's claim at $\alpha = 0.01$. Find the 99% confidence interval of the mean. Does the confidence interval interpretation agree with the results of the hypothesis test? Explain. Assume that the variable is normally distributed.

4. The average time it takes a person in a one-person canoe to complete a certain river course is 47 minutes. Because of rapid currents in the spring, a group of 10 people traverse the course in 42 minutes. The standard deviation, known from previous trips, is 7 minutes. Test the claim that this group's time was different because of the strong currents. Use $\alpha = 0.10$. Find the 90% confidence level of the true mean. Does the confidence interval interpretation agree with the results of the hypothesis test? Explain. Assume that the variable is normally distributed.

5. From past studies the average time college freshmen spend studying is 22 hours per week. The standard deviation is 4 hours. This year, 60 students were surveyed, and the average time that they spent studying

was 20.8 hours. Test the claim that the time students spend studying has changed. Use $\alpha = 0.01$. It is believed that the standard deviation is unchanged. Find the 99% confidence interval of the mean. Do the results agree? Explain.

6. A survey taken several years ago found that the average time a person spent reading the local daily newspaper was 10.8 minutes. The standard deviation of the population was 3 minutes. To see whether the average time had changed since the newspaper's format was revised, the newspaper editor surveyed 36 individuals. The average time that the 36 people spent reading the paper was 12.2 minutes. At $\alpha = 0.02$, is there a change in the average time an individual spends reading the newspaper? Find the 98% confidence interval of the mean. Do the results agree? Explain.

7. What is meant by the power of a test?

8. How is the power of a test related to the type II error?

9. How can the power of a test be increased?

8-8   ## Summary

This chapter introduces the basic concepts of hypothesis testing. A statistical hypothesis is a conjecture about a population. There are two types of statistical hypotheses: the null and the alternative hypotheses. The null hypothesis states that there is no difference, and the alternative hypothesis specifies a difference. To test the null hypothesis, researchers use a statistical test. Many test statistics are computed by using

$$\text{Test statistic} = \frac{(\text{observed value}) - (\text{expected value})}{\text{standard error}}$$

Two common statistical tests are the z test and the t test. The z test is used either when the population standard deviation is known and the variable is normally distributed or when σ is not known and the sample size is greater than or equal to 30. In this case, s is used in place of σ regardless of the shape of the distribution. When the population standard deviation is not known and the variable is normally distributed, the sample standard deviation is used, but a t test should be conducted when the sample size is less than 30. The z test is also used to test proportions when $np \geq 5$ and $nq \geq 5$.

Researchers compute a test statistic from the sample data in order to decide whether the null hypothesis should be rejected. Statistical tests can be one-tailed or two-tailed, depending on the hypotheses.

The null hypothesis is rejected when the difference between the population parameter and the sample statistic is said to be significant. The difference is significant when the test statistic falls in the critical region of the distribution. The critical region is determined by α, the level of significance of the test. The level is the probability of committing a type I error. This error occurs when the null hypothesis is rejected when it is true. Three generally agreed upon significance levels are 0.10, 0.05, and 0.01. A second kind of error, the type II error, can occur when the null hypothesis is not rejected when it is false.

Finally, one can test a single variance by using a chi-square test.

All hypothesis-testing situations using the traditional method should include the following steps:

1. State the null and alternative hypotheses and identify the claim.

2. State an alpha level and find the critical value(s).

3. Compute the test statistic.

4. Make the decision to reject or not reject the null hypothesis.

5. Summarize the results.

All hypothesis-testing situations using the P-value method should include the following steps:

1. State the hypotheses and identify the claim.

2. Compute the test statistic.

3. Find the P-value.

4. Make the decision.

5. Summarize the results.

For step-by-step guidance on the use of technology for this chapter, visit the Online Learning Centre at www.mcgrawhill.ca/olc/bluman. Summary procedures for Minitab, SPSS, Excel, and TI-83 Plus or TI-84 Plus can also be found in Appendix E.

Important Terms

α (alpha) 339

alternative hypothesis 335

β (beta) 339

chi-square test 375

critical or rejection region 340

critical value 340

hypothesis testing 334

left-tailed test 340

level of significance 339

noncritical or nonrejection region 340

null hypothesis 335

one-tailed test 340

power of a test 385

P-value 351

right-tailed test 340

statistical hypothesis 335

statistical test 337

t test 358

test statistic 337

two-tailed test 341

type I error 338

type II error 338

z test 346

Important Formulas

Formula for the z test for means:

$$z = \frac{\overline{X} - \mu}{\sigma/\sqrt{n}} \quad \textbf{for any value } n$$

$$z = \frac{\overline{X} - \mu}{s/\sqrt{n}} \quad \textbf{for } n \geq 30$$

Formula for the t test for means:

$$t = \frac{\overline{X} - \mu}{s/\sqrt{n}} \quad \textbf{for } n < 30$$

Formula for the z test for proportions:

$$z = \frac{X - \mu}{\sigma} \quad \text{or} \quad z = \frac{\hat{p} - p}{\sqrt{pq/n}}$$

Formula for the chi-square test for variance or standard deviation:

$$\chi^2 = \frac{(n - 1)s^2}{\sigma^2}$$

Review Exercises

For Exercises 1 through 19, perform each of the following steps.

 a. State the hypotheses and identify the claim.
 b. Find the critical value(s).
 c. Compute the test statistic.
 d. Make the decision.
 e. Summarize the results.

Use the traditional method of hypothesis testing unless otherwise specified.

1. A meteorologist claims that the average of the highest temperatures in Eastern Canada is 37°C. A random sample of 50 cities is selected, and the highest temperatures are recorded. The data are shown. At $\alpha = 0.05$, can the claim be rejected?

38.3	35.6	37.0	40.3	35.0
37.6	39.0	36.1	38.5	32.2
36.0	38.3	38.5	35.1	34.5
37.8	39.0	37.0	36.0	35.5
35.0	36.7	35.4	30.6	36.5
38.0	38.0	36.8	37.0	35.5
33.9	37.0	36.1	36.5	31.1
37.4	37.0	40.6	39.1	33.3
32.2	34.0	38.4	32.8	38.9
36.7	34.0	35.6	32.8	32.8

Source: Environment Canada Weather Database.

2. A stockbroker thought that the average number of shares of stocks traded daily in the stock market was about 500 million. To test the claim, a researcher selected a random sample of 40 days and found the mean number of shares traded each day was 506 million shares. The standard deviation of the sample was 10.3. At $\alpha = 0.05$ is there enough evidence to reject the broker's claim? Based on the results, do you agree or disagree with the broker?

3. Nationwide, graduates entering the actuarial field earn $40,000. A college placement officer feels that this number is too low. She surveys 36 graduates entering the actuarial field and finds the average salary to be $41,000 with a standard deviation of $3000. Can her claim be supported at $\alpha = 0.05$?

Source: BeAnActuary.org.

4. Nationwide, the average salary of actuaries who achieve the rank of Fellow is $150,000. An insurance executive wants to see how this compares with Fellows within his company. He checks the salaries of eight Fellows and finds the average salary to be $155,500 with a standard deviation of $15,000. Can he conclude that Fellows in his company make more than the national average, using $\alpha = 0.05$?

Source: BeAnActuary.org.

5. The normal July maximum temperature for Metropolitan Toronto is 26.8°C. News reports indicated that July 2006 was hotter than normal. A random sample of 10 days in July 2006 shows an average daily maximum temperature of 28.6°C with a standard deviation of 3.5°C. At $\alpha = 0.10$, can it be concluded that July 2006 was hotter than normal? Assume the variable is normally distributed.

   Source: Environment Canada Weather Database.

6. The Tennis Industry Association stated that the average age of a tennis fan is 32 years. To test the claim, a researcher selected a random sample of 18 tennis fans and found that the mean of their ages was 31.3 years and the standard deviation was 2.8 years. At $\alpha = 0.05$ does it appear that the average age is lower than what was stated by the Tennis Industry Association? Use the *P*-value method, and assume the variable is approximately normally distributed.

7. A park manager suggests that the average attendance for national parks last year was 6 million. The number of visits for 10 parks this year is shown. At $\alpha = 0.02$, has the average attendance changed? The data are in millions of people. Assume the variable is normally distributed.

4.7	17.2	14.0	6.1	6.1
4.9	9.3	9.4	6.4	6.1

   Source: USA TODAY.

8. A 2003 report indicated that 57% of women in Canada aged 15 years and over had jobs. A regional manager claims that more women work in the region. A survey of 1000 randomly selected women finds that 622 work. At $\alpha = 0.05$, is the manager correct?

   Source: Statistics Canada—Women in Canada.

9. A transportation report indicates that 10.5% of workers commute to work using public transit. A city councillor feels that this figure is low for her municipality and commissions a study. A survey of 400 workers indicates that 51 use public transit to get to work. At $\alpha = 0.05$, is she right in her assumption?

   Source: Encyclopedia Britannica.

10. The Tennis Industry Association reported that 41% of tennis fans were female. If, in a sample of 30 tennis fans, 15 were female, do the results suggest that the percentage may have changed? Use $\alpha = 0.02$.

11. A radio manufacturer claims that 65% of teenagers 13 to 16 years old have their own portable radios. A researcher wishes to test the claim and selects a random sample of 80 teenagers. She finds that 57 have their own portable radios. At $\alpha = 0.05$, should the claim be rejected? Use the *P*-value method.

12. A football coach claims that the average weight of all the opposing teams' members is 100 kilograms (kg). To test the claim, a sample of 50 players is taken from all the opposing teams. The mean is found to be 104 kg, and the standard deviation is 7 kg. At $\alpha = 0.01$, test the coach's claim. Find the *P*-value and make the decision.

13. An advertisement claims that Fasto Stomach Calm will provide relief from indigestion in less than 10 minutes. For a test of the claim, 35 individuals were given the product; the average time until relief was 9.25 minutes. From past studies, the standard deviation is known to be 2 minutes. Can one conclude that the claim is justified? Find the *P*-value and let $\alpha = 0.05$.

14. A film editor feels that the standard deviation for the number of minutes in a video is 3.4 minutes. A sample of 24 videos has a standard deviation of 4.2 minutes. At $\alpha = 0.05$, is the sample standard deviation different from what the editor hypothesized?

15. The standard deviation of the fuel consumption of a certain automobile is hypothesized to be greater than or equal to 1.6 litres per 100 kilometres (L/100 km). A sample of 20 automobiles produced a standard deviation of 0.9 L/100 km. Is the standard deviation really less than previously thought? Use $\alpha = 0.05$ and the *P*-value method.

16. A real estate agent claims that the standard deviation of the rental rates of condominiums in Metropolitan Toronto is $500. A random sample of rental rates in dollars is shown. At $\alpha = 0.02$, can the claim be refuted? Assume the variable is normally distributed.

2258	1658	2151	1100	1677	1988
3007	1244	2653	2230	1757	1550
2692	1544	2140	1519	1969	1450

   Source: MLS Rental Report, Toronto Real Estate Board.

17. A manufacturer claims that the standard deviation of the drying time of a certain type of paint is 18 minutes. A sample of five test panels produced a standard deviation of 21 minutes. Test the claim at $\alpha = 0.05$.

18. To see whether people are keeping their car tires inflated to the correct level at 241.3 kilopascals (kPa), a tire company manager selects a sample of 36 tires and checks the pressure. The mean of the sample is 230.9 kPa, and the standard deviation is 20.7 kPa. Are the tires properly inflated? Use $\alpha = 0.10$. Find the 90% confidence interval of the mean. Do the results agree? Explain.

19. A biologist knows that the average length of a leaf of a certain full-grown plant is 10.2 centimetres (cm). The standard deviation of the population is 1.5 cm. A sample of 20 leaves of that type of plant given a new type of plant food had an average length of 10.7 cm. Is there reason to believe that the new food is responsible for a change in the growth of the leaves? Use $\alpha = 0.01$. Find the 99% confidence interval of the mean. Do the results concur? Explain. Assume that the variable is approximately normally distributed.

Statistics Today

How Much Better Is Better?—Revisited

Now that you have learned the techniques of hypothesis testing presented in this chapter, you realize that the difference between the sample mean and the population mean must be *significant* before one can conclude that the students really scored above average. The Minister of Education should follow the steps in the hypothesis-testing procedure and be able to reject the null hypothesis before announcing that his/her students scored higher than average.

Data Analysis

The Data Bank is found in Appendix D, or on the World Wide Web by following links from www.mcgrawhill.ca/olc/bluman.

1. From the Data Bank, select a random sample of at least 30 individuals, and test one or more of the following hypotheses by using the z test. Use $\alpha = 0.05$.

   a. For serum cholesterol, H_0: $\mu = 220$ milligram percent (mg%).

   b. For systolic pressure, H_0: $\mu = 120$ millimetres of mercury (mm Hg).

   c. For IQ, H_0: $\mu = 100$.

   d. For sodium level, H_0: $\mu = 140$ milliequivalents per litre (mEq/l).

2. Select a random sample of 15 individuals and test one or more of the hypotheses in Exercise 1 by using the t test. Use $\alpha = 0.05$.

3. Select a random sample of at least 30 individuals, and using the z test for proportions, test one or more of the following hypotheses. Use $\alpha = 0.05$.

   a. For educational level, H_0: $p = 0.50$ for level 2.

   b. For smoking status, H_0: $p = 0.20$ for level 1.

   c. For exercise level, H_0: $p = 0.10$ for level 1.

   d. For gender, H_0: $p = 0.50$ for males.

4. Select a sample of 20 individuals and test the hypothesis H_0: $\sigma^2 = 225$ for IQ level. Use $\alpha = 0.05$.

5. Using the data from Data Set XIII, select a sample of 10 hospitals and test H_0: $\mu = 250$ and H_1: $\mu < 250$ for the number of beds. Use $\alpha = 0.05$.

6. Using the data obtained in Exercise 5, test the hypothesis H_0: $\sigma = 150$ and H_1: $\sigma < 150$. Use $\alpha = 0.05$.

Chapter Quiz

Determine whether each statement is true or false. If the statement is false, explain why.

1. No error is committed when the null hypothesis is rejected when it is false.

2. When one is conducting the t test, the population must be approximately normally distributed.

3. The test statistic separates the critical region from the noncritical region.

4. The values of a chi-square test cannot be negative.

5. The chi-square test for variances is always one-tailed.

Select the best answer.

6. When the value of α is increased, the probability of committing a type I error is

   a. Decreased   c The same

   b. Increased   d. None of the above

7. If one wishes to test the claim that the mean of the population is 100, the appropriate alternative hypothesis is

   a. $\overline{X} \neq 100$ c. $\mu < 100$

   b. $\mu > 100$ d. $\mu \neq 100$

8. The degrees of freedom for the chi-square test for variances or standard deviations are

   a. 1

   b. n

   c. $n - 1$

   d. None of the above

9. For the z test, if σ is unknown and $n \geq 30$, one can substitute _____ for σ.

   a. n

   b. s

   c. χ^2

   d. t

Complete the following statements with the best answer.

10. Rejecting the null hypothesis when it is true is called a(n) _____ error.

11. The probability of a type II error is referred to as _____.

12. A conjecture about a population parameter is called a(n) _____.

13. To test the hypothesis H_0: $\mu \leq 87$, one would use a(n) _____-tailed test.

14. The degrees of freedom for the t test are _____.

For the following exercises where applicable:

    a. State the hypotheses and identify the claim.
    b. Find the critical value(s).
    c. Compute the test statistic.
    d. Make the decision.
    e. Summarize the results.

Use the traditional method of hypothesis testing unless otherwise specified.

15. A sociologist wishes to see if it is true that for a certain group of professional women, the average age at which they have their first child is 28.6 years. A random sample of 36 women is selected, and their ages at the birth of their first children are recorded. At $\alpha = 0.05$, does the evidence refute the sociologist's assertion?

32	28	26	33	35	34
29	24	22	25	26	28
28	34	33	32	30	29
30	27	33	34	28	25
24	33	25	37	35	33
34	36	38	27	29	26

16. A real estate agent believes that the average closing cost of purchasing a new home is $6500 over the purchase price. She selects 40 new home sales at random and finds that the average closing costs are $6600. The standard deviation of the population is $120. Test her belief at $\alpha = 0.05$.

17. A recent study stated that if a person chewed gum, the average number of sticks of gum he or she chewed daily was 8. To test the claim, a researcher selected a random sample of 36 gum chewers and found the mean number of sticks of gum chewed per day was 9. The standard deviation was 1. At $\alpha = 0.05$, is the number of sticks of gum a person chews per day actually greater than 8?

18. A travel agent claims that the average of the number of rooms in hotels in a large city is 500. At $\alpha = 0.01$ is the claim realistic? The data for a sample of six hotels are shown. Assume the variable is approximately normally distributed.

713   300   292   311   598   401   618

Give a reason why the claim might be deceptive.

19. In a Montreal modelling agency, a researcher wishes to see if the average height of female models is really less than 170 centimetres (cm), as the chief claims. A sample of 20 models has an average of 167.1 cm. The standard deviation of the sample is 4.3 cm. At $\alpha = 0.05$, is the average height of the models really less than 170 cm? Use the P-value method. Assume the population data is normally distributed.

20. A taxi company claims that its drivers have an average of at least 12.4 years' experience. In a study of 15 taxi drivers, the average experience was 11.2 years. The standard deviation was 2. At $\alpha = 0.10$, is the number of years' experience of the taxi drivers really less than the taxi company claimed?

21. A recent study in a small city stated that the average age of robbery victims was 63.5 years. A sample of 20 recent victims had a mean of 63.7 years and a standard deviation of 1.9 years. At $\alpha = 0.05$, is the average age higher than originally believed? Use the P-value method. Assume the variable is approximately normally distributed.

22. A magazine article stated that the average age of women who are getting married for the first time is 26 years. A researcher decided to test this hypothesis at $\alpha = 0.02$. She selected a sample of 25 women who were recently married for the first time and found the average was 25.1 years. The standard deviation was 3 years. Should the null hypothesis be rejected on the basis of the sample? Assume the variable is approximately normally distributed.

23. A survey in *Men's Health* magazine reported that 39% of cardiologists said that they took vitamin E supplements. To see if this is still true, a researcher randomly selected 100 cardiologists and found that 36 said that they took vitamin E supplements. At $\alpha = 0.05$ test the claim that 39% of the cardiologists took vitamin E supplements. A recent study said that taking too much vitamin E might be harmful. How might this study make the results of the previous study invalid?

24. A dietitian read in a survey that at least 55% of adults do not eat breakfast at least 3 days a week. To verify this, she selected a random sample of 80 adults and asked them how many days a week they skipped breakfast. A total of 50% responded that they skipped breakfast at least 3 days a week. At $\alpha = 0.10$, test the claim.

25. A Harris Poll found that 35% of people said that they drink a caffeinated beverage to combat midday drowsiness. A recent survey found that 19 out of 48 people stated that they drank a caffeinated beverage to combat midday drowsiness. At $\alpha = 0.02$ is the claim of the percentage found in the Harris Poll believable?

26. A magazine claims that 75% of all teenage boys have their own radios. A researcher wished to test the claim and selected a random sample of 60 teenage boys. She found that 54 had their own radios. At $\alpha = 0.01$, should the claim be rejected?

27. Find the P-value for the z test in Exercise 15.

28. Find the *P*-value for the *z* test in Exercise 16.

29. A copyeditor thinks the standard deviation for the number of pages in a romance novel is greater than 6. A sample of 25 novels has a standard deviation of 9 pages. At $\alpha = 0.05$, is it higher, as the editor hypothesized?

30. It has been hypothesized that the standard deviation of the germination time of radish seeds is 8 days. The standard deviation of a sample of 60 radish plants' germination times was 6 days. At $\alpha = 0.01$, test the claim.

31. The standard deviation of the pollution by-products released in the burning of 1 gallon of gas is 2.3 ounces.

A sample of 20 automobiles tested produced a standard deviation of 1.9 ounces. Is the standard deviation really less than previously thought? Use $\alpha = 0.05$.

32. A manufacturer claims that the standard deviation of the strength of wrapping cord is 4.1 kilograms (kg). A sample of 10 wrapping cords produced a standard deviation of 5.0 kg. At $\alpha = 0.05$, test the claim. Use the *P*-value method.

33. Find the 90% confidence interval of the mean in Exercise 15. Is μ contained in the interval?

34. Find the 95% confidence interval for the mean in Exercise 16. Is μ contained in the interval?

Critical Thinking Challenges

● ● ●

The power of a test $(1 - \beta)$ can be calculated when a specific value of the mean is hypothesized in the alternative hypothesis; for example, let H_0: $\mu = 50$ and let H_1: $\mu = 52$. To find the power of a test, it is necessary to find the value of β. This can be done by the following steps:

Step 1 For a specific value of α find the corresponding value of $\overline{X}$, $z = \dfrac{\overline{X} - \mu}{\upsilon/\sqrt{n}}$, where μ is the hypothesized value given in H_0. Use a right-tailed test.

Step 2 Using the value of $\overline{X}$ found in step 1 and the value of μ in the alternative hypothesis, find the area corresponding to z in the formula $z = \dfrac{\overline{X} - \mu}{\sigma/\sqrt{n}}$.

Step 3 Subtract this area from 0.5000. This is the value of β.

Step 4 Subtract the value of β from 1. This will give you the power of a test. See Figure 8–40.

1. Find the power of a test, using the hypotheses given previously and $\alpha = 0.05$, $\sigma = 3$, and $n = 30$.

2. Select several other values for μ in H_1 and compute the power of the test. Generalize the results.

Figure 8–40

Relationship Among α, β, and the Power of a Test

Data Projects

● ● ●

Use Minitab, SPSS, the TI-83 Plus, the TI-84 Plus, or a computer program of your choice to complete these exercises.

1. Choose a variable such as the number of kilometres students live from the college or the number of daily

admissions to an ice skating rink for a 1-month period. Before you collect the data, decide what a likely average might be. Then complete the following.

a. Write a brief statement of the purpose of the study.
b. Define the population.

c. State the hypotheses for the study.

d. Select an α value.

e. State how the sample was selected.

f. Show the raw data.

g. Decide which statistical test is appropriate, and compute the test statistic (z or t). Why is the test appropriate?

h. Find the critical value(s).

i. State the decision.

j. Summarize the results.

2. Decide on a question that could be answered with "yes" or "no" or "not sure (undecided)." For example, "Are you satisfied with the variety of food the cafeteria serves?" Before you collect the data, hypothesize what you expect the proportion of students who will respond yes to be. Then complete the following.

a. Write a brief statement of the purpose of the study.

b. Define the population.

c. State the hypotheses for the study.

d. Select an α value.

e. State how the sample was selected.

f. Show the raw data.

g. Decide which statistical test is appropriate, and compute the test statistic (z or t). Why is the test appropriate?

h. Find the critical value(s).

i. State the decision.

j. Summarize the results.

Do you think the project supported your initial hypothesis? Explain your answer.

You may use the following websites to obtain raw data:

Visit the data sets at the book's website found at www.mcgrawhill.ca/olc/bluman

http://lib.stat.cmu.edu/DASL

www.statcan.ca

Answers to Applying the Concepts ●●●

Section 8–2 Eggs and Your Health

1. The study was prompted by claims that linked foods high in cholesterol to high blood serum cholesterol.

2. The population under study is people in general.

3. A sample of 500 subjects was collected.

4. The hypothesis was that eating eggs did not increase blood serum cholesterol.

5. Blood serum cholesterol levels were collected.

6. Most likely but we are not told which test.

7. The conclusion was that eating a moderate amount of eggs will not significantly increase blood serum cholesterol level.

Section 8–3 Car Thefts

1. H_0: $\mu = 50$ and H_1: $\mu \neq 50$

2. This sample can be considered large for our purposes.

3. The variable is derived from a normally distributed population or the Central Limit Theorem applies.

4. We will use the z distribution.

5. Since we are interested in whether the automobile theft rate has changed, we use a two-tailed test.

6. Answers may vary. At the $\alpha = 0.05$ significance level, the critical values are $z = \pm 1.96$.

7. The sample mean is $\overline{X} = 58.3$, and the sample standard deviation is 42.5. Our test statistic is

$$z = \frac{58.3 - 50}{42.5/\sqrt{36}} \approx 1.17$$

8. Since 1.17 is between ± 1.96, we do not reject the null hypothesis.

9. There is not enough evidence to conclude that the automobile theft rate has changed.

10. Answers will vary. Based on our sample data, it appears that the automobile theft rate has not changed from 50 vehicles per 10,000 people. Although the sample data suggests an increase, the evidence is insufficient to indicate a change has occurred.

11. Based on our sample, we would expect 58.3 automobile thefts per 10,000 people, so we would expect (58.3)(5) = 291.5, or about 292 automobile thefts in the city.

Section 8–4 How Much Nicotine Is in Those Cigarettes?

1. We have $15 - 1 = 14$ degrees of freedom.

2. This is a small-sample test.

3. We are only testing one sample.

4. This is a right-tailed test, since the hypotheses of the tobacco company are H_0: $\mu = 40$ and H_1: $\mu > 40$.

5. The P-value is 0.008, which is less than the significance level of 0.01. We reject the tobacco company's claim.

6. Since the test statistic (2.72) is greater than the critical value (2.62), we reject the tobacco company's claim.

7. There is no conflict in this output, since the results based on the P-value and on the critical value agree.

8. Answers will vary. It appears that the company's claim is false and that there is more than 40 mg of nicotine in its cigarettes.

Section 8–5   Quitting Smoking

1. The statistical hypotheses were that StopSmoke helps more people quit smoking than the other leading brands.

2. The null hypotheses were that StopSmoke has the same effectiveness as or is not as effective as the other leading brands.

3. The alternative hypotheses were that StopSmoke helps more people quit smoking than the other leading brands. (The alternative hypotheses are the statistical hypotheses.)

4. No statistical tests were run that we know of.

5. Had tests been run, they would have been one-tailed tests.

6. Some possible significance levels are 0.01, 0.05, and 0.10.

7. A type I error would be concluding that StopSmoke is better when it really is not.

8. A type II error would be concluding that StopSmoke is not better when it really is.

9. These studies proved nothing. Had statistical tests been used, we could have tested the effectiveness of StopSmoke.

10. Answers will vary. One possible answer is that more than likely the statements are talking about practical significance and not statistical significance, since we have no indication that any statistical tests were conducted.

Section 8–6   Testing Fuel Consumption Claims

1. The hypotheses are H_0: $\mu = 9.6$ and H_1: $\mu > 9.6$. The value of the test statistics is $z = 2.11$, and the associated P-value is 0.0179. We would reject the DaimlerChrysler's claim that the Dodge Caravans are getting 9.6 L/100 km and conclude that they actually use more than 9.6 L/100 km.

2. The hypotheses are H_0: $\sigma = 0.5$ and H_1: $\sigma > 0.5$. The value of our test statistic is

$$\chi^2 = \frac{(n-1)s^2}{\sigma^2} = \frac{(40-1)(1.5)^2}{(0.5)^2} = 351.0$$

and the associated P-value is approximately zero. We would reject DaimlerChrysler's claim that the standard deviation is 0.5 L/100 km.

3. Answers will vary. It is recommended that DaimlerChrysler increase their claim about the vehicle fuel consumption in L/100 km of the Dodge Caravans. DaimlerChrysler should also try to increase variability in L/100 km and provide confidence intervals for the litres per 100 kilometres.

4. Answers will vary. There are cases when a mean may be fine, but if there is a lot of variability about the mean, there will be complaints (due to the lack of consistency).

Section 8–7   Confidence Intervals and Hypothesis Testing

1. Answers will vary.
2. Answers will vary.
3. Answers will vary.
4. Answers will vary.
5. Answers will vary.
6. Answers will vary.

CHAPTER

9

Testing the Difference Between Two Means, Two Variances, and Two Proportions

Objectives

After completing this chapter, you should be able to

1. Test the difference between two large sample means, using the *z* test.

2. Test the difference between two variances or standard deviations.

3. Test the difference between two means for small independent samples.

4. Test the difference between two means for small dependent samples.

5. Test the difference between two proportions.

Outline

9–1 **Introduction**

9–2 **Testing the Difference Between Two Means: Large Samples**

9–3 **Testing the Difference Between Two Variances**

9–4 **Testing the Difference Between Two Means: Small Independent Samples**

9–5 **Testing the Difference Between Two Means: Small Dependent Samples**

9–6 **Testing the Difference Between Proportions**

9–7 **Summary**

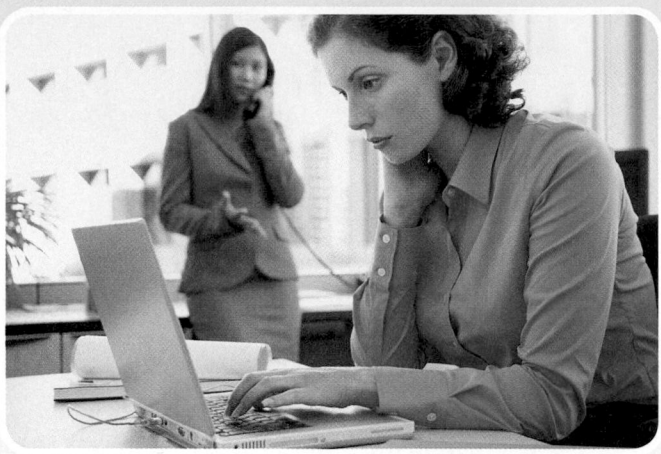

Statistics Today

A Woman's Path To Pay Equity

Women in Canada earn less than their male counterparts employed in many comparable labour activities. Statistics Canada has reported that the gender earnings gap was even larger with self-employed than with the wage workforce. In order to study gender differences in wage and self-employed earnings, census data from the two groups was collected. Unlike techniques used in Chapter 8, this study used procedures explained in this chapter and found some interesting results. Refer to Statistics Today—Revisited, page 443, to see the techniques used and the results of the study.

Sources: Neil Wolff, School of Business, Ryerson University, "Earning Equity: A Comparative Study of Changing Gender Earnings Differentials between Earners and Self-Employed" paper submitted to the Conference on Gender & Diversity in Organization, Halifax, Nova Scotia, 2002; "Excerpts from A Profile of the Self-Employed, 1997", adapted from Statistics Canada publication *Canadian Economic Observer*, Catalogue 11-010, November 1997, Volume 10, no. 11, Released October 24, 1997.

9–1   Introduction

The basic concepts of hypothesis testing were explained in Chapter 8. With the z, t, and χ^2 tests, a sample mean, variance, or proportion can be compared to a specific population mean, variance, or proportion to determine whether the null hypothesis should be rejected.

There are, however, many instances when researchers wish to compare two sample means, using experimental and control groups. For example, the average lifetimes of two different brands of bus tires might be compared to see whether there is any difference in tread wear. Two different brands of fertilizer might be tested to see whether one is better than the other for growing plants. Or two brands of cough syrup might be tested to see whether one brand is more effective than the other.

In the comparison of two means, the same basic steps for hypothesis testing shown in Chapter 8 are used, and the z and t tests are also used. When comparing two means by using the t test, the researcher must decide if the two samples are *independent* or *dependent*. The concepts of independent and dependent samples will be explained in Sections 9–4 and 9–5.

Furthermore, when the samples are independent, there are two different formulas that can be used depending on whether or not the variances are equal. To determine if the variances are equal, use the F test shown in Section 9–3. Finally, the z test can be used to compare two proportions, as shown in Section 9–6.

9–2   Testing the Difference Between Two Means: Large Samples

Suppose a researcher wishes to determine whether there is a difference in the average age of nursing students who enroll in a nursing program at a college and those who enroll in a nursing program at a university. In this case, the researcher is not interested

Objective ①

Test the difference between two large sample means, using the z test.

in the average age of all beginning nursing students; instead, he is interested in *comparing* the means of the two groups. His research question is: Does the mean age of nursing students who enroll at a college differ from the mean age of nursing students who enroll at a university? Here, the hypotheses are

$$H_0: \mu_1 = \mu_2$$
$$H_1: \mu_1 \neq \mu_2$$

where

μ_1 = mean age of all beginning nursing students at the college
μ_2 = mean age of all beginning nursing students at the university

Another way of stating the hypotheses for this situation is

$$H_0: \mu_1 - \mu_2 = 0$$
$$H_1: \mu_1 - \mu_2 \neq 0$$

If there is no difference in population means, subtracting them will give a difference of zero. If they are different, subtracting will give a number other than zero. Both methods of stating hypotheses are correct and will be illustrated in this chapter.

Assumptions for the z Test to Determine the Difference Between Two Means

1. The samples must be independent of each other. That is, there can be no relationship between the subjects in each sample.
2. The populations from which the samples were obtained must be normally distributed, and the standard deviations of the variable must be known, or the sample sizes must be greater than or equal to 30.

The theory behind testing the difference between two means is based on selecting pairs of samples and comparing the means of the pairs. The population means are not typically known.

All possible pairs of samples are taken from populations. The means for each pair of samples are computed and then subtracted, and the differences are plotted. If both populations have the same mean, then most of the differences will be zero or close to zero. Occasionally, there will be a few large differences due to chance alone, some positive and others negative. If the differences are plotted, the curve will be shaped like a normal distribution and have a mean of zero, as shown in Figure 9–1.

The variance of the difference $\overline{X}_1 - \overline{X}_2$ is equal to the sum of the individual variances of $\overline{X}_1$ and $\overline{X}_2$. That is,

$$\sigma^2_{\overline{X}_1 - \overline{X}_2} = \sigma^2_{\overline{X}_1} + \sigma^2_{\overline{X}_2}$$

Figure 9–1

Differences of Means of Pairs of Samples

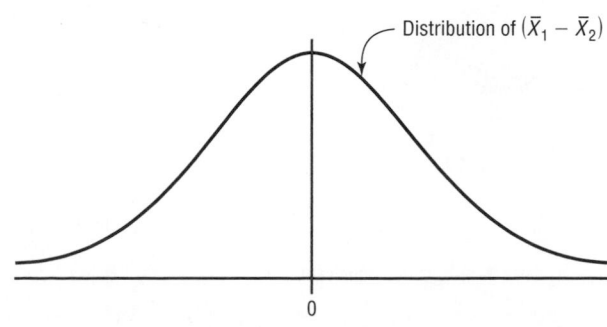
Distribution of $(\overline{X}_1 - \overline{X}_2)$

where $\qquad \sigma_{\bar{X}_1}^2 = \dfrac{\sigma_1^2}{n_1}$ and $\qquad \sigma_{\bar{X}_2}^2 = \dfrac{\sigma_2^2}{n_2}$

So the standard deviation of $\overline{X}_1 - \overline{X}_2$ is

$$\sqrt{\dfrac{\sigma_1^2}{n_1} + \dfrac{\sigma_2^2}{n_2}}$$

Formula for the z Test for Comparing Two Means from Independent Populations

$$z = \dfrac{(\overline{X}_1 - \overline{X}_2) - (\mu_1 - \mu_2)}{\sqrt{\dfrac{\sigma_1^2}{n_1} + \dfrac{\sigma_2^2}{n_2}}}$$

This formula is based on the general format of

$$\text{Test statistic} = \dfrac{(\text{observed value}) - (\text{expected value})}{\text{standard error}}$$

where $\overline{X}_1 - \overline{X}_2$ is the observed difference, and the expected difference $\mu_1 - \mu_2$ is zero when the null hypothesis is $\mu_1 = \mu_2$, since that is equivalent to $\mu_1 - \mu_2 = 0$. Finally, the standard deviation of the difference, referred to as the standard error of the difference is

$$\sqrt{\dfrac{\sigma_1^2}{n_1} + \dfrac{\sigma_2^2}{n_2}}$$

In the comparison of two sample means, the difference may be due to chance, in which case the null hypothesis will not be rejected, and the researcher can assume that the means of the populations are basically the same. The difference in this case is not significant. See Figure 9–2(a). On the other hand, if the difference is significant, the null hypothesis is rejected and the researcher can conclude that the population means are different. See Figure 9–2(b).

Figure 9–2

Hypothesis-Testing Situations in the Comparison of Means

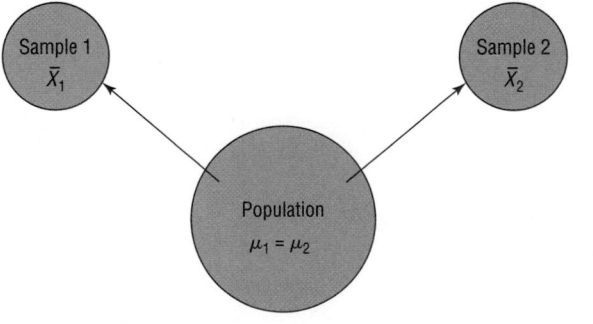

(a) Difference is not significant

Do not reject H_0: $\mu_1 = \mu_2$ since $\overline{X}_1 - \overline{X}_2$ is not significant.

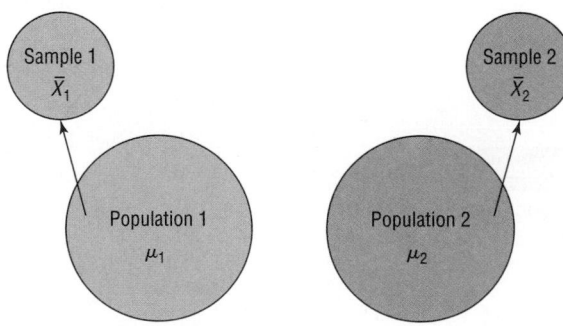

(b) Difference is significant

Reject H_0: $\mu_1 = \mu_2$ since $\overline{X}_1 - \overline{X}_2$ is significant.

These tests can also be one-tailed, using the following hypotheses:

Right-tailed		**Left-tailed**	
$H_0: \mu_1 = \mu_2$ $\quad$ or $\quad$ $H_0: \mu_1 - \mu_2 = 0$		$H_0: \mu_1 = \mu_2$ $\quad$ or $\quad$ $H_0: \mu_1 - \mu_2 = 0$	
$H_1: \mu_1 > \mu_2$ $\quad\quad$ $H_1: \mu_1 - \mu_2 > 0$		$H_1: \mu_1 < \mu_2$ $\quad\quad$ $H_1: \mu_1 - \mu_2 < 0$	

The same critical values used in Section 8–3 are used here. They can be obtained from Tables E–1 and E–2 in Appendix C.

If σ_1^2 and σ_2^2 are not known, the researcher can use the variances obtained from each sample s_1^2 and s_2^2, but both sample sizes must be 30 or more. The formula then is

$$z = \frac{(\overline{X}_1 - \overline{X}_2) - (\mu_1 - \mu_2)}{\sqrt{\dfrac{s_1^2}{n_1} + \dfrac{s_2^2}{n_2}}}$$

provided that $n_1 \geq 30$ and $n_2 \geq 30$.

When one or both sample sizes are less than 30 and σ_1 and σ_2 are unknown, the t test must be used, as shown in Section 9–4.

The basic format for hypothesis testing using the traditional method is reviewed here.

Step 1 State the hypotheses and identify the claim.

Step 2 Find the critical value(s).

Step 3 Compute the test statistic.

Step 4 Make the decision.

Step 5 Summarize the results.

Example 9–1

A survey found that the average hotel room rate in Toronto is $175.53 and the average room rate in Vancouver is $171.31. Assume that the data were obtained from two samples of 50 hotels each and the standard deviations were $9.52 and $10.89, respectively. At $\alpha = 0.05$, can it be concluded that there is a significant difference in the rates?

Source: *Canadian Lodging Outlook* (June 2006).

Solution

Step 1 State the hypotheses and identify the claim.

$$H_0: \mu_1 = \mu_2 \quad \text{and} \quad H_1: \mu_1 \neq \mu_2 (\text{claim})$$

Step 2 Find the critical values. Since $\alpha = 0.05$, the critical values are $+1.96$ and -1.96.

Step 3 Compute the test statistic.

$$z = \frac{(\overline{X}_1 - \overline{X}_2) - (\mu_1 - \mu_2)}{\sqrt{\dfrac{s_1^2}{n_1} + \dfrac{s_2^2}{n_2}}} = \frac{(175.53 - 171.31) - 0}{\sqrt{\dfrac{9.52^2}{50} + \dfrac{10.89^2}{50}}} \approx 2.06$$

Step 4 Make the decision. Reject the null hypothesis at $\alpha = 0.05$, since $2.06 > 1.96$. See Figure 9–3.

Figure 9–3

Critical Values and Test Statistic for Example 9–1

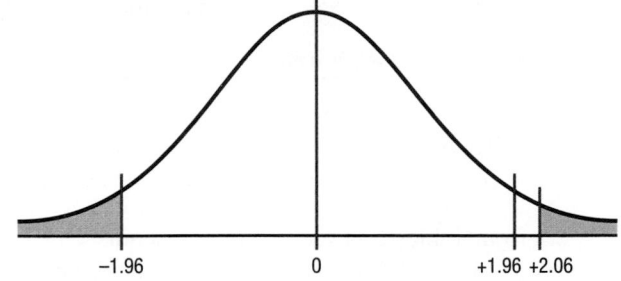

| −1.96 | 0 | +1.96 +2.06 |

> **Step 5** Summarize the results. There is enough evidence to support the claim that the means are not equal. Hence, there is a significant difference in the rates.

For example, if the test statistic for a two-tailed test is $+2.06$, the P-value obtained using Table E–2 is 0.0394. This value is obtained by subtracting the cumulative area to the left of $z = 2.06$, which is 0.9803, from 1.000 and multiplying by 2 (two-tailed test). The result is $2(1.0000 - 0.9803) = 2(0.0197) = 0.0394$. If $\alpha = 0.05$, the decision would be to reject the null hypothesis, since the P-value $< \alpha$.

The P-value method for hypothesis testing for this chapter also follows the same format as stated in Chapter 8. The steps are reviewed here.

Step 1 State the hypotheses and identify the claim.

Step 2 Compute the test statistic.

Step 3 Find the P-value.

Step 4 Make the decision.

Step 5 Summarize the results.

Example 9–2 illustrates these steps.

Example 9–2

A researcher hypothesizes that the average number of sports that colleges offer for males is greater than the average number of sports that colleges offer for females. A sample of the number of sports offered by colleges is shown. At $\alpha = 0.10$, is there enough evidence to support the claim?

Males					Females				
6	11	11	8	15	6	8	11	13	8
6	14	8	12	18	7	5	13	14	6
6	9	5	6	9	6	5	5	7	6
6	9	18	7	6	10	7	6	5	5
15	6	11	5	5	16	10	7	8	5
9	9	5	5	8	7	5	5	6	5
8	9	6	11	6	9	18	13	7	10
9	5	11	5	8	7	8	5	7	6
7	7	5	10	7	11	4	6	8	7
10	7	10	8	11	14	12	5	8	5

Source: USA TODAY.

Solution

Step 1 State the hypotheses and identify the claim.

$$H_0: \mu_1 = \mu_2 \quad \text{and} \quad H_1: \mu_1 > \mu_2 \text{ (claim)}$$

Step 2 Compute the test statistic. Using a calculator or the formulas in Chapter 3, find the mean and standard deviation for each data set.

For the males $\quad \overline{X}_1 = 8.6 \quad$ and $\quad s_1 = 3.3$

For the females $\quad \overline{X}_2 = 7.9 \quad$ and $\quad s_2 = 3.3$

Substitute in the formula.

$$z = \frac{(\overline{X}_1 - \overline{X}_2) - (\mu_1 - \mu_2)}{\sqrt{\dfrac{s_1^2}{n_1} + \dfrac{s_2^2}{n_2}}} = \frac{(8.6 - 7.9) - 0}{\sqrt{\dfrac{3.3^2}{50} + \dfrac{3.3^2}{50}}} \approx 1.06*$$

Step 3 Find the *P*-value. For $z = +1.06$, the cumulative area to the left from Table E–2 is 0.8554. For a right-tailed test, the required area is $1.0000 - 0.8554 = 0.1446$ or a *P*-value of 0.1446.

Step 4 Make the decision. Since the *P*-value is larger than α (that is, $0.1446 > 0.10$), the decision is to not reject the null hypothesis. See Figure 9–4.

Figure 9–4

P-Value and α Value for Example 9–2

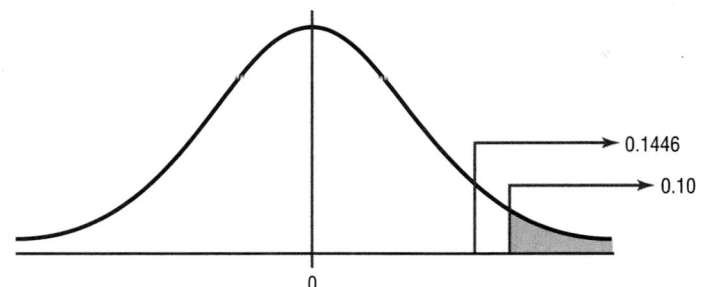

Note: Calculator results may differ due to rounding.

Step 5 Summarize the results. There is not enough evidence to support the claim that colleges offer more sports for males than they do for females.

Sometimes, the researcher is interested in testing a specific difference in means other than zero. For example, he or she might hypothesize that the nursing students at a college are, on the average, 3.2 years older than those at a university. In this case, the hypotheses are

$$H_0: \mu_1 - \mu_2 = 3.2 \quad \text{and} \quad H_1: \mu_1 - \mu_2 > 3.2$$

The formula for the *z* test is still

$$z = \frac{(\overline{X}_1 - \overline{X}_2) - (\mu_1 - \mu_2)}{\sqrt{\dfrac{\sigma_1^2}{n_1} + \dfrac{\sigma_2^2}{n_2}}}$$

where $\mu_1 - \mu_2$ is the hypothesized difference or expected value. In this case, $\mu_1 - \mu_2 = 3.2$.

Confidence intervals for the difference between two means can also be found. When one is hypothesizing a difference of zero, if the confidence interval contains zero, the null hypothesis is not rejected. If the confidence interval does not contain zero, the null hypothesis is rejected.

Confidence intervals for the difference between two means can be found by using this formula:

Formula for Confidence Interval for Difference Between Two Means: Large Samples

$$(\overline{X}_1 - \overline{X}_2) - z_{\alpha/2}\sqrt{\frac{\sigma_1^2}{n_1} + \frac{\sigma_2^2}{n_2}} < \mu_1 - \mu_2 < (\overline{X}_1 - \overline{X}_2) + z_{\alpha/2}\sqrt{\frac{\sigma_1^2}{n_1} + \frac{\sigma_2^2}{n_2}}$$

When $n_1 \geq 30$ and $n_2 \geq 30$, s_1^2 and s_2^2 can be used in place of σ_1^2 and σ_2^2.

Example 9–3

Find the 95% confidence interval for the difference between the means for the data in Example 9–1.

Solution

$$(\overline{X}_1 - \overline{X}_2) - z_{\alpha/2}\sqrt{\frac{\sigma_1^2}{n_1} + \frac{\sigma_2^2}{n_2}} < \mu_1 - \mu_2 < (\overline{X}_1 - \overline{X}_2) + z_{\alpha/2}\sqrt{\frac{\sigma_1^2}{n_1} + \frac{\sigma_2^2}{n_2}}$$

$$(175.53 - 171.31) - 1.96\sqrt{\frac{9.52^2}{50} + \frac{10.89^2}{50}} < \mu_1 - \mu_2$$

$$< (175.53 - 171.31) + 1.96\sqrt{\frac{9.52^2}{50} + \frac{10.89^2}{50}}$$

$$4.22 - 4.01 < \mu_1 - \mu_2 < 4.22 + 4.01$$

$$0.21 < \mu_1 - \mu_2 < 8.23$$

Since the confidence interval does not contain zero, the decision is to reject the null hypothesis, which agrees with the previous result.

Applying the Concepts 9–2

Home Runs

For a sports radio talk show, you are asked to research the question whether more home runs are hit by major league baseball players in the National League or by players in the American League. You decide to use the home run leaders from each league for the last 40 years as your data. The numbers are shown.

National League

47	49	73	50	65	70	49	47	40	43
46	35	38	40	47	39	49	37	37	36
40	37	31	48	48	45	52	38	38	36
44	40	48	45	45	36	39	44	52	47

American League

47	57	52	47	48	56	56	52	50	40
46	43	44	51	36	42	49	49	40	43
39	39	22	41	45	46	39	32	36	32
32	32	37	33	44	49	44	44	49	32

Using the data given, answer the following questions.

1. Define a population.
2. What kind of sample was used?
3. Do you feel that it is representative?
4. What are your hypotheses?
5. What significance level will you use?
6. What statistical test will you use?
7. What are the test results?
8. What is your decision?
9. What can you conclude?
10. Do you feel that using the data given really answers the original question asked?
11. What other data might be used to answer the question?

See page 448 for the answers.

Exercises 9–2

1. Explain the difference between testing a single mean and testing the difference between two means.

2. When a researcher selects all possible pairs of samples from a population in order to find the difference between the means of each pair, what will be the shape of the distribution of the differences when the original distributions are normally distributed? What will be the mean of the distribution? What will be the standard deviation of the distribution?

3. What two assumptions must be met when one is using the z test to test differences between two means? When can the sample standard deviations s_1 and s_2 be used in place of the population standard deviations σ_1 and σ_2?

4. Show two different ways to state that the means of two populations are equal.

For Exercises 5 through 17, perform each of the following steps.

 a. State the hypotheses and identify the claim.
 b. Find the critical value(s).
 c. Compute the test statistic.
 d. Make the decision.
 e. Summarize the results.

Use the traditional method of hypothesis testing unless otherwise specified.

5. A researcher wishes to see if the average length of the major rivers in North America is the same as the average length of the major rivers in Europe. The data (in

kilometres) of a sample of rivers are shown. At $\alpha = 0.01$, is there enough evidence to reject the claim?

North America			Europe		
1173	901	698	774	1165	1320
529	531	579	856	575	813
724	3726	1392	2858	1806	798
531	660	1667	1970	1020	370
529	1287	719	2285	525	1007
966	2108	1049	1411	933	338
2000	974	579	719	912	406
845	1490	1162	1326	1500	966
1368	499	692	1020	1809	2535
856	604	3185	909	652	3685
1143	877	417	1086	731	
483	756	684			

Source: *The World Almanac and Book of Facts.*

6. A study was conducted to see if there was a difference between spouses and significant others in coping skills when living with or caring for a person with multiple sclerosis. These skills were measured by questionnaire responses. The results of the two groups are given on one factor, ambivalence. At $\alpha = 0.10$, is there a difference in the means of the two groups?

Spouses	Significant others
$\overline{X}_1 = 2.0$	$\overline{X}_2 = 1.7$
$s_1 = 0.6$	$s_2 = 0.7$
$n_1 = 120$	$n_2 = 34$

Source: Elsie E. Gulick, "Coping Among Spouses or Significant Others of Persons with Multiple Sclerosis," *Nursing Research.*

7. A medical researcher wishes to see whether the pulse rates of smokers are higher than the pulse rates of nonsmokers. Samples of 100 smokers and 100 nonsmokers are selected. The results are shown here. Can the researcher conclude, at $\alpha = 0.05$, that smokers have higher pulse rates than nonsmokers?

Smokers	Nonsmokers
$\overline{X}_1 = 90$	$\overline{X}_2 = 88$
$s_1 = 5$	$s_2 = 6$
$n_1 = 100$	$n_2 = 100$

8. At age 9 the average weight (21.3 kg) and the average height (124.5 cm) for both boys and girls are exactly the same. A random sample of 9-year-olds yielded these results. Estimate the mean difference in height between boys and girls with 95% confidence. Does your interval support the given claim?

	Boys	Girls
Sample size	60	50
Mean height, cm	123.5	126.2
Sample variance	98	120

Source: www.healthepic.com.

9. Using data from the "Noise Levels in an Urban Hospital" study cited in Exercise 19 in Exercise set 7–2, test the claim that the noise level in the corridors is higher than that in the clinics. Use $\alpha = 0.02$. The data are shown here.

Corridors	Clinics
$\overline{X}_1 = 61.2$ dBA	$\overline{X}_2 = 59.4$ dBA
$s_1 = 7.9$	$s_2 = 7.9$
$n_1 = 84$	$n_2 = 34$

Source: M. Bayo, A. Garcia, and A. Garcia, "Noise Levels in an Urban Hospital and Workers' Subjective Responses," *Archives of Environmental Health* 50, no. 3.

10. A real estate agent compares the selling prices of Alberta homes in Calgary and Edmonton to see if there is a difference in the price. The results of the study are shown. Is there enough evidence to reject the claim that the average cost of a home in both locations is the same? Use $\alpha = 0.01$.

Calgary	Edmonton
$\overline{X}_1 = \$358,103*$	$\overline{X}_2 = \$303,304*$
$s_1 = \$21,471$	$s_2 = \$14,636$
$n_1 = 35$	$n_2 = 40$

*Based on data from the Multiple Listing Service.

11. In a study of women science majors, the following data were obtained on two groups, those who left their profession within a few months after graduation (leavers) and those who remained in their profession after they graduated (stayers). Test the claim that those who stayed had a higher science grade point average than those who left. Use $\alpha = 0.05$.

Leavers	Stayers
$\overline{X}_1 = 3.16$	$\overline{X}_2 = 3.28$
$s_1 = 0.52$	$s_2 = 0.46$
$n_1 = 103$	$n_2 = 225$

Source: Paula Rayman and Belle Brett, "Women Science Majors: What Makes a Difference in Persistence after Graduation?" *The Journal of Higher Education.*

12. A published survey of Canada's universities nationwide indicated an average entering grade of 82.9. Assume that a survey of 500 Saint Mary's University students attain a mean grade of 80.6. If the standard deviation in each case is 3.1, can we conclude that Saint Mary's University has a lower average entry grade than the national average? Use $\alpha = 0.05$.

Source: *Maclean's* University Survey.

13. A school administrator hypothesizes that colleges spend more for male sports than they do for female sports. A sample of two different colleges is selected, and the annual expenses (in dollars) per student at each school are shown. At $\alpha = 0.01$, is there enough evidence to support the claim?

Males

7,040	6,576	1,664	12,919	8,605
22,220	3,377	10,128	7,723	2,063
8,033	9,463	7,656	11,456	12,244
6,670	12,371	9,626	5,472	16,175
8,383	623	6,797	10,160	8,725
14,029	13,763	8,811	11,480	9,544
15,048	5,544	10,652	11,267	10,126
8,796	13,351	7,120	9,505	9,571
7,551	5,811	9,119	9,732	5,286
5,254	7,550	11,015	12,403	12,703

Females

10,333	6,407	10,082	5,933	3,991
7,435	8,324	6,989	16,249	5,922
7,654	8,411	11,324	10,248	6,030
9,331	6,869	6,502	11,041	11,597
5,468	7,874	9,277	10,127	13,371
7,055	6,909	8,903	6,925	7,058
12,745	12,016	9,883	14,698	9,907
8,917	9,110	5,232	6,959	5,832
7,054	7,235	11,248	8,478	6,502
7,300	993	6,815	9,959	10,353

Source: *USA TODAY.*

14. Is there a difference in average kilometres for each of two taxi companies during a randomly selected week? The data are shown. Use $\alpha = 0.05$. Assume that the populations are normally distributed. Use the *P*-value method.

Black Top Taxi Company	Yellow Cab Company
$\overline{X}_1 = 1347$	$\overline{X}_2 = 1212$
$s_1 = 48$	$s_2 = 64$
$n_1 = 35$	$n_2 = 40$

15. In the study cited in Exercise 11, the researchers collected the data shown here on a self-esteem questionnaire. At $\alpha = 0.05$, can it be concluded that there is a difference in the self-esteem scores of the two groups? Use the P-value method.

Leavers	Stayers
$\overline{X}_1 = 3.05$	$\overline{X}_2 = 2.96$
$s_1 = 0.75$	$s_2 = 0.75$
$n_1 = 103$	$n_2 = 225$

Source: Paula Rayman and Belle Brett, "Women Science Majors: What Makes a Difference in Persistence after Graduation?" *The Journal of Higher Education.*

16. The dean of students wants to see whether there is a significant difference in ages of resident students and commuting students. She selects a sample of 50 students from each group. The ages are shown here. At $\alpha = 0.05$, decide if there is enough evidence to reject the claim of no difference in the ages of the two groups. Use the standard deviations from the samples and the P-value method.

Resident students

22	25	27	23	26	28	26	24
25	20	26	24	27	26	18	19
18	30	26	18	18	19	32	23
19	19	18	29	19	22	18	22
26	19	19	21	23	18	20	18
22	21	19	21	21	22	18	20
19	23						

Commuter students

18	20	19	18	22	25	24	35
23	18	23	22	28	25	20	24
26	30	22	22	22	21	18	20
19	26	35	19	19	18	19	32
29	23	21	19	36	27	27	20
20	21	18	19	23	20	19	19
20	25						

17. Two groups of students are given a problem-solving test, and the results are compared. Find the 90% confidence interval of the true difference in means.

Mathematics majors	Computer science majors
$\overline{X}_1 = 83.6$	$\overline{X}_2 = 79.2$
$s_1 = 4.3$	$s_2 = 3.8$
$n_1 = 36$	$n_2 = 36$

18. The average credit card debt for a recent year was $9205. Five years earlier the average credit card debt was $6618. Assume sample sizes of 35 were used and the standard deviations of both samples were $1928. Is there enough evidence to believe that the average credit card debt has increased? Use $\alpha = 0.05$. Give a possible reason as to why or why not the debt was increased.

Source: CardWeb.com.

19. Two brands of cigarettes are selected, and their nicotine content is compared. The data are shown here. Find the 99% confidence interval of the true difference in the means.

Brand A	Brand B
$X_1 = 28.6$ milligrams	$X_2 = 32.9$ milligrams
$\sigma_1 = 5.1$ milligrams	$\sigma_2 = 4.4$ milligrams
$n_1 = 30$	$n_2 = 40$

20. Two brands of batteries are tested, and their voltage is compared. The data follow. Find the 95% confidence interval of the true difference in the means. Assume that both variables are normally distributed.

Brand X	Brand Y
$\overline{X}_1 = 9.2$ volts	$\overline{X}_2 = 8.8$ volts
$\sigma_1 = 0.3$ volt	$\sigma_2 = 0.1$ volt
$n_1 = 27$	$n_2 = 30$

Extending the Concepts

21. A researcher claims that students in a private school have exam scores that are at most 8 points higher than those of students in public schools. Random samples of 60 students from each type of school are selected and given an exam. The results are shown. At $\alpha = 0.05$, test the claim.

Private school	Public school
$\overline{X}_1 = 110$	$\overline{X}_2 = 104$
$s_1 = 15$	$s_2 = 15$
$n_1 = 60$	$n_2 = 60$

<table>
<tr><td style="background-color:#808080">9–3</td><td></td></tr>
</table>

| 9–3 | **Testing the Difference Between Two Variances** |

In addition to comparing two means, statisticians are interested in comparing two variances or standard deviations. For example, is the variation in the temperatures for a certain month for two cities different?

In another situation, a researcher may be interested in comparing the variance of the cholesterol of men with the variance of the cholesterol of women. For the comparison of two variances or standard deviations, an **F test** is used. The F test should not be confused with the chi-square test, which compares a single sample variance to a specific population variance, as shown in Chapter 8.

Objective ②

Test the difference between two variances or standard deviations.

If two independent samples are selected from two normally distributed populations in which the variances are equal ($\sigma_1^2 = \sigma_2^2$) and if the variances s_1^2 and s_2^2 are compared as $\dfrac{s_1^2}{s_2^2}$, the sampling distribution of the variances is called the **F distribution.**

Characteristics of the F Distribution

1. The values of F cannot be negative, because variances are always positive or zero.
2. The distribution is positively skewed.
3. The mean value of F is approximately equal to 1.
4. The F distribution is a family of curves based on the degrees of freedom of the variance of the numerator and the degrees of freedom of the variance of the denominator.

Figure 9–5 shows the shapes of several curves for the F distribution.

Figure 9–5

The F Family of Curves

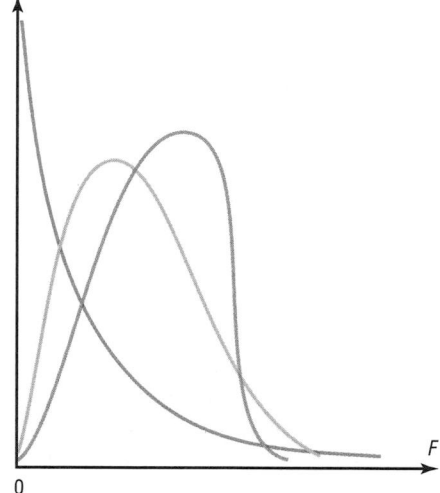

Formula for the F Test

$$F = \frac{s_1^2}{s_2^2}$$

where the larger of the two variances is placed in the numerator regardless of the subscripts. (See note on page 413.)

The F test has two terms for the degrees of freedom: that of the numerator, $n_1 - 1$, and that of the denominator, $n_2 - 1$, where n_1 is the sample size from which the larger variance was obtained.

When one is finding the *F* test value, *the larger of the variances is placed in the numerator of the F formula;* this is not necessarily the variance of the larger of the two sample sizes.

Table H in Appendix C gives the *F* critical values for $\alpha = 0.005, 0.01, 0.025, 0.05,$ and 0.10 (each α value involves a separate table in Table H). These are one-tailed values; if a two-tailed test is being conducted, then the $\alpha/2$ value must be used. For example, if a two-tailed test with $\alpha = 0.05$ is being conducted, then the $0.05/2 = 0.025$ table of Table H should be used.

Example 9–4	Find the critical value for a right-tailed *F* test when $\alpha = 0.05$, the degrees of freedom for the numerator (abbreviated d.f.N.) are 15, and the degrees of freedom for the denominator (d.f.D.) are 21.

Solution

Since this test is right-tailed with $\alpha = 0.05$, use the 0.05 table. The d.f.N. is listed across the top, and the d.f.D. is listed in the left column. The critical value is found where the row and column intersect in the table. In this case, it is 2.18. See Figure 9–6.

Figure 9–6

Finding the Critical Value in Table H for Example 9–4

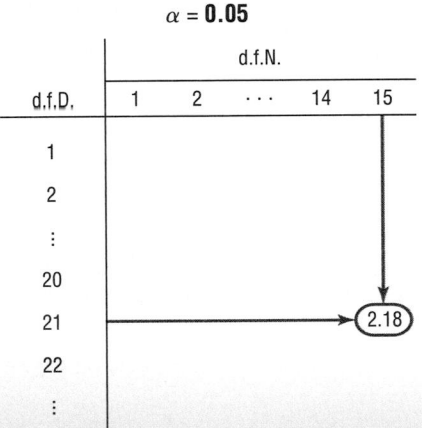

As noted previously, when the *F* test is used, the larger variance is always placed in the numerator of the formula. When one is conducting a two-tailed test, α is split; and even though there are two values, only the right tail is used. The reason is that the *F* test value is always greater than or equal to 1.

Example 9–5	Find the critical value for a two-tailed *F* test with $\alpha = 0.05$ when the sample size from which the variance for the numerator was obtained was 21 and the sample size from which the variance for the denominator was obtained was 12.

Solution

Since this is a two-tailed test with $\alpha = 0.05$, the $0.05/2 = 0.025$ table must be used. Here, d.f.N. $= 21 - 1 = 20$, and d.f.D. $= 12 - 1 = 11$; hence, the critical value is 3.23. See Figure 9–7.

Figure 9–7

Finding the Critical Value in Table H for Example 9–5

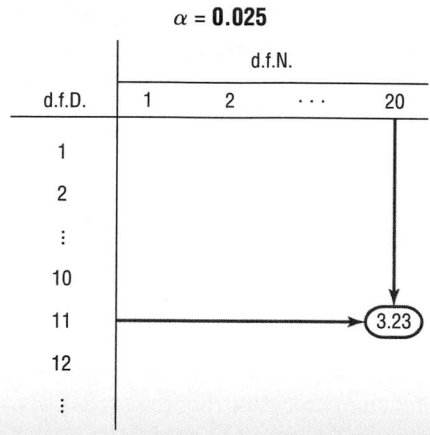

$\alpha = 0.025$

When the degree of freedom values cannot be found in the table, the closest value on the smaller side should be used. For example, if d.f.N. = 14, this value is between the given table values of 12 and 15; therefore, 12 should be used, to be on the safe side.

When one is testing the equality of two variances, these hypotheses are used:

Right-tailed	Left-tailed	Two-tailed
$H_0: \sigma_1^2 = \sigma_2^2$	$H_0: \sigma_1^2 = \sigma_2^2$	$H_0: \sigma_1^2 = \sigma_2^2$
$H_1: \sigma_1^2 > \sigma_2^2$	$H_1: \sigma_1^2 < \sigma_2^2$	$H_1: \sigma_1^2 \neq \sigma_2^2$

There are four key points to keep in mind when one is using the F test.

Notes for the Use of the F Test

1. The larger variance should always be placed in the numerator of the formula regardless of the subscripts. (See note on page 413.)

$$F = \frac{s_1^2}{s_2^2}$$

2. For a two-tailed test, the α value must be divided by 2 and the critical value placed on the right side of the F curve.
3. If the standard deviations instead of the variances are given in the problem, they must be squared for the formula for the F test.
4. When the degrees of freedom cannot be found in Table H, the closest value on the smaller side should be used.

Assumptions for Testing the Difference Between Two Variances

1. The populations from which the samples were obtained must be normally distributed. (*Note:* The test should not be used when the distributions depart from normality.)
2. The samples must be independent of each other.

Remember also that in tests of hypotheses using the traditional method, these five steps should be taken:

Step 1   State the hypotheses and identify the claim.

Step 2   Find the critical value.

Unusual Stat

2.1% of Canadian newborns weigh 4500 grams or more.

Step 3   Compute the test statistic.

Step 4   Make the decision.

Step 5   Summarize the results.

Example 9–6

A medical researcher wishes to see whether the variance of the heart rates (in beats per minute) of smokers is different from the variance of heart rates of people who do not smoke. Two samples are selected, and the data are as shown. Using $\alpha = 0.05$, is there enough evidence to support the claim?

Smokers	Nonsmokers
$n_1 = 26$	$n_2 = 18$
$s_1^2 = 36$	$s_2^2 = 10$

Solution

Step 1   State the hypotheses and identify the claim.

$$H_0: \sigma_1^2 = \sigma_2^2 \qquad \text{and} \qquad H_1: \sigma_1^2 \neq \sigma_2^2 \text{ (claim)}$$

Step 2   Find the critical value. Use the 0.025 table in Table H since $\alpha = 0.05$ and this is a two-tailed test. Here, d.f.N. $= 26 - 1 = 25$, and d.f.D. $= 18 - 1 = 17$. The critical value is 2.56 (d.f.N. $= 24$ was used). See Figure 9–8.

Figure 9–8

Critical Value for
Example 9–6

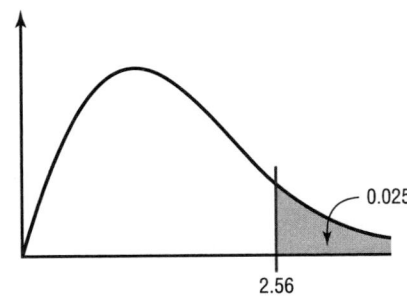

0.025

2.56

Step 3   Compute the test statistic.

$$F = \frac{s_1^2}{s_2^2} = \frac{36}{10} = 3.6$$

Step 4   Make the decision. Reject the null hypothesis, since $3.6 > 2.56$.

Step 5   Summarize the results. There is enough evidence to support the claim that the variance of the heart rates of smokers and nonsmokers is different.

Example 9–7

The standard deviation of the average waiting time to see a doctor for non-life-threatening problems in the emergency room at an urban hospital is 32 minutes. At a second hospital, the standard deviation is 28 minutes. If a sample of 16 patients was used in the first case and 18 in the second case, is there enough evidence to conclude that the standard deviation of the waiting times in the first hospital is greater than the standard deviation of the waiting times in the second hospital? Use $\alpha = 0.01$.

Solution

Step 1 State the hypotheses and identify the claim.

$$H_0: \sigma_1^2 = \sigma_2^2 \qquad \text{and} \qquad H_1: \sigma_1^2 > \sigma_2^2 \text{ (claim)}$$

Step 2 Find the critical value. Here, d.f.N. $= 16 - 1 = 15$, and d.f.D. $= 18 - 1 = 17$. From the 0.01 table, the critical value is 3.31.

Step 3 Compute the test statistic.

$$F = \frac{s_1^2}{s_2^2} = \frac{32^2}{28^2} \approx 1.31$$

Step 4 Do not reject the null hypothesis since $1.31 < 3.31$.

Step 5 Summarize the results. There is not enough evidence to support the claim that the standard deviation of the waiting times of the first hospital is greater than the standard deviation of the waiting times of the second hospital.

Finding P-values for the F test statistic is somewhat more complicated since it requires looking through all the F tables (Table H in Appendix C) using the specific d.f.N. and d.f.D. values. For example, suppose that a certain test has $F = 3.58$, d.f.N. $= 5$, and d.f.D. $= 10$. To find the P-value interval for $F = 3.58$, one must first find the corresponding F values for d.f.N. $= 5$ and d.f.D. $= 10$ for α equal to 0.005 on page 668, 0.01 on page 669, 0.025 on page 670, 0.05 on page 671, and 0.10 on page 672 in Table H. Then make a table as shown.

α	0.10	0.05	0.025	0.01	0.005
F	2.52	3.33	4.24	5.64	6.87
Reference page	xx	xx	xx	xx	xx

Now locate the two F values that the test value 3.58 falls between. In this case, 3.58 falls between 3.33 and 4.24, corresponding to 0.05 and 0.025. Hence, the P-value for a right-tailed test for $F = 3.58$ falls between 0.025 and 0.05 (that is, $0.025 < P\text{-value} < 0.05$). For a right-tailed test, then, one would reject the null hypothesis at $\alpha = 0.05$ but not at $\alpha = 0.01$. The P-value obtained from a calculator is 0.0408. Remember that for a two-tailed test the values found in Table H for α must be doubled. In this case, $0.05 < P\text{-value} < 0.10$ for $F = 3.58$.

Once you understand the concept, you can dispense with making a table as shown and find the P-value directly from Table H.

Example 9–8

The CEO of an airport hypothesizes that the variance in the number of passengers for American airports is greater than the variance in the number of passengers for Canadian airports. At $\alpha = 0.10$, is there enough evidence to support the hypothesis? The data in millions of passengers per year are shown for selected airports. Use the P-value method. Assume the variable is normally distributed.

American airports		Canadian airports	
76.0	66.7	23.8	13.4
56.2	52.8	7.5	7.3
35.6	35.5		

Sources: www.tc.gc.ca/pol/en/T-Facts3/main.asp?id=43&table=10.Table 43&file=air &Lang=&title=AIR%20-%20 Passenger %20 Traffic, Statistics Canada, Air Carrier Statements St. 2, 4 & 6 dated February 2002 and updated September 30, 2003, reproduced with the permission of the Minister of Public Works and Government Services Canada, 2007.

Solution

Step 1 State the hypotheses and identify the claim.

$$H_0: \sigma_1^2 = \sigma_2^2 \qquad \text{and} \qquad H_0: \sigma_1^2 > \sigma_2^2 \text{ (claim)}$$

Step 2 Compute the test statistic. Using the formula in Chapter 3 or a calculator, find the variance for each group.

$$s_1^2 \approx 266.43 \qquad \text{and} \qquad s_2^2 \approx 59.85$$

Substitute in the formula and solve.

$$F = \frac{s_1^2}{s_2^2} = \frac{266.43}{59.85} \approx 4.45$$

Step 3 Find the P-value in Table H, using d.f.N. $= 5$ and d.f.D. $= 3$.

α	0.10	0.05	0.025	0.01	0.005
F	5.31	9.01	14.88	28.24	45.39

Since 4.45 is less than 5.31, the P-value is greater than 0.10. (The P-value obtained from a calculator is 0.124.)

Step 4 Make the decision. The decision is to not reject the null hypothesis since P-value > 0.10.

Step 5 Summarize the results. There is not enough evidence to support the claim that the variance in the number of passengers for American airports is greater than the variance in the number of passengers for Canadian airports.

If the exact degrees of freedom are not specified in Table H, the closest smaller value should be used. For example, if $\alpha = 0.05$ (right-tailed test), d.f.N. $= 18$, and d.f.D. $= 20$, use the column d.f.N. $= 15$ and the row d.f.D. $= 20$ to get $F = 2.20$.

Note: It is not absolutely necessary to place the larger variance in the numerator when one is performing the F test. Critical values for left-tailed hypotheses tests can be found by interchanging the degrees of freedom and taking the reciprocal of the value found in Table H.

Also, one should use caution when performing the F test since the data can run contrary to the hypotheses on rare occasions. For example, if the hypotheses are $H_0: \sigma_1^2 = \sigma_2^2$ and $H_1: \sigma_1^2 > \sigma_2^2$, but if $s_1^2 < s_2^2$, then the F test should not be performed and one would not reject the null hypothesis.

Applying the Concepts 9–3

Variability and Automatic Transmissions

Assume the following data values are from the June 1996 issue of *Automotive Magazine*. An article compared various parameters of North American and Japanese-made sports cars. This report centres on the price of an optional automatic transmission. Which sector has the greater variability in the price of automatic transmissions? Input the data and answer the following questions.

Japanese cars		North American cars	
Nissan 300ZX	$1940	Dodge Stealth	$2363
Mazda RX7	1810	Saturn	1230
Mazda MX6	1871	Mercury Cougar	1332
Nissan NX	1822	Ford Probe	932
Mazda Miata	1920	Eagle Talon	1790
Honda Prelude	1730	Chevy Lumina	1833

1. What is the null hypothesis?

2. What test statistic is used to test for any significant differences in the variances?

3. Is there a significant difference in the variability in the prices between the two car sectors?

4. What effect does a small sample size have on the standard deviations?

5. What degrees of freedom are used for the statistical test?

6. Could two sets of data have significantly different variances without having significantly different means?

See page 448 for the answers.

Exercises 9–3

1. When one is computing the F test value, what condition is placed on the variance that is in the numerator?

2. Why is the critical region always on the right side in the use of the F test?

3. What are the two different degrees of freedom associated with the F distribution?

4. What are the characteristics of the F distribution?

5. Using Table H, find the critical value for each.

   a. Sample 1: $s_1^2 = 128$, $n_1 = 23$
      Sample 2: $s_2^2 = 162$, $n_2 = 16$
      Two-tailed, $\alpha = 0.01$

   b. Sample 1: $s_1^2 = 37$, $n_1 = 14$
      Sample 2: $s_2^2 = 89$, $n_2 = 25$
      Right-tailed, $\alpha = 0.01$

   c. Sample 1: $s_1^2 = 232$, $n_1 = 30$
      Sample 2: $s_2^2 = 387$, $n_2 = 46$
      Two-tailed, $\alpha = 0.05$

   d. Sample 1: $s_1^2 = 164$, $n_1 = 21$
      Sample 2: $s_2^2 = 53$, $n_2 = 17$
      Two-tailed, $\alpha = 0.10$

   e. Sample 1: $s_1^2 = 92.8$, $n_1 = 11$
      Sample 2: $s_2^2 = 43.6$, $n_2 = 11$
      Right-tailed, $\alpha = 0.05$

6. (ans) Using Table H, find the P-value interval for each F test statistic.

   a. $F = 2.97$, d.f.N. $= 9$, d.f.D. $= 14$, right-tailed
   b. $F = 3.32$, d.f.N. $= 6$, d.f.D. $= 12$, two-tailed
   c. $F = 2.28$, d.f.N. $= 12$, d.f.D. $= 20$, right-tailed
   d. $F = 3.51$, d.f.N. $= 12$, d.f.D. $= 21$, right-tailed
   e. $F = 4.07$, d.f.N. $= 6$, d.f.D. $= 10$, two-tailed
   f. $F = 1.65$, d.f.N. $= 19$, d.f.D. $= 28$, right-tailed
   g. $F = 1.77$, d.f.N. $= 28$, d.f.D. $= 28$, right-tailed
   h. $F = 7.29$, d.f.N. $= 5$, d.f.D. $= 8$, two-tailed

For Exercises 7 through 20, perform the following steps. Assume that all variables are normally distributed.

   a. State the hypotheses and identify the claim.
   b. Find the critical value.
   c. Compute the test statistic.
   d. Make the decision.
   e. Summarize the results.

Use the traditional method of hypothesis testing unless otherwise specified.

7. The standard deviation for the number of weeks 15 *New York Times* hardcover fiction books spent on their bestseller list is 6.17 weeks. The standard deviation for the 15 *New York Times* hardcover nonfiction list is 13.12 weeks. At $\alpha = 0.10$, can we conclude that there is a difference in the variances?

   Source: *The New York Times.*

8. A researcher claims that the standard deviation of the ages of cats is smaller than the standard deviation of the ages of dogs who are owned by families in a large city. A randomly selected sample of 29 cats has a standard deviation of 2.7 years, and a random sample of 16 dogs has a standard deviation of 3.5 years. Is the researcher correct? Use $\alpha = 0.05$. If there is a difference, suggest a reason for the difference.

9. A tax collector wishes to see if the variances of the values of the tax-exempt properties are different for two large cities. The values of the tax-exempt properties for two samples are shown. The data are given in millions of dollars. At $\alpha = 0.05$, is there enough evidence to support the tax collector's claim that the variances are different?

City A				City B			
113	22	14	8	82	11	5	15
25	23	23	30	295	50	12	9
44	11	19	7	12	68	81	2
31	19	5	2	20	16	4	5

10. In the hospital study cited in Exercise 19 in Exercise set 7–2, it was found that the standard deviation of the sound levels from 20 areas designated as "casualty doors" was 4.1 dBA and the standard deviation of 24 areas designated as operating theatres was 7.5 dBA. At $\alpha = 0.05$, can one substantiate the claim that there is a difference in the standard deviations?

Source: M. Bayo, A. Garcia, and A. Garcia, "Noise Levels in an Urban Hospital and Workers' Subjective Responses," *Archives of Environmental Health.*

11. The numbers of calories contained in 113-gram servings of randomly selected flavours of ice cream from two national brands are listed here. At the 0.05 level of significance, is there sufficient evidence to conclude that the variance in the number of calories differs between the two brands?

Brand A		Brand B	
330	300	280	310
310	350	300	370
270	380	250	300
310	300	290	310

Source: *The Doctor's Pocket Calorie, Fat and Carbohydrate Counter.*

12. A researcher wishes to see if the variance in the number of passenger vehicles crossing the Canada–U.S. border southbound each year is different from the variance in the number of vehicles crossing the border northbound. Recent annual data (in thousands) are shown. At $\alpha = 0.05$, can it be concluded that the variances are different?

Southbound	Northbound
39,146	38,584
39,531	38,858
38,950	38,950
36,597	36,693
37,220	36,460
36,915	36,172
34,308	34,012
32,539	32,020
30,220	29,953

Source: North American Transportation Statistics.

13. The standard deviation of the ages of a sample of people who were playing the slot machines is 6.8 years. The standard deviation of the ages of a sample of people who were playing roulette is 3.2 years. If each sample contained 25 people, can it be concluded that the standard deviations of the ages are different? Use $\alpha = 0.05$. If there is a difference, suggest a reason for the difference.

14. The number of grams of carbohydrates contained in 30-gram servings of randomly selected chocolate and nonchocolate candy is listed here. Is there sufficient evidence to conclude that the variance in carbohydrate content varies between chocolate and nonchocolate candy? Use $\alpha = 0.10$.

Chocolate:	29	25	17	36	41	25	32	29
	38	34	24	27	29			

Nonchocolate:	41	41	37	29	30	38	39	10
	29	55	29					

Source: *The Doctor's Pocket Calorie, Fat and Carbohydrate Counter.*

15. The yearly tuition costs in dollars for random samples of medical schools that specialize in research and in primary care are listed. At $\alpha = 0.05$, can it be concluded that a difference between the variances of the two groups exists?

Research			Primary care		
30,897	34,280	31,943	26,068	21,044	30,897
34,294	31,275	29,590	34,208	20,877	29,691
20,618	20,500	29,310	33,783	33,065	35,000
21,274			27,297		

Source: *U.S. News & World Report Best Graduate Schools.*

16. A researcher wants to find out if the variance of the number of small farms (<73 hectares) in Saskatchewan is less than the variance of the number of small farms in Alberta. A random sample of farm geographical divisions is selected, and the data are shown. At $\alpha = 0.01$, can it be concluded that the variance of the number of small farms in Saskatchewan is less than the variance of the number of small farms in Alberta?

Saskatchewan			Alberta		
3006	3388	2849	1971	1804	1031
1956	4424	2004	3540	6436	4347
3169	4605	5400	3911	3323	1228

Source: Statistics Canada—Census 2001—Farm Data.

17. Test the claim that the variance of heights of the tallest buildings in Montreal is equal to the variance in heights of the tallest buildings in Calgary at $\alpha = 0.10$. The data are given in metres.

Montreal			Calgary		
205	188	158	250	197	167
195	180	181	215	191	164
190	173	198	191	177	162

Source: www.answers.com.

18. A researcher claims that the variation in the salaries of elementary school teachers is greater than the variation in the salaries of secondary school teachers. A sample of the salaries of 30 elementary school teachers has a variance of $8324, and a sample of the salaries of 30 secondary school teachers has a variance of $2862. At $\alpha = 0.05$, can the researcher conclude that the variation in the elementary school teachers' salaries is greater than the variation in the secondary teachers' salaries? Use the P-value method.

19. The weights, in grams, of a sample of running shoes for men and women are shown. Calculate the variances for each sample, and test the claim that the variances are equal at $\alpha = 0.05$. Use the P-value method.

Men			Women		
370.1	323.5	391.9	329.7	317.3	273.7
382.6	345.2	457.2	298.6	295.5	295.5
286.2	335.9	401.2	314.1	348.4	289.3
348.4	363.9	413.7	292.4	320.4	295.5
429.2	398.1	451.0	304.8	320.4	342.1

20. Upright vacuum cleaners have either a hard body type or a soft body type. Shown are the weights in pounds of a sample of each type. At $\alpha = 0.05$, can the claim that there is a difference in the variances of the weights of the two types be substantiated?

Hard body types				Soft body types			
21	17	17	20	24	13	11	13
16	17	15	20	12	15		
23	16	17	17				
13	15	16	18				
18							

9-4 Testing the Difference Between Two Means: Small Independent Samples

In Section 9–2, the z test was used to test the difference between two means when the population standard deviations were known and the variables were normally or approximately normally distributed, or when both sample sizes were greater than or equal to 30. In many situations, however, these conditions cannot be met—that is, the population standard deviations are not known, and one or both sample sizes are less than 30. In these cases, a t test is used to test the difference between means when the two samples are independent and when the samples are taken from two normally or approximately normally distributed populations. Samples are **independent samples** when the measurements in one sample are not related to the measurements in the other sample.

There are actually two different options for the use of t tests. *One option is used when the variances of the populations are not equal, and the other option is used when the variances are equal.* To determine whether two sample variances are equal, the researcher can use an F test, as shown in Section 9–3.

Note, however, that not all statisticians are in agreement about using the F test before using the t test. Some believe that conducting the F and t tests at the same level of significance will change the overall level of significance of the t test. Their reasons are beyond the scope of this textbook.

Objective 3

Test the difference between two means for small independent samples.

Formulas for the t Tests—For Testing the Difference Between Two Means—Small Independent Samples

Variances are assumed to be unequal:

$$t = \frac{(\bar{X}_1 - \bar{X}_2) - (\mu_1 - \mu_2)}{\sqrt{\dfrac{s_1^2}{n_1} + \dfrac{s_2^2}{n_2}}}$$

where the degrees of freedom are equal to the smaller of $n_1 - 1$ or $n_2 - 1$.
Variances are assumed to be equal:

$$t = \frac{(\bar{X}_1 - \bar{X}_2) - (\mu_1 - \mu_2)}{\sqrt{\dfrac{(n_1 - 1)s_1^2 + (n_2 - 1)s_2^2}{n_1 + n_2 - 2}}\sqrt{\dfrac{1}{n_1} + \dfrac{1}{n_2}}}$$

where the degrees of freedom are equal to $n_1 + n_2 - 2$.

When the variances are unequal, the first formula

$$t = \frac{(\overline{X}_1 - \overline{X}_2) - (\mu_1 - \mu_2)}{\sqrt{\dfrac{s_1^2}{n_1} + \dfrac{s_2^2}{n_2}}}$$

follows the format of

$$\text{Test statistic} = \frac{(\text{observed value}) - (\text{expected value})}{\text{standard error}}$$

where $\overline{X}_1 - \overline{X}_2$ is the observed difference between sample means and where the expected value $\mu_1 - \mu_2$ is equal to zero when no difference between population means is hypothesized. The denominator $\sqrt{s_1^2/n_1 + s_2^2/n_2}$ is the standard error of the difference between two means. Since mathematical derivation of the standard error is somewhat complicated, it will be omitted here.

When the variances are assumed to be equal, the second formula

$$t = \frac{(\overline{X}_1 - \overline{X}_2) - (\mu_1 - \mu_2)}{\sqrt{\dfrac{(n_1 - 1)s_1^2 + (n_2 - 1)s_2^2}{n_1 + n_2 - 2}}\sqrt{\dfrac{1}{n_1} + \dfrac{1}{n_2}}}$$

also follows the format of

$$\text{Test statistic} = \frac{(\text{observed value}) - (\text{expected value})}{\text{standard error}}$$

For the numerator, the terms are the same as in the first formula. However, a note of explanation is needed for the denominator of the second test statistic. Since both populations are assumed to have the same variance, the standard error is computed with what is called a pooled estimate of the variance. A **pooled estimate of the variance** is a weighted average of the variance using the two sample variances and the *degrees of freedom* of each variance as the weights. Again, since the algebraic derivation of the standard error is somewhat complicated, it is omitted.

In summary, then, to use the t test, first use the F test to determine whether the variances are equal. Then use the appropriate t test formula. This procedure involves two five-step processes.

Example 9–9

The average size of a farm in Ontario is 85 hectares (ha). The average farm size of a farm in Quebec is 93 ha. Assume the data were obtained from two samples with standard deviations of 17 ha and 6 ha, respectively, and sample sizes of 8 and 10, respectively. Can it be concluded at $\alpha = 0.05$ that the average size of the farms in the two provinces is different? Assume the populations are normally distributed.

Source: Adapted from Statistics Canada publication *Farming Facts, 2002*, Catalogue 21-522-XPE.

Solution

Here we will use the F test to determine whether the variances are equal. The null hypothesis is that the variances are equal.

Step 1 State the hypotheses and identify the claim.

$$H_0\text{: } \sigma_1^2 = \sigma_2^2 \text{ (claim)} \qquad \text{and} \qquad H_1\text{: } \sigma_1^2 \neq \sigma_2^2$$

Step 2 Find the critical value. The critical value for the F test found in Table H (Appendix C) for $\alpha = 0.05$ is 4.20, since there are 7 and 9 degrees of freedom. (Note: Use the 0.025 table.)

Step 3 Compute the test statistic.

$$F = \frac{s_1^2}{s_2^2} = \frac{17^2}{6^2} = 8.03$$

Step 4 Make the decision. Reject the null hypothesis since 8.03 falls in the critical region. See Figure 9–9.

Figure 9–9

Critical and *F* Test Values for Example 9–9

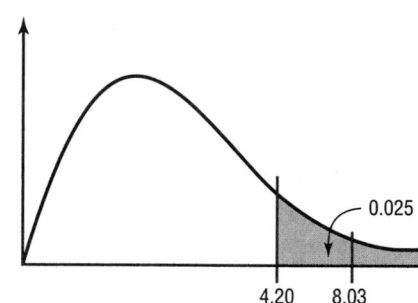

Step 5 Summarize the results. It can be concluded that the variances are not equal.
Since the variances are not equal, the first formula will be used to test the equality of the means.

Step 1 State the hypotheses and identify the claim for the means.

$$H_0: \mu_1 = \mu_2 \qquad \text{and} \qquad H_1: \mu_1 \neq \mu_2 \text{ (claim)}$$

Step 2 Find the critical values. Since the test is two-tailed, since $\alpha = 0.05$, and since the variances are unequal, the degrees of freedom are the smaller of $n_1 - 1$ or $n_2 - 1$. In this case the degrees of freedom are $8 - 1 = 7$. Hence, from Table F, the critical values are $+2.365$ and -2.365.

Step 3 Compute the test statistic. Since the variances are unequal, use the first formula.

$$t = \frac{(\overline{X}_1 - \overline{X}_2) - (\mu_1 - \mu_2)}{\sqrt{\dfrac{s_1^2}{n_1} + \dfrac{s_2^2}{n_2}}} = \frac{(85 - 93) - 0}{\sqrt{\dfrac{17^2}{8} + \dfrac{6^2}{10}}} \approx -1.269$$

Step 4 Make the decision. Do not reject the null hypothesis, since $-1.269 > -2.365$. See Figure 9–10.

Figure 9–10

Critical Values and Test Statistic for Example 9–9

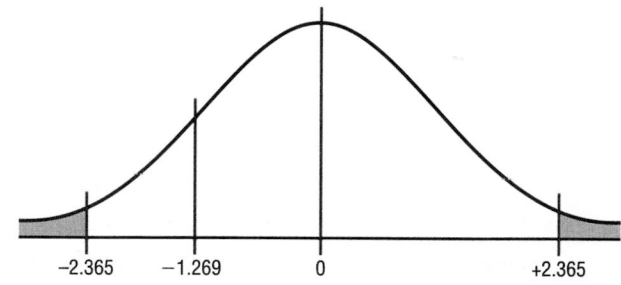

Step 5 Summarize the results. There is not enough evidence to support the claim that the average size of the farms is different.

Example 9–10   A researcher wishes to determine whether the salaries of professional nurses employed by private hospitals in the United States are higher than those of nurses employed by government-owned hospitals. She selects a sample of nurses from each type of hospital and calculates the means and standard deviations of their salaries. At $\alpha = 0.01$, can she conclude that the private hospitals pay more than the government hospitals? Assume that the populations are approximately normally distributed. Use the P-value method.

Private	Government
$\overline{X}_1 = \$26{,}800$	$\overline{X}_2 = \$25{,}400$
$s_1 = \$600$	$s_2 = \$450$
$n_1 = 10$	$n_2 = 8$

Solution

The F test will be used to determine whether the variances are equal. The null hypothesis is that the variances are equal.

Step 1   State the hypotheses and identify the claim.

$$H_0: \sigma_1^2 = \sigma_2^2 \text{ (claim)} \qquad \text{and} \qquad H_1: \sigma_1^2 \neq \sigma_2^2$$

Step 2   Compute the test statistic.

$$F = \frac{s_1^2}{s_2^2} = \frac{600^2}{450^2} \approx 1.78$$

Step 3   Find the P-value in Table H, using d.f.N. $= 9$ and d.f.D. $= 7$. Since $1.78 < 2.72$, P-value > 0.20. (The P-value obtained from a calculator is 0.460.)

Step 4   Make the decision. Do not reject the null hypothesis since P-value > 0.01 (the α value).

Step 5   Summarize the results. There is not enough evidence to reject the claim that the variances are equal; therefore, the second formula is used to test the difference between the two means, as shown next.

Step 1   State the hypotheses and identify the claim.

$$H_0: \mu_1 \leq \mu_2 \qquad \text{and} \qquad H_1: \mu_1 > \mu_2 \text{ (claim)}$$

Step 2   Compute the test statistic. Use the second formula, since the variances are assumed to be equal.

$$t = \frac{(\overline{X}_1 - \overline{X}_2) - (\mu_1 - \mu_2)}{\sqrt{\dfrac{(n_1 - 1)s_1^2 + (n_2 - 1)s_2^2}{n_1 + n_2 - 2}} \sqrt{\dfrac{1}{n_1} + \dfrac{1}{n_2}}}$$

$$= \frac{(26{,}800 - 25{,}400) - 0}{\sqrt{\dfrac{(10 - 1)(600)^2 + (8 - 1)(450)^2}{10 + 8 - 2}} \sqrt{\dfrac{1}{10} + \dfrac{1}{8}}}$$

$$= 5.47$$

Step 3   Find the P-value, using Table F. The P-value for $t = 5.47$ with d.f. $= 16$ (that is, $10 + 8 - 2$) is P-value < 0.005. (The P-value obtained from a calculator is 0.00002.)

Step 4 Make the decision. Since P-value < 0.01 (the α value), the decision is to reject the null hypothesis.

Step 5 Summarize the results. There is enough evidence to support the claim that the salaries paid to nurses employed by private hospitals in the United States are higher than those paid to nurses employed by government-owned hospitals.

When raw data are given in the exercises, use your calculator or the formulas in Chapter 3 to find the means and variances for the data sets. Then follow the procedures shown in this section to test the hypotheses.

Confidence intervals can also be found for the difference between two means with these formulas:

Confidence Intervals for the Difference of Two Means: Small Independent Samples

Variances unequal

$$(\overline{X}_1 - \overline{X}_2) - t_{\alpha/2}\sqrt{\frac{s_1^2}{n_1} + \frac{s_2^2}{n_2}} < \mu_1 - \mu_2 < (\overline{X}_1 - \overline{X}_2) + t_{\alpha/2}\sqrt{\frac{s_1^2}{n_1} + \frac{s_2^2}{n_2}}$$

d.f. = smaller value of $n_1 - 1$ or $n_2 - 1$

Variances equal

$$(\overline{X}_1 - \overline{X}_2) - t_{\alpha/2}\sqrt{\frac{(n_1-1)s_1^2 + (n_2-1)s_2^2}{n_1 + n_2 - 2}} \cdot \sqrt{\frac{1}{n_1} + \frac{1}{n_2}}$$

$$< \mu_1 - \mu_2 < (\overline{X}_1 - \overline{X}_2) + t_{\alpha/2}\sqrt{\frac{(n_1-1)s_1^2 + (n_2-1)s_2^2}{n_1 + n_2 - 2}} \cdot \sqrt{\frac{1}{n_1} + \frac{1}{n_2}}$$

d.f. = $n_1 + n_2 - 2$

Remember that when one is testing the difference between two means from independent samples, two different statistical test formulas can be used. One formula is used when the variances are equal, the other when the variances are not equal. As shown in Section 9–3, some statisticians use an F test to determine whether the two variances are equal.

Example 9–11

Find the 95% confidence interval for the data in Example 9–9.

Solution

Substitute in the formula.

$$(\overline{X}_1 - \overline{X}_2) - t_{\alpha/2}\sqrt{\frac{s_1^2}{n_1} + \frac{s_2^2}{n_2}} < \mu_1 - \mu_2 < (\overline{X}_1 - \overline{X}_2) + t_{\alpha/2}\sqrt{\frac{s_1^2}{n_1} + \frac{s_2^2}{n_2}}$$

$$(85 - 93) - 2.365\sqrt{\frac{17^2}{8} + \frac{6^2}{10}} < \mu_1 - \mu_2 < (85 - 93) + 2.365\sqrt{\frac{17^2}{8} + \frac{6^2}{10}}$$

$$-22.91 < \mu_1 - \mu_2 < 6.91$$

Since 0 is contained in the interval, the decision is to not reject the null hypothesis $H_0\colon \mu_1 = \mu_2$.

Applying the Concepts 9–4

Too Long on the Telephone

A company collects data on the lengths of telephone calls made by employees in two different divisions. The mean and standard deviation for the sales division are 10.26 and 8.56, respectively. The mean and standard deviation for the shipping and receiving division are 6.93 and 4.93, respectively. A hypothesis test was run, and the computer output follows.

Test statistic $F = 3.07849$
P-value $= 0.01071$
Significance level $= 0.01$
Degrees of freedom $= 56$
Confidence interval limits $= -0.18979, 6.84979$
Test statistic $t = 1.89566$
Critical value $t = -2.0037, 2.0037$
P-value $= 0.06317$
Significance level $= 0.05$

1. Are the samples independent or dependent?
2. Why was the F test done?
3. Were the results of the F test significant?
4. How many were in the study?
5. Which number from the output is compared to the significance level to check if the null hypothesis should be rejected?
6. Which number from the output gives the probability of a type I error that is calculated from the sample data?
7. Which number from the output is the result of dividing the two sample variances?
8. Was a right-, left-, or two-tailed test done? Why?
9. What are your conclusions?
10. What would your conclusions be if the level of significance were initially set at 0.10?

See page 449 for the answers.

Exercises 9–4

For Exercises 1 through 11, perform each of these steps. Assume that all variables are normally or approximately normally distributed. Be sure to test for equality of variance first.

a. State the hypotheses and identify the claim.
b. Find the critical value(s).
c. Compute the test statistic.
d. Make the decision.
e. Summarize the results.

Use the traditional method of hypothesis testing unless otherwise specified.

1. A real estate agent wishes to determine whether tax assessors and real estate appraisers agree on the values of homes. A random sample of the two groups appraised 10 homes. The data are shown here. Is there a significant difference in the values of the homes for each group? Let $\alpha = 0.05$. Find the 95% confidence interval for the difference of the means.

Real estate appraisers	Tax assessors
$\overline{X}_1 = \$83,256$	$\overline{X}_2 = \$88,354$
$s_1 = \$3256$	$s_2 = \$2341$
$n_1 = 10$	$n_2 = 10$

2. A researcher suggests that male nurses earn more than female nurses. A survey of 16 male nurses and 20 female nurses reports these data. Is there enough evidence to support the claim that male nurses earn more than female nurses? Use $\alpha = 0.05$.

Female	Male
$\overline{X}_2 = \$23{,}750$	$\overline{X}_1 = \$23{,}800$
$s_2 = \$250$	$s_1 = \$300$
$n_2 = 20$	$n_1 = 16$

3. An agent claims that there is no difference between the pay of safeties and linebackers in the National Football League. A survey of 15 safeties found an average salary of $501,580, and a survey of 15 linebackers found an average salary of $513,360. If the standard deviation in each case was $20,000, is the agent correct? Use $\alpha = 0.05$.

Source: NFL Players Assn./USA TODAY.

4. The data show the number of students attending cyber charter schools in Allegheny County and the number of students attending cyber schools in counties surrounding Allegheny County. At $\alpha = 0.01$ is there enough evidence to support the claim that the average number of students in school districts in Allegheny County who attend cyber schools is greater than those who attend cyber schools in school districts outside Allegheny County? Give a factor that should be considered in interpreting this answer.

Allegheny County	Outside Allegheny County
25 75 38 41 27 32	57 25 38 14 10 29

Source: Pittsburgh Tribune-Review.

5. A health-care worker wishes to see if the average number of family day-care homes per county is greater than the average number of day-care centres per county. The number of centres for a selected sample of counties is shown. At $\alpha = 0.01$, can it be concluded that the average number of family day-care homes is greater than the average number of day-care centres?

Number of family day-care homes			Number of day-care centres		
25	57	34	5	28	37
42	21	44	16	16	48

Source: Pittsburgh Tribune-Review.

6. A researcher wishes to test the claim that, on average, more juveniles than adults are classified as missing persons. Records for the last 5 years are shown. At $\alpha = 0.10$, is there enough evidence to support the claim?

Juveniles	65,513	65,934	64,213	61,954	59,167
Adults	31,364	34,478	36,937	35,946	38,209

Source: USA TODAY.

7. The local branch of the Canada Revenue Agency spent an average of 21 minutes helping each of 10 people prepare their tax returns. The standard deviation was 5.6 minutes. A volunteer tax preparer spent an average of 27 minutes helping 14 people prepare their taxes. The standard deviation was 4.3 minutes. At $\alpha = 0.02$, is there a difference in the average time spent by the two services? Find the 98% confidence interval for the two means.

8. Females and males alike from the general adult population volunteer an average of 4.2 hours per week. A random sample of 20 female college students and 18 male college students indicated these results concerning the amount of time spent in volunteer service per week. At the 0.01 level of significance, is there sufficient evidence to conclude that a difference exists between the mean number of volunteer hours per week for male and female college students?

	Male	Female
Sample mean	2.5	3.8
Sample variance	2.2	3.5
Sample size	18	20

Source: N.Y. Times Almanac.

9. The average cost of a movie ticket in London is $19.63 while the average cost of a movie ticket in New York City is $10.25. Assume the standard deviations are $3.20 and $2.57, respectively, and both samples consisted of 25 theatres. At $\alpha = 0.10$ can it be concluded that movie tickets cost more in London than they do in New York City? Suggest a reason for the difference, if one exists.

Source: USA TODAY.

10. Health Care Knowledge Systems reported that an insured woman spends on average 2.3 days in the hospital for a routine childbirth, while an uninsured woman spends on average 1.9 days. Assume two samples of 16 women each were used and the standard deviations are both equal to 0.6 day. At $\alpha = 0.01$, test the claim that the means are equal. Find the 99% confidence interval for the differences of the means. Use the P-value method.

Source: Michael D. Shook and Robert L. Shook, The Book of Odds.

11. The times (in minutes) it took 6 white mice to learn to run a simple maze and the times it took 6 brown mice to learn to run the same maze are given here. At $\alpha = 0.05$, does the colour of the mice make a difference in their learning rate? Find the 95% confidence interval for the difference of the means. Use the P-value method.

White mice	18	24	20	13	15	12
Brown mice	25	16	19	14	16	10

12. A random sample of enrolments from medical schools that specialize in research and from those that are noted for primary care is listed. Find the 90% confidence interval for the difference in the means.

Research				Primary care			
474	577	605	663	783	605	427	728
783	467	670	414	546	474	371	107
813	443	565	696	442	587	293	277
692	694	277	419	662	555	527	320
884							

Source: *U.S. News & World Report Best Graduate Schools.*

13. Tuition fees for a random sample of Canadian and international undergraduate students (in dollars) are

listed. Find the 95% confidence interval for the difference in the means.

Canadian		International	
4,092	4,184	16,620	11,079
6,557	4,133	20,981	12,450
4,689	1,668	8,765	11,970
2,700		5,700	8,780

Source: Association of Universities and Colleges of Canada.

9–5 Testing the Difference Between Two Means: Small Dependent Samples

Objective

Test the difference between two means for small dependent samples.

In Section 9–4, the *t* test was used to compare two sample means when the samples were independent. In this section, a different version of the *t* test is explained. This version is used when the samples are dependent. Samples are considered to be **dependent samples** when the subjects are paired or matched in some way.

For example, suppose a medical researcher wants to see whether a drug will affect the reaction time of its users. To test this hypothesis, the researcher must pretest the subjects in the sample first. That is, they are given a test to ascertain their normal reaction times. Then after taking the drug, the subjects are tested again, using a posttest. Finally, the means of the two tests are compared to see whether there is a difference. Since the same subjects are used in both cases, the samples are *related;* subjects scoring high on the pretest will generally score high on the posttest, even after consuming the drug. Likewise, those scoring lower on the pretest will tend to score lower on the posttest. To take this effect into account, the researcher employs a *t* test, using the differences between the pretest values and the posttest values. Thus only the gain or loss in values is compared.

Here are some other examples of dependent samples. A researcher may want to design an SAT Reasoning Test preparation course to help students raise their test scores the second time they take the SAT Reasoning Test. Hence, the differences between the two exams are compared. A medical specialist may want to see whether a new counselling program will help subjects lose weight. Therefore, the preweights of the subjects will be compared with the postweights.

Besides samples in which the same subjects are used in a pre–post situation, there are other cases where the samples are considered dependent. For example, students might be matched or paired according to some variable that is pertinent to the study; then one student is assigned to one group, and the other student is assigned to a second group. For instance, in a study involving learning, students can be selected and paired according to their IQs. That is, two students with the same IQ will be paired. Then one will be assigned to one sample group (which might receive instruction by computers), and the other student will be assigned to another sample group (which might receive instruction by the lecture discussion method). These assignments will be done randomly. Since a student's IQ is important to learning, it is a variable that should be controlled. By matching subjects on IQ, the researcher can eliminate the variable's influence, for the most part. Matching, then, helps to reduce type II error by eliminating extraneous variables.

Two notes of caution should be mentioned. First, when subjects are matched according to one variable, the matching process does not eliminate the influence of other variables. Matching students according to IQ does not account for their mathematical ability or their familiarity with computers. Since not all variables influencing a study can be controlled, it is up to the researcher to determine which variables should be used in matching. Second, when the same subjects are used for a pre–post study, sometimes the knowledge that they are participating in a study can influence the results. For example, if people are placed in a special program, they may be more highly motivated to succeed simply because they have been selected to participate; the program itself may have little effect on their success.

When the samples are dependent, a special *t* test for dependent means is used. This test employs the difference in values of the matched pairs. The hypotheses are as follows:

Two-tailed	Left-tailed	Right-tailed
$H_0: \mu_D = 0$	$H_0: \mu_D = 0$	$H_0: \mu_D = 0$
$H_1: \mu_D \neq 0$	$H_1: \mu_D < 0$	$H_1: \mu_D > 0$

where μ_D is the symbol for the expected mean of the difference of the matched pairs. The general procedure for finding the test value involves several steps.

First, find the differences of the values of the pairs of data.

$$D = X_1 - X_2$$

Second, find the mean $\overline{D}$ of the differences, using the formula

$$\overline{D} = \frac{\Sigma D}{n}$$

where n is the number of data pairs. Third, find the standard deviation s_D of the differences, using the formula

$$s_D = \sqrt{\frac{\Sigma D^2 - \dfrac{(\Sigma D)^2}{n}}{n - 1}}$$

Fourth, find the estimated standard error $s_{\overline{D}}$ of the differences, which is

$$s_{\overline{D}} = \frac{s_D}{\sqrt{n}}$$

Finally, find the test statistic, using the formula

$$t = \frac{\overline{D} - \mu_D}{s_D/\sqrt{n}} \qquad \text{with d.f.} = n - 1$$

The formula in the final step follows the basic format of

$$\text{Test statistic} = \frac{(\text{observed value}) - (\text{expected value})}{\text{standard error}}$$

where the observed value is the mean of the differences. The expected value μ_D is zero if the hypothesis is $\mu_D = 0$. The standard error of the difference is the standard deviation of the difference, divided by the square root of the sample size. Both populations must be normally or approximately normally distributed. Example 9–12 illustrates the hypothesis testing procedure in detail.

Example 9–12

A physical education director claims by taking a special vitamin, a weightlifter can increase his strength. Eight athletes are selected and given a test of strength, using the standard bench press. After 2 weeks of regular training, supplemented with the vitamin, they are tested again. Test the effectiveness of the vitamin regimen at $\alpha = 0.05$. Each value in these data represents the maximum number of kilograms the athlete can bench-press. Assume that the variable is approximately normally distributed.

Athlete	1	2	3	4	5	6	7	8
Before (X_1)	95	104	83	92	119	115	99	98
After (X_2)	99	107	81	93	122	113	101	98

Solution

Step 1 State the hypotheses and identify the claim. For the vitamin to be effective, the before weights must be significantly less than the after weights; hence, the mean of the differences must be less than zero.

$$H_0\text{: } \mu_D = 0 \qquad \text{and} \qquad H_1\text{: } \mu_D < 0 \text{ (claim)}$$

Step 2 Find the critical value. The degrees of freedom are $n - 1$. In this case, d.f. = $8 - 1 = 7$. The critical value for a left-tailed test with $\alpha = 0.05$ is -1.895.

Step 3   Compute the test statistic.

a. Make a table.

Before (X_1)	After (X_2)	A $D = X_1 - X_2$	B $D^2 = (X_1 - X_2)^2$
95	99		
104	107		
83	81		
92	93		
119	122		
115	113		
99	101		
98	98		

Unusual Stat

Canadians consume, on average, 45 kilograms of sugar per year.

b. Find the differences and place the results in column A.

$$95 - 99 = -4$$
$$104 - 107 = -3$$
$$83 - 81 = 2$$
$$92 - 93 = -1$$
$$119 - 122 = -3$$
$$115 - 113 = 2$$
$$99 - 101 = -2$$
$$98 - 98 = 0$$
$$\Sigma D = -9$$

c. Find the mean of the differences.

$$\overline{D} = \frac{\Sigma D}{n} = \frac{-9}{8} = -1.125$$

d. Square the differences and place the results in column B.

$$(-4)^2 = 16$$
$$(-3)^2 = 9$$
$$(2)^2 = 4$$
$$(-1)^2 = 1$$
$$(-3)^2 = 9$$
$$(2)^2 = 4$$
$$(-2)^2 = 4$$
$$(0)^2 = 0$$
$$\Sigma D^2 = 47$$

The completed table is shown.

Before (X_1)	After (X_2)	A $D = X_1 - X_2$	B $D^2 = (X_1 - X_2)^2$
95	99	-4	16
104	107	-3	9
83	81	2	4
92	93	-1	1
119	122	-3	9
115	113	2	4
99	101	-2	4
98	98	0	0
		$\Sigma D = -9$	$\Sigma D^2 = 47$

e. Find the standard deviation of the differences.

$$s_D = \sqrt{\dfrac{\Sigma D^2 - \dfrac{(\Sigma D)^2}{n}}{n-1}} = \sqrt{\dfrac{47 - \dfrac{(-9)^2}{8}}{8-1}} \approx 2.295$$

f. Find the test statistic.

$$t = \dfrac{\overline{D} - \mu_0}{s_D/\sqrt{n}} = \dfrac{-1.125 - 0}{2.295/\sqrt{8}} \approx -1.386$$

Step 4 Make the decision. The decision is to not reject the null hypothesis at $\alpha = 0.05$, since $-1.386 > -1.895$, as shown in Figure 9–11.

Figure 9–11

Critical Value and Test Statistic for Example 9–12

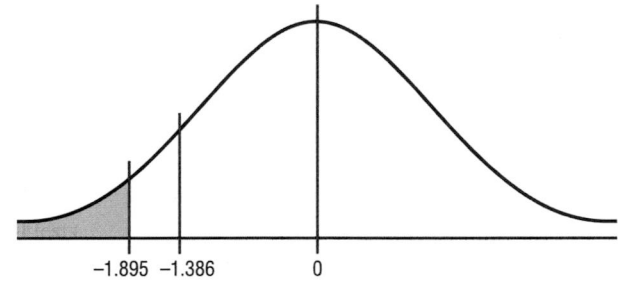

−1.895 −1.386   0

Step 5 Summarize the results. There is not enough evidence to support the claim that the vitamin supplement increases the strength of weightlifters.

The formulas for this *t* test are summarized next.

Formulas for the *t* Test for Dependent Samples

$$t = \dfrac{\overline{D} - \mu_D}{s_D/\sqrt{n}}$$

with d.f. $= n - 1$ and where

$$\overline{D} = \dfrac{\Sigma D}{n} \qquad \text{and} \qquad s_D = \sqrt{\dfrac{\Sigma D^2 - \dfrac{(\Sigma D)^2}{n}}{n-1}}$$

Example 9–13

A dietitian wishes to see if a person's cholesterol level will change if the diet is supplemented by a certain mineral. Six subjects were pretested, and then they took the mineral supplement for a 6-week period. The results are shown in the table. (Cholesterol level is measured in milligrams per decilitre.) Can it be concluded that the cholesterol level has been changed at $\alpha = 0.10$? Assume the variable is approximately normally distributed.

Subject	1	2	3	4	5	6
Before (X_1)	210	235	208	190	172	244
After (X_2)	190	170	210	188	173	228

Solution

Step 1 State the hypotheses and identify the claim. If the diet is effective, the before cholesterol levels should be different from the after levels.

$$H_0: \mu_D = 0 \qquad \text{and} \qquad H_1: \mu_D \neq 0 \ (\text{claim})$$

Step 2 Find the critical value. The degrees of freedom are 5. At $\alpha = 0.10$, the critical values are ± 2.015.

Step 3 Compute the test statistic.

a. Make a table.

Before (X_1)	After (X_2)	A $D = X_1 - X_2$	B $D^2 = (X_1 - X_2)^2$
210	190		
235	170		
208	210		
190	188		
172	173		
244	228		

b. Find the differences and place the results in column A.

$$
\begin{aligned}
210 - 190 &= \ \ 20 \\
235 - 170 &= \ \ 65 \\
208 - 210 &= -2 \\
190 - 188 &= \ \ \ \ 2 \\
172 - 173 &= -1 \\
244 - 228 &= \ \ 16 \\
\hline
\Sigma D &= 100
\end{aligned}
$$

c. Find the mean of the differences.

$$\overline{D} = \frac{\Sigma D}{n} = \frac{100}{6} \approx 16.7$$

d. Square the differences and place the results in column B.

$$
\begin{aligned}
(20)^2 &= \ \ \ 400 \\
(65)^2 &= 4225 \\
(-2)^2 &= \ \ \ \ \ \ 4 \\
(2)^2 &= \ \ \ \ \ \ 4 \\
(-1)^2 &= \ \ \ \ \ \ 1 \\
(16)^2 &= \ \ \ 256 \\
\hline
\Sigma D^2 &= 4890
\end{aligned}
$$

Then complete the table as shown.

Before (X_1)	After (X_2)	A $D = X_1 - X_2$	B $D^2 = (X_1 - X_2)^2$
210	190	20	400
235	170	65	4225
208	210	−2	4
190	188	2	4
172	173	−1	1
244	228	16	256
		$\Sigma D = 100$	$\Sigma D^2 = 4890$

e. Find the standard deviation of the differences.

$$s_D = \sqrt{\frac{\Sigma D^2 - \frac{(\Sigma D)^2}{n}}{n-1}} = \sqrt{\frac{4890 - \frac{(100)^2}{6}}{5}} \approx 25.4$$

f. Find the test statistic.

$$t = \frac{\overline{D} - \mu_D}{s_D/\sqrt{n}} = \frac{16.7 - 0}{25.4/\sqrt{6}} \approx 1.610$$

Step 4 Make the decision. The decision is to not reject the null hypothesis, since the test statistic 1.610 is in the noncritical region, as shown in Figure 9–12.

Figure 9–12

Critical Values and Test Statistic for Example 9–13

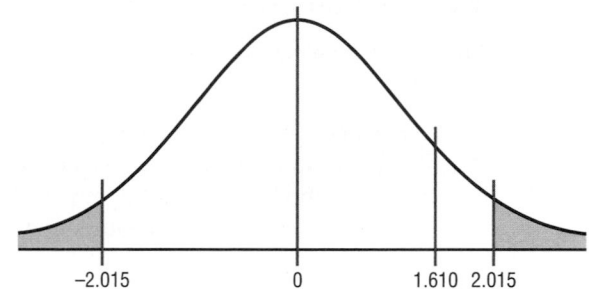

-2.015   0   1.610 2.015

Step 5 Summarize the results. There is not enough evidence to support the claim that the mineral changes a person's cholesterol level.

The steps for this *t* test are summarized in the Procedure Table.

Procedure Table

Testing the Difference Between Means for Dependent Samples

Step 1 State the hypotheses and identify the claim.

Step 2 Find the critical value(s).

Step 3 Compute the test statistic.

a. Make a table, as shown.

X_1	X_2	A $D = X_1 - X_2$	B $D^2 = (X_1 - X_2)^2$
⋮	⋮		
		$\Sigma D =$ _____	$\Sigma D^2 =$ _____

b. Find the differences and place the results in column A.

$$D = X_1 - X_2$$

c. Find the mean of the differences.

$$\overline{D} = \frac{\Sigma D}{n}$$

d. Square the differences and place the results in column B. Complete the table.

$$D^2 = (X_1 - X_2)^2$$

Procedure Table *(continued)*

    e. Find the standard deviation of the differences.

$$s_D = \sqrt{\dfrac{\Sigma D^2 - \dfrac{(\Sigma D)^2}{n}}{n - 1}}$$

    f. Find the test statistic.

$$t = \dfrac{\overline{D} - \mu_D}{s_D / \sqrt{n}} \qquad \text{with d.f.} = n - 1$$

Step 4   Make the decision.

Step 5   Summarize the results.

The P-values for the t test are found in Table F. For a two-tailed test with d.f. $= 5$ and $t = 1.610$, the P-value is found between 1.476 and 2.015; hence, $0.10 < P$-value < 0.20. Thus, the null hypothesis cannot be rejected at $\alpha = 0.10$.

If a specific difference is hypothesized, this formula should be used

$$t = \dfrac{\overline{D} - \mu_D}{s_D / \sqrt{n}}$$

where μ_D is the hypothesized difference.

For example, if a dietitian claims that people on a specific diet will lose an average of 1.5 kilograms in a week, the hypotheses are

$$H_0\colon \mu_D = 1.5 \qquad \text{and} \qquad H_1\colon \mu_D \neq 1.5$$

The value 1.5 will be substituted in the test statistic formula for μ_D.

Confidence intervals can be found for the mean differences with this formula.

Confidence Interval for the Mean Difference

$$\overline{D} - t_{\alpha/2}\dfrac{s_D}{\sqrt{n}} < \mu_D < \overline{D} + t_{\alpha/2}\dfrac{s_D}{\sqrt{n}}$$

d.f. $= n - 1$

Example 9–14

Find the 90% confidence interval for the data in Example 9–13.

Solution

Substitute in the formula.

$$\overline{D} - t_{\alpha/2}\dfrac{s_D}{\sqrt{n}} < \mu_D < \overline{D} + t_{\alpha/2}\dfrac{s_D}{\sqrt{n}}$$

$$16.7 - 2.015 \cdot \dfrac{25.4}{\sqrt{6}} < \mu_D < 16.7 + 2.015 \cdot \dfrac{25.4}{\sqrt{6}}$$

$$16.7 - 20.89 < \mu_D < 16.7 + 20.89$$

$$-4.19 < \mu_D < 37.59$$

Since 0 is contained in the interval, the decision is to not reject the null hypothesis $H_0\colon \mu_D = 0$.

Speaking of
Statistics

Can Video Games Save Lives?

Can playing video games help doctors perform surgery? The answer is yes. A study showed that surgeons who played video games for a least 3 hours each week made about 37% fewer mistakes and finished operations 27% faster than those who did not play video games.

The type of surgery that they performed is called *laparoscopic* surgery, where the surgeon inserts a tiny video camera into the body and uses a joystick to maneuver the surgical instruments while watching the results on a television monitor. This study compared two groups and used proportions. What statistical test do you think was used to compare the percentages? (See Section 9–6.)

Applying the Concepts 9–5

Air Quality

As a researcher for the Ontario Ministry of Environment, you have been asked to determine if Ontario's air quality index (AQI) has changed in the past 2 years. You select a random sample of 10 cities and find the air quality index on the same day in two consecutive years. The data are shown. (Note: The lower the AQI, the better the air quality.)

Year 1	25	39	29	33	42	17	35	10	21	30
Year 2	42	28	48	46	44	32	48	30	25	46

Source: Ontario—Ministry of Environment.

Based on the data, answer the following questions.

1. What is the purpose of the study?
2. Are the samples independent or dependent?
3. What are the hypotheses that you would use?
4. What is (are) the critical value(s) that you would use?
5. What statistical test would you use?
6. How many degrees of freedom are there?
7. What is your conclusion?
8. Could an independent means test have been used?
9. Do you think this was a good way to answer the original questions?

See page 449 for the answers.

Exercises 9–5

1. Classify each as independent or dependent samples.

a. Heights of identical twins

b. Test scores of the same students in English and psychology

c. The effectiveness of two different brands of aspirin

d. Effects of a drug on reaction time, measured by a before- and an after-test

e. The effectiveness of two different diets on two different groups of individuals

For Exercises 2 through 10, perform each of these steps. Assume that all variables are normally or approximately normally distributed.

a. State the hypotheses and identify the claim.

b. Find the critical value(s).

c. Compute the test statistic.

d. Make the decision.

e. Summarize the results.

Use the traditional method of hypothesis testing unless otherwise specified.

2. A program for reducing the number of days missed by food handlers in a certain restaurant chain was conducted. The owners hypothesized that after the program the workers would miss fewer days of work due to illness. The table shows the number of days 10 workers missed per month before and after completing the program. Is there enough evidence to support the claim, at $\alpha = 0.05$, that the food handlers missed fewer days after the program?

Before	2	3	6	7	4	5	3	1	0	0
After	1	4	3	8	3	3	1	0	1	0

3. As an aid for improving students' study habits, nine students were randomly selected to attend a seminar on the importance of education in life. The table shows the number of hours each student studied per week before and after the seminar. At $\alpha = 0.10$, did attending the seminar increase the number of hours the students studied per week?

Before	9	12	6	15	3	18	10	13	7
After	9	17	9	20	2	21	15	22	6

4. A doctor is interested in determining whether a film about exercise will change 10 persons' attitudes about exercise. The results of his questionnaire are shown. A higher numerical value shows a more favourable attitude toward exercise. Is there enough evidence to support the claim, at $\alpha = 0.05$, that there was a change in attitude? Find the 95% confidence interval for the difference of the two means.

Before	12	11	14	9	8	6	8	5	4	7
After	13	12	10	9	8	8	7	6	5	5

5. Students in a statistics class were asked to report the number of hours they slept on weeknights and on weekends. At $\alpha = 0.05$, is there sufficient evidence that there is a difference in the mean number of hours slept?

Student	1	2	3	4	5	6	7	8
Hours, Sun.–Thurs.	8	5.5	7.5	8	7	6	6	8
Hours, Fri.–Sat.	4	7	10.5	12	11	9	6	9

6. A sample of municipalities' legal costs (in thousands of dollars) for two recent consecutive years is as shown. At $\alpha = 0.05$ is there a difference in the costs? Suggest a reason for the difference, if one exists.

Year 1	61	26	9	16	61	71	14	86	17	24
Year 2	62	40	10	23	38	118	18	67	21	20

Source: *Pittsburgh Tribune-Review.*

7. A composition teacher wishes to see whether a new grammar program will reduce the number of grammatical errors her students make when writing a two-page essay. The data are shown here. At $\alpha = 0.025$, can it be concluded that the number of errors has been reduced?

Student	1	2	3	4	5	6
Errors before	12	9	0	5	4	3
Errors after	9	6	1	3	2	3

8. A sample of legal costs (in thousands of dollars) for school districts for two recent consecutive years is shown. At $\alpha = 0.05$ is there a difference in the costs? Suggest a reason for the difference, if one exists.

Year 1	108	36	65	108	87	94	10	40
Year 2	138	28	67	181	97	126	18	67

Source: *Pittsburgh Tribune-Review.*

9. A researcher wanted to compare the pulse rates of identical twins to see whether there was any difference. Eight sets of twins were selected. The rates are given in the table as number of beats per minute. At $\alpha = 0.01$, is there a significant difference in the average pulse rates of twins? Find the 99% confidence interval for the difference of the two. Use the P-value method.

Twin A	87	92	78	83	88	90	84	93
Twin B	83	95	79	83	86	93	80	86

10. A reporter hypothesizes that the average assessed values of land in a large city have changed during a 5-year period. A random sample of wards is selected, and the data (in millions of dollars) are shown. At $\alpha = 0.05$, can it be concluded that the average taxable assessed values have changed? Use the P-value method.

Ward	A	B	C	D	E	F	G	H	I	J	K	L	M	N	O	P
1994	184	414	22	99	116	49	24	50	282	25	141	45	12	37	9	17
1999	161	382	22	109	120	52	28	50	297	40	148	56	20	38	9	19

Source: *Pittsburgh Tribune-Review.*

Extending the Concepts

11. Instead of finding the mean of the differences between X_1 and X_2 by subtracting $X_1 - X_2$, one can find it by finding the means of X_1 and X_2 and then subtracting the means. Show that these two procedures will yield the same results.

9–6   Testing the Difference Between Proportions

Objective ❺

Test the difference between two proportions.

The z test with some modifications can be used to test the equality of two proportions. For example, a researcher might ask, Is the proportion of men who exercise regularly less than the proportion of women who exercise regularly? Is there a difference in the percentage of students who own a personal computer and the percentage of nonstudents who own one? Is there a difference in the proportion of college graduates who pay cash for purchases and the proportion of non-college graduates who pay cash?

Recall from Chapter 7 that the symbol $\hat{p}$ ("p hat") is the sample proportion used to estimate the population proportion, denoted by p. For example, if in a sample of 30 college students, 9 are on probation, then the sample proportion is $\hat{p} = \frac{9}{30}$, or 0.3. The population proportion p is the number of all students who are on probation, divided by the number of students who attend the college. The formula for $\hat{p}$ is

$$\hat{p} = \frac{X}{n}$$

where

X = number of units that possess the characteristic of interest
n = sample size

When one is testing the difference between two population proportions p_1 and p_2, the hypotheses can be stated thus, if no difference between the proportions is hypothesized.

$$H_0: p_1 = p_2 \qquad H_0: p_1 - p_2 = 0$$
$$H_1: p_1 \neq p_2 \quad \text{or} \quad H_1: p_1 - p_2 \neq 0$$

Similar statements using $\geq$ and $<$ or $\leq$ and $>$ can be formed for one-tailed tests.

For two proportions, $\hat{p}_1 = X_1/n_1$ is used to estimate p_1 and $\hat{p}_2 = X_2/n_2$ is used to estimate p_2. The standard error of the difference is

$$\sigma_{(\hat{p}_1 - \hat{p}_2)} = \sqrt{\sigma_{p_1}^2 + \sigma_{p_2}^2} = \sqrt{\frac{p_1 q_1}{n_1} + \frac{p_2 q_2}{n_2}}$$

where $\sigma_{p_1}^2$ and $\sigma_{p_2}^2$ are the variances of the proportions, $q_1 = 1 - p_1$, $q_2 = 1 - p_2$, and n_1 and n_2 are the respective sample sizes.

Since p_1 and p_2 are unknown, a weighted estimate of p can be computed by using the formula

$$\bar{p} = \frac{n_1 \hat{p}_1 + n_2 \hat{p}_2}{n_1 + n_2}$$

and $\overline{q} = 1 - \overline{p}$. This weighted estimate is based on the hypothesis that $p_1 = p_2$. Hence, $\overline{p}$ is a better estimate than either $\hat{p}_1$ or $\hat{p}_2$, since it is a combined average using both $\hat{p}_1$ and $\hat{p}_2$.

Since $\hat{p}_1 = X_1/n_1$ and $\hat{p}_2 = X_2/n_2$, $\overline{p}$ can be simplified to

$$\overline{p} = \frac{X_1 + X_2}{n_1 + n_2}$$

Finally, the standard error of the difference in terms of the weighted estimate is

$$\sigma_{(\hat{p}_1 - \hat{p}_2)} = \sqrt{\overline{p}\,\overline{q}\left(\frac{1}{n_1} + \frac{1}{n_2}\right)}$$

The formula for the test statistic is shown next.

Formula for the z Test for Comparing Two Proportions

$$z = \frac{(\hat{p}_1 - \hat{p}_2) - (p_1 - p_2)}{\sqrt{\overline{p}\,\overline{q}\left(\frac{1}{n_1} + \frac{1}{n_2}\right)}}$$

where

$$\overline{p} = \frac{X_1 + X_2}{n_1 + n_2} \qquad \hat{p}_1 = \frac{X_1}{n_1}$$

$$\overline{q} = 1 - \overline{p} \qquad \hat{p}_2 = \frac{X_2}{n_2}$$

This formula follows the format

$$\text{Test statistic} = \frac{(\text{observed value}) - (\text{expected value})}{\text{standard error}}$$

There are two requirements for use of the z test: (1) The samples must be independent of each other, and (2) $n_1 p_1$ and $n_1 q_1$ must be 5 or more, and $n_2 p_2$ and $n_2 q_2$ must be 5 or more.

Example 9–15

Researchers found that 12 out of 34 small nursing homes had a resident vaccination rate of less than 80%, while 17 out of 24 large nursing homes had a vaccination rate of less than 80%. At $\alpha = 0.05$, test the claim that there is no difference in the proportions of the small and large nursing homes with a resident vaccination rate of less than 80%.

Source: Nancy Arden, Arnold S. Monto, and Suzanne E. Ohmit, "Vaccine Use and the Risk of Outbreaks in a Sample of Nursing Homes During an Influenza Epidemic," *American Journal of Public Health.*

Solution

Let $\hat{p}_1$ be the proportion of the small nursing homes with a vaccination rate of less than 80% and $\hat{p}_2$ be the proportion of the large nursing homes with a vaccination rate of less than 80%. Then

$$\hat{p}_1 = \frac{X_1}{n_1} = \frac{12}{34} = 0.35 \qquad \text{and} \qquad \hat{p}_2 = \frac{X_2}{n_2} = \frac{17}{24} = 0.71$$

$$\overline{p} = \frac{X_1 + X_2}{n_1 + n_2} = \frac{12 + 17}{34 + 24} = \frac{29}{58} = 0.5$$

$$\overline{q} = 1 - \overline{p} = 1 - 0.5 = 0.5$$

Now, follow the steps in hypothesis testing.

Step 1 State the hypotheses and identify the claim.

$$H_0: p_1 = p_2 \text{ (claim)} \qquad \text{and} \qquad H_1: p_1 \neq p_2$$

Step 2 Find the critical values. Since $\alpha = 0.05$, the critical values are $+1.96$ and -1.96.

Step 3 Compute the test statistic.

$$z = \frac{(\hat{p}_1 - \hat{p}_2) - (p_1 - p_2)}{\sqrt{\bar{p}\,\bar{q}\left(\dfrac{1}{n_1} + \dfrac{1}{n_2}\right)}}$$

$$= \frac{(0.35 - 0.71) - 0}{\sqrt{(0.5)(0.5)\left(\dfrac{1}{34} + \dfrac{1}{24}\right)}} = \frac{-0.36}{0.1333} = -2.7$$

Step 4 Make the decision. Reject the null hypothesis, since $-2.7 < -1.96$. See Figure 9–13.

Figure 9–13

Critical Values and Test Statistic for Example 9–15

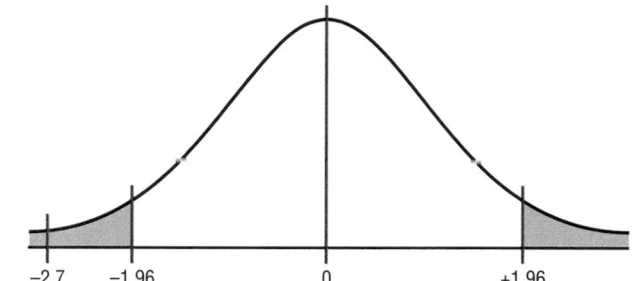

-2.7   -1.96   0   +1.96

Step 5 Summarize the results. There is enough evidence to reject the claim that there is no difference in the proportions of small and large nursing homes with a resident vaccination rate of less than 80%.

Example 9–16

In a sample of 200 surgeons, 15% thought the government should control health care. In a sample of 200 general practitioners, 21% felt the same way. At $\alpha = 0.01$, is there a difference in the proportions?

Solution

Since the statistics are given in percentages, $\hat{p}_1 = 15\%$ or 0.15 and $\hat{p}_2 = 21\%$ or 0.21. To compute $\bar{p}$, one must find X_1 and X_2.

$$X_1 = \hat{p}_1 n_1 = 0.15(200) = 30$$

$$X_2 = \hat{p}_2 n_2 = 0.21(200) = 42$$

$$\bar{p} = \frac{X_1 + X_2}{n_1 + n_2} = \frac{30 + 42}{200 + 200} = \frac{72}{400} = 0.18$$

$$\bar{q} = 1 - \bar{p} = 1 - 0.18 = 0.82$$

Step 1 State the hypotheses and identify the claim.

$$H_0: p_1 = p_2 \qquad \text{and} \qquad H_1: p_1 \neq p_2 \text{ (claim)}$$

Step 2 Find the critical values. Since $\alpha = 0.01$, the critical values are $+2.58$ and -2.58.

Step 3 Compute the test statistic.

$$z = \frac{(\hat{p}_1 - \hat{p}_2) - (p_1 - p_2)}{\sqrt{\overline{p}\,\overline{q}\left(\dfrac{1}{n_1} + \dfrac{1}{n_2}\right)}}$$

$$= \frac{(0.15 - 0.21) - 0}{\sqrt{(0.18)(0.82)\left(\dfrac{1}{200} + \dfrac{1}{200}\right)}} = -1.56$$

Step 4 Make the decision. Do not reject the null hypothesis since $-1.56 > -2.58$. See Figure 9–14.

Figure 9–14

Critical Values and Test Statistic for Example 9–16

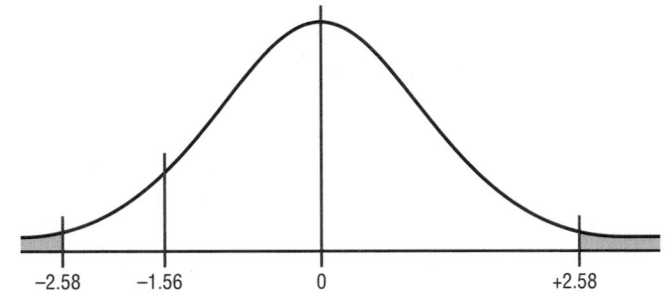

-2.58 -1.56 0 $+2.58$

Step 5 Summarize the results. There is not enough evidence to support the claim that there is a difference in proportions.

The *P*-value for the difference of proportions can be found from Tables E–1 and E–2, as shown in Section 8–3. For Example 9–16, 3.99 is beyond 3.09; hence, the null hypothesis can be rejected since the *P*-value is less than 0.001.

The formula for the confidence interval for the difference between two proportions is shown next.

Confidence Interval for the Difference Between Two Proportions

$$(\hat{p}_1 - \hat{p}_2) - z_{\alpha/2}\sqrt{\frac{\hat{p}_1\hat{q}_1}{n_1} + \frac{\hat{p}_2\hat{q}_2}{n_2}} < p_1 - p_2 < (\hat{p}_1 - \hat{p}_2) + z_{\alpha/2}\sqrt{\frac{\hat{p}_1\hat{q}_1}{n_1} + \frac{\hat{p}_2\hat{q}_2}{n_2}}$$

Example 9–17

Find the 95% confidence interval for the difference of proportions for the data in Example 9–15.

Solution

$$\hat{p}_1 = \frac{12}{34} = 0.35 \qquad \hat{q}_1 = 0.65$$

$$\hat{p}_2 = \frac{17}{24} = 0.71 \qquad \hat{q}_2 = 0.29$$

Substitute in the formula.

$$(\hat{p}_1 - \hat{p}_2) - z_{\alpha/2}\sqrt{\frac{\hat{p}_1\hat{q}_1}{n_1} + \frac{\hat{p}_2\hat{q}_2}{n_2}} < p_1 - p_2$$

$$< (\hat{p}_1 - \hat{p}_2) + z_{\alpha/2}\sqrt{\frac{\hat{p}_1\hat{q}_1}{n_1} + \frac{\hat{p}_2\hat{q}_2}{n_2}}$$

$$(0.35 - 0.71) - 1.96\sqrt{\frac{(0.35)(0.65)}{34} + \frac{(0.71)(0.29)}{24}}$$

$$< p_1 - p_2 < (0.35 - 0.71) + 1.96\sqrt{\frac{(0.35)(0.65)}{34} + \frac{(0.71)(0.29)}{24}}$$

$$-0.36 - 0.242 < p_1 - p_2 < -0.36 + 0.242$$

$$-0.602 < p_1 - p_2 < -0.118$$

Since 0 is not contained in the interval, the decision is to reject the null hypothesis $H_0: p_1 = p_2$.

Applying the Concepts 9–6

Smoking and Education

You are researching the hypothesis that there is no difference in the percent of public school students who smoke and the percent of private school students who smoke. You find these results from a recent survey.

School	Percent who smoke
Public	32.3
Private	14.5

Based on these figures, answer the following questions.

1. What hypotheses would you use if you wanted to compare percentages of the public school students who smoke with the private school students who smoke?
2. What critical value(s) would you use?
3. What statistical test would you use to compare the two percentages?
4. What information would you need to complete the statistical test?
5. Suppose you found that 1000 individuals in each group were surveyed. Could you perform the statistical test?
6. If so, complete the test and summarize the results.

See page 449 for the answers.

Exercises 9–6

1a. Find the proportions $\hat{p}$ and $\hat{q}$ for each.

    a. $n = 48, X = 34$
    b. $n = 75, X = 28$
    c. $n = 100, X = 50$
    d. $n = 24, X = 6$
    e. $n = 144, X = 12$

1b. Find each X, given $\hat{p}$.

    a. $\hat{p} = 0.16, n = 100$
    b. $\hat{p} = 0.08, n = 50$
    c. $\hat{p} = 6\%, n = 800$
    d. $\hat{p} = 52\%, n = 200$
    e. $\hat{p} = 20\%, n = 150$

2. Find $\bar{p}$ and $\bar{q}$ for each.

   a. $X_1 = 60$, $n_1 = 100$, $X_2 = 40$, $n_2 = 100$
   b. $X_1 = 22$, $n_1 = 50$, $X_2 = 18$, $n_2 = 30$
   c. $X_1 = 18$, $n_1 = 60$, $X_2 = 20$, $n_2 = 80$
   d. $X_1 = 5$, $n_1 = 32$, $X_2 = 12$, $n_2 = 48$
   e. $X_1 = 12$, $n_1 = 75$, $X_2 = 15$, $n_2 = 50$

For Exercises 3 through 14, perform these steps.

   a. State the hypotheses and identify the claim.
   b. Find the critical value(s).
   c. Compute the test statistic.
   d. Make the decision.
   e. Summarize the results.

Use the traditional method of hypothesis testing unless otherwise specified.

3. A sample of 150 people from a certain industrial community showed that 80 people suffered from a lung disease. A sample of 100 people from a rural community showed that 30 suffered from the same lung disease. At $\alpha = 0.05$, is there a difference between the proportions of people who suffer from the disease in the two communities?

4. A study is conducted to determine if the percent of women who receive financial aid in undergraduate school is different from the percent of men who receive financial aid in undergraduate school. A random sample of undergraduates revealed these results. At $\alpha = 0.01$, is there significant evidence to reject the null hypothesis?

	Women	Men
Sample size	250	300
Number receiving aid	200	180

Source: U.S. Department of Education, National Center for Education Statistics.

5. Labour statistics indicate that 77% of cashiers and servers are women. A random sample of cashiers and servers in a large metropolitan area found that 112 of 150 cashiers and 150 of 200 servers were women. At the 0.05 level of significance, is there sufficient evidence to conclude that a difference exists between the proportion of servers and the proportion of cashiers who are women?

Source: *N.Y. Times Almanac.*

6. An Edmonton report indicated that in a sample of 284 dog bites, 31 were from the Rottweiler breed. In a Winnipeg survey, a sample of 166 dog bites revealed that 11 were from the Rottweiler breed. Is there a significant difference in the proportions from the two cities? Use $\alpha = 0.05$. Find the 95% confidence interval for the difference of the two proportions.

Source: Dog Legislation Council of Canada.

7. A survey found that 83% of the men questioned preferred computer-assisted instruction to lecture and 75% of the women preferred computer-assisted instruction to lecture. There were 100 individuals in each sample. At $\alpha = 0.05$, test the claim that there is no difference in the proportion of men and the proportion of women who favour computer-assisted instruction over lecture. Find the 95% confidence interval for the difference of the two proportions.

8. In a sample of 50 men, 44 said that they had less leisure time today than they had 10 years ago. In a sample of 50 women, 48 women said that they had less leisure time than they had 10 years ago. At $\alpha = 0.10$ is there a difference in the proportion? Find the 90% confidence interval for the difference of the two proportions. Does the confidence interval contain 0? Give a reason why this information would be of interest to a researcher.

Source: Based on statistics from Market Directory.

9. In a sample of 80 North Americans, 55% wished that they were rich. In a sample of 90 Europeans, 45% wished that they were rich. At $\alpha = 0.01$, is there a difference in the proportions? Find the 99% confidence interval for the difference of the two proportions.

10. In a sample of 200 men, 130 said they used seat belts. In a sample of 300 women, 63 said they used seat belts. Test the claim that men are more safety conscious than women, at $\alpha = 0.01$. Use the *P*-value method.

11. A survey found that in a sample of 75 families, 26 owned dogs. A survey done 15 years ago found that in a sample of 60 families, 26 owned dogs. At $\alpha = 0.05$ has the proportion of dog owners changed over the 15-year period? Find the 95% confidence interval of the true difference in the proportions. Does the confidence interval contain 0? Why would this fact be important to a researcher?

Source: Based on statistics from the American Veterinary Medical Association.

12. A recent study showed that in a sample of 100 people, 30% had visited California's Disneyland. In another sample of 100 people, 24% had visited Florida's Disney World. Are the proportions of people who visited each park different? Use $\alpha = 0.02$ and the *P*-value method.

13. A sample of 200 teenagers shows that 50 believe that war is inevitable, and a sample of 300 people over age 60 shows that 93 believe war is inevitable. Is the proportion of teenagers who believe war is inevitable different from the proportion of people over age 60 who do? Use $\alpha = 0.01$. Find the 99% confidence interval for the difference of the two proportions.

14. In a sample of 50 high school seniors, 8 had their own cars. In a sample of 75 college freshmen, 20 had their own cars. At $\alpha = 0.05$, can it be concluded that a higher proportion of college freshmen have their own cars? Use the *P*-value method.

15. Find the 99% confidence interval for the difference in the population proportions for the data of a study in

which 43% of 150 respondents in Atlantic Canada are in favour of replacing the existing Senate with an elected Senate and 57% of 125 Alberta respondents favour an elected Senate.

Source: CanWest News Service, *Ottawa Citizen.*

16. The City of Hamilton councillors feel that a higher percentage of women work there than in the neighbouring Regional Municipality of Niagara. To test this, they randomly select 1000 women in each area and find that in Hamilton, 579 women work, and in Niagara, 557 women work. Using $\alpha = 0.05$, do you think that City of Hamilton councillors are correct?

Source: Statistics Canada, 2001 Census.

17. In a sample of 100 store customers, 43 used a MasterCard. In another sample of 100, 58 used a Visa card. At $\alpha = 0.05$, is there a difference in the proportion of people who use each type of credit card?

18. Find the 95% confidence interval for the true difference in proportions for the data of a study in which 40% of the 200 males surveyed opposed the death penalty and 56% of the 100 females surveyed opposed the death penalty.

19. The percentages of adults 25 years of age and older who have completed 4 or more years of college are 23.6% for females and 27.8% for males. A random sample of women and men who were 25 years old or older was surveyed with these results. Estimate the true difference in proportions with 95% confidence, and compare your interval with the *Almanac* statistics.

	Women	Men
Sample size	350	400
No. who completed 4 or more years	100	115

Source: *N.Y. Times Almanac.*

Extending the Concepts

20. If there is a significant difference between p_1 and p_2 and between p_2 and p_3, can one conclude that there is a significant difference between p_1 and p_3?

9–7 Summary

Many times researchers are interested in comparing two population parameters, such as means or proportions. This comparison can be accomplished by using special z and t tests. If the samples are independent and the variances are known, the z test is used. The z test is also used when the variances are unknown but both sample sizes are 30 or more. If the variances are not known and one or both sample sizes are less than 30, the t test must be used. For independent samples, a further requirement is that one must determine whether the variances of the populations are equal. The F test is used to determine whether the variances are equal. Different formulas are used in each case. If the samples are dependent, the t test for dependent samples is used. Finally, a z test is used to compare two proportions.

For step-by-step guidance on the use of technology for this chapter, visit the Online Learning Centre at www.mcgrawhill.ca/olc/bluman. Summary procedures for Minitab, SPSS, Excel, and TI-83 Plus or TI-84 Plus can also be found in Appendix E.

Important Terms

● ● ●

dependent samples 423

F distribution 408

F test 408

independent samples 416

pooled estimate of the variance 417

Important Formulas

● ● ●

Formula for the z test for comparing two means from independent populations:

$$z = \frac{(\overline{X}_1 - \overline{X}_2) - (\mu_1 - \mu_2)}{\sqrt{\dfrac{\sigma_1^2}{n_1} + \dfrac{\sigma_2^2}{n_2}}}$$

Formula for the confidence interval for difference of two means (large samples):

$$(\overline{X}_1 - \overline{X}_2) - z_{\alpha/2}\sqrt{\frac{\sigma_1^2}{n_1} + \frac{\sigma_2^2}{n_2}} < \mu_1 - \mu_2$$

$$< (\overline{X}_1 - \overline{X}_2) + z_{\alpha/2}\sqrt{\frac{\sigma_1^2}{n_1} + \frac{\sigma_2^2}{n_2}}$$

Formula for the F test for comparing two variances:

$$F = \frac{s_1^2}{s_2^2} \qquad \begin{array}{l} \text{d.f.N.} = n_1 - 1 \\ \text{d.f.D.} = n_2 - 1 \end{array}$$

Formula for the t test for comparing two means (small independent samples, variances not equal):

$$t = \frac{(\overline{X}_1 - \overline{X}_2) - (\mu_1 - \mu_2)}{\sqrt{\dfrac{s_1^2}{n_1} + \dfrac{s_2^2}{n_2}}}$$

and d.f. = the smaller of $n_1 - 1$ or $n_2 - 1$.

Formula for the t test for comparing two means (independent samples, variances equal):

$$t = \frac{(\overline{X}_1 - \overline{X}_2) - (\mu_1 - \mu_2)}{\sqrt{\dfrac{(n_1 - 1)s_1^2 + (n_2 - 1)s_2^2}{n_1 + n_2 - 2}}\sqrt{\dfrac{1}{n_1} + \dfrac{1}{n_2}}}$$

and d.f. = $n_1 + n_2 - 2$.

Formula for the confidence interval for the difference of two means (small independent samples, variances unequal):

$$(\overline{X}_1 - \overline{X}_2) - t_{\alpha/2}\sqrt{\frac{s_1^2}{n_1} + \frac{s_2^2}{n_2}} < \mu_1 - \mu_2$$

$$< (\overline{X}_1 - \overline{X}_2) + t_{\alpha/2}\sqrt{\frac{s_1^2}{n_1} + \frac{s_2^2}{n_2}}$$

and d.f. = smaller of $n_1 - 1$ and $n_2 - 2$.

Formula for the confidence interval for the difference of two means (small independent samples, variances equal):

$$(\overline{X}_1 - \overline{X}_2) - t_{\alpha/2}\sqrt{\frac{(n_1 - 1)s_1^2 + (n_2 - 1)s_2^2}{n_1 + n_2 - 2}} \cdot \sqrt{\frac{1}{n_1} + \frac{1}{n_2}}$$

$$< \mu_1 - \mu_2$$

$$< (\overline{X}_1 - \overline{X}_2) + t_{\alpha/2}\sqrt{\frac{(n_1 - 1)s_1^2 + (n_2 - 1)s_2^2}{n_1 + n_2 - 2}} \cdot \sqrt{\frac{1}{n_1} + \frac{1}{n_2}}$$

and d.f. = $n_1 + n_2 - 2$.

Formula for the t test for comparing two means from dependent samples:

$$t = \frac{\overline{D} - \mu_D}{s_D/\sqrt{n}}$$

where $\overline{D}$ is the mean of the differences

$$\overline{D} = \frac{\Sigma D}{n}$$

and s_D is the standard deviation of the differences

$$s_D = \sqrt{\frac{\Sigma D^2 - \dfrac{(\Sigma D)}{n}}{n - 1}}$$

Formula for confidence interval for the mean of the difference for dependent samples:

$$\overline{D} - t_{\alpha/2}\frac{s_D}{\sqrt{n}} < \mu_D < \overline{D} + t_{\alpha/2}\frac{s_D}{\sqrt{n}}$$

and d.f. = $n - 1$.

Formula for the z test for comparing two proportions:

$$z = \frac{(\hat{p}_1 - \hat{p}_2) - (p_1 - p_2)}{\sqrt{\overline{p}\,\overline{q}\left(\dfrac{1}{n_1} + \dfrac{1}{n_2}\right)}}$$

where

$$\overline{p} = \frac{X_1 + X_2}{n_1 + n_2} \qquad \hat{p}_1 = \frac{X_1}{n_1}$$

$$\overline{q} = 1 - \overline{p} \qquad \hat{p}_2 = \frac{X_2}{n_2}$$

Formula for confidence interval for the difference of two proportions:

$$(\hat{p}_1 - \hat{p}_2) - z_{\alpha/2}\sqrt{\frac{\hat{p}_1\hat{q}_1}{n_1} + \frac{\hat{p}_2\hat{q}_2}{n_2}} < p_1 - p_2$$

$$< (\hat{p}_1 - \hat{p}_2) + z_{\alpha/2}\sqrt{\frac{\hat{p}_1\hat{q}_1}{n_1} + \frac{\hat{p}_2\hat{q}_2}{n_2}}$$

Review Exercises

For each exercise, perform these steps. Assume that all variables are normally or approximately normally distributed.

   a. State the hypotheses and identify the claim.
   b. Find the critical value(s).
   c. Compute the test statistic.
   d. Make the decision.
   e. Summarize the results.

Use the traditional method of hypothesis testing unless otherwise specified.

1. Two groups of drivers are surveyed to see how many kilometres per week they drive for pleasure trips. The data are shown. At $\alpha = 0.01$, can it be concluded that single drivers do more driving for pleasure trips on average than married drivers?

Single drivers					Married drivers				
171	177	185	195	212	156	167	222	164	185
192	156	190	196	217	214	193	192	219	154
177	188	187	222	229	224	174	188	233	183
185	183	166	158	159	225	219	182	182	241
174	188	245	237	188	163	183	187	182	217
248	138	185	187	167	185	175	237	171	142
172	214	222	229	225	182	192	159	174	169

2. An educator wishes to compare the variances of the amount of money spent per student in two provinces. The data are given. At $\alpha = 0.05$, is there a significant difference in the variances of the amounts the provinces spend per student?

Province 1	Province 2
$s_1^2 = \$585$	$s_1^2 = \$261$
$n_1 = 18$	$n_2 = 16$

3. In the hospital study cited in Exercise 19 in Exercise set 7–2, the standard deviation of the noise levels of the 11 intensive care units was 4.1 dBA, and the standard deviation of the noise levels of 24 nonmedical care areas, such as kitchens and machine rooms, was 13.2 dBA. At $\alpha = 0.10$, is there a significant difference between the standard deviations of these two areas?

Source: M. Bayo, A. Garcia, and A. Garcia, "Noise Levels in an Urban Hospital and Workers' Subjective Responses," *Archives of Environmental Health.*

4. A researcher wants to compare the variances of the heights (in centimetres) of Major League Baseball players with those of players in the Minor Leagues. A sample of 25 players from each league is selected, and the variances of the heights for each league are 5.7 and 12.3 respectively. At $\alpha = 0.10$, is there a significant difference between the variances of the heights for the two leagues?

5. A traffic safety commissioner believes the variation in the number of speeding tickets given on U.S. Route 19 is greater than the variation in the number of speeding tickets given on U.S. Route 22. Ten weeks are randomly selected; the standard deviation of the number of tickets issued for Route 19 is 6.3, and the standard deviation of the number of tickets issued for Route 22 is 2.8. At $\alpha = 0.05$, can the commissioner conclude that the variance of speeding tickets issued on Route 19 is greater than the variance of speeding tickets issued on Route 22? Use the *P*-value method.

6. The variations in the number of absentees per day in two schools are being compared. A sample of 30 days is selected; the standard deviation of the number of absentees in school A is 4.9, and for school B it is 2.5. At $\alpha = 0.01$, can one conclude that there is a difference in the two standard deviations?

7. A researcher claims the variation in the number of days that factory workers miss per year due to illness is greater than the variation in the number of days that hospital workers miss per year. A sample of 42 workers from a large hospital has a standard deviation of 2.1 days, and a sample of 65 workers from a large factory has a standard deviation of 3.2 days. Test the claim at $\alpha = 0.10$.

8. The average price of 15 cans of tomato soup from different stores is \$0.73, and the standard deviation is \$0.05. The average price of 24 cans of chicken noodle soup is \$0.91, and the standard deviation is \$0.03. At $\alpha = 0.01$, is there a significant difference in price?

9. The average temperatures (°C) for a 25-day period for Victoria, British Columbia, and St. John's, Newfoundland, are shown. Based on the samples, at $\alpha = 0.10$, can it be concluded that it is warmer in Victoria?

Victoria					St. John's				
22.4	25.3	24.8	24.4	25.9	20.5	24.7	20.5	23.5	20.5
21.9	17.3	23.2	25.6	24.8	18.0	23.2	21.4	20.1	17.8
21.8	21.4	20.2	24.7	25.9	15.3	18.9	22.4	19.6	14.6
22.3	20.7	20.3	17.3	23.8	15.5	15.5	22.2	20.9	12.8
25.7	18.8	18.1	19.6	20.4	16.7	23.7	22.6	23.8	19.3
25.6	22.6	24.9	20.7	20.0	22.9	17.9	18.9	22.7	16.6

Source: Environment Canada.

10. A sample of 15 teachers from Nova Scotia has an average salary of \$44,168 with a standard deviation of \$4077. A sample of 30 teachers from New Brunswick

has an average salary of $40,482 with a standard deviation of $1964. Is there a significant difference in teachers' salaries between the two provinces? Use $\alpha = 0.02$. Find the 98% confidence interval for the difference of the two means.

Source: Education Canada Network: Canadian Teacher Salaries.

11. The data show the amounts (in thousands of dollars) of the contracts for soft drinks in local school districts. At $\alpha = 0.10$ can it be concluded that there is a difference in the averages? Use the *P*-value method. Give a reason why the result would be of concern to a cafeteria manager.

Pepsi						Coca-Cola		
46	120	80	500	100	59	420	285	57

Source: Local school districts.

12. In an effort to improve the vocabulary of 10 students, a teacher provides a weekly 1-hour tutoring session for them. A pretest is given before the sessions, and a posttest is given afterward. The results are shown in the table. At $\alpha = 0.01$, can the teacher conclude that the tutoring sessions helped to improve the students' vocabularies?

Before	1	2	3	4	5	6	7	8	9	10
Pretest	83	76	92	64	82	68	70	71	72	63
Posttest	88	82	100	72	81	75	79	68	81	70

13. In an effort to increase production of an automobile part, the factory manager decides to play music in the manufacturing area. Eight workers are selected, and the number of items each produced for a specific day is recorded. After one week of music, the same workers are monitored again. The data are given in the table. At $\alpha = 0.05$, can the manager conclude that the music has increased production?

Worker	1	2	3	4	5	6	7	8
Before	6	8	10	9	5	12	9	7
After	10	12	9	12	8	13	8	10

14. St. Petersburg, Russia, has 207 foggy days out of 365 days while Stockholm, Sweden, has 166 foggy days out of 365. At $\alpha = 0.02$, can it be concluded that the proportions of foggy days for the two cities are different? Find the 98% confidence interval for the difference of the two proportions.

Source: Jack Williams, *USA TODAY.*

15. A recent survey found that in a study of 120 families, 18 owned a bird. Fifteen years ago, a survey found that in a sample of 100 families, 5 owned a bird. At $\alpha = 0.05$ has the proportion of families who owned a bird changed? Find the confidence interval for the difference of the proportions. Does the confidence interval contain 0? Why would this be important for a researcher to know?

Source: Based on statistics from the American Veterinary Medical Association.

A Woman's Path To Pay Equity?–Revisited

Statistics Today

Using a z test, the researchers compared the difference between gender self-employment and wage compensation gap means. Statistically significant results indicated that the average income gap between self-employed workers was $10,904 compared to an average income gap of $38,626 for wage earners both in favour of the male gender. Using statistical methods presented in later chapters, the researchers predicted that the gender income gap for both self-employed and wage earners will decrease with age but self-employed females will experience a lesser amount of income gap differential.

Data Analysis

The Data Bank is found in Appendix D, or on the World Wide Web by following links from www.mcgrawhill. ca/olc/bluman.

1. From the Data Bank, select a variable and compare the mean of the variable for a random sample of at least 30 men with the mean of the variable for the random sample of at least 30 women. Use a z test.

2. Repeat the experiment in Exercise 1, using a different variable and two samples of size 15. Compare the means by using a t test. Assume that the variances are equal.

3. Compare the proportion of men who are smokers with the proportion of women who are smokers. Use the data in the Data Bank. Choose random samples of size 30 or more. Use the z test for proportions.

4. Select two samples of 20 values from the data in Data Set IV in Appendix D. Test the hypothesis that the mean heights of the buildings are equal.

5. Using the same data obtained in Exercise 4, test the hypothesis that the variances are equal.

Chapter Quiz

Determine whether each statement is true or false. If the statement is false, explain why.

1. When one is testing the difference between two means for small samples, it is not important to distinguish whether the samples are independent of each other.

2. If the same diet is given to two groups of randomly selected individuals, the samples are considered to be dependent.

3. When computing the F test value, one always places the larger variance in the numerator of the fraction.

4. Tests for variances are always two-tailed.

Select the best answer.

5. To test the equality of two variances, one would use a(n) _____ test.

   a. z
   b. t
   c. χ^2
   d. F

6. To test the equality of two proportions, one would use a(n) _____ test.

   a. z
   b. t
   c. χ^2
   d. F

7. The mean value of the F is approximately equal to

   a. 0
   b. 0.5
   c. 1
   d. It cannot be determined.

8. What test can be used to test the difference between two small sample means?

   a. z
   b. t
   c. χ^2
   d. F

Complete these statements with the best answer.

9. If one hypothesizes that there is no difference between means, this is represented as H_0: _____.

10. When one is testing the difference between two means, a(n) _____ estimate of the variances is used when the variances are equal.

11. When the t test is used for testing the equality of two means, the populations must be _____.

12. The values of F cannot be _____.

13. The formula for the F test for variances is _____.

For each of these problems, perform the following steps.

   a. State the hypotheses and identify the claim.
   b. Find the critical value(s).
   c. Compute the test statistic.
   d. Make the decision.
   e. Summarize the results.

Use the traditional method of hypothesis testing unless otherwise specified.

14. A researcher wishes to see if there is a difference in the cholesterol levels of two groups of men. A random sample of 30 men between the ages of 25 and 40 is selected and tested. The average level is 223. A second sample of 25 men between the ages of 41 and 56 is selected and tested. The average of this group is 229. The population standard deviation for both groups is 6. At $\alpha = 0.01$, is there a difference in the cholesterol levels between the two groups? Find the 99% confidence interval for the difference of the two means.

15. The data shown are the rental fees (in dollars) for two random samples of apartments in a large city. At $\alpha = 0.10$, can it be concluded that the average rental fee for apartments in the East is greater than the average rental fee in the West?

East					West				
495	390	540	445	420	525	400	310	375	750
410	550	499	500	550	390	795	554	450	370
389	350	450	530	350	385	395	425	500	550
375	690	325	350	799	380	400	450	365	425
475	295	350	485	625	375	360	425	400	475
275	450	440	425	675	400	475	430	410	450
625	390	485	550	650	425	450	620	500	400
685	385	450	550	425	295	350	300	360	400

Source: Pittsburgh Post-Gazette.

16. A politician wishes to compare the variances of the amount of money spent for road repair in two different counties. The data are given here. At $\alpha = 0.05$, is there a significant difference in the variances of the amounts spent in the two counties? Use the P-value method.

County A	County B
$s_1 = \$11{,}596$	$s_2 = \$14{,}837$
$n_1 = 15$	$n_2 = 18$

17. A researcher wants to compare the variances of the heights (in centimetres) of university basketball players with those of college players. A sample of 30 players from each type of school is selected, and the variances of the heights for each type are 15.68 and 20.32, respectively. At $\alpha = 0.10$, is there a significant difference between the variances of the heights in the two types of schools?

18. The data shown are based on a survey taken in February and July and indicate the number of hours per day of household television usage. At $\alpha = 0.05$, test the claim that there is no difference in the standard deviations of the number of hours that televisions are used.

February			July		
7.6	9.3	8.2	7.4	10.3	9.4
7.4	7.9	6.8	4.6	7.3	7.1
7.5	7.1	6.4	6.8	7.7	8.2
4.3	10.6	9.8	5.4	6.2	7.1

19. The variances in the amount of fat in two different types of ground beef are compared. Eight samples of the first type, Super Lean, have a variance of 18.2 grams; 12 of the second type, Ultimate Lean, have a variance of 9.4 grams. At $\alpha = 0.10$, can it be concluded that there is a difference in the variances of the two types of ground beef?

20. It is hypothesized that the variance in the number of murders committed in selected cities on the U.S. East Coast is greater than the variance of the number of murders committed on the U.S. West Coast. A sample of six selected cities on the West Coast has a standard deviation of 206. A sample of six cities on the East Coast has a standard deviation of 215. Test the hypothesis at $\alpha = 0.10$. Suggest a factor that may have influenced the results of this study.

Source: Based on FBI statistics.

21. The variations in the number of retail thefts per day in two shopping malls are being compared. A sample of 21 days is selected. The standard deviation of the number of retail thefts in mall A is 6.8, and for mall B it is 5.3. At $\alpha = 0.05$, can it be concluded that there is a difference in the two standard deviations?

22. The average price of a sample of 12 bottles of diet salad dressing taken from different stores is $1.43. The standard deviation is $0.09. The average price of a sample of 16 low-calorie frozen desserts is $1.03. The standard deviation is $0.10. At $\alpha = 0.01$, is there a significant difference in price? Find the 99% confidence interval of the difference in the means.

23. The data shown represent the number of accidents people had when using jet skis and other types of wet bikes. At $\alpha = 0.05$, can it be concluded that the average number of accidents per year has increased from one period to the next?

1987–1991			1992–1996		
376	650	844	1650	2236	3002
1162	1513		4028	4010	

Source: USA TODAY.

24. A sample of 12 health-care workers from British Columbia shows an average annual salary of $39,420 with a standard deviation of $1659, while a sample of 26 health-care workers from Manitoba has an average salary of $30,215 with a standard deviation of $4116. Is there a significant difference between the two provinces in health-care worker salaries at $\alpha = 0.02$? Find the 98% confidence interval of the difference in the means.

Source: Statistics Canada.

25. The average income of 15 families who reside in a large U.S. metropolitan East Coast city is $62,456. The standard deviation is $9652. The average income of 11 families who reside in a rural area of the U.S. Midwest is $60,213, with a standard deviation of $2009. At $\alpha = 0.05$, can it be concluded that the families who live in the cities have a higher income than those who live in the rural areas? Use the *P*-value method.

26. In an effort to improve the mathematical skills of 10 students, a teacher provides a weekly 1-hour tutoring session for the students. A pretest is given before the sessions, and a posttest is given after. The results are shown here. At $\alpha = 0.01$, can it be concluded that the sessions help to improve the students' mathematical skills?

Student	1	2	3	4	5	6	7	8	9	10
Pretest	82	76	91	62	81	67	71	69	80	85
Posttest	88	80	98	80	80	73	74	78	85	93

27. To increase egg production, a farmer decided to increase the amount of time the lights in his hen house were on. Ten hens were selected, and the number of eggs each produced was recorded. After 1 week of lengthened light time, the same hens were monitored again. The data are given here. At $\alpha = 0.05$, can it be concluded that the increased light time increased egg production?

Hen	1	2	3	4	5	6	7	8	9	10
Before	4	3	8	7	6	4	9	7	6	5
After	6	5	9	7	4	5	10	6	9	6

28. In a sample of 80 workers from a factory in city A, it was found that 5% were unable to read, while in a sample of 50 workers in city B, 8% were unable to read. Can it be concluded that there is a difference in the proportions of nonreaders in the two cities? Use $\alpha = 0.10$. Find the 90% confidence interval for the difference of the two proportions.

29. A recent survey of 200 American households showed that 8 had a single male as the head of household. Forty years ago, a survey of 200 households showed that 6 had a single male as the head of household. At $\alpha = 0.05$ can it be concluded that the proportion has changed? Find the 95% confidence interval of the difference of the two proportions. Does the confidence interval contain 0? Why is this important to know?

Source: Based on data from the U.S. Census Bureau.

Critical Thinking Challenges ● ● ●

1. The study cited in the article entitled "Only the Timid Die Young" (p. 446) stated that "Timid rats were 60% more likely to die at any given time than were their outgoing brothers." Based on the results, answer the following questions.

   a. Why were rats used in the study?
   b. What are the variables in the study?
   c. Why were infants included in the article?
   d. What is wrong with extrapolating the results to humans?
   e. Suggest some ways humans might be used in a study of this type.

2. Based on the study presented in the article entitled "Sleeping Brain, Not at Rest," answer these questions.

   a. What were the variables used in the study?
   b. How were they measured?
   c. Suggest a statistical test that might have been used to arrive at the conclusion.
   d. Based on the results, what would you suggest for students preparing for an exam?

ONLY THE TIMID DIE YOUNG

DO OVERACTIVE STRESS HORMONES DAMAGE HEALTH?

ABOUT 15 OUT OF 100 CHILDREN ARE BORN SHY, BUT ONLY THREE WILL BE SHY AS ADULTS.

FEARFUL TYPES MAY MEET THEIR maker sooner, at least among rats. Researchers have for the first time connected a personality trait—fear of novelty—to an early death.

Sonia Cavigelli and Martha McClintock, psychologists at the University of Chicago, presented unfamiliar bowls, tunnels and bricks to a group of young male rats. Those hesitant to explore the mystery objects were classified as "neophobic."

The researchers found that the neophobic rats produced high levels of stress hormones, called glucocorticoids—typically involved in the fight-or-flight stress response—when faced with strange situations. Those rats continued to have high levels of the hormones at random times throughout their lives, indicating that timidity is a fixed and stable trait. The team then set out to examine the cumulative effects of this personality trait on the rats' health.

Timid rats were 60 percent more likely to die at any given time than were their outgoing brothers. The causes of death were similar for both groups. "One hypothesis as to why the neophobic rats died earlier is that the stress hormones negatively affected their immune system," Cavigelli says. Neophobes died, on average, three months before their rat brothers, a significant gap, considering that most rats lived only two years.

Shyness—the human equivalent of neophobia—can be detected in infants as young as 14 months. Shy people also produce more stress hormones than "average," or thrill-seeking humans. But introverts don't necessarily stay shy for life, as rats apparently do. Jerome Kagan, a professor of psychology at Harvard University, has found that while 15 out of every 100 children will be born with a shy temperament, only three will appear shy as adults. None, however, will be extroverts.

Extrapolating from the doomed fate of neophobic rats to their human counterparts is difficult. "But it means that something as simple as a personality trait could have physiological consequences," Cavigelli says.

—*Carlin Flora*

SLEEPING BRAIN, NOT AT REST

Regions of the brain that have spent the day learning sleep more heavily at night.

In a study published in the journal *Nature*, Giulio Tononi, a psychiatrist at the University of Wisconsin–Madison, had subjects perform a simple point-and-click task with a computer adjusted so that its cursor didn't track in the right direction. Afterward, the subjects' brain waves were recorded while they slept, then examined for "slow wave" activity, a kind of deep sleep.

Compared with people who'd completed the same task with normal cursors, Tononi's subjects showed elevated slow wave activity in brain areas associated with spatial orientation, indicating that their brains were adjusting to the day's learning by making cellular-level changes. In the morning, Tononi's subjects performed their tasks better than they had before going to sleep.

—*Richard A. Love*

Reprinted with permission from *Psychology Today*, Copyright © 2004, Sussex Publishers, Inc.

Data Projects

● ● ●

Where appropriate, use Minitab, SPSS, the TI-83 Plus, the TI-84 Plus, or a computer program of your choice to complete the following exercises.

1. Choose a variable for which you would like to determine if there is a difference in the averages for two groups. Make sure that the samples are independent. For example, you may wish to see if men see more movies or spend more money on lunch than women. Select a sample of data values (10 to 50) and complete the following:

   a. Write a brief statement of the purpose of the study.
   b. Define the population.
   c. State the hypotheses for the study.
   d. Select an α value.
   e. State how the sample was selected.
   f. Show the raw data.
   g. Decide which statistical test is appropriate and compute the test statistic (z or t). Why is the test appropriate?
   h. Find the critical value(s).
   i. State the decision.
   j. Summarize the results.

2. Choose a variable that will permit the use of dependent samples. For example, you might wish to see if a person's weight has changed after a diet. Select a sample of data (10 to 50) value pairs (e.g., before and after), and then complete the following:

   a. Write a brief statement of the purpose of the study.
   b. Define the population.
   c. State the hypotheses for the study.
   d. Select an α value.
   e. State how the sample was selected.
   f. Show the raw data.
   g. Decide which statistical test is appropriate and compute the test statistic (z or t). Why is the test appropriate?
   h. Find the critical value(s).
   i. State the decision.
   j. Summarize the results.

3. Choose a variable that will enable you to compare proportions of two groups. For example, you might want to see if the proportion of first-year students who buy used books is lower than (or higher than or the same as) the proportion of second-year students who buy used books. After collecting 30 or more responses from the two groups, complete the following:

   a. Write a brief statement of the purpose of the study.
   b. Define the population.
   c. State the hypotheses for the study.
   d. Select an α value.
   e. State how the sample was selected.
   f. Show the raw data.
   g. Decide which statistical test is appropriate and compute the test statistic (z or t). Why is the test appropriate?
   h. Find the critical value(s).
   i. State the decision.
   j. Summarize the results.

You may use the following websites to obtain raw data:

**Visit the data sets at the book's website found at
www.mcgrawhill.ca/olc/bluman
http://lib.stat.cmu.edu/DASL
www.statcan.ca**

Hypothesis-Testing Summary 1

1. Comparison of a sample mean with a specific population mean.

   Example: $H_0: \mu = 100$

   a. Use the z test when σ is known:

   $$z = \frac{\overline{X} - \mu}{\sigma/\sqrt{n}}$$

   b. Use the t test when σ is unknown:

   $$t = \frac{\overline{X} - \mu}{s/\sqrt{n}} \qquad \text{with d.f.} = n - 1$$

2. Comparison of a sample variance or standard deviation with a specific population variance or standard deviation.

   Example: $H_0: \sigma^2 = 225$

   Use the chi-square test:

   $$\chi^2 = \frac{(n-1)s^2}{\sigma^2} \qquad \text{with d.f.} = n - 1$$

3. Comparison of two sample means.

   Example: $H_0: \mu_1 = \mu_2$

   a. Use the z test when the population variances are known:

   $$z = \frac{(\overline{X}_1 - \overline{X}_2) - (\mu_1 - \mu_2)}{\sqrt{\dfrac{\sigma_1^2}{n_1} + \dfrac{\sigma_2^2}{n_2}}}$$

   b. Use the t test for independent samples when the population variances are unknown and the sample variances are unequal:

   $$t = \frac{(\overline{X}_1 - \overline{X}_2) - (\mu_1 - \mu_2)}{\sqrt{\dfrac{s_1^2}{n_1} + \dfrac{s_2^2}{n_2}}}$$

   with d.f. = the smaller of $n_1 - 1$ or $n_2 - 1$.

   c. Use the t test for independent samples when the population variances are unknown and assumed to be equal:

   $$t = \frac{(\overline{X}_1 - \overline{X}_2) - (\mu_1 - \mu_2)}{\sqrt{\dfrac{(n_1 - 1)s_1^2 + (n_2 - 1)s_2^2}{n_1 + n_2 - 2}}\sqrt{\dfrac{1}{n_1} + \dfrac{1}{n_2}}}$$

   with d.f. = $n_1 + n_2 - 2$.

   d. Use the t test for means for dependent samples:

   Example: $H_0: \mu_D = 0$

   $$t = \frac{\overline{D} - \mu_D}{s_D/\sqrt{n}} \qquad \text{with d.f.} = n - 1$$

   where n = number of pairs.

4. Comparison of a sample proportion with a specific population proportion.

   Example: $H_0: p = 0.32$

   Use the z test:

   $$z = \frac{X - \mu}{\sigma} \qquad \text{or} \qquad z = \frac{\hat{p} - p}{\sqrt{pq/n}}$$

5. Comparison of two sample proportions.

   Example: $H_0: p_1 = p_2$

   Use the z test:

   $$z = \frac{(\hat{p}_1 - \hat{p}_2) - (p_1 - p_2)}{\sqrt{\overline{p}\,\overline{q}\left(\dfrac{1}{n_1} + \dfrac{1}{n_2}\right)}}$$

   where

   $$\overline{p} = \frac{X_1 + X_2}{n_1 + n_2} \qquad \hat{p}_1 = \frac{X_1}{n_1}$$

   $$\overline{q} = 1 - \overline{p} \qquad \hat{p}_2 = \frac{X_2}{n_2}$$

6. Comparison of two sample variances or standard deviations.

   Example: $H_0: \sigma_1^2 = \sigma_2^2$

   Use the F test:

   $$F = \frac{s_1^2}{s_2^2}$$

   where

s_1^2 = larger variance	d.f.N. $= n_1 - 1$
s_2^2 = smaller variance	d.f.D. $= n_2 - 1$

Answers to Applying the Concepts ● ● ●

Section 9–2 Home Runs

1. The population is all home runs hit by Major League Baseball players.

2. A cluster sample was used.

3. Answers will vary. While this sample is not representative of all Major League Baseball players per se, it does allow us to compare the leaders in each league.

4. H_0: $\mu_1 = \mu_2$ and H_1: $\mu_1 \neq \mu_2$

5. Answers will vary. Possible answers include the 0.05 and 0.01 significance levels.

6. We will use the z test for the difference in means.

7. Out test statistic is $z = \dfrac{44.75 - 42.88}{\sqrt{\dfrac{8.88^2}{40} + \dfrac{7.82^2}{40}}} = 1.00$, and our

   P-value is 0.3173.

8. We fail to reject the null hypothesis.

9. There is not enough evidence to conclude that there is a difference in the number of home runs hit by National League versus American League baseball players.

10. Answers will vary. One possible answer is that since we do not have a random sample of data from each league, we cannot answer the original question asked.

11. Answers will vary. One possible answer is that we could get a random sample of data from each league from a recent season.

Section 9–3 Variability and Automatic Transmissions

1. The null hypothesis is that the variances are the same: H_0: $\sigma_1^2 = \sigma_2^2$.

2. We will use an F test.

3. The value of the test statistic is $F = \dfrac{s_1^2}{s_2^2} = \dfrac{77.7^2}{514.8^2} = 0.02$, and the P-value is 0.0006. There is a significant difference in the variability of the prices between the two car sectors.

4. Small sample sizes are highly impacted by outliers.

5. The degrees of freedom for the numerator and denominator are both 5.

6. Yes, two sets of data can centre on the same mean but have very different standard deviations.

Section 9–4 Too Long on the Telephone

1. These samples are independent.

2. The F test was done to test for any significant difference in the variances.

3. The results of the F test are not significant at the 0.01 level, since the P-value is greater than 0.01.

4. There were $56 + 2 = 58$ people in the study.

5. We compare the P-value of 0.06317 to the significance level to check if the null hypothesis should be rejected.

6. The P-value of 0.06317 also gives the probability of a type I error.

7. The F value of 3.07849 is the result of dividing the two sample variances.

8. Since two critical values are shown, we know that a two-tailed test was done.

9. Since the P-value of 0.06317 is greater than the significance value of 0.05, we fail to reject the null hypothesis and find that we do not have enough evidence to conclude that there is a difference in the lengths of telephone calls made by employees in the two divisions of the company.

10. If the significance level had been 0.10, we would have rejected the null hypothesis, since the P-value would have been less than the significance level.

Section 9–5 Air Quality

1. The purpose of the study is to determine if the air quality index in Ontario has changed over a 2-year period.

2. These are dependent samples, since we have two readings from each of the 10 cities.

3. The hypotheses we will test are H_0: $\mu_D = 0$ and H_1: $\mu_D \neq 0$.

4. We will use the 0.05 significance level and critical values of $t = \pm 2.262$.

5. We will use the t test for dependent samples.

6. There are $10 - 1 = 9$ degrees of freedom.

7. Our test statistic is $t = \dfrac{-10.8 - 0}{9.682/\sqrt{10}} = -3.527$

   We reject the null hypothesis and find that there is enough evidence to conclude that the air quality in Ontario has changed over the past 2 years.

8. No, we could not use an independent means test since we have two readings from each city.

9. Answers will vary. One possible answer is that there may be other measures of air quality that we could have examined to answer the question.

Section 9–6 Smoking and Education

1. Our hypotheses are H_0: $p_1 = p_2$ and H_1: $p_1 \neq p_2$.

2. At the 0.05 significance level, our critical values are $z = \pm 1.96$.

3. We will use the z test for the difference between proportions.

4. To complete the statistical test, we would need the sample sizes.

5. Knowing the sample sizes were 1000, we can now complete the test.

6. Our test statistic is

$$z = \frac{0.323 - 0.145}{\sqrt{(0.234)(0.766)\left(\frac{1}{1000} + \frac{1}{1000}\right)}} = 9.40,$$

and our P-value is very close to zero. We reject the null hypothesis and find that there is enough evidence to conclude that there is a difference in the proportions of public school students and private school students who smoke.

10 Correlation and Regression

Objectives

After completing this chapter, you should be able to

1. Draw a scatter plot for a set of ordered pairs.
2. Compute the correlation coefficient.
3. Test the hypothesis H_0: $\rho = 0$.
4. Compute the equation of the regression line.
5. Compute the coefficient of determination.
6. Compute the standard error of the estimate.
7. Find a prediction interval.
8. Be familiar with the concept of multiple regression.

Outline

10–1 Introduction

10–2 Scatter Plots

10–3 Correlation

10–4 Regression

10–5 Coefficient of Determination and Standard Error of the Estimate

10–6 Multiple Regression (Optional)

10–7 Summary

Statistics Today

Like Parent, Like Child?

Do parents influence a child's participation in the employment insurance (EI) program? A Statistics Canada family and labour study examined the relationship between a young adult's use of EI and having a parent who collected EI. The Canada–Sweden joint study also compared other factors, such as past experience with the program and time to a first EI claim, as well as the entire sequence of claims over time. Using methods of correlation and regression, which are explained in this chapter, they were able to determine the effect of parental factors in an offspring's involvement in the EI program. See Statistics Today— Revisited, page 494.

Source: "Excerpts from the Intergenerational Influences on the Receipt of Unemployment Insurance in Canada and Sweden," adapted from Statistics Canada publication *Analytical Studies Branch Research Paper Series,* Catalogue 11F0019MIE2001159, www.statcan.ca/bsolc/english/bsolc?catno=11F0019M2001159.

10–1   Introduction

In Chapters 7 and 8, two areas of inferential statistics—confidence intervals and hypothesis testing—were explained. Another area of inferential statistics involves determining whether a relationship between two or more numerical or quantitative variables exists. For example, a businessperson may want to know whether the volume of sales for a given month is related to the amount of advertising the firm does that month. Educators are interested in determining whether the number of hours a student studies is related to the student's score on a particular exam. Medical researchers are interested in questions such as, Is caffeine related to heart damage? or Is there a relationship between a person's age and his or her blood pressure? A zoologist may want to know whether the birth weight of a certain animal is related to its life span. These are only a few of the many questions that can be answered by using the techniques of correlation and regression analysis. **Correlation** is a statistical method used to determine whether a relationship between variables exists. **Regression** is a statistical method used to describe the nature of the relationship between variables, that is, positive or negative, linear or nonlinear.

The purpose of this chapter is to answer these questions statistically:

1. Are two or more variables related?

2. If so, what is the strength of the relationship?

3. What type of relationship exists?

4. What kind of predictions can be made from the relationship?

To answer the first two questions, statisticians use a numerical measure to determine whether two or more variables are related and to determine the strength of the relationship between or among the variables. This measure is called a *correlation coefficient.* For example, there are many variables that contribute to heart disease, among them lack of exercise, smoking, heredity, age, stress, and diet. Of these variables, some are more important than others; therefore, a physician who wants to help a patient must know which factors are most important.

To answer the third question, one must ascertain what type of relationship exists. There are two types of relationships: *simple* and *multiple.* In a simple relationship, there are two variables—an **independent variable,** also called an explanatory variable or a predictor variable, and a **dependent variable,** also called a response variable. A simple relationship analysis is called *simple regression,* and there is one independent variable that is used to predict the dependent variable. For example, a manager may wish to see whether the number of years the salespeople have been working for the company has anything to do with the amount of sales they make. This type of study involves a simple relationship, since there are only two variables—years of experience and amount of sales.

In a multiple relationship, called *multiple regression,* two or more independent variables are used to predict one dependent variable. For example, an educator may wish to investigate the relationship between a student's success in college and factors such as the number of hours devoted to studying, the student's GPA, and the student's high school background. This type of study involves several variables.

Simple relationships can also be positive or negative. A **positive relationship** exists when both variables increase or decrease at the same time. For instance, a person's height and weight are related; and the relationship is positive, since the taller a person is, generally, the more the person weighs. In a **negative relationship**, as one variable increases, the other variable decreases, and vice versa. For example, if one measures the strength of people over 60 years of age, one will find that as age increases, strength generally decreases. The word *generally* is used here because there are exceptions.

Finally, the fourth question asks what type of predictions can be made. Every day, predictions are made in all facets of modern life. Examples include weather forecasting, stock market analyses, sales predictions, crop predictions, gasoline predictions, and sports predictions. Some predictions are more accurate than others, due to the strength of the relationship. That is, the stronger the relationship is between variables, the more accurate the prediction is.

10–2   Scatter Plots

Objective

Draw a scatter plot for a set of ordered pairs.

In simple correlation and regression studies, the researcher collects data on two numerical or quantitative variables to see whether a relationship exists between the variables. For example, if a researcher wishes to see whether there is a relationship between number of hours of study and test scores on an exam, she must select a random sample of students, determine the hours each studied, and obtain their grades on the exam. A table can be made for the data, as shown here.

Student	Hours of study x	Grade y (%)
A	6	82
B	2	63
C	1	57
D	5	88
E	2	68
F	3	75

As stated previously, the two variables for this study are called the independent variable and the dependent variable. The independent variable is the variable in regression that can be controlled or manipulated. In this case, "number of hours of study" is the independent variable and is designated as the x variable. The dependent variable is the variable in regression that cannot be controlled or manipulated. The grade the student received on the exam is the dependent variable, designated as the y variable. The reason for this distinction between the variables is that one assumes that the grade the student earns *depends* on the number of hours the student studied. Also, one assumes that, to some extent, the student can regulate or *control* the number of hours he or she studies for the exam.

The determination of the x and y variables is not always clear-cut and is sometimes an arbitrary decision. For example, if a researcher studies the effects of age on a person's blood pressure, the researcher can generally assume that age affects blood pressure. Hence, the variable *age* can be called the *independent variable,* and the variable *blood pressure* can be called the *dependent variable.* On the other hand, if a researcher is studying the attitudes of husbands on a certain issue and the attitudes of their wives on the same issue, it is difficult to say which variable is the independent variable and which is the dependent variable. In this study, the researcher can arbitrarily designate the variables as independent and dependent.

The independent and dependent variables can be plotted on a graph called a *scatter plot.* The independent variable x is plotted on the horizontal axis, and the dependent variable y is plotted on the vertical axis.

A **scatter plot** is a graph of the ordered pairs (x, y) of numbers consisting of the independent variable x and the dependent variable y.

The scatter plot is a visual way to describe the nature of the relationship between the independent and dependent variables. The scales of the variables can be different, and the coordinates of the axes are determined by the smallest and largest data values of the variables.

The procedure for drawing a scatter plot is shown in Examples 10–1 through 10–3.

Example 10–1

Construct a scatter plot for the data obtained in a study of age and systolic blood pressure of six randomly selected subjects. The data are shown in the table.

Subject	Age x	Pressure y
A	43	128
B	48	120
C	56	135
D	61	143
E	67	141
F	70	152

Solution

Step 1 Draw and label the x and y axes.

Step 2 Plot each point on the graph, as shown in Figure 10–1.

Figure 10–1

Scatter Plot for
Example 10–1

Example 10–2

Construct a scatter plot for the data obtained in a study on the number of absences and the final grades of seven randomly selected students from a statistics class. The data are shown here.

Student	Number of absences x	Final grade y (%)
A	6	82
B	2	86
C	15	43
D	9	74
E	12	58
F	5	90
G	8	78

Solution

Step 1 Draw and label the x and y axes.

Step 2 Plot each point on the graph, as shown in Figure 10–2.

Figure 10–2

Scatter Plot for
Example 10–2

Example 10–3

Construct a scatter plot for the data obtained in a study on the number of hours that nine people exercise each week and the amount of milk (in litres) each person consumes per week. The data are shown.

Subject	Hours x	Amount y
A	3	1.4
B	0	0.2
C	2	0.9
D	5	1.9
E	8	0.3
F	5	0.9
G	10	1.7
H	2	2.1
I	1	1.4

Solution

Step 1   Draw and label the *x* and *y* axes.

Step 2   Plot each point on the graph, as shown in Figure 10–3.

Figure 10–3

Scatter Plot for Example 10–3

After the plot is drawn, it should be analyzed to determine which type of relationship, if any, exists. For example, the plot shown in Figure 10–1 suggests a positive relationship, since as a person's age increases, blood pressure tends to increase also. The plot of the data shown in Figure 10–2 suggests a negative relationship, since as the number of absences increases, the final grade decreases. Finally, the plot of the data shown in Figure 10–3 shows no specific type of relationship, since no pattern is discernible.

Note that the data shown in Figures 10–1 and 10–2 also suggest a linear relationship, since the points seem to fit a straight line, although not perfectly. Sometimes a scatter plot, such as the one in Figure 10–4, shows a nonlinear relationship between the data. In this situation, the methods shown in this section and in Section 10–3 cannot be used. Methods for nonlinear relationships are beyond the scope of this book.

Figure 10–4

Scatter Plot Suggesting
a Nonlinear Relationship

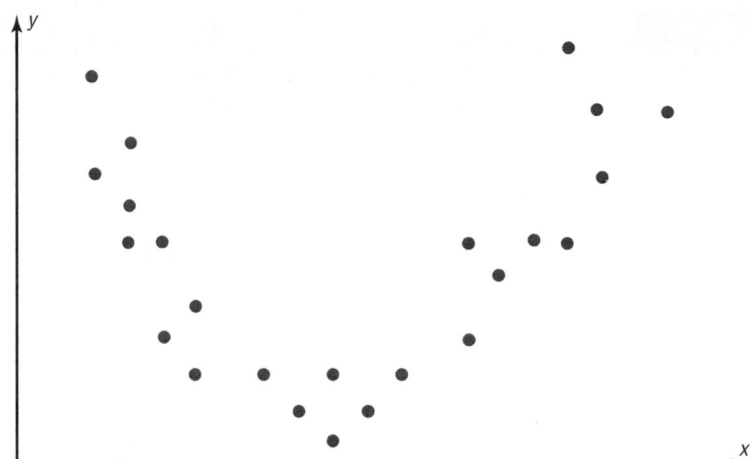

Figure 10–4

Scatter Plot Suggesting
a Nonlinear Relationship

In summary, check the following patterns in a scatter plot to identify possible relationships.

Shape of plot—linear or nonlinear

Direction of data points—direct (positive slope) or indirect (negative slope)

Strength of relationship—strong (minimal or no scatter), weak (scatter with pattern), none (scatter without pattern)

Outliers—extreme data points outside of pattern

10–3   Correlation

Correlation Coefficient

Objective ❷

Compute the
correlation coefficient.

As stated in Section 10–1, statisticians use a measure called the *correlation coefficient* to determine the strength of the relationship between two variables. There are several types of correlation coefficients. The one explained in this section is called the **Pearson product moment correlation coefficient** (PPMC), named after statistician Karl Pearson, who pioneered the research in this area.

> The **correlation coefficient** computed from the sample data measures the strength and direction of a linear relationship between two variables. The symbol for the sample correlation coefficient is r. The symbol for the population correlation coefficient is ρ (Greek letter rho).

The *range of the correlation coefficient* is from -1 to $+1$. If there is a *strong positive linear relationship* between the variables, the value of r will be close to $+1$. If there is a *strong negative linear relationship* between the variables, the value of r will be close to -1. When there is no linear relationship between the variables or only a weak relationship, the value of r will be close to 0. See Figure 10–5.

The graphs in Figure 10–6 show the relationship between the correlation coefficients and their corresponding scatter plots. Notice that as the value of the correlation coefficient increases from 0 to $+1$ (parts *a*, *b*, and *c*), data values become closer to an increasingly stronger relationship. As the value of the correlation coefficient decreases

Figure 10–5

Range of Values for the
Correlation Coefficient

Strong negative
linear relationship   No linear
relationship   Strong positive
linear relationship

-1 0 $+1$

Figure 10–6

Relationship Between
the Correlation
Coefficient and the
Scatter Plot

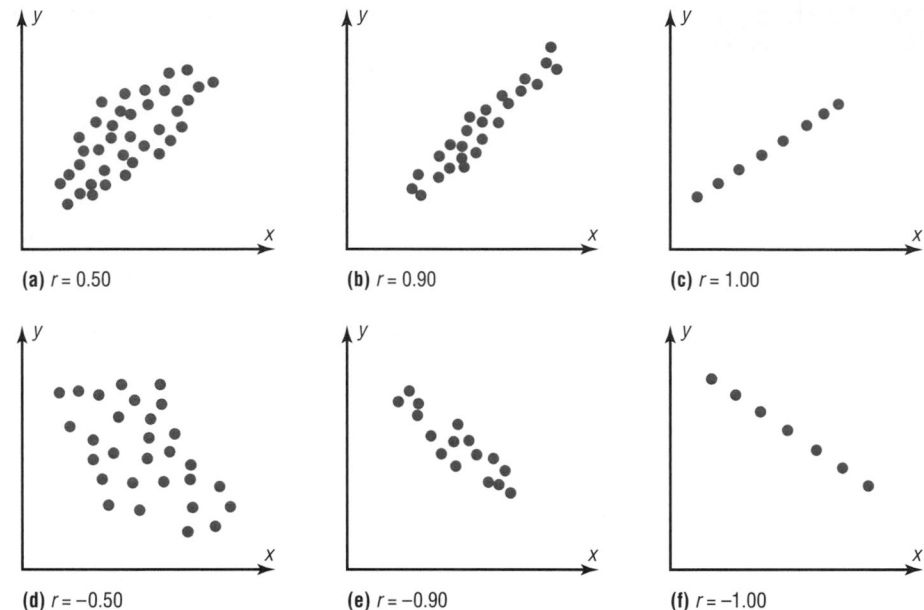

(a) $r = 0.50$

(b) $r = 0.90$

(c) $r = 1.00$

(d) $r = -0.50$

(e) $r = -0.90$

(f) $r = -1.00$

from 0 to -1 (parts d, e, and f), the data values also become closer to a straight line. Again this suggests a stronger relationship.

There are several ways to compute the value of the correlation coefficient. One method is to use the formula shown here.

Formula for the Correlation Coefficient r

$$r = \frac{n(\Sigma xy) - (\Sigma x)(\Sigma y)}{\sqrt{[n(\Sigma x^2) - (\Sigma x)^2][n(\Sigma y^2) - (\Sigma y)^2]}}$$

where n is the number of data pairs.

Rounding Rule for the Correlation Coefficient   Round the value of r to three decimal places.

The formula looks somewhat complicated, but using a table to compute the values, as shown in Example 10–4, makes it somewhat easier to determine the value of r.

Example 10–4

Compute the value of the correlation coefficient for the data obtained in the study of age and blood pressure given in Example 10–1.

Solution

Step 1   Make a table, as shown here.

Subject	Age x	Pressure y	xy	x^2	y^2
A	43	128			
B	48	120			
C	56	135			
D	61	143			
E	67	141			
F	70	152			

Step 2 Find the values of xy, x^2, and y^2 and place these values in the corresponding columns of the table.
The completed table is shown.

Subject	Age x	Pressure y	xy	x^2	y^2
A	43	128	5,504	1,849	16,384
B	48	120	5,760	2,304	14,400
C	56	135	7,560	3,136	18,225
D	61	143	8,723	3,721	20,449
E	67	141	9,447	4,489	19,881
F	70	152	10,640	4,900	23,104
	$\Sigma x = 345$	$\Sigma y = 819$	$\Sigma xy = 47,634$	$\Sigma x^2 = 20,399$	$\Sigma y^2 = 112,443$

Step 3 Substitute in the formula and solve for r.

$$r = \frac{n(\Sigma xy) - (\Sigma x)(\Sigma y)}{\sqrt{[n(\Sigma x^2) - (\Sigma x)^2][n(\Sigma y^2) - (\Sigma y)^2]}}$$

$$= \frac{(6)(47,634) - (345)(819)}{\sqrt{[(6)(20,399) - (345)^2][(6)(112,443) - (819)^2]}} \approx 0.897$$

The correlation coefficient suggests a strong positive relationship between age and blood pressure.

Example 10–5

Compute the value of the correlation coefficient for the data obtained in the study of the number of absences and the final grade of the seven students in the statistics class given in Example 10–2.

Solution

Step 1 Make a table.

Step 2 Find the values of xy, x^2, and y^2 and place these values in the corresponding columns of the table.

Student	Number of absences x	Final grade y (%)	xy	x^2	y^2
A	6	82	492	36	6,724
B	2	86	172	4	7,396
C	15	43	645	225	1,849
D	9	74	666	81	5,476
E	12	58	696	144	3,364
F	5	90	450	25	8,100
G	8	78	624	64	6,084
	$\Sigma x = 57$	$\Sigma y = 511$	$\Sigma xy = 3745$	$\Sigma x^2 = 579$	$\Sigma y^2 = 38,993$

Step 3 Substitute in the formula and solve for r.

$$r = \frac{n(\Sigma xy) - (\Sigma x)(\Sigma y)}{\sqrt{[n(\Sigma x^2) - (\Sigma x)^2][n(\Sigma y^2) - (\Sigma y)^2]}}$$

$$= \frac{(7)(3745) - (57)(511)}{\sqrt{[(7)(579) - (57)^2][(7)(38,993) - (511)^2]}} \approx -0.944$$

The value of r suggests a strong negative relationship between a student's final grade and the number of absences a student has. That is, the more absences a student has, the lower is his or her grade.

Example 10–6

Compute the value of the correlation coefficient for the data given in Example 10–3 for the number of hours a person exercises and the amount of milk a person consumes per week.

Solution

Step 1 Make a table.

Step 2 Find the values of xy, x^2, and y^2 and place these values in the corresponding columns of the table.

Subject	Hours x	Amount y	xy	x^2	y^2
A	3	1.4	4.2	9	1.96
B	0	0.2	0.0	0	0.04
C	2	0.9	1.8	4	0.81
D	5	1.9	9.5	25	3.61
E	8	0.3	2.4	64	0.09
F	5	0.9	4.5	25	0.81
G	10	1.7	17.0	100	2.89
H	2	2.1	4.2	4	4.41
I	1	1.4	1.4	1	1.96
	$\Sigma x = 36$	$\Sigma y = 10.8$	$\Sigma xy = 45$	$\Sigma x^2 = 232$	$\Sigma y^2 = 16.58$

Step 3 Substitute into the formula and solve for r:

$$r = \frac{n(\Sigma xy) - (\Sigma x)(\Sigma y)}{\sqrt{[n(\Sigma x^2) - (\Sigma x)^2][n(\Sigma y^2) - (\Sigma y)^2]}}$$

$$r = \frac{9(45) - (36)(10.8)}{\sqrt{[9(232) - (36)^2][9(16.58) - (10.8)^2]}} \approx 0.101$$

The value of r indicates a very weak positive relationship between the variables.

In Example 10–4, the value of r was high (close to 1.00); in Example 10–6, the value of r was much lower (close to 0). This question then arises: When is the value of r due to chance, and when does it suggest a significant linear relationship between the variables? This question will be answered next.

Objective ③

Test the hypothesis H_0: $\rho = 0$.

The Significance of the Correlation Coefficient

As stated before, the range of the correlation coefficient is between -1 and $+1$. When the value of r is near $+1$ or -1, there is a strong linear relationship. When the value of r is near 0, the linear relationship is weak or nonexistent. Since the value of r is computed from data obtained from samples, there are two possibilities when r is not equal to zero: either the value of r is high enough to conclude that there is a significant linear relationship between the variables, or the value of r is due to chance.

To make this decision, one uses a hypothesis-testing procedure. The traditional method is similar to the one used in previous chapters.

Step 1 State the hypotheses.

Step 2 Find the critical values.

Step 3 Compute the test statistic.

Step 4 Make the decision.

Step 5 Summarize the results.

The population correlation coefficient is computed from taking all possible (x,y) pairs; it is designated by the Greek letter ρ (rho). The sample correlation coefficient can then be used as an estimator of ρ if the following assumptions are valid.

1. The variables x and y are *linearly* related.
2. The variables are *random* variables.
3. The two variables have a *bivariate normal distribution*.

This means for any given value of x, the y variable is normally distributed.

Formally defined, the **population correlation coefficient** ρ is the correlation computed by using all possible pairs of data values (x, y) taken from a population.

In hypothesis testing, one of these is true:

H_0: $\rho = 0$ This null hypothesis means that there is no correlation between the x and y variables in the population.

H_1: $\rho \neq 0$ This alternative hypothesis means that there is a significant correlation between the variables in the population.

When the null hypothesis is rejected at a specific level, it means that there is a significant difference between the value of r and 0. When the null hypothesis is not rejected, it means that the value of r is not significantly different from 0 (zero) and is probably due to chance.

Several methods can be used to test the significance of the correlation coefficient. Three methods will be shown in this section. The first uses the t test.

Formula for the t Test for the Correlation Coefficient

$$t = r\sqrt{\frac{n-2}{1-r^2}}$$

with degrees of freedom equal to $n - 2$.

Although hypothesis tests can be one-tailed, most hypotheses involving the correlation coefficient are two-tailed. Recall that ρ represents the population correlation coefficient. Also, if there is no linear relationship, the value of the correlation coefficient will be 0. Hence, the hypotheses will be

$$H_0: \rho = 0 \quad \text{and} \quad H_1: \rho \neq 0$$

One does not have to identify the claim here, since the question will always be whether there is a significant linear relationship between the variables.

The two-tailed critical values are used. These values are found in Table F in Appendix C. Also, when one is testing the significance of a correlation coefficient, both variables x and y must come from normally distributed populations.

Example 10–7

Test the significance of the correlation coefficient found in Example 10–4. Use $\alpha = 0.05$ and $r = 0.897$.

Solution

Step 1   State the hypotheses.

$$H_0: \rho = 0 \qquad \text{and} \qquad H_1: \rho \neq 0$$

Step 2   Find the critical values. Since $\alpha = 0.05$ and there are $6 - 2 = 4$ degrees of freedom, the critical values obtained from Table F are ± 2.776, as shown in Figure 10–7.

Figure 10–7

Critical Values for Example 10–7

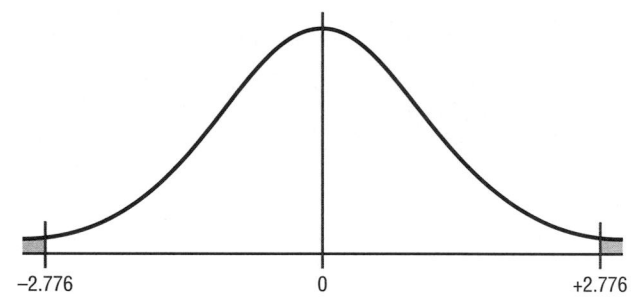

     -2.776 0 $+2.776$

Step 3   Compute the test statistic.

$$t = r\sqrt{\frac{n - 2}{1 - r^2}} = (0.897)\sqrt{\frac{6 - 2}{1 - (0.897)^2}} \approx 4.059$$

Step 4   Make the decision. Reject the null hypothesis, since the test statistic falls in the critical region, as shown in Figure 10–8.

Figure 10–8

Critical Values and Test Statistic for Example 10–7

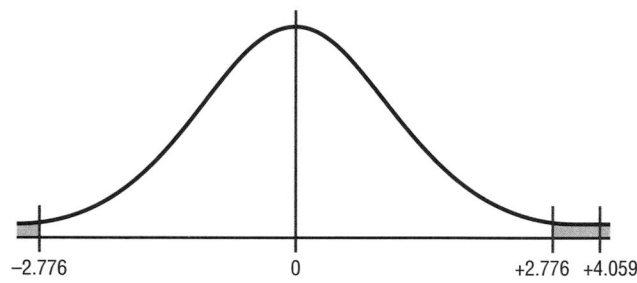

     -2.776 0 $+2.776$ $+4.059$

Step 5   Summarize the results. There is a significant relationship between the variables of age and blood pressure.

The second method that can be used to test the significance of r is the *P*-value method. The method is the same as that shown in Chapters 8 and 9. It uses the following steps.

Step 1   State the hypotheses.

Step 2   Find the test statistic. (In this case, use the t test.)

Figure 10–9

Finding the Critical
Value from Table I

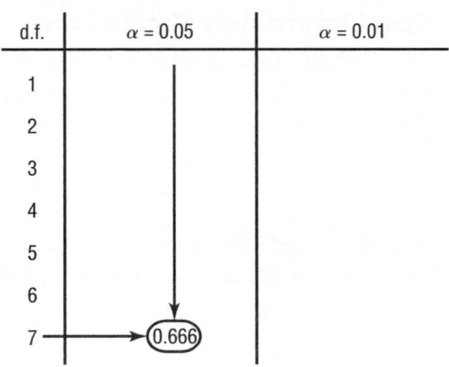

d.f.	$\alpha = 0.05$	$\alpha = 0.01$
1		
2		
3		
4		
5		
6		
7	0.666	

Step 3 Find the *P*-value. (In this case, use Table F.)

Step 4 Make the decision.

Step 5 Summarize the results.

Referring to Example 10–7, we see that the *t* value obtained in step 3 is 4.059 and d.f. = 4. Using Table F with d.f. = 4 and the row Two tails, the value 4.059 falls between 3.747 and 4.604; hence, $0.01 < P\text{-value} < 0.02$. (The *P*-value obtained from a calculator is 0.015.) That is, the *P*-value falls between 0.01 and 0.02. The decision then is to reject the null hypothesis since $P\text{-value} < 0.05$.

The third method of testing the significance of *r* is to use Table I in Appendix C. This table shows the values of the correlation coefficient that are significant for a specific α level and a specific number of degrees of freedom. For example, for 7 degrees of freedom and $\alpha = 0.05$, the table gives a critical value of 0.666. Any value of *r* greater than $+0.666$ or less than -0.666 will be significant, and the null hypothesis will be rejected. See Figure 10–9. When Table I is used, one need not compute the *t* test value. Table I is for two-tailed tests only.

Example 10–8

Using Table I, test the significance of the correlation coefficient $r = 0.067$, obtained in Example 10–6, at $\alpha = 0.01$.

Solution

$$H_0: \rho = 0 \qquad \text{and} \qquad H_1: \rho \neq 0$$

Since the sample size is 9, there are 7 degrees of freedom. When $\alpha = 0.01$ and with 7 degrees of freedom, the value obtained from Table I is 0.798. For a significant relationship, a value of *r* greater than $+0.798$ or less than -0.798 is needed. Since $r = 0.067$, the null hypothesis is not rejected. Hence, there is not enough evidence to say that there is a significant linear relationship between the variables. See Figure 10–10.

Figure 10–10

Rejection and
Nonrejection Regions
for Example 10–8

Correlation and Causation

Researchers must understand the nature of the linear relationship between the independent variable x and the dependent variable y. When a hypothesis test indicates that a significant linear relationship exists between the variables, researchers must consider the possibilities outlined next.

Possible Relationships Between Variables

When the null hypothesis has been rejected for a specific α value, any of the following five possibilities can exist.

1. *There is a direct cause-and-effect relationship between the variables.* That is, x causes y. For example, water causes plants to grow, poison causes death, and heat causes ice to melt.

2. *There is a reverse cause-and-effect relationship between the variables.* That is, y causes x. For example, suppose a researcher believes excessive coffee consumption causes nervousness, but the researcher fails to consider that the reverse situation may occur. That is, it may be that an extremely nervous person craves coffee to calm his or her nerves.

3. *The relationship between the variables may be caused by a third variable.* For example, if a statistician correlated the number of deaths due to drowning and the number of cans of soft drink consumed daily during the summer, he or she would probably find a significant relationship. However, the soft drink is not necessarily responsible for the deaths, since both variables may be related to heat and humidity.

4. *There may be a complexity of interrelationships among many variables.* For example, a researcher may find a significant relationship between students' high school grades and university grades. But there probably are many other variables involved, such as IQ, hours of study, influence of parents, motivation, age, and instructors.

5. *The relationship may be coincidental.* For example, a researcher may be able to find a significant relationship between the increase in the number of people who are exercising and the increase in the number of people who are committing crimes. But common sense dictates that any relationship between these two values must be due to coincidence.

When two variables are highly correlated, item 3 in the box states that there exists a possibility that the correlation is due to a third variable. If this is the case and the third variable is unknown to the researcher or not accounted for in the study, it is called a **lurking variable.** An attempt should be made by the researcher to identify such variables and to use methods to control their influence.

Also, one should be cautious when the data for one or both of the variables involve averages rather than individual data. It is not wrong to use averages, but the results cannot be generalized to individuals since averaging tends to smooth out the variability among individual data values. The result could be a higher correlation than actually exists.

Thus, when the null hypothesis is rejected, the researcher must consider all possibilities and select the appropriate one as determined by the study. Remember, correlation does not necessarily imply causation.

Applying the Concepts 10–3

Stopping Distances

Manitoba Public Insurance published a brochure titled "Watch Your Speed." The purpose of the study was to educate the public on the most common factors associated with vehicle crashes. An area that was focused on in the study was the stopping distance (metres) required to completely stop a vehicle at various speeds (kilometres per hour). Use the following table to answer the questions.

Speed (km/h)	Stopping distance (m)
30	18
50	35
70	57
100	98
110	114

Assume km/h is going to be used to predict stopping distance.

1. Which of the two variables is the independent variable?
2. Which is the dependent variable?
3. What type of variable is the independent variable?
4. What type of variable is the dependent variable?
5. Construct a scatter plot for the data.
6. Is there a linear relationship between the two variables?
7. Redraw the scatter plot, and change the distances between the independent-variable numbers. Does the relationship look different?
8. Is the relationship positive or negative?
9. Can stopping distance be accurately predicted from km/h?
10. List some other variables that affect stopping distance.
11. Compute the value of r.
12. Is r significant at $\alpha = 0.05$?

See page 497 for the answers.

Exercises 10–3

1. What is meant by the statement that two variables are related?

2. How is a linear relationship between two variables measured in statistics? Explain.

3. What is the symbol for the sample correlation coefficient? The population correlation coefficient?

4. What is the range of values for the correlation coefficient?

5. What is meant when the relationship between the two variables is positive? Negative?

6. Give examples of two variables that are positively correlated and two that are negatively correlated.

7. Give an example of a correlation study, and identify the independent and dependent variables.

8. What is the diagram of the independent and dependent variables called? Why is drawing this diagram important?

9. What is the name of the correlation coefficient used in this section?

10. What statistical test is used to test the significance of the correlation coefficient?

11. When two variables are correlated, can the researcher be sure that one variable causes the other? Why or why not?

For Exercises 12 through 27, perform the following steps.

  a. Draw the scatter plot for the variables.
  b. Compute the value of the correlation coefficient.
  c. State the hypotheses.
  d. Test the significance of the correlation coefficient at $\alpha = 0.05$, using Table I.
  e. Give a brief explanation of the type of relationship.

12. A medical researcher wishes to see if there is a relationship between prescription drug prices for identical drugs and identical dosages that are prescribed for humans and for animals. The prices are shown. Is there a relationship between the prices?

Speaking of

Statistics

In correlation and regression studies, it is difficult to control all variables. This study shows some of the consequences when researchers overlook certain aspects in studies. Suggest ways that the extraneous variables might be controlled in future studies.

Source: Reprinted with permission of the Associated Press.

Coffee Not Disease Culprit, Study Says

NEW YORK (AP)—Two new studies suggest that coffee drinking, even up to $5\frac{1}{2}$ cups per day, does not increase the risk of heart disease, and other studies that claim to have found increased risks might have missed the true culprits, a researcher says.

"It might not be the coffee cup in one hand, it might be the cigarette or coffee roll in the other," said Dr. Peter W. F. Wilson, the author of one of the new studies.

He noted in a telephone interview Thursday that many coffee drinkers, particularly heavy coffee drinkers, are smokers. And one of the new studies found that coffee drinkers had excess fat in their diets.

The findings of the new studies conflict sharply with a study reported in November 1985 by Johns Hopkins University scientists in Baltimore.

The Hopkins scientists found that coffee drinkers who consumed five or more cups of coffee per day had three times the heart-disease risk of non-coffee drinkers.

The reason for the discrepancy appears to be that many of the coffee drinkers in the Hopkins study also smoked—and it was the smoking that increased their heart-disease risk, said Wilson.

Wilson, director of laboratories for the Framingham Heart Study in Framingham, Mass., said Thursday at a conference sponsored by the American Heart Association in Charleston, S.C., that he had examined the coffee intake of 3,937 participants in the Framingham study during 1956–66 and an additional 2,277 during the years 1972–1982.

In contrast to the subjects in the Hopkins study, most of these coffee drinkers consumed two or three cups per day, Wilson said. Only 10 percent drank six or more cups per day.

He then looked at blood cholesterol levels and heart and blood vessel disease in the two groups. "We ran these analyses for coronary heart disease, heart attack, sudden death and stroke and in absolutely every analysis, we found no link with coffee," Wilson said.

He found that coffee consumption was linked to a significant decrease in total blood cholesterol in men, and to a moderate increase in total cholesterol in women.

Prices for humans x	0.67	0.64	1.20	0.51	0.87	0.74	0.50	1.22
Prices for animals y	0.13	0.18	0.42	0.25	0.57	0.57	0.49	1.28

Source: House Committee on Government Reform.

(The information in this exercise will be used for Exercise 12 in Section 10–4.)

13. A researcher wishes to determine if a person's age is related to the number of hours he or she exercises per week. The data for the sample are shown here. (The information in this exercise will be used for Exercises 13 and 36 in Section 10–4 and Exercise 13 in Section 10–5.)

Age x	18	26	32	38	52	59
Hours y	10	5	2	3	1.5	1

14. An environmentalist wants to determine the relationships between the number (in thousands) of forest fires over the year and the number (in hundreds of thousands) of hectares burned. The data for 8 recent years are shown. Describe the relationship.

Number of fires x	72	69	58	47	84	62	57	45
Number of hectares burned y	25	17	8	11	21	6	12	6

Source: National Emergency Fire Causes.

(The information in this exercise will be used for Exercises 14 and 36 in Section 10–4 and Exercises 14 and 18 in Section 10–5.)

15. The director of an alumni association for a small college wants to determine whether there is any type of relationship between the amount of an alumnus's contribution (in dollars) and the years the alumnus has been out of school. The data follow. (The information in this exercise will be used for Exercises 15, 36, and 37 in Section 10–4 and Exercises 15 and 19 in Section 10–5.)

Years x	1	5	3	10	7	6
Contribution y	500	100	300	50	75	80

16. A store manager wishes to find out whether there is a relationship between the age of her employees and the number of sick days they take each year. The data for the sample are shown. (The information in this exercise will be used for Exercises 16 and 37 in Section 10–4 and Exercises 16 and 20 in Section 10–5.)

Age x	18	26	39	48	53	58
Days y	16	12	9	5	6	2

17. A criminology student wants to determine if there is a relationship between the robbery and homicide crime rates in Canada. Data is collected from 7 randomly selected cities. Crime rates are calculated per 100,000 population. Is there a relationship between the two types of crimes in Canada's cities?

Robbery crimes x	229	148	141	150	91	88	84
Homicide crimes y	4.9	2.6	3.4	1.7	1.9	1.3	1.1

Source: Statistics Canada.

(The information in this exercise will be used for Exercise 17 of Section 10–4.)

18. A football fan wishes to see how the number of pass attempts (not completions) relates to the number of yards gained for quarterbacks in past National Football League (NFL) season playoff games. The data are shown for five quarterbacks. Describe the relationships.

Pass attempts x	116	90	82	108	92
Yards gained y	1001	823	851	873	839

(The information in this exercise will be used for Exercises 18 and 38 in Section 10–4.)

19. A meteorologist wants to see if there is a relationship between the number of tornadoes that occur each year and the number of deaths attributed to the tornadoes. The data are shown for 10 recent years. Is there a relationship?

No. of tornadoes x	1133	1132	1297	1173	1082
No. of deaths y	53	39	39	33	69
No. of tornadoes x	1234	1148	1424	1342	898
No. of deaths y	30	67	130	94	40

(The information in this exercise will be used for Exercise 19 of Section 10–4.)

20. An emergency medical service wishes to see whether a relationship exists between the outside temperature (°C) and the number of emergency calls it receives for an 8-hour period. The data are shown. (The information in this exercise will be used for Exercises 20 and 38 in Section 10–4.)

Temperature (°C) x	20	23	28	31	34	37	38
Number of calls y	7	4	8	10	11	9	13

21. A random sample of cities in Eastern Canada is selected to determine if there is a relationship between the number of Black and number of Asian visible minorities. (The information in this exercise will be used for Exercises 21 and 36 in Section 10–4.)

Black x	350	13,085	1,440	325	3,640
Asian y	1,735	9,665	1,110	425	5,065

Source: Statistics Canada.

22. The results of a survey of the average monthly rents (in dollars) for one-bedroom apartments and two-bedroom apartments in randomly selected metropolitan areas are shown. Determine if there is a relationship between the rents. (The information in this exercise will be used for Exercise 22 in Section 10–4.)

One-bedroom x	782	486	451	529	618	520	845
Two-bedroom y	1223	902	739	954	1055	875	1455

Source: *N.Y. Times Almanac.*

23. The average daily temperature (°C) and the corresponding average monthly precipitation (cm) for the month of July are shown for 7 randomly selected Canadian cities. Determine if there is a relationship between the two variables. (The information in this exercise will be used for Exercise 23 in 10–4.)

Temperature (°C) x	21.8	23.2	26.3	26.1	26.4	24.9	23.1
Precipitation (cm) y	17.6	29.9	58.9	72.0	88.1	118.5	81.6

Source: Environment Canada.

24. A random sample of Major League Baseball Hall of Fame pitchers' career wins and their total number of strikeouts is shown next. Is there a relationship between the variables? (The information in this exercise will be used for Exercise 24 in Section 10–4.)

Wins x	329	150	236	300	284	207
Strikeouts y	4136	1155	1956	2266	3192	1277

Wins x	247	314	273	324
Strikeouts y	1068	3534	1987	3574

Source: N.Y. Times Almanac.

25. The number of calories and the number of milligrams of cholesterol for a random sample of fast-food chicken sandwiches from 7 restaurants are shown here. Is there a relationship between the variables? (The information in this exercise will be used in Exercise 25 in Section 10–4.)

Calories x	390	535	720	300	430	500	440
Cholesterol y	43	45	80	50	55	52	60

Source: The Doctor's Pocket Calorie, Fat, and Carbohydrate Counter.

26. An architect wants to determine if a relationship exists between the number of storeys in a building and the height (in metres) of the building. The data for a random sample of 7 buildings in Vancouver are shown. Explain the relationship.

Storeys x	48	28	30	37	35	30	32
Height y	150	146	142	141	138	127	122

Source: www.answers.com.

27. A hospital administrator wants to see if there is a relationship between the number of licensed beds and the number of staffed beds in U.S. hospitals. The data for a specific day are shown. Describe the relationship.

Licensed beds x	144	32	175	185	208	100	169
Staffed beds y	112	32	162	141	103	80	118

Source: Pittsburgh Tribune-Review.

(The information in this exercise will be used for Exercise 28 of this section and Exercise 27 in Section 10–4.)

Extending the Concepts

28. One of the formulas for computing r is

$$r = \frac{\Sigma(x - \bar{x})(y - \bar{y})}{(n - 1)(s_x)(s_y)}$$

Using the data in Exercise 27, compute r with this formula. Compare the results.

29. Compute r for the data set shown. Explain the reason for this value of r. Now, interchange the values of x and y and compute r again. Compare this value with the previous one. Explain the results of the comparison.

x	1	2	3	4	5
y	3	5	7	9	11

30. Compute r for the following data and test the hypothesis $H_0: \rho = 0$. Draw the scatter plot; then explain the results.

x	−3	−2	−1	0	1	2	3
y	9	4	1	0	1	4	9

10–4   Regression

Objective

Compute the equation of the regression line.

In studying relationships between two variables, collect the data and then construct a scatter plot. The purpose of the scatter plot, as indicated previously, is to determine the nature of the relationship. The possibilities include a positive linear relationship, a negative linear relationship, a nonlinear relationship, or no discernible relationship. After the scatter plot is drawn, the next steps are to compute the value of the correlation coefficient and to test the significance of the relationship. If the value of the correlation coefficient is significant, the next step that is often performed by researchers is to determine the equation of the **regression line,** which is the data's line of best fit. (*Note:* Determining the regression line when r is not significant and then making predictions using the regression line are meaningless.) The purpose of the regression line is to enable the researcher to see the trend and make predictions on the basis of the data.

Figure 10–11

Scatter Plot with Three Lines Fit to the Data

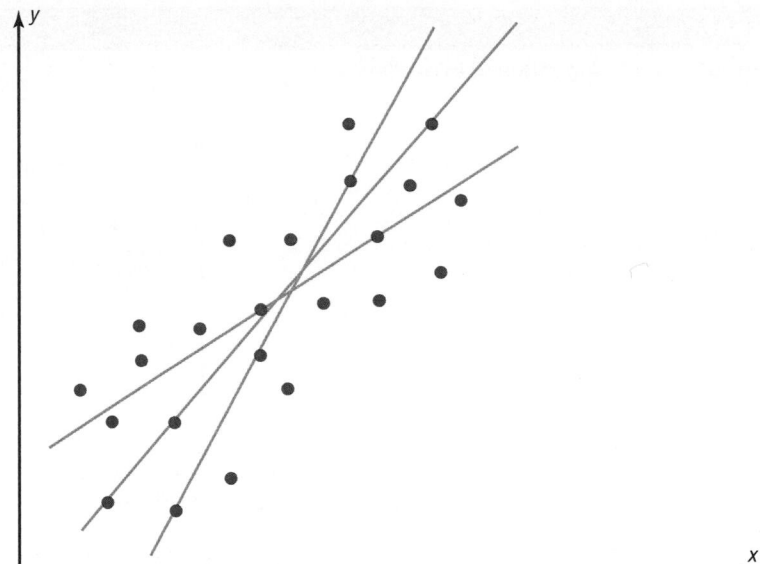

Figure 10–12

Line of Best Fit for a Set of Data Points

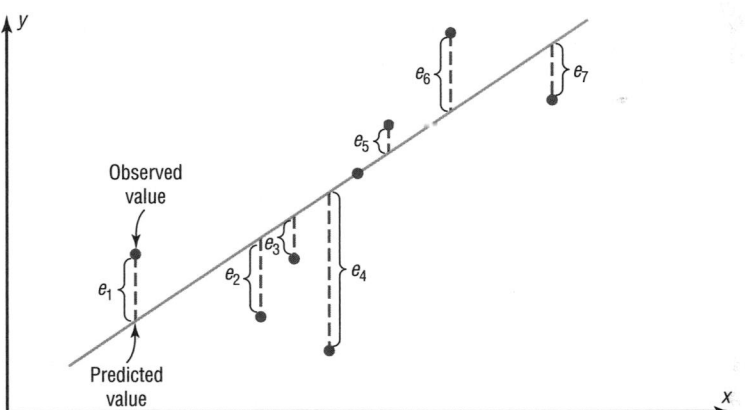

ℋ*istorical Note*

Francis Galton drew the line of best fit visually. An assistant of Karl Pearson's named G. Yule devised the mathematical solution using the least-squares method, employing a mathematical technique developed by Adrien-Marie Legendre about 100 years earlier.

Line of Best Fit

Figure 10–11 shows a scatter plot for the data of two variables. It shows that several lines can be drawn on the graph near the points. Given a scatter plot, one must be able to draw the *line of best fit. Best fit* means that the sum of the squares of the errors in the y direction from each point to the line is at a minimum. The reason one needs a line of best fit is that the values of y will be predicted from the values of x; hence, the closer the points are to the line, the better the fit and the prediction will be. See Figure 10–12. When r is positive, the line slopes upward and to the right. When r is negative, the line slopes downward from left to right.

Determination of the Regression Line Equation

In algebra, the equation of a line is usually given as $y = mx + b$, where m is the slope of the line and b is the y intercept. (Students who need an algebraic review of the properties of a line should refer to Appendix A, Section A–3, before studying this section.) In statistics, the equation of the regression line is written as $y' = a + bx$, where a is the y' intercept and b is the slope of the line. See Figure 10–13.

Figure 10–13

A Line as Represented in Algebra and in Statistics

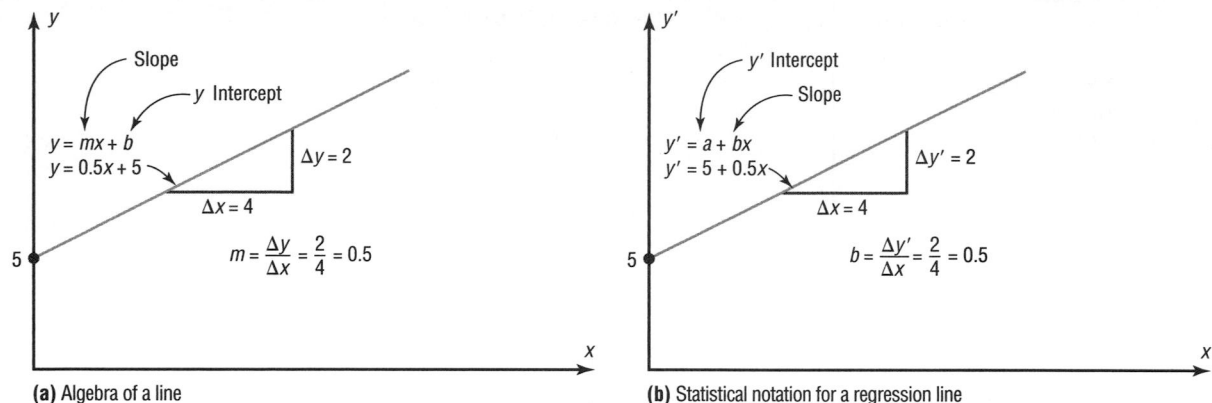

(a) Algebra of a line

(b) Statistical notation for a regression line

There are several methods for finding the equation of the regression line. Two formulas are given here. *These formulas use the same values that are used in computing the value of the correlation coefficient.* The mathematical development of these formulas is beyond the scope of this book.

Formulas for the Regression Line $y' = a + bx$

$$a = \frac{(\Sigma y)(\Sigma x^2) - (\Sigma x)(\Sigma xy)}{n(\Sigma x^2) - (\Sigma x)^2}$$

$$b = \frac{n(\Sigma xy) - (\Sigma x)(\Sigma y)}{n(\Sigma x^2) - (\Sigma x)^2}$$

where a is the y' intercept and b is the slope of the line.

Rounding Rule for the Intercept and Slope   Round the values of a and b to three decimal places.

Example 10–9

Find the equation of the regression line for the data in Example 10–4, and graph the line on the scatter plot of the data.

Solution

The values needed for the equation are $n = 6$, $\Sigma x = 345$, $\Sigma y = 819$, $\Sigma xy = 47{,}634$, and $\Sigma x^2 = 20{,}399$. Substituting in the formulas, one gets

$$a = \frac{(\Sigma y)(\Sigma x^2) - (\Sigma x)(\Sigma xy)}{n(\Sigma x^2) - (\Sigma x)^2} = \frac{(819)(20{,}399) - (345)(47{,}634)}{(6)(20{,}399) - (345)^2} \approx 81.048$$

$$b = \frac{n(\Sigma xy) - (\Sigma x)(\Sigma y)}{n(\Sigma x^2) - (\Sigma x)^2} = \frac{(6)(47{,}634) - (345)(819)}{(6)(20{,}399) - (345)^2} \approx 0.964$$

Hence, the equation of the regression line $y' = a + bx$ is

$$y' = 81.048 + 0.964x$$

The graph of the line is shown in Figure 10–14.

Figure 10–14

Regression Line for
Example 10–9

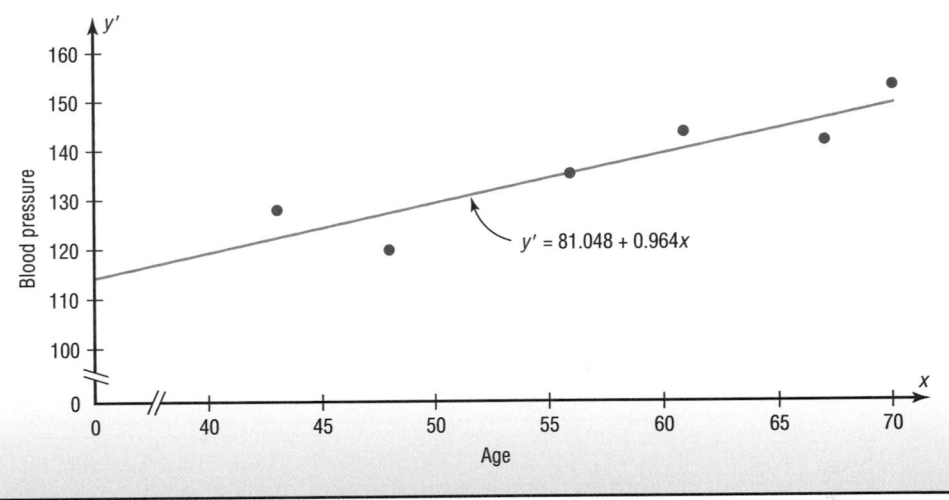

Note: When one is drawing the scatter plot and the regression line, it is sometimes desirable to *truncate* the graph (see Chapter 2). The motive is to show the line drawn in the range of the independent and dependent variables. For example, the regression line in Figure 10–14 is drawn between the x values of approximately 43 and 82 and the y' values of approximately 120 and 152. The range of the x values in the original data shown in Example 10–4 is $70 - 43 = 27$, and the range of the y' values is $152 - 120 = 32$. Notice that the x axis has been truncated; the distance between 0 and 40 is not shown in the proper scale compared to the distance between 40 and 50, 50 and 60, etc. The y' axis has been similarly truncated.

The important thing to remember is that when the x axis and sometimes the y' axis have been truncated, do not use the y' intercept value a to graph the line. To be on the safe side when graphing the regression line, use a value for x selected from the range of x values.

Example 10–10

Find the equation of the regression line for the data in Example 10–5, and graph the line on the scatter plot.

Solution

The values needed for the equation are $n = 7$, $\Sigma x = 57$, $\Sigma y = 511$, $\Sigma xy = 3745$, and $\Sigma x^2 = 579$. Substituting in the formulas, one gets

$$a = \frac{(\Sigma y)(\Sigma x^2) - (\Sigma x)(\Sigma xy)}{n(\Sigma x^2) - (\Sigma x)^2} = \frac{(511)(579) - (57)(3745)}{(7)(579) - (57)^2} = 102.493$$

$$b = \frac{n(\Sigma xy) - (\Sigma x)(\Sigma y)}{n(\Sigma x^2) - (\Sigma x)^2} = \frac{(7)(3745) - (57)(511)}{(7)(579) - (57)^2} = -3.622$$

Hence, the equation of the regression line $y' = a + bx$ is

$$y' = 102.493 - 3.622x$$

The graph of the line is shown in Figure 10–15.

Figure 10–15

Regression Line for
Example 10–10

$y' = 102.493 - 3.622x$

Final grade

Number of absences

The sign of the correlation coefficient and the sign of the slope of the regression line will always be the same. That is, if r is positive, then b will be positive; if r is negative, then b will be negative. The reason is that the numerators of the formulas are the same and determine the signs of r and b, and the denominators are always positive. The regression line will always pass through the point whose x coordinate is the mean of the x values and whose y coordinate is the mean of the y values, that is, $(\bar{x}, \bar{y})$.

The regression line can be used to make predictions for the dependent variable. The method for making predictions is shown in Example 10–11.

Example 10–11

Using the equation of the regression line found in Example 10–9, predict the blood pressure for a person who is 50 years old.

Solution

Substituting 50 for x in the regression line $y' = 81.048 + 0.964x$ gives

$$y' = 81.048 + (0.964)(50) = 129.248 \text{ (rounded to 129)}$$

In other words, the predicted systolic blood pressure for a 50-year-old person is 129.

The value obtained in Example 10–11 is a point prediction, and with point predictions, no degree of accuracy or confidence can be determined. More information on prediction is given in Section 10–5.

The magnitude of the change in one variable when the other variable changes exactly 1 unit is called a **marginal change.** The value of slope b of the regression line equation represents the marginal change. For example, the slope of the regression line equation in Example 10–9 is 0.964. This means that for each increase of 1 year, the value of y (systolic blood pressure reading) changes by 0.964 unit on average. In other words, for each year a person ages, her or his blood pressure rises about 1 unit.

When r is not significantly different from 0, the best predictor of y is the mean of the data values of y. For valid predictions, the value of the correlation coefficient must be significant. Also, two other assumptions must be met.

Figure 10–16

Assumptions for Predictions

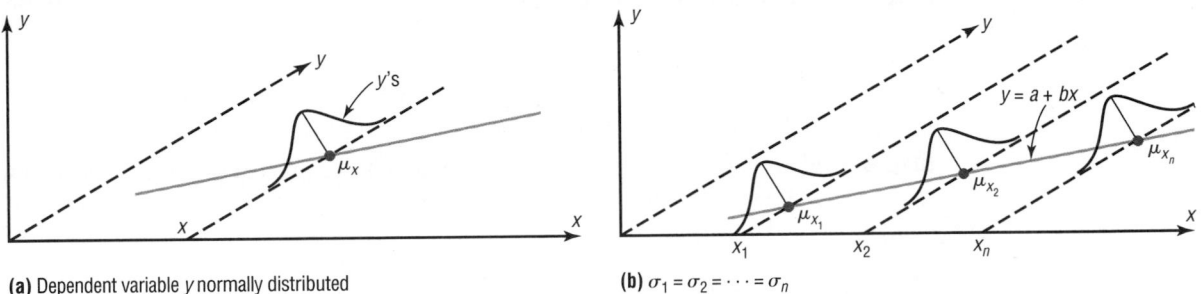

(a) Dependent variable y normally distributed

(b) $\sigma_1 = \sigma_2 = \cdots = \sigma_n$

Assumptions for Valid Predictions in Regression

1. For any specific value of the independent variable x, the value of the dependent variable y must be normally distributed about the regression line. See Figure 10–16(a).
2. The standard deviation of each of the dependent variables must be the same for each value of the independent variable. See Figure 10–16(b).

Extrapolation, or making predictions beyond the bounds of the data, must be interpreted cautiously. For example, in 1979, some experts predicted that North America would run out of oil by the year 2003. This prediction was based on the current consumption and on known oil reserves at that time. However, since then, the automobile industry has produced many new fuel-efficient vehicles. Also, there are many as yet undiscovered oil fields. Finally, science may someday discover a way to run a car on something as unlikely but as common as peanut oil. In addition, the price of a litre of gasoline was predicted to reach $2.50 a few years later. Fortunately this has not come to pass. *Remember that when predictions are made, they are based on present conditions or on the premise that present trends will continue.* This assumption may or may not prove true in the future.

The steps for finding the value of the correlation coefficient and the regression line equation are summarized in this Procedure Table:

Interesting Fact

It is estimated that wearing a motorcycle helmet reduces the risk of a fatal accident by 30%.

Procedure Table

Finding the Correlation Coefficient and the Regression Line Equation

Step 1   Make a table, as shown in step 2.

Step 2   Find the values of xy, x^2, and y^2. Place them in the appropriate columns and sum each column.

x	y	xy	x^2	y^2
.	.	.	.	.
.	.	.	.	.
.	.	.	.	.
$\Sigma x =$	$\Sigma y =$	$\Sigma xy =$	$\Sigma x^2 =$	$\Sigma y^2 =$

Procedure Table *(continued)*

Step 3   Substitute in the formula to find the value of r.

$$r = \frac{n(\Sigma xy) - (\Sigma x)(\Sigma y)}{\sqrt{[n(\Sigma x^2) - (\Sigma x)^2][n(\Sigma y^2) - (\Sigma y)^2]}}$$

Step 4   When r is significant, substitute in the formulas to find the values of a and b for the regression line equation $y' = a + bx$.

$$a = \frac{(\Sigma y)(\Sigma x^2) - (\Sigma x)(\Sigma xy)}{n(\Sigma x^2) - (\Sigma x)^2} \qquad b = \frac{n(\Sigma xy) - (\Sigma x)(\Sigma y)}{n(\Sigma x^2) - (\Sigma x)^2}$$

A scatter plot should be checked for outliers. An outlier is a point that seems out of place when compared with the other points (see Chapter 3). Some of these points can affect the equation of the regression line. When this happens, the points are called **influential points** or **influential observations.**

When a point on the scatter plot appears to be an outlier, it should be checked to see if it is an influential point. An influential point tends to "pull" the regression line toward the point itself. To check for an influential point, the regression line should be graphed with the point included in the data set. Then a second regression line should be graphed that excludes the point from the data set. If the position of the second line is changed considerably, the point is said to be an influential point. Points that are outliers in the x direction tend to be influential points.

Researchers should use their judgment as to whether to include influential observations in the final analysis of the data. If the researcher has substantive reasons, then it should be excluded so that it does not influence the results of the study. However, if the researcher feels that it is necessary, then he or she may want to obtain additional data values whose x values are near the x value of the influential point and then include them in the study.

"Explain that to me."

Source: Reprinted with special permission of King Features Syndicate.

Applying the Concepts 10–4

Stopping Distances Revisited

In a study on speed and stopping distance, researchers looked for a method to estimate how fast a person was travelling before an accident by measuring the length of their skid marks. An area that was focused on in the study was the distance required to completely stop a vehicle at various speeds. Use the following table to answer the questions.

Speed (km/h)	Stopping distance (m)
30	18
50	35
70	57
100	98
110	114

Assume km/h is going to be used to predict stopping distance.

1. Find the linear regression equation.
2. What does the slope tell you about km/h and the stopping distance? How about the y intercept?
3. Find the stopping distance when km/h = 60.
4. Find the stopping distance when km/h = 120.
5. Comment on predicting beyond the given data values.

See page 497 for the answers.

Exercises 10–4

1. What two things should be done before one performs a regression analysis?

2. What are the assumptions for regression analysis?

3. What is the general form for the regression line used in statistics?

4. What is the symbol for the slope? For the y intercept?

5. What is meant by the *line of best fit?*

6. When all the points fall on the regression line, what is the value of the correlation coefficient?

7. What is the relationship between the sign of the correlation coefficient and the sign of the slope of the regression line?

8. As the value of the correlation coefficient increases from 0 to 1, or decreases from 0 to −1, how do the points of the scatter plot fit the regression line?

9. How is the value of the correlation coefficient related to the accuracy of the predicted value for a specific value of x?

10. If the value of r is not significant, what can be said about the regression line?

11. When the value of r is not significant, what value should be used to predict y?

For Exercises 12 through 27, use the same data as for the corresponding exercises in Section 10–3. For each exercise, find the equation of the regression line and find the y' value for the specified x value. Remember that no regression should be done when r is not significant.

12. Price of drugs for humans and animals

Humans x	0.67	0.64	1.20	0.51	0.87	0.74	0.50	1.22
Animals y	0.13	0.18	0.42	0.25	0.57	0.57	0.49	1.28

Find y' when $x = 0.75$.

13. Ages and exercise

Age x	18	26	32	38	52	59
Hours y	10	5	2	3	1.5	1

Find y' when $x = 35$ years.

14. Number (in thousands) of forest fires over the year and the number (in hundreds of thousands) of hectares burned.

Number of fires x	72	69	58	47	84	62	57	45
Number of hectares burned y	25	17	8	11	21	6	12	6

Find y' when $x = 60$.

15. Years and contribution

Years x	1	5	3	10	7	6
Contribution y, $	500	100	300	50	75	80

Find y' when $x = 4$ years.

16. Age and sick days

Age x	18	26	39	48	53	58
Days y	16	12	9	5	6	2

Find y' when $x = 47$ years.

17. Robbery and homicide crime rates (per 100,000 population)

Robbery crimes x	229	148	141	150	91	88	84
Homicide crimes y	4.9	2.6	3.4	1.7	1.9	1.3	1.1

Find y', when $x = 100$.

18. Pass attempts and yards gained

Attempts x	116	90	82	108	92
Yards y	1001	823	851	873	837

Find y' when $x = 95$.

19. Tornadoes and deaths

Tornadoes x	1113	1132	1297	1173	1082
Deaths y	53	39	39	33	69

Tornadoes x	1234	1148	1424	1342	898
Deaths y	30	67	130	94	40

Find y' when $x = 1000$.

20. Temperature (°C) and number of emergency calls

Temperature (°C) x	20	23	28	31	34	37	38
Number of calls y	7	4	8	10	11	9	13

Find y' when $x = 30$°C.

21. Number of Black and number of Asian visible minorities

Black x	350	13,085	1,440	325	3,640
Asian y	1,735	9,665	1,110	425	5,065

Predict y' when $x = 2,500$.

22. Rents for one-bedroom and two-bedroom apartments

One-bedroom x, $	782	486	451	529	618	520	845
Two-bedroom y, $	1223	902	739	954	1055	875	1455

Find y' when $x = \$700$.

23. Average daily temperature (°C) and average monthly precipitation (cm)

Temperature (°C) x	21.8	23.2	26.3	26.1	26.4	24.9	23.1
Precipitation (cm) y	17.6	29.9	58.9	72.0	88.1	118.5	81.6

Find y' when $x = 25$°C.

Source: Environment Canada.

24. Wins and strikeouts for Major League Baseball Hall of Fame pitchers

Wins x	329	150	236	300	284	207
Strikeouts y	4136	1155	1956	2266	3192	1277
Wins x	247	314	273	324		
Strikeouts y	1068	3534	1987	3574		

Find y' when $x = 260$ wins.

25. Calories and cholesterol

Calories x	390	535	720	300	430	500	440
Cholesterol y	43	45	80	50	55	52	60

Find y' when $x = 600$ calories.

26. Building storeys and building height (in metres)

Storeys x	48	28	30	37	35	30	32
Height y	150	146	142	141	138	127	122

Find y' when $x = 40$ storeys.

27. Licensed beds and staffed beds

Licensed beds x	144	32	175	185	208	100	169
Staffed beds y	112	32	162	141	103	80	118

Find y' when $x = 44$.

For Exercises 28 through 33, do a complete regression analysis by performing these steps.

  a. Draw a scatter plot.

  b. Compute the correlation coefficient.

  c. State the hypotheses.

  d. Test the hypotheses at $\alpha = 0.05$. Use Table I. If hypothesis test produces a significant result, proceed to steps *e-g*, otherwise stop

  e. Determine the regression line equation.

  f. Plot the regression line on the scatter plot.

  g. Summarize the results.

28. These data were obtained for the years 1993 through 1998 and indicate the number of fireworks (in millions) used and the related injuries. Predict the number of injuries if 100 million fireworks are used during a given year.

Fireworks in use x	67.6	87.1	117	115	118	113
Related injuries y	12,100	12,600	12,500	10,900	7,800	7,000

Source: National Council of Fireworks Safety, American Pyrotechnic Assoc.

29. These data were obtained from a survey of the number of years people smoked and the percentage of lung damage they sustained. Predict the percentage of lung damage for a person who has smoked for 30 years.

Years x	22	14	31	36	9	41	19
Damage y	20	14	54	63	17	71	23

30. A medical researcher wishes to describe the relationship between the prescription cost of a brand name drug and its generic equivalent. The data (in dollars) are shown. Describe the relationship.

Brand name x	96	93	59	80	44	47	15	56
Generic y	42	31	17	16	8	12	6	22

31. The following data compares the number of business head offices in a random sample of Canadian cities between 1999 and 2005. Predict the number of head offices in 2005 for a city with 200 head offices in 1999.

1999 x	596	100	826	114	279	139	355
2005 y	536	101	918	129	316	157	335

Source: Statistics Canada.

32. A television executive selects 10 television shows and compares the average number of viewers the show had last year with the average number of viewers this year. The data (in millions) are shown. Describe the relationship.

Viewers last year x	26.6	17.85	20.3	16.8	20.8
Viewers this year y	28.9	19.2	26.4	13.7	20.2
Viewers last year x	16.7	19.1	18.9	16.0	15.8
Viewers this year y	18.8	25.0	21.0	16.8	15.3

Source: Nielson Media Research.

33. An educator wants to see how the number of absences for a student in her class affects the student's final grade. The data obtained from a sample are shown.

No. of absences x	10	12	2	0	8	5
Final grade y	70	65	96	94	75	82

For Exercises 34 and 35, do a complete regression analysis and test the significance of r at $\alpha = 0.05$, using the P-value method.

34. A physician wishes to know whether there is a relationship between a father's weight (in kilograms) and his newborn son's weight (in kilograms). The data are given here.

Father's weight x	79.8	72.6	84.8	95.3	88.9	64.4	93.0	97.5
Son's weight y	3.0	3.7	4.2	3.2	4.0	4.2	3.4	3.9

35. Is a person's age related to his or her net worth? A sample of 10 billionaires is selected, and the person's age and net worth are compared. The data are given here.

Age x	56	39	42	60	84	37	68	66	73	55
Net worth (in billions) y	18	14	12	14	11	10	10	7	7	5

Source: The Associated Press.

Extending the Concepts

36. For Exercises 13, 15, and 21 in Section 10–3, find the mean of the x and y variables. Then substitute the mean of the x variable into the corresponding regression line equations found in Exercises 12, 13, and 14 in this section and find y'. Compare the value of y' with $\bar{y}$ for each exercise. Generalize the results.

37. The y intercept value a can also be found by using the equation

$$a = \bar{y} - b\bar{x}$$

Verify this result by using the data in Exercises 15 and 16 of Sections 10–3 and 10–4.

38. The value of the correlation coefficient can also be found by using the formula

$$r = \frac{bs_x}{s_y}$$

where s_x is the standard deviation of the x value and s_y is the standard deviation of the y values. Verify this result for Exercises 18 and 20 of Section 10–3.

10–5 Coefficient of Determination and Standard Error of the Estimate

The previous sections stated that if the correlation coefficient is significant, the equation of the regression line can be determined. Also, for various values of the independent variable x, the corresponding values of the dependent variable y can be predicted. Several other measures are associated with the correlation and regression techniques. They include the coefficient of determination, the standard error of estimate, and the prediction interval. But before these concepts can be explained, the different types of variation associated with the regression model must be defined.

Types of Variation for the Regression Model

Consider the following hypothetical regression model.

x	1	2	3	4	5
y	10	8	12	16	20

The equation of the regression line is $y' = 4.8 + 2.8x$, and $r = 0.919$. The sample y values are 10, 8, 12, 16, and 20. The predicted values, designated by y', for each x can be found by substituting each x value into the regression equation and finding y'. For example, when $x = 1$,

$$y' = 4.8 + 2.8x = 4.8 + (2.8)(1) = 7.6$$

Now, for each x, there is an observed y value and a predicted y' value, for example, when $x = 1$, $y = 10$, and $y' = 7.6$. Recall that the closer the observed values are to the predicted values, the better the fit is and the closer r is to $+1$ or -1.

The *total variation* $\Sigma(y - \bar{y})^2$ is the sum of the squares of the vertical distances each point is from the mean. The total variation can be divided into two parts: that which is attributed to the relationship of x and y and that which is due to chance. The variation obtained from the relationship (i.e., from the predicted y' values) is $\Sigma(y' - \bar{y})^2$ and is called the *explained variation*. Most of the variations can be explained by the relationship. The closer the value r is to $+1$ or -1, the better the points fit the line and the closer $\Sigma(y' - \bar{y})^2$ is to $\Sigma(y - \bar{y})^2$. In fact, if all points fall on the regression line, $\Sigma(y' - \bar{y})^2$ will equal $\Sigma(y - \bar{y})^2$, since y' would be equal to y in each case.

On the other hand, the variation due to chance, found by $\Sigma(y - y')^2$, is called the *unexplained variation*. This variation cannot be attributed to the relationship. When the unexplained variation is small, the value of r is close to $+1$ or -1. If all points fall on the regression line, the unexplained variation $\Sigma(y - y')^2$ will be 0. Hence, the *total variation* is equal to the sum of the explained variation and the unexplained variation. That is,

$$\Sigma(y - \bar{y})^2 = \Sigma(y' - \bar{y})^2 + \Sigma(y - y')^2$$

These values are shown in Figure 10–17. For a single point, the differences are called *deviations*. For the hypothetical regression model given earlier, for $x = 1$ and $y = 10$, one gets $y' = 7.6$ and $\bar{y} = 13.2$.

The procedure for finding the three types of variation is illustrated next.

Step 1 Find the predicted y' values.

For $x = 1$ $y' = 4.8 + 2.8x = 4.8 + (2.8)(1) = 7.6$

For $x = 2$ $y' = 4.8 + (2.8)(2) = 10.4$

For $x = 3$ $y' = 4.8 + (2.8)(3) = 13.2$

For $x = 4$ $y' = 4.8 + (2.8)(4) = 16.0$

For $x = 5$ $y' = 4.8 + (2.8)(5) = 18.8$

Figure 10–17

Deviations for the Regression Equation

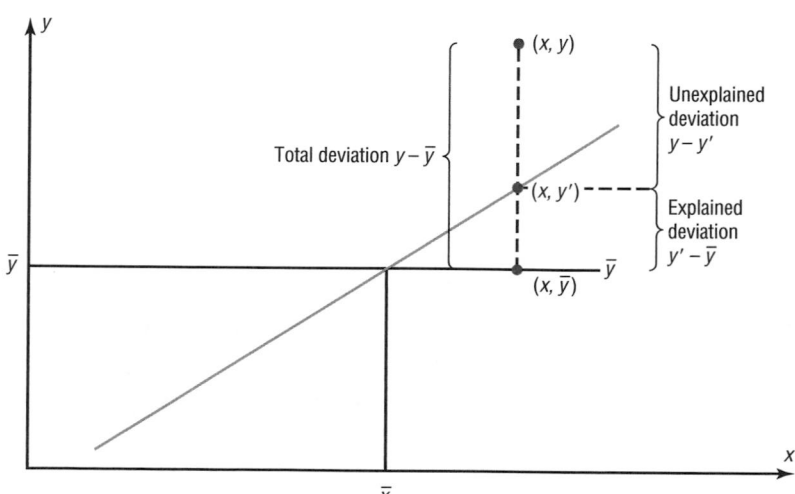

Hence, the values for this example are as follows:

x	y	y'
1	10	7.6
2	8	10.4
3	12	13.2
4	16	16.0
5	20	18.8

Step 2 Find the mean of the y values.

$$\bar{y} = \frac{10 + 8 + 12 + 16 + 20}{5} = 13.2$$

Step 3 Find the total variation $\Sigma(y - \bar{y})^2$.

$$(10 - 13.2)^2 = 10.24$$
$$(8 - 13.2)^2 = 27.04$$
$$(12 - 13.2)^2 = 1.44$$
$$(16 - 13.2)^2 = 7.84$$
$$(20 - 13.2)^2 = \underline{46.24}$$
$$\Sigma(y - \bar{y})^2 = 92.8$$

Step 4 Find the explained variation $\Sigma(y' - \bar{y})^2$.

$$(7.6 - 13.2)^2 = 31.36$$
$$(10.4 - 13.2)^2 = 7.84$$
$$(13.2 - 13.2)^2 = 0.00$$
$$(16 - 13.2)^2 = 7.84$$
$$(18.8 - 13.2)^2 = \underline{31.36}$$
$$\Sigma(y' - \bar{y})^2 = 78.4$$

Step 5 Find the unexplained variation $\Sigma(y - y')^2$.

$$(10 - 7.6)^2 = 5.76$$
$$(8 - 10.4)^2 = 5.76$$
$$(12 - 13.2)^2 = 1.44$$
$$(16 - 16)^2 = 0.00$$
$$(20 - 18.8)^2 = \underline{1.44}$$
$$\Sigma(y - y')^2 = 14.4$$

Notice that

Total variation = Explained variation + Unexplained variation

$$92.8 = \quad 78.4 \quad + \quad 14.4$$

Note: The values $(y - y')$ are called *residuals*. A **residual** is the difference between the actual value of y and the predicted value y' for a given x value. The mean of the residuals is always zero. As stated previously, the regression line determined by the formulas in Section 10–4 is the line that best fits the points of the scatter plot. The regression line computation minimizes the sum of the squared residuals. For this reason, a regression line is also called a **least-squares line.**

Objective

Compute the coefficient of determination.

Coefficient of Determination

The *coefficient of determination* is the ratio of the explained variation to the total variation and is denoted by r^2. That is,

$$r^2 = \frac{\text{explained variation}}{\text{total variation}}$$

For the example, $r^2 = 78.4/92.8 = 0.845$. The term r^2 is usually expressed as a percentage. So in this case, 84.5% of the total variation is explained by the regression line using the independent variable.

Another way to arrive at the value for r^2 is to square the correlation coefficient. In this case, $r = 0.919$ and $r^2 = 0.845$, which is the same value found by using the variation ratio.

> The **coefficient of determination** is a measure of the variation of the dependent variable that is explained by the regression line and the independent variable. The symbol for the coefficient of determination is r^2.

Of course, it is usually easier to find the coefficient of determination by squaring r and converting it to a percentage. Therefore, if $r = 0.90$, then $r^2 = 0.81$, which is equivalent to 81%. This result means that 81% of the variation in the dependent variable is accounted for by the variations in the independent variable.

Objective

Compute the standard error of the estimate.

Standard Error of the Estimate

When a y' value is predicted for a specific x value, the prediction is a point prediction. However, a prediction interval about the y' value can be constructed, just as a confidence interval was constructed for an estimate of the population mean. The prediction interval uses a statistic called the *standard error of the estimate*.

> The **standard error of the estimate**, denoted by s_{est}, is the standard deviation of the observed y values about the predicted y' values. The formula for the standard error of estimate is
>
> $$s_{est} = \sqrt{\frac{\Sigma(y - y')^2}{n - 2}}$$

The standard error of the estimate is similar to the standard deviation, but the mean is not used. As can be seen from the formula, the standard error of the estimate is the square root of the unexplained variation—that is, the variation due to the difference of the observed values and the expected values—divided by $n - 2$. So the closer the observed values are to the predicted values, the smaller the standard error of the estimate will be.

Example 10–12 shows how to compute the standard error of the estimate.

Example 10–12   A researcher collects the following data and determines that there is a significant relationship between the age of a copy machine and its monthly maintenance cost. The regression equation is $y' = 55.57 + 8.13x$. Find the standard error of the estimate.

Machine	Age x (years)	Monthly cost y
A	1	$ 62
B	2	78
C	3	70
D	4	90
E	4	93
F	6	103

Solution

Step 1 Make a table, as shown.

x	y	y'	$y - y'$	$(y - y')^2$
1	62			
2	78			
3	70			
4	90			
4	93			
6	103			

Step 2 Using the regression line equation $y' = 55.57 + 8.13x$, compute the predicted values y' for each x and place the results in the column labelled y'.

$x = 1$ $y' = 55.57 + (8.13)(1) = 63.70$
$x = 2$ $y' = 55.57 + (8.13)(2) = 71.83$
$x = 3$ $y' = 55.57 + (8.13)(3) - 79.96$
$x = 4$ $y' = 55.57 + (8.13)(4) = 88.09$
$x = 6$ $y' = 55.57 + (8.13)(6) = 104.35$

Step 3 For each y, subtract y' and place the answer in the column labelled $y - y'$.

$62 - 63.70 = -1.70$ $90 - 88.09 = 1.91$
$78 - 71.83 = 6.17$ $93 - 88.09 = 4.91$
$70 - 79.96 = -9.96$ $103 - 104.35 = -1.35$

Step 4 Square the numbers found in step 3 and place the squares in the column labelled $(y - y')^2$.

Step 5 Find the sum of the numbers in the last column. The completed table is shown.

x	y	y'	$y - y'$	$(y - y')^2$
1	62	63.70	−1.70	2.89
2	78	71.83	6.17	38.0689
3	70	79.96	−9.96	99.2016
4	90	88.09	1.91	3.6481
4	93	88.09	4.91	24.1081
6	103	104.35	−1.35	1.8225
				169.7392

Step 6 Substitute in the formula and find s_{est}.

$$s_{est} = \sqrt{\frac{\Sigma(y - y')^2}{n - 2}} = \sqrt{\frac{169.7392}{6 - 2}} \approx 6.51$$

In this case, the standard deviation of observed values about the predicted values is 6.51.

The standard error of the estimate can also be found by using the formula

$$s_{est} = \sqrt{\frac{\Sigma y^2 - a\,\Sigma y - b\,\Sigma xy}{n-2}}$$

Example 10–13

Find the standard error of the estimate for the data for Example 10–12 by using the preceding formula. The equation of the regression line is $y' = 55.57 + 8.13x$.

Solution

Step 1   Make a table.

Step 2   Find the product of x and y values, and place the results in the third column.

Step 3   Square the y values, and place the results in the fourth column.

Step 4   Find the sums of the second, third, and fourth columns. The completed table is shown here.

x	y	xy	y^2
1	62	62	3,844
2	78	156	6,084
3	70	210	4,900
4	90	360	8,100
4	93	372	8,649
6	103	618	10,609
	$\Sigma y = 496$	$\Sigma xy = 1{,}778$	$\Sigma y^2 = 42{,}186$

Step 5   From the regression equation $y' = 55.57 + 8.13x$, $a = 55.57$ and $b = 8.13$.

Step 6   Substitute in the formula and solve for s_{est}.

$$s_{est} = \sqrt{\frac{\Sigma y^2 - a\,\Sigma y - b\,\Sigma xy}{n-2}}$$

$$= \sqrt{\frac{42{,}186 - (55.57)(496) - (8.13)(1778)}{6-2}} \approx 6.48$$

This value is close to the value found in Example 10–12. The difference is due to rounding.

Objective

Find a prediction interval.

Prediction Interval

The standard error of estimate can be used for constructing a **prediction interval** (similar to a confidence interval) about a y' value.

When a specific value x is substituted into the regression equation, one gets y', which is a point estimate for y. For example, if the regression line equation for the age of a machine and the monthly maintenance cost is $y' = 55.57 + 8.13x$ (Example 10–12), then the predicted maintenance cost for a 3-year-old machine would be $y' = 55.57 + 8.13(3)$, or $79.96. Since this is a point estimate, one has no idea how accurate it is. But one can construct a prediction interval about the estimate. By selecting an α value, one can achieve a $(1 - \alpha) \cdot 100\%$ confidence that the interval contains the population mean of the y values that correspond to the given value of x.

The reason is that there are possible sources of prediction errors in finding the regression line equation. One source occurs when finding the standard error of the estimate s_{est}. Two others are errors made in estimating the slope and the y' intercept, since the equation of the regression line will change somewhat if different random samples are used when calculating the equation.

Formula for the Prediction Interval about a Value y′

$$y' - t_{\alpha/2}s_{est}\sqrt{1 + \frac{1}{n} + \frac{n(x - \overline{X})^2}{n\,\Sigma x^2 - (\Sigma x)^2}} < y < y' + t_{\alpha/2}s_{est}\sqrt{1 + \frac{1}{n} + \frac{n(x - \overline{X})^2}{n\,\Sigma x^2 - (\Sigma x)^2}}$$

with d.f. $= n - 2$

Example 10–14

For the data in Example 10–12, find the 95% prediction interval for the monthly maintenance cost of a machine that is 3 years old.

Solution

Step 1 Find Σx, Σx^2, and $\overline{X}$.

$$\Sigma x = 20 \qquad \Sigma x^2 = 82 \qquad \overline{X} = \frac{20}{6} = 3.3$$

Step 2 Find y' for $x = 3$.

$$y' = 55.57 + 8.13x$$
$$y' = 55.57 + 8.13(3) = 79.96$$

Step 3 Find s_{est}.

$$s_{est} = 6.48$$

as shown in Example 10–13.

Step 4 Substitute in the formula and solve: $t_{\alpha/2} = 2.776$, d.f. $= 6 - 2 = 4$ for 95%.

$$y' - t_{\alpha/2}s_{est}\sqrt{1 + \frac{1}{n} + \frac{n(x - \overline{X})^2}{n\Sigma x^2 - (\Sigma x)^2}} < y < y'$$

$$+ t_{\alpha/2}s_{est}\sqrt{1 + \frac{1}{n} + \frac{n(x - \overline{X})^2}{n\,\Sigma x^2 - (\Sigma x)^2}}$$

$$79.96 - (2.776)(6.48)\sqrt{1 + \frac{1}{n} + \frac{6(3 - 3.3)^2}{6(82) - (20)^2}} < y < 79.96$$

$$+ (2.776)(6.48)\sqrt{1 + \frac{1}{6} + \frac{6(3 - 3.3)^2}{6(82) - (20)^2}}$$

$$79.96 - (2.776)(6.48)(1.08) < y < 79.96 + (2.776)(6.48)(1.08)$$
$$79.96 - 19.43 < y < 79.96 + 19.43$$
$$60.53 < y < 99.39$$

Hence, one can be 95% confident that the interval $60.53 < y < 99.39$ contains the actual value of y.

Applying the Concepts 10–5

Interpreting Simple Linear Regression

Answer the questions about the following computer-generated information.

Linear correlation coefficient $r = 0.794556$

Coefficient of determination $= 0.631319$

Standard error of estimate $= 12.9668$

Explained variation $= 5182.41$

Unexplained variation $= 3026.49$

Total variation $= 8208.90$

Equation of regression line $y' = 0.725983X + 16.5523$

Level of significance $= 0.1$

Test statistic $= 0.794556$

Critical value $= 0.378419$

1. Are both variables moving in the same direction?
2. Which number measures the distances from the prediction line to the actual values?
3. Which number is the slope of the regression line?
4. Which number is the y intercept of the regression line?
5. Which number can be found in a table?
6. Which number is the allowable risk of making a type I error?
7. Which number measures the variation explained by the regression?
8. Which number measures the scatter of points about the regression line?
9. What is the null hypothesis?
10. Which number is compared to the critical value to see if the null hypothesis should be rejected?
11. Should the null hypothesis be rejected?

See page 498 for the answers.

Exercises 10–5

1. What is meant by the *explained variation?* How is it computed?

2. What is meant by the *unexplained variation?* How is it computed?

3. What is meant by the *total variation?* How is it computed?

4. Define the coefficient of determination.

5. How is the coefficient of determination found?

For Exercises 6 through 11, find the coefficients of determination and nondetermination and explain the meaning of each.

6. $r = 0.81$

7. $r = 0.70$

8. $r = 0.45$

9. $r = 0.37$

10. $r = 0.15$

11. $r = 0.05$

12. Define the standard error of the estimate for regression. When can the standard error of the estimate be used to construct a prediction interval about a value y'?

13. Compute the standard error of the estimate for Exercise 13 in Section 10–3. The regression line equation was found in Exercise 13 in Section 10–4.

14. Compute the standard error of the estimate for Exercise 14 in Section 10–3. The regression line equation was found in Exercise 14 in Section 10–4.

15. Compute the standard error of the estimate for Exercise 15 in Section 10–3. The regression line equation was found in Exercise 15 in Section 10–4.

16. Compute the standard error of the estimate for Exercise 16 in Section 10–3. The regression line equation was found in Exercise 16 in Section 10–4.

17. For the data in Exercises 13 in Sections 10–3 and 10–4 and 13 in Section 10–5, find the 90% prediction interval when $x = 20$ years.

18. For the data in Exercises 14 in Sections 10–3 and 10–4 and 14 in Section 10–5, find the 95% prediction interval when $x = 60$.

19. For the data in Exercises 15 in Sections 10–3 and 10–4 and 15 in Section 10–5, find the 90% prediction interval when $x = 4$ years.

20. For the data in Exercises 16 in Sections 10–3 and 10–4 and 16 in Section 10–5, find the 98% prediction interval when $x = 47$ years.

10–6   Multiple Regression (Optional)

Objective

Be familiar with the concept of multiple regression.

The previous sections explained the concepts of simple linear regression and correlation. In simple linear regression, the regression equation contains one independent variable x and one dependent variable y' and is written as

$$y' = a + bx$$

where a is the y' intercept and b is the slope of the regression line.

In **multiple regression,** there are several independent variables and one dependent variable, and the equation is

$$y' = a + b_1x_1 + b_2x_2 + \cdots + b_kx_k$$

where $x_1, x_2, \ldots, x_k$ are the independent variables.

For example, suppose a Dean of Graduate Studies wishes to see whether there is a relationship between a student's grade point average, age, and the GMAT entrance examination. The two independent variables are GPA (denoted by x_1) and age (denoted by x_2). The dean will collect the data for all three variables for a sample of graduate students. Rather than conduct two separate simple regression studies, one using the GPA and GMAT scores and another using ages and GMAT scores, the dean can conduct one study using multiple regression analysis with two independent variables—GPA and ages—and one dependent variable—GMAT scores.

*U*nusual Stat

The most popular single-digit number played by people who purchase lottery tickets is 7.

Speaking of

Statistics

In this study, researchers found a correlation between the cleanliness of the homes children are raised in and the years of schooling completed and earning potential for those children. What interfering variables were controlled? How might these have been controlled? Summarize the conclusions of the study.

SUCCESS

HOME SMART HOME

KIDS WHO GROW UP IN A CLEAN HOUSE FARE BETTER AS ADULTS

Good-bye, GPA. So long, SATs. New research suggests that we may be able to predict children's future success from the level of cleanliness in their homes.

A University of Michigan study presented at the annual meeting of the American Economic Association uncovered a surprising correlation: children raised in clean homes were later found to have completed more school and to have higher earning potential than those raised in dirty homes. The clean homes may indicate a family that values organization and similarly helpful skills at school and work, researchers say.

Cleanliness ratings for about 5000 households were assessed between 1968 and 1972, and respondents were interviewed 25 years later to determine educational achievement and professional earnings of the young adults who had grown up there, controlling for variables such as race, socio-economic status and level of parental education. The data showed that those raised in homes rated "clean" to "very clean" had completed an average of 1.6 more years of school than those raised in "not very clean" or "dirty" homes. Plus, the first group's annual wages averaged about $3100 more than the second's.

But don't buy stock in Mr. Clean and Pine Sol just yet. "We're not advocating that everyone go out and clean their homes right this minute," explains Rachel Dunifon, a University of Michigan doctoral candidate and a researcher on the study. Rather, the main implication of the study, Dunifon says, is that there is significant evidence that non-cognitive factors, such as organization and efficiency, play a role in determining academic and financial success.

— *Jackie Fisherman*

Source: Reprinted with permission from *Psychology Today,* Copyright © (2001) Sussex Publishers, Inc.

A multiple regression correlation R can also be computed to determine if a significant relationship exists between the independent variables and the dependent variable. Multiple regression analysis is used when a statistician thinks there are several independent variables contributing to the variation of the dependent variable. This analysis then can be used to increase the accuracy of predictions for the dependent variable over one independent variable alone.

Two other examples for multiple regression analysis are when a store manager wants to see whether the amount spent on advertising and the amount of floor space used for a display affect the amount of sales of a product, and when a sociologist wants to see whether the amount of time children spend watching television and playing video games is related to their weight. Multiple regression analysis can also be conducted by using more than two independent variables, denoted by $x_1, x_2, x_3, \ldots, x_m$. Since these computations are quite complicated and for the most part would be done on a computer, this chapter will show the computations for two independent variables only.

For example, the dean wishes to see whether a student's grade point average and age are related to the student's score on the GMAT entrance examination. She selects five students and obtains the following data.

Student	GPA x_1	Age x_2	GMAT score y
A	3.2	22	550
B	2.7	27	570
C	2.5	24	525
D	3.4	28	670
E	2.2	23	490

The multiple regression equation obtained from the data is

$$y' = -44.81 + 87.64x_1 + 14.533x_2$$

If a student has a GPA of 3.0 and is 25 years old, her predicted GMAT score can be computed by substituting these values in the equation for x_1 and x_2, respectively, as shown.

$$y' = -44.8 + 87.64(3.0) + 14.533(25)$$
$$= 581.44 \text{ or } 581$$

Hence, if a student has a GPA of 3.0 and is 25 years old, the student's predicted GMAT score is 581.

The Multiple Regression Equation

A multiple regression equation with two independent variables (x_1 and x_2) and one dependent variable would have the form

$$y' = a + b_1x_1 + b_2x_2$$

A multiple regression with three independent variables (x_1, x_2, and x_3) and one dependent variable would have the form

$$y' = a + b_1x_1 + b_2x_2 + b_3x_3$$

General Form of the Multiple Regression Equation

The general form of the multiple regression equation with k independent variables is

$$y' = a + b_1x_1 + b_2x_2 + \cdots + b_kx_k$$

The x's are the independent variables. The value for a is more or less an intercept, although a multiple regression equation with two independent variables constitutes a plane rather than a line. The b's are called *partial regression coefficients*. Each b represents the amount of change in y' for one unit of change in the corresponding x value when the other x values are held constant. In the example just shown, the regression equation was $y' = -44.81 + 87.64x_1 + 14.533x_2$. In this case, for each unit of change in the student's GPA, there is a change of 87.64 units in the GMAT score with the student's age x_2 being held constant. And for each unit of change in x_2 (the student's age), there is a change of 14.533 units in the GMAT score with the GPA held constant.

Assumptions for Multiple Regression

The assumptions for multiple regression are similar to those for simple regression.

1. For any specific value of the independent variable, the values of the y variable are normally distributed. (This is called the *normality* assumption.)

2. The variances (or standard deviations) for the y variables are the same for each value of the independent variable. (This is called the *equal-variance* assumption.)

3. There is a linear relationship between the dependent variable and the independent variables. (This is called the *linearity* assumption.)

4. The independent variables are not correlated. (This is called the *nonmulticolinearity* assumption.)

5. The values for the y variables are independent. (This is called the *independence* assumption.)

In multiple regression, as in simple regression, the strength of the relationship between the independent variables and the dependent variable is measured by a correlation coefficient. This **multiple correlation coefficient** is symbolized by R. The value of R can range from 0 to $+1$; R can never be negative. The closer to $+1$, the stronger the relationship; the closer to 0, the weaker the relationship. The value of R takes into account all the independent variables and can be computed by using the values of the individual correlation coefficients. The formula for the multiple correlation coefficient when there are two independent variables is shown next.

Formula for the Multiple Correlation Coefficient

The formula for R is

$$R = \sqrt{\frac{r_{yx_1}^2 + r_{yx_2}^2 - 2r_{yx_1} \cdot r_{yx_2} \cdot r_{x_1x_2}}{1 - r_{x_1x_2}^2}}$$

where r_{yx_1} is the value of the correlation coefficient for variables y and x_1; r_{yx_2} is the value of the correlation coefficient for variables y and x_2; and $r_{x_1x_2}$ is the value of the correlation coefficient for variables x_1 and x_2.

In this case, R is 0.989, as shown in Example 10–15. The multiple correlation coefficient is always higher than the individual correlation coefficients. For this specific example, the multiple correlation coefficient is higher than the two individual correlation coefficients computed by using grade point average and GMAT scores ($r_{yx_1} = 0.845$) or age and GMAT scores ($r_{yx_2} = 0.791$). *Note:* $r_{x_1x_2} = 0.371$.

Example 10–15   For the data regarding GMAT scores, find the value of R.

Solution

The values of the correlation coefficients are

$$r_{yx_1} = 0.845$$
$$r_{yx_2} = 0.791$$
$$r_{x_1x_2} = 0.371$$

Substituting in the formula, one gets

$$R = \sqrt{\frac{r_{yx_1}^2 + r_{yx_2}^2 - 2r_{yx_1} \cdot r_{yx_2} \cdot r_{x_1x_2}}{1 - r_{x_1x_2}^2}}$$

$$= \sqrt{\frac{(0.845)^2 + (0.791)^2 - 2(0.845)(0.791)(0.371)}{1 - 0.371^2}}$$

$$= \sqrt{\frac{0.8437569}{0.862359}} = \sqrt{0.9784288} = 0.989$$

Hence, the correlation between a student's grade point average and age with the student's GMAT score on the graduate entrance examination is 0.989. In this case, there is a strong relationship among the variables; the value of R is close to 1.00.

As with simple regression, R^2 is the *coefficient of multiple determination,* and it is the amount of variation explained by the regression model. The expression $1 - R^2$ represents the amount of unexplained variation, called the *error* or *residual variation.* Since $R = 0.989$, $R^2 = 0.978$ and $1 - R^2 = 1 - 0.978 = 0.022$.

Testing the Significance of R

An F test is used to test the significance of R. The hypotheses are

$$H_0: \rho = 0 \quad \text{and} \quad H_1: \rho \neq 0$$

where ρ represents the population correlation coefficient for multiple correlation.

F Test for Significance of R

The formula for the F test is

$$F = \frac{R^2/k}{(1 - R^2)/(n - k - 1)}$$

where n is the number of data groups $(x_1, x_2, \dots, y)$ and k is the number of independent variables.

The degrees of freedom are d.f.N. $= n - k$ and d.f.D. $= n - k - 1$.

Example 10–16

Test the significance of the R obtained in Example 10–15 at $\alpha = 0.05$.

Solution

$$F = \frac{R^2/k}{(1 - R^2)/(n - k - 1)}$$

$$= \frac{0.978/2}{(1 - 0.978)/(5 - 2 - 1)} = \frac{0.489}{0.011} = 44.45$$

The critical value obtained from Table H with $\alpha = 0.05$, d.f.N. $= 3$, and d.f.D. $= 5 - 2 - 1 = 2$ is 19.16. Hence, the decision is to reject the null hypothesis and conclude that there is a significant relationship among the student's GPA, age, and GMAT score on the graduate entrance examination.

Adjusted R^2

Since the value of R^2 is dependent on n (the number of data pairs) and k (the number of variables), statisticians also calculate what is called an **adjusted R^2,** denoted by R^2_{adj}. This is based on the number of degrees of freedom.

Formula for the Adjusted R^2

The formula for the adjusted R^2 is

$$R^2_{\text{adj}} = 1 - \left[\frac{(1 - R^2)(n - 1)}{n - k - 1} \right]$$

The adjusted R^2 is smaller than R^2 and takes into account the fact that when n and k are approximately equal, the value of R may be artificially high, due to sampling error rather than a true relationship among the variables. This occurs because the chance variations of all the variables are used in conjunction with each other to derive the regression equation. Even if the individual correlation coefficients for each independent variable and the dependent variable were all zero, the multiple correlation coefficient due to sampling error could be higher than zero.

Hence, both R^2 and R^2_{adj} are usually reported in a multiple regression analysis.

Example 10–17

Calculate the adjusted R^2 for the data in Example 10–16. The value for R is 0.989.

Solution

$$R^2_{\text{adj}} = 1 - \left[\frac{(1 - R^2)(n - 1)}{n - k - 1}\right]$$

$$= 1 - \left[\frac{(1 - 0.989^2)(5 - 1)}{5 - 2 - 1}\right]$$

$$= 1 - 0.043758$$

$$\approx 0.956$$

In this case, when the number of data pairs and the number of independent variables are accounted for, the adjusted multiple coefficient of determination is 0.956.

Applying the Concepts 10–6

More Math Means More Money

In a study to determine a person's yearly income 10 years after high school, it was found that the two biggest predictors are number of math courses taken and number of hours worked per week during a person's senior year of high school. The multiple regression equation generated from a sample of 20 individuals is

$$y' = 6000 + 4540x_1 + 1290x_2$$

Let x_1 represent the number of mathematics courses taken and x_2 represent hours worked. The correlation between income and mathematics courses is 0.63. The correlation between income and hours worked is 0.84, and the correlation between mathematics courses and hours worked is 0.31. Use this information to answer the following questions.

1. What is the dependent variable?
2. What are the independent variables?
3. What are the multiple regression assumptions?
4. Explain what 4540 and 1290 in the equation tell us.
5. What is the predicted income if a person took 8 math classes and worked 20 hours per week during her or his senior year in high school?
6. What does a multiple correlation coefficient of 0.77 mean?
7. Compute R^2.
8. Compute the adjusted R^2.
9. Would the equation be considered a good predictor of income?
10. What are your conclusions about the relationship between courses taken, hours worked, and yearly income?

See page 498 for the answers.

Exercises 10–6

1. Explain the similarities and differences between simple linear regression and multiple regression.

2. What is the general form of the multiple regression equation? What does a represent? What do the b's represent?

3. Why would a researcher prefer to conduct a multiple regression study rather than separate regression studies using one independent variable and the dependent variable?

4. What are the assumptions for multiple regression?

5. How do the values of the individual correlation coefficients compare to the value of the multiple correlation coefficient?

6. A researcher has determined that a significant relationship exists among an employee's age x_1, grade point average x_2, and income y. The multiple regression equation is $y' = -34,127 + 132x_1 + 20,805x_2$. Predict the income of a person who is 32 years old and has a GPA of 3.4.

7. A manufacturer found that a significant relationship exists among the number of hours an assembly line employee works per shift x_1, the total number of items produced x_2, and the number of defective items produced y. The multiple regression equation is $y' = 9.6 + 2.2x_1 - 1.08x_2$. Predict the number of defective items produced by an employee who has worked 9 hours and produced 24 items.

8. A real estate agent found that there is a significant relationship among the number of hectares on a farm x_1, the number of rooms in the farmhouse x_2, and the selling price in thousands of dollars y of farms in a specific area. The regression equation is $y' = 44.9 - 0.0266x_1 + 7.56x_2$. Predict the selling price of a farm that has 371 hectares and a farmhouse with six rooms.

9. An educator has found a significant relationship among a college graduate's IQ x_1, score on the verbal section of the SAT Reasoning Test x_2, and income for the first year following graduation from college y. Predict the income of a college graduate whose IQ is 120 and verbal SAT Reasoning Test score is 650. The regression equation is $y' = 5000 + 97x_1 + 35x_2$.

10. A medical researcher found a significant relationship among a person's age x_1, cholesterol level x_2, sodium level of the blood x_3, and systolic blood pressure y. The regression equation is $y' = 97.7 + 0.691x_1 + 219x_2 - 299x_3$. Predict the systolic blood pressure of a person who is 35 years old and has a cholesterol level of 194 milligrams per decilitre (mg/dl) and a sodium blood level of 142 milliequivalents per litre (mEq/l).

11. Explain the meaning of the multiple correlation coefficient R.

12. What is the range of values R can assume?

13. Define R^2 and R^2_{adj}.

14. What are the hypotheses used to test the significance of R?

15. What test is used to test the significance of R?

16. What is the meaning of the adjusted R^2? Why is it computed?

10-7 Summary

Many relationships among variables exist in the real world. One way to determine whether a relationship exists is to use the statistical techniques known as correlation and regression. The strength and direction of the relationship are measured by the value of the correlation coefficient. It can assume values between and including $+1$ and -1. The closer the value of the correlation coefficient is to $+1$ or -1, the stronger the linear relationship is between the variables. A value of $+1$ or -1 indicates a perfect linear relationship. A positive relationship between two variables means that for small values of the independent variable, the values of the dependent variable will be small, and that for large values of the independent variable, the values of the dependent variable will be large. A negative relationship between two variables means that for small values of the independent variable, the values of the dependent variable will be large, and that for large values of the independent variable, the values of the dependent variable will be small.

Relationships can be linear or curvilinear. To determine the shape, one draws a scatter plot of the variables. If the relationship is linear, the data can be approximated by a straight line, called the *regression line,* or the *line of best fit.* The closer the value of *r* is to $+1$ or -1, the closer the points will fit the line.

"At this point in my report, I'll ask all of you to follow me to the conference room directly below us!"

Source: Cartoon by Bradford Veley, Marquette, Michigan. Reprinted with permission.

In addition, relationships can be multiple. That is, there can be two or more independent variables and one dependent variable. A coefficient of correlation and a regression equation can be found for multiple relationships, just as they can be found for simple relationships.

The coefficient of determination is a better indicator of the strength of a relationship than the correlation coefficient. It is better because it identifies the percentage of variation of the dependent variable that is directly attributable to the variation of the independent variable. The coefficient of determination is obtained by squaring the correlation coefficient and converting the result to a percentage.

Another statistic used in correlation and regression is the standard error of the estimate, which is an estimate of the standard deviation of the *y* values about the predicted y' values. The standard error of the estimate can be used to construct a prediction interval about a specific value point estimate y' of the mean of the *y* values for a given value of *x.*

Finally, remember that a significant relationship between two variables does not necessarily mean that one variable is a direct cause of the other variable. In some cases this is true, but other possibilities that should be considered include a complex relationship involving other (perhaps unknown) variables, a third variable interacting with both variables, or a relationship due solely to chance.

For step-by-step guidance on the use of technology for this chapter, visit the Online Learning Centre at www.mcgrawhill.ca/olc/bluman. Summary procedures for Minitab, SPSS, Excel, and TI-83 Plus or TI-84 Plus can also be found in Appendix E.

Important Terms

●●●

adjusted R^2 489	correlation 452	extrapolation 473	influential point or observation 474
coefficient of determination 480	correlation coefficient 457	independent variable 453	least-squares line 479
	dependent variable 453		

lurking variable 464

marginal change 472

multiple correlation
coefficient 488

multiple regression 485

negative relationship 453

Pearson product moment
correlation coefficient 457

population correlation
coefficient 461

positive relationship 453

prediction interval 482

regression 452

regression line 468

residual 479

scatter plot 454

standard error of the
estimate 480

Important Formulas ● ● ●

Formula for the correlation coefficient:

$$r = \frac{n(\Sigma xy) - (\Sigma x)(\Sigma y)}{\sqrt{[n(\Sigma x^2) - (\Sigma x)^2][n(\Sigma y^2) - (\Sigma y)^2]}}$$

Formula for the t test for the correlation coefficient:

$$t = r\sqrt{\frac{n-2}{1-r^2}} \qquad \text{d.f.} = n - 2$$

The regression line equation: $y' = a + bx$, where

$$a = \frac{(\Sigma y)(\Sigma x^2) - (\Sigma x)(\Sigma xy)}{n(\Sigma x^2) - (\Sigma x)^2}$$

$$b = \frac{n(\Sigma xy) - (\Sigma x)(\Sigma y)}{n(\Sigma x^2) - (\Sigma x)^2}$$

Formula for the standard error of the estimate:

$$s_{est} = \sqrt{\frac{\Sigma(y - y')^2}{n - 2}}$$

or

$$s_{est} = \sqrt{\frac{\Sigma y^2 - a\,\Sigma y - b\,\Sigma xy}{n - 2}}$$

Formula for the prediction interval for a value y':

$$y' - t_{\alpha/2}\, s_{est}\sqrt{1 + \frac{1}{n} + \frac{n(x - \overline{X})^2}{n\Sigma x^2 - (\Sigma x)^2}} < y$$

$$< y' + t_{\alpha/2}\, s_{est}\sqrt{1 + \frac{1}{n} + \frac{n(x - \overline{X})^2}{n\Sigma x^2 - (\Sigma x)^2}}$$

$$\text{d.f.} = n - 2$$

Formula for the multiple correlation coefficient:

$$R = \sqrt{\frac{r_{yx_1}^2 + r_{yx_2}^2 - 2r_{yx_1} \cdot r_{yx_2} \cdot r_{x_1x_2}}{1 - r_{x_1x_2}^2}}$$

Formula for the F test for the multiple correlation coefficient:

$$F = \frac{R^2/k}{(1 - R^2)/(n - k - 1)}$$

with d.f.N $= n - k$ and d.f.D $= n - k - 1$.

Formula for the adjusted R^2:

$$R_{adj}^2 = 1 - \left[\frac{(1 - R^2)(n - 1)}{n - k - 1}\right]$$

Review Exercises ● ● ●

For Exercises 1 through 7, do a complete regression analysis by performing the following steps.

   a. Draw the scatter plot.
   b. Compute the value of the correlation coefficient.
   c. Test the significance of the correlation coefficient at $\alpha = 0.01$, using Table I.
   d. Determine the regression line equation.
   e. Plot the regression line on the scatter plot.
   f. Predict y' for a specific value of x.

1. These data represent the number of hits and the number of strikeouts for 15 players on a college baseball team. If there is a significant relationship between the variables, predict the number of strikeouts a baseball player is likely to have if he has 30 hits.

Hits x	54	16	41	43	24	21	6	2
Strikeouts y	12	6	30	33	21	29	10	4

Hits x	54	41	29	39	11	24	1
Strikeouts y	26	20	23	27	10	12	3

Source: University of Findlay baseball statistics.

2. A researcher wishes to determine if there is a relationship between sports involvement and gender in Canada. Statistics Canada collected data on thousands of individuals that included both active and passive participation levels. If a significant relationship exists, predict the number of females participating in sports if 1500 males participate.

Male x	5140	2338	2076	962	537	842	4040
Female y	3169	2261	916	766	399	864	3611

Source: Statistics Canada.

3. A study is done to see whether there is a relationship between a mother's age and the number of children she has. The data are shown here. If there is a significant relationship, predict the number of children of a mother whose age is 34.

Mother's age x	18	22	29	20	27	32	33	36
No. of children y	2	1	3	1	2	4	3	5

4. A study is conducted to determine the relationship between a driver's age and the number of accidents he or she has over a 1-year period. The data are shown here. (This information will be used for Exercise 8.) If there is a significant relationship, predict the number of accidents of a driver who is 28.

Driver's age x	16	24	18	17	23	27	32
No. of accidents y	3	2	5	2	0	1	1

5. A researcher desires to know whether the typing speed of a secretary (in words per minute) is related to the time (in hours) that it takes the secretary to learn to use a new word processing program. The data are shown.

Speed x	48	74	52	79	83	56	85	63	88	74	90	92
Time y	7	4	8	3.5	2	6	2.3	5	2.1	4.5	1.9	1.5

If there is a significant relationship, predict the time it will take the average secretary who has a typing speed of 72 words per minute to learn the word processing program. (This information will be used for Exercises 9 and 11.)

6. A study was conducted with vegetarians to see whether the number of grams of protein each ate per day was related to diastolic blood pressure. The data are given here. (This information will be used for Exercises 10 and 12.) If there is a significant relationship, predict the diastolic pressure of a vegetarian who consumes 8 grams of protein per day.

Grams x	4	6.5	5	5.5	8	10	9	8.2	10.5
Pressure y	73	79	83	82	84	92	88	86	95

7. An auditor needs to determine if there is a relationship between the age (years) of a vehicle and the annual cost (dollars) of vehicle repair (excluding collision work). A random sample were selected and the vehicle's age and car repair history were obtained. If there is a relationship, what would you expect the annual cost of repair to be for a 7-year-old vehicle?

Vehicle's age x	1	3	4	6	8	9	11	13
Repair cost y	141	510	701	978	1187	1207	1160	1151

Source: DesRosiers Automotive Consultants.

8. For Exercise 4, find the standard error of the estimate.

9. For Exercise 5, find the standard error of the estimate.

10. For Exercise 6, find the standard error of the estimate.

11. For Exercise 5, find the 90% prediction interval for time when the speed is 72 words per minute.

12. For Exercise 6, find the 95% prediction interval for pressure when the number of grams is 8.

13. (Opt.) A study found a significant relationship among a person's years of experience on a particular job x_1, the number of workdays missed per month x_2, and the person's age y. The regression equation is $y' = 12.8 + 2.09x_1 + 0.423x_2$. Predict a person's age if he or she has been employed for 4 years and has missed 2 workdays a month.

14. (Opt.) Find R when $r_{yx_1} = 0.681$ and $r_{yx_2} = 0.872$ and $r_{x_1x_2} = 0.746$.

15. (Opt.) Find R^2_{adj} when $R = 0.873$, $n = 10$, and $k = 3$.

Statistics Today

Like Parent, Like Child?–Revisited

The researchers found that parental use of employment insurance (EI) plays a role in shortening the time to the first use of this program by the sample of Canadian men under study. An interesting statistic indicated that 24% of Canadian males who collected EI had parents who were prior recipients. Using the Pearson correlation coefficient, researchers found correlations with statistically significant r values of 0.648, 0.644, and 0.629 in Newfoundland, Prince Edward Island, and Saskatchewan recipients. Researchers also indicated that all of the estimates of parental past and future EI collection are statistically significant, having associated P-values of less than 0.001. It should be noted that the researchers compared Canadian results with a similar Swedish study that found no significant correlation with parental and child employment insurance involvement.

Data Analysis

The Data Bank is found in Appendix D, or on the World Wide Web by following links from **www.mcgrawhill.ca/olc/bluman.**

1. From the Data Bank, choose two variables that might be related: for example, IQ and educational level; age and cholesterol level; exercise and weight; or weight and systolic pressure. Do a complete correlation and regression analysis by performing the following steps. Select a random sample of at least 10 subjects.

    a. Draw a scatter plot.

    b. Compute the correlation coefficient.

    c. Test the hypothesis H_0: $\rho = 0$.

    d. Find the regression line equation.

    e. Summarize the results.

2. Repeat Exercise 1, using samples of values of 10 or more obtained from Data Set V in Appendix D. Let x = the number of suspensions and y = the enrolment size.

3. Repeat Exercise 1, using samples of 10 or more values obtained from Data Set XIII. Let x = the number of beds and y = the number of personnel employed.

Chapter Quiz

Determine whether each statement is true or false. If the statement is false, explain why.

1. A negative relationship between two variables means that for the most part, as the x variable increases, the y variable increases.

2. A correlation coefficient of -1 implies a perfect linear relationship between the variables.

3. Even if the correlation coefficient is high or low, it may not be significant.

4. When the correlation coefficient is significant, one can assume x causes y.

5. It is not possible to have a significant correlation by chance alone.

6. In multiple regression, there are several dependent variables and one independent variable.

Select the best answer.

7. The strength of the relationship between two variables is determined by the value of

    a. r *c.* x

    b. a *d.* s_{est}

8. To test the significance of r, a(n) _____ test is used.

    a. t *c.* χ^2

    b. F *d.* None of the above

9. The test of significance for r has _____ degrees of freedom.

    a. 1   *c.* $n - 1$

    b. n *d.* $n - 2$

10. The equation of the regression line used in statistics is

    a. $x = a + by$ *c.* $y' = a + bx$

    b. $y = bx + a$ *d.* $x = ay + b$

11. The coefficient of determination is

    a. r *c.* a

    b. r^2 *d.* b

Complete the following statements with the best answer.

12. A statistical graph of two variables is called a(n) _____.

13. The x variable is called the _____ variable.

14. The range of r is from _____ to _____.

15. The sign of r and _____ will always be the same.

16. The regression line is called the _____.

17. If all the points fall on a straight line, the value of r will be _____ or _____.

For Exercises 18 through 21, do a complete regression analysis.

    a. Draw the scatter plot.

    b. Compute the value of the correlation coefficient.

    c. Test the significance of the correlation coefficient at $\alpha = 0.05$.

    d. Determine the regression line equation.

    e. Plot the regression line on the scatter plot.

    f. Predict y' for a specific value of x.

18. A medical researcher wants to determine the relationship between the price per dose of prescription drugs in Canada and the price of the same drug in the United States. The data, in Canadian dollars (C$), are shown. Describe the relationship. Predict the U.S. drug price of $3.75.

Canada price (C$) x	9.17	1.61	1.31	1.70	1.84	0.57	0.96
United States price (C$) y	23.66	2.27	2.93	2.90	1.40	2.12	0.92

Source: CBC News Online.

19. A study is conducted to determine the relationship between a driver's age and the number of accidents he or she has over a 1-year period. The data are shown here. If there is a significant relationship, predict the number of accidents of a driver who is 64.

Driver's age x	63	65	60	62	66	67	59
No. of accidents y	2	3	1	0	3	1	4

20. A researcher desires to know if the age of a child is related to the number of cavities he or she has. The data are shown here. If there is a significant relationship, predict the number of cavities for a child of 11.

Age of child x	6	8	9	10	12	14
No. of cavities y	2	1	3	4	6	5

21. A study is conducted with a group of dieters to see if the number of grams of fat each consumes per day is related to cholesterol level. The data are shown here. If there is a significant relationship, predict the cholesterol level of a dieter who consumes 8.5 grams of fat per day.

Fat grams x	6.8	5.5	8.2	10	8.6	9.1	8.6	10.4
Cholesterol level y	183	201	193	283	222	250	190	218

22. For Exercise 20, find the standard error of the estimate.

23. For Exercise 21, find the standard error of the estimate.

24. For Exercise 20, find the 90% prediction interval of the number of cavities for a 7-year-old.

25. For Exercise 21, find the 95% prediction interval of the cholesterol level of a person who consumes 10 grams of fat.

26. (Opt.) A study was conducted, and a significant relationship was found among the number of hours a teenager watches television per day x_1, the number of hours the teenager talks on the telephone per day x_2, and the teenager's weight y. The regression equation is $y' = 98.7 + 3.82x_1 + 6.51x_2$. Predict a teenager's weight if she averages 3 hours of TV and 1.5 hours on the phone per day.

27. (Opt.) Find R when $r_{yx_1} = 0.561$ and $r_{yx_2} = 0.714$ and $r_{x_1x_2} = 0.625$.

28. (Opt.) Find R^2_{adj} when $R = 0.774$, $n = 8$, and $k = 2$.

Critical Thinking Challenges

When the points in a scatter plot show a curvilinear trend rather than a linear trend, statisticians have methods of fitting curves rather than straight lines to the data, thus obtaining a better fit and a better prediction model. One type of curve that can be used is the logarithmic regression curve. The data shown are the number of items of a new product sold over a period of 15 months at a certain store. Notice that sales rise during the beginning months and then level off later on.

Month x	1	3	6	8	10	12	15
No. of items sold y	10	12	15	19	20	21	21

1. Draw the scatter plot for the data.
2. Find the equation of the regression line.

3. Describe how the line fits the data.
4. Using the log key on your calculator, transform the x values into log x values.
5. Using the log x values instead of the x values, find the equation of a and b for the regression line.
6. Next, plot the curve $y = a + b \log x$ on the graph.
7. Compare the line $y = a + bx$ with the curve $y = a + b \log x$ and decide which one fits the data better.
8. Compute r, using the x and y values; then compute r, using the log x and y values. Which is higher?
9. In your opinion, which (the line or the logarithmic curve) would be a better predictor for the data? Why?

Data Projects

Where appropriate, use Minitab, SPSS, the TI-83 Plus, the TI-84 Plus, or a computer program of your choice to complete the following exercises.

1. Select two variables that might be related, such as the age of a person and the number of cigarettes the person smokes, or the number of credits a student has and the number of hours the student watches television. Sample at least 10 people.

   a. Write a brief statement as to the purpose of the study.
   b. Define the population.
   c. State how the sample was selected.
   d. Show the raw data.
   e. Draw a scatter plot for the data values.
   f. Write a statement analyzing the scatter plot.
   g. Compute the value of the correlation coefficient.

h. Test the significance of r. (State the hypotheses, select α, find the critical values, make the decision, and analyze the results.)

i. Find the equation of the regression line and draw it on the scatter plot. (*Note:* Even if r is not significant, complete this step.)

j. Summarize the overall results.

2. For the data in Exercise 1, use Minitab or similar technology to answer these.

a. Does a linear correlation exist between x and y?

b. If so, find the regression equation.

c. Explain how good a model the regression equation is by finding the coefficient of determination and coefficient of correlation and interpreting the strength of these values.

d. Find the prediction interval for y. Use the α value that you selected in Exercise 1.

You may use the following websites to obtain raw data:

Visit the data sets at the book's website found at www.mcgrawhill.ca/olc/bluman
http://lib.stat.cmu.edu/DASL
www.statcan.ca

Answers to Applying the Concepts

Section 10–3   Stopping Distances

1. The independent variable is kilometres per hour (km/h).

2. The dependent variable is stopping distance (metres).

3. Kilometres per hour is a continuous quantitative variable.

4. Stopping distance is a continuous quantitative variable.

5. A scatter plot of the data is shown.

6. There might be a linear relationship between the two variable, but there is a bit of a curve in the data.

7. Changing the distances between the km/h increments will change the appearance of the relationship.

8. There is a positive relationship between the two variables—higher speeds are associated with longer stopping distances.

9. The strong relationship between the two variables suggests that stopping distance can be accurately predicted from km/h. We might still have some concern about the curve in the data.

10. Answers will vary. Some other variables that might affect stopping distance include road distances, driver response time, and condition of the brakes.

11. The correlation coefficient is $r = 0.995$.

12. The value for $r = 0.995$ is significant at $\alpha = 0.05$. This confirms the strong, positive relationship between the variables.

Section 10–4   Stopping Distances Revisited

1. The linear regression equation is

$$y' = -22.96 + 1.21x.$$

2. The slope says that for each additional kilometre per hour a vehicle is travelling, we expect the stopping distance to increase 1.21 metres, on average. The y intercept is the stopping distance we would expect for a vehicle travelling 0 km/h. Although meaningless in this context, it is an important part of the model.

3. $y' = -22.96 + 1.21(60) = 49.64$. The stopping distance for a vehicle travelling 60 km/h is approximately 50 metres.

4. $y' = -22.96 + 1.21\,(120) = 122.24$. The stopping distance for a vehicle travelling 120 km/h is approximately 122 metres.

5. It is not appropriate to make predictions of stopping distance for speeds outside of the given data values (for example, the 120 km/h above) because we know nothing about the relationship between the two variables outside of the range of the data.

Section 10–5   Interpreting Simple Linear Regression

1. Both variables are moving in the same direction. In others words, the two variables are positively associated. We know this because the correlation coefficient is positive.

2. The unexplained variation of 3026.49 measures the distances from the prediction line to the actual values.

3. The slope of the regression line is 0.725983.

4. The y intercept is 16.5523.

5. The critical value of 0.378419 can be found in a table.

6. The allowable risk of making a type I error is 0.10, the level of significance.

7. The variation explained by the regression is 0.631319, or about 63.1%.

8. The average scatter of points about the regression line is 12.9668, the standard error of the estimate.

9. The null hypothesis is that there is no correlation, $H_0: \rho = 0$.

10. We compare the test statistic of 0.794556 to the critical value to see if the null hypothesis should be rejected.

11. Since $0.794556 > 0.378419$, we reject the null hypothesis and find that there is enough evidence to conclude that the correlation is not equal to zero.

Section 10–6   More Math Means More Money

1. The dependent variable is yearly income 10 years after high school.

2. The independent variables are number of math courses taken and number of hours worked per week during the senior year of high school.

3. Multiple regression assumes that the independent variables are not highly correlated.

4. We expect a person's yearly income 10 years after high school to be $4540 more, on average, for each additional math course taken, all other variables held constant. We expect a person's yearly income 10 years after high school to be $1290 more, on average, for each additional hour worked per week during the senior year of high school, all other variables held constant.

5. $y' = 6000 + 4540(8) + 1290(20) = 68,120$. The predicted yearly income 10 years after high school is $68,120.

6. The multiple correlation coefficient of 0.77 means that there is a fairly strong positive relationship between the independent variables (number of math courses and hours worked during senior year of high school) and the dependent variable (yearly income 10 years after high school).

7. $R^2 = (0.77)^2 = 0.5929$

8. $R^2_{\text{adj}} = 1 - \left[\dfrac{(1 - R^2)(n - 1)}{n - k - 1} \right]$

$= 1 - \left[\dfrac{(1 - 0.5929)(20 - 1)}{20 - 2 - 1} \right]$

$= 1 - \left[\dfrac{(0.4071)(19)}{17} \right] = 0.5450$

9. The equation appears to be a fairly good predictor of income, since 54.5% of the variation in yearly income 10 years after high school is explained by the regression model.

10. Answers will vary. One possible answer is that yearly income 10 years after high school increases with more math classes and more hours of work during the senior year of high school. The number of math classes has a higher coefficient, so more math does mean more money!

CHAPTER 11

Other Chi-Square Tests

Objectives

After completing this chapter, you should be able to

1. Test a distribution for goodness of fit, using chi-square.

2. Test two variables for independence, using chi-square.

3. Test proportions for homogeneity, using chi-square.

Outline

11–1 Introduction

11–2 Test for Goodness of Fit

11–3 Tests Using Contingency Tables

11–4 Summary

Statistics Today

Statistics and Heredity

An Austrian monk, Gregor Mendel (1822–1884) studied genetics, and his principles are the foundation for modern genetics. Mendel used his spare time to grow a variety of peas at the monastery. One of his many experiments involved crossbreeding peas that had smooth yellow seeds with peas that had wrinkled green seeds. He noticed that the results occurred with regularity.

That is, some of the offspring had smooth yellow seeds, some had smooth green seeds, some had wrinkled yellow seeds, and some had wrinkled green seeds. Furthermore, after several experiments, the percentages of each type seemed to remain approximately the same. Mendel formulated his theory based on the assumption of dominant and recessive traits and tried to predict the results. He then crossbred his peas and examined 556 seeds over the next generation.

Finally, he compared the actual results with the theoretical results to see if his theory was correct. To do this, he used a "simple" chi-square test, which is explained in this chapter. See Statistics Today—Revisited, page 524.

Source: J. Hodges, Jr., D. Krech, and R. Crutchfield, *Stat Lab, An Empirical Introduction to Statistics* (New York: McGraw-Hill, 1975), pp. 228–229. Used with permission.

11–1   Introduction

The chi-square distribution was used in Chapters 7 and 8 to find a confidence interval for a variance or standard deviation and to test a hypothesis about a single variance or standard deviation.

It can also be used for tests concerning *frequency distributions*, such as "If a sample of buyers is given a choice of automobile colours, will each colour be selected with the same frequency?" The chi-square distribution can be used to test the *independence* of two variables, for example, "Are the opinions of elected Members of Parliament on gun control independent of party affiliations?" That is, do the Conservatives feel one way and the Liberals feel differently, or do they have the same opinion?

Finally, the chi-square distribution can be used to test the *homogeneity of proportions.* For example, is the proportion of high school seniors who attend college immediately after graduating the same for western, central, or eastern parts of Canada?"

This chapter explains the chi-square distribution and its applications. In addition to the applications mentioned here, chi-square has many other uses in statistics.

11–2   Test for Goodness of Fit

Objective

Test a distribution for goodness of fit, using chi-square.

In addition to being used to test a single variance, the chi-square statistic can be used to see whether a frequency distribution fits a specific pattern. For example, to meet customer demands, a manufacturer of running shoes may wish to see whether buyers show a preference for a specific style. A traffic engineer may wish to see whether accidents occur more often on some days than on others, so that she can increase police patrols accordingly. An emergency service may want to see whether it receives more calls at certain times of the day than at others, so that it can provide adequate staffing.

When one is testing to see whether a frequency distribution fits a specific pattern, the chi-square **goodness-of-fit test** is used. For example, suppose a market analyst wished to see whether consumers have any preference among five flavours of a new fruit soda. A sample of 100 people provided these data:

Cherry	Strawberry	Orange	Lime	Grape
32	28	16	14	10

If there were no preference, one would expect each flavour to be selected with equal frequency. In this case, the equal frequency is $100/5 = 20$. That is, *approximately* 20 people would select each flavour.

Since the frequencies for each flavour were obtained from a sample, these actual frequencies are called the **observed frequencies.** The frequencies obtained by calculation (as if there were no preference) are called the **expected frequencies.** A completed table for the test is shown.

Frequency	Cherry	Strawberry	Orange	Lime	Grape
Observed	32	28	16	14	10
Expected	20	20	20	20	20

The observed frequencies will almost always differ from the expected frequencies due to sampling error; that is, the values differ from sample to sample. But the question is: Are these differences significant (a preference exists), or are they due to chance? The chi-square goodness-of-fit test will enable the researcher to determine the answer.

Before computing the test statistic, one must state the hypotheses. The null hypothesis should be a statement indicating that there is no difference or no change. For this example, the hypotheses are as follows:

H_0: Consumers show no preference for flavours of the fruit soda.

H_1: Consumers show a preference.

In the goodness-of-fit test, the degrees of freedom are equal to the number of categories minus 1. For this example, there are five categories (cherry, strawberry, orange, lime, and grape); hence, the degrees of freedom are $5 - 1 = 4$. This is so because the number of subjects in each of the first four categories is free to vary. But in order for the sum to be 100—the total number of subjects—the number of subjects in the last category is fixed.

Formula for the Chi-Square Goodness-of-Fit Test

$$\chi^2 = \sum \frac{(O - E)^2}{E}$$

with degrees of freedom equal to the number of categories minus 1, and where

O = observed frequency
E = expected frequency

Two assumptions are needed for the goodness-of-fit test. These assumptions are given next.

Assumptions for the Chi-Square Goodness-of-Fit Test

1. The data are obtained from a random sample.
2. The expected frequency for each category must be 5 or more.

This test is a right-tailed test, since when the $O - E$ values are squared, the answer will be positive or zero. This formula is explained in Example 11–1.

Example 11–1	Is there enough evidence to reject the claim that there is no preference in the selection of fruit soda flavours, using the data shown previously? Let $\alpha = 0.05$.

Solution

Step 1 State the hypotheses and identify the claim.

H_0: Consumers show no preference for flavours (claim).

H_1: Consumers show a preference.

Step 2 Find the critical value. The degrees of freedom are $5 - 1 = 4$, and $\alpha = 0.05$. Hence, the critical value from Table G in Appendix C is 9.488.

Step 3 Compute the test statistic by subtracting the expected value from the corresponding observed value, squaring the result and dividing by the expected value, and finding the sum. The expected value for each category is 20, as shown previously.

$$\chi^2 = \sum \frac{(O - E)^2}{E}$$

$$= \frac{(32 - 20)^2}{20} + \frac{(28 - 20)^2}{20} + \frac{(16 - 20)^2}{20} + \frac{(14 - 20)^2}{20}$$

$$+ \frac{(10 - 20)^2}{20} = 18.0$$

Step 4 Make the decision. The decision is to reject the null hypothesis, since $18.0 > 9.488$, as shown in Figure 11–1.

Figure 11–1

Critical Value and Test Statistic for Example 11–1

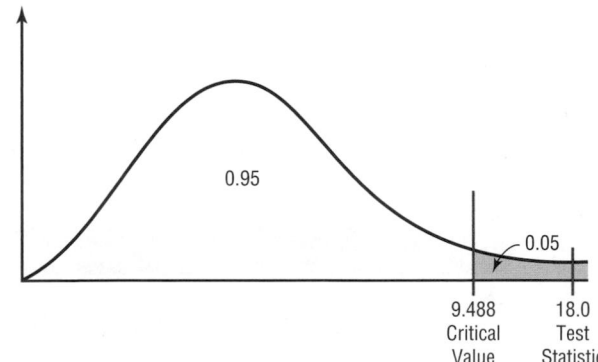

Step 5 Summarize the results. There is enough evidence to reject the claim that consumers show no preference for the flavours.

P-value Method

Using procedures explained in Section 8–6, the approximate *P*-value for Example 11–1 with d.f. = 4 and test statistic $\chi^2 = 18.0$ is less than 0.005. The exact *P*-value using technology is 0.001. Since the *P*-value (0.001) < significance level ($\alpha = 0.05$), reject H_0. Refer to Example 11–3 illustrating *P*-value method.

To get some idea of why this test is called the goodness-of-fit test, examine graphs of the observed values and expected values. See Figure 11–2. From the graphs, one can see whether the observed values and expected values are close together or far apart.

Figure 11–2

Graphs of the
Observed and
Expected Values for
Soda Flavours

When the observed values and expected values are close together, the chi-square test value will be small. Then the decision will be to not reject the null hypothesis—hence, there is "a good fit." See Figure 11–3(a). When the observed values and the expected values are far apart, the chi-square test value will be large. Then the null hypothesis will be rejected—hence, there is "not a good fit." See Figure 11–3(b).

Figure 11–3

Results of the
Goodness-of-Fit Test

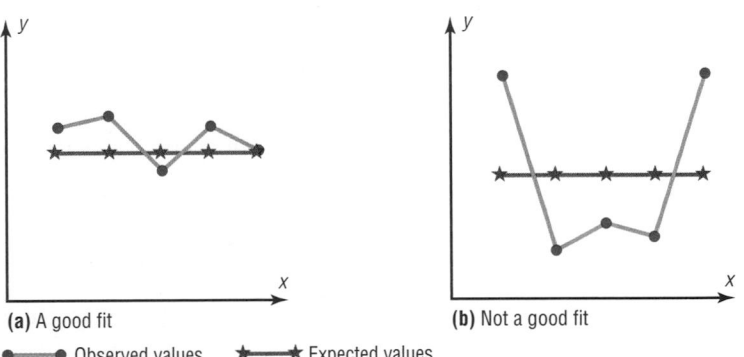

The steps for the chi-square goodness-of-fit test are summarized in this Procedure Table.

Procedure Table

The Chi-Square Goodness-of-Fit Test (Traditional Method)

Step 1   State the hypotheses and identify the claim.

Step 2   Find the critical value. The test is always right-tailed.

Procedure Table *(continued)*

Step 3   Compute the test statistic.

Find the sum of the $\dfrac{(O - E)^2}{E}$ values.

Step 4   Make the decision.

Step 5   Summarize the results.

When there is perfect agreement between the observed and the expected values, $\chi^2 = 0$. Also, χ^2 can never be negative. Finally, the test is right-tailed because "H_0: Good fit" and "H_1: Not a good fit" mean that χ^2 will be small in the first case and large in the second case.

Example 11–2   Canadian retirees returning to paid employment were asked why they did so. Financial considerations were mentioned by 38% of retirees, 22% disliked retirement, 19% alluded to the intrinsic rewards offered by work (challenging tasks, social contacts, sense of purpose), 14% felt they were needed or wanted to help out, and 7% cited other considerations, such as pressure from family members, improved health, or no longer having to provide caregiving. To see if these percentages are consistent with residents of Canada's Atlantic region, a researcher surveyed 300 retirees who had returned to work. The reasons cited were broken down as follows: 128 for financial reasons, 59 disliked retirement, 51 mentioned intrinsic rewards, 37 felt that they were needed, and 25 cited other considerations. At $\alpha = 0.10$, test the claim that the percentages are the same for retirees working in Canada's Atlantic region.

Source: Adapted from Statistics Canada publication *Perspectives on Labour and Income,* Catalogue 75-001-XIE, September 2005.

Solution

Step 1   State the hypotheses and identify the claim.

H_0: Canadian retirees reasons for returning to work are distributed as follows: 38% for financial reasons, 22% disliked retirement, 19% desired intrinsic rewards, 14% felt needed, and 7% cited other considerations.

H_1: The distribution is different than stated in the null hypothesis.

Step 2   Find the critical value. Since $\alpha = 0.10$ and the degrees of freedom are $5 - 1 = 4$, then the critical value is 7.779.

Step 3   Compute the test statistic. The expected values are computed as follows:

$0.38 \times 300 = 114$ $0.19 \times 300 = 57$ $0.07 \times 300 = 21$
$0.22 \times 300 = 66$ $0.14 \times 300 = 42$

$$\chi^2 = \sum \frac{(O - E)^2}{E}$$

$$= \frac{(128 - 114)^2}{114} + \frac{(59 - 66)^2}{66} + \frac{(51 - 57)^2}{57} + \frac{(37 - 42)^2}{42} + \frac{(25 - 21)^2}{21}$$

$$\approx 4.4504$$

Step 4   Make the decision. Since the test statistic ($\chi^2 = 4.4504$) is less than the critical value ($\chi^2 = 7.779$), fail to reject the null hypothesis. See Figure 11–4.

Figure 11–4

Critical Value and
Test Statistic for
Example 11–2

4.4504	7.779
Test	Critical
Statistic	Value

Step 5   Summarize the results. There is not enough evidence to reject the claim. It can be concluded that the proportions are not significantly different from those stated in the null hypothesis.

P-value Method

Using procedures explained in Section 8–6, the approximate P-value for Example 11–2 with d.f. = 4 and test statistic $\chi^2 = 4.4504$ is between 0.90 and 0.10. The exact P-value using technology is 0.348. Since the P-value (0.348) > significance level ($\alpha = 0.10$), fail to reject H_0. Refer to Example 11–3 illustrating P-value method.

P-value Method for Chi-Square Tests

The P-value method was explained in Section 8–6, "χ^2 Test for a Variance or Standard Deviation." The P-value steps for the χ^2 Goodness-of-Fit Test are shown below.

Procedure Table

The Chi-Square Goodness-of-Fit Test (P-value Method)

Step 1   State the hypotheses and identify the claim.

Step 2   Compute the test statistic.

Step 3   Find P-value.

Step 4   Make the decision.

Step 5   Summarize the results.

The P-value can be approximated using Table G—The Chi-Square Distribution in Appendix C or more precisely using statistical software (e.g., Minitab, SPSS) or a spreadsheet application (e.g., Excel), or a programmable calculator (e.g., TI-83 Plus or TI-84 Plus). Refer to Appendix E for a summary of these procedures.

Example 11–3

The advisor of a varsity sports team at a large university believes that the group consists of 10% freshmen, 20% sophomores, 40% juniors, and 30% seniors. The membership for the club this year consisted of 14 freshmen, 19 sophomores, 51 juniors, and 16 seniors. At $\alpha = 0.10$, test the advisor's claim. Use P-value method.

Solution

Step 1 State the hypotheses and identify the claim.

H_0: The club consists of 10% freshmen, 20% sophomores, 40% juniors, and 30% seniors (claim).

H_1: The distribution is not the same as stated in the null hypothesis.

Step 2 Compute the test statistic. The expected values are computed as follows:

$$0.10 \times 100 = 10 \qquad 0.40 \times 100 = 40$$
$$0.20 \times 100 = 20 \qquad 0.30 \times 100 = 30$$

$$\chi^2 = \sum \frac{(O - E)^2}{E}$$

$$= \frac{(14 - 10)^2}{10} + \frac{(19 - 20)^2}{20} + \frac{(51 - 40)^2}{40} + \frac{(16 - 30)^2}{30}$$

$$\approx 11.208$$

Step 3 Find P-value.

The P-value, obtained from Table G in Appendix C, for the test statistic, $\chi^2 = 11.208$, with d.f. $= 3$ is between 0.025 and 0.01. See Figure 11–5.

Figure 11–5

Finding the P-value

							P-value is between 0.025 and 0.01			
Degrees of Freedom	0.995	0.99	0.975	0.95	0.90	0.10	0.05	0.025	0.01	0.005
1	0.000	0.000	0.001	0.004	0.016	2.706	3.841	5.024	6.635	7.879
2	0.010	0.020	0.051	0.103	0.211	4.605	5.991	7.378	9.210	10.597
3	0.072	0.115	0.216	0.352	0.584	6.251	7.815	9.348	11.345	12.838
4	0.207	0.297	0.484	0.711	1.064	7.779	9.486	11.143	13.277	14.860

Test statistic is 11.208

Note: The P-value obtained from statistical software, spreadsheet, or calculator is 0.011.

Step 4 Make the decision.

Since the P-value (0.011) is less than the significance level ($\alpha = 0.10$), reject the null hypothesis, as shown in Figure 11–6.

Step 5 Summarize the results.

There is enough evidence to reject the advisor's claim.

Traditional Method

The critical value for $\alpha = 0.10$, d.f. $= 3$, is 6.251. Reject the null hypothesis, since the test statistic ($\chi^2 = 11.208$) > critical value ($\chi^2 = 6.251$), as shown in Figure 11–6.

Figure 11–6

Comparison of χ^2
Traditional Method and
P-value Method

P-value
= 0.011

$\alpha = 0.10$

6.251
Critical
Value

11.208
Test
Statistic

For use of the chi-square goodness-of-fit test, statisticians have determined that the expected frequencies should be at least 5, as stated in the assumptions. The reasoning is as follows: The chi-square distribution is continuous, whereas the goodness-of-fit test is discrete. However, the continuous distribution is a good approximation and can be used when the expected value for each class is at least 5. If an expected frequency of a class is less than 5, then that class can be combined with another class so that the expected frequency is 5 or more.

Applying the Concepts 11–2

Never the Same Amounts

M&M/Mars, the makers of Skittles candies, states that the flavour blend is 20% for each flavour. Skittles is a combination of lemon, lime, orange, strawberry, and grape flavoured candies. The following data list the results of four randomly selected bags of Skittles and their flavour blends. Use the data to answer the questions.

Bag	Flavour				
	Green	**Orange**	**Red**	**Purple**	**Yellow**
1	7	20	10	7	14
2	20	5	5	13	17
3	4	16	13	21	4
4	12	9	16	3	17
Total	43	50	44	44	52

1. Are the variables quantitative or qualitative?

2. What type of test can be used to compare the observed values to the expected values?

3. Perform a chi-square test on the total values.

4. What hypotheses did you use?

5. What were the degrees of freedom for the test? What is the critical value?

6. What is your conclusion?

See page 528 for the answers.

Exercises 11–2

1. How does the goodness-of-fit test differ from the chi-square variance test?

2. How are the degrees of freedom computed for the goodness-of-fit test?

3. How are the expected values computed for the goodness-of-fit test?

4. When the expected frequencies are less than 5 for a specific class, what should be done so that one can use the goodness-of-fit test?

For Exercises 5 through 19, perform these steps.

    a.   State the hypotheses and identify the claim.

    b.   Find the critical value.

    c.   Compute the test statistic.

    d.   Make the decision.

    e.   Summarize the results.

Use the traditional method of hypothesis testing unless otherwise specified.

5. A researcher for an automobile manufacturer wishes to see if the ages of automobiles are equally distributed among three categories: less than 3 years old, 3 to 7 years old, and 8 years or older. A sample of 30 adult automobile owners is selected, and the results are shown. At $\alpha = 0.05$ can it be considered that the ages of the automobiles are equally distributed among the three categories? What would the results suggest to a tire manufacturer?

Category	Less than three years	3 to 7 years	8 years or older
Number	8	10	12

Source: Based on information from Goodyear.

6. A researcher wishes to see if the five ways (drinking decaffeinated beverages, taking a nap, going for a walk, eating a sugary snack, other) people use to combat midday drowsiness are equally distributed among office workers. A sample of 60 office workers is selected, and the following data are obtained. At $\alpha = 0.10$ can it be concluded that there is no preference? Why would the results be of interest to an employer?

Method	Beverage	Nap	Walk	Snack	Other
Number	21	16	10	8	5

Source: Based on information from Harris Interactive.

7. An automotive industry report indicates the market share for new vehicles sold in Canada were General Motors, 29.0%; DaimlerChrysler, 14.3%; Ford, 14.1%; Toyota, 10.2%; Other Manufacturers, 32.4%. A recent survey of new car sales in a particular region indicated that of 100 cars sold 26 were General Motors, 16 were DaimlcrChrysler, 14 were Ford, 13 were Toyota, and 31 were Other Manufacturers. At $\alpha = 0.05$, is there

sufficient evidence to conclude that the proportions differ from those stated in the report?

Source: DesRosiers Automotive Consultants Inc.

8. According to a recent census report, 68% of families have two parents present, 23% have only a mother present, 5% have only a father present, and 4% have no parent present. A random sample of families from a large school district revealed these results:

Two parents	Mother only	Father only	No parent
120	40	30	10

Is there sufficient evidence to conclude that the proportions of families by type of parent(s) present differ from those reported by the census?

Source: *N.Y. Times Almanac.*

9. An ABC News poll asked adults whether they felt genetically modified food was safe to eat. Thirty-five percent felt it was safe, 52% felt it was not safe, and 13% had no opinion. A random sample of 120 adults was asked the same question at a local fair. Forty people felt that genetically modified food was safe, 60 felt that it was not safe, and 20 had no opinion. At the 0.01 level of significance, is there sufficient evidence to conclude that the proportions differ from those reported in the survey?

Source: ABCNews.com Poll, www.pollingreport.com.

10. A recent U.S. survey asked adults nationwide if they thought that the U.S. federal government should continue to fund NASA's efforts to send unstaffed missions to Mars. Fifty-six percent said they should continue, 40% said that they should not continue, and 4% had no opinion. A random sample of 200 U.S. college students resulted in these numbers:

Should continue: 126

Should not continue: 65

No opinion: 9

Is there sufficient evidence at $\alpha = 0.05$ to conclude that the opinions of the college students differ from those of the report?

Source: CNN/*USA TODAY*/Gallup Poll, www.pollingreport.com.

11. A national publication reported that 21% of loans granted by credit unions were for home mortgages, 39% were for automobile purchases, 20% were for credit card and other unsecured loans, 12% were for real estate other than home loans, and 8% were for other miscellaneous needs. In order to see if her credit union customers had similar needs, a manager surveyed a random sample of 100 loans and found that 25 were for home mortgages, 44 for automobile purchases, 19 for credit card and unsecured loans, 8 for real estate other than home loans, and 4 for miscellaneous needs. At $\alpha = 0.05$, is the distribution the same as reported in the newspaper?

Source: *USA TODAY.*

12. Statistics Canada reports national sources of greenhouse gas emissions by sector. The breakdown is business sector, 81.2%; non-business sector, 2.6%; and household sector, 16.2%. A provincial environment official wants to see if her province is the same. Her study of 300 emission sources finds business sector, 230; non-business sector, 6; and household sector, 64. At $\alpha = 0.05$, can she claim the percentages are the same?

Source: Statistics Canada.

13. A publication from Physicians for a Smoke-Free Canada indicates that Rothman's brands have 22% of Canada's cigarette market share; Imperial Tobacco brands have 59.8%; MacDonald brands have 12.4%; and other brands have 5.8%. A provincial health official wants to determine if her province has the same allocation. A random sample of 800 cigarette smokers indicates that 200 smoked Rothman's brands, 410 smoked Imperial Tobacco brands, 134 smoked MacDonald brands, and 56 smoked other brands. At $\alpha = 0.01$, test the claim that the health official's survey has the same cigarette preferences as the physician's publication.

Source: Physicians for a Smoke-Free Canada.

14. The population distribution of Canada's federal prisons by serious offences are the following: crimes of violence, 52%; property crimes, 19%; drug offences, 14%; other offences, 15%. A warden wants to see how his prison compares so he surveys 500 prisoners and finds 275 committed crimes of violence; 88 committed property crimes; 77 committed drug offences; and 60 committed other offences. Can the warden conclude that the percentages are the same for his prison? Use $\alpha = 0.05$.

Source: Statistics Canada.

15. The population of provincial prisons nationwide by serious offences are the following: crimes of violence,

15.5%; property crimes, 24.1%; impaired driving, 5.5%; drug offences, 4.7%, other criminal code offences, 29.8%; and other statutes, 20.4%. A provincial corrections officer wants to check how this compares to her province. She surveys 1000 inmates and finds 150 were sentenced for crimes of violence, 243 for property crimes, 57 for impaired driving, 60 for drug offences, 305 for other criminal code offences, and 185 for other statutes. Can she conclude that the percentages for her prison are the same as national statistics? Use $\alpha = 0.05$.

Source: Statistics Canada.

16. A researcher wants to know if attendance to live performing arts is equally distributed among Canada's language groups: Anglophone, Francophone, and Allophone (*spoken language other than English or French*). A sample of 188 adults was asked if they attended a live performance in the past year. The results are shown. At $\alpha = 0.05$, can it be concluded that the frequencies are equal? Use the *P*-value method. Interpret your answer.

Category	Anglophone	Francophone	Allophone
Frequency	65	67	56

Source: Decima Research.

17. A medical researcher wants to determine if the way Canadians pay for their retail medical prescription is distributed as follows: 24% out-of-pocket, 34.6% private insurers, and 41.4% public insurance. A sample of 50 people found that 11 paid out-of-pocket, 16 paid using private insurers, and 23 paid with public insurance. At $\alpha = 0.05$, is the assumption correct? Use the *P*-value method. What would be an implication of the results?

Source: Canadian Institute for Health Information.

Extending the Concepts

18. Three coins are tossed 72 times, and the number of heads is shown. At $\alpha = 0.05$, test the null hypothesis that the coins are balanced and randomly tossed. (*Hint:* Use the binomial distribution.)

No. of heads	0	1	2	3
Frequency	3	10	17	42

19. Select a three-digit lottery number over a period of 50 days. Count the number of times each digit, 0 through 9, occurs. Test the claim, at $\alpha = 0.05$, that the digits occur at random.

11–3   Tests Using Contingency Tables

When data can be tabulated in table form in terms of frequencies, several types of hypotheses can be tested by using the chi-square test.

Two such tests are the independence of variables test and the homogeneity of proportions test. The test of independence of variables is used to determine whether two variables are independent of or related to each other when a single sample is selected. The test of homogeneity of proportions is used to determine whether the proportions for a variable are equal when several samples are selected from different populations. Both tests use the chi-square distribution and a contingency table, and the test value is found in the same way. The independence test will be explained first.

Objective

Test two variables for independence, using chi-square.

Test for Independence

The chi-square **independence test** can be used to test the independence of two variables. For example, suppose a new postoperative procedure is administered to a number of patients in a large hospital. One can ask the question, Do the doctors feel differently about this procedure from the nurses, or do they feel basically the same way? Note that the question is not whether they prefer the procedure but whether there is a difference of opinion between the two groups.

To answer this question, a researcher selects a sample of nurses and doctors and tabulates the data in table form, as shown.

Group	Prefer new procedure	Prefer old procedure	No preference
Nurses	100	80	20
Doctors	50	120	30

As the survey indicates, 100 nurses prefer the new procedure, 80 prefer the old procedure, and 20 have no preference; 50 doctors prefer the new procedure, 120 like the old procedure, and 30 have no preference. Since the main question is whether there is a difference in opinion, the null hypothesis is stated as follows:

H_0: The opinion about the procedure is *independent* of the profession.

The alternative hypothesis is stated as follows:

H_1: The opinion about the procedure is *dependent* on the profession.

If the null hypothesis is not rejected, the test means that both professions feel basically the same way about the procedure and the differences are due to chance. If the null hypothesis is rejected, the test means that one group feels differently about the procedure from the other. Remember that rejection does *not* mean that one group favours the procedure and the other does not. Perhaps both groups favour it or both dislike it, but in different proportions.

To test the null hypothesis by using the chi-square independence test, one must compute the expected frequencies, assuming that the null hypothesis is true. These frequencies are computed by using the observed frequencies given in the table.

When data are arranged in table form for the chi-square independence test, the table is called a **contingency table.** The table is made up of R rows and C columns. The table here has two rows and three columns.

Group	Prefer new procedure	Prefer old procedure	No preference
Nurses	100	80	20
Doctors	50	120	30

Note that row and column headings do not count in determining the number of rows and columns.

A contingency table is designated as an $R \times C$ (rows by columns) table. In this case, $R = 2$ and $C = 3$; hence, this table is a 2×3 contingency table. Each block in the table is called a *cell* and is designated by its row and column position. For example, the cell with a frequency of 80 is designated as $C_{1,2}$, or row 1, column 2. The cells are shown below.

	Column 1	**Column 2**	**Column 3**
Row 1	$C_{1,1}$	$C_{1,2}$	$C_{1,3}$
Row 2	$C_{2,1}$	$C_{2,2}$	$C_{2,3}$

The degrees of freedom for any contingency table are (rows − 1) times (columns − 1); that is, d.f. = $(R − 1)(C − 1)$. In this case, $(2 − 1)(3 − 1) = (1)(2) = 2$. The reason for this formula for d.f. is that all the expected values except one are free to vary in each row and in each column.

Using the previous table, one can compute the expected frequencies for each block (or cell), as shown next.

1. Find the sum of each row and each column, and find the grand total, as shown.

Group	**Prefer new procedure**	**Prefer old procedure**	**No preference**	**Total**
Nurses	100	80	20	Row 1 sum 200
Doctors	+50	+120	+30	Row 2 sum 200
Total	150	200	50	400
	Column 1 sum	Column 2 sum	Column 3 sum	Grand total

2. For each cell, multiply the corresponding row sum by the column sum and divide by the grand total, to get the expected value:

$$\text{Expected value} = \frac{\text{row sum} \times \text{column sum}}{\text{grand total}}$$

The rationale for the computation of the expected frequencies for a contingency table uses proportions. For $C_{1,1}$ a total of 150 out of 400 people prefer the new procedure. And since there are 200 nurses, one would expect, if the null hypothesis were true, (150/400)(200), or 75, of the nurses to be in favour of the new procedure.

For example, for $C_{1,2}$, the expected value, denoted by $E_{1,2}$, is (refer to the previous tables)

$$E_{1,2} = \frac{(200)(200)}{400} = 100$$

For each cell, the expected values are computed as follows:

$$E_{1,1} = \frac{(200)(150)}{400} = 75 \quad E_{1,2} = \frac{(200)(200)}{400} = 100 \quad E_{1,3} = \frac{(200)(50)}{400} = 25$$

$$E_{2,1} = \frac{(200)(150)}{400} = 75 \quad E_{2,2} = \frac{(200)(200)}{400} = 100 \quad E_{2,3} = \frac{(200)(50)}{400} = 25$$

The expected values can now be placed in the corresponding cells along with the observed values, as shown.

Group	**Prefer new procedure**	**Prefer old procedure**	No preference	Total
Nurses	100 (75)	80 (100)	20 (25)	200
Doctors	50 (75)	120 (100)	30 (25)	200
Total	150	200	50	400

The formula for the test statistic for the independence test is the same as the one used for the goodness-of-fit test. It is

$$\chi^2 = \sum \frac{(O - E)^2}{E}$$

For the previous example, compute the $(O - E)^2 / E$ values for each cell, and then find the sum.

$$
\begin{aligned}
\chi^2 &= \sum \frac{(O - E)^2}{E} \\
&= \frac{(100 - 75)^2}{75} + \frac{(80 - 100)^2}{100} + \frac{(20 - 25)^2}{25} + \frac{(50 - 75)^2}{75} \\
&\quad + \frac{(120 - 100)^2}{100} + \frac{(30 - 25)^2}{25} \\
&= 26.67
\end{aligned}
$$

The final steps are to make the decision and summarize the results. This test is always a right-tailed test, and the degrees of freedom are $(R-1)(C-1) = (2-1)(3-1) = 2$. If $\alpha = 0.05$, the critical value from Table G is 5.991. Hence, the decision is to reject the null hypothesis, since $26.67 > 5.991$. See Figure 11–7.

Figure 11–7

Critical Value and Test Statistic for the Postoperative Procedures Example

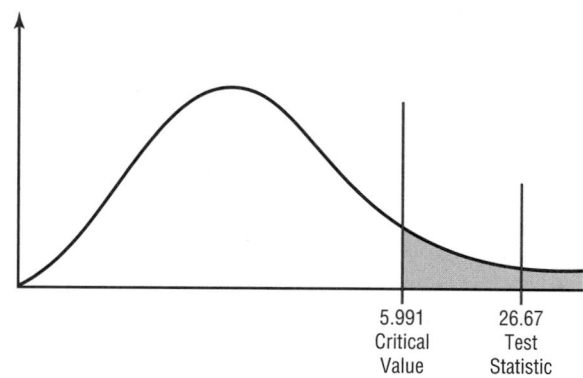

5.991	26.67
Critical	Test
Value	Statistic

The conclusion is that there is enough evidence to support the claim that opinion is related to (dependent on) profession—that is, doctors and nurses differ in their opinions about the procedure.

Examples 11–4 and 11–5 illustrate the procedure for the chi-square test of independence.

P-value Method

The *P*-value method for the χ^2 Independence Test is essentially the same as the procedure explained in Section 11–2 for the χ^2 Goodness-of-Fit Test. In essence, the critical value is not required in Step 2 before the calculation of the test statistic. After the test statistic is calculated, the *P*-value is either approximated using Table G in Appendix C or solved using technology. The decision rule for the *P*-value is shown below.

Decision Rule—*P*-value Method

If the P-value is less than or equal to the significance level (α), reject the null hypothesis; otherwise, fail to reject the null hypothesis.

For Example 11–5, the approximate *P*-value from Table G for d.f. $= 2$ and a test statistic $\chi^2 = 0.281$ is less than 0.005. The exact *P*-value using technology is 1.620 *E*-6 or 1.620×10^{-6} or 0.00000162. Since the *P*-value (0.00000162) $<$ significance level ($\alpha = 0.05$), reject H_0.

Example 11–4

A sociologist wishes to see whether the number of years of college a person has completed is related to her or his place of residence. A sample of 88 people is selected and classified as shown.

Location	No college	Four-year degree	Advanced degree	Total
Urban	15	12	8	35
Suburban	8	15	9	32
Rural	6	8	7	21
Total	29	35	24	88

At $\alpha = 0.05$, can the sociologist conclude that a person's location is dependent on the number of years of college?

Solution

Step 1   State the hypotheses and identify the claim.

H_0: A person's place of residence is independent of the number of years of college completed.

H_1: A person's place of residence is dependent on the number of years of college completed (claim).

Step 2   Find the critical value. The critical value is 9.488, since the degrees of freedom are $(3 - 1)(3 - 1) = (2)(2) = 4$.

Step 3   Compute the test statistic. To compute the test statistic, one must first compute the expected values.

$$E_{1,1} = \frac{(35)(29)}{88} = 11.53 \quad E_{1,2} = \frac{(35)(35)}{88} = 13.92 \quad E_{1,3} = \frac{(35)(24)}{88} = 9.55$$

$$E_{2,1} = \frac{(32)(29)}{88} = 10.55 \quad E_{2,2} = \frac{(32)(35)}{88} = 12.73 \quad E_{2,3} = \frac{(32)(24)}{88} = 8.73$$

$$E_{3,1} = \frac{(21)(29)}{88} = 6.92 \quad E_{3,2} = \frac{(21)(35)}{88} = 8.35 \quad E_{3,3} = \frac{(21)(24)}{88} = 5.73$$

The completed table is shown.

Location	No college	Four-year degree	Advanced degree	Total
Urban	15 (11.53)	12 (13.92)	8 (9.55)	35
Suburban	8 (10.55)	15 (12.73)	9 (8.73)	32
Rural	6 (6.92)	8 (8.35)	7 (5.73)	21
Total	29	35	24	88

Then the chi-square test value is

$$\chi^2 = \sum \frac{(O - E)^2}{E}$$

$$= \frac{(15 - 11.53)^2}{11.53} + \frac{(12 - 13.92)^2}{13.92} + \frac{(8 - 9.55)^2}{9.55}$$

$$+ \frac{(8 - 10.55)^2}{10.55} + \frac{(15 - 12.73)^2}{12.73} + \frac{(9 - 8.73)^2}{8.73}$$

$$+ \frac{(6 - 6.92)^2}{6.92} + \frac{(8 - 8.35)^2}{8.35} + \frac{(7 - 5.73)^2}{5.73} \approx 3.006$$

Figure 11–8

Critical Value and Test
Statistic for Example
11–4

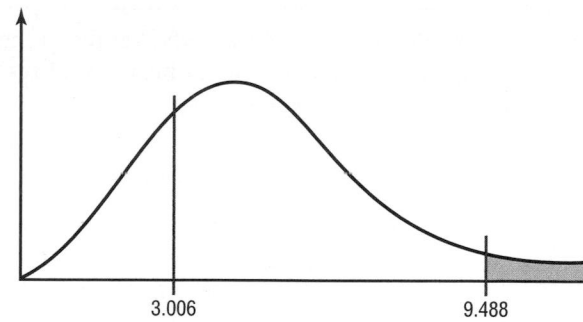

3.006   9.488

Step 4   Make the decision. The decision is to not reject the null hypothesis since
3.006 < 9.488. See Figure 11–8.

Step 5   Summarize the results. There is not enough evidence to support the claim that
a person's place of residence is dependent on the number of years of college
completed.

P-value Method

Using procedures explained in Section 11–2, the approximate *P*-value for Example
11–4 with d.f. = 4 and a test statistic $\chi^2 = 3.01$ is between 0.90 and 0.10. The exact
P-value using technology is 0.557. Since the *P*-value (0.557) > significance level
($\alpha = 0.05$), fail to reject H_0.

Example 11–5

A researcher wishes to determine whether there is a relationship between the gender of
an individual and the amount of alcohol consumed. A sample of 68 people is selected,
and the following data are obtained. Use the *P*-value method.

Gender	Alcohol consumption			Total
	Low	**Moderate**	**High**	
Male	10	9	8	27
Female	13	16	12	41
Total	23	25	20	68

At $\alpha = 0.10$, can the researcher conclude that alcohol consumption is related to gender?

Solution

Step 1   State the hypotheses and identify the claim.

H_0: The amount of alcohol that a person consumes is independent of the
individual's gender.

H_1: The amount of alcohol that a person consumes is dependent on the
individual's gender (claim).

Step 2   Compute the test statistic. First, compute the expected values.

$$E_{1,1} = \frac{(27)(23)}{68} = 9.13 \quad E_{1,2} = \frac{(27)(25)}{68} = 9.93 \quad E_{1,3} = \frac{(27)(20)}{68} = 7.94$$

$$E_{2,1} = \frac{(41)(23)}{68} = 13.87 \quad E_{2,2} = \frac{(41)(25)}{68} = 15.07 \quad E_{2,3} = \frac{(41)(20)}{68} = 12.06$$

The completed table is shown.

	Alcohol consumption			
Gender	**Low**	**Moderate**	**High**	**Total**
Male	10 (9.13)	9 (9.93)	8 (7.94)	27
Female	13 (13.87)	16 (15.07)	12 (12.06)	41
Total	23	25	20	68

Then the test statistic is

$$\chi^2 = \sum \frac{(O - E)^2}{E}$$

$$= \frac{(10 - 9.13)^2}{9.13} + \frac{(9 - 9.93)^2}{9.93} + \frac{(8 - 7.94)^2}{7.94}$$

$$+ \frac{(13 - 13.87)^2}{13.87} + \frac{(16 - 15.07)^2}{15.07} + \frac{(12 - 12.06)^2}{12.06}$$

$$\approx 0.281$$

Step 3 Find *P*-value.

The *P*-value, obtained from Table G in Appendix C, for the test statistic, $\chi^2 = 0.281$, with d.f. = 2 is between 0.90 and 0.10. See Figure 11–9.

Figure 11–9

Finding the *P*-value

P-value is between 0.90 and 0.10

Degrees of Freedom	0.995	0.99	0.975	0.95	0.90	0.10	0.05	0.025	0.01	0.005
1	0.000	0.000	0.001	0.004	0.016	2.706	3.841	5.024	6.635	7.879
2	0.010	0.020	0.051	0.103	0.211	4.605	5.991	7.378	9.210	10.597
3	0.072	0.115	0.216	0.352	0.584	6.251	7.815	9.348	11.345	12.838
4	0.207	0.297	0.484	0.711	1.064	7.779	9.486	11.143	13.277	14.860

Test statistic is 0.281

Note: The *P*-value obtained from statistical software, spreadsheet, or calculator is 0.869.

Step 4 Make the decision.

Since the *P*-value (0.869) is greater than the significance level ($\alpha = 0.10$), fail to reject the null hypothesis, as shown in Figure 11–10.

Figure 11–10

Comparison of χ^2 Traditional Method and *P*-value Method

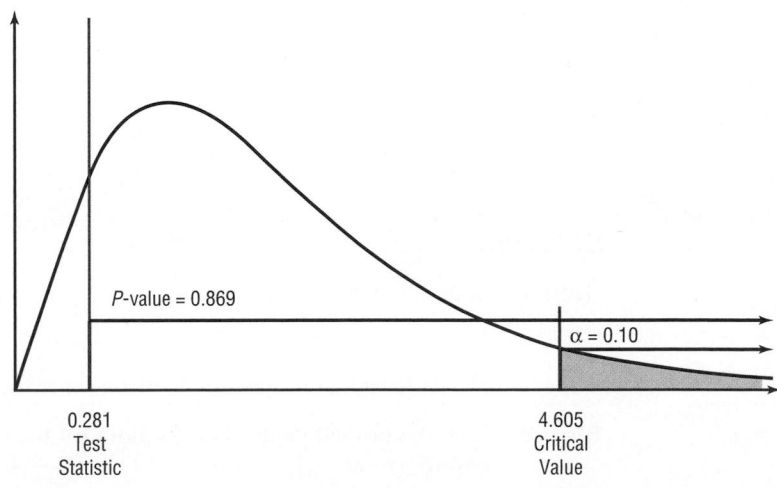

P-value = 0.869

$\alpha = 0.10$

0.281
Test
Statistic

4.605
Critical
Value

Step 5   Summarize the results.

There is not enough evidence to support the claim that the amount of alcohol a person consumes is dependent on the individual's gender.

Traditional Method

The critical value for $\alpha = 0.10$, d.f. $= (2-1)(3-1) = 2$, is 4.605. Fail to reject the null hypothesis, since the test statistic ($\chi^2 = 0.281$) < critical value ($\chi^2 = 4.605$), as shown in Figure 11–10.

Objective 3

Test proportions for homogeneity, using chi-square.

Test for Homogeneity of Proportions

The second chi-square test that uses a contingency table is called the **homogeneity of proportions test.** In this situation, samples are selected from several different populations, and the researcher is interested in determining whether the proportions of elements that have a common characteristic are the same for each population. The sample sizes are specified in advance, making either the row totals or column totals in the contingency table known before the samples are selected. For example, a researcher may select a sample of 50 freshmen, 50 sophomores, 50 juniors, and 50 seniors and then find the proportion of students who are smokers in each level. The researcher will then compare the proportions for each group to see if they are equal. The hypotheses in this case would be

$H_0: p_1 = p_2 = p_3 = p_4$

H_1: At least one proportion is different from the others.

If one does not reject the null hypothesis, it can be assumed that the proportions are equal and the differences in them are due to chance. Hence, the proportion of students who smoke is the same for grade levels freshmen through senior. When the null hypothesis is rejected, it can be assumed that the proportions are not all equal. The computational procedure is the same as that for the test of independence shown in Example 11–6.

Example 11–6

A researcher selected a sample of 50 seniors from each of three area high schools and asked each senior, "Do you drive to school in a car owned by either you or your parents?" The data are shown in the table. At $\alpha = 0.05$, test the claim that the proportion of students who drive their own or their parents' car is the same at all three schools.

	School 1	School 2	School 3	Total
Yes	18	22	16	56
No	32	28	34	94
Total	50	50	50	150

Interesting Fact

Water is the most critical nutrient in your body. It is needed for just about everything that happens. Water is lost fast. A ½ litre daily is lost just exhaling, 2½ litres through normal waste and body cooling, and 1 to 2 litres per hour running, biking, or working out.

Solution

Step 1   State the hypotheses.

$H_0: p_1 = p_2 = p_3$

H_1: At least one proportion is different from the others.

Step 2   Find the critical value. The formula for the degrees of freedom is the same as before: (rows $-$ 1)(columns $-$ 1) $= (2-1)(3-1) = 1(2) = 2$. The critical value is 5.991.

Step 3 Compute the test statistic. First, compute the expected values.

$$E_{1,1} = \frac{(56)(50)}{150} = 18.67 \qquad E_{2,1} = \frac{(94)(50)}{150} = 31.33$$

$$E_{1,2} = \frac{(56)(50)}{150} = 18.67 \qquad E_{2,2} = \frac{(94)(50)}{150} = 31.33$$

$$E_{1,3} = \frac{(56)(50)}{150} = 18.67 \qquad E_{2,3} = \frac{(94)(50)}{150} = 31.33$$

The completed table is shown here.

	School 1	School 2	School 3	Total
Yes	18 (18.67)	22 (18.67)	16 (18.67)	56
No	32 (31.33)	28 (31.33)	34 (31.33)	94
Total	50	50	50	150

The test statistic is

$$\chi^2 = \sum \frac{(O - E)^2}{E}$$
$$= \frac{(18 - 18.67)^2}{18.67} + \frac{(22 - 18.67)^2}{18.67} + \frac{(16 - 18.67)^2}{18.67}$$
$$+ \frac{(32 - 31.33)^2}{31.33} + \frac{(28 - 31.33)^2}{31.33} + \frac{(34 - 31.33)^2}{31.33}$$
$$\approx 1.596$$

Step 4 Make the decision. The decision is to not reject the null hypothesis, since the test statistic ($\chi^2 = 1.596$) < critical value ($\chi^2 = 5.991$).

Step 5 Summarize the results. There is not enough evidence to reject the null hypothesis that the proportions of high school students who drive their own or their parents' car to school are equal for each school.

P-Value Method

Using procedures explained in Section 11–2, the approximate P-value for Example 11–6 for d.f. = 2 and a test statistic $\chi^2 = 1.596$ is between 0.90 and 0.10. The exact P-value using technology is 0.450. Since the P-value (0.450) > significance level ($\alpha = 0.05$), fail to reject H_0.

The steps for the chi-square independence and homogeneity tests are summarized in this Procedure Table.

Procedure Table

The Chi-Square Independence and Homogeneity Tests (Traditional Method)

Step 1 State the hypotheses and identify the claim.

Step 2 Find the critical value in the right tail. Use Table G.

Step 3 Compute the test statistic. To compute the test statistic, first find the expected values. For each cell of the contingency table, use the formula

$$E = \frac{(\text{row sum})(\text{column sum})}{\text{grand total}}$$

Procedure Table *(continued)*

to get the expected value. To find the test statistic, use the formula

$$\chi^2 = \sum \frac{(O - E)^2}{E}$$

Step 4   Make the decision.

Step 5   Summarize the results.

The assumptions for the two chi-square tests are given next.

Assumptions for the Chi-Square Independence and Homogeneity Tests

1. The data are obtained from a random sample.
2. The expected value in each cell must be 5 or more.

If the expected values are not 5 or more, combine categories.

Applying the Concepts 11–3

Satellite Dishes in Restricted Areas

Should satellite dishes be allowed in environmentally sensitive or deed-restricted areas? An opinion poll was taken to see if how a person felt about satellite dish restrictions was related to his or her age. A chi-square test was run, creating the following computer-generated information.

Degrees of freedom d.f. = 6
Test statistic χ^2 = 61.25
Critical value = 12.6
P-value = 0.00 (2.5 $\|$ E^{-11})
Significance level = 0.05

	18–29	30–49	50–64	65 and up
For	96 (79.5)	96 (79.5)	90 (79.5)	36 (79.5)
Against	201 (204.75)	189 (204.75)	195 (204.75)	234 (204.75)
Don't know	3 (15.75)	15 (15.75)	15 (15.75)	30 (15.75)

1. Which number from the output is compared to the significance level to check if the null hypothesis should be rejected?

2. Which number from the output gives the probability of a type I error that is calculated from your sample data?

3. Was a right-, left-, or two-tailed test run? Why?

4. Can you tell how many rows and columns there were by looking at the degrees of freedom?

5. Does increasing the sample size change the degrees of freedom?

6. What are your conclusions? Look at the observed and expected frequencies in the table to draw some of your own specific conclusions about response and age.

7. What would your conclusions be if the level of significance were initially set at 0.10?

8. Does chi-square tell you which cell's observed and expected frequencies are significantly different?

See page 528 for the answers.

Exercises 11–3

1. How is the chi-square independence test similar to the goodness-of-fit test? How is it different?

2. How are the degrees of freedom computed for the independence test?

3. Generally, how would the null and alternative hypotheses be stated for the chi-square independence test?

4. What is the name of the table used in the independence test?

5. How are the expected values computed for each cell in the table?

6. Explain how the chi-square independence test differs from the chi-square homogeneity of proportions test.

7. How are the null and alternative hypotheses stated for the test of homogeneity of proportions?

For Exercises 8 through 31, perform the following steps.

a. State the hypotheses and identify the claim.
b. Find the critical value.
c. Compute the test statistic.
d. Make the decision.
e. Summarize the results.

Use the traditional method of hypothesis testing unless otherwise specified.

8. A study is conducted as to whether there is a relationship between joggers and the consumption of nutritional supplements. A random sample of 210 subjects is selected, and they are classified as shown. At $\alpha = 0.05$, test the claim that jogging and the consumption of supplements are not related. Why might supplement manufacturers use the results of this study?

Jogging status	Daily	Weekly	As needed
Joggers	34	52	23
Nonjoggers	18	65	18

9. Is the type of pet owned dependent on annual household income? Use $\alpha = 0.05$.

	Type of pet			
Income ($)	Dog	Cat	Bird	Horse
Under 12,500	127	139	173	95
12,500–24,999	191	197	209	203
25,000–39,999	216	215	220	218
40,000–59,999	215	212	175	231
60,000 and over	254	237	223	254

Source: *N.Y. Times Almanac.*

10. This table lists the number of military personnel by status (full-time active duty or primary reserves) in each branch of the Canadian Forces. At $\alpha = 0.05$, is there sufficient evidence to conclude that a relationship exists between military personnel status and branch of the Canadian Forces?

	Active	Reserve
Army	33,000	24,000
Navy	11,200	4,200
Air Force	19,400	2,300

Source: Department of National Defence.

11. Is the composition of the House of Commons related to the province of the Member of Parliament? Use $\alpha = 0.05$.

	Conservative	Liberal	New Democrat
British Columbia	18	8	10
Manitoba	8	3	3
Ontario	41	53	12
New Brunswick	3	6	1

Source: Parliament of Canada.

12. Is the size of the U.S. population by age related to the state that it's in? Use $\alpha = 0.05$. (Population values are in thousands.)

	Under 5	5–17	18–24	25–44	45–64	65+
Pennsylvania	721	2140	1025	3515	2702	1899
Ohio	740	2104	1065	3359	2487	1501

Source: *N.Y. Times Almanac.*

13. Some 300 men and 210 women were asked about how many ads in all media they think they saw or heard during one day. The results are shown.

	Number				
	1–30	31–50	51–100	101–300	301 or more
Men	45	60	90	54	51
Women	50	50	54	30	26

At $\alpha = 0.01$, is the number of ads people feel that they see or hear related to the gender of the person?

Source: Based on information from *USA TODAY.*

14. An instructor wishes to see if the way people obtain information is independent of their educational background. A survey of 400 high school and college graduates yielded this information. At $\alpha = 0.05$, test the claim that the way people obtain information is independent of their educational background.

	Television	Newspapers	Other sources
High school	159	90	51
College	27	42	31

Source: *USA TODAY.*

15. A study was conducted to see if there was a relationship between the gender of an attorney and the type of practice he or she is engaged in. A sample of 240

attorneys is selected, and the results are shown. At $\alpha = 0.05$, can it be assumed that gender and employment are independent?

Gender	Private practice	Law firm	Government
Male	112	16	12
Female	64	18	18

16. A researcher wants to see if there is a relationship between crime rates and Canadian city. Data rates shown are calculated per 100,000 population.

	Homicide	Robbery	Break-ins
Edmonton	4.3	142	1025
Winnipeg	3.7	263	1070
Hamilton	1.6	102	681

Using $\alpha = 0.05$, can it be concluded that the crime rates and Canadian city are independent.

Source: Statistics Canada.

17. A study is being conducted to determine whether the age of the customer is related to the type of movie he or she rents. A sample of renters gives the data shown here. At $\alpha = 0.10$, is the type of movie selected related to the customer's age?

Age	Documentary	Comedy	Mystery
12–20	14	9	8
21–29	15	14	9
30–38	9	21	39
39–47	7	22	17
48 and over	6	38	12

Type of movie header spans Documentary/Comedy/Mystery.

18. A researcher wishes to see if the gender of the person who prepares dinner is independent of the time when the person decides what to eat for dinner. A sample of 70 men and women is selected, and the results are shown. At $\alpha = 0.05$, can it be concluded that the variables are independent? Summarize the results in your own words.

Gender	In the afternoon	In the morning	Day or days before
Female	20	9	10
Male	16	12	3

19. A survey at a ballpark shows this selection of snacks purchased. At $\alpha = 0.10$, is the snack chosen independent of the gender of the consumer?

Gender	Hot dog	Peanuts	Popcorn
Male	12	21	19
Female	13	8	25

Snack header spans Hot dog/Peanuts/Popcorn.

20. To test the effectiveness of a new drug, a researcher gives one group of individuals the new drug and another group a placebo. The results of the study are shown

here. At $\alpha = 0.10$, can the researcher conclude that the drug is effective? Use the P-value method.

Medication	Effective	Not effective
Drug	32	9
Placebo	12	18

21. A book publisher wishes to determine whether there is a difference in the type of book selected by males and females for recreational reading. A random sample provides the data given here. At $\alpha = 0.05$, test the claim that the type of book selected is independent of the gender of the individual. Use the P-value method.

Gender	Mystery	Romance	Self-help
Male	243	201	191
Female	135	149	202

Type of book header spans Mystery/Romance/Self-help.

22. Environics Research Group has reported that 54% of Canadian health care professionals have signed an organ donor card. A researcher surveys 50 randomly selected Canadian drivers in the health care profession in each of three regions to determine the percentage who have signed an organ donor card. The results are shown here. At $\alpha = 0.01$, test the claim that the proportion of those who have signed donor cards is equal in all three regions.

Donor Card	Region A	Region B	Region C
Signed	19	27	24
Not signed	31	23	26
Total	50	50	50

Source: Canadian Council for Donation and Transplantation (CCDT).

23. Statistics Canada report that 23% of Canadians are obese. A physical educator wants to determine if the school district's students have the same percentage as the national average. Measurements for obesity (20% for males, 25% for females over ideal weight), are taken at four district schools. The results are shown here. At $\alpha = 0.05$, test the claim that the proportions who are obese in each district are equal.

	West	East	South	North
Obese	22	28	20	24
Not obese	98	92	100	96

Source: Statistics Canada.

24. An advertising firm has decided to ask 92 randomly selected individuals to fill out a brief survey related to their shopping experience in three shopping malls. According to previous reports, 33% of Canadians refuse to participate in surveys. The results are shown here. At $\alpha = 0.01$, test the claim that the proportion of those who are willing to participate in each mall are equal.

	Mall A	Mall B	Mall C
Will participate	52	45	36
Will not participate	40	47	56
	92	92	92

Source: Statistics Canada.

25. A researcher wishes to see if the proportions of low-paid workers based on education level have changed during the last 20 years. A sample of 100 workers is selected, and the results are shown. At $\alpha = 0.05$, test the claim that the proportions have not changed.

Education level	Less than high school	High school diploma	Post-secondary certificate	University degree
20 years ago	22	17	12	6
Now	26	21	14	7
Total	48	38	26	13

Source: Statistics Canada.

26. According to a recent survey, 59% of the population aged 8 to 17 would prefer that their mother work outside the home, regardless of what she does now. A school district psychologist decided to select 3 samples of 60 students each in elementary, middle, and high school to see how the students in her district felt about the issue. At $\alpha = 0.10$, test the claim that the proportions of the students who prefer that their mother have a job are equal.

	Elementary	Middle	High
Prefers mother work	29	38	51
Prefers mother not work	31	22	9
Total	60	60	60

Source: Daniel Weiss, 100% American.

27. A researcher surveyed 100 randomly selected lawyers in each of four areas of the country and asked them if they had performed *pro bono* work for 25 or fewer hours in the last year. The results are shown here. At $\alpha = 0.10$, is there enough evidence to reject the claim that the proportions of those who accepted *pro bono* work for 25 hours or less are the same in each area?

	North	South	East	West
Yes	43	39	22	28
No	57	61	78	72
Total	100	100	100	100

Source: Daniel Weiss, *100% American.*

28. On average, 79% of North American fathers are in the delivery room when their children are born. A physician's assistant surveyed 300 first-time fathers to determine if they had been in the delivery room when their children were born. The results are shown here. At $\alpha = 0.05$, is there enough evidence to reject the claim that the proportions of those who were in the delivery room at the time of birth are the same?

	Hospital A	Hospital B	Hospital C	Hospital D
Present	66	60	57	56
Not present	9	15	18	19
Total	75	75	75	75

Source: Daniel Weiss, *100% American.*

29. A national Canadian survey of children's playground injuries indicated that 20% of injuries resulted in a medical visit. An insurance investigator wants to show that the proportion of playground injuries requiring a medical visit is the same across the country. Four regions are sampled with the results shown in the table below. At $\alpha = 0.05$, test the claim that the proportions are the same. Use the *P*-value method.

	West	Prairies	Central	Atlantic
Medical visit	7	8	4	6
No medical visit	23	22	26	24
	30	30	30	30

Source: Calgary Health Region.

30. In 2004, 55% of Nova Scotians voted to prohibit "big stores" from opening on Sundays. In 2006, the Supreme Court of Canada sided with two grocery chains to allow Sunday shopping, Nova Scotians have strong opinions on this issue. An advocate for workers' rights wants to show that all regions of Nova Scotia are equally in favour of a ban on Sunday shopping. Four regions are selected and 125 potential shoppers are surveyed. The results are shown below. At $\alpha = 0.10$, test the claim that the proportions of Nova Scotians in favour of maintaining the ban on Sunday openings is equal in each region. Use the *P*-value method.

	Region 1	Region 2	Region 3	Region 4
In favour of ban	66	70	56	63
Not in favour of ban	59	55	69	62
	125	125	125	125

Source: CBC.ca.

31. The vice president of a large supermarket chain wished to determine if her customers made a list before going grocery shopping. She surveyed 288 customers in three stores. The results are shown here. At $\alpha = 0.10$, test the claim that the proportions of the customers in the three stores who made a list before going shopping are equal.

	Store A	Store B	Store C
Made list	77	74	68
No list	19	22	28
Total	96	96	96

Source: Daniel Weiss, *100% American.*

Extending the Concepts

32. For a 2 × 2 table, a, b, c, and d are the observed values for each cell, as shown.

a	b
c	d

The chi-square test value can be computed as

$$\chi^2 = \frac{n(ad - bc)^2}{(a + b)(a + c)(c + d)(b + d)}$$

where $n = a + b + c + d$. Compute the χ^2 test statistic by using the above formula and the formula $\Sigma (O - E)^2/E$, and compare the results for the following table.

12	15
9	23

33. For the contingency table shown in Exercise 32, compute the chi-square test statistic by using the Yates correction for continuity.

34. When the chi-square test value is significant and there is a relationship between the variables, the strength of this relationship can be measured by using the *contingency coefficient*. The formula for the contingency coefficient is

$$C = \sqrt{\frac{\chi^2}{\chi^2 + n}}$$

where χ^2 is the test statistic and n is the sum of frequencies of the cells. The contingency coefficient will always be less than 1. Compute the contingency coefficient for Exercises 8 and 20.

Speaking of
Statistics

Does Colour Affect Your Appetite?

It has been suggested that colour is related to appetite in humans. For example, if the walls in a restaurant are painted certain colours, it is thought that the customer will eat more food. A study was done at the University of Illinois and the University of Pennsylvania. When people were given six varieties of jellybeans mixed in a bowl or separated by colour, they ate about twice as many from the bowl with the mixed jellybeans as from the bowls that were separated by colour.

It is thought that when the jellybeans were mixed, people felt that it offered a greater variety of choices, and the variety of choices increased their appetites.

In this case one variable—colour—is categorical, and the other variable—amount of jellybeans eaten—is numerical. Could a chi-square goodness-of-fit test be used here? If so, suggest how it could be set up.

11–4   Summary

Three uses of the chi-square distribution were explained in this chapter. It can be used as a goodness-of-fit test to determine whether the frequencies of a distribution are the same as the hypothesized frequencies. For example, is the number of defective parts produced by a factory the same each day? This test is always a right-tailed test.

The test of independence is used to determine whether two variables are related or are independent. This test uses a contingency table and is always a right-tailed test. An example of its use is a test to determine whether the attitudes of urban residents about the recycling of trash differ from the attitudes of rural residents.

Finally, the homogeneity of proportions test is used to determine if several proportions are all equal when samples are selected from different populations.

The chi-square distribution is also used for other types of statistical hypothesis tests, such as the Kruskal-Wallis test, which is explained in Chapter 13.

For step-by-step guidance on the use of technology for this chapter, visit the Online Learning Centre at www.mcgrawhill.ca/olc/bluman. Summary procedures for Minitab, SPSS, Excel, and TI-83 Plus or TI-84 Plus can also be found in Appendix E.

Important Terms

contingency table 510

expected frequency 501

goodness-of-fit test 301

homogeneity of proportions test 516

independence test 510

observed frequency 501

Important Formulas

Formula for the chi-square test for goodness of fit:

$$\chi^2 = \sum \frac{(O - E)^2}{E}$$

with degrees of freedom equal to the number of categories minus 1 and where

O = observed frequency

E = expected frequency

Formula for the chi-square independence and homogeneity of proportions tests:

$$\chi^2 = \sum \frac{(O - E)^2}{E}$$

with degrees of freedom equal to (rows − 1) times (columns − 1). Formula for the expected value for each cell:

$$E = \frac{(\text{row sum})(\text{column sum})}{\text{grand total}}$$

Review Exercises

For Exercises 1 through 10, follow these steps.

a. State the hypotheses and identify the claim.
b. Find the critical value(s).
c. Compute the test statistic.
d. Make the decision.
e. Summarize the results.

Use the traditional method of hypothesis testing unless otherwise specified.

1. A storeowner wishes to see if people have a favourite day of the week to shop. A sample of 400 people is selected, and each is asked his or her preference. The data are shown. At $\alpha = 0.05$, test the claim that

shoppers have no preference. Give one example of how retail merchants would be able to use the numbers in this study.

Day	Sun.	Mon.	Tues.	Wed.	Thurs.	Fri.	Sat.
Number	28	16	20	26	74	96	140

Source: Based on information from the International Mass Retail Association.

2. A researcher reads that the marital status of Canadian adults is distributed as follows: married, 48%; single, 42%; widowed 5%; divorced 5%. She selects a sample of 150 people, and the results are shown. At $\alpha = 0.01$, can it be concluded that marital status is distributed as she has read? Give one factor that might influence the results of this study.

Marital status	Married	Single	Widowed	Divorced
Number	64	79	3	4

Source: Statistics Canada.

3. The federal government has proposed labelling tires by fuel efficiency to save fuel and cut emissions. A survey was taken to see who would use these labels. At $\alpha = 0.10$, is the gender of the individual related to whether or not a person would use these labels? The data from a sample are shown here.

Gender	Yes	No	Undecided
Men	114	30	6
Women	136	16	8

Source: USA TODAY.

4. A police investigator read that the reasons why gun sales to applicants were denied were distributed as follows: criminal history of felonies, 75%; domestic violence conviction, 11%; and drug abuse, fugitive, etc., 14%. A sample of applicants in a large study who were refused sales is obtained and is distributed as follows. At $\alpha = 0.10$, can it be concluded that the distribution is as stated? Do you think the results might be different in a rural area?

Reason	Criminal history	Domestic violence	Drug abuse etc.
Number	120	42	38

Source: Based on FBI statistics.

5. A survey was taken on how a lump-sum pension would be invested by 45-year-olds and 65-year-olds. The data are shown here. At $\alpha = 0.05$, is there a relationship between the age of the investor and the way the money would be invested?

	Large company stock funds	Small company stock funds	Inter-national stock funds	CDs or money market funds	Bonds
Age 45	20	10	10	15	45
Age 65	42	24	24	6	24

Source: USA TODAY.

6. A car manufacturer wishes to determine whether the type of car purchased is related to the individual's gender. The data obtained from a sample are shown here. At $\alpha = 0.01$, is the gender of the purchaser related to the type of car purchased?

Gender of purchaser	Type of vehicle purchased			
	Sedan	Compact	Station wagon	SUV
Male	33	27	23	17
Female	21	34	41	18

Statistics Today

Statistics and Heredity—Revisited

Using probability, Mendel predicted the following:

	Smooth		Wrinkled	
	Yellow	Green	Yellow	Green
Expected	0.5625	0.1875	0.1875	0.0625

The observed results were these:

	Smooth		Wrinkled	
	Yellow	Green	Yellow	Green
Observed	0.5666	0.1942	0.1816	0.0556

Using chi-square tests on the data, Mendel found that his predictions were accurate in most cases (i.e., a good fit), thus supporting his theory. He reported many highly successful experiments. Mendel's genetic theory is simple but useful in predicting the results of hybridization.

A Fly in the Ointment

Although Mendel's theory is basically correct, an English statistician named R. A. Fisher examined Mendel's data some 50 years later. He found that the observed (actual) results agreed too closely with the expected (theoretical) results and concluded that the data had in some way been falsified. The results were too good to be true. Several explanations have been proposed, ranging from deliberate misinterpretation to an assistant's error, but no one can be sure how this happened.

7. A guidance counsellor wishes to determine if the proportions of high school girls in his school district who have jobs are equal to the national average of 36%. He surveys 80 female students, ages 16 through 18, to determine if they work or not. The results are shown. At $\alpha = 0.01$, test the claim that the proportions of girls who work are equal. Use the P-value method.

	16-year-olds	17-year-olds	18-year-olds
Work	45	31	38
Don't work	35	49	42
Total	80	80	80

Source: Michael D. Shook and Robert L. Shook, *The Book of Odds.*

8. The risk of injury is higher for males compared to females (57% versus 43%). A hospital emergency room supervisor wishes to determine if the proportions of injuries to males in his hospital are the same for each of four months. He surveys 100 injuries treated in his ER for each month. The results are shown here. At $\alpha = 0.05$, can he reject the claim that the proportions of injuries for males are equal for each of the four months?

	May	June	July	August
Male	51	47	58	63
Female	49	53	42	37
Total	100	100	100	100

Source: Michael D. Shook and Robert L. Shook, *The Book of Odds.*

9. A researcher surveyed 50 randomly selected subjects in four cities and asked if they felt that their anger was the most difficult behaviour to control. The results are shown. At $\alpha = 0.10$, is there enough evidence to reject the claim that the proportion of those who felt this way in each city is the same?

	City A	City B	City C	City D
Yes	12	15	10	21
No	38	35	40	29
Total	50	50	50	50

10. A researcher surveyed 50 randomly selected males and 50 randomly selected females to see how they paid their bills. The data are shown. At $\alpha = 0.01$, test the claim that the proportions are not equal. What might be a reason for the difference, if one exists?

Type of payment	Cheques	Electronically	In person
Males	27	15	8
Females	22	19	9
Total	49	34	17

Source: Based on information from Gallup.

Data Analysis

The Data Bank is located in Appendix D, or on the World Wide Web by following links from www. mcgrawhill.ca/olc/bluman.

1. Select a sample of 40 individuals from the Data Bank. Use the chi-square goodness-of-fit test to see if the marital status of individuals is equally distributed.

2. Use the chi-square test of independence to test the hypothesis that smoking is independent of gender. Use a sample of at least 75 people.

3. Using the data from Data Set X in Appendix D, classify the data as 1–3, 4–6, 7–9, etc. Use the chi-square goodness-of-fit test to see if the number of times each ball is drawn is equally distributed.

Chapter Quiz

Determine whether each statement is true or false. If the statement is false, explain why.

1. The chi-square test of independence is always two-tailed.

2. The test statistics for the chi-square goodness-of-fit test and the independence test are computed by using the same formula.

3. When the null hypothesis is rejected in the goodness-of-fit test, it means there is close agreement between the observed and expected frequencies.

Select the best answer.

4. The values of the chi-square variable cannot be
   a. Positive
   b. 0
   c. Negative
   d. None of the above

5. The null hypothesis for the chi-square test of independence is that the variables are
   a. Dependent
   b. Independent

   c. Related

   d. Always 0

6. The degrees of freedom for the goodness-of-fit test are

   a. 0

   b. 1

   c. Sample size − 1

   d. Number of categories − 1

Complete the following statements with the best answer.

7. The degrees of freedom for a 4 × 3 contingency table are _____ .

8. An important assumption for the chi-square test is that the observations must be _____ .

9. The chi-square goodness-of-fit test is always _____ tailed.

10. In the chi-square independence test, the expected frequency for each class must always be _____ .

For Exercises 11 through 19, follow these steps.

   a. State the hypotheses and identify the claim.

   b. Find the critical value.

   c. Compute the test statistic.

   d. Make the decision.

   e. Summarize the results.

Use the traditional method of hypothesis testing unless otherwise specified.

11. A survey of why people lost their jobs produced the following results. At $\alpha = 0.05$, test the claim that the number of responses is equally distributed. Do you think the results might be different if the study were done 10 years ago?

Reason	Company closing	Position abolished	Insufficient work
Number	26	18	28

Source: Based on information from U.S. Department of Labor.

12. A food service manager read that the place where people consumed takeout food is distributed as follows: home, 53%; car, 19%; work, 14%; other, 14%. A survey of 300 individuals showed the following results. At $\alpha = 0.01$, can it be concluded that the distribution is as stated? Where would a fast-food restaurant want to target its advertisements?

Place	Home	Car	Work	Other
Number	142	57	51	50

Source: Beef Industry Council.

13. A survey found that 62% of the respondents stated that they never watched the home shopping channels on cable television, 23% stated that they watched the channels rarely, 11% stated that they watched them occasionally, and 4% stated that they watched them frequently. A group of 200 college students was surveyed, and 105 stated that they never watched the home shopping channels, 72 stated that they watched them rarely, 13 stated that they watched them occasionally, and 10 stated that they watched them frequently. At $\alpha = 0.05$, can it be concluded that the college students differ in their preference for the home shopping channels?

Source: Based on information obtained from *USA TODAY* Snapshots.

14. The U.S. 2000 Census indicated the following percentages for means of commuting to work for workers over 15 years of age.

Alone	75.7
Carpooling	12.2
Public	4.7
Walked	2.9
Other	1.2
Worked at home	3.3

A random sample of workers found that 320 drove alone, 100 carpooled, 30 used public transportation, 20 walked, 10 used other forms of transportation, and 20 worked at home. Is there sufficient evidence to conclude that the proportions of workers using each type of transportation differ from those in the U.S. Census report? Use $\alpha = 0.05$.

Source: Census Bureau, *Washington Observer-Reporter.*

15. A survey of women and men asked what their favourite ice cream flavour was. The results are shown. At $\alpha = 0.05$, can it be concluded that the favourite flavour is independent of gender?

	Flavour			
	Vanilla	Chocolate	Strawberry	Other
Women	62	36	10	2
Men	49	37	5	9

16. A pizza shop owner wishes to determine if the type of pizza a person selects is related to the age of the individual. The data obtained from a sample are shown here. At $\alpha = 0.10$, is the age of the purchaser related to the type of pizza ordered? Use the *P*-value method.

	Type of pizza			
Age	Plain	Pepperoni	Mushroom	Double cheese
10–19	12	21	39	71
20–29	18	76	52	87
30–39	24	50	40	47
40–49	52	30	12	28

17. A survey at a ballpark shows the following selection of pennants sold to fans. The data are presented here. At $\alpha = 0.10$, is the colour of the pennant purchased independent of the gender of the individual?

	Blue	Yellow	Red
Men	519	659	876
Women	487	702	787

18. In a survey of children ages 8 through 11, these data were obtained as to what their parents should do with the money from a $400 tax credit.

	Keep it for themselves	Give it to their children	Don't know
Girls	162	132	6
Boys	147	147	6

At $\alpha = 0.10$, is there a relationship between the feelings of the children and the gender of the children?

Source: Based on information from *USA TODAY* Snapshot.

19. A survey of 60 men and 60 women asked if they would be happy spending the rest of their careers with their present employers. The results are shown. At $\alpha = 0.10$, can it be concluded that the proportions are equal? If they are not equal, give a possible reason for the difference.

	Yes	No	Undecided
Men	40	15	5
Women	36	9	15
Total	76	24	20

Source: Based on information from a Maritz Poll.

Critical Thinking Challenges

1. Use your calculator or the Minitab or similar technology random number generator to generate 100 two-digit random numbers. Make a grouped frequency distribution, using the chi-square goodness-of-fit test to see if the distribution is random. To do this, use an expected frequency of 10 for each class. Can it be concluded that the distribution is random? Explain.

2. Simulate the provincial lottery by using your calculator or Minitab or similar technology to generate 100 three-digit random numbers. Group these numbers 100–199,

200–299, etc. Use the chi-square goodness-of-fit test to see if the numbers are random. The expected frequency for each class should be 10. Explain why.

3. Purchase a bag of M&M candy and count the number of pieces of each colour. Using the information as your sample, state a hypothesis for the distribution of colours and compare your hypothesis to one obtained from the *USA TODAY* Snapshot. What did you discover?

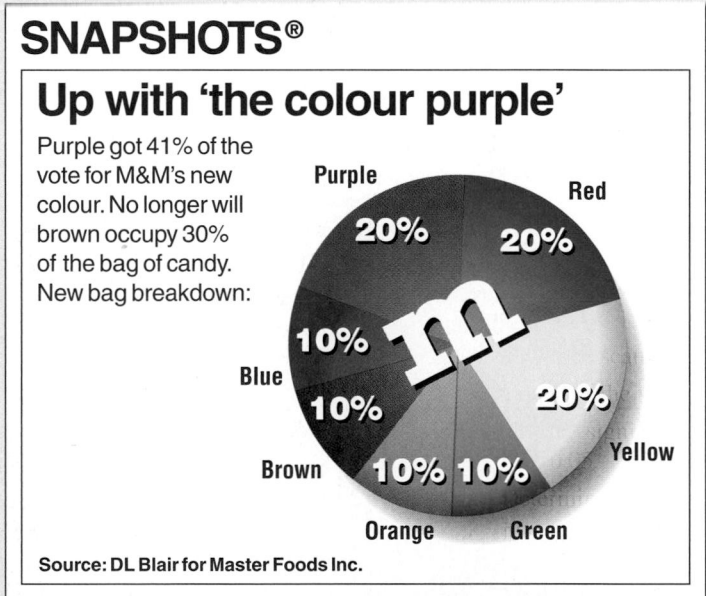

SNAPSHOTS®

Up with 'the colour purple'

Purple got 41% of the vote for M&M's new colour. No longer will brown occupy 30% of the bag of candy. New bag breakdown:

Purple 20% Red 20% Blue 10% Yellow 20% Brown 10% Orange 10% Green 10%

Source: DL Blair for Master Foods Inc.

Source: Copyright 2002. *USA TODAY.* Reprinted with permission.

Data Projects

Where appropriate, use Minitab, SPSS, the TI-83 Plus, the TI-84 Plus, or a computer program of your choice to complete the following exercises.

1. Select a variable and collect some data over a period of a week or several months. For example, you may want to record the number of phone calls you received over 7 days, or the number of times you used your credit card each month for the past several months. Using the chi-square goodness-of-fit test, see if the occurrences are equally distributed over the period.

a. State the purpose of the study.
b. Define the population.
c. State how the sample was selected.
d. State the hypotheses.
e. Select an α value.
f. Compute the chi-square test value.
g. Make the decision.
h. Write a paragraph summarizing the results.

2. Collect some data on a variable and construct a frequency distribution.

a. Using the method shown in Section 11–2, decide if the variable you have chosen is approximately normally distributed.
b. Write a short paper describing your findings, and cite some reasons why the variable you selected is or is not approximately normally distributed.

3. Collect some data on a variable that can be divided into groups. For example, you may want to see if there

is a difference in the colour of cars men own versus the colour of cars women own. Using the chi-square independence test, determine if the one variable is independent of the other.

a. State the purpose of the study.
b. Define the population.
c. State how the sample was selected.
d. State the hypotheses for the study.
e. Select an α value.
f. Compute the chi-square test value.
g. Make the decision.
h. Summarize the results.

You may use the following websites to obtain raw data: Visit the data sets at the book's website found at
www.mcgrawhill.ca/olc/bluman
http://lib.stat.cmu.edu/DASL
www.statcan.ca

Answers to Applying the Concepts ● ● ●

Section 11–2 Never the Same Amounts

1. The variables are quantitative.

2. We can use a chi-square goodness-of-fit test.

3. There are a total of 233 candies, so we would expect 46.6 of each colour. Our test statistic is $\chi^2 = 1.442$.

4. H_0: The colours are equally distributed.

   H_1: The colours are not equally distributed.

5. There are $5 - 1 = 4$ degrees of freedom for the test. The critical value depends on the choice of significance level. At the 0.05 significance level, the critical value is 9.488.

6. Since $1.442 < 9.488$, we fail to reject the null hypothesis. There is not enough evidence to conclude that the colours are not equally distributed.

Section 11–3 Satellite Dishes in Restricted Areas

1. We compare the P-value to the significance level of 0.05 to check if the null hypothesis should be rejected.

2. The P-value gives the probability of a type I error.

3. This is a right-tailed test, since chi-square tests of independence are always right-tailed.

4. You cannot tell how many rows and columns there were just by looking at the degrees of freedom.

5. Increasing the sample size does not increase the degrees of freedom, since the degrees of freedom are based on the number of rows and columns.

6. We will reject the null hypothesis. There are a number of cells where the observed and expected frequencies are quite different.

7. If the significance level were initially set at 0.10, we would still reject the null hypothesis.

8. No, the chi-square value does not tell us which cells have observed and expected frequencies that are very different.

CHAPTER **12** Analysis of Variance

Objectives

After completing this chapter, you should be able to

1. Use the one-way ANOVA technique to determine if there is a significant difference among three or more means.

2. Determine which means differ, using the Scheffé or Tukey test if the null hypothesis is rejected in the ANOVA.

3. Use the two-way ANOVA technique to determine if there is a significant difference in the main effects or interaction.

Outline

12–1 Introduction

12–2 One-Way Analysis of Variance

12–3 The Scheffé Test and the Tukey Test

12–4 Two-Way Analysis of Variance

12–5 Summary

Is Seeing Really Believing?

Statistics Today

Many adults look on the eyewitness testimony of children with skepticism. They believe that young witnesses' testimony is less accurate than the testimony of adults in court cases. Several statistical studies have been done on this subject.

In a preliminary study, three researchers selected fourteen 8-year-olds, fourteen 12-year-olds, and 14 adults. The researchers showed each group the same video of a crime being committed. The next day, each witness responded to direct and cross-examination questioning. Then the researchers, using statistical methods explained in this chapter, were able to determine if there were differences in the accuracy of the testimony of the three groups on direct examination and on cross-examination. The statistical methods used here differ from the ones explained in Chapter 9 because there are three groups rather than two. See Statistics Today—Revisited, page 557.

Source: C. Luus, G. Wells, and J. Turtle, "Child Eyewitnesses: Seeing Is Believing," *Journal of Applied Psychology* 80, no. 2, pp. 317–26.

12–1   Introduction

The *F* test, used to compare two variances shown in Chapter 9, can also be used to compare three or more means. This technique is called *analysis of variance,* or *ANOVA.* It is used to test claims involving three or more means. (*Note:* The *F* test can also be used to test the equality of two means. But since it is equivalent to the *t* test in this case, the *t* test is usually used instead of the *F* test when there are only two means.) For example, suppose a researcher wishes to see whether the means of the time it takes three groups of students to solve a computer problem using computer languages Java, C++, and PHP are different. The researcher will use the ANOVA technique for this test. The *z* and *t* tests should not be used when three or more means are compared, for reasons given later in this chapter.

For three groups, the *F* test can only show whether a difference exists among the three means. It cannot reveal where the difference lies—that is, between $\overline{X}_1$ and $\overline{X}_2$, or $\overline{X}_1$ and $\overline{X}_3$, or $\overline{X}_2$ and $\overline{X}_3$. If the *F* test indicates that there is a difference among the means, other statistical tests are used to find where the difference exists. The most commonly used tests are the Scheffé test and the Tukey test, which are also explained in this chapter.

The analysis of variance that is used to compare three or more means is called a *one-way analysis of variance* since it contains only one variable. In the previous example, the variable is the type of computer language used. The analysis of variance can be extended to studies involving two variables, such as type of computer language used and mathematical background of the students. These studies involve a *two-way analysis of variance.* Section 12–4 explains the two-way analysis of variance.

12–2 One-Way Analysis of Variance

When an F test is used to test a hypothesis concerning the means of three or more populations, the technique is called **analysis of variance** (commonly abbreviated as **ANOVA**). At first glance, one might think that to compare the means of three or more samples, the t test can be used, comparing two means at a time. But there are several reasons why the t test should not be done.

First, when one is comparing two means at a time, the rest of the means under study are ignored. With the F test, all the means are compared simultaneously. Second, when one is comparing two means at a time and making all pairwise comparisons, the probability of rejecting the null hypothesis when it is true is increased, since the more t tests that are conducted, the greater is the likelihood of getting significant differences by chance alone. Third, the more means there are to compare, the more t tests are needed. For example, for the comparison of 3 means two at a time, 3 t tests are required. For the comparison of 5 means two at a time, 10 tests are required. And for the comparison of 10 means two at a time, 45 tests are required.

Assumptions for the F Test for Comparing Three or More Means

1. The populations from which the samples were obtained must be normally or approximately normally distributed.
2. The samples must be independent of one another.
3. The variances of the populations must be equal.

Even though one is comparing three or more means in this use of the F test, *variances* are used in the test instead of means.

With the F test, two different estimates of the population variance are made. The first estimate is called the **between-group variance,** and it involves finding the variance of the means. The second estimate, the **within-group variance,** is made by computing the variance using all the data and is not affected by differences in the means. If there is no difference in the means, the between-group variance estimate will be approximately equal to the within-group variance estimate, and the F test statistic will be approximately equal to 1. The null hypothesis will not be rejected. However, when the means differ significantly, the between-group variance will be much larger than the within-group variance; the F test statistic will be significantly greater than 1; and the null hypothesis will be rejected. Since variances are compared, this procedure is called *analysis of variance* (ANOVA).

For a test of the difference among three or more means, the following hypotheses should be used:

H_0: $\mu_1 = \mu_2 = \cdots = \mu_n$
H_1: At least one mean is different from the others.

As stated previously, a significant test statistic means that there is a high probability that this difference in means is not due to chance, but it does not indicate where the difference lies.

The degrees of freedom for this F test are d.f.N. $= k - 1$, where k is the number of groups, and d.f.D. $= N - k$, where N is the sum of the sample sizes of the groups $N = n_1 + n_2 + \cdots + n_k$. The sample sizes need not be equal. The F test to compare means is always right-tailed.

Examples 12–1 and 12–2 illustrate the computational procedure for the ANOVA technique for comparing three or more means, and the steps are summarized in the Procedure Table shown after the examples.

Example 12–1

 A researcher wishes to try three different techniques to lower the blood pressure of individuals diagnosed with high blood pressure. The subjects are randomly assigned to three groups; the first group takes medication, the second group exercises, and the third group follows a special diet. After four weeks, the reduction in each person's blood pressure is recorded. At $\alpha = 0.05$, test the claim that there is no difference among the means. The data are shown.

Medication	Exercise	Diet
10	6	5
12	8	9
9	3	12
15	0	8
13	2	4
$\overline{X}_1 = 11.8$	$\overline{X}_2 = 3.8$	$\overline{X}_3 = 7.6$
$s_1^2 = 5.7$	$s_2^2 = 10.2$	$s_3^2 = 10.3$

Solution

Step 1 State the hypotheses and identify the claim.

H_0: $\mu_1 = \mu_2 = \mu_3$ (claim)

H_1: At least one mean is different from the others.

Step 2 Find the critical value. Since $k = 3$ and $N = 15$,

d.f.N. $= k - 1 = 3 - 1 = 2$

d.f.D. $= N - k = 15 - 3 = 12$

The critical value is 3.89, obtained from Table H in Appendix C with $\alpha = 0.05$.

Step 3 Compute the test statistic, using the procedure outlined here.

a. Find the mean and variance of each sample (these values are shown below the data).

b. Find the grand mean. The *grand mean,* denoted by $\overline{X}_{GM}$, is the mean of all values in the samples.

$$\overline{X}_{GM} = \frac{\Sigma X}{N} = \frac{10 + 12 + 9 + \cdots + 4}{15} = \frac{116}{15} = 7.73$$

When samples are equal in size, find $\overline{X}_{GM}$ by summing the $\overline{X}$'s and dividing by k, where $k =$ the number of groups.

c. Find the between-group variance, denoted by s_B^2.

$$s_B^2 = \frac{\Sigma n_i (\overline{X}_i - \overline{X}_{GM})^2}{k - 1}$$

$$= \frac{5(11.8 - 7.73)^2 + 5(3.8 - 7.73)^2 + 5(7.6 - 7.73)^2}{3 - 1}$$

$$= \frac{160.13}{2} = 80.07$$

Note: This formula finds the variance among the means by using the sample sizes as weights and considers the differences in the means.

d. Find the within-group variance, denoted by s_W^2.

$$s_W^2 = \frac{\Sigma(n_i - 1)s_i^2}{\Sigma(n_i - 1)}$$

$$= \frac{(5 - 1)(5.7) + (5 - 1)(10.2) + (5 - 1)(10.3)}{(5 - 1) + (5 - 1) + (5 - 1)}$$

$$= \frac{104.80}{12} = 8.73$$

Note: This formula finds an overall variance by calculating a weighted average of the individual variances. It does not involve using differences of the means.

e. Find the F test statistic.

$$F = \frac{s_B^2}{s_W^2} = \frac{80.07}{8.73} = 9.17$$

Step 4 Make the decision. The decision is to reject the null hypothesis, since $9.17 > 3.89$.

Step 5 Summarize the results. There is enough evidence to reject the claim and conclude that at least one mean is different from the others.

The numerator of the fraction obtained in step 3, part *c*, of the computational procedure is called the **sum of squares between groups,** denoted by SS_B. The numerator of the fraction obtained in step 3, part *d*, of the computational procedure is called the **sum of squares within groups,** denoted by SS_W. This statistic is also called the *sum of squares for the error.* SS_B is divided by d.f.N. to obtain the between-group variance. SS_W is divided by $N - k$ to obtain the within-group or error variance. These two variances are sometimes called **mean squares,** denoted by MS_B and MS_W. These terms are used to summarize the analysis of variance and are placed in a summary table, as shown in Table 12–1.

Table 12-1	Analysis of Variance Summary Table			
Source	**Sum of squares**	**d.f.**	**Mean square**	***F***
Between	SS_B	$k - 1$	MS_B	
Within (error)	SS_W	$N - k$	MS_W	
Total				

In the table,

$$SS_B = \text{sum of squares between groups}$$

$$SS_W = \text{sum of squares within groups}$$

$$k = \text{number of groups}$$

$$N = n_1 + n_2 + \cdots + n_k = \text{sum of sample sizes for groups}$$

$$MS_B = \frac{SS_B}{k-1}$$

$$MS_W = \frac{SS_W}{N-k}$$

$$F = \frac{MS_B}{MS_W}$$

The totals are obtained by adding the corresponding columns. For Example 12–1, the **ANOVA summary table** is shown in Table 12–2.

Table 12–2	Analysis of Variance Summary Table for Example 12–1			
Source	Sum of squares	d.f.	Mean square	F
Between	160.13	2	80.07	9.17
Within (error)	104.80	12	8.73	
Total	264.93	14		

Most computer programs will print out an ANOVA summary table.

Example 12–2

A researcher wants to determine if there is a significant difference in the rate of auto thefts by census metropolitan area (CMA) in Canada. The data are shown. At $\alpha = 0.05$, can it be concluded that there is a significant difference in the average rate of auto thefts in each CMA? Rates are expressed per 10,000 population.

More than 500,000	Between 250,000–500,000	Less than 250,000
37	54	57
78	41	18
115	71	57
58	51	20
75	35	83
$\overline{X}_1 = 72.5$	$\overline{X}_2 = 50.3$	$\overline{X}_1 = 47.1$
$s_1^2 = 826.3$	$s_2^2 = 185.3$	$s_3^2 = 764.1$

Source: Adapted from Statistics Canada publication *Juristat,* Motor Vehicle Theft in Canada—2001, Catalogue 85–002, Volume 23, no. 1.

Solution

Step 1 State the hypotheses and identify the claim.

H_0: $\mu_1 = \mu_2 = \mu_3$

H_1: At least one mean is different from the other (claim)

Step 2 Find the critical value. Since $k = 3$, $N = 15$, and $\alpha = 0.05$.

d.f.N. $= k - 1 = 3 - 1 = 2$

d.f.D. $= N - k = 15 - 3 = 12$

The critical value is 3.89.

Step 3 Compute the test statistic.

    a. Find the mean and variance of each sample (these values are shown below the data columns in the example).

    b. Find the grand mean.

$$\overline{X}_{GM} = \frac{\Sigma X}{N} = \frac{37 + 78 + 115 + \cdots + 83}{15} = \frac{849}{15} = 56.6$$

    c. Find the between-group variance.

$$s_B^2 = \frac{\Sigma n_i(\overline{X}_i - \overline{X}_{GM})^2}{k - 1}$$

$$= \frac{5(72.5 - 56.6)^2 + 5(50.3 - 56.6)^2 + 5(47.1 - 56.6)^2}{3 - 1}$$

$$= \frac{1913.75}{2} = 956.88$$

    d. Find the within-group variance.

$$s_W^2 = \frac{\Sigma(n_i - 1)s_i^2}{\Sigma(n_i - 1)}$$

$$= \frac{(5 - 1)(826.3) + (5 - 1)(185.3) + (5 - 1)(764.1)}{(5 - 1) + (5 - 1) + (5 - 1)}$$

$$= \frac{7102.8}{12} = 591.9$$

    e. Find the F test statistic.

$$F = \frac{s_B^2}{s_W^2} = \frac{956.88}{591.9} = 1.62$$

Step 4 Make the decision. Since $1.62 < 3.89$, the decision is to not reject the null hypothesis.

Step 5 Summarize the results. There is not enough evidence to support the claim that there is a difference among the means. The ANOVA summary table for this example is shown in Table 12–3.

Table 12-3	Analysis of Variance Summary Table for Example 12-2			
Source	**Sum of squares**	**d.f.**	**Mean square**	**F**
Between	1913.75	2	956.88	1.62
Within	7102.80	12	591.90	
Total	9016.55	14		

The steps for computing the F test statistic for the ANOVA are summarized in this Procedure Table.

Procedure Table

Finding the F Test Statistic for the Analysis of Variance

Step 1 Find the mean and variance of each sample:

$$(\overline{X}_1, s_1^2), (\overline{X}_2, s_2^2), \ldots, (\overline{X}_k, s_k^2)$$

Step 2 Find the grand mean.

$$\overline{X}_{GM} = \frac{\Sigma X}{N}$$

Step 3 Find the between-group variance.

$$s_B^2 = \frac{\Sigma n_i (\overline{X}_i - \overline{X}_{GM})^2}{k - 1}$$

Step 4 Find the within-group variance.

$$s_W^2 = \frac{\Sigma (n_i - 1) s_i^2}{\Sigma (n_i - 1)}$$

Step 5 Find the F test statistic.

$$F = \frac{s_B^2}{s_W^2}$$

The degrees of freedom are

d.f.N. $= k - 1$

where k is the number of groups, and

d.f.D. $= N - k$

where N is the sum of the sample sizes of the groups,

$$N = n_1 + n_2 + \cdots + n_k$$

P-Values for ANOVA

The procedure in Section 9–3 showed the method to find approximate P-values for ANOVA using Table H in Appendix C. For Example 12–2, find the two α values in the tables for the F distribution (Table H) using d.f.N. $= 2$ and d.f.D. $= 12$, where $F = 1.62$ falls between. In this case 1.62 is less than 2.81 corresponding to $\alpha = 0.10$. Since the P-value > 0.05 (the originally chosen value for α), the decision is to not reject the null hypothesis. (The exact P-value acquired using appropriate technology is 0.238.)

12–3 The Scheffé Test and the Tukey Test

When the null hypothesis is rejected using the F test, the researcher may want to know where the difference among the means is. Several procedures have been developed to determine where the significant differences in the means lie after the ANOVA procedure has been performed. Among the most commonly used tests are the *Scheffé test* and the *Tukey test*.

Objective ❷

Determine which means differ, using the Scheffé or Tukey test if the null hypothesis is rejected in the ANOVA.

Scheffé Test

To conduct the **Scheffé test,** one must compare the means two at a time, using all possible combinations of means. For example, if there are three means, the following comparisons must be done:

$$\overline{X}_1 \text{ versus } \overline{X}_2 \qquad \overline{X}_1 \text{ versus } \overline{X}_3 \qquad \overline{X}_2 \text{ versus } \overline{X}_3$$

Formula for the Scheffé Test

$$F_S = \frac{(\overline{X}_i - \overline{X}_j)^2}{s_W^2[(1/n_i) + (1/n_j)]}$$

where $\overline{X}_i$ and $\overline{X}_j$ are the means of the samples being compared, n_i and n_j are the respective sample sizes, and s_W^2 is the within-group variance.

To find the critical value F' for the Scheffé test, multiply the critical value for the F test by $k - 1$:

$$F' = (k - 1)(\text{C.V.})$$

There is a significant difference between the two means being compared when F_S is greater than F'. Example 12–3 illustrates the use of the Scheffé test.

Example 12–3

Using the Scheffé test, test each pair of means in Example 12–1 to see whether a specific difference exists, at $\alpha = 0.05$.

Solution

a. For $\overline{X}_1$ versus $\overline{X}_2$,

$$F_S = \frac{(\overline{X}_1 - \overline{X}_2)^2}{s_W^2[(1/n_1) + (1/n_2)]} = \frac{(11.8 - 3.8)^2}{8.73[(1/5) + (1/5)]} = 18.33.$$

b. For $\overline{X}_2$ versus $\overline{X}_3$,

$$F_S = \frac{(\overline{X}_2 - \overline{X}_3)^2}{s_W^2[(1/n_2) + (1/n_3)]} = \frac{(3.8 - 7.6)^2}{8.73[(1/5) + (1/5)]} = 4.14.$$

c. For $\overline{X}_1$ versus $\overline{X}_3$,

$$F_S = \frac{(\overline{X}_1 - \overline{X}_3)^2}{s_W^2[(1/n_1) + (1/n_3)]} = \frac{(11.8 - 7.6)^2}{8.73[(1/5) + (1/5)]} = 5.05.$$

The critical value for the analysis of variance for Example 12–1 was 3.89, found by using Table H with $\alpha = 0.05$, d.f.N. $= k - 1 = 2$, and d.f.D. $= N - k = 12$. In this case, it is multiplied by $k - 1$ as shown.

The critical value for F' at $\alpha = 0.05$, with d.f.N. $= 2$ and d.f.D. $= 12$, is

$$F' = (k - 1)(\text{C.V.}) = (3 - 1)(3.89) = 7.78$$

Since only the F test statistic for part a ($\overline{X}_1$ versus $\overline{X}_2$) is greater than the critical value, 7.78, the only significant difference is between $\overline{X}_1$ and $\overline{X}_2$, that is, between medication and exercise.

Speaking of
Statistics

This study involved three groups. The results showed that patients in all three groups felt better after two years. State possible null and alternative hypotheses for this study. Was the null hypothesis rejected? Explain how the statistics could have been used to arrive at the conclusion.

HEALTH

TRICKING KNEE PAIN

You sign up for a clinical trial of arthroscopic surgery used to relieve knee pain caused by arthritis. You're sedated and wake up with tiny incisions. Soon your bum knee feels better. Two years later you find out you had "placebo" surgery. In a study at the Houston VA Medical Center, researchers divided 180 patients into three groups: two groups had damaged cartilage removed, while the third got simulated surgery. Yet an equal number of patients in all groups felt better after two years. Some 650,000 people have the surgery annually, but they're wasting their money, says Dr. Nelda P. Wray, who led the study. And the patients who got fake surgery? "They aren't angry at us," she says. "They still report feeling better."

— STEPHEN P. WILLIAMS

On occasion, when the *F* test statistic is greater than the critical value, the Scheffé test may not show any significant differences in the pairs of means. This result occurs because the difference may actually lie in the average of two or more means when compared with the other mean. The Scheffé test can be used to make these types of comparisons, but the technique is beyond the scope of this book.

Tukey Test

The **Tukey test** can also be used after the analysis of variance has been completed to make pairwise comparisons between means when the groups have the same sample size. The symbol for the test statistic in the Tukey test is *q*.

Formula for the Tukey Test

$$q = \frac{\overline{X}_i - \overline{X}_j}{\sqrt{s_W^2/n}}$$

where $\overline{X}_i$ and $\overline{X}_j$ are the means of the samples being compared, *n* is the size of the samples, and s_W^2 is the within-group variance.

When the absolute value of q is greater than the critical value for the Tukey test, there is a significant difference between the two means being compared. The procedures for finding q and the critical value from Table N in Appendix C for the Tukey test are shown in Example 12–4.

| **Example 12–4** | Using the Tukey test, test each pair of means in Example 12–1 to see whether a specific difference exists, at $\alpha = 0.05$. |

Solution

a. For $\overline{X}_1$ versus $\overline{X}_2$,

$$q = \frac{\overline{X}_1 - \overline{X}_2}{\sqrt{s_W^2/n}} = \frac{11.8 - 3.8}{\sqrt{8.73/5}} = \frac{8}{1.32} = 6.06$$

b. For $\overline{X}_1$ versus $\overline{X}_3$,

$$q = \frac{\overline{X}_1 - \overline{X}_3}{\sqrt{s_W^2/n}} = \frac{11.8 - 7.6}{\sqrt{8.73/5}} = \frac{4.2}{1.32} = 3.18$$

c. For $\overline{X}_2$ versus $\overline{X}_3$,

$$q = \frac{\overline{X}_2 - \overline{X}_3}{\sqrt{s_W^2/n}} = \frac{3.8 - 7.6}{\sqrt{8.73/5}} = \frac{-3.8}{1.32} = -2.88$$

To find the critical value for the Tukey test, use Table N in Appendix C. The number of means k is found in the row at the top, and the degrees of freedom for s_W^2 are found in the left column (denoted by v). Since $k = 3$, d.f. $= 12$, and $\alpha = 0.05$, the critical value is 3.77. See Figure 12–1. Hence, the only q value that is greater in absolute value than the critical value is the one for the difference between $\overline{X}_1$ and $\overline{X}_2$. The conclusion, then, is that there is a significant difference in means for medication and exercise. These results agree with the Scheffé analysis.

| **Figure 12–1**

Finding the Critical
Value in Table N for
the Tukey Test
(Example 12–4) | |

The student might wonder why there are two different tests that can be used after the ANOVA. Actually, there are several other tests that can be used in addition to the Scheffé and Tukey tests. It is up to the researcher to select the most appropriate test. The Scheffé test is the most general, and it can be used when the samples are of different sizes. Furthermore, the Scheffé test can be used to make comparisons such as the average of $\overline{X}_1$ and $\overline{X}_2$ compared with $\overline{X}_3$. However, the Tukey test is more powerful than the Scheffé test for making pairwise comparisons for the means. A rule of thumb for pairwise comparisons is to use the Tukey test when the samples are equal in size and the Scheffé test when the samples differ in size. This rule will be followed in this textbook.

Applying the Concepts 12–3

Colours That Make You Smarter

The following set of data values was obtained from a study of people's perceptions on whether the colour of a person's clothing is related to how intelligent the person looks. The subjects rated the person's intelligence on a scale of 1 to 10. Group 1 subjects were randomly shown people with clothing in shades of blue and grey. Group 2 subjects were randomly shown people with clothing in shades of brown and yellow. Group 3 subjects were randomly shown people with clothing in shades of pink and orange. The results follow.

Group 1	Group 2	Group 3
8	7	4
7	8	9
7	7	6
7	7	7
8	5	9
8	8	8
6	5	5
8	8	8
8	7	7
7	6	5
7	6	4
8	6	5
8	6	4

1. Use ANOVA to test for any significant differences between the means.
2. What is the purpose of this study?
3. Could the Scheffé test be used to test all possible pairwise comparisons?
4. Use the Tukey test to test all possible pairwise comparisons.
5. Are there any contradictions in the results?
6. Explain why separate t tests are not accepted in this situation.
7. When would Tukey's test be preferred over the Scheffé method? Explain.

See page 562 for the answers.

Exercises 12–3

1. What test is used to compare three or more means?

2. State three reasons why multiple t tests cannot be used to compare three or more means.

3. What are the assumptions for ANOVA?

4. Define between-group variance and within-group variance.

5. What is the F test formula for comparing three or more means?

6. State the hypotheses used in the ANOVA test.

7. What two tests are used to compare individual means if the null hypothesis is rejected in using the ANOVA technique?

If the null hypothesis is rejected in Exercises 8 through 19, use the Scheffé test when the sample sizes are unequal to test the differences between the means, and use the Tukey test when the sample sizes are equal. Assume that all variables are normally distributed, that the samples are independent, and that the population variances are equal. Also, for each exercise, perform the following steps.

a. State the hypotheses and identify the claim.
b. Find the critical value.
c. Compute the test statistic.
d. Make the decision.
e. Summarize the results, and explain where the differences in the means are.

Use the traditional method of hypothesis testing unless otherwise specified.

8. The amount of sodium (in milligrams) in one serving for a random sample of three different kinds of foods is listed here. At the 0.05 level of significance, is there sufficient evidence to conclude that a difference in mean sodium amounts exists among condiments, cereals, and desserts?

Condiments	Cereals	Desserts
270	260	100
130	220	180
230	290	250
180	290	250
80	200	300
70	320	360
200	140	300
		160

Source: *The Doctor's Pocket Calorie, Fat, and Carbohydrate Counter.*

9. The number of grams of fibre per serving for a random sample of three different kinds of foods is listed. Is there sufficient evidence at the 0.05 level of significance to conclude that there is a difference in mean fibre content among breakfast cereals, fruits, and vegetables?

Breakfast cereals	Fruits	Vegetables
3	5.5	10
4	2	1.5
6	4.4	3.5
4	1.6	2.7
10	3.8	2.5
5	4.5	6.5
6	2.8	4
8		3
5		

Source: *The Doctor's Pocket Calorie, Fat, and Carbohydrate Counter.*

10. A random sample of enrolments in selected apprenticeship trades for the Maritime provinces is shown. At $\alpha = 0.10$, test the claim that the mean enrolments are the same in the Maritime provinces.

NB	NL	NS	PEI
765	1155	755	190
770	1195	1180	140
310	1980	415	25
710	1050	940	40
840	2250	1260	185
1085	2995	1280	85

Source: Statistics Canada.

11. The lengths (in metres) of a random sample of suspension bridges in North America, Europe, and Asia are shown. At $\alpha = 0.05$, is there sufficient evidence to conclude that there is a difference in mean lengths?

North America	Europe	Asia
1298	1624	1990
1067	1410	1385
701	1325	1118
564	1006	1030
668	1013	876
564	988	
472		

Source: http://www.tkk.fi/Units/Bridge/longspan.html.

12. A researcher wishes to see whether there is any difference in the weight gains of athletes following one of three special diets. Athletes are randomly assigned to three groups and placed on the diet for 6 weeks. The weight gains (in pounds) are shown here. At $\alpha = 0.05$, can the researcher conclude that there is a difference in the diets?

Diet A	Diet B	Diet C
3	10	8
6	12	3
7	11	2
4	14	5
	8	
	6	

A computer printout for this problem is shown. Use the *P*-value method and the information in this printout to test the claim.

Computer Printout for Exercise 12

```
ANALYSIS OF VARIANCE SOURCE TABLE
Source          df     Sum of Squares    Mean Square      F       P-value

Bet Groups       2         101.095         50.548        7.740    0.00797
W/I Groups      11          71.833          6.530

Total           13         172.929

DESCRIPTIVE STATISTICS
Condit           N           Means         St Dev

diet A           4          5.000          1.826
diet B           6         10.167          2.858
diet C           4          4.500          2.646
```

13. Tuition fees for a selection of Canadian university undergraduate students in Arts and Sciences programs in three provinces are listed. At $\alpha = 0.05$, is there a difference in the means? If so, give a possible reason for the difference.

Alberta	Ontario	Quebec
3468	4603	2136
4767	4691	2171
5035	4647	2263
5171	4924	2842
	4982	2965
	5012	

Source: macleans.ca.

14. Random samples of populations (in thousands) of Canadian cities in three regions of the country are listed. Is there evidence to conclude a difference in means at the 0.01 level of significance?

Atlantic	Great Lakes	Pacific
373	693	330
181	390	159
126	323	93
58	177	83
36	152	81
	91	55
	80	

Source: *Statistics Canada Catalogue no. 97-550-XWE2006002. Ottawa. Released March 13, 2007.*

15. The numbers of farms in a random selection of agricultural regions in Canada's Prairie provinces are listed. Test the claim at $\alpha = 0.05$ that the mean number of farms is the same across each Prairie province.

Manitoba	Saskatchewan	Alberta
885	1089	3123
1369	1273	3316
1556	1592	6204
1907	1968	7122
2485	2116	8655
2509	2527	
3021	2770	
	3479	
	4050	
	4438	

Source: Statistics Canada.

16. The price, in cents, of a litre of gasoline on the same day in three Canadian cities at a random sample of Petro-Canada gas stations is shown. Using $\alpha = 0.05$, can one conclude that there is a difference in the means?

Toronto	Calgary	Vancouver
74.2	79.9	91.4
76.5	82.9	94.5
80.2	84.9	95.3
82.9	88.4	97.9
84.4	91.9	100.8

Source: GasBuddy Organization Inc.

17. A research organization tested microwave ovens. At $\alpha = 0.10$, is there a significant difference in the average prices of the three types of oven?

Watts		
1000	**900**	**800**
270	240	180
245	135	155
190	160	200
215	230	120
250	250	140
230	200	180
	200	140
	210	130

A computer printout for this exercise is shown. Use the *P*-value method and the information in this printout to test the claim.

Computer Printout for Exercise 17

```
ANALYSIS OF VARIANCE SOURCE TABLE
Source        df      Sum of Squares    Mean Square       F      P-value

Bet Groups     2        21729.735        10864.867      10.118    0.00102
W/I Groups    19        20402.083         1073.794

Total         21        42131.818

DESCRIPTIVE STATISTICS
Condit         N           Means           St Dev

 1000          6          233.333          28.23
  900          8          203.125          39.36
  800          8          155.625          28.21
```

18. Three random samples of New Year's Eve hotel prices per night in popular Canadian destinations are shown. At $\alpha = 0.05$, is there a difference in the mean prices among the three cities?

Niagara Falls	Banff	Quebec City
425	363	219
339	299	149
249	290	125
215	211	100
206	160	
194		

Source: expedia.ca.

19. The data consist of the number of students who were sent to alternative forms of education for schools in four different counties. At $\alpha = 0.01$, is there a difference in the means? Give a few reasons why some people would be enrolled in an alternative type of school.

County A	County B	County C	County D
2	6	4	0
0	0	0	3
8	1	2	0
1	5	3	1
0	3	2	1

12–4 Two-Way Analysis of Variance

Objective ③

Use the two-way ANOVA technique to determine if there is a significant difference in the main effects or interaction.

The analysis of variance technique shown previously is called a **one-way ANOVA** since there is only *one independent variable*. The **two-way ANOVA** is an extension of the one-way analysis of variance; it involves *two independent variables*. The independent variables are also called **factors.**

The two-way analysis of variance is quite complicated, and many aspects of the subject should be considered when one is using a research design involving a two-way ANOVA. For the purposes of this textbook, only a brief introduction to the subject will be given.

In doing a study that involves a two-way analysis of variance, the researcher is able to test the effects of two independent variables or factors on one *dependent variable*. In addition, the interaction effect of the two variables can be tested.

For example, suppose a researcher wishes to test the effects of two different types of plant food and two different types of soil on the growth of certain plants. The two independent variables are the type of plant food and the type of soil, while the dependent variable is the plant growth. Other factors, such as water, temperature, and sunlight, are held constant.

To conduct this experiment, the researcher sets up four groups of plants. See Figure 12–2.

Figure 12–2

Treatment Groups for the Plant Food–Soil Type Experiment

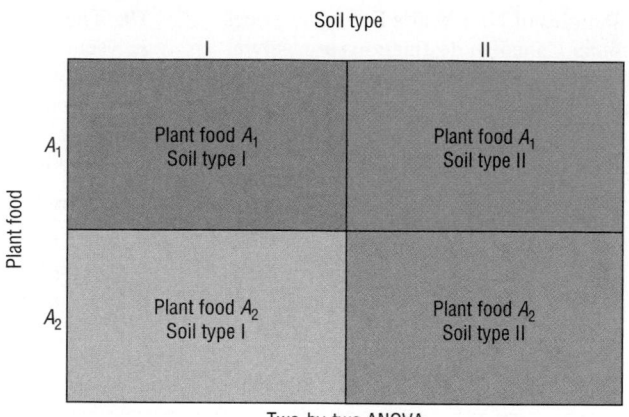

Assume that the plant food type is designated by the letters A_1 and A_2 and the soil type by the Roman numerals I and II. The groups for such a two-way ANOVA are sometimes called **treatment groups.** The four groups are

Group 1	Plant food A_1, soil type I
Group 2	Plant food A_1, soil type II
Group 3	Plant food A_2, soil type I
Group 4	Plant food A_2, soil type II

The plants are assigned to the groups at random. This design is called a 2×2 (read "two-by-two") design, since each variable consists of two **levels,** that is, two different treatments.

The two-way ANOVA enables the researcher to test the effects of the plant food and the soil type in a single experiment rather than in separate experiments involving the plant food alone and the soil type alone. Furthermore, the researcher can test an additional hypothesis about the effect of the *interaction* of the two variables—plant food and soil type—on plant growth. For example, is there a difference between the growth of plants using plant food A_1 and soil type II and the growth of plants using plant food A_2 and soil type I? When a difference of this type occurs, the experiment is said to have a significant **interaction effect.** That is, the types of plant food affect the plant growth differently in different soil types.

There are many different kinds of two-way ANOVA designs, depending on the number of levels of each variable. Figure 12–3 shows a few of these designs. As stated previously, the plant food–soil type experiment uses a 2×2 ANOVA.

The design in Figure 12–3(a) is called a 3×2 design, since the factor in the rows has three levels and the factor in the columns has two levels. Figure 12–3(b) is a 3×3 design, since each factor has three levels. Figure 12–3(c) is a 4×3 design.

The two-way ANOVA design has several null hypotheses. There is one for each independent variable and one for the interaction. In the plant food–soil type problem, the hypotheses are as follows:

1. H_0: There is no interaction effect between type of plant food used and type of soil used on plant growth.

H_1: There is an interaction effect between food type and soil type on plant growth.

2. H_0: There is no difference in means of heights of plants grown using different foods.

H_1: There is a difference in means of heights of plants grown using different foods.

Figure 12–3

Some Types of
Two-Way ANOVA
Designs

(a) 3 × 2 design

(b) 3 × 3 design

(c) 4 × 3 design

3. H_0: There is no difference in means of heights of plants grown in different soil types.

H_1: There is a difference in means of heights of plants grown in different soil types.

The first set of hypotheses concerns the interaction effect; the second and third sets test the effects of the independent variables, which are sometimes called the **main effects.**

As with the one-way ANOVA, a between-group variance estimate is calculated, and a within-group variance estimate is calculated. An F test is then performed for each of the independent variables and the interaction. The results of the two-way ANOVA are summarized in a two-way table, as shown in Table 12–4 for the plant experiment.

Table 12–4	ANOVA Summary Table for Plant Food and Soil Type			
Source	**Sum of squares**	**d.f.**	**Mean square**	**F**
Plant food				
Soil type				
Interaction				
Within (error)				
Total				

In general, the two-way ANOVA summary table is set up as shown in Table 12–5.

Table 12–5	ANOVA Summary Table			
Source	**Sum of squares**	**d.f.**	**Mean square**	**F**
A	SS_A	$a - 1$	MS_A	F_A
B	SS_B	$b - 1$	MS_B	F_B
$A \times B$	$SS_{A \times B}$	$(a - 1)(b - 1)$	$MS_{A \times B}$	$F_{A \times B}$
Within (error)	SS_W	$ab(n - 1)$	MS_W	
Total				

In the table,

$$SS_A = \text{sum of squares for factor } A$$
$$SS_B = \text{sum of squares for factor } B$$
$$SS_{A \times B} = \text{sum of squares for interaction}$$
$$SS_W = \text{sum of squares for error term (within-group)}$$
$$a = \text{number of levels of factor } A$$
$$b = \text{number of levels of factor } B$$
$$n = \text{number of subjects in each group}$$

$$MS_A = \frac{SS_A}{a-1}$$

$$MS_B = \frac{SS_B}{b-1}$$

$$MS_{A \times B} = \frac{SS_{A \times B}}{(a-1)(b-1)}$$

$$MS_W = \frac{SS_W}{ab(n-1)}$$

$$F_A = \frac{MS_A}{MS_W} \qquad \text{with d.f.N.} = a-1, \text{d.f.D.} = ab(n-1)$$

$$F_B = \frac{MS_B}{MS_W} \qquad \text{with d.f.N.} = b-1, \text{d.f.D.} = ab(n-1)$$

$$F_{A \times B} = \frac{MS_{A \times B}}{MS_W} \qquad \text{with d.f.N.} = (a-1)(b-1), \text{d.f.D.} = ab(n-1)$$

The assumptions for the two-way analysis of variance are basically the same as those for the one-way ANOVA, except for sample size.

Assumptions for the Two-Way ANOVA

1. The populations from which the samples were obtained must be normally or approximately normally distributed.
2. The samples must be independent.
3. The variances of the populations from which the samples were selected must be equal.
4. The groups must be equal in sample size.

The computational procedure for the two-way ANOVA is quite lengthy. For this reason, it will be omitted in Example 12–5, and only the two-way ANOVA summary table will be shown. The table used in Example 12–5 is similar to the one generated by most computer programs. The student should be able to interpret the table and summarize the results.

Example 12–5*   A researcher wishes to see whether the type of gasoline used and the type of automobile driven have any effect on gasoline consumption. Two types of gasoline, regular and high-octane, will be used, and two types of automobiles, two-wheel- and four-wheel-drive will be used in each group. There will be two automobiles in each group, for a total of eight automobiles used. Using a two-way analysis of variance, the researcher will perform the following steps.

Step 1   State the hypotheses.

*Generated results using Excel Analysis Toolpak.

Step 2 Find the critical value for each F test, using $\alpha = 0.05$.

Step 3 Complete the summary table to get the test statistic.

Step 4 Make the decision.

Step 5 The data (litres per 100 kilometres) are shown here, and the summary table is given in Table 12–6.

	Type of automobile	
Gas	**Two-wheel-drive**	**Four-wheel-drive**
Regular	8.8	8.2
	9.3	8.0
High-octane	7.3	9.0
	7.2	9.7

Table 12–6	ANOVA Summary Table for Example 12–5			
Source	**Sum of squares**	**d.f.**	**Mean square**	**F**
Gasoline A	0.183			
Automobile B	0.712			
Interaction ($A \times B$)	4.758			
Within (error)	0.413			
Total	6.066			

Note: Results generated using Excel Data Analysis Toolpak.

Solution

Step 1 State the hypotheses. The hypotheses for the interaction are these:

H_0: There is no interaction effect between type of gasoline used and type of automobile a person drives on gasoline consumption.

H_1: There is an interaction effect between type of gasoline used and type of automobile a person drives on gasoline consumption.

The hypotheses for the gasoline types are:

H_0: There is no difference between the means of gasoline consumption for two types of gasoline.

H_1: There is a difference between the means of gasoline consumption for two types of gasoline.

The hypotheses for the types of automobile driven are:

H_0: There is no difference between the means of gasoline consumption for two-wheel-drive and four-wheel-drive automobiles.

H_1: There is a difference between the means of gasoline consumption for two-wheel-drive and four-wheel-drive automobiles.

Step 2 Find the critical values for each F test. In this case, each independent variable, or factor, has two levels. Hence, a 2×2 ANOVA table is used. Factor A is designated as the gasoline type. It has two levels, regular and high-octane; therefore, $a = 2$. Factor B is designated as the automobile type. It also has two levels; therefore, $b = 2$. The degrees of freedom for each factor are as follows:

Factor A:	d.f.N. $= a - 1 = 2 - 1 = 1$
Factor B:	d.f.N. $= b - 1 = 2 - 1 = 1$
Interaction ($A \times B$):	d.f.N. $= (a - 1)(b - 1)$
	$= (2 - 1)(2 - 1) = 1 \cdot 1 = 1$
Within (error):	d.f.D. $= ab(n - 1)$
	$= 2 \cdot 2(2 - 1) = 4$

where n is the number of data values in each group. In this case, $n = 2$.

The critical value for the F_A test is found by using $\alpha = 0.05$, d.f.N. $= 1$, and d.f.D. $= 4$. In this case, $F_A = 7.71$. The critical value for the F_B test is found by using $\alpha = 0.05$, d.f.N. $= 1$, and d.f.D. $= 4$; F_B is also 7.71. Finally, the critical value for the $F_{A \times B}$ test is found by using d.f.N. $= 1$ and d.f.D. $= 4$; it is also 7.71.

Note: If there are different levels of the factors, the critical values will not all be the same. For example, if factor A has three levels and factor b has four levels, and if there are two subjects in each group, then the degrees of freedom are as follows:

d.f.N. $= a - 1 = 3 - 1 = 2$	factor A
d.f.N. $= b - 1 = 4 - 1 = 3$	factor B
d.f.N. $= (a - 1)(b - 1) = (3 - 1)(4 - 1)$	
$= 2 \cdot 3 = 6$	factor $A \times B$
d.f.N. $= ab(n - 1) = 3 \cdot 4(2 - 1) = 12$	within (error) factor

Step 3 Complete the ANOVA summary table to get the test statistics. The mean squares are computed first.

$$MS_A = \frac{SS_A}{a - 1} = \frac{0.183}{2 - 1} = 0.183$$

$$MS_B = \frac{SS_B}{b - 1} = \frac{0.712}{2 - 1} = 0.712$$

$$MS_{A \times B} = \frac{SS_{A \times B}}{(a - 1)(b - 1)} = \frac{4.758}{(2 - 1)(2 - 1)} = 4.758$$

$$MS_w = \frac{SS_w}{ab(n - 1)} = \frac{0.4130}{4} = 0.103$$

The F test statistics are computed next.

$$F_A = \frac{MS_A}{MS_W} = \frac{0.183}{0.103} = 1.777 \qquad \text{d.f.N.} = a - 1 = 1 \qquad \text{d.f.D.} = ab(n - 1) = 4$$

$$F_B = \frac{MS_B}{MS_W} = \frac{0.712}{0.103} = 6.913 \qquad \text{d.f.N.} = b - 1 = 1 \qquad \text{d.f.D.} = ab(n - 1) = 4$$

$$F_{A \times B} = \frac{MS_{A \times B}}{MS_W} = \frac{4.758}{0.103} = 46.194 \quad \text{d.f.N.} = (a - 1)(b - 1) = 1 \quad \text{d.f.D.} = ab(n - 1) = 4$$

The completed ANOVA table is shown in Table 12–7.

Table 12–7	Completed ANOVA Summary Table for Example 12–5			
Source	**Sum of squares**	**d.f.**	**Mean square**	**F**
Gasoline A	0.183	1	0.183	1.777
Automobile B	0.712	1	0.712	6.913
Interaction ($A \times B$)	4.758	1	4.758	46.194
Within (error)	0.413	4	0.103	
Total	6.066	7		

Step 4 Make the decision. Since $F_{A \times B} = 46.194$ is greater than the critical value 7.71, the null hypothesis concerning the interaction effect should be rejected.

Step 5 Summarize the results. Since the null hypothesis for the interaction effect was rejected, it can be concluded that the combination of type of gasoline and type of automobile does affect gasoline consumption.

In the preceding analysis, the effect of the type of gasoline used and the effect of the type of automobile driven are called the *main effects*. If there is no significant interaction effect, the main effects can be interpreted independently. However, if there is a significant interaction effect, the main effects must be interpreted cautiously.

To interpret the results of a two-way analysis of variance, researchers suggest drawing a graph, plotting the means of each group, analyzing the graph, and interpreting the results. In Example 12–5, find the means for each group or cell by adding the data values in each cell and dividing by n. The means for each cell are shown in the chart here.

	Type of automobile	
Gas	**Two-wheel-drive**	**Four-wheel-drive**
Regular	$\overline{X} = \dfrac{8.8 + 9.3}{2} = 9.05$	$\overline{X} = \dfrac{8.2 + 8.0}{2} = 8.1$
High-octane	$\overline{X} = \dfrac{7.3 + 7.2}{2} = 7.25$	$\overline{X} = \dfrac{9.0 + 9.7}{2} = 9.35$

The graph of the means for each of the variables is shown in Figure 12–4. In this graph, the lines cross each other. When such an intersection occurs and the interaction is significant, the interaction is said to be a **disordinal interaction.** When there is a disordinal interaction, one should not interpret the main effects without considering the interaction effect.

The other type of interaction that can occur is an *ordinal interaction.* Figure 12–5 shows a graph of means in which an ordinal interaction occurs between two variables. The lines do not cross each other, nor are they parallel. If the F test value for the ineraction is significant and the lines do not cross each other, then the interaction is said to be an **ordinal interaction** and the main effects can be interpreted independently of each other.

Finally, when there is no significant interaction effect, the lines in the graph will be parallel or approximately parallel. When this situation occurs, the main effects can be interpreted independently of each other because there is no significant interaction. Figure 12–6 shows the graph of two variables when the interaction effect is not significant; the lines are parallel.

Figure 12–4

Graph of the Means of
the Variables in
Example 12–5

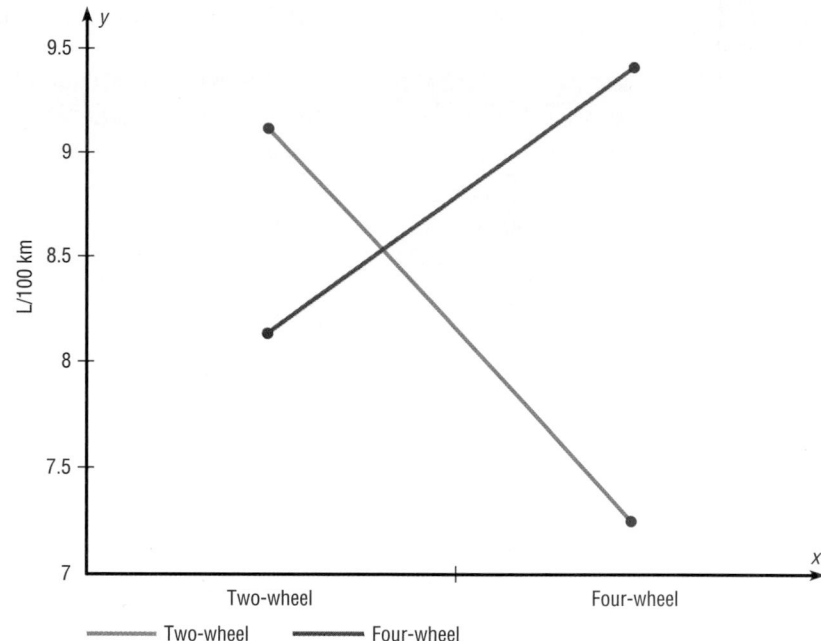

Figure 12–5

Graph of Two Variables
Indicating an Ordinal
Interaction

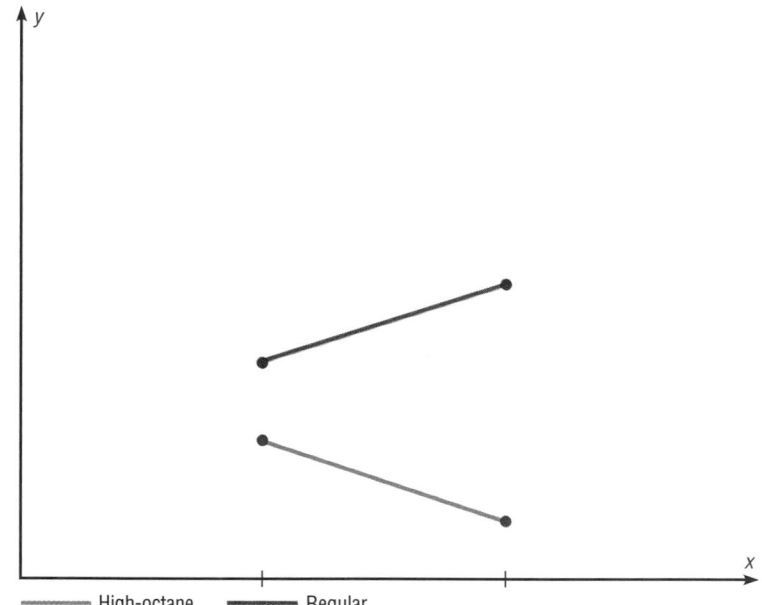

Example 12–5 was an example of a 2×2 two-way analysis of variance, since each
independent variable had two levels. For other types of variance problems, such as a
3×2 or a 4×3 ANOVA, interpretation of the results can be quite complicated.
Procedures using tests such as the Tukey and Scheffé tests for analyzing the cell means
exist and are similar to the tests shown for the one-way ANOVA, but they are beyond
the scope of this textbook. Many other designs for analysis of variance are available to
researchers, such as three-factor designs and repeated-measure designs; they are also
beyond the scope of this book.

Figure 12–6

Graph of Two Variables
Indicating No Interaction

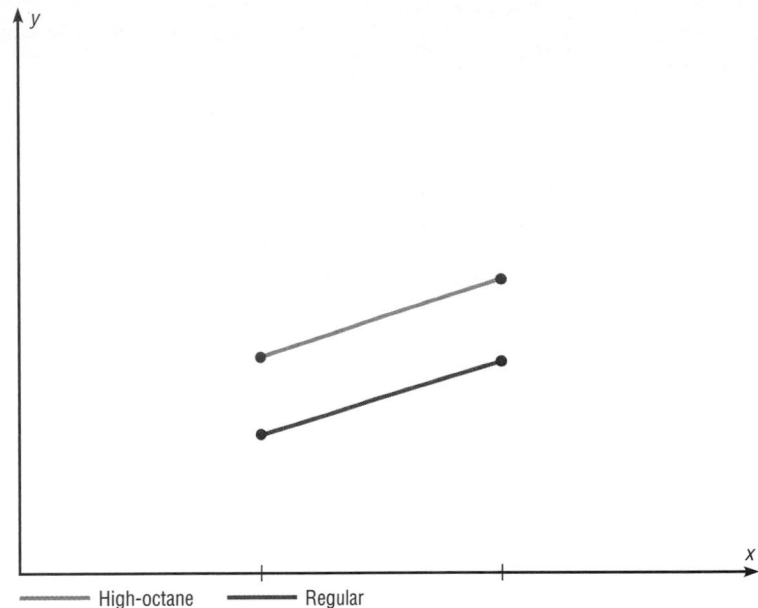

In summary, the two-way ANOVA is an extension of the one-way ANOVA. The former can be used to test the effects of two independent variables and a possible interaction effect on a dependent variable.

Applying the Concepts 12–4

Automobile Sales Techniques

The following outputs are from the result of an analysis of how car sales are affected by the experience of the salesperson and the type of sales technique used. Experience was broken up into four levels, and two different sales techniques were used. Analyze the results and draw conclusions about level of experience with respect to the two different sales techniques and how they affect car sales.

Two-Way Analysis of Variance

```
Analysis of Variance for Sales
Source        DF        SS        MS
Experience     3     3414.0    1138.0
Presentation   1        6.0       6.0
Interaction    3      414.0     138.0
Error         16      838.0      52.4
Total         23     4672.0
                         Individual 95% CI
Experience    Mean    -----+---------+---------+---------+------
1             62.0     (-----*-----)
2             63.0     (-----*-----)
3             78.0                 (-----*-----)
4             91.0                            (-----*-----)
                      -----+---------+---------+---------+------
                        60.0      70.0      80.0      90.0


                         Individual 95% CI
Presentation  Mean    ------+---------+---------+---------+-----
1             74.0       (-----------------*------------------)
2             73.0     (-----------------*-----------------)
                      ------+---------+---------+---------+-----
```

See page 562 for the answers.

Exercises 12–4

1. How does the two-way ANOVA differ from the one-way ANOVA?

2. Explain what is meant by *main effects* and *interaction effect*.

3. How are the values for the mean squares computed?

4. How are the *F* test statistics computed?

5. In a two-way ANOVA, variable *A* has three levels and variable *B* has two levels. There are five data values in each cell. Find each degrees-of-freedom value.

    a. d.f.N. for factor *A*

    b. d.f.N. for factor *B*

    c. d.f.N. for factor $A \times B$

    d. d.f.D. for the within (error) factor

6. In a two-way ANOVA, variable *A* has six levels and variable *B* has five levels. There are seven data values in each cell. Find each degrees-of-freedom value.

    a. d.f.N. for factor *A*

    b. d.f.N. for factor *B*

    c. d.f.N. for factor $A \times B$

    d. d.f.D. for the within (error) factor

7. What are the two types of interactions that can occur in the two-way ANOVA?

8. When can the main effects for the two-way ANOVA be interpreted independently?

9. Describe what the graph of the variables would look like for each situation in a two-way ANOVA experiment.

    a. No interaction effect occurs.

    b. An ordinal interaction effect occurs.

    c. A disordinal interaction effect occurs.

For Exercises 10 through 15, perform these steps. Assume that all variables are normally or approximately normally distributed, that the samples are independent, and that the population variances are equal.

   a. State the hypotheses.

   b. Find the critical value for each *F* test.

   c. Complete the summary table and find the test statistic.

   d. Make the decision.

   e. Summarize the results. (Draw a graph of the cell means if necessary.)

10. A company wishes to test the effectiveness of its advertising. A product is selected, and two types of ads are written; one is serious and one is humorous. Also the ads are run on both television and radio. Sixteen potential customers are selected and assigned randomly to one of four groups. After seeing or listening to the ad, each customer is asked to rate its effectiveness on a scale of 1 to 20. Various points are assigned for clarity, conciseness, etc. The data are shown here. At $\alpha = 0.01$, analyze the data, using a two-way ANOVA.

Type of ad	Medium	
	Radio	**Television**
Humorous	6, 10, 11, 9	15, 18, 14, 16
Serious	8, 13, 12, 10	19, 20, 13, 17

ANOVA Summary Table for Exercise 10

Source	SS	d.f.	MS	F
Type	10.563			
Medium	175.563			
Interaction	0.063			
Within	66.250			
Total	252.439			

11. A medical researcher wishes to test the effects of two diets and the time of day on the sodium level in a person's blood. Eight people are randomly selected, and two are randomly assigned to each of the four groups. Analyze the data shown in the tables here, using a two-way ANOVA at $\alpha = 0.05$. The sodium content is measured in milliequivalents per litre.

Time	Diet type			
	I		**II**	
8:00 A.M.	135	145	138	141
8:00 P.M.	155	162	171	191

ANOVA Summary Table for Exercise 11

Source	SS	d.f.	MS	F
Time	1800.0			
Diet	242.0			
Interaction	264.5			
Within	279.0			
Total	2585.5			

12. A contractor wishes to see whether there is a difference in the time (in days) it takes two subcontractors to build three different types of homes. At $\alpha = 0.05$, analyze the data shown here, using a two-way ANOVA. See above for raw data.

ANOVA Summary Table for Exercise 12

Source	SS	d.f.	MS	F
Subcontractor	1672.553			
Home type	444.867			
Interaction	313.267			
Within	328.800			
Total	2759.487			

Data for Exercise 12

Subcontractor	Home type		
	I	**II**	**III**
A	25, 28, 26, 30, 31	30, 32, 35, 29, 31	43, 40, 42, 49, 48
B	15, 18, 22, 21, 17	21, 27, 18, 15, 19	23, 25, 24, 17, 13

13. Two special training programs in outdoor survival are available for army recruits. One lasts one week and the other lasts two weeks. The officer wishes to test the effectiveness of the programs and see whether there are any gender differences. Six subjects are randomly assigned to each of the programs according to gender. After completing the program, each is given a written test on his or her knowledge of survival skills. The test consists of 100 questions. The scores of the groups are shown here. Use $\alpha = 0.10$ and analyze the data, using a two-way ANOVA.

Gender	Duration	
	One week	**Two weeks**
Female	86, 92, 87, 88, 78, 95	78, 62, 56, 54, 65, 63
Male	52, 67, 53, 42, 68, 71	85, 94, 82, 84, 78, 91

ANOVA Summary Table for Exercise 13

Source	SS	d.f.	MS	F
Gender	57.042			
Duration	7.042			
Interaction	3978.375			
Within	1365.500			
Total	5407.959			

14. Two types of outdoor paint, enamel and latex, were tested to see how long (in months) each lasted before it began to crack, flake, and peel. They were tested in four geographic locations in North America to study the effects of climate on the paint. At $\alpha = 0.01$, analyze the data shown, using a two-way ANOVA shown on the next page. Each group contained five test panels. See below for raw data.

Data for Exercise 14

Type of paint	Geographic location			
	North	**East**	**South**	**West**
Enamel	60, 53, 58, 62, 57	54, 63, 62, 71, 76	80, 82, 62, 88, 71	62, 76, 55, 48, 61
Latex	36, 41, 54, 65, 53	62, 61, 77, 53, 64	68, 72, 71, 82, 86	63, 65, 72, 71, 63

ANOVA Summary Table for Exercise 14

Source	SS	d.f.	MS	F
Paint type	12.1			
Location	2501.0			
Interaction	268.1			
Within	2326.8			
Total	5108.0			

15. A company sells three items: swimming pools, spas, and saunas. The owner decides to see whether the age of the sales representative and the type of item affect monthly sales. At $\alpha = 0.05$, analyze the data shown, using a two-way ANOVA. Sales are given in hundreds of dollars for a randomly selected month, and five salespeople were selected for each group.

ANOVA Summary Table for Exercise 15

Source	SS	d.f.	MS	F
Age	168.033			
Product	1,762.067			
Interaction	7,955.267			
Within	2,574.000			
Total	12,459.367			

Data for Exercise 15

Age of salesperson	Product		
	Pool	**Spa**	**Sauna**
Over 30	56, 23, 52, 28, 35	43, 25, 16, 27, 32	47, 43, 52, 61, 74
30 or under	16, 14, 18, 27, 31	58, 62, 68, 72, 83	15, 14, 22, 16, 27

12–5   Summary

The F test, as shown in Chapter 9, can be used to compare two sample variances to determine whether they are equal. It can also be used to compare three or more means. When three or more means are compared, the technique is called analysis of variance (ANOVA). The ANOVA technique uses two estimates of the population variance. The between-group variance is the variance of the sample means; the within-group variance is the overall variance of all the values. When there is no significant difference among the means, the two estimates will be approximately equal and the F test statistic will be close to 1. If there is a significant difference among the means, the between-group variance estimate will be larger than the within-group variance estimate and a significant test statistic will result.

If there is a significant difference among means, the researcher may wish to see where this difference lies. Several statistical tests can be used to compare the sample means after the ANOVA technique has been done. The most common are the Scheffé test and the Tukey test. When the sample sizes are the same, the Tukey test can be used. The Scheffé test is more general and can be used when the sample sizes are equal or not equal.

When there is one independent variable, the analysis of variance is called a one-way ANOVA. When there are two independent variables, the analysis of variance is called a two-way ANOVA. The two-way ANOVA enables the researcher to test the effects of two independent variables and a possible interaction effect on one dependent variable.

For step-by-step guidance on the use of technology for this chapter, visit the Online Learning Centre at www.mcgrawhill.ca/olc/bluman. Summary procedures for Minitab, SPSS, Excel, and TI-83 Plus or TI-84 Plus can also be found in Appendix F.

Important Terms   ● ● ●

analysis of variance (ANOVA) 531	factors 543	ordinal interaction 549	treatment groups 544
ANOVA summary table 534	interaction effect 544	Scheffé test 537	Tukey test 538
between-group variance 531	level 544	sum of squares between groups 533	two-way ANOVA 543
disordinal interaction 549	main effect 545	sum of squares within groups 533	within-group variance 531
	mean square 533		
	one-way ANOVA 543		

Important Formulas   ● ● ●

Formulas for the ANOVA test:

$$\overline{X}_{GM} = \frac{\Sigma X}{N}$$

$$F = \frac{s_B^2}{s_W^2}$$

where

$$s_B^2 = \frac{\Sigma n_i (\overline{X}_i - \overline{X}_{GM})^2}{k - 1} \qquad s_W^2 = \frac{\Sigma (n_i - 1) s_i^2}{\Sigma (n_i - 1)}$$

d.f.N. $= k - 1$ $\qquad N = n_1 + n_2 + \cdots + n_k$

d.f.D. $= N - k$ $\qquad k = $ **number of groups**

Formulas for the Scheffé test:

$$F_s = \frac{(\overline{X}_i - \overline{X}_j)^2}{s_W^2[(1/n_i) + (1/n_j)]} \qquad \text{and} \qquad F' = (k-1)(\text{C.V.})$$

Formula for the Tukey test:

$$q = \frac{\overline{X}_i - \overline{X}_j}{\sqrt{s_W^2/n}}$$

d.f.N. = k and **d.f.D. = degrees of freedom s_W^2**

Formulas for the two-way ANOVA:

$$\text{MS}_A = \frac{\text{SS}_A}{a-1} \qquad\qquad F_A = \frac{\text{MS}_A}{\text{MS}_W} \qquad \textbf{d.f.N.} = a - 1$$

$$\textbf{d.f.D.} = ab(n-1)$$

$$\text{MS}_B = \frac{\text{SS}_B}{b-1} \qquad\qquad F_B = \frac{\text{MS}_B}{\text{MS}_W} \qquad \textbf{d.f.N.} = b - 1$$

$$\textbf{d.f.D.} = ab(n-1)$$

$$\text{MS}_{A \times B} = \frac{\text{SS}_{A \times B}}{(a-1)(b-1)} \qquad F_{A \times B} = \frac{\text{MS}_{A \times B}}{\text{MS}_W} \qquad \textbf{d.f.N.} = (a-1)(b-1)$$

$$\textbf{d.f.D.} = ab(n-1)$$

$$\text{MS}_W = \frac{\text{SS}_W}{ab(n-1)}$$

Review Exercises ● ● ●

If the null hypothesis is rejected in Exercises 1 through 9, use the Scheffé test when the sample sizes are unequal to test the differences between the means, and use the Tukey test when the sample sizes are equal. For these exercises, perform these steps.

a. State the hypotheses and identify the claim.
b. Find the critical value(s).
c. Compute the test statistic.
d. Make the decision.
e. Summarize the results, and explain where the differences in means are.

Use the traditional method of hypothesis testing unless otherwise specified.

1. The data represent the lengths (in metres) of three types of bridges in the United States. At $\alpha = 0.01$, test the claim that there is no significant difference in the means of the lengths of the types of bridges.

Simple truss	Segmented concrete	Continuous plate
227	250	192
218	229	175
213	241	160
198	205	155
197	201	146
191	195	140
185	194	137
182	189	137
168	158	137
166	137	130
163	119	128
161	113	110

Source: World Almanac and Book of Facts.

2. Is there a difference in the price per bottle of three different types of wine? The data show the costs per bottle (in dollars) of three different types of wines. Use $\alpha = 0.01$ to answer the question. Why would some wines be more expensive than others?

Type 1	Type 2	Type 3
11	15	13
10	7	11
20	9	18
10	10	10
17	4	22
9	5	15

3. The number of carbohydrates per serving in randomly selected cereals from three manufacturers is shown. At the 0.05 level of significance, is there sufficient evidence to conclude a difference in the average number of carbohydrates?

Manufacturer 1	Manufacturer 2	Manufacturer 3
25	23	24
26	44	39
24	24	28
26	24	25
26	36	23
41	27	32
26	25	
43		

Source: The Doctor's Pocket Calorie, Fat, and Carbohydrate Counter.

4. The number of grams of fat per serving for three different kinds of pizza from several manufacturers is listed below. At the 0.01 level of significance, is there

sufficient evidence that a difference exists in mean fat content?

Cheese	Pepperoni	Supreme/Deluxe
18	20	16
11	17	27
19	15	17
20	18	17
16	23	12
21	23	27
16	21	20

Source: The Doctor's Pocket Calorie, Fat, and Carbohydrate Counter.

5. The iron content in three different types of food is shown. At the 0.10 level of significance, is there sufficient evidence to conclude that a difference in mean iron content exists for meats and fish, breakfast cereals, and nutritional high-protein drinks?

Meats and fish	Breakfast cereals	Nutritional drinks
3.4	8	3.6
2.5	2	3.6
5.5	1.5	4.5
5.3	3.8	5.5
2.5	3.8	2.7
1.3	6.8	3.6
2.7	1.5	6.3
	4.5	

Source: The Doctor's Pocket Calorie, Fat, and Carbohydrate Counter.

6. The data consist of the weights (in grams) of three different types of digital camera. Use $\alpha = 0.05$ to see if the means are equal.

2–3 Megapixels	4–5 Megapixels	6–8 Megapixels
187	435	591
249	342	840
218	467	653
342	746	715
124	529	746
249	311	1026

7. A researcher wishes to see if there is a difference in the average number of violent crimes in different metropolitan areas across Canada. Random samples of cities were selected, and the violent crime rate (per 100,000 population) for a specific year was reported. At $\alpha = 0.05$, is there a difference in the means? If so, suggest a reason for the difference.

Pacific	Prairies	Central	Atlantic
1028	934	836	1343
1136	1718	489	788
	1578	910	1169
	1242	564	
		691	

Source: Statistics Canada.

8. A teacher wishes to test the math anxiety level of her students in two classes at the beginning of the semester. The classes are Calculus I and Statistics. Furthermore, she wishes to see whether there is a difference owing to the students' ages. Math anxiety is measured by the score on a 100-point anxiety test. Use $\alpha = 0.10$ and a two-way analysis of variance to see whether there is a difference. Five students are randomly assigned to each group. The data are shown here.

	Class	
Age	**Calculus I**	**Statistics**
Under 20	43, 52, 61, 57, 55	19, 20, 31, 36, 24
20 or over	56, 55, 42, 48, 61	63, 78, 67, 71, 75

ANOVA Summary Table for Exercise 8

Source	SS	d.f.	MS	F
Age	2376.2			
Class	105.8			
Interaction	2645.0			
Within	763.2			
Total	5890.2			

Is Seeing Really Believing?–Revisited

Statistics Today

To see if there were differences in the testimonies of the witnesses in the three age groups, the witnesses responded to 17 questions, 10 on direct examination and 7 on cross-examination. These were then scored for accuracy. An analysis of variance test with age as the independent variable was used to compare the total number of questions answered correctly by the groups. The results showed no significant differences among the age groups for the direct examination questions. However, there was a significant difference among the groups on the cross-examination questions. Further analysis showed the 8-year-olds were significantly less accurate under cross-examination compared to the other two groups. The 12-year-old and adult eyewitnesses did not differ in the accuracy of their cross-examination responses.

9. A medical researcher wishes to test the effects of two different diets and two different exercise programs on the glucose level in a person's blood. The glucose level is measured in milligrams per decilitre (mg/dl).Three subjects are randomly assigned to each group. Analyze the data shown here, using a two-way ANOVA with $\alpha = 0.05$.

Exercise program	Diet	
	A	**B**
I	62, 64, 66	58, 62, 53
II	65, 68, 72	83, 85, 91

ANOVA Summary Table for Exercise 9

Source	SS	d.f.	MS	F
Exercise	816.750			
Diet	102.083			
Interaction	444.083			
Within	108.000			
Total	1470.916			

Data Analysis

● ● ●

The Data Bank is found in Appendix D, or on the World Wide Web by following links from www.mcgrawhill.ca/olc/bluman.

1. From the Data Bank, select a random sample of subjects, and test the hypothesis that the mean cholesterol levels of the nonsmokers, less-than-one-pack-a-day smokers, and one-pack-plus smokers are equal. Use an ANOVA test. If the null hypothesis is rejected, conduct the Scheffé test to find where the difference is. Summarize the results.

2. Repeat Exercise 2 for the mean IQs of the various educational levels of the subjects.

3. Using the Data Bank, randomly select 12 subjects and randomly assign them to one of the four groups in the following classifications.

	Smoker	Nonsmoker
Male		
Female		

Use one of these variables—weight, cholesterol, or systolic pressure—as the dependent variable, and perform a two-way ANOVA on the data. Use a computer program to generate the ANOVA table.

Chapter Quiz

● ● ●

Determine whether each statement is true or false. If the statement is false, explain why.

1. In analysis of variance, the null hypothesis should be rejected only when there is a significant difference among all pairs of means.

2. The F test does not use the concept of degrees of freedom.

3. When the F test statistic is close to 1, the null hypothesis should be rejected.

4. The Tukey test is generally more powerful than the Scheffé test for pairwise comparisons.

Select the best answer.

5. Analysis of variance uses the _____ test.

   a. z *c.* χ^2
   b. t *d.* F

6. The null hypothesis in ANOVA is that all the means are _____.

   a. Equal   *c.* Variable
   b. Unequal   *d.* None of the above

7. When one conducts an F test, _____ estimates of the population variance are compared.

   a. Two   *c.* Any number of
   b. Three   *d.* No

8. If the null hypothesis is rejected in ANOVA, one can use the _____ test to see where the difference in the means is found.

   a. z or t *c.* Scheffé or Tukey
   b. F or χ^2 *d.* Any of the above

Complete the following statements with the best answer.

9. When three or more means are compared, one uses the _____ technique.

10. If the null hypothesis is rejected in ANOVA, the _____ test should be used when sample sizes are equal.

11. In a two-way ANOVA, one can test _____ main hypotheses and one interactive hypothesis.

For Exercises 12 through 16 use the traditional method of hypothesis testing unless otherwise specified.

12. In a recent federal election, a sample of the percentage of voters who voted in various regions across Canada is

shown. At $\alpha = 0.05$, is there a difference in the mean percentage of voters who voted in each region.

North	West	Central	East
54.1	71.0	72.4	66.9
56.2	63.2	72.8	62.4
54.0	63.7	64.7	70.7
	48.4	64.1	

Source: Elections Canada.

13. A media researcher wishes to see if there is a difference in the ages of viewers of three late-night television talk shows. Three samples of viewers are selected, and the ages of the viewers are shown. At $\alpha = 0.01$, is there a difference in the means of the ages of the viewers? Why is the average age of a viewer important to a television show writer?

David Letterman	Jay Leno	Conan O'Brien
53	48	40
46	51	36
48	57	35
42	46	42
35	38	39

Source: Based on information from Nielsen Media Research.

14. Prices (in dollars) of men's, women's, and children's athletic shoes are shown. At the 0.05 level of significance, can it be concluded that there is a difference in mean price?

Women's	Men's	Children's
59	65	40
36	70	45
44	66	40
49	59	56
48	48	46
50	70	36

15. The birth weights (in kilograms) of randomly selected newborns at three area hospitals are shown. Using the 0.10 level of significance, test the claim that the mean weights are equal.

Hospital A	Hospital B	Hospital C
3.5	5.7	4.3
3.7	1.5	2.5
5.2	2.9	3.0
3.0	4.8	3.9
3.3	1.7	4.7
3.7	1.1	3.4

16. Several students volunteered for an alumni phone-a-thon to solicit alumni gifts. The number of calls made by randomly selected students from each class is listed. At $\alpha = 0.05$, is there sufficient evidence to conclude a difference in means?

Freshmen	Sophomores	Juniors	Seniors
25	17	20	20
29	25	24	25
32	20	25	26
15	26	30	32
18	30	15	19
26	28	18	20
35			

17. A researcher conducted a study of two different diets and two different exercise programs. Three randomly selected subjects were assigned to each group for one month. The values indicate the amount of weight each lost.

Exercise program	Diet	
	A	B
I	5, 6, 4	8, 10, 15
II	3, 4, 8	12, 16, 11

Answer the following questions for the information in the printout shown below.

a. What procedure is being used?
b. What are the names of the two variables?
c. How many levels does each variable contain?
d. What are the hypotheses for the study?
e. What are the F statistics for the hypotheses? State which are significant, using the P-values.
f. Based on the answers to part *e*, which hypotheses can be rejected?

Computer Printout for Problem 17

```
Datafile: NONAME.SST    Procedure: Two-way ANOVA

TABLE OF MEANS:
                          DIET
                    A .....      B .....      Row Mean
EX PROG I .....     5.000        11.000       8.000
       II .....     5.000        13.000       9.000
    Col Mean        5.000        12.000
    Tot Mean        8.500

 SOURCE TABLE:
       Source     df    Sums of Squares    Mean Square    F Ratio    p-value
         DIET     1          147.000         147.000       21.000     0.00180
      EX PROG     1            3.000           3.000        0.429     0.53106
   DIET X EX P    1            3.000           3.000        0.429     0.53106
       Within     8           56.000           7.000
        Total    11          209.000
```

Critical Thinking Challenges

Shown here are the abstract and two tables from a research study entitled "Adult Children of Alcoholics: Are They at Greater Risk for Negative Health Behaviors?" by Arlene E. Hall. Based on the abstract and the tables, answer these questions.

1. What was the purpose of the study?

2. How many groups were used in the study?

3. By what means were the data collected?

4. What was the sample size?

5. What type of sampling method was used?

6. How might the population be defined?

7. What may have been the hypothesis for the ANOVA part of the study?

8. Why was the one-way ANOVA procedure used, as opposed to another test, such as the t test?

9. What part of the ANOVA table did the conclusion "ACOAs had significantly lower wellness scores (WS) than non-ACOAs" come from?

10. What level of significance was used?

11. In the following excerpts from the article, the researcher states that

> . . . using the Tukey-HSD procedure revealed a significant difference between ACOAs and non-ACOAs, $p = 0.05$, but no significant difference was found between ACOAs and Unsures or between non-ACOAs and Unsures.

Using Tables 12–8 and 12–9 and the means, explain why the Tukey test would have enabled the researcher to draw this conclusion.

Abstract *The purpose of the study was to examine and compare the health behaviors of adult children of alcoholics (ACOAs) and their non ACOA peers within a university population. Subjects were 980 undergraduate students from a major university in the East. Three groups (ACOA, non-ACOA, and Unsure) were identified from subjects' responses to three direct questions regarding parental drinking behaviors. A questionnaire was used to collect data for the study. Included were questions related to demographics, parental drinking behaviors, and the College Wellness Check (WS), a health risk appraisal designed especially for college students (Dewey & Cabral, 1986). Analysis of variance procedures revealed that ACOAs had significantly lower wellness scores (WS) than non-ACOAs. Chi-square analyses of the individual variables revealed that ACOAs and non-ACOAs were significantly different on 15 of the 50 variables of the WS. A discriminant analysis procedure revealed the similarities between Unsure subjects and ACOA subjects. The results provide valuable information regarding ACOAs in a nonclinical setting and contribute to our understanding of the influences related to their health risk behaviors.*

Table 12–8	Means and Standard Deviations for the Wellness Scores (WS) Group by ($N = 945$)		
Group	**N**	**$\overline{X}$**	**S.D**
ACOAs	143	69.0	13.6
Non-ACOAs	746	73.2	14.5
Unsure	56	70.1	14.0
Total	945	212.3	42.1

Table 12–9	ANOVA of Group Means for the Wellness Scores (WS)			
Source	**d.f.**	**SS**	**MS**	**F**
Between groups	2	2,403.5	1,201.7	5.9*
Within groups	942	193,237.4	205.1	
Total	944	195,640.8		

$*p < 0.01$

Source: Arlene E. Hall, "Adult Children of Alcoholics: Are They at Greater Risk for Negative Health Behaviors?" *Journal of Health Education* 12, no. 4, pp. 232–238.

Data Projects

Where appropriate, use Minitab, SPSS, the TI-83 Plus, the TI-84 Plus, or a computer program of your choice to complete these exercises.

Select a variable and collect data for at least three different groups (samples). For example, you could ask students, faculty, and clerical staff how many cups of coffee they drink per day or how many hours they watch television per day. Compare the means, using the one-way ANOVA technique, and then answer each of these.

a. What is the purpose of the study?
b. Define the population.
c. How were the samples selected?

d. What α value was used?

e. State the hypotheses.

f. What was the F test statistic?

g. What was the decision?

h. Summarize the results.

You may use the following websites to obtain raw data:

Visit the data sets at the book's website found at www.mcgrawhill.ca/olc/bluman

http://lib.stat.cmu.edu/DASL

www.statcan.ca

Hypothesis-Testing Summary 2* ● ● ●

7. Test of the significance of the correlation coefficient.

Example: $H_0: \rho = 0$

Use a t test:

$$t = r\sqrt{\frac{n-2}{1-r^2}} \quad \text{with d.f.} = n - 2$$

8. Formula for the F test for the multiple correlation coefficient.

Example: $H_0: \rho = 0$

$$F = \frac{R^2/k}{(1 - R^2)/(n - k - 1)}$$

d.f.N. $= n - k$ d.f.D. $= n - k - 1$

9. Comparison of a sample distribution with a specific population.

Example: H_0: There is no difference between the two distributions.

Use the chi-square goodness-of-fit test:

$$\chi^2 = \sum \frac{(O - E)^2}{E}$$

d.f. = no. of categories $- 1$

10. Comparison of the independence of two variables.

Example: H_0: Variable A is independent of variable B.

Use the chi-square independence test:

$$\chi^2 = \sum \frac{(O - E)^2}{E}$$

d.f. $= (R - 1)(C - 1)$

11. Test for homogeneity of proportions.

Example: $H_0: p_1 = p_2 = p_3$

Use the chi-square test:

$$\chi^2 = \sum \frac{(O - E)^2}{E}$$

d.f. $= (R - 1)(C - 1)$

12. Comparison of three or more sample means.

Example: $H_0: \mu_1 = \mu_2 = \mu_3$

Use the analysis of variance test:

$$F = \frac{s_B^2}{s_W^2}$$

where

$$s_B^2 = \frac{\sum n_i (\bar{X}_i - \bar{X}_{\text{GM}})^2}{k - 1}$$

$$s_W^2 = \frac{\sum (n_i - 1)s_i^2}{\sum (n_i - 1)}$$

d.f.N. $= k - 1$ $N = n_1 + n_2 + \cdots + n_k$

d.f.D. $= N - k$ $k = $ number of groups

13. Test when the F test statistic for the ANOVA is significant. Use the Scheffé test to find what pairs of means are significantly different.

$$F_S = \frac{(\bar{X}_i - \bar{X}_j)^2}{s_w^2[(1/n_i) + (1/n_j)]}$$

$$F' = (k - 1)(\text{C.V.})$$

Use the Tukey test to find which pairs of means are significantly different.

$$q = \frac{\bar{X}_j - \bar{X}_j}{\sqrt{s_W^2/n}} \quad \begin{array}{l} \text{d.f.N.} = k \\ \text{d.f.D.} = \text{degrees of freedom for } s_W^2 \end{array}$$

14. Test for the two-way ANOVA.

Example:

H_0: There is no significant difference for the main effects.

H_1: There is no significant difference for the interaction-effect.

$$\text{MS}_A = \frac{\text{SS}_A}{a - 1}$$

$$\text{MS}_B = \frac{\text{SS}_B}{b - 1}$$

$$MS_{A \times B} = \frac{SS_{A \times B}}{(a-1)(b-1)}$$

$$MS_W = \frac{SS_W}{ab(n-1)}$$

$$F_A = \frac{MS_A}{MS_W} \qquad \text{d.f.N.} = a - 1$$
$$\text{d.f.D.} = ab(n-1)$$

$$F_B = \frac{MS_B}{MS_W} \qquad \text{d.f.N.} = (b-1)$$
$$\text{d.f.D.} = ab(n-1)$$

$$F_{A \times B} = \frac{MS_{A \times B}}{MS_W} \qquad \text{d.f.N.} = (a-1)(b-1)$$
$$\text{d.f.D.} = ab(n-1)$$

*This summary is a continuation of Hypothesis-Testing Summary 1, at the end of Chapter 9.

Answers to Applying the Concepts ●●●

Section 12–3   Colours That Make You Smarter

1. The ANOVA produces a test statistic of $F = 3.06$, with a P-value of 0.059. We would fail to reject the null hypothesis and find that there is not enough evidence to conclude that the colour of a person's clothing is related to people's perceptions of how intelligent the person looks.

2. Answers will vary. One possible answer is that the purpose of the study was to determine if the colour of a person's clothing is related to people's perceptions of how intelligent the person looks.

3. We could use the Scheffé test to test all possible pairwise comparisons.

4. Tukey's pairwise comparisons

```
Family error rate = 0.0500
Individual error rate = 0.0195

Critical value = 3.46
Intervals for (column level mean) - (row level mean)
              1              2
    2       -0.399
             2.091

    3       -0.014        -0.861
             2.476         1.630
```

5. There are no contradictions in the results. Tukey's pairwise comparisons do not show any differences between any of the means, and the ANOVA failed to reject the null hypothesis of the means being equal.

6. We would have to perform three separate t tests, which would inflate the error rate.

7. We prefer to use Tukey's test over the Scheffé method when the sample sizes are all equal.

Section 12–4   Automobile Sales Techniques

There is no significant difference between levels 1 and 2 of experience. Level 3 and level 4 salespersons did significantly better than those at levels 1 and 2, with level 4 showing the best results, on average. If type of presentation is taken into consideration, the interaction plot shows a significant difference. The best combination seems to be level 4 experience with presentation style 1.

CHAPTER 13 Nonparametric Statistics

Objectives

After completing this chapter, you should be able to

1 State the advantages and disadvantages of nonparametric methods.

2 Test hypotheses, using the sign test.

3 Test hypotheses, using the Wilcoxon rank sum test.

4 Test hypotheses, using the signed-rank test.

5 Test hypotheses, using the Kruskal-Wallis test.

6 Compute the Spearman rank correlation coefficient.

7 Test hypotheses, using the runs test.

Outline

13–1 Introduction

13–2 Advantages and Disadvantages of Nonparametric Methods

13–3 The Sign Test

13–4 The Wilcoxon Rank Sum Test

13–5 The Wilcoxon Signed-Rank Test

13–6 The Kruskal-Wallis Test

13–7 The Spearman Rank Correlation Coefficient and the Runs Test

13–8 Summary

Statistics Today

Too Much or Too Little?

Suppose a manufacturer of ketchup wishes to check the bottling machines to see if they are functioning properly. That is, are they dispensing the right amount of ketchup per bottle? A 375-millilitre bottle is currently used. Because of the natural variation in the manufacturing process, the amount of ketchup in a bottle will not always be exactly 375 millilitres. Some bottles will contain less than 375 millilitres, and others will contain more than 375 millilitres. To see if the variation is due to chance or to a malfunction in the manufacturing process, a runs test can be used. The runs test is a nonparametric statistical technique. See Statistics Today—Revisited, page 599. This chapter explains such techniques, which can be used to help the manufacturer determine the answer to the question.

13–1   Introduction

Statistical tests, such as the z, t, and F tests, are called parametric tests. **Parametric tests** are statistical tests for population parameters such as means, variances, and proportions that involve assumptions about the populations from which the samples were selected. One assumption is that these populations are normally distributed. But what if the population in a particular hypothesis-testing situation is *not* normally distributed? Statisticians have developed a branch of statistics known as **nonparametric statistics** or **distribution-free statistics** to use when the population from which the samples are selected is not normally distributed. Nonparametric statistics can also be used to test hypotheses that do not involve specific population parameters, such as μ, σ, or p.

For example, a sportswriter may wish to know whether there is a relationship between the rankings of two judges on the diving abilities of 10 Olympic swimmers. In another situation, a sociologist may wish to determine whether men and women enrol at random for a specific drug rehabilitation program. The statistical tests used in these situations are nonparametric or distribution-free tests. The term *nonparametric* is used for both situations.

The nonparametric tests explained in this chapter are the sign test, the Wilcoxon rank sum test, the Wilcoxon signed-rank test, the Kruskal-Wallis test, and the runs test. In addition, the Spearman rank correlation coefficient, a statistic for determining the relationship between ranks, is explained.

13–2

Advantages and Disadvantages of Nonparametric Methods

As stated previously, nonparametric tests and statistics can be used in place of their parametric counterparts (z, t, and F) when the assumption of normality cannot be met. However, one should not assume that these statistics are a better alternative than the parametric statistics. There are both advantages and disadvantages in the use of nonparametric methods.

Advantages

Objective 1

State the advantages and disadvantages of nonparametric methods.

There are five advantages that nonparametric methods have over parametric methods:

1. They can be used to test population parameters when the variable is not normally distributed.
2. They can be used when the data are nominal or ordinal.
3. They can be used to test hypotheses that do not involve population parameters.
4. In most cases, the computations are easier than those for the parametric counterparts.
5. They are easy to understand.

Disadvantages

There are three disadvantages of nonparametric methods:

1. They are *less sensitive* than their parametric counterparts when the assumptions of the parametric methods are met. Therefore, larger differences are needed before the null hypothesis can be rejected.
2. They tend to use *less information* than the parametric tests. For example, the sign test requires the researcher to determine only whether the data values are above or below the median, not how much above or below the median each value is.
3. They are *less efficient* than their parametric counterparts when the assumptions of the parametric methods are met. That is, larger sample sizes are needed to overcome the loss of information. For example, the nonparametric sign test is about 60% as efficient as its parametric counterpart, the z test. Thus, a sample size of 100 is needed for use of the sign test, compared with a sample size of 60 for use of the z-test to obtain the same results.

Since there are both advantages and disadvantages to the nonparametric methods, the researcher should use caution in selecting these methods. If the parametric assumptions can be met, the parametric methods are preferred. However, when parametric assumptions cannot be met, the nonparametric methods are a valuable tool for analyzing the data.

Ranking

Interesting Fact

Older men have the biggest ears. James Heathcote, M.D., says, "On average, our ears seem to grow 0.22 millimetre a year. This is roughly a centimetre during the course of 50 years."

Many nonparametric tests involve the **ranking** of data, that is, the positioning of a data value in a data array according to some rating scale. Ranking is an ordinal variable. For example, suppose a judge decides to rate five speakers on an ascending scale of 1 to 10, with 1 being the best and 10 being the worst, for categories such as voice, gestures, logical presentation, and platform personality. The ratings are shown in the chart.

Speaker	A	B	C	D	E
Rating	8	6	10	3	1

The rankings are shown next.

Speaker	E	D	B	A	C
Rating	1	3	6	8	10
Ranking	1	2	3	4	5

Since speaker E received the lowest score, 1 point, he or she is ranked first. Speaker D received the next-lower score, 3 points; he or she is ranked second; and so on.

What happens if two or more speakers receive the same number of points? Suppose the judge awards points as follows:

Speaker	A	B	C	D	E
Rating	8	6	10	6	3

The speakers are then ranked as follows:

Speaker	E	D	B	A	C
Rating	3	6	6	8	10
Ranking	1	Tie for 2nd and 3rd		4	5

When there is a tie for two or more places, the average of the ranks must be used. In this case, each would be ranked as

$$\frac{2 + 3}{2} = \frac{5}{2} = 2.5$$

Hence, the rankings are as follows:

Speaker	E	D	B	A	C
Rating	3	6	6	8	10
Ranking	1	2.5	2.5	4	5

Many times, the data are already ranked, so no additional computations must be done. For example, if the judge does not have to award points but can simply select the speakers who are best, second-best, third-best, and so on, then these ranks can be used directly.

P-values can also be found for nonparametric statistical tests, and the *P*-value method can be used to test hypotheses that use nonparametric tests. For this chapter, the *P*-value method will be limited to some of the nonparametric tests that use the standard normal distribution or the chi-square distribution.

Applying the Concepts 13–2

Ranking Data

The following table lists the percentages of patients who experienced side effects from a drug used to lower a person's cholesterol level.

Side effect	Percent
Chest pain	4.0
Rash	4.0
Nausea	7.0
Heartburn	5.4
Fatigue	3.8
Headache	7.3
Dizziness	10.0
Chills	7.0
Cough	2.6

Rank each value in the table.

See page 603 for the answer.

Exercises 13–2

1. What is meant by *nonparametric statistics?*

2. When should nonparametric statistics be used?

3. List the advantages and disadvantages of nonparametric statistics.

For Exercises 4 through 10, rank each set of data.

4. 3, 8, 6, 1, 4, 10, 7

5. 22, 66, 32, 43, 65, 43, 71, 34

6. 83, 460, 582, 177, 241

7. 9, 7, 4, 9, 8, 6, 6, 10, 13, 16, 18, 15

8. 22, 25, 28, 28, 18, 32, 37, 41, 41, 43

9. 188, 256, 197, 188, 321, 530, 763

10. 2.8, 6.8, 2.6, 3.1, 1.5, 8.9, 3.15, 2.12, 3.1

13–3   The Sign Test

Single-Sample Sign Test

Objective 2

Test hypotheses, using the sign test.

The simplest nonparametric test, the **sign test** for single samples, is used to test the value of a median for a specific sample. When using the sign test, the researcher hypothesizes the specific value for the median of a population; then he or she selects a sample of data and compares each value with the conjectured median. If the data value is above the conjectured median, it is assigned a plus sign. If it is below the conjectured median, it is assigned a minus sign. And if it is exactly the same as the conjectured median, it is assigned a 0. Then the numbers of plus and minus signs are compared. If the null hypothesis is true, the number of plus signs should be approximately equal to the number of minus signs. If the null hypothesis is not true, there will be a disproportionate number of plus or minus signs.

Test Statistic for the Sign Test

The test statistic is the smaller number of plus or minus signs.

For example, if there are 8 positive signs and 3 negative signs, the test statistic is 3. When the sample size is 25 or less, Table J in Appendix C is used to determine the critical value. For a specific α, if the test statistic is less than or equal to the critical value obtained from the table, the null hypothesis should be rejected. The values in Table J are obtained from the binomial distribution. The derivation is omitted here.

Example 13–1

A convenience store owner hypothesizes that the median number of snow cones she sells per day is 40. A random sample of 20 days yields the following data for the number of snow cones sold each day.

18	43	40	16	22
30	29	32	37	36
39	34	39	45	28
36	40	34	39	52

At $\alpha = 0.05$, test the owner's hypothesis.

Solution

Step 1   State the hypotheses and identify the claim.

H_0: median = 40 (claim)   and H_1: median $\neq$ 40

Step 2 Find the critical value. Compare each value of the data with the median. If the value is greater than the median, replace the value with a plus sign. If it is less than the median, replace it with a minus sign. And if it is equal to the median, replace it with a 0. The completed table follows.

−	+	0	−	−
−	−	−	−	−
−	−	−	+	−
−	0	−	−	+

Refer to Table J in Appendix C, using $n = 18$ (the total number of plus and minus signs; omit the zeros) and $\alpha = 0.05$ for a two-tailed test; the critical value is 4. See Figure 13–1.

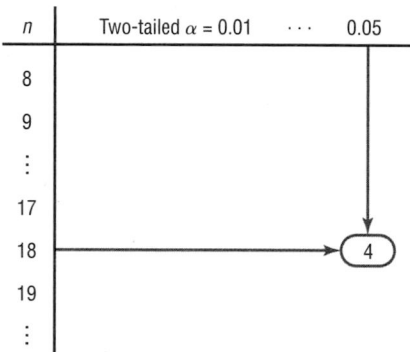

Figure 13–1

Finding the Critical Value in Table J for Example 13–1

Step 3 Compute the test statistic. Count the number of plus and minus signs obtained in step 2, and use the smaller value as the test statistic. Since there are 3 plus signs and 15 minus signs, 3 is the test statistic.

Step 4 Make the decision. Compare the test statistic 3 with the critical value 4. If the test statistic is less than or equal to the critical value, the null hypothesis is rejected. In this case, the null hypothesis is rejected since $3 < 4$.

Step 5 Summarize the results. There is enough evidence to reject the claim that the median number of snow cones sold per day is 40.

When the sample size is 26 or more, the normal approximation can be used to find the test statistic. The formula is given. The critical value is found in Table E–1 or Table E–2 in Appendix C.

Formula for the z Test Statistic in the Sign Test When $n \geq 26$

$$z = \frac{(X + 0.5) - (n/2)}{\sqrt{n}/2}$$

where

X = smaller number of + or − signs
n = sample size

Example 13–2	Based on past experience, a manufacturer claims that the median (MD) lifetime of a rubber washer is at least 8 years. A sample of 50 washers showed that 21 lasted more than 8 years. At $\alpha = 0.05$, is there enough evidence to reject the manufacturer's claim?

Solution

Step 1   State the hypotheses and identify the claim.

$$H_0: \text{MD} \geq 8 \ (\text{claim}) \qquad \text{and} \qquad H_1: \text{MD} < 8$$

Step 2   Find the critical value. Since $\alpha = 0.05$ and $n = 50$, and since this is a left-tailed test, the critical value is -1.645, obtained from Table E–1.

Step 3   Compute the test statistic.

$$z = \frac{(X + 0.5) - (n/2)}{\sqrt{n}/2} = \frac{(21 + 0.5) - (50/2)}{\sqrt{50}/2} = \frac{-3.5}{3.5355} = -0.99$$

Step 4   Make the decision. Since the test statistic of -0.99 is greater than -1.65, the decision is to not reject the null hypothesis.

Step 5   Summarize the results. There is not enough evidence to reject the claim that the median lifetime of the washers is at least 8 years.

In Example 13–2, the sample size was 50, and 21 washers lasted more than 8 years, so $50 - 21$, or 29, washers did not last 8 years. The value of X corresponds to the smaller of the two numbers 21 and 29. In this case, $X = 21$ is used in the formula. The reason is that there would be 21 positive signs, since subtracting 8 years from the value in years of a washer that lasted longer than 8 years results in a positive answer. When 8 is subtracted from the value in years of a washer that did not last 8 years, the answer is negative. Assuming that no washer lasted exactly 8 years results in 21 positive answers and 29 negative answers. Since 21 is the smaller of the two numbers, the value of X is 21.

Suppose a researcher hypothesized that the median age of houses in a certain municipality was 40 years. In a random sample of 100 houses, 68 were older than 40 years. Then the value used for X in the formula would be $100 - 68$, or 32, since it is the smaller of the two numbers 68 and 32. When 40 is subtracted from the age of a house older than 40 years, the answer is positive. When 40 is subtracted from the age of a house that is less than 40 years old, the result is negative. There would be 68 positive signs and 32 negative signs (assuming that no house was exactly 40 years old). Hence, 32 would be used for X, since it is the smaller of the two values.

Paired-Sample Sign Test

The sign test can also be used to test sample means in a comparison of two dependent samples, such as a before-and-after test. Recall that when dependent samples are taken from normally distributed populations, the t test is used (Section 9–5). When the condition of normality cannot be met, the nonparametric sign test can be used, as shown in Example 13–3.

Example 13–3	A medical researcher believed the number of ear infections in swimmers can be reduced if the swimmers use earplugs. A sample of 10 people was selected, and the number of infections for a four-month period was recorded. During the first two months, the swimmers did not use the earplugs; during the second two months, they

did. At the beginning of the second two-month period, each swimmer was examined to make sure that no infections were present. The data are shown here. At $\alpha = 0.05$, can the researcher conclude that using earplugs reduced the number of ear infections?

Number of ear infections

Swimmer	Before, X_B	After, X_A
A	3	2
B	0	1
C	5	4
D	4	0
E	2	1
F	4	3
G	3	1
H	5	3
I	2	2
J	1	3

Solution

Step 1   State the hypotheses and identify the claim.

H_0: The number of ear infections will not be reduced.

H_1: The number of ear infections will be reduced (claim).

Step 2   Find the critical value. Subtract the after values X_A from the before values X_B and indicate the difference by a positive or negative sign or 0, according to the value, as shown in the table.

Swimmer	Before, X_B	After, X_A	Sign of difference
A	3	2	+
B	0	1	−
C	5	4	+
D	4	0	+
E	2	1	+
F	4	3	+
G	3	1	+
H	5	3	+
I	2	2	0
J	1	3	−

From Table J, with $n = 9$ (the total number of positive and negative signs; the 0 is not counted) and $\alpha = 0.05$ (one-tailed), at most 1 negative sign is needed to reject the null hypothesis because 1 is the smallest entry in the $\alpha = 0.05$ column of Table J.

Step 3   Compute the test statistic. Count the number of positive and negative signs found in step 2, and use the smaller value as the test statistic. There are 2 negative signs, so the test statistic is 2.

Step 4   Make the decision. There are 2 negative signs. The decision is to not reject the null hypothesis. The reason is that with $n = 9$, C.V. $= 1$ and $1 < 2$.

Step 5   Summarize the results. There is not enough evidence to support the claim that the use of earplugs reduced the number of ear infections.

When conducting a one-tailed sign test, the researcher must scrutinize the data to determine whether they support the null hypothesis. If the data support the null hypothesis, there is no need to conduct the test. In Example 13–3, the null hypothesis states that the number of ear infections will not be reduced. The data would support the null hypothesis if there were more negative signs than positive signs. The reason is that the before values X_B in most cases would be smaller than the after values X_A, and the $X_B - X_A$ values would be negative more often than positive. This would indicate that there is not enough evidence to reject the null hypothesis. The researcher would stop here, since there is no need to continue the procedure.

On the other hand, if the number of ear infections were reduced, the X_B values, for the most part, would be larger than the X_A values, and the $X_B - X_A$ values would most often be positive, as in Example 13–3. Hence, the researcher would continue the procedure. A word of caution is in order, and a little reasoning is required.

When the sample size is 26 or more, the normal approximation can be used in the same manner as in Example 13–2. The steps for conducting the sign test for single or paired samples are given in the Procedure Table.

Procedure Table

Sign Test for Single and Paired Samples

Step 1   State the hypotheses and identify the claim.

Step 2   Find the critical value(s). For the single-sample test, compare each value with the conjectured median. If the value is larger than the conjectured median, replace it with a positive sign. If it is smaller than the conjectured median, replace it with a negative sign.

         For the paired-sample sign test, subtract the after values from the before values, and indicate the difference with a positive or negative sign or 0, according to the value. Use Table J and n = total number of positive and negative signs.

         Check the data to see whether they support the null hypothesis. If they do, do not reject the null hypothesis. If not, continue with step 3.

Step 3   Compute the test statistic. Count the number of positive and negative signs found in step 2, and use the smaller value as the test statistic.

Step 4   Make the decision. Compare the test statistic with the critical value in Table J. If the test statistic is less than or equal to the critical value, reject the null hypothesis.

Step 5   Summarize the results.

         Note: If the sample size n is 26 or more, use Table E–1 or Table E–2 and the following formula for the test statistic:

$$z = \frac{(X + 0.5) - (n/2)}{\sqrt{n}/2}$$

where

$\qquad X$ = smaller number of + or − signs

$\qquad n$ = sample size

Applying the Concepts 13-3

Clean Air

An environmentalist suggests that the median of the number of days per year that a large city failed to meet the U.S. Environmental Protection Agency (EPA) acceptable standards for clean air is 11 days per month. A random sample of 20 months shows the number of days per month that the air quality was below the EPA's standards.

15	14	1	9	0	3	3	1	10	8
6	16	21	22	3	19	16	5	23	13

1. What is the claim?
2. What test would you use to test the claim? Why?
3. What would the hypotheses be?
4. Select a value for α and find the corresponding critical value.
5. What is the test statistic?
6. What is your decision?
7. Summarize the results.
8. Could a parametric test be used?

See page 603 for the answers.

Exercises 13-3

1. Why is the sign test the simplest nonparametric test to use?

2. What population parameter can be tested with the sign test?

3. In the sign test, what is used as the test statistic when $n < 26$?

4. When $n \geq 26$, what is used in place of Table J for the sign test?

For Exercises 5 through 20, perform these steps.

  a. State the hypotheses and identify the claim.
  b. Find the critical value(s).
  c. Compute the test statistic.
  d. Make the decision.
  e. Summarize the results.

Use the traditional method of hypothesis testing unless otherwise specified.

5. An oceanographer believes that the median height of the waves at Ocean City is 0.9 metres. The wave heights (in metres) are measured for a random sample of 20 days. The data are shown here. At $\alpha = 0.05$, is there enough evidence to reject the oceanographer's claim?

1.1	0.6	0.7	0.6	0.8
1.0	1.2	1.0	0.9	0.9
0.6	0.6	1.0	1.1	0.9
0.5	0.7	1.1	1.2	1.3

6. An athletic director suggests the median number for the paid attendance at 20 local football games is 3000. The data for a sample are shown. At $\alpha = 0.05$, is there enough evidence to reject the claim? If you were printing the programs for the games, would you use this figure as a guide?

6210	3150	2700	3012	4875
3540	6127	2581	2642	2573
2792	2800	2500	3700	6030
5437	2758	3490	2851	2720

Source: *Pittsburgh Post Gazette.*

7. An educator hypothesizes that the median of the number of students enrolled in cyber schools in school districts in southwestern Pennsylvania is 25. At $\alpha = 0.05$, is there enough evidence to reject the educator's claim? The data are shown here. What benefit would this information provide to the school board of a local school district?

12	41	26	14	4
38	27	27	9	11
17	11	66	5	14
8	35	16	25	17

Source: *Tribune-Review.*

8. A government economist estimates that the median cost per pound of beef is $5.00. A sample of 22 livestock buyers shows the following costs (in dollars) per pound of beef. Is there enough evidence to reject the economist's hypothesis at $\alpha = 0.10$?

5.35	5.16	4.97	4.83	5.05	5.19
4.78	4.93	4.86	5.00	4.63	5.06
5.19	5.00	5.05	5.10	5.16	5.25
5.16	5.42	5.13	5.27		

9. For a specific year, the median price of natural gas was $10.86 per 1000 cubic feet. A researcher wishes to see if there is enough evidence to reject the claim. Out of 42 households, 18 paid less that $10.86 per 1000 cubic feet for natural gas. Test the claim at $\alpha = 0.05$. How could a prospective home buyer use this information?

Source: Based on information from the U.S. Energy Information Administration.

10. One hundred people were placed on a special exercise program. After one month, 58 lost weight, 12 gained weight, and 30 weighed the same as before. Test the hypothesis that the exercise program is effective at $\alpha = 0.10$. (*Note:* It will be effective if fewer than 50% of the people did not lose weight.)

11. Of 50 students surveyed, 29 favoured single-room dormitories. At $\alpha = 0.02$, test the hypothesis that more than 50% of the students favour single-room dormitories. Use the *P*-value method.

12. A researcher read that the median age for viewers of the Carson Daly show is 39. To test the claim, 75 viewers were surveyed, and 27 were under the age of 39. At $\alpha = 0.02$ test the claim. Give one reason why an advertiser might like to know the results of this study.

Source: Nielsen Media Research.

13. One hundred students are asked if they favour increasing the school year by 20 days. The responses are 62 no, 36 yes, and 2 undecided. At $\alpha = 0.10$, test the hypothesis that 50% of the students are against extending the school year. Use the *P*-value method.

14. A criminologist suggests that the median number of unintentional firearms deaths per year in Canada is 56. The number of deaths for a sample of 11 years is shown. At $\alpha = 0.05$, is there enough evidence to reject the claim? If you took proper firearm safety precautions, would you feel relatively safe?

71	66	31	92	76	67
59	49	48	27	52	

Source: Statistics Canada.

15. A study was conducted to see whether a certain diet medication had an effect on the weights (in kilograms) of eight women. Their weights were taken before and six weeks after daily administration of the medication. The data are shown here. At $\alpha = 0.05$, can one conclude that the medication had an effect (increase or decrease) on the weights of the women?

Subject	A	B	C	D	E	F	G	H
Weight before	84.8	73.9	91.2	71.7	63.0	64.9	89.8	69.9
Weight after	80.7	73.5	85.3	70.8	60.3	68.0	79.4	68.0

16. Two different laboratory machines measure the sodium content (in milligrams) of the same 10 blood samples. The data are shown here. At $\alpha = 0.01$, test the claim that both machines gave the same reading.

Sample	1	2	3	4	5	6	7	8	9	10
Machine 1	138	136	142	151	154	141	140	138	132	136
Machine 2	140	136	141	150	153	144	143	136	131	138

17. An educator designed a reasoning skills course. Nine students were selected and given a pretest to determine their reasoning abilities. After completing the course, the same students were given an equivalent form of the test to see whether their reasoning skills had improved. The data are shown here. At $\alpha = 0.05$, did the course improve their reasoning skills?

Student	1	2	3	4	5	6	7	8	9
Pretest	80	76	74	83	92	78	91	74	88
Posttest	82	78	73	85	95	79	93	78	90

18. A researcher wishes to test the effects of a pill on a person's appetite. Twelve subjects are allowed to eat a meal of their choice, and their caloric intake is measured. The next day, the same subjects take the pill and eat a meal of their choice. The caloric intake of the second meal is measured. The data are shown here. At $\alpha = 0.02$, can the researcher conclude that the pill had an effect on a person's appetite?

Subject	1	2	3	4	5	6	7
Meal 1	856	732	900	1321	843	642	738
Meal 2	843	721	872	1341	805	531	740

Subject	8	9	10	11	12
Meal 1	1005	888	756	911	998
Meal 2	900	805	695	878	914

19. A researcher wishes to determine if the number of viewers for 10 returning television shows has not changed since last year. The data are given in millions of viewers. At $\alpha = 0.01$, test the claim that the number of viewers has not changed. Depending on your answer, would a television executive plan to air these programs for another year?

Show	1	2	3	4	5	6
Last year	28.9	26.4	20.8	25.0	21.0	19.2
This year	26.6	20.5	20.2	19.1	18.9	17.8

Show	7	8	9	10
Last year	13.7	18.8	16.8	15.3
This year	16.8	16.7	16.0	15.8

Source: Based on information from Nielson Media Research.

20. A manufacturer believes that if routine maintenance (cleaning and oiling of machines) is increased to once a day rather than once a week, the number of defective parts produced by the machines will decrease. Nine machines are selected, and the number of defective parts produced over a 24-hour operating period is counted. Maintenance is then increased to once a day for a week, and the number of defective parts each machine produces is again counted over a 24-hour operating period. The data are shown here. At $\alpha = 0.01$, can the

manufacturer conclude that increased maintenance reduces the number of defective parts manufactured by the machines?

Machine	1	2	3	4	5	6	7	8	9
Before	6	18	5	4	16	13	20	9	3
After	5	16	7	4	18	12	14	7	1

Extending the Concepts

The confidence interval for the median of a set of values less than or equal to 25 in number can be found by ordering the data from smallest to largest, finding the median, and using Table J. For example, to find the 95% confidence interval of the true median for 17, 19, 3, 8, 10, 15, 1, 23, 2, 12, order the data:

1, 2, 3, 8, 10, 12, 15, 17, 19, 23

From Table J, select $n = 10$ and $\alpha = 0.05$, and find the critical value. Use the two-tailed row. In this case, the critical value is 1. Add 1 to this value to get 2. In the ordered list, count from the left two numbers and from the right two numbers, and use these numbers to get the confidence interval, as shown:

1, 2, 3, 8, 10, 12, 15, 17, 19, 23

$2 \leq MD \leq 19$

Always add 1 to the number obtained from the table before counting. For example, if the critical value is 3, then count 4 values from the left and right.

For Exercises 21 through 25, find the confidence interval of the median, indicated in parentheses, for each set of data.

21. 3, 12, 15, 18, 16, 15, 22, 30, 25, 4, 6, 9 (95%)

22. 101, 115, 143, 106, 100, 142, 157, 163, 155, 141, 145, 153, 152, 147, 143, 115, 164, 160, 147, 150 (90%)

23. 8.2, 7.1, 6.3, 5.2, 4.8, 9.3, 7.2, 9.3, 4.5, 9.6, 7.8, 5.6, 4.7, 4.2, 9.5, 5.1 (98%)

24. 1, 8, 2, 6, 10, 15, 24, 33, 56, 41, 58, 54, 5, 3, 42, 31, 15, 65, 21 (99%)

25. 12, 15, 18, 14, 17, 19, 25, 32, 16, 47, 14, 23, 27, 42, 33, 35, 39, 41, 21, 19 (95%)

13–4   The Wilcoxon Rank Sum Test

Objective

Test hypotheses, using the Wilcoxon rank sum test.

Interesting Fact

One in four married women now earns more than her husband.

The sign test does not consider the magnitude of the data. For example, whether a value is 1 point or 100 points below the median, it will receive a negative sign. And when one compares values in the pretest/posttest situation, the magnitude of the differences is not considered. The Wilcoxon tests consider differences in magnitudes by using ranks.

The two tests considered in this section and in Section 13–5 are the **Wilcoxon rank sum test,** which is used for independent samples, and the **Wilcoxon signed-rank test,** which is used for dependent samples. Both tests are used to compare distributions. The parametric equivalents are the z and t tests for independent samples (Sections 9–2 and 9–4) and the t test for dependent samples (Section 9–5). For the parametric tests, as stated previously, the samples must be selected from approximately normally distributed populations, but the only assumption for the Wilcoxon signed-rank tests is that the population of differences has a symmetric distribution.

In the Wilcoxon tests, the values of the data for both samples are combined and then ranked. If the null hypothesis is true—meaning that there is no difference in the population distributions—then the values in each sample should be ranked approximately the same. Therefore, when the ranks are summed for each sample, the sums should be approximately equal, and the null hypothesis will not be rejected. If there is a large difference in the sums of the ranks, then the distributions are not identical, and the null hypothesis will be rejected.

The first test to be considered is the Wilcoxon rank sum test for independent samples. For this test, both sample sizes must be greater than or equal to 10. The formulas needed for the test are given next.

Formula for the Wilcoxon Rank Sum Test When Samples Are Independent

$$z = \frac{R - \mu_R}{\sigma_R}$$

where

$$\mu_R = \frac{n_1(n_1 + n_2 + 1)}{2}$$

$$\sigma_R = \sqrt{\frac{n_1 n_2 (n_1 + n_2 + 1)}{12}}$$

R = sum of ranks for smaller sample size (n_1)
n_1 = smaller of sample sizes
n_2 = larger of sample sizes
$n_1 \geq 10$ and $n_2 \geq 10$

Note that if both samples are the same size, either size can be used as n_1.

Example 13–4 illustrates the Wilcoxon rank sum test for independent samples.

Example 13–4

Two independent samples of army and navy recruits are selected, and the time in minutes it takes each recruit to complete an obstacle course is recorded, as shown in the table. At $\alpha = 0.05$, is there a difference in the times it takes the recruits to complete the course?

Army	15	18	16	17	13	22	24	17	19	21	26	28	Mean = 19.67
Navy	14	9	16	19	10	12	11	8	15	18	25		Mean = 14.27

Solution

Step 1 State the hypotheses and identify the claim.

H_0: There is no difference in the times it takes the recruits to complete the obstacle course.

H_1: There is a difference in the times it takes the recruits to complete the obstacle course (claim).

Step 2 Find the critical value. Since $\alpha = 0.05$ and this test is a two-tailed test, use the z values of $+1.96$ and -1.96 from Tables E–1 and E–2.

Step 3 Compute the test statistic.

a. Combine the data from the two samples, arrange the combined data in order, and rank each value. Be sure to indicate the group.

Time	8	9	10	11	12	13	14	15	15	16	16	17
Group	N	N	N	N	N	A	N	A	N	A	N	A
Rank	1	2	3	4	5	6	7	8.5	8.5	10.5	10.5	12.5

Time	17	18	18	19	19	21	22	24	25	26	28
Group	A	N	A	A	N	A	A	A	N	A	A
Rank	12.5	14.5	14.5	16.5	16.5	18	19	20	21	22	23

b. Sum the ranks of the group with the smaller sample size. (*Note:* If both groups have the same sample size, either one can be used.) In this case, the sample size for the navy is smaller.

$$R = 1 + 2 + 3 + 4 + 5 + 7 + 8.5 + 10.5 + 14.5 + 16.5 + 21$$
$$= 93$$

c. Substitute in the formulas to find the test statistic.

$$\mu_R = \frac{n_1(n_1 + n_2 + 1)}{2} = \frac{(11)(11 + 12 + 1)}{2} = 132$$

$$\sigma_R = \sqrt{\frac{n_1 n_2(n_1 + n_2 + 1)}{12}} = \sqrt{\frac{(11)(12)(11 + 12 + 1)}{12}}$$

$$= \sqrt{264} = 16.2$$

$$z = \frac{R - \mu_R}{\sigma_R} = \frac{93 - 132}{16.2} = -2.41$$

Step 4   Make the decision. The decision is to reject the null hypothesis, since $-2.41 < -1.96$.

Step 5   Summarize the results. There is enough evidence to support the claim that there is a difference in the times it takes the recruits to complete the course.

The steps for the Wilcoxon rank sum test are given in the Procedure Table.

Procedure Table

Wilcoxon Rank Sum Test

Step 1   State the hypotheses and identify the claim.

Step 2   Find the critical value(s). Use Tables E–1 and E–2.

Step 3   Compute the test statistic.

  a. Combine the data from the two samples, arrange the combined data in order, and rank each value.

  b. Sum the ranks of the group with the smaller sample size. (*Note:* If both groups have the same sample size, either one can be used.)

  c. Use these formulas to find the test statistic.

$$\mu_R = \frac{n_1(n_1 + n_2 + 1)}{2}$$

$$\sigma_R = \sqrt{\frac{n_1 n_2(n_1 + n_2 + 1)}{12}}$$

$$z = \frac{R - \mu_R}{\sigma_R}$$

  where R is the sum of the ranks of the data in the smaller sample and n_1 and n_2 are each greater than or equal to 10.

Step 4   Make the decision.

Step 5   Summarize the results.

Applying the Concepts 13–4

School Lunch

A nutritionist decided to see if there was a difference in the number of calories served for lunch in elementary and secondary schools. She selected a random sample of eight elementary schools and another random sample of eight secondary schools in Ontario. The data are shown.

Elementary	Secondary
648	694
589	730
625	750
595	810
789	860
727	702
702	657
564	761

1. Are the samples independent or dependent?
2. What are the hypotheses?
3. What nonparametric test would you use to test the claim?
4. What critical value would you use?
5. What is the test statistic?
6. What is your decision?
7. What is the corresponding parametric test?
8. What assumption would you need to meet to use the parametric test?
9. If this assumption were not met, would the parametric test yield the same results?

See page 603 for the answers.

Exercises 13–4

1. What are the minimum sample sizes for the Wilcoxon rank sum test?

2. What are the parametric equivalent tests for the Wilcoxon rank sum test?

3. What distribution is used for the Wilcoxon rank sum test?

For Exercises 4 through 11, use the Wilcoxon rank sum test. Assume that the samples are independent. Also perform each of these steps.

   a. State the hypotheses and identify the claim.
   b. Find the critical value(s).
   c. Compute the test statistic.
   d. Make the decision.
   e. Summarize the results.

Use the traditional method of hypothesis testing unless otherwise specified.

4. A random sample of men and women in prison was asked to give the length of sentence each received for a certain type of crime. At $\alpha = 0.05$, test the claim that there is no difference in the sentence received by each gender. The data (in months) are shown here.

Males	8	12	6	14	22	27	32	24	26
Females	7	5	2	3	21	26	30	9	4

Males	19	15	13		
Females	17	23	12	11	16

5. A researcher wishes to see if there is a difference in the number of jetplanes grounded for repairs and the number of jetplanes in storage. A sample of data for the past several years is shown. At $\alpha = 0.05$, test the claim that there is no difference in the number of planes that are stored and the number of planes grounded. Based on these results, should an airline plan for more storage facilities or repair facilities?

Year	1	2	3	4	5	6
In storage	179	149	140	152	191	432
Grounded	647	716	1480	1338	1285	208

Year	7	8	9	10
In storage	727	345	1054	371
Grounded	511	806	615	913

Source: Back Aviation Solutions.

6. To test the claim that there is no difference in the lifetimes of two brands of handheld video games, a researcher selects a sample of 11 video games of each brand. The lifetimes (in months) of each brand are shown here. At $\alpha = 0.01$, can the researcher conclude that there is a difference in the distributions of lifetimes for the two brands?

Brand A	42	34	39	42	22	47	51	34	41	39	28
Brand B	29	39	38	43	45	49	53	38	44	43	32

7. A researcher wishes to see if the stopping distance (metres) for midsize automobiles is different from the stopping distance for compact automobiles at a speed of 110 kilometres per hour. The data are shown. At $\alpha = 0.10$, test the claim that the stopping distances are the same. If one of your safety concerns is stopping distance, would it make a difference which type of automobile you purchase?

Automobile	1	2	3	4	5	6	7	8	9	10
Midsize	57	58	59	59	57	59	57	57	65	62
Compact	61	64	63	91	60	62	66	65	60	59

Source: Based on information from the National Highway Traffic Safety Administration.

8. Two groups of employees were given a questionnaire to ascertain their degree of job satisfaction. The scale ranged from 0 to 100. The groups were divided into those who had under 5 years of work experience and those who had 5 or more years of experience. The data are shown here. At $\alpha = 0.10$, test the claim that there is no difference in the job satisfaction of the two groups, as measured by the questionnaire. Use the *P*-value method.

Under 5	78	98	83	86	75	77	72	68
5 and over	94	79	82	85	73	66	64	59

Under 5	56	93	97	99	93
5 and over	52	58	63	68	88

9. A joint union and management safety committee wants to determine if the number of worker fatalities is different in two Canadian provinces with similar populations—Manitoba and Nova Scotia. A sample of data from the two provinces over the past several years is selected, and the numbers of worker fatalities are shown. At $\alpha = 0.05$, test the claim that there is no difference in the number of worker fatalities in the two provinces.

Manitoba	25	20	27	22	34	14	30
Nova Scotia	40	22	23	13	17	23	41

Source: Centre for Study of Living Standards.

10. Supervisors were asked to rate the productivity of employees on their jobs. A researcher wishes to see whether married men receive higher ratings than single men. A rating scale of 1 to 50 yielded the data shown here. At $\alpha = 0.01$, is there evidence to support this claim?

Single men	48	46	42	50	38	36	40	31	28	24	49	34
Married men	44	35	41	37	42	43	29	31	37	32	36	

11. A study was conducted to see whether there is a difference in the time it takes employees of a factory to assemble the product. Samples of high school graduates and nongraduates were timed. At $\alpha = 0.05$, is there a difference in the distributions for the two groups in the times needed to assemble the product? The data (in minutes) are shown here.

Graduates	3.6	3.2	4.4	3.0	5.6	6.3	8.2
Nongraduates	2.7	3.8	5.3	1.6	1.9	2.4	2.9
Graduates	7.1	5.8	7.3	6.4	4.2	4.7	
Nongraduates	1.7	2.6	2.0	3.1	3.4	3.9	

13–5   The Wilcoxon Signed-Rank Test

Objective 4

Test hypotheses, using the signed-rank test.

When the samples are dependent, as they would be in a before-and-after test using the same subjects, the Wilcoxon signed-rank test can be used in place of the *t* test for dependent samples. Again, this test does not require the condition of normality. Table K is used to find the critical values.

The procedure for this test is shown in Example 13–5.

Example 13–5

In a large department store, the owner wishes to see whether the number of shoplifting incidents per day will change if the number of uniformed security officers is doubled. A sample of 7 days before security is increased and 7 days after the increase shows the number of shoplifting incidents.

	Number of shoplifting incidents	
Day	Before	After
Monday	7	5
Tuesday	2	3
Wednesday	3	4
Thursday	6	3
Friday	5	1
Saturday	8	6
Sunday	12	4

Is there enough evidence to support the claim, at $\alpha = 0.05$, that there is a difference in the number of shoplifting incidents before and after the increase in security?

Solution

Step 1 State the hypotheses and identify the claim.

H_0: There is no difference in the number of shoplifting incidents before and after the increase in security.

H_1: There is a difference in the number of shoplifting incidents before and after the increase in security (claim).

Step 2 Find the critical value from Table K. Since $n = 7$ and $\alpha = 0.05$ for this two-tailed test, the critical value is 2. See Figure 13–2.

Figure 13–2

Finding the Critical Value in Table K for Example 13–5

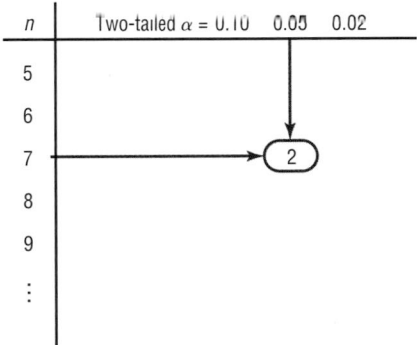

Step 3 Find the test statistic.

a. Make a table as shown here.

Day	Before, X_B	After, X_A	Difference $D = X_B - X_A$	Absolute value $|D|$	Rank	Signed rank
Mon.	7	5				
Tues.	2	3				
Wed.	3	4				
Thurs.	6	3				
Fri.	5	1				
Sat.	8	6				
Sun.	12	4				

b. Find the differences (before minus after), and place the values in the Difference column.

$7 - 5 = 2$ $6 - 3 = 3$ $8 - 6 = 2$

$2 - 3 = -1$ $5 - 1 = 4$ $12 - 4 = 8$

$3 - 4 = -1$

c. Find the absolute value of each difference, and place the results in the Absolute value column. (*Note:* The absolute value of any number except 0 is the positive value of the number. Any differences of 0 should be ignored.)

$$|2| = 2 \qquad |3| = 3 \qquad |2| = 2$$
$$|-1| = 1 \qquad |4| = 4 \qquad |8| = 8$$
$$|-1| = 1$$

d. Rank each absolute value from lowest to highest, and place the rankings in the Rank column. In the case of a tie, assign the values that rank plus 0.5.

Value	2	1	1	3	4	2	8
Rank	3.5	1.5	1.5	5	6	3.5	7

e. Give each rank a plus or minus sign, according to the sign in the Difference column. The completed table is shown here.

Day	Before, X_B	After, X_A	Difference $D = X_B - X_A$	Absolute value $\lvert D \rvert$	Rank	Signed rank
Mon.	7	5	2	2	3.5	+3.5
Tues.	2	3	-1	1	1.5	-1.5
Wed.	3	4	-1	1	1.5	-1.5
Thurs.	6	3	3	3	5	+5
Fri.	5	1	4	4	6	+6
Sat.	8	6	2	2	3.5	+3.5
Sun.	12	4	8	8	7	+7

f. Find the sum of the positive ranks and the sum of the negative ranks separately.

Positive rank sum $\quad (+3.5) + (+5) + (+6) + (+3.5) + (+7) = +25$

Negative rank sum $\quad (-1.5) + (-1.5) \qquad\qquad\qquad\quad = -3$

g. Select the smaller of the absolute values of the sums ($\lvert -3 \rvert$), and use this absolute value as the test statistic w_s. In this case, $w_s = \lvert -3 \rvert = 3$.

Step 4 Make the decision. Reject the null hypothesis if the test statistic is less than or equal to the critical value. In this case, $3 > 2$; hence, the decision is not to reject the null hypothesis.

Step 5 Summarize the results. There is not enough evidence to support the claim that there is a difference in the number of shoplifting incidents. Hence, the security increase probably made no difference in the number of shoplifting incidents.

The rationale behind the signed-rank test can be explained by a diet example. If the diet is working, then the majority of the postweights will be smaller than the preweights. When the postweights are subtracted from the preweights, the majority of the signs will be positive, and the absolute value of the sum of the negative ranks will be small. This sum will probably be smaller than the critical value obtained from Table K, and the null hypothesis will be rejected. On the other hand, if the diet does not work, some people will gain weight, other people will lose weight, and still other people will remain about the same weight. In this case, the sum of the positive ranks and the absolute value of the sum of the negative ranks will be approximately equal and will be about one-half of the sum of the absolute value of all the ranks. In this case, the smaller of the absolute values of the two sums will still be larger than the critical value obtained from Table K, and the null hypothesis will not be rejected.

When $n \geq 30$, the normal distribution can be used to approximate the Wilcoxon distribution. The same critical values from Tables E–1 and E–2 used for the z test for specific α values are used. The formula is

$$z = \frac{w_s - \dfrac{n(n+1)}{4}}{\sqrt{\dfrac{n(n+1)(2n+1)}{24}}}$$

where
   n = number of pairs where difference is not 0
   w_s = smaller sum in absolute value of signed ranks

The steps for the Wilcoxon signed-rank test are given in the Procedure Table.

Procedure Table

Wilcoxon Signed-Rank Test

Step 1 State the hypotheses and identify the claim.

Step 2 Find the critical value from Table K.

Step 3 Compute the test statistic.

   a. Make a table, as shown.

Before, X_B	After, X_A	Difference $D = X_B - X_A$	Absolute value $|D|$	Rank	Signed rank

   b. Find the differences (before − after), and place the values in the Difference column.

   c. Find the absolute value of each difference, and place the results in the Absolute value column.

   d. Rank each absolute value from lowest to highest, and place the rankings in the Rank column.

   e. Give each rank a positive or negative sign, according to the sign in the Difference column.

   f. Find the sum of the positive ranks and the sum of the negative ranks separately.

   g. Select the smaller of the absolute values of the sums, and use this absolute value as the test statistic w_s.

Step 4 Make the decision. Reject the null hypothesis if the test statistic is less than or equal to the critical value.

Step 5 Summarize the results.

   Note: When $n \geq 30$, use Tables E–1 and E–2 and the test statistic

$$z = \frac{w_s - \dfrac{n(n+1)}{4}}{\sqrt{\dfrac{n(n+1)(2n+1)}{24}}}$$

   where
      n = number of pairs where difference is not 0
      w_s = smaller sum in absolute value of signed ranks

Applying the Concepts 13–5

Pain Medication

A researcher decides to see how effective a pain medication is. Eight subjects were asked to determine the severity of their pain by using a scale of 1 to 10, with 1 being very minor and 10 being very severe. Then each was given the medication, and after 1 hour, they were asked to rate the severity of their pain, using the same scale.

Subject	1	2	3	4	5	6	7	8
Before	8	6	2	3	4	6	2	7
After	6	5	3	1	2	6	1	6

1. What is the purpose of the study?
2. Are the samples independent or dependent?
3. What are the hypotheses?
4. What nonparametric test could be used to test the claim?
5. What significance level would you use?
6. What is your decision?
7. What parametric test could you use?
8. Would the results be the same?

See page 603 for the answers.

Exercises 13–5

1. What is the parametric equivalent test for the Wilcoxon signed-rank test?

For Exercises 2 and 3, find the sum of the signed ranks. Assume that the samples are dependent. State which sum is used as the test value.

2.
Pretest	18	32	35	37	25	41	52	43	56	62
Posttest	20	21	26	37	29	40	31	37	51	65

3.
Pretest	108	97	115	162	156	105	153
Posttest	110	97	103	168	143	112	141

For Exercises 4 through 8, use Table K to determine whether the null hypothesis should be rejected.

4. $w_s = 62$, $n = 21$, $\alpha = 0.05$, two-tailed test

5. $w_s = 18$, $n = 15$, $\alpha = 0.02$, two-tailed test

6. $w_s = 53$, $n = 25$, $\alpha = 0.05$, one-tailed test

7. $w_s = 142$, $n = 28$, $\alpha = 0.05$, one-tailed test

8. $w_s = 109$, $n = 27$, $\alpha = 0.025$, one-tailed test

9. Eight drugs were selected, and the prices for the human doses and the animal doses for the same amounts were compared. At $\alpha = 0.05$, can it be concluded that the prices for the animal doses are significantly less than the prices for the human doses? If the null hypothesis is rejected, give one reason why animal doses might cost less than human doses.

Human dose	0.67	0.64	1.20	0.51	0.87	0.74	0.50	1.22
Animal dose	0.13	0.18	0.42	0.25	0.57	0.57	0.49	1.28

Source: U.S. House Committee on Government Reform.

10. In a corporation, female and male workers were matched according to years of experience working for the company. Their salaries were then compared. The data (in thousands of dollars) are shown in the table. At $\alpha = 0.10$, is there a difference in the salaries of the males and females?

Males	18	43	32	27	15	45	21	22
Females	16	38	35	29	15	46	25	28

11. A Quebec marketing executive wished to compare the number of hours per week that Quebec francophones watched television programming versus Quebec anglophones. Data is collected for the same six age categories for both groups. At $\alpha = 0.05$, can it be concluded that the Quebec francophones watch more television per week than Quebec anglophones? Do the results help the marketing executive focus her advertising efforts?

Francophones	22.9	12.0	17.0	20.0	25.4	37.0
Anglophones	19.8	9.5	15.7	16.5	22.0	29.7

Source: Statistics Canada.

12. Eight couples are given a questionnaire designed to measure marital compatibility. After completing a workshop, they are given a second questionnaire to see whether there is a change in their attitudes toward each other. The data are as shown here. At $\alpha = 0.10$, is there any difference in the scores of the couples?

Before	43	52	37	29	51	62	57	61
After	48	59	36	29	60	68	59	72

13. A researcher wishes to compare the prices for prescription drugs in the United States with those in Canada. The same drugs and dosages were compared in each country. At $\alpha = 0.05$, can it be concluded that the drugs in Canada are cheaper?

Drug	1	2	3	4	5	6
United States	3.31	2.27	2.54	3.13	23.40	3.16
Canada	1.47	1.07	1.34	1.34	21.44	1.47

Drug	7	8	9	10
United States	1.98	5.27	1.96	1.11
Canada	1.07	3.39	2.22	1.13

Source: IMS Health and other sources.

13–6   The Kruskal-Wallis Test

Objective 5

Test hypotheses, using the Kruskal-Wallis test.

The analysis of variance uses the F test to compare the means of three or more populations. The assumptions for the ANOVA test are that the populations are normally distributed and that the population variances are equal. When these assumptions cannot be met, the nonparametric **Kruskal-Wallis test,** sometimes called the *H test,* can be used to compare three or more means.

In this test, each sample size must be 5 or more. In these situations, the distribution can be approximated by the chi-square distribution with $k - 1$ degrees of freedom, where k = number of groups. This test also uses ranks. The formula for the test is given next.

In the Kruskal-Wallis test, one considers all the data values as a group and then ranks them. Next, the ranks are separated and the H formula is computed. This formula approximates the variance of the ranks. If the samples are from different populations, the sums of the ranks will be different and the H value will be large; hence, the null hypothesis will be rejected if the H value is large enough. If the samples are from the same population, the sums of the ranks will be approximately the same and the H value will be small; therefore, the null hypothesis will not be rejected. This test is always a right-tailed test. The chi-square table, Table G, with d.f. $= k - 1$, should be used for critical values.

Formula for the Kruskal-Wallis Test

$$H = \frac{12}{N(N + 1)}\left(\frac{R_1^2}{n_1} + \frac{R_2^2}{n_2} + \cdots + \frac{R_k^2}{n_k}\right) - 3(N + 1)$$

where
    R_1 = sum of ranks of sample 1
    n_1 = size of sample 1
    R_2 = sum of ranks of sample 2
    n_2 = size of sample 2
    .
    .
    .
    R_k = sum of ranks of sample k
    n_k = size of sample k
    $N = n_1 + n_2 + \cdots + n_k$
    k = number of samples

Example 13–6 illustrates the procedure for conducting the Kruskal-Wallis test.

Example 13–6

A researcher tests three different brands of breakfast drink to see how many milliequivalents of potassium per quart each contains. These data are obtained.

Brand A	Brand B	Brand C
4.7	5.3	6.3
3.2	6.4	8.2
5.1	7.3	6.2
5.2	6.8	7.1
5.0	7.2	6.6

At $\alpha = 0.05$, is there enough evidence to reject the hypothesis that all brands contain the same amount of potassium?

Solution

Step 1   State the hypotheses and identify the claim.

H_0: There is no difference in the amount of potassium contained in the brands (claim).

H_1: There is a difference in the amount of potassium contained in the brands.

Step 2   Find the critical value. Use the chi-square table, Table G, with d.f. $= k - 1$ ($k =$ number of groups). With $\alpha = 0.05$ and d.f. $= 3 - 1 = 2$, the critical value is 5.991.

Step 3   Compute the test statistic.

a. Arrange all the data from lowest to highest, and rank each value.

Amount	Brand	Rank
3.2	A	1
4.7	A	2
5.0	A	3
5.1	A	4
5.2	A	5
5.3	B	6
6.2	C	7
6.3	C	8
6.4	B	9
6.6	C	10
6.8	B	11
7.1	C	12
7.2	B	13
7.3	B	14
8.2	C	15

b. Find the sum of the ranks of each brand.

Brand A $1 + 2 + 3 + 4 + 5 = 15$

Brand B $6 + 9 + 11 + 13 + 14 = 53$

Brand C $7 + 8 + 10 + 12 + 15 = 52$

c. Substitute in the formula.

$$H = \frac{12}{N(N+1)}\left(\frac{R_1^2}{n_1} + \frac{R_2^2}{n_2} + \frac{R_3^2}{n_3}\right) - 3(N+1)$$

where

$$N = 15 \qquad R_1 = 15 \qquad R_2 = 53 \qquad R_3 = 52$$
$$n_1 = n_2 = n_3 = 5$$

Therefore,

$$H = \frac{12}{15(15+1)}\left(\frac{15^2}{5} + \frac{53^2}{5} + \frac{52^2}{5}\right) - 3(15+1) = 9.38$$

Step 4 Make the decision. Since the test statistic 9.38 is greater than the critical value 5.991, the decision is to reject the null hypothesis.

Step 5 Summarize the results. There is enough evidence to reject the claim that there is no difference in the amount of potassium contained in the three brands. Hence, not all brands contain the same amount of potassium.

The steps for the Kruskal-Wallis test are given in the Procedure Table.

Procedure Table

Kruskal-Wallis Test

Step 1 State the hypotheses and identify the claim.

Step 2 Find the critical value. Use the chi-square table, Table G, with d.f. $= k - 1$ ($k =$ number of groups).

Step 3 Compute the test statistic.
   a. Arrange the data from lowest to highest and rank each value.
   b. Find the sum of the ranks of each group.
   c. Substitute in the formula.

$$H = \frac{12}{N(N+1)}\left(\frac{R_1^2}{n_1} + \frac{R_2^2}{n_2} + \cdots + \frac{R_k^2}{n_k}\right) - 3(N+1)$$

where
$$N = n_1 + n_2 + \cdots + n_k$$
$$R_k = \text{sum of ranks for } k\text{th group}$$
$$k = \text{number of groups}$$

Step 4 Make the decision.

Step 5 Summarize the results.

Applying the Concepts 13–6

Height of Waterfalls

You are doing research for an article on the waterfalls on our planet. You want to make a statement about the heights of waterfalls on three continents. Three samples of waterfall heights (in metres) are shown.

North America	Africa	Asia
183	124	67
366	155	253
55	192	187
189	221	335
357	146	270
135	614	101

1. What questions are you trying to answer?
2. What nonparametric test would you use to find the answer?
3. What are the hypotheses?
4. Select a significance level and run the test. What is the H value?
5. What is your conclusion?
6. What is the corresponding parametric test?
7. What assumptions would you need to make to conduct this test?

See page 604 for the answers.

Exercises 13–6

For Exercises 1 through 11, perform these steps.

    a. State the hypotheses and identify the claim.
    b. Find the critical value.
    c. Compute the test statistic.
    d. Make the decision.
    e. Summarize the results.

Use the traditional method of hypothesis testing unless otherwise specified.

1. Samples of four different cereals show the following number of calories for the suggested servings of each brand. At $\alpha = 0.05$, is there a difference in the number of calories for the different brands?

Brand A	Brand B	Brand C	Brand D
112	110	109	106
120	118	116	122
135	123	125	130
125	128	130	117
108	102	128	116
121	101	132	114

2. A test to measure self-esteem is given to three different samples of individuals based on birth order. The scores range from 0 to 50. The data are shown here. At $\alpha = 0.05$, is there a difference in the scores?

Oldest child	Middle child	Youngest child
48	50	47
46	49	45
42	42	46
41	43	30
37	39	32
32	28	41

3. A researcher wishes to compare the prices of three types of lawnmowers. At $\alpha = 0.10$, can it be concluded that there is a difference in the prices? Based on your answer, do you feel that the cost should be a factor in determining which type of lawnmower a person would purchase?

Gas-powered self-propelled	Gas-powered push	Electric
290	320	188
325	360	245
210	200	470
300	229	395
330	160	

4. Three brands of microwave dinners were advertised as low in sodium. Samples of the three different brands show the following milligrams of sodium. At $\alpha = 0.05$, is there a difference in the amount of sodium among the brands?

Brand A	Brand B	Brand C
810	917	893
702	912	790
853	952	603
703	958	744
892	893	623
732		743
713		609
613		

5. A nutritionist wishes to compare the number of carbohydrates in one serving of three low-carbohydrate foods. At $\alpha = 0.01$, is there a difference in the number of calories? Based on your answer, which type of food would you recommend if a person wished to limit carbohydrates?

Pasta	Ice cream	Bread
11	5	43
22	13	62
16	10	71
29	8	49
25	12	50

6. A recent study recorded the number of job offers received by newly graduated chemical engineers at three colleges. The data are shown here. At $\alpha = 0.05$, is there a difference in the average number of job offers received by the graduates at the three colleges?

College A	College B	College C
6	2	10
8	1	12
7	0	9
5	3	13
6	6	4

7. A criminologist wishes to see if there is a difference in the number of firearm-related deaths by manner/intent and age group. The data for each age group are shown here. At $\alpha = 0.10$, is there a difference in the number of firearm-related deaths for each manner/intent category?

Suicide	Homicide	Unintentional
4	7	3
87	38	3
173	59	15
247	27	7
122	6	3

Source: Statistics Canada.

8. An electronics store manager wishes to compare the costs (in dollars) of three types of computer printer. The data are shown. At $\alpha = 0.05$, can it be concluded that there is a difference in the prices? Based on your answer, do you think that a certain type of printer generally costs more than the other types?

Inkjet printers	Multifunction printers	Laser printers
149	98	192
199	119	159
249	149	198
239	249	198
99	99	229
79	199	

9. In a large city, the number of crimes per week in five precincts is recorded for five weeks. The data are shown here. At $\alpha = 0.01$, is there a difference in the number of crimes?

Precinct 1	Precinct 2	Precinct 3	Precinct 4	Precinct 5
105	87	74	56	103
108	86	83	43	98
99	91	78	52	94
97	93	74	58	89
92	82	60	62	88

10. A recent study examined the number of unemployed people in five cities who are actively seeking employment. They are listed here according to the education each received. At $\alpha = 0.05$, is there a difference in the number of unemployed based on education received? Use the P-value method.

High school diploma	College degree	Postgraduate degree
49	23	7
43	49	38
51	54	23
108	87	52
68	28	26

11. Three different methods of first aid instruction are given to students. The same final examination is given to each class. The data are shown here. At $\alpha = 0.10$, is there a difference in the final examination scores? Use the P-value method.

Method A	Method B	Method C
98	97	99
100	88	94
95	82	96
92	84	89
86	75	81
76	73	72
71	74	

13–7 The Spearman Rank Correlation Coefficient and the Runs Test

The techniques of regression and correlation were explained in Chapter 10. To determine whether two variables are linearly related, one uses the Pearson product moment correlation coefficient. Its values range from $+1$ to -1. One assumption for testing the hypothesis that $\rho = 0$ for the Pearson coefficient is that the populations from which the samples are obtained are normally distributed. If this requirement cannot be met, the nonparametric equivalent, called the **Spearman rank correlation coefficient** (denoted by r_s), can be used when the data are ranked.

Objective ⑥

Compute the Spearman rank correlation coefficient.

Rank Correlation Coefficient

The computations for the rank correlation coefficient are simpler than those for the Pearson coefficient and involve ranking each set of data. The difference in ranks is found, and r_s is computed by using these differences. If both sets of data have the same ranks, r_s will be $+1$. If the sets of data are ranked in exactly the opposite way, r_s will be -1. If there is no relationship between the rankings, r_s will be near 0.

Formula for Computing the Spearman Rank Correlation Coefficient

$$r_s = 1 - \frac{6 \, \Sigma d^2}{n(n^2 - 1)}$$

where
d = difference in ranks
n = number of data pairs

This formula is algebraically equivalent to the formula for r given in Chapter 10, except that ranks are used instead of raw data.

The computational procedure is shown in Example 13–7. For a test of the significance of r_s, Table L is used for values of n up to 30. For larger values, the normal distribution can be used. (See Exercises 24 through 28 in the exercise section.)

Example 13–7

Two students were asked to rate 8 different textbooks for a specific course on an ascending scale from 0 to 20 points. Points were assigned for each of several categories, such as reading level, use of illustrations, and use of colour. At $\alpha = 0.05$, test the hypothesis that there is a significant linear correlation between the two students' ratings. The data are shown in the following table.

Textbook	Student 1's rating	Student 2's rating
A	4	4
B	10	6
C	18	20
D	20	14
E	12	16
F	2	8
G	5	11
H	9	7

Solution

Step 1 State the hypotheses.

$H_0: \rho = 0$ and $H_1: \rho \neq 0$

Step 2 Find the critical value. Use Table L to find the value for $n = 8$ and $\alpha = 0.05$. It is 0.738. See Figure 13–3.

Figure 13–3

**Finding the Critical
Value in Table L for
Example 13–7**

n	$\alpha = 0.10$	$\alpha = 0.05$	$\alpha = 0.02$
5			
6			
7			
8		(0.738)	
9			
⋮			

Step 3 Find the test statistic.

    a. Rank each data set, as shown in the table.

Textbook	Student 1	Rank	Student 2	Rank
A	4	7	4	8
B	10	4	6	7
C	18	2	20	1
D	20	1	14	3
E	12	3	16	2
F	2	8	8	5
G	5	6	11	4
H	9	5	7	6

Let X_1 be the first student's rankings and X_2 be the second student's rankings.

    b. Subtract the rankings $(X_1 - X_2)$.

$$7 - 8 = -1 \qquad 4 - 7 = -3 \qquad \text{etc.}$$

    c. Square the differences.

$$(-1)^2 = 1 \qquad (-3)^2 = 9 \qquad \text{etc.}$$

    d. Find the sum of the squares.

$$1 + 9 + 1 + 4 + 1 + 9 + 4 + 1 = 30$$

The results can be summarized in a table, as shown here.

X_1	X_2	$d = X_1 - X_2$	d^2
7	8	−1	1
4	7	−3	9
2	1	1	1
1	3	−2	4
3	2	1	1
8	5	3	9
6	4	2	4
5	6	−1	1
			$\Sigma d^2 = 30$

    e. Substitute in the formula to find r_s.

$$r_s = 1 - \frac{6\Sigma d^2}{n(n^2 - 1)}$$

where n = the number of data pairs. For this problem,

$$r_s = 1 - \frac{(6)(30)}{8(8^2 - 1)} = 1 - \frac{180}{504} = 0.643$$

Step 4 Make the decision. Do not reject the null hypothesis since $r_s = 0.643$, which is less than the critical value of 0.738.

Step 5 Summarize the results. There is not enough evidence to say that there is a correlation between the rankings of the two students.

The steps for finding and testing the Spearman rank correlation coefficient are given in the Procedure Table.

Procedure Table

Finding and Testing the Spearman Rank Correlation Coefficient

Step 1 State the hypotheses.

Step 2 Rank each data set.

Step 3 Subtract the rankings $(X_1 - X_2)$.

Step 4 Square the differences.

Step 5 Find the sum of the squares.

Step 6 Substitute in the formula.

$$r_s = 1 - \frac{6\Sigma d^2}{n(n^2 - 1)}$$

where
d = difference in ranks
n = number of pairs of data

Step 7 Find the critical value.

Step 8 Make the decision.

Step 9 Summarize the results.

Objective

Test hypotheses, using the runs test.

The Runs Test

When samples are selected, one assumes that they are selected at random. How does one know if the data obtained from a sample are truly random? Before the answer to this question is given, consider the following situations for a researcher interviewing 20 people for a survey. Let their genders be denoted by M for male and F for female. Suppose the participants were chosen as follows:

Situation 1   M M M M M M M M M M F F F F F F F F F F

It does not look as if the people in this sample were selected at random, since 10 males were selected first, followed by 10 females.

Consider a different selection:

Situation 2   F M F M F M F M F M F M F M F M F M F M

In this case, it seems as if the researcher selected a female, then a male, etc. This selection is probably not random either.

Finally, consider the following selection:

Situation 3   F F F M M F M F M M F F M M F F M M M F

This selection of data looks as if it may be random, since there is a mix of males and females and no apparent pattern to their selection.

Rather than try to guess whether the data of a sample have been selected at random, statisticians have devised a nonparametric test to determine randomness. This test is called the **runs test.**

> A **run** is a succession of identical letters preceded or followed by a different letter or no letter at all, such as the beginning or end of the succession.

For example, the first situation presented has two runs:

Run 1:   M M M M M M M M M M

Run 2:   F F F F F F F F F F

The second situation has 20 runs. (Each letter constitutes one run.) The third situation has 11 runs.

Run 1:	F F F	Run 5:	F	Run 9:	F F
Run 2:	M M	Run 6:	M M	Run 10:	M M M
Run 3:	F	Run 7:	F F	Run 11:	F
Run 4:	M	Run 8:	M M		

Example 13–8

Determine the number of runs in each sequence.

a. F F F M M F F F F M

b. H H H T T T T

c. A A B B A A B B A A B B

Solution

a. There are four runs, as shown.

$$\underbrace{F\,F\,F}_{1}\quad\underbrace{M\,M}_{2}\quad\underbrace{F\,F\,F\,F}_{3}\quad\underbrace{M}_{4}$$

b. There are two runs, as shown.

$$\underbrace{H\,H\,H}_{1}\quad\underbrace{T\,T\,T\,T}_{2}$$

c. There are six runs, as shown.

$$\underbrace{A\,A}_{1}\quad\underbrace{B\,B}_{2}\quad\underbrace{A\,A}_{3}\quad\underbrace{B\,B}_{4}\quad\underbrace{A\,A}_{5}\quad\underbrace{B\,B}_{6}$$

The test for randomness considers the number of runs rather than the frequency of the letters. For example, for data to be selected at random, there should not be too few or too many runs, as in situations 1 and 2. The runs test does not consider the questions of how many males or females were selected or how many of each are in a specific run.

To determine whether the number of runs is within the random range, use Table M in Appendix C. The values are for a two-tailed test with $\alpha = 0.05$. For a sample of 12 males and 8 females, the table values shown in Figure 13–4 mean that any number of runs from 7 to 15 would be considered random. If the number of runs is 6 or less or 16 or more, the sample is probably not random, and the null hypothesis should be rejected.

Example 13–9 shows the procedure for conducting the runs test by using letters as data. Example 13–10 shows how the runs test can be used for numerical data.

Figure 13–4

Finding the Critical Value in Table M

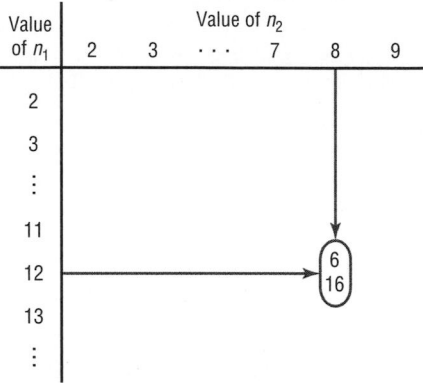

Example 13–9

On a commuter train, the conductor wishes to see whether the passengers enter the train at random. He observes the first 25 people, with the following sequence of males (M) and females (F).

$$\text{F F F M M F F F F M F M M M F F F F M M F F F M M}$$

Test for randomness at $\alpha = 0.05$.

Solution

Step 1   State the hypotheses and identify the claim.

H_0: The passengers board the train at random, according to gender (claim).

H_1: The null hypothesis is not true.

Step 2   Find the number of runs. Arrange the letters according to runs of males and females, as shown.

Run	Gender
1	F F F
2	M M
3	F F F F
4	M
5	F
6	M M M
7	F F F F
8	M M
9	F F F
10	M M

There are 15 females (n_1) and 10 males (n_2).

Step 3   Find the critical value. Find the number of runs in Table M for $n_1 = 15$, $n_2 = 10$, and $\alpha = 0.05$. The values are 7 and 18. *Note:* In this situation the critical value is found after the number of runs is determined.

Step 4   Make the decision. Compare these critical values with the number of runs. Since the number of runs is 10, and 10 is between 7 and 18, do not reject the null hypothesis.

Step 5   Summarize the results. There is not enough evidence to reject the hypothesis that the passengers board the train at random according to gender.

Example 13–10   Twenty people enrolled in a drug abuse program. Test the claim that the ages of the people, according to the order in which they enrol, occur at random, at $\alpha = 0.05$. The data are 18, 36, 19, 22, 25, 44, 23, 27, 27, 35, 19, 43, 37, 32, 28, 43, 46, 19, 20, 22.

Solution

Step 1   State the hypotheses and identify the claim.

H_0: The ages of the people, according to the order in which they enrol in a drug program, occur at random (claim).

H_1: The null hypothesis is not true.

Step 2   Find the number of runs.

a. Find the median of the data. Arrange the data in ascending order.

18 19 19 19 20 22 22 23 25 27 27

28 32 35 36 37 43 43 44 46

The median is 27.

b. Replace each number in the original sequence with an A if it is above the median and with a B if it is below the median. Eliminate any numbers that are equal to the median.

B A B B B A B A B A A A A A A B B B

c. Arrange the letters according to runs.

Run	Letters
1	B
2	A
3	B B B
4	A
5	B
6	A
7	B
8	A A A A A
9	B B B

Step 3   Find the critical value. Table M shows that with $n_1 = 9$, $n_2 = 9$, and $\alpha = 0.05$, the number of runs should be between 5 and 15.

Step 4   Make the decision. Since there are 9 runs, and 9 falls between 5 and 15, the null hypothesis is not rejected.

Step 5   Summarize the results. There is not enough evidence to reject the hypothesis that the ages of the people who enrol occur at random.

The steps for the runs test are given in the Procedure Table.

Procedure Table

The Runs Test

Step 1 State the hypotheses and identify the claim.

Step 2 Find the number of runs.

Note: When the data are numerical, find the median. Then compare each data value with the median and classify it as above or below the median. Other methods such as odd-even can also be used. (Discard any value that is equal to the median.)

Step 3 Find the critical value. Use Table M.

Step 4 Make the decision. Compare the actual number of runs with the critical value.

Step 5 Summarize the results.

Applying the Concepts 13–7

Tall Trees

As a biologist, you wish to see if there is a relationship between the heights of the trees and their diameters. You find the following data for the diameter (in metres) of the tree at 1.4 metres from the ground and corresponding heights (in metres).

Diameter (m)	Height (m)
26.0	79.6
24.1	97.8
11.5	66.8
12.8	85.6
19.3	48.5
16.4	25.3
18.0	58.2
14.9	43.0
11.2	70.7
13.9	32.9

Source: *The World Almanac and Book of Facts.*

1. What questions are you trying to answer?
2. What type of nonparametric analysis could be used to answer the questions?
3. What would be the corresponding parametric test that could be used?
4. Which test do you think would be better?
5. Perform both tests and write a short statement comparing the results.

See page 604 for the answer.

Exercises 13–7

For Exercises 1 through 4, find the critical value from Table L for the rank correlation coefficient, given sample size n and α. Assume that the test is two-tailed.

1. $n = 14, \alpha = 0.01$
2. $n = 28, \alpha = 0.02$
3. $n = 10, \alpha = 0.05$
4. $n = 9, \alpha = 0.01$

For Exercises 5 through 14, perform these steps.

a. Find the Spearman rank correlation coefficient.
b. State the hypotheses.
c. Find the critical value. Use $\alpha = 0.05$.
d. Make the decision.
e. Summarize the results.

Use the traditional method of hypothesis testing unless otherwise specified.

5. The table shows the total number of forest fires in select Canadian provinces for a given year caused by human activity (e.g., camping, logging, construction, arson, etc.) or Mother Nature (i.e. lightning). At $\alpha = 0.10$, is there a relationship between the number of forest fires caused by human activity and Mother Nature?

Prov	Human Activity	Mother Nature
AB	336	428
BC	644	842
MB	203	105
NB	256	20
NS	398	27
ON	422	168
QC	401	74
SK	239	180

Source: Statistics Canada.

6. Six cities are selected, and the number of daily passenger trips (in thousands) for subways and commuter rail service is obtained. At $\alpha = 0.05$, is there a relationship between the variables? Suggest one reason why the transportation authority might use the results of this study.

City	1	2	3	4	5	6
Subway	845	494	425	313	108	41
Rail	39	291	142	103	33	39

Source: American Public Transportation Association.

7. The table shows the average maximum sentence length for certain crimes and the actual time served in months. At $\alpha = 0.05$, is there a relationship between the two?

Crime	Sentence	Time served
Murder	227	97
Rape	120	45
Robbery	106	40
Burglary	77	26
Drug offenses	60	18
Weapons offenses	49	21

Source: World Almanac and Book of Facts.

8. Six different summer theatre actors were ranked by male and female patrons on the basis of diction and appearance. The data are shown here (1 is the highest rating). At $\alpha = 0.05$, is there a relationship between the rankings?

Actors	A	B	C	D	E	F
Males	6	3	2	5	1	4
Females	4	5	1	6	3	2

9. Eight music videos were ranked by teenagers and their parents on style and clarity, with 1 being the highest ranking. The data are shown here. At $\alpha = 0.05$, is there a relationship between the rankings?

Music videos	1	2	3	4	5	6	7	8
Teenagers	4	6	2	8	1	7	3	5
Parents	1	7	5	4	3	8	2	6

10. Eight school districts are randomly selected, and the number of employees who retired and the payment for their unused sick days are obtained. At $\alpha = 0.05$, is there a relationship between the data? How can a school board use the results of this study?

No. of employees	10	5	17	8	10	10	11	9
Amount paid in thousands of dollars	83	30	29	35	40	18	90	54

11. Shown is data illustrating select Canadian monthly fuel prices (C$/litre) and the monthly price of a barrel of oil (US$/barrel). At $\alpha = 0.05$, is there a relationship between the prices?

Fuel Price	1.02	0.92	0.87	0.95	0.89	1.12
Barrel of Oil Price	60.04	59.55	52.15	62.35	64.05	75.05

Source: GasBuddy.com.

12. A meteorologist wishes to see if the number of deaths from tornadoes is related to the number of tornadoes per year. At $\alpha = 0.05$, is there a relationship? The data for a randomly selected 11-year period are shown. How could an insurance agency use this information?

Number of deaths	53	39	39	33	69	30
Number of tornadoes	1133	1132	1297	1173	1082	1234
Number of deaths	25	67	130	40	94	
Number of tornadoes	1173	1148	1424	898	1342	

Source: NOAA.

13. Shown are the number of students enrolled in cyber school for 5 randomly selected school districts and the per-student costs for the cyber school education. At $\alpha = 0.10$, is there a relationship between the two variables? How might this information be useful to school administrators?

Number of students	10	6	17	8	11
Per-student cost	7200	9393	7385	4500	8203

Source: Tribune-Review.

14. Shown are the price for a human dose of several prescription drugs and the price for an equivalent dose for animals. At $\alpha = 0.10$, is there a relationship between the variables?

Humans	0.67	0.64	1.20	0.51	0.87	0.74	0.50	1.22
Animals	0.13	0.18	0.42	0.25	0.57	0.57	0.49	1.28

Source: U.S. House Committee on Government Reform.

15. A school dentist wanted to test the claim, at $\alpha = 0.05$, that the number of cavities in Grade 4 students is random. Forty students were checked, and the

number of cavities each had is shown here. Test for randomness of the values above or below the median.

0	4	6	0	6	2	5	3	1	5	1
2	2	1	3	7	3	6	0	2	6	0
2	3	1	5	2	1	3	0	2	3	7
3	1	5	1	1	2	2				

16. A drawing was held each day for a month. Categorize the winning numbers as odd or even. The data follow. Test for randomness, at $\alpha = 0.05$.

409	872	235	338	472	481	318	129	229
084	291	991	356	212	457	473	834	304
361	301	051	652	405	458	094	633	809
299	712	802						

17. The winning numbers for Ontario's Pick 3 lottery for June are listed here. Classify each as odd or even and test for randomness, at $\alpha = 0.05$.

655	683	374	890	580	304
268	175	167	519	361	918
966	765	085	550	861	689
245	511	695	551	492	683
918	244	089	849	769	389

Source: Ontario Lottery and Gaming Corporation.

18. An irate student believes that the answers to his history professor's final true/false examination are not random. Test the claim, at $\alpha = 0.05$. The answers to the questions are shown.

T T T F F T T T F F F F F F T

T T F F F T T T F T F F T T F

19. A machine manufactures audiocassette cases that are either defective (D) or acceptable (A). The sequence is shown here. At $\alpha = 0.05$, test for randomness.

D A A A A A A A D D A D D A A A

D D A A A A A A A D D D A A A

20. Twenty shoppers are in a checkout line at a grocery store. At $\alpha = 0.05$, test for randomness of their gender: male (M) or female (F). The data are shown here.

F M M F F M F M M F

F M M M F F F F F M

21. A supervisor records the number of employees absent over a 30-day period. Test for randomness, at $\alpha = 0.05$.

27	6	19	24	18	12	15	17	18	20
0	9	4	12	3	2	7	7	0	5
32	16	38	31	27	15	5	9	4	10

22. A ski lodge manager observes the weather for the month of February. If his customers are able to ski, he records S; if weather conditions do not permit skiing, he records N. Test for randomness, at $\alpha = 0.05$.

S S S S S S N N N N N N N N

N S S S N N S S S S S S S S

23. These data are the scores on an IQ exam in the order that the students finished the test. At $\alpha = 0.05$, test for randomness.

101	98	99	110	119	121	118
106	96	88	91	97	92	106
94	93	100	89	86	95	99

Extending the Concepts

When $n \geq 30$, the formula $r = \dfrac{\pm z}{\sqrt{n-1}}$ can be used to find the critical values for the rank correlation coefficient. For example, if $n = 40$ and $\alpha = 0.05$ for a two-tailed test,

$$r = \frac{\pm 1.96}{\sqrt{40-1}} = \pm 0.314$$

Hence, any r_s greater than or equal to $+0.314$ or less than or equal to -0.314 is significant.

For Exercises 24 through 28, find the critical r value for each (assume that the test is two-tailed).

24. $n = 50, \alpha = 0.05$

25. $n = 30, \alpha = 0.01$

26. $n = 35, \alpha = 0.02$

27. $n = 60, \alpha = 0.10$

28. $n = 40, \alpha = 0.01$

13–8   Summary

In many research situations, the assumptions (particularly that of normality) for the use of parametric statistics cannot be met. Also, some statistical studies do not involve parameters such as means, variances, and proportions. For both situations, statisticians have developed nonparametric statistical methods, also called *distribution-free methods*.

There are several advantages to the use of nonparametric methods. The most important one is that no knowledge of the population distributions is required. Other advantages include ease of computation and understanding. The major disadvantage is that they are less efficient than their parametric counterparts when the assumptions for the parametric methods are met. In other words, larger sample sizes are needed to get results as accurate as those given by their parametric counterparts.

This list gives the nonparametric statistical tests presented in this chapter, along with their parametric counterparts.

Nonparametric test	Parametric test	Condition
Single-sample sign test	z or t test	One sample
Paired-sample sign test	z or t test	Two dependent samples
Wilcoxon rank sum test	z or t test	Two independent samples
Wilcoxon signed-rank test	t test	Two dependent samples
Kruskal-Wallis test	ANOVA	Three or more independent samples
Spearman rank correlation coefficient	Pearson's correlation coefficient	Relationships between variables
Runs test	None	Randomness

When the assumptions of the parametric tests can be met, the parametric tests should be used instead of their nonparametric counterparts.

For step-by-step guidance on the use of technology for this chapter, visit the Online Learning Centre at www.mcgrawhill.ca/olc/bluman. Summary procedures for Minitab, SPSS, Excel, and TI-83 Plus or TI-84 Plus can also be found in Appendix E.

Important Terms   ● ● ●

distribution-free statistics 564

Kruskal-Wallis test 583

nonparametric statistics 564

parametric tests 564

ranking 565

run 591

runs test 591

sign test 567

Spearman rank correlation coefficient 588

Wilcoxon rank sum test 574

Wilcoxon signed-rank test 574

Important Formulas   ● ● ●

Formula for the z test statistic in the sign test:

$$z = \frac{(X + 0.5) - (n/2)}{\sqrt{n}/2}$$

where

n = sample size (greater than or equal to 26)
X = smaller number of positive or negative signs

Formula for the Wilcoxon rank sum test:

$$z = \frac{R - \mu_R}{\sigma_R}$$

where

$$\mu_R = \frac{n_1(n_1 + n_2 + 1)}{2}$$

$$\sigma_R = \sqrt{\frac{n_1 n_2 (n_1 + n_2 + 1)}{12}}$$

R = sum of ranks for smaller sample size (n_1)

n_1 = smaller of sample sizes

n_2 = larger of sample sizes

$n_1 \geq 10$ and $n_2 \geq 10$

Formula for the Wilcoxon signed-rank test:

$$z = \frac{w_s - \dfrac{n(n+1)}{4}}{\sqrt{\dfrac{n(n+1)(2n+1)}{24}}}$$

where

n = number of pairs where difference is not 0 and $n \geq 30$

w_s = smaller sum in absolute value of signed ranks

Formula for the Kruskal-Wallis test:

$$H = \frac{12}{N(N+1)} \left(\frac{R_1^2}{n_1} + \frac{R_2^2}{n_2} + \cdots + \frac{R_k^2}{n_k} \right) - 3(N+1)$$

where

R_1 = sum of ranks of sample 1

n_1 = size of sample 1

R_2 = sum of ranks of sample 2

n_2 = size of sample 2

.
.
.

R_k = sum of ranks of sample k

n_k = size of sample k

$N = n_1 + n_2 + \cdots + n_k$

k = number of samples

Formula for the Spearman rank correlation coefficient:

$$r_s = 1 - \frac{6 \Sigma d^2}{n(n^2 - 1)}$$

where

d = difference in ranks

n = number of data pairs

Review Exercises

For Exercises 1 through 13, follow this procedure:

    a. State the hypotheses and identify the claim.

    b. Find the critical value(s).

    c. Compute the test statistic.

    d. Make the decision.

    e. Summarize the results.

Use the traditional method of hypothesis testing unless otherwise specified.

1. A researcher believes that the median number of wet days per month in Yosemite National Park is 5. A sample of the number of wet days per month for last year is shown. At $\alpha = 0.05$, is there enough evidence to reject the researcher's claim?

8   6   7   6   4   2   1   1   1   2   6   7

Source: Jack Williams, *The USA TODAY Weather Almanac.*

2. A tire manufacturer claims that the median lifetime of a certain brand of truck tires is 65,000 kilometres. A sample of 30 tires shows that 12 lasted longer than 65,000 kilometres. Is there enough evidence to reject the claim at $\alpha = 0.05$? Use the sign test.

3. A special diet including hormones is fed to adult hogs to see whether they will gain weight. The before and after weights (in kilograms) are given here. Use the paired-sample sign test at $\alpha = 0.05$ to determine whether there is a weight gain.

Before	145	196	207	162	168	179	164	163	145
After	151	195	208	164	173	179	166	161	143

4. Shown here are the record high temperatures (°C) for Dawson Creek, British Columbia, and for Whitehorse, Yukon, for 12 months. Using the Wilcoxon rank sum test at $\alpha = 0.05$, do you find a difference in the record high temperatures? Use the *P*-value method.

Dawson Creek	11	16	14	22	30	32	34	34	31	27	19	11
Whitehorse	8	10	11	21	30	32	33	30	27	19	11	8

Source: Jack Williams, The *USA TODAY* Weather Almanac.

5. Samples of students majoring in business and engineering are selected, and the amount (in dollars) each spent on a required textbook for the fall semester is recorded. The data are shown here. For the Wilcoxon rank sum test at $\alpha = 0.10$, is there a difference in the amount spent by each group?

Business		Engineering	
48	36	98	73
52	62	72	78
74	50	63	93
63	46	78	88
51	53	55	86
49	58	58	85
		64	

6. Twelve automobiles were tested to see how many litres per 100 kilometres (L/100 km) each one obtained. Under similar driving conditions, they were tested

again, using a special additive. The data are shown here. At $\alpha = 0.05$, did the additive improve fuel efficiency. Use the Wilcoxon signed-rank test.

Before		After	
17.3	12.9	10.4	9.9
12.9	12.1	10.7	11.3
14.6	12.9	9.3	9.3
15.4	14.1	8.2	8.6
12.3	11.0	15.5	13.7
12.5	13.7	14.4	12.7

7. The number of sick days taken by seven assembly-line workers was recorded for one year. The owners of the company then installed brighter lighting and permitted the employees to take a 10-minute break in the morning and afternoon. The number of sick days taken was recorded for another year. The data are shown here. From the Wilcoxon signed-rank test at $\alpha = 0.05$, can one conclude that the number of sick days taken was reduced?

Before	6	15	18	14	27	17	9
After	8	12	16	9	23	14	15

8. Samples of three types of ropes are tested for breaking strength. The data (in kilograms) are shown here. At $\alpha = 0.05$, is there a difference in the breaking strength of the ropes? Use the Kruskal-Wallis test.

Cotton	Nylon	Hemp
104	161	230
196	137	239
229	164	264
221	184	225
205	196	208
172	171	230
210	164	255
241	181	259
166	169	226
169	165	215
205	139	229
221	138	254
210	144	241
212	146	227

9. Rats were fed three different diets for one month to see whether diet has any effect on learning. Each rat was then taught to traverse a simple maze. The number of trials it took each rat to learn the correct path is shown in the table. At $\alpha = 0.05$, does diet have any effect on learning? Use the Kruskal-Wallis test.

Diet 1	8	6	12	15	9	7	5
Diet 2	2	3	6	8	7	4	
Diet 3	9	15	17	8	4	13	18	20

10. A statistics instructor wishes to see whether there is a relationship between the number of homework exercises a student completes and her or his exam score. The data are shown here. Using the Spearman rank correlation coefficient, test the hypothesis that there is no relationship at $\alpha = 0.05$.

Homework problems	63	55	58	87	89	52	46	75	105
Exam score	85	71	75	98	93	63	72	89	100

11. Shown are the average number of viewers for 10 television shows for two consecutive years. At $\alpha = 0.05$, is there a relationship between the number of viewers?

Last year	28.9	26.4	20.8	25.0	21.0	19.2
This year	26.6	20.5	20.2	19.1	18.9	17.8
Last year	13.7	18.8	16.8	15.3		
This year	16.8	16.7	16.0	15.8		

12. In a recent survey, 20 college students were asked, as they arrived for class, if they worked during the academic year (W) or did not work (N). At $\alpha = 0.05$, test for randomness. The data are shown here. Assume the probabilities are the same.

W N N N W W W N W N
N W W N N W N N W N

13. An instructor wishes to see whether grades of students who finish an exam occur at random. Shown here are the grades of 30 students in the order that they finished an exam. (Read from left to right across each row, and then proceed to the next row.) Test for randomness, at $\alpha = 0.05$.

87	93	82	77	64	98
100	93	88	65	72	73
56	63	85	92	95	91
88	63	72	79	55	53
65	68	54	71	73	72

Too Much or Too Little?—Revisited

Statistics Today

In this case, the manufacturer would select a sequence of bottles and see how many bottles contained more than 375 millilitres, denoted by plus, and how many bottles contained less than 375 millilitres, denoted by minus. The sequence could then be analyzed according to the number of runs, as explained in Section 13–7. If the sequence were not random, then the machine would need to be checked to see if it was malfunctioning. Another method that can be used to see if machines are functioning properly is *statistical quality control*. This method is beyond the scope of this book.

Data Analysis ●●●

The Data Bank is found in Appendix D, or on the World Wide Web by following links from www.mcgrawhill.ca/olc/bluman.

1. From the Data Bank, choose a sample and use the sign test to test one of the following hypotheses.

   a. For serum cholesterol, test H_0: median = 220 milligram percent (mg%).

   b. For systolic pressure, test H_0: median = 120 millimetres of mercury (mm Hg).

   c. For IQ, test H_0: median = 100.

   d. For sodium level, test H_0: median = 140 mEq/l.

2. From the Data Bank, select a sample of subjects. Use the Kruskal-Wallis test to see if the sodium levels of smokers and nonsmokers are equal.

3. From the Data Bank select a sample of 50 subjects. Use the Wilcoxon rank sum test to see if the means of the sodium levels of the males differ from those of the females.

Chapter Quiz ●●●

Determine whether each statement is true or false. If the statement is false, explain why.

1. Nonparametric statistics cannot be used to test the difference between two means.

2. Nonparametric statistics are more sensitive than their parametric counterparts.

3. Nonparametric statistics can be used to test hypotheses about parameters other than means, proportions, and standard deviations.

4. Parametric tests are preferred over their nonparametric counterparts, if the assumptions can be met.

Select the best answer.

5. The _____ test is used to test means when samples are dependent and the normality assumption cannot be met.

   a. Wilcoxon signed-rank   c. Sign
   b. Wilcoxon rank sum   d. Kruskal-Wallis

6. The Kruskal-Wallis test uses the _____ distribution.

   a. z   c. χ^2
   b. t   d. F

7. The nonparametric counterpart of ANOVA is the _____.

   a. Wilcoxon signed-rank test
   b. Sign test
   c. Runs test
   d. None of the above

8. To see if two rankings are related, one can use the _____.

   a. Runs test
   b. Spearman correlation coefficient
   c. Sign test
   d. Kruskal-Wallis test

Complete the following statements with the best answer.

9. When the assumption of normality cannot be met, one can use _____ tests.

10. When data are _____ or _____ in nature, nonparametric methods are used.

11. To test to see whether a median was equal to a specific value, one would use the _____ test.

12. Nonparametric tests are less _____ than their parametric counterparts.

For the following exercises, use the traditional method of hypothesis testing unless otherwise specified.

13. The owner of a candy store states that she sells on average 300 candy bars per day. A random sample of 18 days shows the number of candy bars sold each day. At $\alpha = 0.10$, is the claim correct? Use the sign test.

271	297	315	282	106	297	268	215
262	305	315	256	311	375	319	297
311	299

14. A battery manufacturer claims that the median lifetime of a certain brand of heavy-duty battery is 1200 hours. A sample of 25 batteries shows that 15 lasted longer than 1200 hours. Test the claim at $\alpha = 0.05$. Use the sign test.

15. A special diet is fed to adult turkeys to see if they will gain weight. The before and after weights (in kilograms) are given here. Use the paired-sample sign test at $\alpha = 0.05$ to see if there is weight gain.

Before	12.7	10.9	13.2	13.6	14.5	15.0	11.3	11.8	12.7
After	13.6	13.2	14.1	14.5	14.5	15.9	13.2	11.3	14.1

16. Two groups of alcoholics, one group male and the other female, were asked at what age they first drank alcohol.

The data are shown here. Using the Wilcoxon rank sum test at $\alpha = 0.05$, is there a difference in the ages of the females and males?

Males	6	12	14	16	17	17	13	12	10	11
Females	8	9	9	12	14	15	12	16	17	19

17. Samples of students majoring in law and nursing are selected, and the amount each spent on textbooks for the spring semester is recorded here, in dollars. Using the Wilcoxon rank sum test at $\alpha = 0.10$, is there a difference in the amount spent by each group?

Law	167	158	162	106	98	206	112	121
Nursing	98	198	209	168	157	126	104	122

Law	133	145	151	199
Nursing	111	138	116	201

18. The grade point average of a group of students was recorded for one month. During the next nine-week grading period, the students attended a workshop on study skills. Their GPAs were recorded at the end of the grading period, and the data appear here. Using the Wilcoxon signed-rank test at $\alpha = 0.05$, can it be concluded that the GPA increased?

Before	3.0	2.9	2.7	2.5	2.1	2.6	1.9	2.0
After	3.2	3.4	2.9	2.5	3.0	3.1	2.4	2.8

19. Samples of three different types of wrapping tape are tested for breaking strength, in kilograms. The data are shown here. At $\alpha = 0.05$, is there a difference in the breaking strength of the tapes? Use the Kruskal-Wallis test.

Type A	102	151	183	176	159	127	164	195	121
Type B	116	92	118	138	105	126	118	136	123
Type C	184	194	218	180	159	186	210	214	181

Type A	160	131	164	166	123
Type B	93	93	99	101	119
Type C	184	209	196	182	170

20. Three different groups of monkeys were fed three different medications for one month to see if the medication has any effect on reaction time. Each monkey was then taught to repeat a series of steps to receive a reward. The number of trials it took each to receive the reward is shown here. At $\alpha = 0.05$, does the medication have an effect on reaction time? Use the Kruskal-Wallis test. Use the P-value method.

Med. 1	8	7	11	14	8	6	5
Med. 2	3	4	6	7	9	3	4
Med. 3	8	14	13	7	5	9	12

21. Is there a relationship between the prescription drug prices in Canada and Great Britain? Use $\alpha = 0.10$.

Canada	1.47	1.07	1.34	1.34	1.47	1.07	3.39	1.11	1.13
Great Britain	1.67	1.08	1.67	0.82	1.73	0.95	2.86	0.41	1.70

Source: *USA TODAY.*

22. Is there a relationship between the amount of money (in millions of dollars) spent on the U.S. Head Start Program by the states and the number of students enrolled (in thousands)? Use $\alpha = 0.10$.

Funding	100	50	22	88	49	219
Enrolment	16	7	3	14	8	31

Source: Gannet News Service.

23. At the registry of vital statistics, the birth certificates issued for females (F) and males (M) were tallied. At $\alpha = 0.05$, test for randomness. The data are shown here.

M M F F F F F F F F M M M M F F
M F M F M M M F F F

24. The output in revolutions per minute (rpm) of 10 motors was obtained. The motors were tested again under similar conditions after they had been reconditioned. The data are shown here. At $\alpha = 0.05$, did the reconditioning improve the motors' performance? Use the Wilcoxon signed-rank test.

Before	413	701	397	602	405	512	450	487	388	351
After	433	712	406	650	450	550	450	500	402	415

25. A statistician wishes to determine if a province's lottery numbers are selected at random. The winning numbers selected for the month of February are shown here. Test for randomness at $\alpha = 0.05$.

321	909	715	700	487	808	509	606	943	761
200	123	367	012	444	576	409	128	567	908
103	407	890	193	672	867	003	578

Critical Thinking Challenges ●●●

1. Two commuters ride to work together in one car. To decide who pays the toll for a bridge on the way to work, they flip a coin and the loser pays. Explain why over a period of one year, one person might have to pay the toll 5 days in a row. There is no toll on the return trip. (*Hint:* You may want to use random numbers.)

2. Shown in the column on page 602 are the type and number of medals each country won in the 2000 Summer Olympic Games. You are to rank the countries from highest to lowest. Gold medals are highest, followed by silver, followed by bronze.

There are many different ways to rank objects and events. Here are several suggestions.

a. Rank the countries according to the total medals won.
b. List some advantages and disadvantages of this method.
c. Rank each country separately for the number of gold medals won, then for the number of silver medals won, and then for the number of bronze medals won. Then rank the countries according to the sum of the *ranks* for the categories.
d. Are the rankings of the countries the same as those in step *a*? Explain any differences.
e. List some advantages and disadvantages of this method of ranking.
f. A third way to rank the countries is to assign a weight to each medal. In this case, assign 3 points for each gold medal, 2 points for each silver medal, and 1 point for each bronze medal the country won. Multiply the number of medals by the weights for each medal and find the sum. For example, since Austria won 2 gold medals, 1 silver medal, and 0 bronze medals, its rank sum is $(2 \times 3) + (1 \times 2) + (0 \times 1) = 8$. Rank the countries according to this method.

g. Compare the ranks using this method with those using the other two methods. Are the rankings the same or different? Explain.
h. List some advantages and disadvantages of this method.
i. Select two of the rankings, and run the Spearman rank correlation test to see if they differ significantly.

Summer Olympic Games 2000 Final Medal Standings

Country	Gold	Silver	Bronze
Austria	2	1	0
Canada	3	3	8
Germany	14	17	26
Italy	13	8	13
Norway	4	3	3
Russia	32	28	28
Switzerland	1	6	2
U.S.A.	40	24	33

Source: Reprinted with permission from the World Almanac and Book of Facts. World Almanac Education Group Inc.

Data Projects

Where appropriate, use Minitab, SPSS, the TI-83 Plus, the TI-84 Plus, or a computer program of your choice to complete these nonparametric exercises.

1. There are many nonparametric statistical tests. Decide on a project that will use one of the nonparametric tests, and collect data from a sample.

   a. Describe the purpose of the study.
   b. Define the population.
   c. State how the sample was obtained.
   d. Select an α value.
   e. State the hypotheses for the study.
   f. Decide which nonparametric test will be used and compute the test statistic.
   g. Make the decision.
   h. Summarize the results.
   i. Conduct the corresponding parametric test and compare the results.
   j. Write a brief paragraph on which test is more appropriate, and give reasons why.

2. Select a variable on which you can perform a runs test. For example, you might observe the gender of 20 or 30 individuals waiting in the cafeteria, bookstore checkout, or registration line.

   a. Conduct the runs test and decide whether the sequence is random.
   b. Write a brief summary of the results.

You may use the following websites to obtain raw data:

Visit the data sets at the book's website found at www.mcgrawhill.ca/olc/bluman
http://lib.stat.cmu.edu/DASL
www.statcan.ca

Hypothesis-Testing Summary 3*

15. Test to see whether the median of a sample is a specific value when $n \geq 26$.

Example: H_0: median = 100

Use the sign test:

$$z = \frac{(X + 0.5) - (n/2)}{\sqrt{n}/2}$$

16. Test to see whether two independent samples are obtained from populations that have identical distributions.

Example: H_0: There is no difference in the ages of the subjects.

Use the Wilcoxon rank sum test:

$$z = \frac{R - \mu_R}{\sigma_R}$$

where

$$\mu_R = \frac{n_1(n_1 + n_2 + 1)}{2}$$

$$\sigma_R = \sqrt{\frac{n_1 n_2(n_1 + n_2 + 1)}{12}}$$

17. Test to see whether two dependent samples have identical distributions.

Example: H_0: There is no difference in the effects of a tranquilizer on the number of hours a person sleeps at night.

Use the Wilcoxon signed-rank test:

$$z = \frac{w_s - \dfrac{n(n + 1)}{4}}{\sqrt{\dfrac{n(n + 1)(2n + 1)}{24}}}$$

when $n \geq 30$.

18. Test to see whether three or more samples come from identical populations.

Example: H_0: There is no difference in the weights of the three groups.

Use the Kruskal-Wallis test:

$$H = \frac{12}{N(N + 1)}\left(\frac{R_1^2}{n_1} + \frac{R_2^2}{n_2} + \cdots + \frac{R_k^2}{n_k}\right) - 3(N + 1)$$

19. Rank correlation coefficient.

$$r_s = 1 - \frac{6\sum d^2}{n(n^2 - 1)}$$

20. Test for randomness: Use the runs test.

*This summary is a continuation of Hypothesis Testing Summary 2 at the end of Chapter 12.

Answers to Applying the Concepts   ● ● ●

Section 13–2   Ranking Data

Percent	2.6	3.8	4.0	4.0	5.4	7.0	7.0	7.3	10.0
Rank	1	2	3.5	3.5	5	6.5	6.5	8	9

Section 13–3   Clean Air

1. The claim is that the median number of days that a large city failed to meet EPA standards is 11 days per month.

2. We will use the sign test, since we do not know anything about the distribution of the variable and we are testing the median.

3. H_0: median $= 11$ and H_1: median $\neq 11$.

4. If $\alpha = 0.05$, then the critical value is 5.

5. The test statistic is 9.

6. Since $9 > 5$, we reject the null hypothesis.

7. There is enough evidence to conclude that the median is not 11 days per month.

_____

_____

_____

8. We cannot use a parametric test in this situation.

Section 13–4   School Lunch

1. The samples are independent since two different random samples were selected.

2. H_0: There is no difference in the number of calories served for lunch in elementary and secondary schools.

H_1: There is a difference in the number of calories served for lunch in elementary and secondary schools.

3. We will use the Wilcoxon rank sum test.

4. The critical value is ± 1.96 if we use $\alpha = 0.05$.

5. The test statistic is $z = -2.15$.

6. Since $-2.15 < -1.96$, we reject the null hypothesis and conclude that there is a difference in the number of calories served for lunch in elementary and secondary schools.

7. The corresponding parametric test is the two-sample t test.

8. We would need to know that the samples were normally distributed to use the parametric test.

9. Since t tests are robust against variations from normality, the parametric test would yield the same results.

Section 13–5   Pain Medication

1. The purpose of the study is to see how effective a pain medication is.

2. These are dependent samples, since we have before and after readings on the same subjects.

3. H_0: The severity of pain after is the same as the severity of pain before the medication was administered.

 H_1: The severity of pain after is less than the severity of pain before the medication was administered.

4. We will use the Wilcoxon signed-rank test.

5. We will choose to use a significance level of 0.05.

6. The test statistic is $w_s = 25.5$. The critical value is 4. Since $25.5 > 4$, we reject the null hypothesis. There is enough evidence to conclude that the severity of pain after is less than the severity of pain before the medication was administered.

7. The parametric test that could be used is the t test for small dependent samples.

8. The results for the parametric test would be the same.

Section 13–6   Heights of Waterfalls

1. We are investigating the heights of waterfalls on three continents.

2. We will use the Kruskal-Wallis test.

3. H_0: There is no difference in the heights of waterfalls on the three continents.

 H_1: There is a difference in the heights of waterfalls on the three continents.

4. We will use the 0.05 significance level. The critical value is 5.991. Our test statistic is $H = 0.01$.

5. Since $0.01 < 5.991$, we fail to reject the null hypothesis. There is not enough evidence to conclude that there is a difference in the heights of waterfalls on the three continents.

6. The corresponding parametric test is analysis of variance (ANOVA).

7. To perform an ANOVA, the population must be normally distributed, the samples must be independent of each other, and the variance of the samples must be equal.

Section 13–7   Tall Trees

1. The biologist is trying to see if there is a relationship between the heights and diameters of tall trees.

2. We will use the Spearman rank correlation analysis.

3. The corresponding parametric test is the Pearson product moment correlation analysis.

4. Answers will vary.

5. The Pearson correlation coefficient is $r = 0.329$. The associated P-value is 0.353. We would fail to reject the null hypothesis that the correlation is zero. The Spearman rank correlation coefficient is $r_s = 0.115$. We would reject the null hypothesis at the 0.05 significance level, if $r_s > 0.648$. Since $0.115 < 0.648$, we fail to reject the null hypothesis that the correlation is zero. Both the parametric and nonparametric tests find that the correlation is not statistically significantly different from zero. It appears that no linear relationship exists between the heights and diameters of tall trees.

CHAPTER 14

Sampling and Simulation

Objectives

After completing this chapter, you should be able to

1. Demonstrate a knowledge of the four basic sampling methods.

2. Recognize faulty questions on a survey and other factors that can bias responses.

3. Solve problems, using simulation techniques.

Outline

14–1 **Introduction**

14–2 **Common Sampling Techniques**

14–3 **Surveys and Questionnaire Design**

14–4 **Simulation Techniques**

14–5 **Summary**

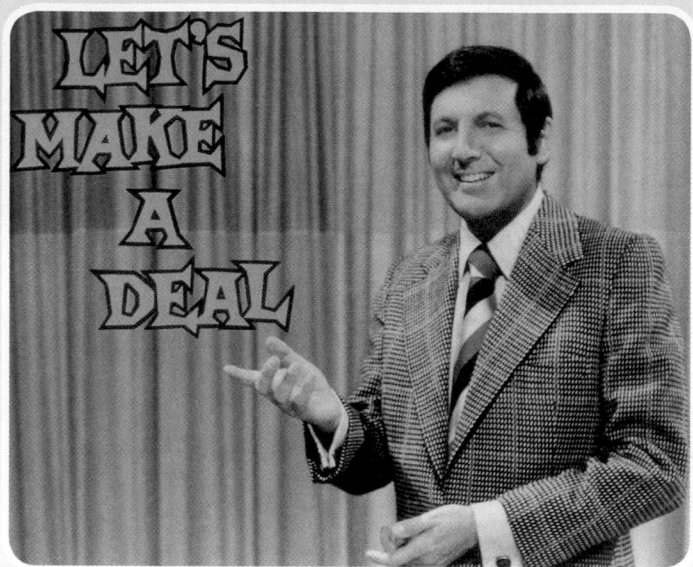

Statistics Today

The Monty Hall Problem

On the game show *Let's Make A Deal,* Canadian-born host Monty Hall gave a contestant a choice of three doors. A valuable prize was behind one door, and nothing was behind the other two doors. When the contestant selected one door, host Monty Hall opened one of the other doors that the contestant didn't select and that had no prize behind it. (Monty Hall knew in advance which door had the prize.) Then he asked the contestant if he or she wanted to change doors or keep the one that the contestant originally selected. Now the question is, Should the contestant switch doors, or does it really matter? This chapter will show you how you can solve this problem by simulation. For the answer, see Statistics Today—Revisited, page 630.

For the answer, see Statistics Today—Revisited, page 630.

14–1   Introduction

Most people have heard of Gallup, Ipsos Reid, and Nielsen. These and other pollsters gather information about the habits and opinions of the Canadian people. Such survey firms and Statistics Canada gather information by selecting samples from well-defined populations. Recall from Chapter 1 that the subjects in the sample should be a subgroup of the subjects in the population. Sampling methods often use what are called *random numbers* to select samples.

Since many statistical studies use surveys and questionnaires, some information about these is presented in Section 14–3.

Random numbers are also used in *simulation techniques.* Instead of studying a real-life situation, which may be costly or dangerous, researchers create a similar situation in a laboratory or with a computer. Then, by studying the simulated situation, researchers can gain the necessary information about the real-life situation in a less expensive or safer manner. This chapter will explain some common methods used to obtain samples as well as the techniques used in simulations.

14–2   Common Sampling Techniques

Objective ❶

Demonstrate a knowledge of the four basic sampling methods.

In Chapter 1, a *population* was defined as all subjects (human or otherwise) under study. Since some populations can be very large, researchers cannot use every single subject, so a sample must be selected. A *sample* is a subgroup of the population. Any subgroup of the population, technically speaking, can be called a sample. However, for researchers to make valid inferences about population characteristics, the sample must be random.

For a sample to be a **random sample,** every member of the population must have an equal chance of being selected.

When a sample is chosen at random from a population, it is said to be an **unbiased sample.** That is, the sample, for the most part, is representative of the population. Conversely, if a sample is selected incorrectly, it may be a biased sample. Samples are said to be **biased samples** when some type of systematic error has been made in the selection of the subjects.

A sample is used to get information about a population for several reasons:

1. *It saves the researcher time and money.*

2. *It enables the researcher to get information that he or she might not be able to obtain otherwise.* For example, if a person's blood is to be analyzed for cholesterol, a researcher cannot analyze every single drop of blood without killing the person. Or if the breaking strength of cables is to be determined, a researcher cannot test to destruction every cable manufactured, since the company would not have any cables left to sell.

3. *It enables the researcher to get more detailed information about a particular subject.* If only a few people are surveyed, the researcher can conduct in-depth interviews by spending more time with each person, thus getting more information about the subject. This is not to say that the smaller the sample, the better; in fact, the opposite is true. In general, larger samples—if correct sampling techniques are used—give more reliable information about the population.

It would be ideal if the sample were a perfect miniature of the population in all characteristics. This ideal, however, is impossible to achieve, because there are so many human traits (height, weight, IQ, etc.). The best that can be done is to select a sample that will be representative with respect to *some* characteristics, preferably those pertaining to the study. For example, if one-half of the population subjects are female, then approximately one-half of the sample subjects should be female. Likewise, other characteristics, such as age, socioeconomic status, and IQ, should be represented proportionately. To obtain unbiased samples, statisticians have developed several basic sampling methods. The most common methods are *random, systematic, stratified,* and *cluster sampling.* Each method will be explained in detail in this section.

In addition to the basic methods, there are other methods used to obtain samples. Some of these methods are also explained in this section.

Simple Random Sampling

A simple random sample is obtained by using methods such as random numbers, which can be generated from calculators, computers, or tables. In *simple random sampling,* the basic requirement is that for a sample of size *n,* all possible samples of this size must have an equal chance of being selected from the population. But before the correct method of obtaining a simple random sample is explained, several incorrect methods commonly used by various researchers and agencies to gain information are discussed.

One incorrect method commonly used is to ask "the person on the street." News reporters use this technique quite often. Selecting people haphazardly on the street does not meet the requirement for simple random sampling, since not all possible samples of a specific size have an equal chance of being selected. Many people will be at home or at work when the interview is being conducted and therefore do not have a chance of being selected.

Another incorrect technique is to ask a question by either radio or television and have the listeners or viewers call the station to give their responses or opinions. Again, this sample is not random, since only those who feel strongly for or against the issue may respond and people may not have heard or seen the program. A third erroneous method is to ask people to respond by mail. Again, only those who are concerned and who have the time are likely to respond.

These methods do not meet the requirement of simple random sampling, since not all possible samples of a specific size have an equal chance of being selected. To meet this requirement, researchers can use one of two methods. The first method is to number each element of the population and then place the numbers on cards. Place the cards in a hat or fishbowl, mix them, and then select the sample by drawing the cards. When using this procedure, researchers must ensure that the numbers are well mixed. On occasion, when this procedure is used, the numbers are not mixed well, and the numbers chosen for the sample are those that were placed in the bowl last.

The second and preferred way of selecting a simple random sample is to use random numbers. Figure 14–1 shows a table of two-digit random numbers generated by a computer. A more detailed table of random numbers is found in Table D of Appendix C.

The theory behind random numbers is that each digit, 0 through 9, has an equal probability of occurring. That is, in every sequence of 10 digits, each digit has a probability of $\frac{1}{10}$ of occurring. This does not mean that in every sequence of 10 digits, one will find each digit. Rather, it means that on the average, each digit will occur once. For example, the digit 2 may occur 3 times in a sequence of 10 digits, but in later sequences, it may not occur at all, thus averaging to a probability of $\frac{1}{10}$.

To obtain a sample by using random numbers, number the elements of the population sequentially and then select each person by using random numbers. This process is shown in Example 14–1.

Simple random samples can be selected with or without replacement. If the same member of the population cannot be used more than once in the study, then the sample is selected without replacement. That is, once a random number is selected, it cannot be used later.

Figure 14–1

Table of Random Numbers

79	41	71	93	60	35	04	67	96	04	79	10	86
26	52	53	13	43	50	92	09	87	21	83	75	17
18	13	41	30	56	20	37	74	49	56	45	46	83
19	82	02	69	34	27	77	34	24	93	16	77	00
14	57	44	30	93	76	32	13	55	29	49	30	77
29	12	18	50	06	33	15	79	50	28	50	45	45
01	27	92	67	93	31	97	55	29	21	64	27	29
55	75	65	68	65	73	07	95	66	43	43	92	16
84	95	95	96	62	30	91	64	74	83	47	89	71
62	62	21	37	82	62	19	44	08	64	34	50	11
66	57	28	69	13	99	74	31	58	19	47	66	89
48	13	69	97	29	01	75	58	05	40	40	18	29
94	31	73	19	75	76	33	18	05	53	04	51	41
00	06	53	98	01	55	08	38	49	42	10	44	38
46	16	44	27	80	15	28	01	64	27	89	03	27
77	49	85	95	62	93	25	39	63	74	54	82	85
81	96	43	27	39	53	85	61	12	90	67	96	02
40	46	15	73	23	75	96	68	13	99	49	64	11

Note: In the explanations and examples of the sampling procedures, a small population will be used, and small samples will be selected from this population. Small populations are used for illustrative purposes only, because the entire population could be included with little difficulty. In real life, however, researchers must usually sample from very large populations, using the procedures shown in this chapter.

Example 14–1

Suppose a researcher wants to produce a television show featuring in-depth interviews with Canada's city mayors on the subject of a new partnership with the federal and provincial governments. Because of time constraints, the 60-minute program will have room for only 10 mayors. The researcher wishes to select the mayors at random. Select a simple random sample of 10 cities from 50.

Solution

Step 1 Number each city from 1 to 50, as shown. In this case, they are numbered alphabetically.

01	Abbotsford	14	Hamilton	27	Oshawa	40	Sudbury
02	Barrie	15	Kamloops	28	Ottawa	41	Surrey
03	Brampton	16	Kingston	29	Quebec City	42	Thunder Bay
04	Brantford	17	Kitchener	30	Red Deer	43	Toronto
05	Burlington	18	Laval	31	Regina	44	Trois-Rivières
06	Burnaby	19	Lethbridge	32	Richmond	45	Vancouver
07	Calgary	20	Lévis	33	Saguenay	46	Victoria
08	Cambridge	21	London	34	Saint John	47	Waterloo
09	Coquitlan	22	Longueuil	35	Saskatoon	48	Whitby
10	Edmonton	23	Mississauga	36	Sault Ste. Marie	49	Windsor
11	Gatineau	24	Montreal	37	Sherbrooke	50	Winnipeg
12	Guelph	25	Niagara Falls	38	St. Catharines		
13	Halifax	26	Oakville	39	St. John's		

Step 2 Using the random numbers shown in Figure 14–1, find a starting point. To find a starting point, one generally closes one's eyes and places one's finger anywhere on the table. In this case, the first number selected was 27 in the fourth column. Going down the column and continuing on to the next column, select the first 10 numbers. They are 27, 95, 27, 73, 60, 43, 56, 34, 93, and 06. See Figure 14–2. (Note that 06 represents 6.)

Figure 14–2

Selecting a Starting Point and 10 Numbers from the Random Number Table

79	41	71	93	60 ✓	35	04	67	96	04	79	10	86
26	52	53	13	43 ✓	50	92	09	87	21	83	75	17
18	13	41	30	56 ✓	20	37	74	49	56	45	46	83
19	82	02	69	34 ✓	27	77	34	24	93	16	77	00
14	57	44	30	93 ✓	76	32	13	55	29	49	30	77
29	12	18	50	06 ✓	33	15	79	50	28	50	45	45
01	27	92	67	93	31	97	55	29	21	64	27	29
55	75	65	68	65	73	07	95	66	43	43	92	16
84	95	95	96	62	30	91	64	74	83	47	89	71
62	62	21	37	82	62	19	44	08	64	34	50	11
66	57	28	69	13	99	74	31	58	19	47	66	89
48	13	69	97	29	01	75	58	05	40	40	18	29
94	31	73	19	75	76	33	18	05	53	04	51	41
00	06	53	*Start here 01	55	08	38	49	42	10	44	38
46	16	44	㉗✓	80	15	28	01	64	27	89	03	27
77	49	85	95 ✓	62	93	25	39	63	74	54	82	85
81	96	43	27 ✓	39	53	85	61	12	90	67	96	02
40	46	15	73 ✓	23	75	96	68	13	99	49	64	11

Now, refer to the list of cities and identify the city corresponding to each number. The sample consists of the following cities:

27	Oshawa	43	Toronto
95		56	
27	Oshawa	34	Saint John
73		93	
60		06	Burnaby

Step 3   Since the numbers 95, 73, 60, 56, and 93 are too large, they are disregarded. And since 27 appears twice, it is also disregarded the second time. Now, one must select six more random numbers between 1 and 50 and omit duplicates, since this sample will be selected without replacement. Make this selection by continuing down the column and moving over to the next column until a total of 10 numbers is selected. The final 10 numbers are 27, 43, 34, 06, 13, 29, 01, 39, 23, and 35. See Figure 14–3.

Figure 14–3

The Final 10 Numbers Selected

79	41	71	93	60	⑤35	04	67	96	04	79	10	86
26	52	53	13	㊸43	50	92	09	87	21	83	75	17
18	13	41	30	56	20	37	74	49	56	45	46	83
19	82	02	69	㉞34	27	77	34	24	93	16	77	00
14	57	44	30	93	76	32	13	55	29	49	30	77
29	12	18	50	⓪06	33	15	79	50	28	50	45	45
01	27	92	67	93	31	97	55	29	21	64	27	29
55	75	65	68	65	73	07	95	66	43	43	92	16
84	95	95	96	62	30	91	64	74	83	47	89	71
62	62	21	37	82	62	19	44	08	64	34	50	11
66	57	28	69	⑬13	99	74	31	58	19	47	66	89
48	13	69	97	㉙29	01	75	58	05	40	40	18	29
94	31	73	19	75	76	33	18	05	53	04	51	41
00	06	53	98	⓪01	55	08	38	49	42	10	44	38
46	16	44	㉗27	80	15	28	01	64	27	89	03	27
77	49	85	95	62	93	25	39	63	74	54	82	85
81	96	43	27	㊴39	53	85	61	12	90	67	96	02
40	46	15	73	㉓23	75	96	68	13	99	49	64	11

These numbers correspond to the following cities:

27	Oshawa	29	Quebec City
43	Toronto	01	Abbotsford
34	Saint John	39	St. John's
06	Burnaby	23	Mississauga
13	Halifax	35	Saskatoon

Thus, the mayors of these 10 cities will constitute the sample.

Simple random sampling has one limitation. If the population is extremely large, it is time-consuming to number and select the sample elements. Also, notice that the random numbers in the table are two-digit numbers. If three digits are needed, then the first digit from the next column can be used, as shown in Figure 14–4. Table D in Appendix C gives five-digit random numbers.

Speaking of
Statistics

Should We Be Afraid of Lightning?

The U.S. National Weather Service collects various types of data about the weather. For example, each year in the United States about 400 million lightning strikes occur. On average, 400 people are struck by lightning, and 85% of those struck are men. About 100 of these people die. The cause of most of these deaths is not burns, even though temperatures as high as 54,000°F are reached, but heart attacks. The lightning strike short-circuits the body's autonomic nervous system, causing the heart to stop beating. In some instances, the heart will restart on its own. In other cases, the heart victim will need emergency resuscitation.

    The most dangerous places to be during a thunderstorm are open fields, golf courses, under trees, and near water, such as a lake or swimming pool. It's best to be inside a building during a thunderstorm although there's no guarantee that the building won't be struck by lightning. Are these statistics descriptive or inferential? Why do you think more men are struck by lightning than women? Should you be afraid of lightning?

79	41	71	93	60	35	04	67	96	04	79	10	86
26	52	53	13	43	50	92	09	87	21	83	75	17
18	13	41	30	56	20	37	74	49	56	45	46	83
19	82	02	69	34	27	77	34	24	93	16	77	00
14	57	44	30	93	76	32	13	55	29	49	30	77
29	12	18	50	06	33	15	79	50	28	50	45	45
01	27	92	67	93	31	97	55	29	21	64	27	29
55	75	65	68	65	73	07	95	66	43	43	92	16
84	95	95	96	62	30	91	64	74	83	47	89	71
62	62	21	37	82	62	19	44	08	64	34	50	11
66	57	28	69	13	99	74	31	58	19	47	66	89
48	13	69	97	29	01	75	58	05	40	40	18	29
94	31	73	19	75	76	33	18	05	53	04	51	41
00	06	53	98	01	55	08	38	49	42	10	44	38
46	16	44	27	80	15	28	01	64	27	89	03	27
77	49	85	95	62	93	25	39	63	74	54	82	85
81	96	43	27	39	53	85	61	12	90	67	96	02
40	46	15	73	23	75	96	68	13	99	49	64	11

Figure 14–4

Method for Selecting Three-Digit Numbers

Use one column and part of the next column for three digits, that is, 404.

Systematic Sampling

A **systematic sample** is a sample obtained by numbering each element in the population and then selecting every third or fifth or tenth, etc., number from the population to be included in the sample. This is done after the first number is selected at random.

The procedure of systematic sampling is illustrated in Example 14–2.

Example 14–2

Using the population of 50 cities in Example 14–1, select a systematic sample of 10 cities.

Solution

Step 1   Number the population units as shown in Example 14–1.

Step 2   Since there are 50 cities and 10 are to be selected, the rule is to select every fifth city. This rule was determined by dividing 50 by 10, which yields 5.

Step 3   Using the table of random numbers, select the first digit (from 1 to 5) at random. In this case, 4 was selected.

Step 4   Select every fifth number on the list, starting with 4. The numbers include the following:

1 2 3 ④ 5 6 7 8 ⑨ 10 11 12 13 ⑭ . . .

The selected cities are as follows:

4	Brantford	29	Quebec City
9	Coquitlan	34	Saint John
14	Hamilton	39	St. John's
19	Lethbridge	44	Trois-Rivières
24	Montreal	49	Windsor

The advantage of systematic sampling is the ease of selecting the sample elements. Also, in many cases, a numbered list of the population units may already exist. For example, the manager of a factory may have a list of employees who work for the company, or there may be an in-house telephone directory.

When doing systematic sampling, one must be careful how the items are arranged on the list. For example, if each unit were arranged, say, as

1. Husband
2. Wife
3. Husband
4. Wife

then the selection of the starting number could produce a sample of all males or all females, depending on whether the starting number is even or odd and whether the number to be added is even or odd. As another example, if the list were arranged in order of heights of individuals, one would get a different average from two samples if the first were selected by using a small starting number and the second by using a large starting number.

Stratified Sampling

A **stratified sample** is a sample obtained by dividing the population into subgroups, called *strata*, according to various homogeneous characteristics and then selecting members from each stratum for the sample.

For example, a population may consist of males and females who are smokers or nonsmokers. The researcher will want to include in the sample people from each group—that is, males who smoke, males who do not smoke, females who smoke, and females who do not smoke. To accomplish this selection, the researcher divides the population into four subgroups and then selects a random sample from each subgroup. This method ensures that the sample is representative on the basis of the characteristics of gender and smoking. Of course, it may not be representative on the basis of other characteristics.

Example 14–3

Using the population of 20 students shown in Figure 14–5, select a sample of 8 students on the basis of gender (male/female) and grade level (freshman/sophomore) by stratification.

Figure 14–5

Population of Students for Example 14–3

1. Ald, Peter	M	Fr	11. Martin, Janice	F	Fr
2. Brown, Danny	M	So	12. Meloski, Gary	M	Fr
3. Bear, Theresa	F	Fr	13. Oeler, George	M	So
4. Carson, Susan	F	Fr	14. Peters, Michele	F	So
5. Collins, Carolyn	F	Fr	15. Peterson, John	M	Fr
6. Davis, William	M	Fr	16. Smith, Nancy	F	Fr
7. Hogan, Michael	M	Fr	17. Thomas, Jeff	M	So
8. Jones, Lois	F	So	18. Toms, Debbie	F	So
9. Lutz, Harry	M	So	19. Unger, Roberta	F	So
10. Lyons, Larry	M	So	20. Zibert, Mary	F	So

Solution

Step 1 Divide the population into two subgroups, consisting of males and females, as shown in Figure 14–6.

Figure 14–6

Population Divided into Subgroups by Gender

Males			Females		
1. Ald, Peter	M	Fr	1. Bear, Theresa	F	Fr
2. Brown, Danny	M	So	2. Carson, Susan	F	Fr
3. Davis, William	M	Fr	3. Collins, Carolyn	F	Fr
4. Hogan, Michael	M	Fr	4. Jones, Lois	F	So
5. Lutz, Harry	M	So	5. Martin, Janice	F	Fr
6. Lyons, Larry	M	So	6. Peters, Michele	F	So
7. Meloski, Gary	M	Fr	7. Smith, Nancy	F	Fr
8. Oeler, George	M	So	8. Toms, Debbie	F	So
9. Peterson, John	M	Fr	9. Unger, Roberta	F	So
10. Thomas, Jeff	M	So	10. Zibert, Mary	F	So

Step 2 Divide each subgroup further into two groups of freshmen and sophomores, as shown in Figure 14–7.

Figure 14–7

Each Subgroup Divided into Subgroups by Grade Level

Group 1			Group 2		
1. Ald, Peter	M	Fr	1. Bear, Theresa	F	Fr
2. Davis, William	M	Fr	2. Carson, Susan	F	Fr
3. Hogan, Michael	M	Fr	3. Collins, Carolyn	F	Fr
4. Meloski, Gary	M	Fr	4. Martin, Janice	F	Fr
5. Peterson, John	M	Fr	5. Smith, Nancy	F	Fr

Group 3			Group 4		
1. Brown, Danny	M	So	1. Jones, Lois	F	So
2. Lutz, Harry	M	So	2. Peters, Michele	F	So
3. Lyons, Larry	M	So	3. Toms, Debbie	F	So
4. Oeler, George	M	So	4. Unger, Roberta	F	So
5. Thomas, Jeff	M	So	5. Zibert, Mary	F	So

Step 3   Determine how many students need to be selected from each subgroup to have a proportional representation of each subgroup in the sample. There are four groups, and since a total of eight students is needed for the sample, two students must be selected from each subgroup.

Step 4   Select two students from each group by using random numbers. In this case, the random numbers are as follows:

Group 1   Students 5 and 4   Group 2   Students 5 and 2

Group 3   Students 1 and 3   Group 4   Students 3 and 4

The stratified sample then consists of the following people:

Peterson, John	M	Fr	Smith, Nancy	F	Fr
Meloski, Gary	M	Fr	Carson, Susan	F	Fr
Brown, Danny	M	So	Toms, Debbie	F	So
Lyons, Larry	M	So	Unger, Roberta	F	So

The major advantage of stratification is that it ensures representation of all population subgroups that are important to the study. There are two major drawbacks to stratification, however. First, if there are many variables of interest, dividing a large population into representative subgroups requires a great deal of effort. Second, if the variables are somewhat complex or ambiguous (such as beliefs, attitudes, or prejudices), it is difficult to separate individuals into the subgroups according to these variables.

Cluster Sampling

A **cluster sample** is a sample obtained by selecting a preexisting or natural group, called a *cluster,* and using the members in the cluster for the sample.

For example, many studies in education use already existing classes, such as the Grade 7 class in Markham Elementary School. The voters of a certain district might be surveyed to determine their preferences for a mayoral candidate in the upcoming election. Or the residents of an entire city block might be polled to ascertain the percentage of households that have two or more incomes. In cluster sampling, researchers may use all units of a cluster if that is feasible, or they may select only part of a cluster to use as a sample. This selection is done by random methods.

There are three advantages to using a cluster sample instead of other types of samples: (1) A cluster sample can reduce costs, (2) it can simplify fieldwork, and (3) it is convenient. For example, in a dental study involving X-raying Grade 4 students' teeth to see how many cavities each child had, it would be a simple matter to select a single classroom and bring the X-ray equipment to the school to conduct the study. If other sampling methods were used, researchers might have to transport the machine to several different schools or transport the students to the dental office.

The major disadvantage of cluster sampling is that the elements in a cluster may not have the same variations in characteristics as elements selected individually from a population. The reason is that groups of people may be more homogeneous (alike) in specific clusters such as neighbourhoods or clubs. For example, the people who live in a

In this study, the researchers found that subjects did better on fill-in-the-blank questions than on multiple-choice questions. Do you agree with the professor's statement, "Trusting your first impulse is your best strategy?" Explain your answer.

TESTS

Is That Your Final Answer?

Beating game shows takes more than smarts: Contestants must also overcome self-doubt and peer pressure. Two new studies suggest today's hottest game shows are particularly challenging because the very mechanisms employed to help contestants actually lead them astray.

Multiple-choice questions are one such offender, as alternative answers seem to make test-takers ignore gut instincts. To learn why, researchers at Southern Methodist University gave two identical tests: one using multiple-choice questions and the other fill-in-the-blank. The results, recently published in the *Journal of Educational Psychology*, show that test-takers were incorrect more often when given false alternatives, and that the longer they considered those alternatives, the more credible the answers looked.

"If you sit and stew, you forget that you know the right answer," says Alan Brown, Ph.D., a psychology professor at Southern Methodist University. "Trusting your first impulse is your best strategy." Audiences can also be trouble, says Jennifer Butler, Ph.D., a Wittenberg University psychology professor. Her recent study in the *Journal of Personality and Social Psychology* found that contestants who see audience participation as peer pressure slow down to avoid making embarrassing mistakes. But this strategy backfires, as more contemplation produces more wrong answers. Worse, Butler says, if perceived peer pressure grows unbearable, contestants may opt out of answering at all, "thinking that it's better to stop than to have your once supportive audience come to believe you're an idiot."

— *Sarah Smith*

Source: Reprinted with permission from *Psychology Today,* Copyright © 2000 Sussex Publishers, Inc.

certain neighbourhood tend to have similar incomes, drive similar cars, live in similar houses, and, for the most part, have similar habits.

Other Types of Sampling Techniques

In addition to the four basic sampling methods, other methods are sometimes used. In **sequence sampling,** which is used in quality control, successive units taken from production lines are sampled to ensure that the products meet certain standards set by the manufacturing company.

In **double sampling,** a very large population is given a questionnaire to determine those who meet the qualifications for a study. After the questionnaires are reviewed, a second, smaller population is defined. Then a sample is selected from this group.

In **multistage sampling,** the researcher uses a combination of sampling methods. For example, suppose a research organization wants to conduct a nationwide survey for a new product being manufactured. A sample can be obtained by using the following combination of methods. First, the researchers divide the 50 cities from across the country into four or five regions (or clusters). Then, several cities from each region are selected at random. Next the selected cities are divided into various areas by using districts and wards (or neighbourhoods). Samples of these areas arc then selected. Finally, streets in these wards are selected at random, and the families living on these streets are given samples of the product to test and are asked to report the results. This hypothetical example illustrates a typical multistage sampling method.

The steps for conducting a sample survey are given in the Procedure Table.

Procedure Table

Conducting a Sample Survey

Step 1   Decide what information is needed.

Step 2   Determine how the data will be collected (phone interview, mail survey, etc.).

Step 3   Select the information-gathering instrument or design the questionnaire if one is not available.

Step 4   Set up a sampling list, if possible.

Step 5   Select the best method for obtaining the sample (random, systematic, stratified, cluster, or other).

Step 6   Conduct the survey and collect the data.

Step 7   Tabulate the data.

Step 8   Conduct the statistical analysis.

Step 9   Report the results.

Applying the Concepts 14–2

The White or Wheat Bread Debate

Read the following study and answer the questions.

A baking company selected 36 women weighing different amounts and randomly assigned them to four different groups. The four groups were white bread only, brown bread only, low-fat white bread only, and low-fat brown bread only. Each group could eat only the type of bread assigned to the group. The study lasted for eight weeks. No other changes in any of the women's diets were allowed. A trained evaluator was used to check for any differences in the women's diets. The results showed that there were no differences in weight gain between the groups over the eight-week period.

1. Did the researchers use a population or a sample for their study?

2. Based on who conducted this study, would you consider the study to be biased?

3. Which sampling method do you think was used to obtain the original 36 women for the study (random, systematic, stratified, or clustered)?

4. Which sampling method would you use? Why?

5. How would you collect a random sample for this study?

6. Does random assignment help representativeness the same as random selection does? Explain.

See page 632 for the answers.

Exercises 14–2

1. Name the four basic sampling techniques.

2. Why are samples used in statistics?

3. What is the basic requirement for a sample?

4. Why should random numbers be used when one is selecting a random sample?

5. List three incorrect methods that are often used to obtain a sample.

Figure 14–8

Student Survey at Utopia University (for Exercises 11 through 15)

Student number	Gender	Class rank	GPA	Kilometres travelled to school	IQ	Major field	Student number	Gender	Class rank	GPA	Kilometres travelled to school	IQ	Major field
1	M	Fr	1.4	1	104	Bio	26	M	Fr	1.1	8	100	Ed
2	M	Fr	2.3	2	95	Ed	27	F	Jr	2.1	3	101	Bus
3	M	So	2.7	6	108	Psy	28	M	Gr	3.7	5	99	Bio
4	F	So	3.2	7	119	Eng	29	M	Se	2.4	8	105	Eng
5	F	Gr	3.8	12	114	Ed	30	M	So	2.1	15	108	Bus
6	M	Jr	4.0	13	91	Psy	31	M	Gr	3.9	2	112	Ed
7	F	Jr	3.0	2	106	Eng	32	F	Jr	2.4	4	111	Psy
8	M	Jr	3.3	6	100	Bio	33	M	Se	2.7	6	107	Eng
9	F	Se	2.7	9	102	Eng	34	F	So	2.5	1	104	Bio
10	F	So	2.3	5	99	Ed	35	M	Se	3.2	3	96	Bus
11	M	Se	1.6	18	100	Bus	36	F	Fr	3.4	7	98	Bio
12	M	Gr	3.2	7	105	Psy	37	M	Gr	3.6	14	105	Ed
13	F	Gr	3.8	3	103	Bus	38	M	Jr	3.8	4	115	Psy
14	F	Se	3.1	5	97	Eng	39	F	Se	2.2	8	113	Eng
15	F	Jr	2.7	5	106	Bio	40	F	So	2.0	8	103	Psy
16	F	Fr	1.4	4	114	Bus	41	F	Fr	2.3	9	103	Eng
17	M	So	3.6	17	102	Ed	42	F	Se	2.5	10	99	Bus
18	M	Fr	2.2	1	101	Psy	43	M	Gr	3.7	13	114	Ed
19	F	Gr	4.0	7	108	Bus	44	M	Fr	3.0	11	121	Bus
20	M	Jr	2.1	4	97	Ed	45	M	Jr	2.1	10	101	Eng
21	F	Fr	2.0	3	113	Bio	46	F	Jr	3.4	2	104	Ed
22	F	So	3.6	4	104	Bio	47	M	So	3.6	9	105	Psy
23	F	Gr	3.3	16	110	Eng	48	M	Se	2.1	1	97	Psy
24	F	Se	2.5	4	99	Psy	49	F	Gr	3.3	12	111	Bio
25	M	So	3.0	5	96	Psy	50	F	Fr	2.2	11	102	Bio

6. What is the principle behind random numbers?

7. List the advantages and disadvantages of random sampling.

8. List the advantages and disadvantages of systematic sampling.

9. List the advantages and disadvantages of stratified sampling.

10. List the advantages and disadvantages of cluster sampling.

Using the student survey at Utopia University, shown in Figure 14–8, as the population, complete Exercises 11 through 15.

11. Using the table of random numbers in Figure 14–1, select 10 students and find the sample mean (average) of the GPA, IQ, and distance travelled to school. Compare these sample means with the population means.

12. Select a sample of 10 students by the systematic method, and compute the sample means of the GPA, IQ, and distance travelled to school of this sample. Compare these sample means with the population means.

13. Select a cluster of 10 students, for example, students 9 through 18, and compute the sample means of their GPA, IQ, and distance travelled to school. Compare these sample means with the population means.

14. Divide the 50 students into subgroups according to class rank. Then select a sample of 2 students from each rank and compute the means of these 10 students for the GPA, IQ, and distance travelled to school each day. Compare these sample means with the population means.

15. In your opinion, which sampling method(s) provided the best sample to represent the population?

Figure 14–9 shows the 50 U.S. states and the number of electoral votes each state has in the Presidential election. Using this listing as a population, complete Exercises 16 through 19.

16. Select a random sample of 10 states and find the mean number of electoral votes for this sample. Compare this mean with the population mean.

Figure 14–9

U. S. States and Number of Electoral Votes for Each (for Exercises 16 through 19)

1. Alabama	9	14. Indiana	12	27. Nebraska	5	40. South Carolina	8
2. Alaska	3	15. Iowa	8	28. Nevada	4	41. South Dakota	3
3. Arizona	7	16. Kansas	7	29. New Hampshire	4	42. Tennessee	11
4. Arkansas	6	17. Kentucky	9	30. New Jersey	16	43. Texas	29
5. California	47	18. Louisiana	10	31. New Mexico	5	44. Utah	5
6. Colorado	8	19. Maine	4	32. New York	36	45. Vermont	3
7. Connecticut	8	20. Maryland	10	33. North Carolina	13	46. Virginia	12
8. Delaware	3	21. Massachusetts	13	34. North Dakota	3	47. Washington	10
9. Florida	21	22. Michigan	20	35. Ohio	23	48. West Virginia	6
10. Georgia	12	23. Minnesota	10	36. Oklahoma	8	49. Wisconsin	11
11. Hawaii	4	24. Mississippi	7	37. Oregon	7	50. Wyoming	3
12. Idaho	4	25. Missouri	11	38. Pennsylvania	25		
13. Illinois	24	26. Montana	4	39. Rhode Island	4		

Source: "Dating Angus Reid" by J.G. Brin, Bubonic Press, www.bubonicpress.com.

17. Select a systematic sample of 10 states and compute the mean number of electoral votes for the sample. Compare this mean with the population mean.

18. Divide the 50 states into five subgroups by geographic location, using a map of the United States. Each subgroup should include 10 states. The subgroups should be northeast, southeast, central, northwest, and southwest. Select two states from each subgroup, and find the mean number of electoral votes for the sample. Compare these means with the population mean.

19. Select a cluster of 10 states and compute the mean number of electoral votes for the sample. Compare this mean with the population mean.

20. Many research studies described in newspapers and magazines do not report the sample size or the sampling method used. Try to find a research article that gives this information; state the sampling method that was used and the sample size.

14–3   Surveys and Questionnaire Design

Objective 2

Recognize faulty questions on a survey and other factors that can bias responses.

Many statistical studies obtain information from *surveys*. A survey is conducted when a sample of individuals is asked to respond to questions about a particular subject. There are two types of surveys: interviewer-administered and self-administered. Interviewer-administered surveys require a person to ask the questions. The interview can be conducted face to face in an office, on a street, or in the mall, or via telephone.

Self-administered surveys can be done by mail or in a group setting such as a classroom.

When analyzing the results of surveys, you should be very careful about the interpretations. The way a question is phrased can influence the way people respond. For example, when a group of people were asked if they favoured a waiting period and background check before guns could be sold, 91% of the respondents were in favour of it and 7% were against it. However, when asked if there should be a national gun registration program costing about 20% of all dollars spent on crime control, only 33% of the respondents were in favour of it and 61% were against it.

As you can see, by phrasing questions in different ways, different responses can be obtained, since the purpose of a national gun registry would include a waiting period and a background check.

When you are writing questions for a questionnaire, it is important to avoid these common mistakes.

1. *Asking biased questions.* By asking questions in a certain way, the researcher can lead the respondents to answer in the way he or she wants them to. For example, asking a question such as "Are you going to vote for the candidate Jones even though the latest survey indicates that he will lose the election?" instead of "Are you going to vote for candidate Jones?" may dissuade some people from answering in the affirmative.

2. *Using confusing words.* In this case, the participant misinterprets the meaning of the words and answers the questions in a biased way. For example, the question "Do you think people would live longer if they were on a diet?" could be misinterpreted since there are many different types of diets—weight loss diets, low-salt diets, medically prescribed diets, etc.

3. *Asking double-barrelled questions.* Sometimes questions contain compound sentences that require the participant to respond to two questions at the same time. For example, the question "Are you in favour of a special tax to support Canada's commitment to reduce greenhouse gases?" asks two questions: "Are you in favour of greenhouse gas reduction?" and "Do you favour a tax to support it?"

4. *Using double negatives in questions.* Questions with double negatives can be confusing to the respondents. For example, the question " Do you feel that it is not appropriate to have areas where people cannot smoke?" is very confusing since *not* is used twice in the sentence.

5. *Ordering questions improperly.* By arranging the questions in a certain order, the researcher can lead the participant to respond in a way that he or she may otherwise not have done. For example, a question might ask the respondent, "At what age should an elderly person not be permitted to drive?" A later question might ask the respondent to list some problems of elderly people. The respondent may indicate that transportation is a problem based on reading the previous question.

Other factors can also bias a survey. For example, the participant may not know anything about the subject of the question but will answer the question anyway to avoid being considered uninformed. For example, many people might respond yes or no to the following question: "Would you be in favour of giving pensions to the widows of unknown soldiers?" In this case, the question makes no sense since if the soldiers were unknown, their widows would also be unknown.

Many people will make responses on the basis of what they think the person asking the questions wants to hear. For example, if a question states, "How often do you lie?" people may *understate* the incidences of their lying.

Participants will, in some cases, respond differently to questions depending on whether their identity is known. This is especially true if the questions concern sensitive issues such as income, sexuality, and abortion. Researchers try to ensure confidentiality (i.e., keeping the respondent's identity secret) rather than anonymity (soliciting unsigned responses); however, many people will be suspicious in either case.

Still other factors that could bias a survey include the time and place of the survey and whether the questions are open-ended or closed-ended. The time and place where a survey is conducted can influence the results. For example, if a survey on airline safety is conducted immediately after a major airline crash, the results may differ from those obtained in a year in which no major airline disasters occurred.

Finally, the type of questions asked influences the responses. In this case, the concern is whether the question is open-ended or closed-ended.

An *open-ended question* would be one such as "List three activities that you plan to spend more time on when you retire." A *closed-ended question* would be one such as "Select three activities that you plan to spend more time on after you retire: travelling; eating out; fishing, hunting; exercising; visiting relatives."

One problem with a closed-ended question is that the respondent is forced to choose the answers that the researcher gives and cannot supply his or her own. But there is also a problem with open-ended questions in that the results may be so varied that attempting to summarize them might be difficult, if not impossible. Hence, you should be aware of what types of questions are being asked before you draw any conclusions from the survey.

There are several other things to consider when you are conducting a study that uses questionnaires. For example, a pilot study should be done to test the design and usage of the questionnaire (i.e., the *validity* of the questionnaire). The pilot study helps the researcher to pretest the questionnaire to determine if it meets the objectives of the study. It also helps the researcher to rewrite any questions that may be misleading, ambiguous, etc.

If the questions are being asked by an interviewer, some training should be given to that person. If the survey is being done by mail, a cover letter and clear directions should accompany the questionnaire.

Questionnaires help researchers to gather needed statistical information for their studies; however, much care must be given to proper questionnaire design and usage; otherwise, the results will be unreliable.

Unusual Stat

Of people who are struck by lightning, 85% are men.

Applying the Concepts 14–3

Smoking Bans and Profits

Assume you are a tavern owner and are concerned about the recent bans on smoking in public places. Will your business lose money if you do not allow smoking in your tavern? You decide to research this question and find two related articles published on the Internet. The first article states that bars and pubs sales were reduced by 23.5% in Ottawa after the smoking ban was enforced. In that study, a telephone survey was used and owners were asked how much business that they thought they lost. The survey was conducted by a special interest group, PUBCO (Pub and Bar Coalition of Canada). It was reported in the second article that there had been a modest increase in business at various taverns that banned smoking in that same area. Sales receipts were collected and analyzed against last year's profits. The second survey was conducted by KPMG Chartered Accountants for the City of Ottawa.

1. How has the public smoking ban affected tavern business in Ottawa?

2. Why do you think the surveys reported conflicting results?

3. Should surveys based on anecdotal responses be allowed to be published?

4. Can the results of a sample be representative of a population and still offer misleading information?

5. How critical is measurement error in survey sampling?

See page 632 for the answers.

Exercises 14–3

Exercises 1 through 8 include questions that contain a flaw. Identify the flaw and rewrite the question, following the guidelines presented in this section.

1. Will you continue to shop at XYZ Department Store even though it does not carry brand names?

2. Would you buy an ABC car even if you knew the manufacturer used imported parts?

3. Should banks charge their chequing account customers a fee to balance their chequebooks when customers are not able to do so?

4. Do you feel that it is not appropriate for shopping malls to have activities for children who cannot read?

5. How long have you studied for this examination?

6. Do you think children would watch less television if they read more?

7. If a plane were to crash on the border of Ontario and Quebec, where should the survivors be buried?

8. Are you in favour of imposing a tax on tobacco to pay for health care related to diseases caused by smoking?

9. Find a study that uses a questionnaire. Select any questions that you feel are improperly written.

10. Many television and radio stations have a phone vote poll. If there is one in your area, select a specific day and write a brief paragraph stating the question of the day and if it could be misleading in any way.

14–4   Simulation Techniques

Objective

Solve problems, using simulation techniques.

Many real-life problems can be solved by employing simulation techniques.

> A **simulation technique** uses a probability experiment to mimic a real-life situation.

Instead of studying the actual situation, which might be too costly, too dangerous, or too time-consuming, scientists and researchers create a similar situation but one that is less expensive, less dangerous, or less time-consuming. For example, NASA uses space shuttle flight simulators so that its astronauts can practise flying the shuttle. Most video games use the computer to simulate real-life sports such as boxing, wrestling, baseball, and hockey.

Simulation techniques go back to ancient times when the game of chess was invented to simulate warfare. Modern techniques date to the mid-1940s when two physicists, John Von Neumann and Stanislaw Ulam, developed simulation techniques to study the behaviour of neutrons in the design of atomic reactors.

Mathematical simulation techniques use probability and random numbers to create conditions similar to those of real-life problems. Computers have played an important role in simulation techniques, since they can generate random numbers, perform experiments, tally the outcomes, and compute the probabilities much faster than human beings. The basic simulation technique is called the *Monte Carlo method*. This topic is discussed next.

The Monte Carlo Method

The **Monte Carlo method** is a simulation technique using random numbers. Monte Carlo simulation techniques are used in business and industry to solve problems that are extremely difficult or involve a large number of variables. The steps for simulating real-life experiments in the Monte Carlo method are as follows:

1. List all possible outcomes of the experiment.

2. Determine the probability of each outcome.

3. Set up a correspondence between the outcomes of the experiment and the random numbers.

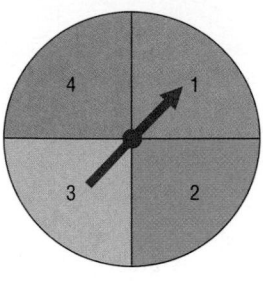

Figure 14–10

Spinner with Four Numbers

4. Select random numbers from a table and conduct the experiment.

5. Repeat the experiment and tally the outcomes.

6. Compute any statistics and state the conclusions.

Before examples of the complete simulation technique are given, an illustration is needed for step 3 (set up a correspondence between the outcomes of the experiment and the random numbers). Tossing a coin, for instance, can be simulated by using random numbers as follows: Since there are only two outcomes, heads and tails, and since each outcome has a probability of $\frac{1}{2}$, the odd digits (1, 3, 5, 7, and 9) can be used to represent a head, and the even digits (0, 2, 4, 6, and 8) can represent a tail.

Suppose a random number 8631 is selected. This number represents four tosses of a single coin and the results T, T, H, H. Or this number could represent one toss of four coins with the same results.

An experiment of rolling a single die can also be simulated by using random numbers. In this case, the digits 1, 2, 3, 4, 5, and 6 can represent the number of spots that appear on the face of the die. The digits 7, 8, 9, and 0 are ignored, since they cannot be rolled.

When two dice are rolled, two random digits are needed. For example, the number 26 represents a 2 on the first die and a 6 on the second die. The random number 37 represents a 3 on the first die, but the 7 cannot be used, so another digit must be selected. As another example, a three-digit daily lotto number can be simulated by using three-digit random numbers. Finally, a spinner with four numbers, as shown in Figure 14–10, can be simulated by letting the random numbers 1 and 2 represent 1 on the spinner, 3 and 4 represent 2 on the spinner, 5 and 6 represent 3 on the spinner, and 7 and 8 represent 4 on the spinner, since each number has a probability of $\frac{1}{4}$ of being selected. The random numbers 9 and 0 are ignored in this situation.

Many real-life games, such as bowling and baseball, can be simulated by using random numbers, as shown in Figure 14–11.

Example 14–4

Using random numbers, simulate the gender of children born.

Solution

There are only two possibilities, female and male. Since the probability of each outcome is 0.5, the odd digits can be used to represent male births and the even digits to represent female births.

Example 14–5

Using random numbers, simulate the outcomes of a tennis game between Bill and Mike, with the additional condition that Bill is twice as good as Mike.

Solution

Since Bill is twice as good as Mike, he will win approximately two games for every one Mike wins; hence, the probability that Bill wins will be $\frac{2}{3}$, and the probability that Mike wins will be $\frac{1}{3}$. The random digits 1 through 6 can be used to represent a game Bill wins; the random digits 7, 8, and 9 can be used to represent Mike's wins. The digit 0 is disregarded. Suppose they play five games, and the random number 86314 is selected. This number means that Bill won games 2, 3, 4, and 5 and Mike won the first game. The sequence is

8	6	3	1	4
M	B	B	B	B

Figure 14–11

Example of Simulation of a Game

Source: Albert Shuylte, "Simulated Bowling Game," Student Math Notes, March 1986. Published by the National Council of Teachers of Mathematics. Reprinted with permission.

Simulated Bowling Game

Let's use the random digit table to simulate a bowling game. Our game is much simpler than commercial simulation games.

First Ball		Second Ball			
		2-Pin Split		No split	
Digit	Results	Digit	Results	Digit	Results
1–3	Strike	1	Spare	1–3	Spare
4–5	2-pin split	2–8	Leave one pin	4–6	Leave 1 pin
6–7	9 pins down	9–0	Miss both pins	7–8	*Leave 2 pins
8	8 pins down			9	+Leave 3 pins
9	7 pins down			0	Leave all pins
0	6 pins down				

*If there are fewer than 2 pins, result is a spare.
+If there are fewer than 3 pins, those pins are left.

Here's how to score bowling:
1. There are 10 frames to a **game** or **line**.
2. You roll two balls for each frame, unless you knock all the pins down with the first ball (a **strike**).
3. Your score for a frame is the sum of the pins knocked down by the two balls, if you don't knock down all 10.
4. If you knock all 10 pins down with two balls (a **spare**, shown as ⌀), your score is 10 pins plus the number knocked down with the next ball.
5. If you knock all 10 pins down with the first ball (a **strike**, shown as ⌧), your score is 10 pins plus the number knocked down by the next **two** balls.
6. A **split** (shown as 0) is when there is a big space between the remaining pins. Place in the circle the number of pins remaining after the second ball.
7. A **miss** is shown as —.

Here is how one person simulated a bowling game using the random digits 7 2 7 4 8 2 2 3 6 1 6 0 4 6 1 5 5, chosen in that order from the table.

Frame

	1	2	3	4	5	6	7	8	9	10
Digit(s)	7/2	7/1	8/2	?	3	6/1	6/0	4/6	1	5/5	
Bowling result	9⌀ 19	9— 28	8⌀ 48	⌧ 77	⌧ 97	9⌀ 116	9— 125	8① 134	⌧ 153	8① 162	162

Now you try several.

Frame

	1	2	3	4	5	6	7	8	9	10
Digit(s)										
Bowling result										

	1	2	3	4	5	6	7	8	9	10
Digit(s)										
Bowling result										

If you wish to, you can change the probabilities in the simulation to better reflect *your* actual bowling ability.

More complex problems can be solved by using random numbers, as shown in Examples 14–6 to 14–8.

Example 14–6

A die is rolled until a 6 appears. Using simulation, find the average number of rolls needed. Try the experiment 20 times.

Solution

Step 1 List all possible outcomes. They are 1, 2, 3, 4, 5, 6.

Step 2 Assign the probabilities. Each outcome has a probability of $\frac{1}{6}$.

Step 3 Set up a correspondence between the random numbers and the outcome. Use random numbers 1 through 6. Omit the numbers 7, 8, 9, and 0.

Step 4 Select a block of random numbers, and count each digit 1 through 6 until the first 6 is obtained. For example, the block 857236 means that it takes 4 rolls to get a 6.

$$
\begin{array}{cccccc}
8 & 5 & 7 & 2 & 3 & 6 \\
  & \uparrow & & \uparrow & \uparrow & \uparrow \\
  & 5 & & 2 & 3 & 6
\end{array}
$$

Step 5 Repeat the experiment 19 more times and tally the data as shown.

Trial	Random number	Number of rolls
1	8 5 7 2 3 6	4
2	2 1 0 4 8 0 1 5 1 1 0 1 5 3 6	11
3	2 3 3 6	4
4	2 4 1 3 0 4 8 3 6	7
5	4 2 1 6	4
6	3 7 5 2 0 3 9 8 7 5 8 1 8 3 7 1 6	9
7	7 7 9 2 1 0 6	3
8	9 9 5 6	2
9	9 6	1
10	8 9 5 7 9 1 4 3 4 2 6	7
11	8 5 4 7 5 3 6	5
12	2 8 9 1 8 6	3
13	6	1
14	0 9 4 2 9 9 3 9 6	4
15	1 0 3 6	3
16	0 7 1 1 9 9 7 3 3 6	5
17	5 1 0 8 5 1 2 7 6	6
18	0 2 3 6	3
19	0 1 0 1 1 5 4 0 9 2 3 3 3 6	10
20	5 2 1 6	4
		Total 96

Step 6 Compute the results and draw a conclusion. In this case, one must find the average.

$$\overline{X} = \frac{\Sigma X}{n} = \frac{96}{20} = 4.8$$

Hence, the average is about 5 rolls.

Note: The theoretical average obtained from the expected value formula is 6. If this experiment is done many times, say 1000 times, the results should be closer to the theoretical results.

Example 14–7

A person selects a key at random from four keys to open a lock. Only one key fits. If the first key does not fit, she tries other keys until one fits. Find the average of the number of keys a person will have to try to open the lock. Try the experiment 25 times.

Solution

Assume that each key is numbered from 1 through 4 and that key 2 fits the lock. Naturally, the person doesn't know this, so she selects the keys at random. For the simulation, select a sequence of random digits, using only 1 through 4, until the digit 2 is reached. The trials are shown here.

Trial	Random digit (key)	Number	Trial	Random digit (key)	Number
1	2	1	14	2	1
2	2	1	15	4 2	2
3	1 2	2	16	1 3 2	3
4	1 4 3 2	4	17	1 2	2
5	3 2	2	18	2	1
6	3 1 4 2	4	19	3 4 2	3
7	4 2	2	20	2	1
8	4 3 2	3	21	2	1
9	4 2	2	22	2	1
10	2	1	23	4 2	2
11	4 2	2	24	4 3 1 2	4
12	3 1 2	3	25	3 1 2	3
13	3 1 2	3			Total 54

Next, find the average:

$$\overline{X} = \frac{\Sigma X}{n} = \frac{1 + 1 + \cdots + 3}{25} = \frac{54}{25} = 2.16$$

The theoretical average is 2.2. Again, only 25 repetitions were used; more repetitions should give a result closer to the theoretical average.

Example 14–8

A box contains five $5 bills, three $10 bills, and two $20 bills. A person selects a bill at random. What is the expected value of the bill? Perform the experiment 25 times.

Solution

Step 1 List all possible outcomes. They are $5, $10, and $20.

Step 2 Assign the probabilities to each outcome.

$$P(\$5) = \frac{5}{10} \quad P(\$10) = \frac{3}{10} \quad P(\$20) = \frac{2}{10}$$

Step 3 Set up a correspondence between the random numbers, and the outcomes. Use random numbers 1 through 5 to represent the $5 bill being selected, 6 through 8 to represent the $10 bill being selected, and 9 and 0 to represent the $20 bill being selected.

Steps 4 and 5 Select the random numbers and tally the results.

Number	Results ($)
4 5 8 2 9	5, 5, 10, 5, 20
2 5 6 4 6	5, 5, 10, 5, 10
9 1 8 0 3	20, 5, 10, 20, 5
8 4 0 6 0	10, 5, 20, 10, 20
9 6 9 4 3	20, 10, 20, 5, 5

Step 6   Compute the average:

$$\overline{X} = \frac{\Sigma X}{n} = \frac{\$5 + \$5 + \$10 + \cdots + \$5}{25} = \frac{\$265}{25} = \$10.60$$

Hence, the average (expected value) is $10.60.

Recall that using the expected value formula $E(X) = \Sigma X \cdot P(X)$ gives a theoretical average of

$$E(X) = \Sigma[X \cdot P(X)] = (0.5)(\$5) + (0.3)(\$10) + (0.2)(\$20) = \$9.50$$

Remember that simulation techniques do not give exact results. The more times the experiment is performed, though, the closer the actual results should be to the theoretical results. (Recall the law of large numbers.)

The steps for solving problems using the Monte Carlo method are summarized in the Procedure Table.

Procedure Table

Simulating Experiments Using the Monte Carlo Method

Step 1   List all possible outcomes of the experiment.

Step 2   Determine the probability of each outcome.

Step 3   Set up a correspondence between the outcomes of the experiment and the random numbers.

Step 4   Select random numbers from a table and conduct the experiment.

Step 5   Repeat the experiment and tally the outcomes.

Step 6   Compute any statistics and state the conclusions.

Applying the Concepts 14–4

Simulations

Answer the following questions:

1. Define simulation technique.
2. Have simulation techniques been used for very many years?
3. Is it cost-effective to do simulation testing on some things such as airplanes or automobiles?
4. Why might simulation testing be better than real-life testing? Give examples.
5. When did physicists develop computer simulation techniques to study neutrons?
6. When could simulations be misleading or harmful? Give examples.
7. Could simulations have prevented previous disasters such as the Hindenburg or the Space Shuttle disaster?
8. What discipline is simulation theory based in?

See page 632 for the answers.

Exercises 14–4

1. Define simulation techniques.

2. Give three examples of simulation techniques.

3. Who is responsible for the development of modern simulation techniques?

4. What role does the computer play in simulation?

5. What are the steps in the simulation of an experiment?

6. What purpose do random numbers play in simulation?

7. What happens when the number of repetitions is increased?

For Exercises 8 through 13, explain how each experiment can be simulated by using random numbers.

8. A spinner contains six equal areas.

9. A basketball player makes 70% of her shots.

10. A certain brand of DVD player manufactured has a 10% defective rate.

11. An archer hits a target 80% of the time.

12. Two players match pennies.

13. Three players play odd man out. (Three coins are tossed; if all three match, the game is repeated and no one wins. If two players match, the third person wins all three coins.)

For Exercises 14 through 21, use random numbers to simulate the experiments. The number in parentheses is the number of times the experiment should be repeated.

14. A coin is tossed until four heads are obtained. Find the average number of tosses necessary. (50)

15. A die is rolled until all faces appear at least once. Find the average number of tosses. (30)

16. A caramel corn company gives four different prizes, one in each box. They are placed in the boxes at random. Find the average number of boxes a person needs to buy to get all four prizes. (40)

17. Two teams are evenly matched. They play a tournament in which the first team to win three games wins the tournament. Find the average number of games the tournament will last. (20)

18. To win a certain lotto, a person must spell the word *big*. Sixty percent of the tickets contain the letter *b,* 30% contain the letter *i,* and 10% contain the letter *g.* Find the average number of tickets a person must buy to win the prize. (30)

19. Two shooters shoot clay pigeons. Gail has an 80% accuracy rate and Paul has a 60% accuracy rate. Paul shoots first. The first person who hits the target wins. Find the probability that each wins. (30).

20. In Exercise 19, find the average number of shots fired. (30)

21. A basketball player has a 60% success rate for shooting foul shots. If she gets two shots, find the probability that she will make one or both shots. (50).

22. Select a game such as baseball or football and write a simulation using random numbers.

23. Explain how cards can be used to generate random numbers.

24. Explain how a pair of dice can be used to generate random numbers.

14–5   Summary

To obtain information and make inferences about a large population, researchers select a sample. A sample is a subgroup of the population. Using a sample rather than a population, researchers can save time and money, get more detailed information, and get information that otherwise would be impossible to obtain.

The four most common methods researchers use to obtain samples are random, systematic, stratified, and cluster sampling methods. In random sampling, some type of random method (usually random numbers) is used to obtain the sample. In systematic sampling, the researcher selects every kth person or item after selecting the *first* one at random. In stratified sampling, the population is divided into subgroups according to various characteristics, and elements are then selected at random from the subgroups. In cluster sampling, the researcher selects an intact group to use as a sample. When the population is large, multistage sampling (a combination of methods) is used to obtain a subgroup of the population.

Researchers must use caution when conducting surveys and designing questionnaires; otherwise, conclusions obtained from these will be inaccurate. Guidelines were presented in Section 14–3.

Most sampling methods use random numbers, which can also be used to simulate many real-life problems or situations. The basic method of simulation is known as the Monte Carlo method. The purpose of simulation is to duplicate situations that are too dangerous, too costly, or too time-consuming to study in real life. Most simulation techniques can be done on the computer or calculator, since they can rapidly generate random numbers, count the outcomes, and perform the necessary computations.

Sampling and simulation are two techniques that enable researchers to gain information that might otherwise be unobtainable.

For step-by-step guidance on the use of technology for this chapter, visit the Online Learning Centre at www.mcgrawhill.ca/olc/bluman. Summary procedures for Minitab, SPSS, Excel, and TI-83 Plus or TI-84 Plus can also be found in Appendix E.

Important Terms   ●●●

biased sample 607	Monte Carlo method 621	sequence sampling 615	systematic sample 611
cluster sample 614	multistage sampling 615	simulation technique 621	unbiased sample 607
double sampling 615	random sample 607	stratified sample 612	

Review Exercises   ●●●

Use Figure 14–12 for Exercises 1 through 8.

1. Select a random sample of 10 people, and find the mean of the weights of the individuals. Compare this mean with the population mean.

2. Select a systematic sample of 10 people, and compute the mean of their weights. Compare this mean with the population mean.

3. Divide the individuals into subgroups of males and females. Select 5 individuals from each group, and find the mean of their weights. Compare these means with the population mean.

4. Select a cluster of 10 people, and find the mean of their weights. Compare this mean with the population mean.

5. Repeat Exercise 1 for blood pressure.

6. Repeat Exercise 2 for blood pressure.

7. Repeat Exercise 3 for blood pressure.

8. Repeat Exercise 4 for blood pressure.

For Exercises 9 through 13, explain how to simulate each experiment by using random numbers.

9. A baseball player strikes out 40% of the time.

10. An airline overbooks 15% of the time.

11. Two players roll a die. The higher number wins.

12. Player 1 rolls two dice. Player 2 rolls one die. If the number on the single die matches one number of

Figure 14–12

Population for Exercises 1 through 8

Individual	Gender	Weight	Systolic blood pressure	Individual	Gender	Weight	Systolic blood pressure	Individual	Gender	Weight	Systolic blood pressure
1	F	122	132	18	F	118	125	35	M	172	116
2	F	128	116	19	F	107	138	36	M	175	123
3	M	183	140	20	M	214	121	37	F	101	114
4	M	165	136	21	F	114	127	38	F	123	113
5	M	192	120	22	M	119	125	39	M	186	145
6	F	116	118	23	F	125	114	40	F	100	119
7	M	206	116	24	M	182	137	41	M	202	135
8	F	131	120	25	F	127	127	42	F	117	121
9	M	155	118	26	F	132	130	43	F	120	130
10	F	106	122	27	M	198	114	44	M	193	125
11	F	103	119	28	F	135	119	45	M	200	115
12	M	169	136	29	M	183	137	46	F	118	132
13	M	173	134	30	F	140	123	47	F	121	143
14	M	195	145	31	M	189	135	48	M	189	128
15	F	107	113	32	M	165	121	49	M	114	118
16	M	201	111	33	M	211	117	50	M	174	138
17	F	114	141	34	F	111	127				

the player who rolled the two dice, player 2 wins. Otherwise, player 1 wins.

13. Two players play rock, paper, scissors. The rules are as follows: Since paper covers rock, paper wins. Since rock breaks scissors, rock wins. Since scissors cut paper, scissors win. Each person selects rock, paper, or scissors by random numbers and then compares results.

For Exercises 14 through 18, use random numbers to simulate the experiments. The number in parentheses is the number of times the experiment should be repeated.

14. A football is placed on the 10-yard line, and a team has four downs to score a touchdown. The team can move the ball only 0 to 5 yards per play. Find the average number of times the team will score a touchdown. (30)

15. In Exercise 14, find the average number of plays it will take to score a touchdown. Ignore the four-downs rule and keep playing until a touchdown is scored. (30)

16. Four dice are rolled 50 times. Find the average of the sum of the number of spots that will appear. (50)

17. A field goal kicker is successful in 60% of his kicks inside the 35-yard line. Find the probability of kicking three field goals in a row. (50)

18. A sales representative finds that there is a 30% probability of making a sale by visiting the potential customer personally. For every 20 calls, find the probability of making three sales in a row. (50)

For Exercises 19 through 22, explain what is wrong with each question. Rewrite each one following the guidelines in this chapter.

19. How often do you run red lights?

20. Do you think students who are not failing should not be tutored?

21. Do you think all automobiles should have heavy-duty bumpers, even though it will raise the price of the cars by $500?

22. Explain the difference between an open-ended question and a closed-ended question.

Data Analysis

The Data Bank is found in Appendix D.

1. From the Data Bank, choose a variable. Select a random sample of 20 individuals, and find the mean of the data.

2. Select a systematic sample of 20 individuals, and using the same variable as in Exercise 1, find the mean.

3. Select a cluster sample of 20 individuals, and using the same variable as in Exercise 1, find the mean.

4. Stratify the data according to marital status and gender, and sample 20 individuals. Compute the mean of the sample variable selected in Exercise 1 (use four groups of five individuals).

5. Compare all four means and decide which one is most appropriate. (*Hint:* Find the population mean.)

Chapter Quiz

● ● ●

Determine whether each statement is true or false. If the statement is false, explain why.

1. When researchers are sampling from large populations, such as adult citizens living in the United States, they may use a combination of sampling techniques to ensure representativeness.

2. Simulation techniques using random numbers are a substitute for performing the actual statistical experiment.

3. When researchers perform simulation experiments, they do not need to use random numbers since they can make up random numbers.

4. Random samples are said to be unbiased.

Statistics Today

The Monty Hall Problem–Revisited

It appears that it does not matter whether the contestant switches doors because he or she is given a choice of two doors, and the chance of winning the prize is 1 out of 2, or $\frac{1}{2}$. This reasoning, however, is incorrect. Consider the three possibilities for the prize. It could be behind door A, B, or C. Also consider the fact that the contestant has selected door A. Now the three situations look like this:

	Door		
Case	A	B	C
1	Prize	Empty	Empty
2	Empty	Prize	Empty
3	Empty	Empty	Prize

In case 1, the contestant selected door A, and if the contestant switched after being shown that there was no prize behind either door B or door C, he'd lose. In case 2, the contestant selected door A, and Monty will open door C, so if the contestant would switch, he would win the prize. In case 3, the contestant selected door A, and Monty will open door B, so if the contestant would switch, he would win the prize. Hence, by switching, the probability of winning is $\frac{2}{3}$ and the probability of losing is $\frac{1}{3}$. The same reasoning can be used no matter which door you select.

You can simulate this problem by using three cards, say, an ace (prize) and two other cards. Have a person arrange the cards in a row and let you select a card. After the person turns over one of the cards (a nonace), then switch. Keep track of the number of times you win. You can also play this game on the Internet by going to the website www.stat.sc.edu/~west/javahtml/LetsMakeaDeal.html

Select the best answer.

5. When all subjects under study are used, the group is called a _____.

   a. Population
   b. Large group
   c. Sample
   d. Study group

6. When a population is divided into subgroups with similar characteristics and then a sample is obtained, this method is called _____ sampling.

   a. Random
   b. Systematic
   c. Stratified
   d. Cluster

7. Interviewing selected people at a local supermarket can be considered an example of _____ sampling.

   a. Random
   b. Systematic
   c. Convenience
   d. Stratified

Complete the following statements with the best answer.

8. In general, when one conducts sampling, the _____ the sample, the more representative it will be.

9. When samples are not representative, they are said to be _____.

10. When all residents of a street are interviewed for a survey, the sampling method used is _____.

Use Figure 14–12 in the Review Exercises (page 629) for Exercises 11 through 14.

11. Select a random sample of 12 people, and find the mean of the blood pressures of the individuals. Compare this with the population mean.

12. Select a systematic sample of 12 people, and compute the mean of their blood pressures. Compare this with the population mean.

13. Divide the individuals into subgroups of six males and six females. Find the means of their blood pressures. Compare these means with the population mean.

14. Select a cluster of 12 people, and find the mean of their blood pressures. Compare this with the population mean.

For Exercises 15 through 19, explain how each could be simulated by using random numbers.

15. A chess player wins 45% of his games.

16. A travel agency has a 5% cancellation rate.

17. Two players select a card from a deck with no face cards. The player who gets the higher card wins.

18. One player rolls two dice. The other player selects a card from a deck. Face cards count as 11 for a jack, 12 for a queen, and 13 for a king. The player with the higher total points wins.

19. Two players toss two coins. If they match, player 1 wins; otherwise, player 2 wins.

For Exercises 20 through 24, use random numbers to simulate the experiments. The number in parentheses is the number of times the experiment should be done.

20. A telephone solicitor finds that there is a 15% probability of selling her product over the phone. For every 20 calls, find the probability of making two sales in a row. (100)

21. A field goal kicker is successful in 65% of his kicks inside the 40-yard line. Find the probability of his kicking four field goals in a row. (40)

22. Two coins are tossed. Find the average number of times two tails will appear. (40)

23. A single card is drawn from a deck. Find the average number of times it takes to draw an ace. (30)

24. A bowler finds that there is a 30% probability that he will make a strike. For every 15 frames he bowls, find the probability of making two strikes. (30)

Critical Thinking Challenges

1. Explain why two different opinion polls might yield different results on a survey. Also, give an example of an opinion poll and explain how the data may have been collected.

2. Use a computer to generate random numbers to simulate the following real-life problem.

In a certain geographic region, 40% of the people have type O blood. On a certain day, the blood centre needs 4 pints of type O blood. On average, how many donors are needed to obtain 4 pints of type O blood?

Data Projects

Where appropriate, use Minitab, SPSS, the TI-83 Plus, the TI-84 Plus, or a computer program of your choice to complete the following exercises.

1. Using the rules given in Figure 14–11 on page 623 of your textbook, play the simulated bowling game at least 10 times. Each game consists of 10 frames.

   a. Analyze the results of the scores by finding the mean, median, mode, range, variance, and standard deviation.
   b. Draw a box plot and explain the nature of the distribution.
   c. Write several paragraphs explaining the results.
   d. Compare this simulation with real bowling. Do you think the game actually simulates bowling? Why or why not?

2. Select a sports game that you like to play or watch on television (e.g., baseball, golf, or hockey). Write a simulated version of the game, using random numbers or dice. Play the game several times and answer these questions.

   a. Does your simulated game represent the real game accurately?
   b. Is your game one of pure chance, or is strategy involved?
   c. What are some shortcomings of your game?
   d. What parts of the real game cannot be simulated in your game?
   e. Is there any way that you could improve your simulated game by changing some rules?

Answers to Applying the Concepts

Section 14–2 The White or Wheat Bread Debate

1. The researchers used a sample for their study.

2. Answers will vary. One possible answer is that we might have doubts about the validity of the study, since the baking company that conducted the experiment has an interest in the outcome of the experiment.

3. The sample was probably a convenience sample.

4. Answers will vary. One possible answer would be to use a simple random sample.

5. Answers will vary. One possible answer is that a list of women's names could be obtained from the city in which the women live. Then a simple random sample could be selected from this list.

6. The random assignment helps to spread variation among the groups. The random selection helps to generalize from the sample back to the population. These are two different issues.

Section 14–3 Smoking Bans and Profits

1. It is uncertain how public smoking bans affected tavern business in Ottawa, since the survey results were conflicting.

2. Since the data were collected in different ways, the survey results were bound to have different answers. Perceptions of the owners will definitely be different from an analysis of actual sales receipts, particularly if the owners assumed that the public smoking bans would hurt business.

3. Answers will vary. One possible answer is that it would be difficult to not allow surveys based on anecdotal responses to be published. At the same time, it would be good for those publishing such results to comment on the limitations of these surveys.

4. We can get results from a representative sample that offers misleading information about the population.

5. Answers will vary. One possible answer is that measurement error is important in survey sampling in order to give ranges for the population parameters that are being investigated.

Section 14–4 Simulations

1. A simulation uses a probability experiment to mimic a real-life situation.

2. Simulation techniques date back to ancient times.

3. It is definitely cost-effective to run simulations for expensive items such as airplanes and automobiles.

4. Simulation testing is safer, faster, and less expensive than many real-life testing situations.

5. Computer simulation techniques were developed in the mid-1940s.

6. Answers will vary. One possible answer is that some simulations are far less harmful than conducting an actual study on the real-life situation of interest.

7. Answers will vary. Simulations could have possibly prevented disasters such as the Hindenburg or the Space Shuttle disaster. For example, data analysis after the Space Shuttle disaster showed that there was a decent chance that something would go wrong on that flight.

8. Simulation theory is based in probability theory.

Appendix A

Algebra Review

A-1 Factorials

A-2 Summation Notation

A-3 The Line

A-1 Factorials

Definition and Properties of Factorials

The notation called factorial notation is used in probability. *Factorial notation* uses the exclamation point and involves multiplication. For example,

$$5! = 5 \cdot 4 \cdot 3 \cdot 2 \cdot 1 = 120$$
$$4! = 4 \cdot 3 \cdot 2 \cdot 1 = 24$$
$$3! = 3 \cdot 2 \cdot 1 = 6$$
$$2! = 2 \cdot 1 = 2$$
$$1! = 1$$

In general, a factorial is evaluated as follows:

$$n! = n(n-1)(n-2) \cdots 3 \cdot 2 \cdot 1$$

Note that the factorial is the product of n factors, with the number decreased by 1 for each factor.

One property of factorial notation is that it can be stopped at any point by using the exclamation point. For example,

$$
\begin{aligned}
5! &= 5 \cdot 4! & \text{since} && 4! &= 4 \cdot 3 \cdot 2 \cdot 1 \\
&= 5 \cdot 4 \cdot 3! & \text{since} && 3! &= 3 \cdot 2 \cdot 1 \\
&= 5 \cdot 4 \cdot 3 \cdot 2! & \text{since} && 2! &= 2 \cdot 1 \\
&= 5 \cdot 4 \cdot 3 \cdot 2 \cdot 1
\end{aligned}
$$

Thus,
$$
\begin{aligned}
n! &= n(n-1)! \\
&= n(n-1)(n-2)! \\
&= n(n-1)(n-2)(n-3)! \qquad \text{etc.}
\end{aligned}
$$

Another property of factorials is

$$0! = 1$$

This fact is needed for formulas.

Operations with Factorials

Factorials cannot be added or subtracted directly. They must be multiplied out. Then the products can be added or subtracted.

Example A-1

Evaluate $3! + 4!$.

Solution

$$
\begin{aligned}
3! + 4! &= (3 \cdot 2 \cdot 1) + (4 \cdot 3 \cdot 2 \cdot 1) \\
&= 6 + 24 = 30
\end{aligned}
$$

Note: $3! + 4! \neq 7!$, since $7! = 5040$.

Example A-2

Evaluate $5! - 3!$.

Solution

$$
\begin{aligned}
5! - 3! &= (5 \cdot 4 \cdot 3 \cdot 2 \cdot 1) - (3 \cdot 2 \cdot 1) \\
&= 120 - 6 = 114
\end{aligned}
$$

Note: $5! - 3! \neq 2!$, since $2! = 2$.

Factorials cannot be multiplied directly. Again, one must multiply them out and then multiply the products.

Example A-3

Evaluate $3! \cdot 2!$.

Solution

$$3! \cdot 2! = (3 \cdot 2 \cdot 1) \cdot (2 \cdot 1) = 6 \cdot 2 = 12$$

Note: $3! \cdot 2! \neq 6!$, since $6! = 720$.

Finally, factorials cannot be divided directly unless they are equal.

Example A-4

Evaluate $6! \div 3!$.

Solution

$$\frac{6!}{3!} = \frac{6 \cdot 5 \cdot 4 \cdot 3 \cdot 2 \cdot 1}{3 \cdot 2 \cdot 1} = \frac{720}{6} = 120$$

Note: $\dfrac{6!}{3!} \neq 2!$ since $2! = 2$

But $\dfrac{3!}{3!} = \dfrac{3 \cdot 2 \cdot 1}{3 \cdot 2 \cdot 1} = \dfrac{6}{6} = 1$

In division, one can take some shortcuts, as shown:

$$\frac{6!}{3!} = \frac{6 \cdot 5 \cdot 4 \cdot 3!}{3!} \quad \text{and} \quad \frac{3!}{3!} = 1$$
$$= 6 \cdot 5 \cdot 4 = 120$$

$$\frac{8!}{6!} = \frac{8 \cdot 7 \cdot 6!}{6!} \quad \text{and} \quad \frac{6!}{6!} = 1$$
$$= 8 \cdot 7 = 56$$

Another shortcut that can be used with factorials is cancellation, after factors have been expanded. For example,

$$\frac{7!}{(4!)(3!)} = \frac{7 \cdot 6 \cdot 5 \cdot 4!}{3 \cdot 2 \cdot 1 \cdot 4!}$$

Now cancel both instances of 4!. Then cancel the $3 \cdot 2$ in the denominator with the 6 in the numerator.

$$\frac{7 \cdot \overset{1}{6} \cdot 5 \cdot \overset{1}{4!}}{\underset{1}{3} \cdot \underset{1}{2} \cdot 1 \cdot \underset{1}{4!}} = 7 \cdot 5 = 35$$

Example A–5

Evaluate $10! \div (6!)(4!)$.

Solution

$$\frac{10!}{(6!)(4!)} = \frac{10 \cdot \overset{3}{9} \cdot \overset{1}{8} \cdot 7 \cdot \overset{1}{6!}}{\underset{1}{4} \cdot \underset{1}{3} \cdot 2 \cdot 1 \cdot \underset{1}{6!}} = 10 \cdot 3 \cdot 7 = 210$$

Exercises

Evaluate each expression.

A–1. 9!

A–2. 7!

A–3. 5!

A–4. 0!

A–5. 1!

A–6. 3!

A–7. $\dfrac{12!}{9!}$

A–8. $\dfrac{10!}{2!}$

A–9. $\dfrac{5!}{3!}$

A–10. $\dfrac{11!}{7!}$

A–11. $\dfrac{9!}{(4!)(5!)}$

A–12. $\dfrac{10!}{(7!)(3!)}$

A–13. $\dfrac{8!}{(4!)(4!)}$

A–14. $\dfrac{15!}{(12!)(3!)}$

A–15. $\dfrac{10!}{(10!)(0!)}$

A–16. $\dfrac{5!}{(3!)(2!)(1!)}$

A–17. $\dfrac{8!}{(3!)(3!)(2!)}$

A–18. $\dfrac{11!}{(7!)(2!)(2!)}$

A–19. $\dfrac{10!}{(3!)(2!)(5!)}$

A–20. $\dfrac{6!}{(2!)(2!)(2!)}$

A–2 Summation Notation

In mathematics, the symbol Σ (Greek capital letter sigma) means to add or find the sum. For example, ΣX means to add the numbers represented by the variable X. Thus, when X represents 5, 8, 2, 4, and 6, then ΣX means $5 + 8 + 2 + 4 + 6 = 25$.

Sometimes, a subscript notation is used, such as

$$\sum_{i=1}^{5} X_i$$

This notation means to find the sum of five numbers represented by X, as shown:

$$\sum_{i=1}^{5} X_i = X_1 + X_2 + X_3 + X_4 + X_5$$

When the number of values is not known, the unknown number can be represented by n, such as

$$\sum_{i=1}^{n} X_i = X_1 + X_2 + X_3 + \cdots + X_n$$

There are several important types of summation used in statistics. The notation ΣX^2 means to square each value before summing. For example, if the values of the X's are 2, 8, 6, 1, and 4, then

$$\Sigma X^2 = 2^2 + 8^2 + 6^2 + 1^2 + 4^2$$
$$= 4 + 64 + 36 + 1 + 16 = 121$$

The notation $(\Sigma X)^2$ means to find the sum of X's and then square the answer. For instance, if the values for X are 2, 8, 6, 1, and 4, then

$$(\Sigma X)^2 = (2 + 8 + 6 + 1 + 4)^2$$
$$= (21)^2 = 441$$

Another important use of summation notation is in finding the mean (shown in Section 3–2). The mean $\bar{X}$ is defined as

$$\bar{X} = \frac{\Sigma X}{n}$$

For example, to find the mean of 12, 8, 7, 3, and 10, use the formula and substitute the values, as shown:

$$\bar{X} = \frac{\Sigma X}{n} = \frac{12 + 8 + 7 + 3 + 10}{5} = \frac{40}{5} = 8$$

The notation $\Sigma(X - \overline{X})^2$ means to perform the following steps.

STEP 1 Find the mean.

STEP 2 Subtract the mean from each value.

STEP 3 Square the answers.

STEP 4 Find the sum.

Example A–6

Find the value of $\Sigma(X - \overline{X})^2$ for the values 12, 8, 7, 3, and 10 of X.

Solution

STEP 1 Find the mean.

$$\overline{X} = \frac{12 + 8 + 7 + 3 + 10}{5} = \frac{40}{5} = 8$$

STEP 2 Subtract the mean from each value.

$$12 - 8 = 4 \qquad 7 - 8 = -1 \qquad 10 - 8 = 2$$
$$8 - 8 = 0 \qquad 3 - 8 = -5$$

STEP 3 Square the answers.

$$4^2 = 16 \qquad (-1)^2 = 1 \qquad 2^2 = 4$$
$$0^2 = 0 \qquad (-5)^2 = 25$$

STEP 4 Find the sum.

$$16 + 0 + 1 + 25 + 4 = 46$$

Example A–7

Find $\Sigma(X - \overline{X})^2$ for the following values of X: 5, 7, 2, 1, 3, 6.

Solution

Find the mean:

$$\overline{X} = \frac{5 + 7 + 2 + 1 + 3 + 6}{6} = \frac{24}{6} = 4$$

Then the steps in Example A–6 can be shortened as follows:

$$\begin{aligned}
\Sigma(X - \overline{X})^2 &= (5 - 4)^2 + (7 - 4)^2 + (2 - 4)^2 \\
&\quad + (1 - 4)^2 + (3 - 4)^2 + (6 - 4)^2 \\
&= 1^2 + 3^2 + (-2)^2 + (-3)^2 \\
&\quad + (-1)^2 + 2^2 \\
&= 1 + 9 + 4 + 9 + 1 + 4 = 28
\end{aligned}$$

Exercises

For each set of values, find ΣX, ΣX^2, $(\Sigma X)^2$, and $\Sigma(X - \overline{X})^2$.

A–21. 9, 17, 32, 16, 8, 2, 9, 7, 3, 18

A–22. 4, 12, 9, 13, 0, 6, 2, 10

A–23. 5, 12, 8, 3, 4

A–24. 6, 2, 18, 30, 31, 42, 16, 5

A–25. 80, 76, 42, 53, 77

A–26. 123, 132, 216, 98, 146, 114

A–27. 53, 72, 81, 42, 63, 71, 73, 85, 98, 55

A–28. 43, 32, 116, 98, 120

A–29. 12, 52, 36, 81, 63, 74

A–30. -9, -12, 18, 0, -2, -15

A–3 The Line

The following figure shows the *rectangular coordinate system* or *Cartesian plane*. This figure consists of two axes: the horizontal axis, called the x axis, and the vertical axis, called the y axis. Each axis has numerical scales. The point of intersection of the axes is called the *origin*.

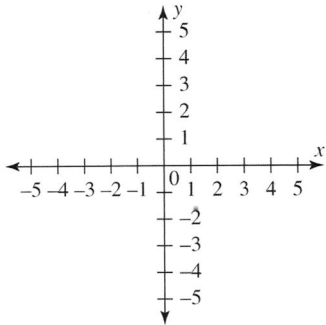

Points can be graphed by using coordinates. For example, the notation for point $P(3, 2)$ means that the x coordinate is 3 and the y coordinate is 2. Hence, P is located at the intersection of $x = 3$ and $y = 2$, as shown.

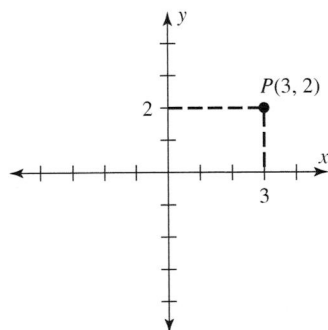

Other points, such as $Q(-5, 2)$, $R(4, 1)$, and $S(-3, -4)$, can be plotted, as shown in the next figure.

When a point lies on the y axis, the x coordinate is 0, as in $(0, 6)(0, -3)$, etc. When a point lies on the x axis, the y coordinate is 0, as in $(6, 0)(-8, 0)$, etc., as shown at the top of the next page.

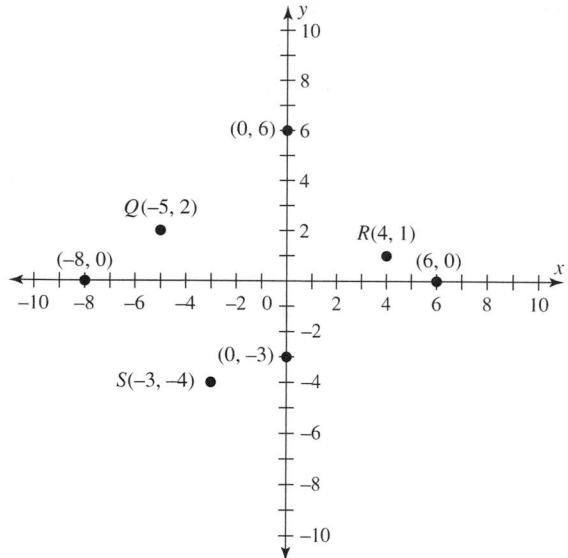

Two points determine a line. There are two properties of a line: its slope and its equation. The *slope m* of a line is determined by the ratio of the rise (called Δy) to the run (Δx).

$$m = \frac{\text{rise}}{\text{run}} = \frac{\Delta y}{\Delta x}$$

For example, the slope of the line shown below is $\frac{3}{2}$, or 1.5, since the height Δy is 3 units and the run Δx is 2 units.

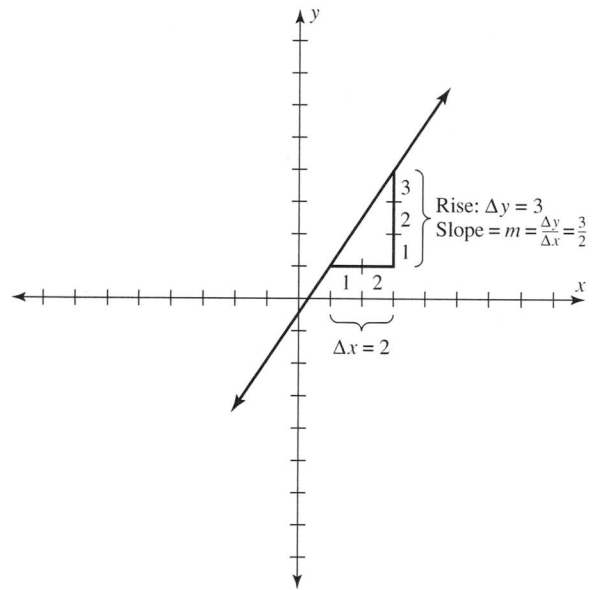

The slopes of lines can be positive, negative, or zero. A line going uphill from left to right has a positive slope. A line going downhill from left to right has a negative slope. And a line that is horizontal has a slope of zero.

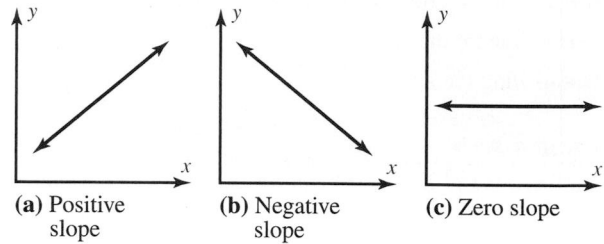

(a) Positive slope   **(b)** Negative slope   **(c)** Zero slope

A point b where the line crosses the x axis is called the *x-intercept* and has the coordinates $(b, 0)$. A point a where the line crosses the y axis is called the *y intercept* and has the coordinates $(0, a)$.

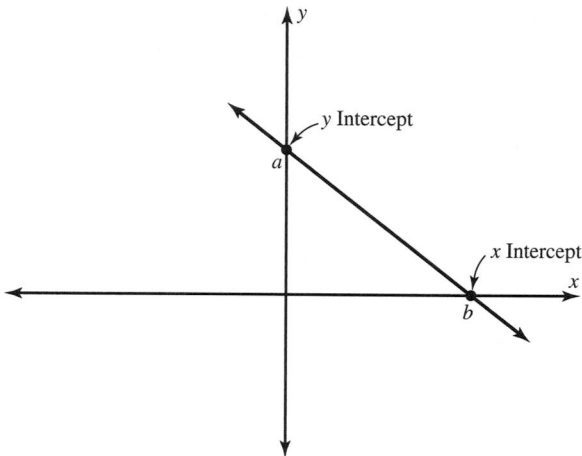

Every line has a unique equation of the form $y = a + bx$. For example, the equations

$$y = 5 + 3x$$
$$y = 8.6 + 3.2x$$
$$y = 5.2 - 6.1x$$

all represent different, unique lines. The number represented by a is the y intercept point; the number represented by b is the slope. The line whose equation is $y = 3 + 2x$ has a y intercept at 3 and a slope of 2, or $\frac{2}{1}$. This line can be shown as in the following graph.

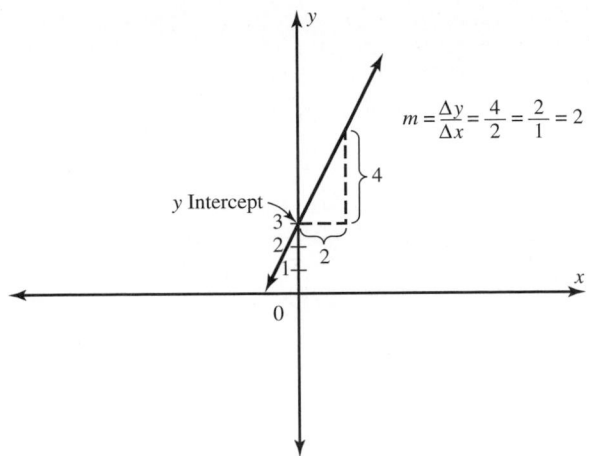

If two points are known, then the graph of the line can be plotted. For example, to find the graph of a line passing through the points $P(2, 1)$ and $Q(3, 5)$, plot the points and connect them as shown below.

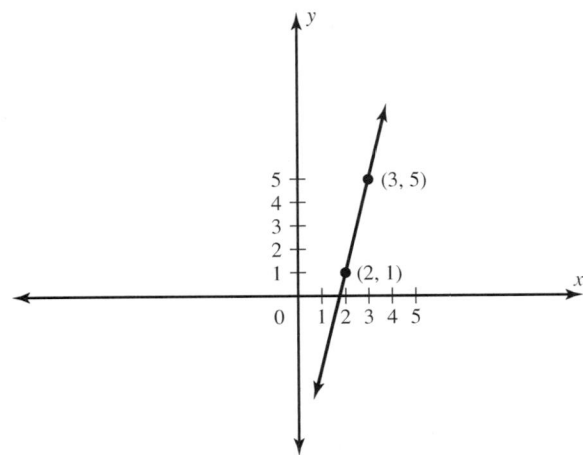

Given the equation of a line, one can graph the line by finding two points and then plotting them.

Example A–8

Plot the graph of the line whose equation is $y = 3 + 2x$.

Solution

Select any number as an x value, and substitute it in the equation to get the corresponding y value. Let $x = 0$.

Then

$$y = 3 + 2x = 3 + 2(0) = 3$$

Hence, when $x = 0$, then $y = 3$, and the line passes through the point $(0, 3)$.

Now select any other value of x, say, $x = 2$.

$$y = 3 + 2x = 3 + 2(2) = 7$$

Hence, a second point is $(2, 7)$. Then plot the points and graph the line.

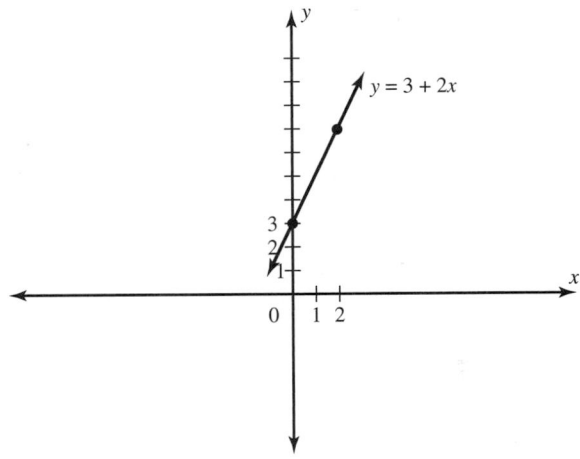

Exercises

Plot the line passing through each set of points.

A–31. $P(3, 2), Q(1, 6)$ **A–34.** $P(-1, -2), Q(-7, 8)$

A–32. $P(0, 5), Q(8, 0)$ **A–35.** $P(6, 3), Q(10, 3)$

A–33. $P(-2, 4), Q(3, 6)$

Find at least two points on each line, and then graph the line containing these points.

A–36. $y = 5 + 2x$ **A–39.** $y = -2 - 2x$

A–37. $y = -1 + x$ **A–40.** $y = 4 - 3x$

A–38. $y = 3 + 4x$

Appendix B-1
Writing the Research Report

After conducting a statistical study, a researcher must write a final report explaining how the study was conducted and giving the results. The formats of research reports, theses, and dissertations vary from school to school; however, they tend to follow the general format explained here.

Front Materials

The front materials typically include the following items:

Title page
Copyright page
Acknowledgments
Table of contents
Table of appendixes
List of tables
List of figures

Chapter 1: Nature and Background of the Study

This chapter should introduce the reader to the nature of the study and present some discussion on the background. It should contain the following information:

Introduction
Statement of the problem
Background of the problem
Rationale for the study
Research questions and/or hypotheses
Assumptions, limitations, and delimitations
Definitions of terms

Chapter 2: Review of Literature

This chapter should explain what has been done in previous research related to the study. It should contain the following information:

Prior research
Related literature

Chapter 3: Methodology

This chapter should explain how the study was conducted. It should contain the following information:

Development of questionnaires, tests, survey instruments, etc.
Definition of the population
Sampling methods used
How the data were collected
Research design used
Statistical tests that will be used to analyze the data

Chapter 4: Analysis of Data

This chapter should explain the results of the statistical analysis of the data. It should state whether the null hypothesis should be rejected. Any statistical tables used to analyze the data should be included here.

Chapter 5: Summary, Conclusions, and Recommendations

This chapter summarizes the results of the study and explains any conclusions that have resulted from the statistical analysis of the data. The researchers should cite and explain any shortcomings of the study. Recommendations obtained from the study should be included here, and further studies should be suggested.

Appendix B-2

Bayes' Theorem

Objective 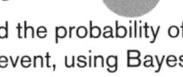 B-1

Find the probability of an event, using Bayes' theorem.

Given two dependent events A and B, the previous formulas for conditional probability allow one to find $P(A \text{ and } B)$, or $P(B|A)$. Related to these formulas is a rule developed by the English Presbyterian minister Thomas Bayes (1702–61). The rule is known as **Bayes' theorem.**

It is possible, given the outcome of the second event in a sequence of two events, to determine the probability of various possibilities for the first event. In Example 4–31, there were two boxes, each containing red balls and blue balls. A box was selected and a ball was drawn. The example asked for the probability that the ball selected was red. Now, a different question can be asked: If the ball is red, what is the probability it came from box 1? In this case, the outcome is known, a red ball was selected, and one is asked to find the probability that it is a result of a previous event, that it

came from box 1. Bayes' theorem can enable one to compute this probability and can be explained by using tree diagrams.

The tree diagram for the solution of Example 4–31 is shown in Figure B–1, along with the appropriate notation and the corresponding probabilities. In this case, A_1 is the event of selecting box 1, A_2 is the event of selecting box 2, R is the event of selecting a red ball, and B is the event of selecting a blue ball.

To answer the question "If the ball selected is red, what is the probability that it came from box 1?" the two formulas

$$P(B|A) = \frac{P(A \text{ and } B)}{P(A)} \tag{1}$$

$$P(A \text{ and } B) = P(A) \cdot P(B|A) \tag{2}$$

can be used. The notation that will be used is that of Example 4–31, shown in Figure B–1. Finding the probability that box 1 was selected given that the ball selected was red can be written symbolically as $P(A_1|R)$. By formula 1,

$$P(A_1|R) = \frac{P(R \text{ and } A_1)}{P(R_1)}$$

Note: $P(R \text{ and } A_1) = P(A_1 \text{ and } R)$.

Figure B–1

Tree Diagram for Example 4–31

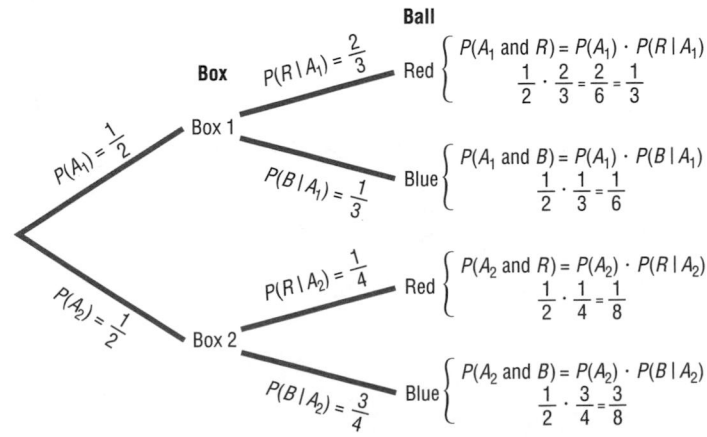

By formula 2,

$$P(A_1 \text{ and } R) = P(A_1) \cdot P(R|A_1)$$

and

$$P(R) = P(A_1 \text{ and } R) + P(A_2 \text{ and } R)$$

as shown in Figure B–1; P(R) was found by adding the products of the probabilities of the branches in which a red ball was selected. Now,

$$P(A_1 \text{ and } R) = P(A_1) \cdot P(R|A_1)$$
$$P(A_2 \text{ and } R) = P(A_2) \cdot P(R|A_2)$$

Substituting these values in the original formula for $P(A_1|R)$, one gets

$$P(A_1|R) = \frac{P(A_1) \cdot P(R|A_1)}{P(A_1) \cdot P(R|A_1) + P(A_2) \cdot P(R|A_2)}$$

Refer to Figure B–1. The numerator of the fraction is the product of the top branch of the tree diagram, which consists of selecting a red ball and selecting box 1. And the denominator is the sum of the products of the two branches of the tree where the red ball was selected.

Using this formula and the probability values shown in Figure B–1, one can find the probability that box 1 was selected given that the ball was red, as shown.

$$P(A_1|R) = \frac{P(A_1) \cdot P(R|A_1)}{P(A_1) \cdot P(R|A_1) + P(A_2) \cdot P(R|A_2)}$$

$$= \frac{\frac{1}{2} \cdot \frac{2}{3}}{\frac{1}{2} \cdot \frac{2}{3} + \frac{1}{2} \cdot \frac{1}{4}} = \frac{\frac{1}{3}}{\frac{1}{3} + \frac{1}{8}} = \frac{\frac{1}{3}}{\frac{8}{24} + \frac{3}{24}} = \frac{\frac{1}{3}}{\frac{11}{24}}$$

$$= \frac{1}{3} \div \frac{11}{24} = \frac{1}{\underset{1}{3}} \cdot \frac{\overset{8}{24}}{11} = \frac{8}{11}$$

This formula is a simplified version of Bayes' theorem.

Before Bayes' theorem is stated, another example is shown.

Example B–1

A shipment of two boxes, each containing six telephones, is received by a store. Box 1 contains one defective phone, and box 2 contains two defective phones. After the boxes are unpacked, a phone is selected and found to be defective. Find the probability that it came from box 2.

Solution

STEP 1 Select the proper notation. Let A_1 represent box 1 and A_2 represent box 2. Let D represent a defective phone and ND represent a phone that is not defective.

STEP 2 Draw a tree diagram and find the corresponding probabilities for each branch. The probability of selecting box 1 is $\frac{1}{2}$, and the probability of selecting box 2 is $\frac{1}{2}$. Since there is one defective phone in box 1, the probability of selecting it is $\frac{1}{6}$. The probability of selecting a nondefective phone from box 1 is $\frac{5}{6}$.

Since there are two defective phones in box 2, the probability of selecting a defective phone from box 2 is $\frac{2}{6}$, or $\frac{1}{3}$; and the probability of selecting a nondefective phone is $\frac{4}{6}$, or $\frac{2}{3}$. The tree diagram is shown in Figure B–2.

STEP 3 Write the corresponding formula. Since the example is asking for the probability that, given a defective phone, it came from box 2, the corresponding formula is as shown.

$$P(A_2|D) = \frac{P(A_2) \cdot P(D|A_2)}{P(A_1) \cdot P(D|A_1) + P(A_2) \cdot P(D|A_2)}$$

$$= \frac{\frac{1}{2} \cdot \frac{2}{6}}{\frac{1}{2} \cdot \frac{1}{6} + \frac{1}{2} \cdot \frac{2}{6}} = \frac{\frac{1}{6}}{\frac{1}{12} + \frac{2}{12}} = \frac{\frac{1}{6}}{\frac{3}{12}}$$

$$= \frac{1}{6} \div \frac{3}{12} = \frac{1}{\underset{1}{6}} \cdot \frac{\overset{2}{12}}{3} = \frac{2}{3}$$

Figure B–2

Tree Diagram for Example B–1

Bayes' theorem can be generalized to events with three or more outcomes and formally stated as in the next box.

Bayes' theorem For two events A and B, where event B follows event A, event A can occur in $A_1, A_2, \ldots, A_n$ mutually exclusive ways, and event B can occur in $B_1, B_2, \ldots, B_m$ mutually exclusive ways,

$$P(A_1|B_1) = \frac{P(A_1) \cdot P(B_1|A_1)}{[P(A_1) \cdot P(B_1|A_1) + P(A_2) \cdot P(B_1|A_2)}{+ \cdots + P(A_n) \cdot P(B_1|A_n)]}$$

for any specific events A_1 and B_1.

The numerator is the product of the probabilities on the branch of the tree that consists of outcomes A_1 and B_1. The denominator is the sum of the products of the probabilities of the branches containing B_1 and A_1, B_1 and A_2, ..., B_1 and A_n.

Example B–2

On a game show, a contestant can select one of four boxes. Box 1 contains one $100 bill and nine $1 bills. Box 2 contains two $100 bills and eight $1 bills. Box 3 contains three $100 bills and seven $1 bills. Box 4 contains five $100 bills and five $1 bills. The contestant selects a box at random and selects a bill from the box at random. If a $100 bill is selected, find the probability that it came from box 4.

Solution

STEP 1 Select the proper notation. Let B_1, B_2, B_3, and B_4 represent the boxes and 100 and 1 represent the values of the bills in the boxes.

STEP 2 Draw a tree diagram and find the corresponding probabilities. The probability of selecting each box is $\frac{1}{4}$, or 0.25. The probabilities of selecting the $100 bill from each box, respectively, are $\frac{1}{10} = 0.1$, $\frac{2}{10} = 0.2$, $\frac{3}{10} = 0.3$, and $\frac{5}{10} = 0.5$. The tree diagram is shown in Figure B–3.

STEP 3 Using Bayes' theorem, write the corresponding formula. Since the example asks for the probability that box 4 was selected, given that $100 was obtained, the corresponding formula is as follows:

$$P(B_4|100) = \frac{P(B_4) \cdot P(100|B_4)}{[P(B_1) \cdot P(100|B_1) + P(B_2) \cdot P(100|B_2)}{+ P(B_3) \cdot P(100|B_3) + P(B_4) \cdot P(100|B_4)]}$$

$$= \frac{0.125}{0.025 + 0.05 + 0.075 + 0.125}$$

$$= \frac{0.125}{0.275} = 0.455$$

Figure B–3

Tree Diagram for Example B–2

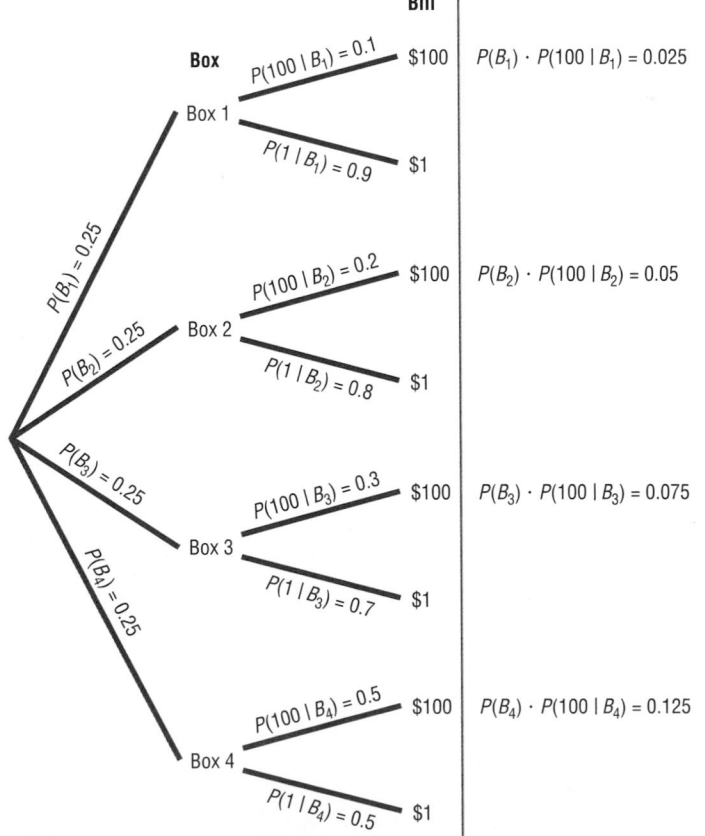

In Example B–2, the original probability of selecting box 4 was 0.25. However, once additional information was obtained—and the condition was considered, that a $100 bill was selected—the revised probability of selecting box 4 became 0.455.

Bayes' theorem can be used to revise probabilities of events once additional information becomes known. Bayes' theorem is used as the basis for a branch of statistics called *Bayesian decision making,* which includes the use of subjective probabilities in making statistical inferences.

Exercises

B–1. An appliance store purchases electric ranges from two companies. From company A, 500 ranges are purchased and 2% are defective. From company B, 850 ranges are purchased and 2% are defective. Given that a range is defective, find the probability that it came from company B.

B–2. Two manufacturers supply blankets to emergency relief organizations. Manufacturer A supplies 3000 blankets, and 4% are irregular in workmanship. Manufacturer B supplies 2400 blankets, and 7% are found to be irregular. Given that a blanket is irregular, find the probability that it came from manufacturer B.

B–3. A test for a certain disease is found to be 95% accurate, meaning that it will correctly diagnose the disease in 95 out of 100 people who have the ailment. For a certain segment of the population, the incidence of the disease is 9%. If a person tests positive, find the probability that the person actually has the disease. The test is also 95% accurate for a negative result.

B–4. Using the test in Exercise B–3, if a person tests negative for the disease, find the probability that the person actually has the disease. Remember, 9% of the population has the disease.

B–5. A corporation has three methods of training employees. Because of time, space, and location, it sends 20% of its employees to location A, 35% to location B, and 45% to location C. Location A has an 80% success rate. That is, 80% of the employees who complete the course will pass the licensing exam. Location B has a 75% success rate, and location C has a 60% success rate. If a person has passed the exam, find the probability that the person went to location B.

B–6. In Exercise B–5, if a person failed the exam, find the probability that the person went to location C.

B–7. A store purchases baseball hats from three different manufacturers. In manufacturer A's box, there are 12 blue hats, 6 red hats, and 6 green hats. In manufacturer B's box, there are 10 blue hats, 10 red hats, and 4 green hats. In manufacturer C's box, there are 8 blue hats, 8 red hats, and 8 green hats. A box is selected at random, and a hat is selected at random from that box. If the hat is red, find the probability that it came from manufacturer A's box.

B–8. In Exercise B–7, if the hat selected is green, find the probability that it came from manufacturer B's box.

B–9. A driver has three ways to get from one city to another. There is an 80% probability of encountering a traffic jam on route 1, a 60% probability on route 2, and a 30% probability on route 3. Because of other factors, such as distance and speed limits, the driver uses route 1 just 50% of the time and routes 2 and 3 each 25% of the time. If the driver calls the dispatcher to inform him that she is in a traffic jam, find the probability that she has selected route 1.

B–10. In Exercise B–9, if the driver did not encounter a traffic jam, find the probability that she selected route 3.

B–11. A store owner purchases telephones from two companies. From company A, 350 telephones are purchased and 2% are defective. From company B, 1050 telephones are purchased and 4% are defective. Given that a phone is defective, find the probability that it came from company B.

B–12. Two manufacturers supply food to a large cafeteria. Manufacturer A supplies 2400 cans of soup, and 3% are found to be dented. Manufacturer B supplies 3600 cans, and 1% are found to be dented. Given that a can of soup is dented, find the probability that it came from manufacturer B.

Appendix B–3

Alternate Approach to the Standard Normal Distribution

The following procedure may be used to replace the cumulative area to the left procedure shown in Section 6–3. This method determines areas from the mean where $z = 0$.

Finding Areas Under the Standard Normal Distribution

For the solution of problems using the standard normal distribution, a four-step procedure may be used with the use of the Procedure Table shown.

STEP 1   Sketch the normal curve and label.

STEP 2   Shade the area desired.

STEP 3   Find the figure that matches the shaded area from the following procedure table.

STEP 4   Follow the directions given in the appropriate block of the procedure table to get the desired area.

Note: Table B–1 gives the area between 0 and any z score to the right of 0, and all areas are positive.

There are seven basic types of problems and all seven are summarized in the Procedure Table, with appropriate examples.

Procedure Table

1. Between 0 and any z score:

Look up the z score in the table to get the area.

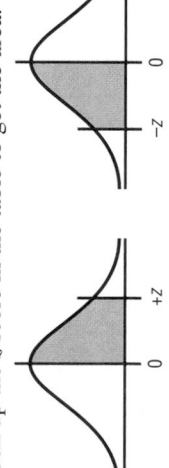

2. In any tail:

a. Look up the z score to get the area.
b. Subtract the area from 0.5000.

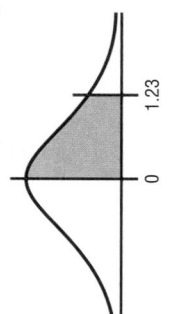

3. Between two z scores on the same side of the mean:

a. Look up both z scores to get the areas.
b. Subtract the smaller area from the larger area.

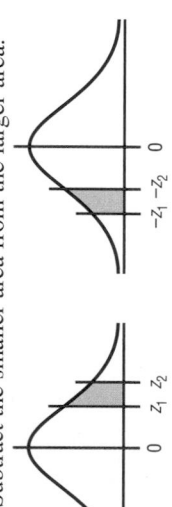

4. Between two z scores on opposite sides of the mean:

a. Look up both z scores to get the areas.
b. Add the areas.

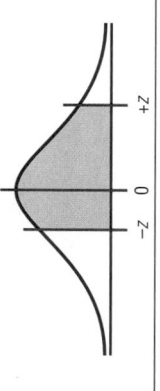

Examples

B–3–1. Find the area between $z = 0$ and $z = 1.23$.

Look up area from $z = 0$ to $z = 1.23$ on Table B-1, as shown below.

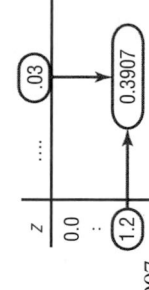

The area between $z = 0$ and $z = 1.23$ is 0.3907.

B–3–2: Find the area to the left of $z = -2.37$.

Look up area from $z = 0$ to $z = 2.37$ on Table B-1, as shown below.

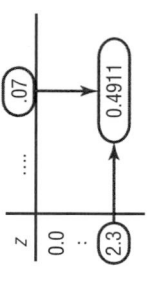

The area from $z = 0$ to $z = 2.37$ is the same as the area from $z = 0$ to $z = -2.37$.
Therefore, the area to the left of $z = -2.37 = 0.5000 - 0.4911 = 0.0089$.

B–3–3: Find the area between $z = 1.23$ and $z = 2.37$.

Look up areas for $z = 0$ to $z = 1.23$ and $z = 0$ to $z = 2.37$, as shown in B–3–1 and B–3–2, respectively.
The area between $z = 1.23$ and $z = 2.37$
$= 0.4911 - 0.3907 = 0.1004$.

B–3–4: Find the area between $z = -1.23$ and $z = 2.37$.

Look up areas for $z = 0$ to $z = 1.23$ and $z = 0$ to $z = 2.37$, as shown in B–3–1 and B–3–2, respectively.

The area between $z = -1.23$ and $z = 2.37$
$= 0.3907 + 0.4911 = 0.8818$.

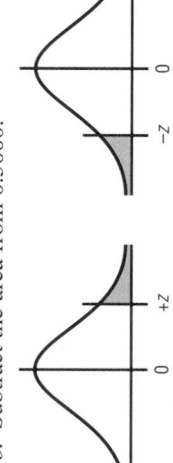

5. To the left of any z score, where z is greater than the mean:

   a. Look up the z score to get the area.

   b. Add 0.5000 to the area.

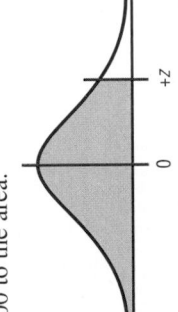

B–3–5: Find the area to the left of $z = 2.37$.

   Look up area for $z = 2.37$, as shown in B–3–2.
The area to the left of $z = 0$ is 0.5000.

   The area to the left of $z = 2.37$
$= 0.4911 + 0.5000 = 0.9911$.

6. To the right of any z score, where z is less than the mean:

   a. Look up the area in the table to get the area.

   b. Add 0.5000 to the area.

B–3–6: Find the area to the right of $z = -2.37$.

   Look up area for $z = 2.37$, as shown in B–3–2.
The area to the right of $z = 0$ is 0.5000.

   The area to the right of $z = -2.37$
$= 0.4911 + 0.5000 = 0.9911$.

7. In any two tails:

   a. Look up the z scores in the table to get the areas.

   b. Subtract both areas from 0.5000.

   c. Add the answers.

B–3–7: Find the area to the left of $z = -1.23$ and to the right of $z = 2.37$.

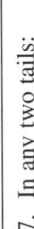

   Look up areas for $z = 0$ to $z = 1.23$ and $z = 0$ to $z = 2.37$, as shown in B–3–1 and B–3–2, respectively.

   Area to the left of $z = -1.23 = 0.5000 - 0.3907 = 0.1093$.
Area to the right of $z = 2.37 = 0.5000 - 0.4911 = 0.0089$.

   The area to the left of $z = -1.23$ and to the right of $z = 2.37$
$= 0.1093 + 0.0089 = 0.1182$.

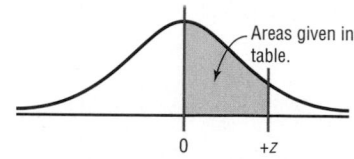

Areas given in table.

Table B-1 The Standard Normal Distribution

z	0.00	.01	.02	.03	.04	.05	.06	.07	.08	.09
0.0	0.0000	0.0040	0.0080	0.0120	0.0160	0.0199	0.0239	0.0279	0.0319	0.0359
0.1	0.0398	0.0438	0.0478	0.0517	0.0557	0.0596	0.0636	0.0675	0.0714	0.0753
0.2	0.0793	0.0832	0.0871	0.0910	0.0948	0.0987	0.1026	0.1064	0.1103	0.1141
0.3	0.1179	0.1217	0.1255	0.1293	0.1331	0.1368	0.1406	0.1443	0.1480	0.1517
0.4	0.1554	0.1591	0.1628	0.1664	0.1700	0.1736	0.1772	0.1808	0.1844	0.1879
0.5	0.1915	0.1950	0.1985	0.2019	0.2054	0.2088	0.2123	0.2157	0.2190	0.2224
0.6	0.2257	0.2291	0.2324	0.2357	0.2389	0.2422	0.2454	0.2486	0.2517	0.2549
0.7	0.2580	0.2611	0.2642	0.2673	0.2704	0.2734	0.2764	0.2794	0.2823	0.2852
0.8	0.2881	0.2910	0.2939	0.2967	0.2995	0.3023	0.3051	0.3078	0.3106	0.3133
0.9	0.3159	0.3186	0.3212	0.3238	0.3264	0.3289	0.3315	0.3340	0.3365	0.3389
1.0	0.3413	0.3438	0.3461	0.3485	0.3508	0.3531	0.3554	0.3577	0.3599	0.3621
1.1	0.3643	0.3665	0.3686	0.3708	0.3729	0.3749	0.3770	0.3790	0.3810	0.3830
1.2	0.3849	0.3869	0.3888	0.3907	0.3925	0.3944	0.3962	0.3980	0.3997	0.4015
1.3	0.4032	0.4049	0.4066	0.4082	0.4099	0.4115	0.4131	0.4147	0.4162	0.4177
1.4	0.4192	0.4207	0.4222	0.4236	0.4251	0.4265	0.4279	0.4292	0.4306	0.4319
1.5	0.4332	0.4345	0.4357	0.4370	0.4382	0.4394	0.4406	0.4418	0.4429	0.4441
1.6	0.4452	0.4463	0.4474	0.4484	0.4495 *	0.4505	0.4515	0.4525	0.4535	0.4545
1.7	0.4554	0.4564	0.4573	0.4582	0.4591	0.4599	0.4608	0.4616	0.4625	0.4633
1.8	0.4641	0.4649	0.4656	0.4664	0.4671	0.4678	0.4686	0.4693	0.4699	0.4706
1.9	0.4713	0.4719	0.4726	0.4732	0.4738	0.4744	0.4750	0.4756	0.4761	0.4767
2.0	0.4772	0.4778	0.4783	0.4788	0.4793	0.4798	0.4803	0.4808	0.4812	0.4817
2.1	0.4821	0.4826	0.4830	0.4834	0.4838	0.4842	0.4846	0.4850	0.4854	0.4857
2.2	0.4861	0.4864	0.4868	0.4871	0.4875	0.4878	0.4881	0.4884	0.4887	0.4890
2.3	0.4893	0.4896	0.4898	0.4901	0.4904	0.4906	0.4909	0.4911	0.4913	0.4916
2.4	0.4918	0.4920	0.4922	0.4925	0.4927	0.4929	0.4931	0.4932	0.4934	0.4936
2.5	0.4938	0.4940	0.4941	0.4943	0.4945	0.4946	0.4948	0.4949 *	0.4951	0.4952
2.6	0.4953	0.4955	0.4956	0.4957	0.4959	0.4960	0.4961	0.4962	0.4963	0.4964
2.7	0.4965	0.4966	0.4967	0.4968	0.4969	0.4970	0.4971	0.4972	0.4973	0.4974
2.8	0.4974	0.4975	0.4976	0.4977	0.4977	0.4978	0.4979	0.4979	0.4980	0.4981
2.9	0.4981	0.4982	0.4982	0.4983	0.4984	0.4984	0.4985	0.4985	0.4986	0.4986
3.0	0.4987	0.4987	0.4987	0.4988	0.4988	0.4989	0.4989	0.4989	0.4990	0.4990
3.1	0.4990	0.4991	0.4991	0.4991	0.4992	0.4992	0.4992	0.4992	0.4993	0.4993
3.2	0.4993	0.4993	0.4994	0.4994	0.4994	0.4994	0.4994	0.4995	0.4995	0.4995
3.3	0.4995	0.4995	0.4995	0.4996	0.4996	0.4996	0.4996	0.4996	0.4996	0.4997
3.4	0.4997	0.4997	0.4997	0.4997	0.4997	0.4997	0.4997	0.4997	0.4997	0.4998
3.5	0.4998	0.4998	0.4998	0.4998	0.4998	0.4998	0.4998	0.4998	0.4998	0.4998
3.6	0.4998	0.4998	0.4999	0.4999	0.4999	0.4999	0.4999	0.4999	0.4999	0.4999

Note: Use 0.4999 for values above z = 3.69

z score	Area
1.645	0.4500
2.575	0.4950

Appendix C

Tables

Table A   Factorials

Table B   The Binomial Distribution

Table C   The Poisson Distribution

Table D   Random Numbers

Tables E–1   Standard Normal Distribution
and E–2

Table F   The t Distribution

Table G   The Chi-Square Distribution

Table H   The F Distribution

Table I   Critical Values for PPMC

Table J   Critical Values for the Sign Test

Table K   Critical Values for the Wilcoxon Signed-Rank Test

Table L   Critical Values for the Rank Correlation Coefficient

Table M   Critical Values for the Number of Runs

Table N   Critical Values for the Tukey Test

Table A	Factorials
n	$n!$
0	1
1	1
2	2
3	6
4	24
5	120
6	720
7	5,040
8	40,320
9	362,880
10	3,628,800
11	39,916,800
12	479,001,600
13	6,227,020,800
14	87,178,291,200
15	1,307,674,368,000
16	20,922,789,888,000
17	355,687,428,096,000
18	6,402,373,705,728,000
19	121,645,100,408,832,000
20	2,432,902,008,176,640,000

Table B		The Binomial Distribution										

		p										
n	*x*	0.05	0.1	0.2	0.3	0.4	0.5	0.6	0.7	0.8	0.9	0.95
2	0	0.902	0.810	0.640	0.490	0.360	0.250	0.160	0.090	0.040	0.010	0.002
	1	0.095	0.180	0.320	0.420	0.480	0.500	0.480	0.420	0.320	0.180	0.095
	2	0.002	0.010	0.040	0.090	0.160	0.250	0.360	0.490	0.640	0.810	0.902
3	0	0.857	0.729	0.512	0.343	0.216	0.125	0.064	0.027	0.008	0.001	
	1	0.135	0.243	0.384	0.441	0.432	0.375	0.288	0.189	0.096	0.027	0.007
	2	0.007	0.027	0.096	0.189	0.288	0.375	0.432	0.441	0.384	0.243	0.135
	3		0.001	0.008	0.027	0.064	0.125	0.216	0.343	0.512	0.729	0.857
4	0	0.815	0.656	0.410	0.240	0.130	0.062	0.026	0.008	0.002		
	1	0.171	0.292	0.410	0.412	0.346	0.250	0.154	0.076	0.026	0.004	
	2	0.014	0.049	0.154	0.265	0.346	0.375	0.346	0.265	0.154	0.049	0.014
	3		0.004	0.026	0.076	0.154	0.250	0.346	0.412	0.410	0.292	0.171
	4			0.002	0.008	0.026	0.062	0.130	0.240	0.410	0.656	0.815
5	0	0.774	0.590	0.328	0.168	0.078	0.031	0.010	0.002			
	1	0.204	0.328	0.410	0.360	0.259	0.156	0.077	0.028	0.006		
	2	0.021	0.073	0.205	0.309	0.346	0.312	0.230	0.132	0.051	0.008	0.001
	3	0.001	0.008	0.051	0.132	0.230	0.312	0.346	0.309	0.205	0.073	0.021
	4			0.006	0.028	0.077	0.156	0.259	0.360	0.410	0.328	0.204
	5				0.002	0.010	0.031	0.078	0.168	0.328	0.590	0.774
6	0	0.735	0.531	0.262	0.118	0.047	0.016	0.004	0.001			
	1	0.232	0.354	0.393	0.303	0.187	0.094	0.037	0.010	0.002		
	2	0.031	0.098	0.246	0.324	0.311	0.234	0.138	0.060	0.015	0.001	
	3	0.002	0.015	0.082	0.185	0.276	0.312	0.276	0.185	0.082	0.015	0.002
	4		0.001	0.015	0.060	0.138	0.234	0.311	0.324	0.246	0.098	0.031
	5			0.002	0.010	0.037	0.094	0.187	0.303	0.393	0.354	0.232
	6				0.001	0.004	0.016	0.047	0.118	0.262	0.531	0.735
7	0	0.698	0.478	0.210	0.082	0.028	0.008	0.002				
	1	0.257	0.372	0.367	0.247	0.131	0.055	0.017	0.004			
	2	0.041	0.124	0.275	0.318	0.261	0.164	0.077	0.025	0.004		
	3	0.004	0.023	0.115	0.227	0.290	0.273	0.194	0.097	0.029	0.003	
	4		0.003	0.029	0.097	0.194	0.273	0.290	0.227	0.115	0.023	0.004
	5			0.004	0.025	0.077	0.164	0.261	0.318	0.275	0.124	0.041
	6				0.004	0.017	0.055	0.131	0.247	0.367	0.372	0.257
	7					0.002	0.008	0.028	0.082	0.210	0.478	0.698
8	0	0.663	0.430	0.168	0.058	0.017	0.004	0.001				
	1	0.279	0.383	0.336	0.198	0.090	0.031	0.008	0.001			
	2	0.051	0.149	0.294	0.296	0.209	0.109	0.041	0.010	0.001		
	3	0.005	0.033	0.147	0.254	0.279	0.219	0.124	0.047	0.009		
	4		0.005	0.046	0.136	0.232	0.273	0.232	0.136	0.046	0.005	
	5			0.009	0.047	0.124	0.219	0.279	0.254	0.147	0.033	0.005
	6			0.001	0.010	0.041	0.109	0.209	0.296	0.294	0.149	0.051
	7				0.001	0.008	0.031	0.090	0.198	0.336	0.383	0.279
	8					0.001	0.004	0.017	0.058	0.168	0.430	0.663

Table B (continued)

n	x	0.05	0.1	0.2	0.3	0.4	0.5	0.6	0.7	0.8	0.9	0.95
9	0	0.630	0.387	0.134	0.040	0.010	0.002					
	1	0.299	0.387	0.302	0.156	0.060	0.018	0.004				
	2	0.063	0.172	0.302	0.267	0.161	0.070	0.021	0.004			
	3	0.008	0.045	0.176	0.267	0.251	0.164	0.074	0.021	0.003		
	4	0.001	0.007	0.066	0.172	0.251	0.246	0.167	0.074	0.017	0.001	
	5		0.001	0.017	0.074	0.167	0.246	0.251	0.172	0.066	0.007	0.001
	6			0.003	0.021	0.074	0.164	0.251	0.267	0.176	0.045	0.008
	7				0.004	0.021	0.070	0.161	0.267	0.302	0.172	0.063
	8					0.004	0.018	0.060	0.156	0.302	0.387	0.299
	9						0.002	0.010	0.040	0.134	0.387	0.630
10	0	0.599	0.349	0.107	0.028	0.006	0.001					
	1	0.315	0.387	0.268	0.121	0.040	0.010	0.002				
	2	0.075	0.194	0.302	0.233	0.121	0.044	0.011	0.001			
	3	0.010	0.057	0.201	0.267	0.215	0.117	0.042	0.009	0.001		
	4	0.001	0.011	0.088	0.200	0.251	0.205	0.111	0.037	0.006		
	5		0.001	0.026	0.103	0.201	0.246	0.201	0.103	0.026	0.001	
	6			0.006	0.037	0.111	0.205	0.251	0.200	0.088	0.011	0.001
	7			0.001	0.009	0.042	0.117	0.215	0.267	0.201	0.057	0.010
	8				0.001	0.011	0.044	0.121	0.233	0.302	0.194	0.075
	9					0.002	0.010	0.040	0.121	0.268	0.387	0.315
	10						0.001	0.006	0.028	0.107	0.349	0.599
11	0	0.569	0.314	0.086	0.020	0.004						
	1	0.329	0.384	0.236	0.093	0.027	0.005	0.001				
	2	0.087	0.213	0.295	0.200	0.089	0.027	0.005	0.001			
	3	0.014	0.071	0.221	0.257	0.177	0.081	0.023	0.004			
	4	0.001	0.016	0.111	0.220	0.236	0.161	0.070	0.017	0.002		
	5		0.002	0.039	0.132	0.221	0.226	0.147	0.057	0.010		
	6			0.010	0.057	0.147	0.226	0.221	0.132	0.039	0.002	
	7			0.002	0.017	0.070	0.161	0.236	0.220	0.111	0.016	0.001
	8				0.004	0.023	0.081	0.177	0.257	0.221	0.071	0.014
	9				0.001	0.005	0.027	0.089	0.200	0.295	0.213	0.087
	10					0.001	0.005	0.027	0.093	0.236	0.384	0.329
	11							0.004	0.020	0.086	0.314	0.569
12	0	0.540	0.282	0.069	0.014	0.002						
	1	0.341	0.377	0.206	0.071	0.017	0.003					
	2	0.099	0.230	0.283	0.168	0.064	0.016	0.002				
	3	0.017	0.085	0.236	0.240	0.142	0.054	0.012	0.001			
	4	0.002	0.021	0.133	0.231	0.213	0.121	0.042	0.008	0.001		
	5		0.004	0.053	0.158	0.227	0.193	0.101	0.029	0.003		
	6			0.016	0.079	0.177	0.226	0.177	0.079	0.016		
	7			0.003	0.029	0.101	0.193	0.227	0.158	0.053	0.004	
	8			0.001	0.008	0.042	0.121	0.213	0.231	0.133	0.021	0.002
	9				0.001	0.012	0.054	0.142	0.240	0.236	0.085	0.017
	10					0.002	0.016	0.064	0.168	0.283	0.230	0.099
	11						0.003	0.017	0.071	0.206	0.377	0.341
	12							0.002	0.014	0.069	0.282	0.540

| Table B | (continued) |

n	x	0.05	0.1	0.2	0.3	0.4	0.5	0.6	0.7	0.8	0.9	0.95
13	0	0.513	0.254	0.055	0.010	0.001						
	1	0.351	0.367	0.179	0.054	0.011	0.002					
	2	0.111	0.245	0.268	0.139	0.045	0.010	0.001				
	3	0.021	0.100	0.246	0.218	0.111	0.035	0.006	0.001			
	4	0.003	0.028	0.154	0.234	0.184	0.087	0.024	0.003			
	5		0.006	0.069	0.180	0.221	0.157	0.066	0.014	0.001		
	6		0.001	0.023	0.103	0.197	0.209	0.131	0.044	0.006		
	7			0.006	0.044	0.131	0.209	0.197	0.103	0.023	0.001	
	8			0.001	0.014	0.066	0.157	0.221	0.180	0.069	0.006	
	9				0.003	0.024	0.087	0.184	0.234	0.154	0.028	0.003
	10				0.001	0.006	0.035	0.111	0.218	0.246	0.100	0.021
	11					0.001	0.010	0.045	0.139	0.268	0.245	0.111
	12						0.002	0.011	0.054	0.179	0.367	0.351
	13							0.001	0.010	0.055	0.254	0.513
14	0	0.488	0.229	0.044	0.007	0.001						
	1	0.359	0.356	0.154	0.041	0.007	0.001					
	2	0.123	0.257	0.250	0.113	0.032	0.006	0.001				
	3	0.026	0.114	0.250	0.194	0.085	0.022	0.003				
	4	0.004	0.035	0.172	0.229	0.155	0.061	0.014	0.001			
	5		0.008	0.086	0.196	0.207	0.122	0.041	0.007			
	6		0.001	0.032	0.126	0.207	0.183	0.092	0.023	0.002		
	7			0.009	0.062	0.157	0.209	0.157	0.062	0.009		
	8			0.002	0.023	0.092	0.183	0.207	0.126	0.032	0.001	
	9				0.007	0.041	0.122	0.207	0.196	0.086	0.008	
	10				0.001	0.014	0.061	0.155	0.229	0.172	0.035	0.004
	11					0.003	0.022	0.085	0.194	0.250	0.114	0.026
	12					0.001	0.006	0.032	0.113	0.250	0.257	0.123
	13						0.001	0.007	0.041	0.154	0.356	0.359
	14							0.001	0.007	0.044	0.229	0.488
15	0	0.463	0.206	0.035	0.005							
	1	0.366	0.343	0.132	0.031	0.005						
	2	0.135	0.267	0.231	0.092	0.022	0.003					
	3	0.031	0.129	0.250	0.170	0.063	0.014	0.002				
	4	0.005	0.043	0.188	0.219	0.127	0.042	0.007	0.001			
	5	0.001	0.010	0.103	0.206	0.186	0.092	0.024	0.003			
	6		0.002	0.043	0.147	0.207	0.153	0.061	0.012	0.001		
	7			0.014	0.081	0.177	0.196	0.118	0.035	0.003		
	8			0.003	0.035	0.118	0.196	0.177	0.081	0.014		
	9			0.001	0.012	0.061	0.153	0.207	0.147	0.043	0.002	
	10				0.003	0.024	0.092	0.186	0.206	0.103	0.010	0.001
	11				0.001	0.007	0.042	0.127	0.219	0.188	0.043	0.005
	12					0.002	0.014	0.063	0.170	0.250	0.129	0.031
	13						0.003	0.022	0.092	0.231	0.267	0.135
	14							0.005	0.031	0.132	0.343	0.366
	15								0.005	0.035	0.206	0.463

Table B	(continued)										

						p						
n	x	0.05	0.1	0.2	0.3	0.4	0.5	0.6	0.7	0.8	0.9	0.95
16	0	0.440	0.185	0.028	0.003							
	1	0.371	0.329	0.113	0.023	0.003						
	2	0.146	0.275	0.211	0.073	0.015	0.002					
	3	0.036	0.142	0.246	0.146	0.047	0.009	0.001				
	4	0.006	0.051	0.200	0.204	0.101	0.028	0.004				
	5	0.001	0.014	0.120	0.210	0.162	0.067	0.014	0.001			
	6		0.003	0.055	0.165	0.198	0.122	0.039	0.006			
	7			0.020	0.101	0.189	0.175	0.084	0.019	0.001		
	8			0.006	0.049	0.142	0.196	0.142	0.049	0.006		
	9			0.001	0.019	0.084	0.175	0.189	0.101	0.020		
	10				0.006	0.039	0.122	0.198	0.165	0.055	0.003	
	11				0.001	0.014	0.067	0.162	0.210	0.120	0.014	0.001
	12					0.004	0.028	0.101	0.204	0.200	0.051	0.006
	13					0.001	0.009	0.047	0.146	0.246	0.142	0.036
	14						0.002	0.015	0.073	0.211	0.275	0.146
	15							0.003	0.023	0.113	0.329	0.371
	16								0.003	0.028	0.185	0.440
17	0	0.418	0.167	0.023	0.002							
	1	0.374	0.315	0.096	0.017	0.002						
	2	0.158	0.280	0.191	0.058	0.010	0.001					
	3	0.041	0.156	0.239	0.125	0.034	0.005					
	4	0.008	0.060	0.209	0.187	0.080	0.018	0.002				
	5	0.001	0.017	0.136	0.208	0.138	0.047	0.008	0.001			
	6		0.004	0.068	0.178	0.184	0.094	0.024	0.003			
	7		0.001	0.027	0.120	0.193	0.148	0.057	0.009			
	8			0.008	0.064	0.161	0.185	0.107	0.028	0.002		
	9			0.002	0.028	0.107	0.185	0.161	0.064	0.008		
	10				0.009	0.057	0.148	0.193	0.120	0.027	0.001	
	11				0.003	0.024	0.094	0.184	0.178	0.068	0.004	
	12				0.001	0.008	0.047	0.138	0.208	0.136	0.017	0.001
	13					0.002	0.018	0.080	0.187	0.209	0.060	0.008
	14						0.005	0.034	0.125	0.239	0.156	0.041
	15						0.001	0.010	0.058	0.191	0.280	0.158
	16							0.002	0.017	0.096	0.315	0.374
	17								0.002	0.023	0.167	0.418

Table B	(continued)										

						p						
n	x	0.05	0.1	0.2	0.3	0.4	0.5	0.6	0.7	0.8	0.9	0.95
18	0	0.397	0.150	0.018	0.002							
	1	0.376	0.300	0.081	0.013	0.001						
	2	0.168	0.284	0.172	0.046	0.007	0.001					
	3	0.047	0.168	0.230	0.105	0.025	0.003					
	4	0.009	0.070	0.215	0.168	0.061	0.012	0.001				
	5	0.001	0.022	0.151	0.202	0.115	0.033	0.004				
	6		0.005	0.082	0.187	0.166	0.071	0.015	0.001			
	7		0.001	0.035	0.138	0.189	0.121	0.037	0.005			
	8			0.012	0.081	0.173	0.167	0.077	0.015	0.001		
	9			0.003	0.039	0.128	0.185	0.128	0.039	0.003		
	10			0.001	0.015	0.077	0.167	0.173	0.081	0.012		
	11				0.005	0.037	0.121	0.189	0.138	0.035	0.001	
	12				0.001	0.015	0.071	0.166	0.187	0.082	0.005	
	13					0.004	0.033	0.115	0.202	0.151	0.022	0.001
	14					0.001	0.012	0.061	0.168	0.215	0.070	0.009
	15						0.003	0.025	0.105	0.230	0.168	0.047
	16						0.001	0.007	0.046	0.172	0.284	0.168
	17							0.001	0.013	0.081	0.300	0.376
	18								0.002	0.018	0.150	0.397
19	0	0.377	0.135	0.014	0.001							
	1	0.377	0.285	0.068	0.009	0.001						
	2	0.179	0.285	0.154	0.036	0.005						
	3	0.053	0.180	0.218	0.087	0.017	0.002					
	4	0.011	0.080	0.218	0.149	0.047	0.007	0.001				
	5	0.002	0.027	0.164	0.192	0.093	0.022	0.002				
	6		0.007	0.095	0.192	0.145	0.052	0.008	0.001			
	7		0.001	0.044	0.153	0.180	0.096	0.024	0.002			
	8			0.017	0.098	0.180	0.144	0.053	0.008			
	9			0.005	0.051	0.146	0.176	0.098	0.022	0.001		
	10			0.001	0.022	0.098	0.176	0.146	0.051	0.005		
	11				0.008	0.053	0.144	0.180	0.098	0.071		
	12				0.002	0.024	0.096	0.180	0.153	0.044	0.001	
	13				0.001	0.008	0.052	0.145	0.192	0.095	0.007	
	14					0.002	0.022	0.093	0.192	0.164	0.027	0.002
	15					0.001	0.007	0.047	0.149	0.218	0.080	0.011
	16						0.002	0.017	0.087	0.218	0.180	0.053
	17							0.005	0.036	0.154	0.285	0.179
	18							0.001	0.009	0.068	0.285	0.377
	19								0.001	0.014	0.135	0.377

Table B		(concluded)										
							p					
n	x	0.05	0.1	0.2	0.3	0.4	0.5	0.6	0.7	0.8	0.9	0.95
20	0	0.358	0.122	0.012	0.001							
	1	0.377	0.270	0.058	0.007							
	2	0.189	0.285	0.137	0.028	0.003						
	3	0.060	0.190	0.205	0.072	0.012	0.001					
	4	0.013	0.090	0.218	0.130	0.035	0.005					
	5	0.002	0.032	0.175	0.179	0.075	0.015	0.001				
	6		0.009	0.109	0.192	0.124	0.037	0.005				
	7		0.002	0.055	0.164	0.166	0.074	0.015	0.001			
	8			0.022	0.114	0.180	0.120	0.035	0.004			
	9			0.007	0.065	0.160	0.160	0.071	0.012			
	10			0.002	0.031	0.117	0.176	0.117	0.031	0.002		
	11				0.012	0.071	0.160	0.160	0.065	0.007		
	12				0.004	0.035	0.120	0.180	0.114	0.022		
	13				0.001	0.015	0.074	0.166	0.164	0.055	0.002	
	14					0.005	0.037	0.124	0.192	0.109	0.009	
	15					0.001	0.015	0.075	0.179	0.175	0.032	0.002
	16						0.005	0.035	0.130	0.218	0.090	0.013
	17						0.001	0.012	0.072	0.205	0.190	0.060
	18							0.003	0.028	0.137	0.285	0.189
	19								0.007	0.058	0.270	0.377
	20								0.001	0.012	0.122	0.358

Note: All values of 0.0005 or less are omitted.

Source: John E. Freund, *Modern Elementary Statistics,* 8th ed., © 1992. Reprinted by permission of Prentice-Hall, Inc., Upper Saddle River, N.J.

Table C	The Poisson Distribution

					λ					
x	0.1	0.2	0.3	0.4	0.5	0.6	0.7	0.8	0.9	1.0
0	.9048	.8187	.7408	.6703	.6065	.5488	.4966	.4493	.4066	.3679
1	.0905	.1637	.2222	.2681	.3033	.3293	.3476	.3595	.3659	.3679
2	.0045	.0164	.0333	.0536	.0758	.0988	.1217	.1438	.1647	.1839
3	.0002	.0011	.0033	.0072	.0126	.0198	.0284	.0383	.0494	.0613
4	.0000	.0001	.0003	.0007	.0016	.0030	.0050	.0077	.0111	.0153
5	.0000	.0000	.0000	.0001	.0002	.0004	.0007	.0012	.0020	.0031
6	.0000	.0000	.0000	.0000	.0000	.0000	.0001	.0002	.0003	.0005
7	.0000	.0000	.0000	.0000	.0000	.0000	.0000	.0000	.0000	.0001

					λ					
x	1.1	1.2	1.3	1.4	1.5	1.6	1.7	1.8	1.9	2.0
0	.3329	.3012	.2725	.2466	.2231	.2019	.1827	.1653	.1496	.1353
1	.3662	.3614	.3543	.3452	.3347	.3230	.3106	.2975	.2842	.2707
2	.2014	.2169	.2303	.2417	.2510	.2584	.2640	.2678	.2700	.2707
3	.0738	.0867	.0998	.1128	.1255	.1378	.1496	.1607	.1710	.1804
4	.0203	.0260	.0324	.0395	.0471	.0551	.0636	.0723	.0812	.0902
5	.0045	.0062	.0084	.0111	.0141	.0176	.0216	.0260	.0309	.0361
6	.0008	.0012	.0018	.0026	.0035	.0047	.0061	.0078	.0098	.0120
7	.0001	.0002	.0003	.0005	.0008	.0011	.0015	.0020	.0027	.0034
8	.0000	.0000	.0001	.0001	.0001	.0002	.0003	.0005	.0006	.0009
9	.0000	.0000	.0000	.0000	.0000	.0000	.0001	.0001	.0001	.0002

					λ					
x	2.1	2.2	2.3	2.4	2.5	2.6	2.7	2.8	2.9	3.0
0	.1225	.1108	.1003	.0907	.0821	.0743	.0672	.0608	.0550	.0498
1	.2572	.2438	.2306	.2177	.2052	.1931	.1815	.1703	.1596	.1494
2	.2700	.2681	.2652	.2613	.2565	.2510	.2450	.2384	.2314	.2240
3	.1890	.1966	.2033	.2090	.2138	.2176	.2205	.2225	.2237	.2240
4	.0992	.1082	.1169	.1254	.1336	.1414	.1488	.1557	.1622	.1680
5	.0417	.0476	.0538	.0602	.0668	.0735	.0804	.0872	.0940	.1008
6	.0146	.0174	.0206	.0241	.0278	.0319	.0362	.0407	.0455	.0504
7	.0044	.0055	.0068	.0083	.0099	.0118	.0139	.0163	.0188	.0216
8	.0011	.0015	.0019	.0025	.0031	.0038	.0047	.0057	.0068	.0081
9	.0003	.0004	.0005	.0007	.0009	.0011	.0014	.0018	.0022	.0027
10	.0001	.0001	.0001	.0002	.0002	.0003	.0004	.0005	.0006	.0008
11	.0000	.0000	.0000	.0000	.0000	.0001	.0001	.0001	.0002	.0002
12	.0000	.0000	.0000	.0000	.0000	.0000	.0000	.0000	.0000	.0001

					λ					
x	3.1	3.2	3.3	3.4	3.5	3.6	3.7	3.8	3.9	4.0
0	.0450	.0408	.0369	.0334	.0302	.0273	.0247	.0224	.0202	.0183
1	.1397	.1304	.1217	.1135	.1057	.0984	.0915	.0850	.0789	.0733
2	.2165	.2087	.2008	.1929	.1850	.1771	.1692	.1615	.1539	.1465
3	.2237	.2226	.2209	.2186	.2158	.2125	.2087	.2046	.2001	.1954
4	.1734	.1781	.1823	.1858	.1888	.1912	.1931	.1944	.1951	.1954

Table C	(continued)								
					λ				
x	3.1	3.2	3.3	3.4	3.5	3.6	3.7	3.8	3.9	4.0
5	.1075	.1140	.1203	.1264	.1322	.1377	.1429	.1477	.1522	.1563
6	.0555	.0608	.0662	.0716	.0771	.0826	.0881	.0936	.0989	.1042
7	.0246	.0278	.0312	.0348	.0385	.0425	.0466	.0508	.0551	.0595
8	.0095	.0111	.0129	.0148	.0169	.0191	.0215	.0241	.0269	.0298
9	.0033	.0040	.0047	.0056	.0066	.0076	.0089	.0102	.0116	.0132
10	.0010	.0013	.0016	.0019	.0023	.0028	.0033	.0039	.0045	.0053
11	.0003	.0004	.0005	.0006	.0007	.0009	.0011	.0013	.0016	.0019
12	.0001	.0001	.0001	.0002	.0002	.0003	.0003	.0004	.0005	.0006
13	.0000	.0000	.0000	.0000	.0001	.0001	.0001	.0001	.0002	.0002
14	.0000	.0000	.0000	.0000	.0000	.0000	.0000	.0000	.0000	.0001

					λ				
x	4.1	4.2	4.3	4.4	4.5	4.6	4.7	4.8	4.9	5.0
0	.0166	.0150	.0136	.0123	.0111	.0101	.0091	.0082	.0074	.0067
1	.0679	.0630	.0583	.0540	.0500	.0462	.0427	.0395	.0365	.0337
2	.1393	.1323	.1254	.1188	.1125	.1063	.1005	.0948	.0894	.0842
3	.1904	.1852	.1798	.1743	.1687	.1631	.1574	.1517	.1460	.1404
4	.1951	.1944	.1933	.1917	.1898	.1875	.1849	.1820	.1789	.1755
5	.1600	.1633	.1662	.1687	.1708	.1725	.1738	.1747	.1753	.1755
6	.1093	.1143	.1191	.1237	.1281	.1323	.1362	.1398	.1432	.1462
7	.0640	.0686	.0732	.0778	.0824	.0869	.0914	.0959	.1002	.1044
8	.0328	.0360	.0393	.0428	.0463	.0500	.0537	.0575	.0614	.0653
9	.0150	.0168	.0188	.0209	.0232	.0255	.0280	.0307	.0334	.0363
10	.0061	.0071	.0081	.0092	.0104	.0118	.0132	.0147	.0164	.0181
11	.0023	.0027	.0032	.0037	.0043	.0049	.0056	.0064	.0073	.0082
12	.0008	.0009	.0011	.0014	.0016	.0019	.0022	.0026	.0030	.0034
13	.0002	.0003	.0004	.0005	.0006	.0007	.0008	.0009	.0011	.0013
14	.0001	.0001	.0001	.0001	.0002	.0002	.0003	.0003	.0004	.0005
15	.0000	.0000	.0000	.0000	.0001	.0001	.0001	.0001	.0001	.0002

					λ				
x	5.1	5.2	5.3	5.4	5.5	5.6	5.7	5.8	5.9	6.0
0	.0061	.0055	.0050	.0045	.0041	.0037	.0033	.0030	.0027	.0025
1	.0311	.0287	.0265	.0244	.0225	.0207	.0191	.0176	.0162	.0149
2	.0793	.0746	.0701	.0659	.0618	.0580	.0544	.0509	.0477	.0446
3	.1348	.1293	.1239	.1185	.1133	.1082	.1033	.0985	.0938	.0892
4	.1719	.1681	.1641	.1600	.1558	.1515	.1472	.1428	.1383	.1339

Table C (continued)

x	λ 5.1	5.2	5.3	5.4	5.5	5.6	5.7	5.8	5.9	6.0
5	.1753	.1748	.1740	.1728	.1714	.1697	.1678	.1656	.1632	.1606
6	.1490	.1515	.1537	.1555	.1571	.1584	.1594	.1601	.1605	.1606
7	.1086	.1125	.1163	.1200	.1234	.1267	.1298	.1326	.1353	.1377
8	.0692	.0731	.0771	.0810	.0849	.0887	.0925	.0962	.0998	.1033
9	.0392	.0423	.0454	.0486	.0519	.0552	.0586	.0620	.0654	.0688
10	.0200	.0220	.0241	.0262	.0285	.0309	.0334	.0359	.0386	.0413
11	.0093	.0104	.0116	.0129	.0143	.0157	.0173	.0190	.0207	.0225
12	.0039	.0045	.0051	.0058	.0065	.0073	.0082	.0092	.0102	.0113
13	.0015	.0018	.0021	.0024	.0028	.0032	.0036	.0041	.0046	.0052
14	.0006	.0007	.0008	.0009	.0011	.0013	.0015	.0017	.0019	.0022
15	.0002	.0002	.0003	.0003	.0004	.0005	.0006	.0007	.0008	.0009
16	.0001	.0001	.0001	.0001	.0001	.0002	.0002	.0002	.0003	.0003
17	.0000	.0000	.0000	.0000	.0000	.0000	.0001	.0001	.0001	.0001

x	λ 6.1	6.2	6.3	6.4	6.5	6.6	6.7	6.8	6.9	7.0
0	.0022	.0020	.0018	.0017	.0015	.0014	.0012	.0011	.0010	.0009
1	.0137	.0126	.0116	.0106	.0098	.0090	.0082	.0076	.0070	.0064
2	.0417	.0390	.0364	.0340	.0318	.0296	.0276	.0258	.0240	.0223
3	.0848	.0806	.0765	.0726	.0688	.0652	.0617	.0584	.0552	.0521
4	.1294	.1249	.1205	.1162	.1118	.1076	.1034	.0992	.0952	.0912
5	.1579	.1549	.1519	.1487	.1454	.1420	.1385	.1349	.1314	.1277
6	.1605	.1601	.1595	.1586	.1575	.1562	.1546	.1529	.1511	.1490
7	.1399	.1418	.1435	.1450	.1462	.1472	.1480	.1486	.1489	.1490
8	.1066	.1099	.1130	.1160	.1188	.1215	.1240	.1263	.1284	.1304
9	.0723	.0757	.0791	.0825	.0858	.0891	.0923	.0954	.0985	.1014
10	.0441	.0469	.0498	.0528	.0558	.0588	.0618	.0649	.0679	.0710
11	.0245	.0265	.0285	.0307	.0330	.0353	.0377	.0401	.0426	.0452
12	.0124	.0137	.0150	.0164	.0179	.0194	.0210	.0227	.0245	.0264
13	.0058	.0065	.0073	.0081	.0089	.0098	.0108	.0119	.0130	.0142
14	.0025	.0029	.0033	.0037	.0041	.0046	.0052	.0058	.0064	.0071
15	.0010	.0012	.0014	.0016	.0018	.0020	.0023	.0026	.0029	.0033
16	.0004	.0005	.0005	.0006	.0007	.0008	.0010	.0011	.0013	.0014
17	.0001	.0002	.0002	.0002	.0003	.0003	.0004	.0004	.0005	.0006
18	.0000	.0001	.0001	.0001	.0001	.0001	.0001	.0002	.0002	.0002
19	.0000	.0000	.0000	.0000	.0000	.0000	.0000	.0001	.0001	.0001

Table C	(continued)								

					λ				
x	7.1	7.2	7.3	7.4	7.5	7.6	7.7	7.8	7.9	8.0
0	.0008	.0007	.0007	.0006	.0006	.0005	.0005	.0004	.0004	.0003
1	.0059	.0054	.0049	.0045	.0041	.0038	.0035	.0032	.0029	.0027
2	.0208	.0194	.0180	.0167	.0156	.0145	.0134	.0125	.0116	.0107
3	.0492	.0464	.0438	.0413	.0389	.0366	.0345	.0324	.0305	.0286
4	.0874	.0836	.0799	.0764	.0729	.0696	.0663	.0632	.0602	.0573
5	.1241	.1204	.1167	.1130	.1094	.1057	.1021	.0986	.0951	.0916
6	.1468	.1445	.1420	.1394	.1367	.1339	.1311	.1282	.1252	.1221
7	.1489	.1486	.1481	.1474	.1465	.1454	.1442	.1428	.1413	.1396
8	.1321	.1337	.1351	.1363	.1373	.1382	.1388	.1392	.1395	.1396
9	.1042	.1070	.1096	.1121	.1144	.1167	.1187	.1207	.1224	.1241
10	.0740	.0770	.0800	.0829	.0858	.0887	.0914	.0941	.0967	.0993
11	.0478	.0504	.0531	.0558	.0585	.0613	.0640	.0667	.0695	.0722
12	.0283	.0303	.0323	.0344	.0366	.0388	.0411	.0434	.0457	.0481
13	.0154	.0168	.0181	.0196	.0211	.0227	.0243	.0260	.0278	.0296
14	.0078	.0086	.0095	.0104	.0113	.0123	.0134	.0145	.0157	.0169
15	.0037	.0041	.0046	.0051	.0057	.0062	.0069	.0075	.0083	.0090
16	.0016	.0019	.0021	.0024	.0026	.0030	.0033	.0037	.0041	.0045
17	.0007	.0008	.0009	.0010	.0012	.0013	.0015	.0017	.0019	.0021
18	.0003	.0003	.0004	.0004	.0005	.0006	.0006	.0007	.0008	.0009
19	.0001	.0001	.0001	.0002	.0002	.0002	.0003	.0003	.0003	.0004
20	.0000	.0000	.0001	.0001	.0001	.0001	.0001	.0001	.0001	.0002
21	.0000	.0000	.0000	.0000	.0000	.0000	.0000	.0000	.0001	.0001

					λ				
x	8.1	8.2	8.3	8.4	8.5	8.6	8.7	8.8	8.9	9.0
0	.0003	.0003	.0002	.0002	.0002	.0002	.0002	.0002	.0001	.0001
1	.0025	.0023	.0021	.0019	.0017	.0016	.0014	.0013	.0012	.0011
2	.0100	.0092	.0086	.0079	.0074	.0068	.0063	.0058	.0054	.0050
3	.0269	.0252	.0237	.0222	.0208	.0195	.0183	.0171	.0160	.0150
4	.0544	.0517	.0491	.0466	.0443	.0420	.0398	.0377	.0357	.0337
5	.0882	.0849	.0816	.0784	.0752	.0722	.0692	.0663	.0635	.0607
6	.1191	.1160	.1128	.1097	.1066	.1034	.1003	.0972	.0941	.0911
7	.1378	.1358	.1338	.1317	.1294	.1271	.1247	.1222	.1197	.1171
8	.1395	.1392	.1388	.1382	.1375	.1366	.1356	.1344	.1332	.1318
9	.1256	.1269	.1280	.1290	.1299	.1306	.1311	.1315	.1317	.1318

Table C	(continued)								

					λ					
x	8.1	8.2	8.3	8.4	8.5	8.6	8.7	8.8	8.9	9.0
10	.1017	.1040	.1063	.1084	.1104	.1123	.1140	.1157	.1172	.1186
11	.0749	.0776	.0802	.0828	.0853	.0878	.0902	.0925	.0948	.0970
12	.0505	.0530	.0555	.0579	.0604	.0629	.0654	.0679	.0703	.0728
13	.0315	.0334	.0354	.0374	.0395	.0416	.0438	.0459	.0481	.0504
14	.0182	.0196	.0210	.0225	.0240	.0256	.0272	.0289	.0306	.0324
15	.0098	.0107	.0116	.0126	.0136	.0147	.0158	.0169	.0182	.0194
16	.0050	.0055	.0060	.0066	.0072	.0079	.0086	.0093	.0101	.0109
17	.0024	.0026	.0029	.0033	.0036	.0040	.0044	.0048	.0053	.0058
18	.0011	.0012	.0014	.0015	.0017	.0019	.0021	.0024	.0026	.0029
19	.0005	.0005	.0006	.0007	.0008	.0009	.0010	.0011	.0012	.0014
20	.0002	.0002	.0002	.0003	.0003	.0004	.0004	.0005	.0005	.0006
21	.0001	.0001	.0001	.0001	.0001	.0002	.0002	.0002	.0002	.0003
22	.0000	.0000	.0000	.0000	.0001	.0001	.0001	.0001	.0001	.0001

					λ					
x	9.1	9.2	9.3	9.4	9.5	9.6	9.7	9.8	9.9	10.0
0	.0001	.0001	.0001	.0001	.0001	.0001	.0001	.0001	.0001	.0000
1	.0010	.0009	.0009	.0008	.0007	.0007	.0006	.0005	.0005	.0005
2	.0046	.0043	.0040	.0037	.0034	.0031	.0029	.0027	.0025	.0023
3	.0140	.0131	.0123	.0115	.0107	.0100	.0093	.0087	.0081	.0076
4	.0319	.0302	.0285	.0269	.0254	.0240	.0226	.0213	.0201	.0189
5	.0581	.0555	.0530	.0506	.0483	.0460	.0439	.0418	.0398	.0378
6	.0881	.0851	.0822	.0793	.0764	.0736	.0709	.0682	.0656	.0631
7	.1145	.1118	.1091	.1064	.1037	.1010	.0982	.0955	.0928	.0901
8	.1302	.1286	.1269	.1251	.1232	.1212	.1191	.1170	.1148	.1126
9	.1317	.1315	.1311	.1306	.1300	.1293	.1284	.1274	.1263	.1251
10	.1198	.1210	.1219	.1228	.1235	.1241	.1245	.1249	.1250	.1251
11	.0991	.1012	.1031	.1049	.1067	.1083	.1098	.1112	.1125	.1137
12	.0752	.0776	.0799	.0822	.0844	.0866	.0888	.0908	.0928	.0948
13	.0526	.0549	.0572	.0594	.0617	.0640	.0662	.0685	.0707	.0729
14	.0342	.0361	.0380	.0399	.0419	.0439	.0459	.0479	.0500	.0521
15	.0208	.0221	.0235	.0250	.0265	.0281	.0297	.0313	.0330	.0347
16	.0118	.0127	.0137	.0147	.0157	.0168	.0180	.0192	.0204	.0217
17	.0063	.0069	.0075	.0081	.0088	.0095	.0103	.0111	.0119	.0128
18	.0032	.0035	.0039	.0042	.0046	.0051	.0055	.0060	.0065	.0071
19	.0015	.0017	.0019	.0021	.0023	.0026	.0028	.0031	.0034	.0037

| Table C | (continued) |

	λ									
x	**9.1**	**9.2**	**9.3**	**9.4**	**9.5**	**9.6**	**9.7**	**9.8**	**9.9**	**10.0**
20	.0007	.0008	.0009	.0010	.0011	.0012	.0014	.0015	.0017	.0019
21	.0003	.0003	.0004	.0004	.0005	.0006	.0006	.0007	.0008	.0009
22	.0001	.0001	.0002	.0002	.0002	.0002	.0003	.0003	.0004	.0004
23	.0000	.0001	.0001	.0001	.0001	.0001	.0001	.0001	.0002	.0002
24	.0000	.0000	.0000	.0000	.0000	.0000	.0000	.0001	.0001	.0001

	λ									
x	**11**	**12**	**13**	**14**	**15**	**16**	**17**	**18**	**19**	**20**
0	.0000	.0000	.0000	.0000	.0000	.0000	.0000	.0000	.0000	.0000
1	.0002	.0001	.0000	.0000	.0000	.0000	.0000	.0000	.0000	.0000
2	.0010	.0004	.0002	.0001	.0000	.0000	.0000	.0000	.0000	.0000
3	.0037	.0018	.0008	.0004	.0002	.0001	.0000	.0000	.0000	.0000
4	.0102	.0053	.0027	.0013	.0006	.0003	.0001	.0001	.0000	.0000
5	.0224	.0127	.0070	.0037	.0019	.0010	.0005	.0002	.0001	.0001
6	.0411	.0255	.0152	.0087	.0048	.0026	.0014	.0007	.0004	.0002
7	.0646	.0437	.0281	.0174	.0104	.0060	.0034	.0018	.0010	.0005
8	.0888	.0655	.0457	.0304	.0194	.0120	.0072	.0042	.0024	.0013
9	.1085	.0874	.0661	.0473	.0324	.0213	.0135	.0083	.0050	.0029
10	.1194	.1048	.0859	.0663	.0486	.0341	.0230	.0150	.0095	.0058
11	.1194	.1144	.1015	.0844	.0663	.0496	.0355	.0245	.0164	.0106
12	.1094	.1144	.1099	.0984	.0829	.0661	.0504	.0368	.0259	.0176
13	.0926	.1056	.1099	.1060	.0956	.0814	.0658	.0509	.0378	.0271
14	.0728	.0905	.1021	.1060	.1024	.0930	.0800	.0655	.0514	.0387
15	.0534	.0724	.0885	.0989	.1024	.0992	.0906	.0786	.0650	.0516
16	.0367	.0543	.0719	.0866	.0960	.0992	.0963	.0884	.0772	.0646
17	.0237	.0383	.0550	.0713	.0847	.0934	.0963	.0936	.0863	.0760
18	.0145	.0256	.0397	.0554	.0706	.0830	.0909	.0936	.0911	.0844
19	.0084	.0161	.0272	.0409	.0557	.0699	.0814	.0887	.0911	.0888
20	.0046	.0097	.0177	.0286	.0418	.0559	.0692	.0798	.0866	.0888
21	.0024	.0055	.0109	.0191	.0299	.0426	.0560	.0684	.0783	.0846
22	.0012	.0030	.0065	.0121	.0204	.0310	.0433	.0560	.0676	.0769
23	.0006	.0016	.0037	.0074	.0133	.0216	.0320	.0438	.0559	.0669
24	.0003	.0008	.0020	.0043	.0083	.0144	.0226	.0328	.0442	.0557
25	.0001	.0004	.0010	.0024	.0050	.0092	.0154	.0237	.0336	.0446
26	.0000	.0002	.0005	.0013	.0029	.0057	.0101	.0164	.0246	.0343
27	.0000	.0001	.0002	.0007	.0016	.0034	.0063	.0109	.0173	.0254
28	.0000	.0000	.0001	.0003	.0009	.0019	.0038	.0070	.0117	.0181
29	.0000	.0000	.0001	.0002	.0004	.0011	.0023	.0044	.0077	.0125

Table C	(concluded)								
					λ				
x	11	12	13	14	15	16	17	18	19	20
30	.0000	.0000	.0000	.0001	.0002	.0006	.0013	.0026	.0049	.0083
31	.0000	.0000	.0000	.0000	.0001	.0003	.0007	.0015	.0030	.0054
32	.0000	.0000	.0000	.0000	.0001	.0001	.0004	.0009	.0018	.0034
33	.0000	.0000	.0000	.0000	.0000	.0001	.0002	.0005	.0010	.0020
34	.0000	.0000	.0000	.0000	.0000	.0000	.0001	.0002	.0006	.0012
35	.0000	.0000	.0000	.0000	.0000	.0000	.0000	.0001	.0003	.0007
36	.0000	.0000	.0000	.0000	.0000	.0000	.0000	.0001	.0002	.0004
37	.0000	.0000	.0000	.0000	.0000	.0000	.0000	.0000	.0001	.0002
38	.0000	.0000	.0000	.0000	.0000	.0000	.0000	.0000	.0000	.0001
39	.0000	.0000	.0000	.0000	.0000	.0000	.0000	.0000	.0000	.0001

Reprinted with permission from W. H. Beyer, *Handbook of Tables for Probability and Statistics,* 2nd ed. Copyright CRC Press, Boca Raton, Fla., 1986.

Table D		Random Numbers											
10480	15011	01536	02011	81647	91646	67179	14194	62590	36207	20969	99570	91291	90700
22368	46573	25595	85393	30995	89198	27982	53402	93965	34095	52666	19174	39615	99505
24130	48360	22527	97265	76393	64809	15179	24830	49340	32081	30680	19655	63348	58629
42167	93093	06243	61680	07856	16376	39440	53537	71341	57004	00849	74917	97758	16379
37570	39975	81837	16656	06121	91782	60468	81305	49684	60672	14110	06927	01263	54613
77921	06907	11008	42751	27756	53498	18602	70659	90655	15053	21916	81825	44394	42880
99562	72905	56420	69994	98872	31016	71194	18738	44013	48840	63213	21069	10634	12952
96301	91977	05463	07972	18876	20922	94595	56869	69014	60045	18425	84903	42508	32307
89579	14342	63661	10281	17453	18103	57740	84378	25331	12566	58678	44947	05584	56941
85475	36857	43342	53988	53060	59533	38867	62300	08158	17983	16439	11458	18593	64952
28918	69578	88231	33276	70997	79936	56865	05859	90106	31595	01547	85590	91610	78188
63553	40961	48235	03427	49626	69445	18663	72695	52180	20847	12234	90511	33703	90322
09429	93969	52636	92737	88974	33488	36320	17617	30015	08272	84115	27156	30613	74952
10365	61129	87529	85689	48237	52267	67689	93394	01511	26358	85104	20285	29975	89868
07119	97336	71048	08178	77233	13916	47564	81056	97735	85977	29372	74461	28551	90707
51085	12765	51821	51259	77452	16308	60756	92144	49442	53900	70960	63990	75601	40719
02368	21382	52404	60268	89368	19885	55322	44819	01188	65255	64835	44919	05944	55157
01011	54092	33362	94904	31273	04146	18594	29852	71585	85030	51132	01915	92747	64951
52162	53916	46369	58586	23216	14513	83149	98736	23495	64350	94738	17752	35156	35749
07056	97628	33787	09998	42698	06691	76988	13602	51851	46104	88916	19509	25625	58104
48663	91245	85828	14346	09172	30168	90229	04734	59193	22178	30421	61666	99904	32812
54164	58492	22421	74103	47070	25306	76468	26384	58151	06646	21524	15227	96909	44592
32639	32363	05597	24200	13363	38005	94342	28728	35806	06912	17012	64161	18296	22851
29334	27001	87637	87308	58731	00256	45834	15398	46557	41135	10367	07684	36188	18510
02488	33062	28834	07351	19731	92420	60952	61280	50001	67658	32586	86679	50720	94953
81525	72295	04839	96423	24878	82651	66566	14778	76797	14780	13300	87074	79666	95725
29676	20591	68086	26432	46901	20849	89768	81536	86645	12659	92259	57102	80428	25280
00742	57392	39064	66432	84673	40027	32832	61362	98947	96067	64760	64584	96096	98253
05366	04213	25669	26422	44407	44048	37937	63904	45766	66134	75470	66520	34693	90449
91921	26418	64117	94305	26766	25940	39972	22209	71500	64568	91402	42416	07844	69618
00582	04711	87917	77341	42206	35126	74087	99547	81817	42607	43808	76655	62028	76630
00725	69884	62797	56170	86324	88072	76222	36086	84637	93161	76038	65855	77919	88006
69011	65797	95876	55293	18988	27354	26575	08625	40801	59920	29841	80150	12777	48501
25976	57948	29888	88604	67917	48708	18912	82271	65424	69774	33611	54262	85963	03547
09763	83473	73577	12908	30883	18317	28290	35797	05998	41688	34952	37888	38917	88050
91567	42595	27958	30134	04024	86385	29880	99730	55536	84855	29080	09250	79656	73211
17955	56349	90999	49127	20044	59931	06115	20542	18059	02008	73708	83517	36103	42791
46503	18584	18845	49618	02304	51038	20655	58727	28168	15475	56942	53389	20562	87338
92157	89634	94824	78171	84610	82834	09922	25417	44137	48413	25555	21246	35509	20468
14577	62765	35605	81263	39667	47358	56873	56307	61607	49518	89656	20103	77490	18062
98427	07523	33362	64270	01638	92477	66969	98420	04880	45585	46565	04102	46880	45709
34914	63976	88720	82765	34476	17032	87589	40836	32427	70002	70663	88863	77775	69348
70060	28277	39475	46473	23219	53416	94970	25832	69975	94884	19661	72828	00102	66794
53976	54914	06990	67245	68350	82948	11398	42878	80287	88267	47363	46634	06541	97809
76072	29515	40980	07391	58745	25774	22987	80059	39911	96189	41151	14222	60697	59583
90725	52210	83974	29992	65831	38857	50490	83765	55657	14361	31720	57375	56228	41546
64364	67412	33339	31926	14883	24413	59744	92351	97473	89286	35931	04110	23726	51900
08962	00358	31662	25388	61642	34072	81249	35648	56891	69352	48373	45578	78547	81788
95012	68379	93526	70765	10593	04542	76463	54328	02349	17247	28865	14777	62730	92277
15664	10493	20492	38391	91132	21999	59516	81652	27195	48223	46751	22923	32261	85653

Reprinted with permission from W. H. Beyer, *Handbook of Tables for Probability and Statistics,* 2nd ed. Copyright CRC Press, Boca Raton, Fla., 1986.

NEGATIVE z Scores

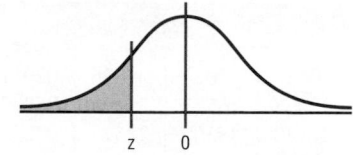

Table E-1		Cumulative Area to the Left of z score								
z	.00	.01	.02	.03	.04	.05	.06	.07	.08	.09
−3.7	0.0001									
−3.6	0.0002	0.0002	0.0001	0.0001	0.0001	0.0001	0.0001	0.0001	0.0001	0.0001
−3.5	0.0002	0.0002	0.0002	0.0002	0.0002	0.0002	0.0002	0.0002	0.0002	0.0002
−3.4	0.0003	0.0003	0.0003	0.0003	0.0003	0.0003	0.0003	0.0003	0.0003	0.0002
−3.3	0.0005	0.0005	0.0005	0.0004	0.0004	0.0004	0.0004	0.0004	0.0004	0.0003
−3.2	0.0007	0.0007	0.0006	0.0006	0.0006	0.0006	0.0006	0.0005	0.0005	0.0005
−3.1	0.0010	0.0009	0.0009	0.0009	0.0008	0.0008	0.0008	0.0008	0.0007	0.0007
−3.0	0.0013	0.0013	0.0013	0.0012	0.0012	0.0011	0.0011	0.0011	0.0010	0.0010
−2.9	0.0019	0.0018	0.0018	0.0017	0.0016	0.0016	0.0015	0.0015	0.0014	0.0014
−2.8	0.0026	0.0025	0.0024	0.0023	0.0023	0.0022	0.0021	0.0021	0.0020	0.0019
−2.7	0.0035	0.0034	0.0033	0.0032	0.0031	0.0030	0.0029	0.0028	0.0027	0.0026
−2.6	0.0047	0.0045	0.0044	0.0043	0.0041	0.0040	0.0039	0.0038	0.0037	0.0036
−2.5	0.0062	0.0060	0.0059	0.0057	0.0055	0.0054	0.0052	0.0051 *	0.0049	0.0048
−2.4	0.0082	0.0080	0.0078	0.0075	0.0073	0.0071	0.0069	0.0068	0.0066	0.0064
−2.3	0.0107	0.0104	0.0102	0.0099	0.0096	0.0094	0.0091	0.0089	0.0087	0.0084
−2.2	0.0139	0.0136	0.0132	0.0129	0.0125	0.0122	0.0119	0.0116	0.0113	0.0110
−2.1	0.0179	0.0174	0.0170	0.0166	0.0162	0.0158	0.0154	0.0150	0.0146	0.0143
−2.0	0.0228	0.0222	0.0217	0.0212	0.0207	0.0202	0.0197	0.0192	0.0188	0.0183
−1.9	0.0287	0.0281	0.0274	0.0268	0.0262	0.0256	0.0250	0.0244	0.0239	0.0233
−1.8	0.0359	0.0351	0.0344	0.0336	0.0329	0.0322	0.0314	0.0307	0.0301	0.0294
−1.7	0.0446	0.0436	0.0427	0.0418	0.0409	0.0401	0.0392	0.0384	0.0375	0.0367
−1.6	0.0548	0.0537	0.0526	0.0516	0.0505 *	0.0495	0.0485	0.0475	0.0465	0.0455
−1.5	0.0668	0.0655	0.0643	0.0630	0.0618	0.0606	0.0594	0.0582	0.0571	0.0559
−1.4	0.0808	0.0793	0.0778	0.0764	0.0749	0.0735	0.0721	0.0708	0.0694	0.0681
−1.3	0.0968	0.0951	0.0934	0.0918	0.0901	0.0885	0.0869	0.0853	0.0838	0.0823
−1.2	0.1151	0.1131	0.1112	0.1093	0.1075	0.1056	0.1038	0.1020	0.1003	0.0985
−1.1	0.1357	0.1335	0.1314	0.1292	0.1271	0.1251	0.1230	0.1210	0.1190	0.1170
−1.0	0.1587	0.1562	0.1539	0.1515	0.1492	0.1469	0.1446	0.1423	0.1401	0.1379
−0.9	0.1841	0.1814	0.1788	0.1762	0.1736	0.1711	0.1685	0.1660	0.1635	0.1611
−0.8	0.2119	0.2090	0.2061	0.2033	0.2005	0.1977	0.1949	0.1922	0.1894	0.1867
−0.7	0.2420	0.2389	0.2358	0.2327	0.2296	0.2266	0.2236	0.2206	0.2177	0.2148
−0.6	0.2743	0.2709	0.2676	0.2643	0.2611	0.2578	0.2546	0.2514	0.2483	0.2451
−0.5	0.3085	0.3050	0.3015	0.2981	0.2946	0.2912	0.2877	0.2843	0.2810	0.2776
−0.4	0.3446	0.3409	0.3372	0.3336	0.3300	0.3264	0.3228	0.3192	0.3156	0.3121
−0.3	0.3821	0.3783	0.3745	0.3707	0.3669	0.3632	0.3594	0.3557	0.3520	0.3483
−0.2	0.4207	0.4168	0.4129	0.4090	0.4052	0.4013	0.3974	0.3936	0.3897	0.3859
−0.1	0.4602	0.4562	0.4522	0.4483	0.4443	0.4404	0.4364	0.4325	0.4286	0.4247
0.0	0.5000	0.4960	0.4920	0.4880	0.4840	0.4801	0.4761	0.4721	0.4681	0.4641

Note: For all values less than −3.70, use 0.0001 for the area.

z score	Area
−1.645	0.0500
−2.575	0.0050

POSITIVE z Scores

Table E–2	Cumulative Area to the Left of z score								
z	.00	.01	.02	.03	.04	.05	.06	.07	.08	.09
0.0	0.5000	0.5040	0.5080	0.5120	0.5160	0.5199	0.5239	0.5279	0.5319	0.5359
0.1	0.5398	0.5438	0.5478	0.5517	0.5557	0.5596	0.5636	0.5675	0.5714	0.5753
0.2	0.5793	0.5832	0.5871	0.5910	0.5948	0.5987	0.6026	0.6064	0.6103	0.6141
0.3	0.6179	0.6217	0.6255	0.6293	0.6331	0.6368	0.6406	0.6443	0.6480	0.6517
0.4	0.6554	0.6591	0.6628	0.6664	0.6700	0.6736	0.6772	0.6808	0.6844	0.6879
0.5	0.6915	0.6950	0.6985	0.7019	0.7054	0.7088	0.7123	0.7157	0.7190	0.7224
0.6	0.7257	0.7291	0.7324	0.7357	0.7389	0.7422	0.7454	0.7486	0.7517	0.7549
0.7	0.7580	0.7611	0.7642	0.7673	0.7704	0.7734	0.7764	0.7794	0.7823	0.7852
0.8	0.7881	0.7910	0.7939	0.7967	0.7995	0.8023	0.8051	0.8078	0.8106	0.8133
0.9	0.8159	0.8186	0.8212	0.8238	0.8264	0.8289	0.8315	0.8340	0.8365	0.8389
1.0	0.8413	0.8438	0.8461	0.8485	0.8508	0.8531	0.8554	0.8577	0.8599	0.8621
1.1	0.8643	0.8665	0.8686	0.8708	0.8729	0.8749	0.8770	0.8790	0.8810	0.8830
1.2	0.8849	0.8869	0.8888	0.8907	0.8925	0.8944	0.8962	0.8980	0.8997	0.9015
1.3	0.9032	0.9049	0.9066	0.9082	0.9099	0.9115	0.9131	0.9147	0.9162	0.9177
1.4	0.9192	0.9207	0.9222	0.9236	0.9251	0.9265	0.9279	0.9292	0.9306	0.9319
1.5	0.9332	0.9345	0.9357	0.9370	0.9382	0.9394	0.9406	0.9418	0.9429	0.9441
1.6	0.9452	0.9463	0.9474	0.9484	0.9495 *	0.9505	0.9515	0.9525	0.9535	0.9545
1.7	0.9554	0.9564	0.9573	0.9582	0.9591	0.9599	0.9608	0.9616	0.9625	0.9633
1.8	0.9641	0.9649	0.9656	0.9664	0.9671	0.9678	0.9686	0.9693	0.9699	0.9706
1.9	0.9713	0.9719	0.9726	0.9732	0.9738	0.9744	0.9750	0.9756	0.9761	0.9767
2.0	0.9772	0.9778	0.9783	0.9788	0.9793	0.9798	0.9803	0.9808	0.9812	0.9817
2.1	0.9821	0.9826	0.9830	0.9834	0.9838	0.9842	0.9846	0.9850	0.9854	0.9857
2.2	0.9861	0.9864	0.9868	0.9871	0.9875	0.9878	0.9881	0.9884	0.9887	0.9890
2.3	0.9893	0.9896	0.9898	0.9901	0.9904	0.9906	0.9909	0.9911	0.9913	0.9916
2.4	0.9918	0.9920	0.9922	0.9925	0.9927	0.9929	0.9931	0.9932	0.9934	0.9936
2.5	0.9938	0.9940	0.9941	0.9943	0.9945	0.9946	0.9948	0.9949 *	0.9951	0.9952
2.6	0.9953	0.9955	0.9956	0.9957	0.9959	0.9960	0.9961	0.9962	0.9963	0.9964
2.7	0.9965	0.9966	0.9967	0.9968	0.9969	0.9970	0.9971	0.9972	0.9973	0.9974
2.8	0.9974	0.9975	0.9976	0.9977	0.9977	0.9978	0.9979	0.9979	0.9980	0.9981
2.9	0.9981	0.9982	0.9982	0.9983	0.9984	0.9984	0.9985	0.9985	0.9986	0.9986
3.0	0.9987	0.9987	0.9987	0.9988	0.9988	0.9989	0.9989	0.9989	0.9990	0.9990
3.1	0.9990	0.9991	0.9991	0.9991	0.9992	0.9992	0.9992	0.9992	0.9993	0.9993
3.2	0.9993	0.9993	0.9994	0.9994	0.9994	0.9994	0.9994	0.9995	0.9995	0.9995
3.3	0.9995	0.9995	0.9995	0.9996	0.9996	0.9996	0.9996	0.9996	0.9996	0.9997
3.4	0.9997	0.9997	0.9997	0.9997	0.9997	0.9997	0.9997	0.9997	0.9997	0.9998
3.5	0.9998	0.9998	0.9998	0.9998	0.9998	0.9998	0.9998	0.9998	0.9998	0.9998
3.6	0.9998	0.9998	0.9999	0.9999	0.9999	0.9999	0.9999	0.9999	0.9999	0.9999
3.7	0.9999									

Note: For all values greater than 3.70, use 0.9999 for the area.

z score	Area
1.645	0.9500
2.575	0.9950

Table F	The *t* Distribution						
	Confidence intervals	**50%**	**80%**	**90%**	**95%**	**98%**	**99%**
	One tail, α	**0.25**	**0.10**	**0.05**	**0.025**	**0.01**	**0.005**
d.f.	**Two tails, α**	**0.50**	**0.20**	**0.10**	**0.05**	**0.02**	**0.01**
1		1.000	3.078	6.314	12.706	31.821	63.657
2		.816	1.886	2.920	4.303	6.965	9.925
3		.765	1.638	2.353	3.182	4.541	5.841
4		.741	1.533	2.132	2.776	3.747	4.604
5		.727	1.476	2.015	2.571	3.365	4.032
6		.718	1.440	1.943	2.447	3.143	3.707
7		.711	1.415	1.895	2.365	2.998	3.499
8		.706	1.397	1.860	2.306	2.896	3.355
9		.703	1.383	1.833	2.262	2.821	3.250
10		.700	1.372	1.812	2.228	2.764	3.169
11		.697	1.363	1.796	2.201	2.718	3.106
12		.695	1.356	1.782	2.179	2.681	3.055
13		.694	1.350	1.771	2.160	2.650	3.012
14		.692	1.345	1.761	2.145	2.624	2.977
15		.691	1.341	1.753	2.131	2.602	2.947
16		.690	1.337	1.746	2.120	2.583	2.921
17		.689	1.333	1.740	2.110	2.567	2.898
18		.688	1.330	1.734	2.101	2.552	2.878
19		.688	1.328	1.729	2.093	2.539	2.861
20		.687	1.325	1.725	2.086	2.528	2.845
21		.686	1.323	1.721	2.080	2.518	2.831
22		.686	1.321	1.717	2.074	2.508	2.819
23		.685	1.319	1.714	2.069	2.500	2.807
24		.685	1.318	1.711	2.064	2.492	2.797
25		.684	1.316	1.708	2.060	2.485	2.787
26		.684	1.315	1.706	2.056	2.479	2.779
27		.684	1.314	1.703	2.052	2.473	2.771
28		.683	1.313	1.701	2.048	2.467	2.763
$(z)\ \infty$		.674	1.282[a]	1.645[b]	1.960	2.326[c]	2.576[d]

[a]This value has been rounded to 1.28 in the textbook.
[b]This value has been rounded to 1.65 in the textbook.
[c]This value has been rounded to 2.33 in the textbook.
[d]This value has been rounded to 2.58 in the textbook.

Source: Adapted from W. H. Beyer, *Handbook of Tables for Probability and Statistics,* 2nd ed., CRC Press, Boca Raton, Fla., 1986. Reprinted with permission.

One tail

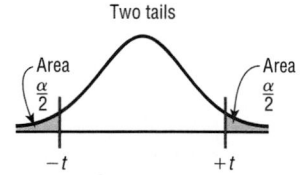

Two tails

| Table G | The Chi-Square Distribution |

Degrees of freedom	α									
	0.995	0.99	0.975	0.95	0.90	0.10	0.05	0.025	0.01	0.005
1	—	—	0.001	0.004	0.016	2.706	3.841	5.024	6.635	7.879
2	0.010	0.020	0.051	0.103	0.211	4.605	5.991	7.378	9.210	10.597
3	0.072	0.115	0.216	0.352	0.584	6.251	7.815	9.348	11.345	12.838
4	0.207	0.297	0.484	0.711	1.064	7.779	9.488	11.143	13.277	14.860
5	0.412	0.554	0.831	1.145	1.610	9.236	11.071	12.833	15.086	16.750
6	0.676	0.872	1.237	1.635	2.204	10.645	12.592	14.449	16.812	18.548
7	0.989	1.239	1.690	2.167	2.833	12.017	14.067	16.013	18.475	20.278
8	1.344	1.646	2.180	2.733	3.490	13.362	15.507	17.535	20.090	21.955
9	1.735	2.088	2.700	3.325	4.168	14.684	16.919	19.023	21.666	23.589
10	2.156	2.558	3.247	3.940	4.865	15.987	18.307	20.483	23.209	25.188
11	2.603	3.053	3.816	4.575	5.578	17.275	19.675	21.920	24.725	26.757
12	3.074	3.571	4.404	5.226	6.304	18.549	21.026	23.337	26.217	28.299
13	3.565	4.107	5.009	5.892	7.042	19.812	22.362	24.736	27.688	29.819
14	4.075	4.660	5.629	6.571	7.790	21.064	23.685	26.119	29.141	31.319
15	4.601	5.229	6.262	7.261	8.547	22.307	24.996	27.488	30.578	32.801
16	5.142	5.812	6.908	7.962	9.312	23.542	26.296	28.845	32.000	34.267
17	5.697	6.408	7.564	8.672	10.085	24.769	27.587	30.191	33.409	35.718
18	6.265	7.015	8.231	9.390	10.865	25.989	28.869	31.526	34.805	37.156
19	6.844	7.633	8.907	10.117	11.651	27.204	30.144	32.852	36.191	38.582
20	7.434	8.260	9.591	10.851	12.443	28.412	31.410	34.170	37.566	39.997
21	8.034	8.897	10.283	11.591	13.240	29.615	32.671	35.479	38.932	41.401
22	8.643	9.542	10.982	12.338	14.042	30.813	33.924	36.781	40.289	42.796
23	9.262	10.196	11.689	13.091	14.848	32.007	35.172	38.076	41.638	44.181
24	9.886	10.856	12.401	13.848	15.659	33.196	36.415	39.364	42.980	45.559
25	10.520	11.524	13.120	14.611	16.473	34.382	37.652	40.646	44.314	46.928
26	11.160	12.198	13.844	15.379	17.292	35.563	38.885	41.923	45.642	48.290
27	11.808	12.879	14.573	16.151	18.114	36.741	40.113	43.194	46.963	49.645
28	12.461	13.565	15.308	16.928	18.939	37.916	41.337	44.461	48.278	50.993
29	13.121	14.257	16.047	17.708	19.768	39.087	42.557	45.722	49.588	52.336
30	13.787	14.954	16.791	18.493	20.599	40.256	43.773	46.979	50.892	53.672
40	20.707	22.164	24.433	26.509	29.051	51.805	55.758	59.342	63.691	66.766
50	27.991	29.707	32.357	34.764	37.689	63.167	67.505	71.420	76.154	79.490
60	35.534	37.485	40.482	43.188	46.459	74.397	79.082	83.298	88.379	91.952
70	43.275	45.442	48.758	51.739	55.329	85.527	90.531	95.023	100.425	104.215
80	51.172	53.540	57.153	60.391	64.278	96.578	101.879	106.629	112.329	116.321
90	59.196	61.754	65.647	69.126	73.291	107.565	113.145	118.136	124.116	128.299
100	67.328	70.065	74.222	77.929	82.358	118.498	124.342	129.561	135.807	140.169

Source: Donald B. Owen, *Handbook of Statistics Tables,* The Chi-Square Distribution Table, © 1962 by Addison-Wesley Publishing Company, Inc. Copyright renewal © 1990. Reprinted by permission of Pearson Education, Inc.

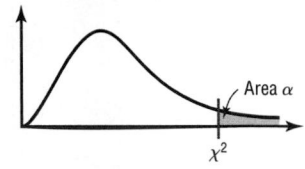

668   Appendix C Tables

Table H   The F Distribution

$\alpha = 0.005$

d.f.N.: degrees of freedom, numerator

d.f.D.: degrees of freedom, denominator	1	2	3	4	5	6	7	8	9	10	12	15	20	24	30	40	60	120	∞
1	16,211	20,000	21,615	22,500	23,056	23,437	23,715	23,925	24,091	24,224	24,426	24,630	24,836	24,940	25,044	25,148	25,253	25,359	25,465
2	198.5	199.0	199.2	199.2	199.3	199.3	199.4	199.4	199.4	199.4	199.4	199.4	199.4	199.5	199.5	199.5	199.5	199.5	199.5
3	55.55	49.80	47.47	46.19	45.39	44.84	44.43	44.13	43.88	43.69	43.39	43.08	42.78	42.62	42.47	42.31	42.15	41.99	41.83
4	31.33	26.28	24.26	23.15	22.46	21.97	21.62	21.35	21.14	20.97	20.70	20.44	20.17	20.03	19.89	19.75	19.61	19.47	19.32
5	22.78	18.31	16.53	15.56	14.94	14.51	14.20	13.96	13.77	13.62	13.38	13.15	12.90	12.78	12.66	12.53	12.40	12.27	12.14
6	18.63	14.54	12.92	12.03	11.46	11.07	10.79	10.57	10.39	10.25	10.03	9.81	9.59	9.47	9.36	9.24	9.12	9.00	8.88
7	16.24	12.40	10.88	10.05	9.52	9.16	8.89	8.68	8.51	8.38	8.18	7.97	7.75	7.65	7.53	7.42	7.31	7.19	7.08
8	14.69	11.04	9.60	8.81	8.30	7.95	7.69	7.50	7.34	7.21	7.01	6.81	6.61	6.50	6.40	6.29	6.18	6.06	5.95
9	13.61	10.11	8.72	7.96	7.47	7.13	6.88	6.69	6.54	6.42	6.23	6.03	5.83	5.73	5.62	5.52	5.41	5.30	5.19
10	12.83	9.43	8.08	7.34	6.87	6.54	6.30	6.12	5.97	5.85	5.66	5.47	5.27	5.17	5.07	4.97	4.86	4.75	4.64
11	12.23	8.91	7.60	6.88	6.42	6.10	5.86	5.68	5.54	5.42	5.24	5.05	4.86	4.76	4.65	4.55	4.44	4.34	4.23
12	11.75	8.51	7.23	6.52	6.07	5.76	5.52	5.35	5.20	5.09	4.91	4.72	4.53	4.43	4.33	4.23	4.12	4.01	3.90
13	11.37	8.19	6.93	6.23	5.79	5.48	5.25	5.08	4.94	4.82	4.64	4.46	4.27	4.17	4.07	3.97	3.87	3.76	3.65
14	11.06	7.92	6.68	6.00	5.56	5.26	5.03	4.86	4.72	4.60	4.43	4.25	4.06	3.96	3.86	3.76	3.66	3.55	3.44
15	10.80	7.70	6.48	5.80	5.37	5.07	4.85	4.67	4.54	4.42	4.25	4.07	3.88	3.79	3.69	3.58	3.48	3.37	3.26
16	10.58	7.51	6.30	5.64	5.21	4.91	4.69	4.52	4.38	4.27	4.10	3.92	3.73	3.64	3.54	3.44	3.33	3.22	3.11
17	10.38	7.35	6.16	5.50	5.07	4.78	4.56	4.39	4.25	4.14	3.97	3.79	3.61	3.51	3.41	3.31	3.21	3.10	2.98
18	10.22	7.21	6.03	5.37	4.96	4.66	4.44	4.28	4.14	4.03	3.86	3.68	3.50	3.40	3.30	3.20	3.10	2.99	2.87
19	10.07	7.09	5.92	5.27	4.85	4.56	4.34	4.18	4.04	3.93	3.76	3.59	3.40	3.31	3.21	3.11	3.00	2.89	2.78
20	9.94	6.99	5.82	5.17	4.76	4.47	4.26	4.09	3.96	3.85	3.68	3.50	3.32	3.22	3.12	3.02	2.92	2.81	2.69
21	9.83	6.89	5.73	5.09	4.68	4.39	4.18	4.01	3.88	3.77	3.60	3.43	3.24	3.15	3.05	2.95	2.84	2.73	2.61
22	9.73	6.81	5.65	5.02	4.61	4.32	4.11	3.94	3.81	3.70	3.54	3.36	3.18	3.08	2.98	2.88	2.77	2.66	2.55
23	9.63	6.73	5.58	4.95	4.54	4.26	4.05	3.88	3.75	3.64	3.47	3.30	3.12	3.02	2.92	2.82	2.71	2.60	2.48
24	9.55	6.66	5.52	4.89	4.49	4.20	3.99	3.83	3.69	3.59	3.42	3.25	3.06	2.97	2.87	2.77	2.66	2.55	2.43
25	9.48	6.60	5.46	4.84	4.43	4.15	3.94	3.78	3.64	3.54	3.37	3.20	3.01	2.92	2.82	2.72	2.61	2.50	2.38
26	9.41	6.54	5.41	4.79	4.38	4.10	3.89	3.73	3.60	3.49	3.33	3.15	2.97	2.87	2.77	2.67	2.56	2.45	2.33
27	9.34	6.49	5.36	4.74	4.34	4.06	3.85	3.69	3.56	3.45	3.28	3.11	2.93	2.83	2.73	2.63	2.52	2.41	2.25
28	9.28	6.44	5.32	4.70	4.30	4.02	3.81	3.65	3.52	3.41	3.25	3.07	2.89	2.79	2.69	2.59	2.48	2.37	2.29
29	9.23	6.40	5.28	4.66	4.26	3.98	3.77	3.61	3.48	3.38	3.21	3.04	2.86	2.76	2.66	2.56	2.45	2.33	2.24
30	9.18	6.35	5.24	4.62	4.23	3.95	3.74	3.58	3.45	3.34	3.18	3.01	2.82	2.73	2.63	2.52	2.42	2.30	2.18
40	8.83	6.07	4.98	4.37	3.99	3.71	3.51	3.35	3.22	3.12	2.95	2.78	2.60	2.50	2.40	2.30	2.18	2.06	1.93
60	8.49	5.79	4.73	4.14	3.76	3.49	3.29	3.13	3.01	2.90	2.74	2.57	2.39	2.29	2.19	2.08	1.96	1.83	1.69
120	8.18	5.54	4.50	3.92	3.55	3.28	3.09	2.93	2.81	2.71	2.54	2.37	2.19	2.09	1.98	1.87	1.75	1.61	1.43
∞	7.88	5.30	4.28	3.72	3.35	3.09	2.90	2.74	2.62	2.52	2.36	2.19	2.00	1.90	1.79	1.67	1.53	1.36	1.00

Table H (continued)

$\alpha = 0.01$

d.f.N.: degrees of freedom, numerator

d.f.D.: degrees of freedom, denominator	1	2	3	4	5	6	7	8	9	10	12	15	20	24	30	40	60	120	∞
1	4052	4999.5	5403	5625	5764	5859	5928	5982	6022	6056	6106	6157	6209	6235	6261	6287	6313	6339	6366
2	98.50	99.00	99.17	99.25	99.30	99.33	99.36	99.37	99.39	99.40	99.42	99.43	99.45	99.46	99.47	99.47	99.48	99.49	99.50
3	34.12	30.82	29.46	28.71	28.24	27.91	27.67	27.49	27.35	27.23	27.05	26.87	26.69	26.60	26.50	26.41	26.32	26.22	26.13
4	21.20	18.00	16.69	15.98	15.52	15.21	14.98	14.80	14.66	14.55	14.37	14.20	14.02	13.93	13.84	13.75	13.65	13.56	13.46
5	16.26	13.27	12.06	11.39	10.97	10.67	10.46	10.29	10.16	10.05	9.89	9.72	9.55	9.47	9.38	9.29	9.20	9.11	9.02
6	13.75	10.92	9.78	9.15	8.75	8.47	8.26	8.10	7.98	7.87	7.72	7.56	7.40	7.31	7.23	7.14	7.06	6.97	6.88
7	12.25	9.55	8.45	7.85	7.46	7.19	6.99	6.84	6.72	6.62	6.47	6.31	6.16	6.07	5.99	5.91	5.82	5.74	5.65
8	11.26	8.65	7.59	7.01	6.63	6.37	6.18	6.03	5.91	5.81	5.67	5.52	5.36	5.28	5.20	5.12	5.03	4.95	4.86
9	10.56	8.02	6.99	6.42	6.06	5.80	5.61	5.47	5.35	5.26	5.11	4.96	4.81	4.73	4.65	4.57	4.48	4.40	4.31
10	10.04	7.56	6.55	5.99	5.64	5.39	5.20	5.06	4.94	4.85	4.71	4.56	4.41	4.33	4.25	4.17	4.08	4.00	3.91
11	9.65	7.21	6.22	5.67	5.32	5.07	4.89	4.74	4.63	4.54	4.40	4.25	4.10	4.02	3.94	3.86	3.78	3.69	3.60
12	9.33	6.93	5.95	5.41	5.06	4.82	4.64	4.50	4.39	4.30	4.16	4.01	3.86	3.78	3.70	3.62	3.54	3.45	3.36
13	9.07	6.70	5.74	5.21	4.86	4.62	4.44	4.30	4.19	4.10	3.96	3.82	3.66	3.59	3.51	3.43	3.34	3.25	3.17
14	8.86	6.51	5.56	5.04	4.69	4.46	4.28	4.14	4.03	3.94	3.80	3.66	3.51	3.43	3.35	3.27	3.18	3.09	3.00
15	8.68	6.36	5.42	4.89	4.56	4.32	4.14	4.00	3.89	3.80	3.67	3.52	3.37	3.29	3.21	3.13	3.05	2.96	2.87
16	8.53	6.23	5.29	4.77	4.44	4.20	4.03	3.89	3.78	3.69	3.55	3.41	3.26	3.18	3.10	3.02	2.93	2.84	2.75
17	8.40	6.11	5.18	4.67	4.34	4.10	3.93	3.79	3.68	3.59	3.46	3.31	3.16	3.08	3.00	2.92	2.83	2.75	2.65
18	8.29	6.01	5.09	4.58	4.25	4.01	3.84	3.71	3.60	3.51	3.37	3.23	3.08	3.00	2.92	2.84	2.75	2.66	2.57
19	8.18	5.93	5.01	4.50	4.17	3.94	3.77	3.63	3.52	3.43	3.30	3.15	3.00	2.92	2.84	2.76	2.67	2.58	2.49
20	8.10	5.85	4.94	4.43	4.10	3.87	3.70	3.56	3.46	3.37	3.23	3.09	2.94	2.86	2.78	2.69	2.61	2.52	2.42
21	8.02	5.78	4.87	4.37	4.04	3.81	3.64	3.51	3.40	3.31	3.17	3.03	2.88	2.80	2.72	2.64	2.55	2.46	2.36
22	7.95	5.72	4.82	4.31	3.99	3.76	3.59	3.45	3.35	3.26	3.12	2.98	2.83	2.75	2.67	2.58	2.50	2.40	2.31
23	7.88	5.66	4.76	4.26	3.94	3.71	3.54	3.41	3.30	3.21	3.07	2.93	2.78	2.70	2.62	2.54	2.45	2.35	2.26
24	7.82	5.61	4.72	4.22	3.90	3.67	3.50	3.36	3.26	3.17	3.03	2.89	2.74	2.66	2.58	2.49	2.40	2.31	2.21
25	7.77	5.57	4.68	4.18	3.85	3.63	3.46	3.32	3.22	3.13	2.99	2.85	2.70	2.62	2.54	2.45	2.36	2.27	2.17
26	7.72	5.53	4.64	4.14	3.82	3.59	3.42	3.29	3.18	3.09	2.96	2.81	2.66	2.58	2.50	2.42	2.33	2.23	2.13
27	7.68	5.49	4.60	4.11	3.78	3.56	3.39	3.26	3.15	3.06	2.93	2.78	2.63	2.55	2.47	2.38	2.29	2.20	2.10
28	7.64	5.45	4.57	4.07	3.75	3.53	3.36	3.23	3.12	3.03	2.90	2.75	2.60	2.52	2.44	2.35	2.26	2.17	2.06
29	7.60	5.42	4.54	4.04	3.73	3.50	3.33	3.20	3.09	3.00	2.87	2.73	2.57	2.49	2.41	2.33	2.23	2.14	2.03
30	7.56	5.39	4.51	4.02	3.70	3.47	3.30	3.17	3.07	2.98	2.84	2.70	2.55	2.47	2.39	2.30	2.21	2.11	2.01
40	7.31	5.18	4.31	3.83	3.51	3.29	3.12	2.99	2.89	2.80	2.66	2.52	2.37	2.29	2.20	2.11	2.02	1.92	1.80
60	7.08	4.98	4.13	3.65	3.34	3.12	2.95	2.82	2.72	2.63	2.50	2.35	2.20	2.12	2.03	1.94	1.84	1.73	1.60
120	6.85	4.79	3.95	3.48	3.17	2.96	2.79	2.66	2.56	2.47	2.34	2.19	2.03	1.95	1.86	1.76	1.66	1.53	1.38
∞	6.63	4.61	3.78	3.32	3.02	2.80	2.64	2.51	2.41	2.32	2.18	2.04	1.88	1.79	1.70	1.59	1.47	1.32	1.00

Table H (continued)

$\alpha = 0.025$

d.f.D.: degrees of freedom, denominator	d.f.N.: degrees of freedom, numerator																		
	1	**2**	**3**	**4**	**5**	**6**	**7**	**8**	**9**	**10**	**12**	**15**	**20**	**24**	**30**	**40**	**60**	**120**	**∞**
1	647.8	799.5	864.2	899.6	921.8	937.1	948.2	956.7	963.3	968.6	976.7	984.9	993.1	997.2	1001	1006	1010	1014	1018
2	38.51	39.00	39.17	39.25	39.30	39.33	39.36	39.37	39.39	39.40	39.41	39.43	39.45	39.46	39.46	39.47	39.48	39.49	39.50
3	17.44	16.04	15.44	15.10	14.88	14.73	14.62	14.54	14.47	14.42	14.34	14.25	14.17	14.12	14.08	14.04	13.99	13.95	13.90
4	12.22	10.65	9.98	9.60	9.36	9.20	9.07	8.98	8.90	8.84	8.75	8.66	8.56	8.51	8.46	8.41	8.36	8.31	8.26
5	10.01	8.43	7.76	7.39	7.15	6.98	6.85	6.76	6.68	6.62	6.52	6.43	6.33	6.28	6.23	6.18	6.12	6.07	6.02
6	8.81	7.26	6.60	6.23	5.99	5.82	5.70	5.60	5.52	5.46	5.37	5.27	5.17	5.12	5.07	5.01	4.96	4.90	4.85
7	8.07	6.54	5.89	5.52	5.29	5.12	4.99	4.90	4.82	4.76	4.67	4.57	4.47	4.42	4.36	4.31	4.25	4.20	4.14
8	7.57	6.06	5.42	5.05	4.82	4.65	4.53	4.43	4.36	4.30	4.20	4.10	4.00	3.95	3.89	3.84	3.78	3.73	3.67
9	7.21	5.71	5.08	4.72	4.48	4.32	4.20	4.10	4.03	3.96	3.87	3.77	3.67	3.61	3.56	3.51	3.45	3.39	3.33
10	6.94	5.46	4.83	4.47	4.24	4.07	3.95	3.85	3.78	3.72	3.62	3.52	3.42	3.37	3.31	3.26	3.20	3.14	3.08
11	6.72	5.26	4.63	4.28	4.04	3.88	3.76	3.66	3.59	3.53	3.43	3.33	3.23	3.17	3.12	3.06	3.00	2.94	2.88
12	6.55	5.10	4.47	4.12	3.89	3.73	3.61	3.51	3.44	3.37	3.28	3.18	3.07	3.02	2.96	2.91	2.85	2.79	2.72
13	6.41	4.97	4.35	4.00	3.77	3.60	3.48	3.39	3.31	3.25	3.15	3.05	2.95	2.89	2.84	2.78	2.72	2.66	2.60
14	6.30	4.86	4.24	3.89	3.66	3.50	3.38	3.29	3.21	3.15	3.05	2.95	2.84	2.79	2.73	2.67	2.61	2.55	2.49
15	6.20	4.77	4.15	3.80	3.58	3.41	3.29	3.20	3.12	3.06	2.96	2.86	2.76	2.70	2.64	2.59	2.52	2.46	2.40
16	6.12	4.69	4.08	3.73	3.50	3.34	3.22	3.12	3.05	2.99	2.89	2.79	2.68	2.63	2.57	2.51	2.45	2.38	2.32
17	6.04	4.62	4.01	3.66	3.44	3.28	3.16	3.06	2.98	2.92	2.82	2.72	2.62	2.56	2.50	2.44	2.38	2.32	2.25
18	5.98	4.56	3.95	3.61	3.38	3.22	3.10	3.01	2.93	2.87	2.77	2.67	2.56	2.50	2.44	2.38	2.32	2.26	2.19
19	5.92	4.51	3.90	3.56	3.33	3.17	3.05	2.96	2.88	2.82	2.72	2.62	2.51	2.45	2.39	2.33	2.27	2.20	2.13
20	5.87	4.46	3.86	3.51	3.29	3.13	3.01	2.91	2.84	2.77	2.68	2.57	2.46	2.41	2.35	2.29	2.22	2.16	2.09
21	5.83	4.42	3.82	3.48	3.25	3.09	2.97	2.87	2.80	2.73	2.64	2.53	2.42	2.37	2.31	2.25	2.18	2.11	2.04
22	5.79	4.38	3.78	3.44	3.22	3.05	2.93	2.84	2.76	2.70	2.60	2.50	2.39	2.33	2.27	2.21	2.14	2.08	2.00
23	5.75	4.35	3.75	3.41	3.18	3.02	2.90	2.81	2.73	2.67	2.57	2.47	2.36	2.30	2.24	2.18	2.11	2.04	1.97
24	5.72	4.32	3.72	3.38	3.15	2.99	2.87	2.78	2.70	2.64	2.54	2.44	2.33	2.27	2.21	2.15	2.08	2.01	1.94
25	5.69	4.29	3.69	3.35	3.13	2.97	2.85	2.75	2.68	2.61	2.51	2.41	2.30	2.24	2.18	2.12	2.05	1.98	1.91
26	5.66	4.27	3.67	3.33	3.10	2.94	2.82	2.73	2.65	2.59	2.49	2.39	2.28	2.22	2.16	2.09	2.03	1.95	1.88
27	5.63	4.24	3.65	3.31	3.08	2.92	2.80	2.71	2.63	2.57	2.47	2.36	2.25	2.19	2.13	2.07	2.00	1.93	1.85
28	5.61	4.22	3.63	3.29	3.06	2.90	2.78	2.69	2.61	2.55	2.45	2.34	2.23	2.17	2.11	2.05	1.98	1.91	1.83
29	5.59	4.20	3.61	3.27	3.04	2.88	2.76	2.67	2.59	2.53	2.43	2.32	2.21	2.15	2.09	2.03	1.96	1.89	1.81
30	5.57	4.18	3.59	3.25	3.03	2.87	2.75	2.65	2.57	2.51	2.41	2.31	2.20	2.14	2.07	2.01	1.94	1.87	1.79
40	5.42	4.05	3.46	3.13	2.90	2.74	2.62	2.53	2.45	2.39	2.29	2.18	2.07	2.01	1.94	1.88	1.80	1.74	1.64
60	5.29	3.93	3.34	3.01	2.79	2.63	2.51	2.41	2.33	2.27	2.17	2.06	1.94	1.88	1.82	1.74	1.67	1.58	1.48
120	5.15	3.80	3.23	2.89	2.67	2.52	2.39	2.30	2.22	2.16	2.05	1.94	1.82	1.76	1.69	1.61	1.53	1.43	1.31
∞	5.02	3.69	3.12	2.79	2.57	2.41	2.29	2.19	2.11	2.05	1.94	1.83	1.71	1.64	1.57	1.48	1.39	1.27	1.00

Table H (continued)

$\alpha = 0.05$

d.f.D.: degrees of freedom, denominator	\multicolumn{19}{c}{d.f.N.: degrees of freedom, numerator}

d.f.D.	1	2	3	4	5	6	7	8	9	10	12	15	20	24	30	40	60	120	∞
1	161.4	199.5	215.7	224.6	230.2	234.0	236.8	238.9	240.5	241.9	243.9	245.9	248.0	249.1	250.1	251.1	252.2	253.3	254.3
2	18.51	19.00	19.16	19.25	19.30	19.33	19.35	19.37	19.38	19.40	19.41	19.43	19.45	19.45	19.46	19.47	19.48	19.49	19.50
3	10.13	9.55	9.28	9.12	9.01	8.94	8.89	8.85	8.81	8.79	8.74	8.70	8.66	8.64	8.62	8.59	8.57	8.55	8.53
4	7.71	6.94	6.59	6.39	6.26	6.16	6.09	6.04	6.00	5.96	5.91	5.86	5.80	5.77	5.75	5.72	5.69	5.66	5.63
5	6.61	5.79	5.41	5.19	5.05	4.95	4.88	4.82	4.77	4.74	4.68	4.62	4.56	4.53	4.50	4.46	4.43	4.40	4.36
6	5.99	5.14	4.76	4.53	4.39	4.28	4.21	4.15	4.10	4.06	4.00	3.94	3.87	3.84	3.81	3.77	3.74	3.70	3.67
7	5.59	4.74	4.35	4.12	3.97	3.87	3.79	3.73	3.68	3.64	3.57	3.51	3.44	3.41	3.38	3.34	3.30	3.27	3.23
8	5.32	4.46	4.07	3.84	3.69	3.58	3.50	3.44	3.39	3.35	3.28	3.22	3.15	3.12	3.08	3.04	3.01	2.97	2.93
9	5.12	4.26	3.86	3.63	3.48	3.37	3.29	3.23	3.18	3.14	3.07	3.01	2.94	2.90	2.86	2.83	2.79	2.75	2.71
10	4.96	4.10	3.71	3.48	3.33	3.22	3.14	3.07	3.02	2.98	2.91	2.85	2.77	2.74	2.70	2.66	2.62	2.58	2.54
11	4.84	3.98	3.59	3.36	3.20	3.09	3.01	2.95	2.90	2.85	2.79	2.72	2.65	2.61	2.57	2.53	2.49	2.45	2.40
12	4.75	3.89	3.49	3.26	3.11	3.00	2.91	2.85	2.80	2.75	2.69	2.62	2.54	2.51	2.47	2.43	2.38	2.34	2.30
13	4.67	3.81	3.41	3.18	3.03	2.92	2.83	2.77	2.71	2.67	2.60	2.53	2.46	2.42	2.38	2.34	2.30	2.25	2.21
14	4.60	3.74	3.34	3.11	2.96	2.85	2.76	2.70	2.65	2.60	2.53	2.46	2.39	2.35	2.31	2.27	2.22	2.18	2.13
15	4.54	3.68	3.29	3.06	2.90	2.79	2.71	2.64	2.59	2.54	2.48	2.40	2.33	2.29	2.25	2.20	2.16	2.11	2.07
16	4.49	3.63	3.24	3.01	2.85	2.74	2.66	2.59	2.54	2.49	2.42	2.35	2.28	2.24	2.19	2.15	2.11	2.06	2.01
17	4.45	3.59	3.20	2.96	2.81	2.70	2.61	2.55	2.49	2.45	2.38	2.31	2.23	2.19	2.15	2.10	2.06	2.01	1.96
18	4.41	3.55	3.16	2.93	2.77	2.66	2.58	2.51	2.46	2.41	2.34	2.27	2.19	2.15	2.11	2.06	2.02	1.97	1.92
19	4.38	3.52	3.13	2.90	2.74	2.63	2.54	2.48	2.42	2.38	2.31	2.23	2.16	2.11	2.07	2.03	1.98	1.93	1.88
20	4.35	3.49	3.10	2.87	2.71	2.60	2.51	2.45	2.39	2.35	2.28	2.20	2.12	2.08	2.04	1.99	1.95	1.90	1.84
21	4.32	3.47	3.07	2.84	2.68	2.57	2.49	2.42	2.37	2.32	2.25	2.18	2.10	2.05	2.01	1.96	1.92	1.87	1.81
22	4.30	3.44	3.05	2.82	2.66	2.55	2.46	2.40	2.34	2.30	2.23	2.15	2.07	2.03	1.98	1.94	1.89	1.84	1.78
23	4.28	3.42	3.03	2.80	2.64	2.53	2.44	2.37	2.32	2.27	2.20	2.13	2.05	2.01	1.96	1.91	1.86	1.81	1.76
24	4.26	3.40	3.01	2.78	2.62	2.51	2.42	2.36	2.30	2.25	2.18	2.11	2.03	1.98	1.94	1.89	1.84	1.79	1.73
25	4.24	3.39	2.99	2.76	2.60	2.49	2.40	2.34	2.28	2.24	2.16	2.09	2.01	1.96	1.92	1.87	1.82	1.77	1.71
26	4.23	3.37	2.98	2.74	2.59	2.47	2.39	2.32	2.27	2.22	2.15	2.07	1.99	1.95	1.90	1.85	1.80	1.75	1.69
27	4.21	3.35	2.96	2.73	2.57	2.46	2.37	2.31	2.25	2.20	2.13	2.06	1.97	1.93	1.88	1.84	1.79	1.73	1.67
28	4.20	3.34	2.95	2.71	2.56	2.45	2.36	2.29	2.24	2.19	2.12	2.04	1.96	1.91	1.87	1.82	1.77	1.71	1.65
29	4.18	3.33	2.93	2.70	2.55	2.43	2.35	2.28	2.22	2.18	2.10	2.03	1.94	1.90	1.85	1.81	1.75	1.70	1.64
30	4.17	3.32	2.92	2.69	2.53	2.42	2.33	2.27	2.21	2.16	2.09	2.01	1.93	1.89	1.84	1.79	1.74	1.68	1.62
40	4.08	3.23	2.84	2.61	2.45	2.34	2.25	2.18	2.12	2.08	2.00	1.92	1.84	1.79	1.74	1.69	1.64	1.58	1.51
60	4.00	3.15	2.76	2.53	2.37	2.25	2.17	2.10	2.04	1.99	1.92	1.84	1.75	1.70	1.65	1.59	1.53	1.47	1.39
120	3.92	3.07	2.68	2.45	2.29	2.17	2.09	2.02	1.96	1.91	1.83	1.75	1.66	1.61	1.55	1.50	1.43	1.35	1.25
∞	3.84	3.00	2.60	2.37	2.21	2.10	2.01	1.94	1.88	1.83	1.75	1.67	1.57	1.52	1.46	1.39	1.32	1.22	1.00

Table H *(concluded)*

α = 0.10

d.f.N.: degrees of freedom, numerator

d.f.D.: degrees of freedom, denominator	1	2	3	4	5	6	7	8	9	10	12	15	20	24	30	40	60	120	∞
1	39.86	49.50	53.59	55.83	57.24	58.20	58.91	59.44	59.86	60.19	60.71	61.22	61.74	62.00	62.26	62.53	62.79	63.06	63.33
2	8.53	9.00	9.16	9.24	9.29	9.33	9.35	9.37	9.38	9.39	9.41	9.42	9.44	9.45	9.46	9.47	9.47	9.48	9.49
3	5.54	5.46	5.39	5.34	5.31	5.28	5.27	5.25	5.24	5.23	5.22	5.20	5.18	5.18	5.17	5.16	5.15	5.14	5.13
4	4.54	4.32	4.19	4.11	4.05	4.01	3.98	3.95	3.94	3.92	3.90	3.87	3.84	3.83	3.82	3.80	3.79	3.78	3.76
5	4.06	3.78	3.62	3.52	3.45	3.40	3.37	3.34	3.32	3.30	3.27	3.24	3.21	3.19	3.17	3.16	3.14	3.12	3.10
6	3.78	3.46	3.29	3.18	3.11	3.05	3.01	2.98	2.96	2.94	2.90	2.87	2.84	2.82	2.80	2.78	2.76	2.74	2.72
7	3.59	3.26	3.07	2.96	2.88	2.83	2.78	2.75	2.72	2.70	2.67	2.63	2.59	2.58	2.56	2.54	2.51	2.49	2.47
8	3.46	3.11	2.92	2.81	2.73	2.67	2.62	2.59	2.56	2.54	2.50	2.46	2.42	2.40	2.38	2.36	2.34	2.32	2.29
9	3.36	3.01	2.81	2.69	2.61	2.55	2.51	2.47	2.44	2.42	2.38	2.34	2.30	2.28	2.25	2.23	2.21	2.18	2.16
10	3.29	2.92	2.73	2.61	2.52	2.46	2.41	2.38	2.35	2.32	2.28	2.24	2.20	2.18	2.16	2.13	2.11	2.08	2.06
11	3.23	2.86	2.66	2.54	2.45	2.39	2.34	2.30	2.27	2.25	2.21	2.17	2.12	2.10	2.08	2.05	2.03	2.00	1.97
12	3.18	2.81	2.61	2.48	2.39	2.33	2.28	2.24	2.21	2.19	2.15	2.10	2.06	2.04	2.01	1.99	1.96	1.93	1.90
13	3.14	2.76	2.56	2.43	2.35	2.28	2.23	2.20	2.16	2.14	2.10	2.05	2.01	1.98	1.96	1.93	1.90	1.88	1.85
14	3.10	2.73	2.52	2.39	2.31	2.24	2.19	2.15	2.12	2.10	2.05	2.01	1.96	1.94	1.91	1.89	1.86	1.83	1.80
15	3.07	2.70	2.49	2.36	2.27	2.21	2.16	2.12	2.09	2.06	2.02	1.97	1.92	1.90	1.87	1.85	1.82	1.79	1.76
16	3.05	2.67	2.46	2.33	2.24	2.18	2.13	2.09	2.06	2.03	1.99	1.94	1.89	1.87	1.84	1.81	1.78	1.75	1.72
17	3.03	2.64	2.44	2.31	2.22	2.15	2.10	2.06	2.03	2.00	1.96	1.91	1.86	1.84	1.81	1.78	1.75	1.72	1.69
18	3.01	2.62	2.42	2.29	2.20	2.13	2.08	2.04	2.00	1.98	1.93	1.89	1.84	1.81	1.78	1.75	1.72	1.69	1.66
19	2.99	2.61	2.40	2.27	2.18	2.11	2.06	2.02	1.98	1.96	1.91	1.86	1.81	1.79	1.76	1.73	1.70	1.67	1.63
20	2.97	2.59	2.38	2.25	2.16	2.09	2.04	2.00	1.96	1.94	1.89	1.84	1.79	1.77	1.74	1.71	1.68	1.64	1.61
21	2.96	2.57	2.36	2.23	2.14	2.08	2.02	1.98	1.95	1.92	1.87	1.83	1.78	1.75	1.72	1.69	1.66	1.62	1.59
22	2.95	2.56	2.35	2.22	2.13	2.06	2.01	1.97	1.93	1.90	1.86	1.81	1.76	1.73	1.70	1.67	1.64	1.60	1.57
23	2.94	2.55	2.34	2.21	2.11	2.05	1.99	1.95	1.92	1.89	1.84	1.80	1.74	1.72	1.69	1.66	1.62	1.59	1.55
24	2.93	2.54	2.33	2.19	2.10	2.04	1.98	1.94	1.91	1.88	1.83	1.78	1.73	1.70	1.67	1.64	1.61	1.57	1.53
25	2.92	2.53	2.32	2.18	2.09	2.02	1.97	1.93	1.89	1.87	1.82	1.77	1.72	1.69	1.66	1.63	1.59	1.56	1.52
26	2.91	2.52	2.31	2.17	2.08	2.01	1.96	1.92	1.88	1.86	1.81	1.76	1.71	1.68	1.65	1.61	1.58	1.54	1.50
27	2.90	2.51	2.30	2.17	2.07	2.00	1.95	1.91	1.87	1.85	1.80	1.75	1.70	1.67	1.64	1.60	1.57	1.53	1.49
28	2.89	2.50	2.29	2.16	2.06	2.00	1.94	1.90	1.87	1.84	1.79	1.74	1.69	1.66	1.63	1.59	1.56	1.52	1.48
29	2.89	2.50	2.28	2.15	2.06	1.99	1.93	1.89	1.86	1.83	1.78	1.73	1.68	1.65	1.62	1.58	1.55	1.51	1.47
30	2.88	2.49	2.28	2.14	2.05	1.98	1.93	1.88	1.85	1.82	1.77	1.72	1.67	1.64	1.61	1.57	1.54	1.50	1.46
40	2.84	2.44	2.23	2.09	2.00	1.93	1.87	1.83	1.79	1.76	1.71	1.66	1.61	1.57	1.54	1.51	1.47	1.42	1.38
60	2.79	2.39	2.18	2.04	1.95	1.87	1.82	1.77	1.74	1.71	1.66	1.60	1.54	1.51	1.48	1.44	1.40	1.35	1.29
120	2.75	2.35	2.13	1.99	1.90	1.82	1.77	1.72	1.68	1.65	1.60	1.55	1.48	1.45	1.41	1.37	1.32	1.26	1.19
∞	2.71	2.30	2.08	1.94	1.85	1.77	1.72	1.67	1.63	1.60	1.55	1.49	1.42	1.38	1.34	1.30	1.24	1.17	1.00

From M. Merrington and C. M. Thompson (1943). Table of Percentage Points of the Inverted Beta (*F*) Distribution. *Biometrika 33*, pp. 74–87. Reprinted with permission from Biometrika.

Table I   Critical Values for PPMC

Reject H_0: $\rho = 0$ if the absolute value of r is greater than the value given in the table. The values are for a two-tailed test; d.f. $= n - 2$.

d.f	$\alpha = 0.05$	$\alpha = 0.01$
1	0.999	0.999
2	0.950	0.999
3	0.878	0.959
4	0.811	0.917
5	0.754	0.875
6	0.707	0.834
7	0.666	0.798
8	0.632	0.765
9	0.602	0.735
10	0.576	0.708
11	0.553	0.684
12	0.532	0.661
13	0.514	0.641
14	0.497	0.623
15	0.482	0.606
16	0.468	0.590
17	0.456	0.575
18	0.444	0.561
19	0.433	0.549
20	0.423	0.537
25	0.381	0.487
30	0.349	0.449
35	0.325	0.418
40	0.304	0.393
45	0.288	0.372
50	0.273	0.354
60	0.250	0.325
70	0.232	0.302
80	0.217	0.283
90	0.205	0.267
100	0.195	0.254

Source: From *Biometrika Tables for Statisticians,* vol. 1 (1962), p. 138. Reprinted with permission.

Table J   Critical Values for the Sign Test

Reject the null hypothesis if the smaller number of positive or negative signs is less than or equal to the value in the table.

n	One-tailed, $\alpha = 0.005$ / Two-tailed, $\alpha = 0.01$	$\alpha = 0.01$ / $\alpha = 0.02$	$\alpha = 0.025$ / $\alpha = 0.05$	$\alpha = 0.05$ / $\alpha = 0.10$
8	0	0	0	1
9	0	0	1	1
10	0	0	1	1
11	0	1	1	2
12	1	1	2	2
13	1	1	2	3
14	1	2	3	3
15	2	2	3	3
16	2	2	3	4
17	2	3	4	4
18	3	3	4	5
19	3	4	4	5
20	3	4	5	5
21	4	4	5	6
22	4	5	5	6
23	4	5	6	7
24	5	5	6	7
25	5	6	6	7

Note: Table J is for one-tailed or two-tailed tests. The term n represents the total number of positive and negative signs. The test value is the number of less frequent signs.

Source: From *Journal of American Statistical Association,* vol. 41 (1946), pp. 557–66. W. J. Dixon and A. M. Mood.

Table K	Critical Values for the Wilcoxon Signed-Rank Test

Reject the null hypothesis if the test value is less than or equal to the value given in the table.

	One-tailed, $\alpha = 0.05$	$\alpha = 0.025$	$\alpha = 0.01$	$\alpha = 0.005$
n	Two-tailed, $\alpha = 0.10$	$\alpha = 0.05$	$\alpha = 0.02$	$\alpha = 0.01$
5	1			
6	2	1		
7	4	2	0	
8	6	4	2	0
9	8	6	3	2
10	11	8	5	3
11	14	11	7	5
12	17	14	10	7
13	21	17	13	10
14	26	21	16	13
15	30	25	20	16
16	36	30	24	19
17	41	35	28	23
18	47	40	33	28
19	54	46	38	32
20	60	52	43	37
21	68	59	49	43
22	75	66	56	49
23	83	73	62	55
24	92	81	69	61
25	101	90	77	68
26	110	98	85	76
27	120	107	93	84
28	130	117	102	92
29	141	127	111	100
30	152	137	120	109

Source: From *Some Rapid Approximate Statistical Procedures,* Copyright 1949, 1964 Lerderle Laboratories, American Cyanamid Co., Wayne, N.J. Reprinted with permission.

Table L	Critical Values for the Rank Correlation Coefficient

Reject H_0: $\rho = 0$ if the absolute value of r_s is greater than the value given in the table.

n	$\alpha = 0.10$	$\alpha = 0.05$	$\alpha = 0.02$	$\alpha = 0.01$
5	0.900	—	—	—
6	0.829	0.886	0.943	—
7	0.714	0.786	0.893	0.929
8	0.643	0.738	0.833	0.881
9	0.600	0.700	0.783	0.833
10	0.564	0.648	0.745	0.794
11	0.536	0.618	0.709	0.818
12	0.497	0.591	0.703	0.780
13	0.475	0.566	0.673	0.745
14	0.457	0.545	0.646	0.716
15	0.441	0.525	0.623	0.689
16	0.425	0.507	0.601	0.666
17	0.412	0.490	0.582	0.645
18	0.399	0.476	0.564	0.625
19	0.388	0.462	0.549	0.608
20	0.377	0.450	0.534	0.591
21	0.368	0.438	0.521	0.576
22	0.359	0.428	0.508	0.562
23	0.351	0.418	0.496	0.549
24	0.343	0.409	0.485	0.537
25	0.336	0.400	0.475	0.526
26	0.329	0.392	0.465	0.515
27	0.323	0.385	0.456	0.505
28	0.317	0.377	0.488	0.496
29	0.311	0.370	0.440	0.487
30	0.305	0.364	0.432	0.478

Source: From N. L. Johnson and F. C. Leone, *Statistical and Experimental Design,* vol. I (1964), p. 412. Reprinted with permission from the Institute of Mathematical Statistics.

Table M — Critical Values for the Number of Runs

This table gives the critical values at $\alpha = 0.05$ for a two-tailed test. Reject the null hypothesis if the number of runs is less than or equal to the smaller value or greater than or equal to the larger value.

Value of n_1	Value of n_2																		
	2	3	4	5	6	7	8	9	10	11	12	13	14	15	16	17	18	19	20
2	1	1	1	1	1	1	1	1	1	1	2	2	2	2	2	2	2	2	2
	6	6	6	6	6	6	6	6	6	6	6	6	6	6	6	6	6	6	6
3	1	1	1	1	2	2	2	2	2	2	2	2	2	3	3	3	3	3	3
	6	8	8	8	8	8	8	8	8	8	8	8	8	8	8	8	8	8	8
4	1	1	1	2	2	2	3	3	3	3	3	3	3	3	4	4	4	4	4
	6	8	9	9	9	10	10	10	10	10	10	10	10	10	10	10	10	10	10
5	1	1	2	2	3	3	3	3	3	4	4	4	4	4	4	4	5	5	5
	6	8	9	10	10	11	11	12	12	12	12	12	12	12	12	12	12	12	12
6	1	2	2	3	3	3	3	4	4	4	4	5	5	5	5	5	5	6	6
	6	8	9	10	11	12	12	13	13	13	13	14	14	14	14	14	14	14	14
7	1	2	2	3	3	3	4	4	5	5	5	5	5	6	6	6	6	6	6
	6	8	10	11	12	13	13	14	14	14	14	15	15	15	16	16	16	16	16
8	1	2	3	3	3	4	4	5	5	5	6	6	6	6	6	7	7	7	7
	6	8	10	11	12	13	14	14	15	15	16	16	16	16	17	17	17	17	17
9	1	2	3	3	4	4	5	5	5	6	6	6	7	7	7	7	8	8	8
	6	8	10	12	13	14	14	15	16	16	16	17	17	18	18	18	18	18	18
10	1	2	3	3	4	5	5	5	6	6	7	7	7	7	8	8	8	8	9
	6	8	10	12	13	14	15	16	16	17	17	18	18	18	19	19	19	20	20
11	1	2	3	4	4	5	5	6	6	7	7	7	8	8	8	9	9	9	9
	6	8	10	12	13	14	15	16	17	17	18	19	19	19	20	20	20	21	21
12	2	2	3	4	4	5	6	6	7	7	7	8	8	8	9	9	9	10	10
	6	8	10	12	13	14	16	16	17	18	19	19	20	20	21	21	21	22	22
13	2	2	3	4	5	5	6	6	7	7	8	8	9	9	9	10	10	10	10
	6	8	10	12	14	15	16	17	18	19	19	20	20	21	21	22	22	23	23
14	2	2	3	4	5	5	6	7	7	8	8	9	9	9	10	10	10	11	11
	6	8	10	12	14	15	16	17	18	19	20	20	21	22	22	23	23	23	24
15	2	3	3	4	5	6	6	7	7	8	8	9	9	10	10	11	11	11	12
	6	8	10	12	14	15	16	18	18	19	20	21	22	22	23	23	24	24	25
16	2	3	4	4	5	6	6	7	8	8	9	9	10	10	11	11	11	12	12
	6	8	10	12	14	16	17	18	19	20	21	21	22	23	23	24	25	25	25
17	2	3	4	4	5	6	7	7	8	9	9	10	10	11	11	11	12	12	13
	6	8	10	12	14	16	17	18	19	20	21	22	23	23	24	25	25	26	26
18	2	3	4	5	5	6	7	8	8	9	9	10	10	11	11	12	12	13	13
	6	8	10	12	14	16	17	18	19	20	21	22	23	24	25	25	26	26	27
19	2	3	4	5	6	6	7	8	8	9	10	10	11	11	12	12	13	13	13
	6	8	10	12	14	16	17	18	20	21	22	23	23	24	25	26	26	27	27
20	2	3	4	5	6	6	7	8	9	9	10	10	11	12	12	13	13	13	14
	6	8	10	12	14	16	17	18	20	21	22	23	24	25	25	26	27	27	28

Source: Adapted from C. Eisenhardt and F. Swed, "Tables for Testing Randomness of Grouping in a Sequence of Alternatives," *The Annals of Statistics,* vol. 14 (1943), pp. 83–86. Reprinted with permission of the Institute of Mathematical Statistics and of the Benjamin/Cummings Publishing Company, in whose publication, *Elementary Statistics,* 3rd ed. (1989), by Mario F. Triola, this table appears.

Table N Critical Values for the Tukey Test

$\alpha = 0.01$

v \ k	2	3	4	5	6	7	8	9	10	11	12	13	14	15	16	17	18	19	20
1	90.03	135.0	164.3	185.6	202.2	215.8	227.2	237.0	245.6	253.2	260.0	266.2	271.8	277.0	281.8	286.3	290.4	294.3	298.0
2	14.04	19.02	22.29	24.72	26.63	28.20	29.53	30.68	31.69	32.59	33.40	34.13	34.81	35.43	36.00	36.53	37.03	37.50	37.95
3	8.26	10.62	12.17	13.33	14.24	15.00	15.64	16.20	16.69	17.13	17.53	17.89	18.22	18.52	18.81	19.07	19.32	19.55	19.77
4	6.51	8.12	9.17	9.96	10.58	11.10	11.55	11.93	12.27	12.57	12.84	13.09	13.32	13.53	13.73	13.91	14.08	14.24	14.40
5	5.70	6.98	7.80	8.42	8.91	9.32	9.67	9.97	10.24	10.48	10.70	10.89	11.08	11.24	11.40	11.55	11.68	11.81	11.93
6	5.24	6.33	7.03	7.56	7.97	8.32	8.61	8.87	9.10	9.30	9.48	9.65	9.81	9.95	10.08	10.21	10.32	10.43	10.54
7	4.95	5.92	6.54	7.01	7.37	7.68	7.94	8.17	8.37	8.55	8.71	8.86	9.00	9.12	9.24	9.35	9.46	9.55	9.65
8	4.75	5.64	6.20	6.62	6.96	7.24	7.47	7.68	7.86	8.03	8.18	8.31	8.44	8.55	8.66	8.76	8.85	8.94	9.03
9	4.60	5.43	5.96	6.35	6.66	6.91	7.13	7.33	7.49	7.65	7.78	7.91	8.03	8.13	8.23	8.33	8.41	8.49	8.57
10	4.48	5.27	5.77	6.14	6.43	6.67	6.87	7.05	7.21	7.36	7.49	7.60	7.71	7.81	7.91	7.99	8.08	8.15	8.23
11	4.39	5.15	5.62	5.97	6.25	6.48	6.67	6.84	6.99	7.13	7.25	7.36	7.46	7.56	7.65	7.73	7.81	7.88	7.95
12	4.32	5.05	5.50	5.84	6.10	6.32	6.51	6.67	6.81	6.94	7.06	7.17	7.26	7.36	7.44	7.52	7.59	7.66	7.73
13	4.26	4.96	5.40	5.73	5.98	6.19	6.37	6.53	6.67	6.79	6.90	7.01	7.10	7.19	7.27	7.35	7.42	7.48	7.55
14	4.21	4.89	5.32	5.63	5.88	6.08	6.26	6.41	6.54	6.66	6.77	6.87	6.96	7.05	7.13	7.20	7.27	7.33	7.39
15	4.17	4.84	5.25	5.56	5.80	5.99	6.16	6.31	6.44	6.55	6.66	6.76	6.84	6.93	7.00	7.07	7.14	7.20	7.26
16	4.13	4.79	5.19	5.49	5.72	5.92	6.08	6.22	6.35	6.46	6.56	6.66	6.74	6.82	6.90	6.97	7.03	7.09	7.15
17	4.10	4.74	5.14	5.43	5.66	5.85	6.01	6.15	6.27	6.38	6.48	6.57	6.66	6.73	6.81	6.87	6.94	7.00	7.05
18	4.07	4.70	5.09	5.38	5.60	5.79	5.94	6.08	6.20	6.31	6.41	6.50	6.58	6.65	6.73	6.79	6.85	6.91	6.97
19	4.05	4.67	5.05	5.33	5.55	5.73	5.89	6.02	6.14	6.25	6.34	6.43	6.51	6.58	6.65	6.72	6.78	6.84	6.89
20	4.02	4.64	5.02	5.29	5.51	5.69	5.84	5.97	6.09	6.19	6.28	6.37	6.45	6.52	6.59	6.65	6.71	6.77	6.82
24	3.96	4.55	4.91	5.17	5.37	5.54	5.69	5.81	5.92	6.02	6.11	6.19	6.26	6.33	6.39	6.45	6.51	6.56	6.61
30	3.89	4.45	4.80	5.05	5.24	5.40	5.54	5.65	5.76	5.85	5.93	6.01	6.08	6.14	6.20	6.26	6.31	6.36	6.41
40	3.82	4.37	4.70	4.93	5.11	5.26	5.39	5.50	5.60	5.69	5.76	5.83	5.90	5.96	6.02	6.07	6.12	6.16	6.21
60	3.76	4.28	4.59	4.82	4.99	5.13	5.25	5.36	5.45	5.53	5.60	5.67	5.73	5.78	5.84	5.89	5.93	5.97	6.01
120	3.70	4.20	4.50	4.71	4.87	5.01	5.12	5.21	5.30	5.37	5.44	5.50	5.56	5.61	5.66	5.71	5.75	5.79	5.83
∞	3.64	4.12	4.40	4.60	4.76	4.88	4.99	5.08	5.16	5.23	5.29	5.35	5.40	5.45	5.49	5.54	5.57	5.61	5.65

Table N *(continued)*

$\alpha = 0.05$

k \ v	2	3	4	5	6	7	8	9	10	11	12	13	14	15	16	17	18	19	20
1	17.97	26.98	32.82	37.08	40.41	43.12	45.40	47.36	49.07	50.59	51.96	53.20	54.33	55.36	56.32	57.22	58.04	58.83	59.56
2	6.08	8.33	9.80	10.88	11.74	12.44	13.03	13.54	13.99	14.39	14.75	15.08	15.38	15.65	15.91	16.14	16.37	16.57	16.77
3	4.50	5.91	6.82	7.50	8.04	8.48	8.85	9.18	9.46	9.72	9.95	10.15	10.35	10.53	10.69	10.84	10.98	11.11	11.24
4	3.93	5.04	5.76	6.29	6.71	7.05	7.35	7.60	7.83	8.03	8.21	8.37	8.52	8.66	8.79	8.91	9.03	9.13	9.23
5	3.64	4.60	5.22	5.67	6.03	6.33	6.58	6.80	6.99	7.17	7.32	7.47	7.60	7.72	7.83	7.93	8.03	8.12	8.21
6	3.46	4.34	4.90	5.30	5.63	5.90	6.12	6.32	6.49	6.65	6.79	6.92	7.03	7.14	7.24	7.34	7.43	7.51	7.59
7	3.34	4.16	4.68	5.06	5.36	5.61	5.82	6.00	6.16	6.30	6.43	6.55	6.66	6.76	6.85	6.94	7.02	7.10	7.17
8	3.26	4.04	4.53	4.89	5.17	5.40	5.60	5.77	5.92	6.05	6.18	6.29	6.39	6.48	6.57	6.65	6.73	6.80	6.87
9	3.20	3.95	4.41	4.76	5.02	5.24	5.43	5.59	5.74	5.87	5.98	6.09	6.19	6.28	6.36	6.44	6.51	6.58	6.64
10	3.15	3.88	4.33	4.65	4.91	5.12	5.30	5.46	5.60	5.72	5.83	5.93	6.03	6.11	6.19	6.27	6.34	6.40	6.47
11	3.11	3.82	4.26	4.57	4.82	5.03	5.20	5.35	5.49	5.61	5.71	5.81	5.90	5.98	6.06	6.13	6.20	6.27	6.33
12	3.08	3.77	4.20	4.51	4.75	4.95	5.12	5.27	5.39	5.51	5.61	5.71	5.80	5.88	5.95	6.02	6.09	6.15	6.21
13	3.06	3.73	4.15	4.45	4.69	4.88	5.05	5.19	5.32	5.43	5.53	5.63	5.71	5.79	5.86	5.93	5.99	6.05	6.11
14	3.03	3.70	4.11	4.41	4.64	4.83	4.99	5.13	5.25	5.36	5.46	5.55	5.64	5.71	5.79	5.85	5.91	5.97	6.03
15	3.01	3.67	4.08	4.37	4.59	4.78	4.94	5.08	5.20	5.31	5.40	5.49	5.57	5.65	5.72	5.78	5.85	5.90	5.96
16	3.00	3.65	4.05	4.33	4.56	4.74	4.90	5.03	5.15	5.26	5.35	5.44	5.52	5.59	5.66	5.73	5.79	5.84	5.90
17	2.98	3.63	4.02	4.30	4.52	4.70	4.86	4.99	5.11	5.21	5.31	5.39	5.47	5.54	5.61	5.67	5.73	5.79	5.84
18	2.97	3.61	4.00	4.28	4.49	4.67	4.82	4.96	5.07	5.17	5.27	5.35	5.43	5.50	5.57	5.63	5.69	5.74	5.79
19	2.96	3.59	3.98	4.25	4.47	4.65	4.79	4.92	5.04	5.14	5.23	5.31	5.39	5.46	5.53	5.59	5.65	5.70	5.75
20	2.95	3.58	3.96	4.23	4.45	4.62	4.77	4.90	5.01	5.11	5.20	5.28	5.36	5.43	5.49	5.55	5.61	5.66	5.71
24	2.92	3.53	3.90	4.17	4.37	4.54	4.68	4.81	4.92	5.01	5.10	5.18	5.25	5.32	5.38	5.44	5.49	5.55	5.59
30	2.89	3.49	3.85	4.10	4.30	4.46	4.60	4.72	4.82	4.92	5.00	5.08	5.15	5.21	5.27	5.33	5.38	5.43	5.47
40	2.86	3.44	3.79	4.04	4.23	4.39	4.52	4.63	4.73	4.82	4.90	4.98	5.04	5.11	5.16	5.22	5.27	5.31	5.36
60	2.83	3.40	3.74	3.98	4.16	4.31	4.44	4.55	4.65	4.73	4.81	4.88	4.94	5.00	5.06	5.11	5.15	5.20	5.24
120	2.80	3.36	3.68	3.92	4.10	4.24	4.36	4.47	4.56	4.64	4.71	4.78	4.84	4.90	4.95	5.00	5.04	5.09	5.13
∞	2.77	3.31	3.63	3.86	4.03	4.17	4.29	4.39	4.47	4.55	4.62	4.68	4.74	4.80	4.85	4.89	4.93	4.97	5.01

Table N *(concluded)*

$\alpha = 0.10$

k / v	2	3	4	5	6	7	8	9	10	11	12	13	14	15	16	17	18	19	20
1	8.93	13.44	16.36	18.49	20.15	21.51	22.64	23.62	24.48	25.24	25.92	26.54	27.10	27.62	28.10	28.54	28.96	29.35	29.71
2	4.13	5.73	6.77	7.54	8.14	8.63	9.05	9.41	9.72	10.01	10.26	10.49	10.70	10.89	11.07	11.24	11.39	11.54	11.68
3	3.33	4.47	5.20	5.74	6.16	6.51	6.81	7.06	7.29	7.49	7.67	7.83	7.98	8.12	8.25	8.37	8.48	8.58	8.68
4	3.01	3.98	4.59	5.03	5.39	5.68	5.93	6.14	6.33	6.49	6.65	6.78	6.91	7.02	7.13	7.23	7.33	7.41	7.50
5	2.85	3.72	4.26	4.66	4.98	5.24	5.46	5.65	5.82	5.97	6.10	6.22	6.34	6.44	6.54	6.63	6.71	6.79	6.86
6	2.75	3.56	4.07	4.44	4.73	4.97	5.17	5.34	5.50	5.64	5.76	5.87	5.98	6.07	6.16	6.25	6.32	6.40	6.47
7	2.68	3.45	3.93	4.28	4.55	4.78	4.97	5.14	5.28	5.41	5.53	5.64	5.74	5.83	5.91	5.99	6.06	6.13	6.19
8	2.63	3.37	3.83	4.17	4.43	4.65	4.83	4.99	5.13	5.25	5.36	5.46	5.56	5.64	5.72	5.80	5.87	5.93	6.00
9	2.59	3.32	3.76	4.08	4.34	4.54	4.72	4.87	5.01	5.13	5.23	5.33	5.42	5.51	5.58	5.66	5.72	5.79	5.85
10	2.56	3.27	3.70	4.02	4.26	4.47	4.64	4.78	4.91	5.03	5.13	5.23	5.32	5.40	5.47	5.54	5.61	5.67	5.73
11	2.54	3.23	3.66	3.96	4.20	4.40	4.57	4.71	4.84	4.95	5.05	5.15	5.23	5.31	5.38	5.45	5.51	5.57	5.63
12	2.52	3.20	3.62	3.92	4.16	4.35	4.51	4.65	4.78	4.89	4.99	5.08	5.16	5.24	5.31	5.37	5.44	5.49	5.55
13	2.50	3.18	3.59	3.88	4.12	4.30	4.46	4.60	4.72	4.83	4.93	5.02	5.10	5.18	5.25	5.31	5.37	5.43	5.48
14	2.49	3.16	3.56	3.85	4.08	4.27	4.42	4.56	4.68	4.79	4.88	4.97	5.05	5.12	5.19	5.26	5.32	5.37	5.43
15	2.48	3.14	3.54	3.83	4.05	4.23	4.39	4.52	4.64	4.75	4.84	4.93	5.01	5.08	5.15	5.21	5.27	5.32	5.38
16	2.47	3.12	3.52	3.80	4.03	4.21	4.36	4.49	4.61	4.71	4.81	4.89	4.97	5.04	5.11	5.17	5.23	5.28	5.33
17	2.46	3.11	3.50	3.78	4.00	4.18	4.33	4.46	4.58	4.68	4.77	4.86	4.93	5.01	5.07	5.13	5.19	5.24	5.30
18	2.45	3.10	3.49	3.77	3.98	4.16	4.31	4.44	4.55	4.65	4.75	4.83	4.90	4.98	5.04	5.10	5.16	5.21	5.26
19	2.45	3.09	3.47	3.75	3.97	4.14	4.29	4.42	4.53	4.63	4.72	4.80	4.88	4.95	5.01	5.07	5.13	5.18	5.23
20	2.44	3.08	3.46	3.74	3.95	4.12	4.27	4.40	4.51	4.61	4.70	4.78	4.85	4.92	4.99	5.05	5.10	5.16	5.20
24	2.42	3.05	3.42	3.69	3.90	4.07	4.21	4.34	4.44	4.54	4.63	4.71	4.78	4.85	4.91	4.97	5.02	5.07	5.12
30	2.40	3.02	3.39	3.65	3.85	4.02	4.16	4.28	4.38	4.47	4.56	4.64	4.71	4.77	4.83	4.89	4.94	4.99	5.03
40	2.38	2.99	3.35	3.60	3.80	3.96	4.10	4.21	4.32	4.41	4.49	4.56	4.63	4.69	4.75	4.81	4.86	4.90	4.95
60	2.36	2.96	3.31	3.56	3.75	3.91	4.04	4.16	4.25	4.34	4.42	4.49	4.56	4.62	4.67	4.73	4.78	4.82	4.86
120	2.34	2.93	3.28	3.52	3.71	3.86	3.99	4.10	4.19	4.28	4.35	4.42	4.48	4.54	4.60	4.65	4.69	4.74	4.78
∞	2.33	2.90	3.24	3.48	3.66	3.81	3.93	4.04	4.13	4.21	4.28	4.35	4.41	4.47	4.52	4.57	4.61	4.65	4.69

Source: "Tables of Range and Studentized Range," *Annals of Mathematical Statistics*, vol. 31, no. 4. Reprinted with permission of the Institute of Mathematical Sciences.

Appendix D
Data Bank

Data Bank Values

This list explains the values given for the categories in the Data Bank.

1. "Age" is given in years.
2. "Educational level" values are defined as follows:
   - 0 = no high school degree
   - 1 = high school graduate
   - 2 = college graduate
   - 3 = graduate degree
3. "Smoking status" values are defined as follows:
   - 0 = does not smoke
   - 1 = smokes less than one pack per day
   - 2 = smokes one or more than one pack per day
4. "Exercise" values are defined as follows:
   - 0 = none
   - 1 = light
   - 2 = moderate
   - 3 = heavy
5. "Weight" is given in pounds.
6. "Serum cholesterol" is given in milligram percent (mg%).
7. "Systolic pressure" is given in millimetres of mercury (mm Hg).
8. "IQ" is given in standard IQ test score values.
9. "Sodium" is given in milliequivalents per litre (mEq/1).
10. "Gender" is listed as male (M) or female (F).
11. "Marital status" values are defined as follows:
    - M = married
    - W = widowed
    - S = single
    - D = divorced

Data Bank

ID number	Age	Educational level	Smoking status	Exercise	Weight	Serum cholesterol	Systolic pressure	IQ	Sodium	Gender	Marital status
1	27	2	1	1	120	193	126	118	136	F	M
2	18	1	0	1	145	210	120	105	137	M	S
3	32	2	0	0	118	196	128	115	135	F	M
4	24	2	0	1	162	208	129	108	142	M	M
5	19	1	2	0	106	188	119	106	133	F	S
6	56	1	0	0	143	206	136	111	138	F	W
7	65	1	2	0	160	240	131	99	140	M	W
8	36	2	1	0	215	215	163	106	151	M	D
9	43	1	0	1	127	201	132	111	134	F	M
10	47	1	1	1	132	215	138	109	135	F	D

Data Bank

ID number	Age	Educational level	Smoking status	Exercise	Weight	Serum cholesterol	Systolic pressure	IQ	Sodium	Gender	Marital status
11	48	3	1	2	196	199	148	115	146	M	D
12	25	2	2	3	109	210	115	114	141	F	S
13	63	0	1	0	170	242	149	101	152	F	D
14	37	2	0	3	187	193	142	109	144	M	M
15	40	0	1	1	234	208	156	98	147	M	M
16	25	1	2	1	199	253	135	103	148	M	S
17	72	0	0	0	143	288	156	103	145	F	M
18	56	1	1	0	156	164	153	99	144	F	D
19	37	2	0	2	142	214	122	110	135	M	M
20	41	1	1	1	123	220	142	108	134	F	M
21	33	2	1	1	165	194	122	112	137	M	S
22	52	1	0	1	157	205	119	106	134	M	D
23	44	2	0	1	121	223	135	116	133	F	M
24	53	1	0	0	131	199	133	121	136	F	M
25	19	1	0	3	128	206	118	122	132	M	S
26	25	1	0	0	143	200	118	103	135	M	M
27	31	2	1	1	152	204	120	119	136	M	M
28	28	2	0	0	119	203	118	116	138	F	M
29	23	1	0	0	111	240	120	105	135	F	S
30	47	2	1	0	149	199	132	123	136	F	M
31	47	2	1	0	179	235	131	113	139	M	M
32	59	1	2	0	206	260	151	99	143	M	W
33	36	2	1	0	191	201	148	118	145	M	D
34	59	0	1	1	156	235	142	100	132	F	W
35	35	1	0	0	122	232	131	106	135	F	M
36	29	2	0	2	175	195	129	121	148	M	M
37	43	3	0	3	194	211	138	129	146	M	M
38	44	1	2	0	132	240	130	109	132	F	S
39	63	2	2	1	188	255	156	121	145	M	M
40	36	2	1	1	125	220	126	117	140	F	S
41	21	1	0	1	109	206	114	102	136	F	M
42	31	2	0	2	112	201	116	123	133	F	M
43	57	1	1	1	167	213	141	103	143	M	W
44	20	1	2	3	101	194	110	111	125	F	S
45	24	2	1	3	106	188	113	114	127	F	D
46	42	1	0	1	148	206	136	107	140	M	S
47	55	1	0	0	170	257	152	106	130	F	M
48	23	0	0	1	152	204	116	95	142	M	M
49	32	2	0	0	191	210	132	115	147	M	M
50	28	1	0	1	148	222	135	100	135	M	M
51	67	0	0	0	160	250	141	116	146	F	W
52	22	1	1	1	109	220	121	103	144	F	M
53	19	1	1	1	131	231	117	112	133	M	S
54	25	2	0	2	153	212	121	119	149	M	D
55	41	3	2	2	165	236	130	131	152	M	M

Data Bank

ID number	Age	Educational level	Smoking status	Exercise	Weight	Serum cholesterol	Systolic pressure	IQ	Sodium	Gender	Marital status
56	24	2	0	3	112	205	118	100	132	F	S
57	32	2	0	1	115	187	115	109	136	F	S
58	50	3	0	1	173	203	136	126	146	M	M
59	32	2	1	0	186	248	119	122	149	M	M
60	26	2	0	1	181	207	123	121	142	M	S
61	36	1	1	0	112	188	117	98	135	F	D
62	40	1	1	0	130	201	121	105	136	F	D
63	19	1	1	1	132	237	115	111	137	M	S
64	37	2	0	2	179	228	141	127	141	F	M
65	65	3	2	1	212	220	158	129	148	M	M
66	21	1	2	2	99	191	117	103	131	F	S
67	25	2	2	1	128	195	120	121	131	F	S
68	68	0	0	0	167	210	142	98	140	M	W
69	18	1	1	2	121	198	123	113	136	F	S
70	26	0	1	1	163	235	128	99	140	M	M
71	45	1	1	1	185	229	125	101	143	M	M
72	44	3	0	0	130	215	128	128	137	F	M
73	50	1	0	0	142	232	135	104	138	F	M
74	63	0	0	0	166	271	143	103	147	F	W
75	48	1	0	3	163	203	131	103	144	M	M
76	27	2	0	3	147	186	118	114	134	M	M
77	31	3	1	1	152	228	116	126	138	M	D
78	28	2	0	2	112	197	120	123	133	F	M
79	36	2	1	2	190	226	123	121	147	M	M
80	43	3	2	0	179	252	127	131	145	M	D
81	21	1	0	1	117	185	116	105	137	F	S
82	32	2	1	0	125	193	123	119	135	F	M
83	29	2	1	0	123	192	131	116	131	F	D
84	49	2	2	1	185	190	129	127	144	M	M
85	24	1	1	1	133	237	121	114	129	M	M
86	36	2	0	2	163	195	115	119	139	M	M
87	34	1	2	0	135	199	133	117	135	F	M
88	36	0	0	1	142	216	138	88	137	F	M
89	29	1	1	1	155	214	120	98	135	M	S
90	42	0	0	2	169	201	123	96	137	M	D
91	41	1	1	1	136	214	133	102	141	F	D
92	29	1	1	0	112	205	120	102	130	F	M
93	43	1	1	0	185	208	127	100	143	M	M
94	61	1	2	0	173	248	142	101	141	M	M
95	21	1	1	3	106	210	111	105	131	F	S
96	56	0	0	0	149	232	142	103	141	F	M
97	63	0	1	0	192	193	163	95	147	M	M
98	74	1	0	0	162	247	151	99	151	F	W
99	35	2	0	1	151	251	147	113	145	F	M
100	28	2	0	3	161	199	129	116	138	M	M

Data Set I   Record Temperatures

Record high temperatures by U.S. state in degrees Celsius

44.4	37.8	53.3	48.9	56.7
47.8	41.1	43.3	46.1	42.8
44.4	37.8	47.8	47.2	46.7
47.8	49.4	45.6	45.6	40.6
42.8	41.7	44.4	45.6	46.1
47.8	47.2	47.8	51.7	41.1
43.3	50.0	42.2	43.3	49.4
45.0	48.9	48.3	43.9	40.0
43.9	48.9	45.0	48.9	47.2
40.6	43.3	47.8	44.4	45.6

Record low temperatures by U.S. state in degrees Celsius

−32.8	−62.2	−40.0	−33.9	−42.8
−51.7	−35.6	−27.2	−54.4	−18.9
−27.2	−11.1	−51.1	−37.8	−37.8
−43.9	−40.0	−38.3	−26.7	−44.4
−40.0	−37.2	−46.1	−51.1	−28.3
−40.0	−56.7	−43.9	−45.6	−43.9
−39.4	−45.6	−46.7	−36.7	−51.1
−28.3	−32.8	−47.8	−41.1	−31.7
−45.6	−50.0	−35.6	−30.6	−56.1
	−34.4	−44.4	−38.3	−48.3

Source: Reprinted with permission from the *World Almanac and Book of Facts 2004.*

Data Set II   Identity Theft Complaints

The data values show the number of complaints of identity theft for 50 selected cities in the year 2002.

2609	1202	2730	483	655
626	393	1268	279	663
817	1165	551	2654	592
128	189	424	585	78
1836	154	248	239	5888
574	75	226	28	205
176	372	84	229	15
148	117	22	211	31
77	41	200	35	30
88	20	84	465	136

Source: Federal Trade Commission.

Data Set III   Length of Major North American Rivers (kilometres)

1173	982	523	631	843
2348	724	748	974	531
1529	1458	529	467	1609
966	2334	1387	856	1432
655	845	1159	2000	1368
1044	1175	566	628	676
1143	547	1115	492	402
756	1165	534	417	3766
901	1706	1246	534	5971
3726	4088	995	1885	740

Data Set III   Length of Major North American Rivers (kilometres)   *(continued)*

694	1287	974	660	2108
805	1271	855	1579	740
1490	604	2076	1947	2108
616	612	483	499	661
3058	698	676	877	916
684	1287	1392	612	716
866	1670	682	563	607
869	1061	1049	505	579
484	824	805	504	982
579	692	1098	1426	719
544	781	1006	1162	845
1287	497	700		

Source: Reprinted with permission from the *World Almanac and Book of Facts 2004.*

Data Set IV   Heights (in Metres) of 80 Tallest Buildings in New York City

381.0	262.4	318.8	290.2	168.2
278.9	237.1	260.9	259.1	282.5
222.2	227.1	230.7	229.2	248.1
228.6	212.4	226.5	225.2	228.6
213.4	204.2	218.2	215.5	222.5
207.9	197.5	209.4	209.4	214.9
198.1	193.2	202.4	205.4	208.8
195.1	191.4	192.0	199.0	205.1
190.5	189.0	191.4	196.6	198.1
187.5	180.4	189.0	192.0	192.0
181.4	176.8	187.1	188.4	191.7
178.9	175.3	179.8	185.6	187.5
175.3	174.3	176.8	179.2	183.8
175.0	171.6	175.3	175.9	178.9
172.2	169.2	171.3	173.7	175.6
169.8	173.7	169.2	171.0	175.0

Heights (in Metres) of 25 Tallest Buildings in Calgary, Alberta

210.0	161.5	140.2	125.0
196.6	160.0	136.9	125.0
196.6	154.5	134.4	124.4
190.8	152.4	132.6	124.1
185.3	143.0	132.6	
176.8	142.6	131.7	
161.5	141.1	128.0	

Source: Reprinted with permission from the *World Almanac and Book of Facts 2004.*

Data Set V School Suspensions

The data values show the number of suspensions and the number of students enrolled in 40 local school districts in southwestern Pennsylvania.

Suspensions	Enrolment	Suspensions	Enrolment
37	1316	63	1588
29	1337	500	6046
106	4904	5	3610
47	5301	117	4329
51	1380	13	1908
46	1670	8	1341
65	3446	71	5582
223	1010	57	1869
10	795	16	1697
60	2094	60	2269
15	926	51	2307
198	1950	48	1564
56	3005	20	4147
72	4575	80	3182
110	4329	43	2982
6	3238	15	3313
37	3064	187	6090
26	2638	182	4874
140	4949	76	8286
39	3354	37	539
42	3547		

Source: U.S. Department of Education, *Pittsburgh Tribune-Review,* March 14, 2004.

Data Set VI Land Measure of U.S. National Parks, in Thousands of Hectares

17	27	94	314	68
15	137	90	19	26
74	1912	25	586	2863
410	1305	478	125	31
210	31	11	88	2
218	1447	263	187	676
1042	43	21	21	96
204	369	38	30	107
163	79	28	5	53
11	3098	898	308	58

Source: The Universal Almanac 1995, p. 45.

Data Set VII Acreage Owned by 35 Municipalities in Southwestern Pennsylvania

384	44	62	218	250
198	60	306	105	600
10	38	87	227	340
48	70	58	223	3700
22	78	165	150	160
130	120	100	234	1200
4200	402	180	200	200

Source: Pittsburgh Tribune-Review.

Data Set VIII Oceans of the World

Ocean	Area (thousands of square kilometres)	Maximum depth (metres)
Arctic	13,986	5,450
Caribbean Sea	2,753	7,680
Mediterranean Sea	2,505	5,020
Norwegian Sea	1,546	4,020
Gulf of Mexico	1,544	4,380
Hudson Bay	1,230	259
Greenland Sea	1,204	4,846
North Sea	575	661
Black Sea	461	2,243
Baltic Sea	422	439
Atlantic Ocean	82,439	9,219
South China Sea	3,447	5,560
Sea of Okhotsk	1,580	3,372
Bering Sea	2,269	4,191
Sea of Japan	1,008	3,743
East China Sea	751	2,782
Yellow Sea	417	91
Pacific Ocean	165,241	11,034
Arabian Sea	3,864	5,800
Bay of Bengal	2,173	5,258
Red Sea	438	2,246
Indian Ocean	73,452	7,450

Source: The Universal Almanac 1995, p. 330.

Data Set IX Commuter and Rapid Rail Systems in the United States

System	Stations	Kilometres	Vehicles Operated
Long Island RR	134	1027	947
N.Y. Metro North	108	862	702
New Jersey Transit	158	1490	582
Chicago RTA	117	671	358
Chicago & NW Transit	62	498	277
Boston Amtrak/MBTA	101	853	291
Chicago, Burlington, Northern	27	121	139
NW Indiana CTD	18	217	39
New York City TA	469	793	4923
Washington Metro Area TA	70	261	534
Metro Boston TA	53	123	368
Chicago TA	137	307	924
Philadelphia SEPTA	76	122	300
San Francisco BART	34	229	415
Metro Atlantic RTA	29	108	136
New York PATH	13	46	282
Miami/Dade Co TA	21	68	82
Baltimore MTA	12	43	48
Philadelphia PATCO	13	51	102
Cleveland RTA	18	61	30
New York, Staten Island RT	22	46	36

Source: The Universal Almanac 1995, p. 287.

Data Set X   Keystone Jackpot Analysis*

Ball	Times drawn	Ball	Times drawn	Ball	Times drawn
1	11	12	10	23	7
2	5	13	11	24	8
3	10	14	5	25	13
4	11	15	8	26	11
5	7	16	14	27	7
6	13	17	8	28	10
7	8	18	11	29	11
8	10	19	10	30	5
9	16	20	7	31	7
10	12	21	11	32	8
11	10	22	6	33	11

*Times each number has been selected in the regular drawings of the Pennsylvania Lottery since November 4, 1995.

Source: Copyright *Pittsburgh Post-Gazette,* October 31, 1996, all rights reserved. Reprinted with permission

Data Set XI   Pages in Statistics Books

The data values represent the number of pages found in statistics textbooks.

616	578	569	511	468
493	564	801	483	847
525	881	757	272	703
741	556	500	668	967
608	465	739	669	651
495	613	774	274	542
739	488	601	727	556
589	724	731	662	680
589	435	742	567	574
733	576	526	443	478
586	282			

Source: Allan G Bluman.

Data Set XII   50 Top Grossing Movies–2000

The data values represent the gross income in millions of dollars for the 50 top movies for the year 2000.

253.4	123.3	90.2	61.3	57.3
215.4	122.8	90.0	61.3	57.2
186.7	117.6	89.1	60.9	56.9
182.6	115.8	77.1	60.8	56.0
161.3	113.7	73.2	60.6	53.3
157.3	113.3	71.2	60.1	53.3
157.0	109.7	70.3	60.0	51.9
155.4	106.8	69.7	59.1	50.9
137.7	101.6	68.5	58.3	50.8
126.6	90.6	68.4	58.1	50.2

Source: Reprinted with permission from the *World Almanac and Book of Facts 2002.* Copyright © 2002 K-III Reference Corporation. All rights reserved

Data Set XIII   Hospital Data*

Number	Number of beds	Admissions	Payroll ($000)	Personnel
1	235	6,559	18,190	722
2	205	6,237	17,603	692
3	371	8,915	27,278	1,187
4	342	8,659	26,722	1,156
5	61	1,779	5,187	237
6	55	2,261	7,519	247
7	109	2,102	5,817	245
8	74	2,065	5,418	223
9	74	3,204	7,614	326
10	137	2,638	7,862	362
11	428	18,168	70,518	2,461
12	260	12,821	40,780	1,422
13	159	4,176	11,376	465
14	142	3,952	11,057	450
15	45	1,179	3,370	145
16	42	1,402	4,119	211
17	92	1,539	3,520	158
18	28	503	1,172	72
19	56	1,780	4,892	195
20	68	2,072	6,161	243
21	206	9,868	30,995	1,142
22	93	3,642	7,912	305
23	68	1,558	3,929	180
24	330	7,611	33,377	1,116
25	127	4,716	13,966	498
26	87	2,432	6,322	240
27	577	19,973	60,934	1,822
28	310	11,055	31,362	981
29	49	1,775	3,987	180
30	449	17,929	53,240	1,899
31	530	15,423	50,127	1,669
32	498	15,176	49,375	1,549
33	60	565	5,527	251
34	350	11,793	34,133	1,207
35	381	13,133	49,641	1,731
36	585	22,762	71,232	2,608
37	286	8,749	28,645	1,194
38	151	2,607	12,737	377
39	98	2,518	10,731	352
40	53	1,848	4,791	185
41	142	3,658	11,051	421
42	73	3,393	9,712	385
43	624	20,410	72,630	2,326
44	78	1,107	4,946	139
45	85	2,114	4,522	221

(continued)

Data Set XIII Hospital Data* *(continued)*

Number	Number of beds	Admissions	Payroll ($000)	Personnel
46	120	3,435	11,479	417
47	84	1,768	4,360	184
48	667	22,375	74,810	2,461
49	36	1,008	2,311	131
50	598	21,259	113,972	4,010
51	1,021	40,879	165,917	6,264
52	233	4,467	22,572	558
53	205	4,162	21,766	527
54	80	469	8,254	280
55	350	7,676	58,341	1,525
56	290	7,499	57,298	1,502
57	890	31,812	134,752	3,933
58	880	31,703	133,836	3,914
59	67	2,020	8,533	280
60	317	14,595	68,264	2,772
61	123	4,225	12,161	504
62	285	7,562	25,930	952
63	51	1,932	6,412	472
64	34	1,591	4,393	205
65	194	5,111	19,367	753
66	191	6,729	21,889	946
67	227	5,862	18,285	731
68	172	5,509	17,222	680
69	285	9,855	27,848	1,180
70	230	7,619	29,147	1,216
71	206	7,368	28,592	1,185
72	102	3,255	9,214	359
73	76	1,409	3,302	198
74	540	396	22,327	788
75	110	3,170	9,756	409
76	142	4,984	13,550	552
77	380	335	11,675	543
78	256	8,749	23,132	907
79	235	8,676	22,849	883
80	580	1,967	33,004	1,059
81	86	2,477	7,507	309
82	102	2,200	6,894	225
83	190	6,375	17,283	618
84	85	3,506	8,854	380
85	42	1,516	3,525	166
86	60	1,573	15,608	236
87	485	16,676	51,348	1,559
88	455	16,285	50,786	1,537
92	36	519	1,526	80
93	34	615	1,342	74
94	37	1,123	2,712	123

Data Set XIII Hospital Data* *(continued)*

Number	Number of beds	Admissions	Payroll ($000)	Personnel
95	100	2,478	6,448	265
96	65	2,252	5,955	237
97	58	1,649	4,144	203
98	55	2,049	3,515	152
99	109	1,816	4,163	194
100	64	1,719	3,696	167
101	73	1,682	5,581	240
102	52	1,644	5,291	222
103	326	10,207	29,031	1,074
104	268	10,182	28,108	1,030
105	49	1,365	4,461	215
106	52	763	2,615	125
107	106	4,629	10,549	456
108	73	2,579	6,533	240
109	163	201	5,015	260
110	32	34	2,880	124
111	385	14,553	52,572	1,724
112	95	3,267	9,928	366
113	339	12,021	54,163	1,607
114	50	1,548	3,278	156
115	55	1,274	2,822	162
116	278	6,323	15,697	722
117	298	11,736	40,610	1,606
118	136	2,099	7,136	255
119	97	1,831	6,448	222
120	369	12,378	35,879	1,312
121	288	10,807	29,972	1,263
122	262	10,394	29,408	1,237
123	94	2,143	7,593	323
124	98	3,465	9,376	371
125	136	2,768	7,412	390
126	70	824	4,741	208
127	35	883	2,505	142
128	52	1,279	3,212	158

*This information was obtained from a sample of hospitals in a selected U.S. state. The hospitals are identified by number instead of name.

Appendix E
Technology Step-by-Step

The following technologies will assist the learner through common statistical procedures for describing and analyzing data.

- Minitab Statistical Software
- SPSS Statistical Software
- Microsoft Excel 2007 Spreadsheet Application
- Texas Instruments TI-83 Plus / TI-84 Plus Programmable Calculator

The technologies listed are representative of scores of statistical tools available to the user. The technologies chosen for this text are popular in business, technology, and educational settings. Each described technology will follow topics in the textbook. *Note:* Procedures shown are representative, not comprehensive. Refer to the technology user guide for a more in-depth description of statistical methods.

Versions and Models

The current versions are Minitab 15, SPSS 15, and Excel 2007. Both the TI-83 Plus and TI-84 Plus calculator models are widely available. Procedures are similar between current versions and models. Procedures explained utilize Minitab 14, SPSS 14, Excel 2003, and TI-83 Plus. The author's operating system is Windows XP Professional.

Minitab
Starting Minitab
In Windows XP, click Start > Programs > Minitab 14 > Minitab 14.

Opening Screen

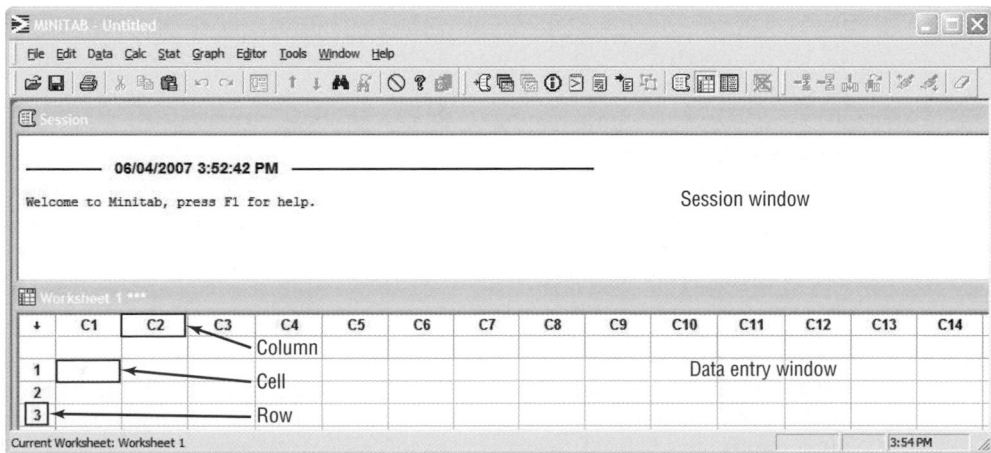

Entering Data

Input data in the worksheet window in the columns and rows. Column labels may be typed into the cells below the column headings above row 1.

Save a Worksheet File and Worksheet Project

Click 💾 or File > Save Current Worksheet or File > Save Project with file or project name to desired folder.

Open a Worksheet File and Worksheet Project

Click 📂 or File > Open Worksheet or File > Open Project from saved folder.

Minitab Commands

Menus may be used to access available commands depending on the desired procedure. Procedure shown uses menu commands.

Alternatively, commands can be input directly in the Session window, commands are typed at the MTB> prompt, subcommands at the SUBC> prompt and data at the DATA> prompt. Press Enter to execute commands. *Note:* Command may need to be enabled in menu. Click Editor > Enable Commands.

Categorical Frequency Table (Qualitative or Discrete Data)

Input data in column and type heading. Select Stat > Tables > Tally Individual Variables. Double-click column with data to display under Variables:, then select Display: Counts | Percents | Cumulative counts. Click OK.

Grouped Frequency Distribution (Quantitative Variable)

Input data in column and type heading label. Select Data > Code > Numeric to Text. Double-click column name containing data to display under Code data from columns:. Type new column name under Into columns:. Type class limits separated with a colon under Original values [e.g., 1:4 12]:, then type the text category classes, usually separated with a dash, under New:. Continue to type each additional class, and then click OK. Click Stat > Tables > Tally Individual Variables, then double-click column with new data (class limits) to display under Variables:, then select Display: Counts | Percents | Cumulative counts. Click OK.

Histogram

Enter data with column label on worksheet. Select Graph > Histogram > Simple > OK. In Histogram dialogue, double-click column label containing data to display under Graph variables:. Click Labels > Select Titles/Footnotes {type chart title and subtitle} > OK.

Other Chart Types

Input appropriate data for the chart type in the worksheet. Pie charts, bar charts, dot plots, stem and leaf plots, and time series plots are accessed in the Graph menu. Pareto charts can be created via the Stat > Quality Tools > Pareto menu. In all cases, the dialogue box will prompt the user for required information.

Descriptive Measures

Enter data with column label on worksheet. Click Data > Basic Statistics > Display Descriptive Statistics. Double-click column containing data to display under Variables:. Click Statistics and select desired descriptive measures—mean, median, range, standard deviation and variance. Click OK twice to display selected descriptive statistics.

Measures of Position

Input data in the worksheet. Access Calc > Standardize menu. In the Standardize dialogue, double-click column containing data to display under Input column(s): and identify column to Store results in:. Click OK to convert data to standard (z) scores.

Relative Frequency Probabilities

Input data for X values and frequencies in two columns in worksheet. Label column headings. Select Calc > Calculator menu. Identify column, or type a new column label, in Store result in variable:. In Expression: window, double-click column with frequency data, then click / (division sign), then under Functions: scroll down and select Sum, then double-click column with frequency data. Expression should be similar to 'f' / SUM('f'). Click OK to display relative frequency probabilities.

Contingency Table

Input appropriate data in two columns. Label column headings. Select Stat > Tables > Cross Tabulation and Chi-Square. Double-click desired columns under Categorical variables: For rows and For columns:. Select Count | Row percents | Column percents | Total Percents as required. Click OK.

Factorials, Permutations, and Combinations

Minitab Release 14 does not have built-in functions for Factorials, Permutations, and Combinations and does not handle very large values without an overflow. The solution is with the use of a natural logarithm expression.
Select Calc > Calculator. In Store result in variable:, indicate desired column. In Expression, type the following (replace n and r with desired values), then click OK.

Factorial $\rightarrow$ EXPO (LNGAMMA($n + 1$) $-$ LNGAMMA ($r + 1$) $-$ LNGAMMA($n - r + 1$))
Permutation $\rightarrow$ EXPO (LNGAMMA($n + 1$) $-$ LNGAMMA($n - x + 1$))
Combination $\rightarrow$ EXPO (LNGAMMA($n + 1$) $-$ LNGAMMA($r + 1$) $-$ LNGAMMA($n - r + 1$))

Note: In Minitab Release 15 replace above expressions, respectively, with FACTORIAL(n), PERMUTATION(n,r) and COMBINATION(n,r).

Binomial Probability Distribution

Input data (X values) in column and type heading label. Label 2nd column for probabilities (i.e., $P(X)$). Select Calc > Probability Distributions > Binomial. In dialogue box, check Probability, and specify Number of trials: and Probability of success:. Indicate location of Input column: {X values} and Optional storage: {$P(X)$}. Click OK to display probabilities.
    Note: If a single binomial probability is desired, type X value in Input constant: instead of using Input column.
    Note: If cumulative or inverse cumulative binomial probabilities are desired, check appropriate boxes instead of Probability: in dialogue box.

Graph Binomial Distribution

Create a binomial probability distribution in worksheet. Select Graph > Scatterplot > Simple. Click Data View > Select Data Display, and check only Project Lines > OK. Click Labels {type an appropriate title and subtitle} > OK. *Optional:* change Scale > Gridlines > OK twice to display graph.

Poisson Probability Distribution

Input data (X values) in column and type heading label. Label 2nd column heading for probabilities (i.e., $P(X)$). Select Calc > Probability Distributions > Poisson. In dialogue box, check Probability and specify Mean:. Identify location of Input column: {X values} and Optional storage: {$P(X)$}. Click OK to display probabilities.
    Note: If a single binomial probability is desired, type X value in Input constant: instead of using Input column.
    Note: If cumulative or inverse cumulative binomial probabilities are desired, check appropriate boxes instead of Probability: in dialogue box.

Standard Normal Distribution

Select Calc > Probability Distributions > Normal. In dialogue box, check Cumulative Probability, and specify Mean: 0 and Standard Deviation: 1. Select Input constant: {type desired z score}. Click OK to display area to the left of z score.

Note: To calculate areas to the right of z score, store probability for area to the left as a variable (i.e., K1) in Optional Storage:. Select Calc > Calculator > {type new variable (i.e., K2) in Store result in variable:}. Type Expression: {i.e., 1 − K1}. Click OK. To display areas to the left and right, respectively, select Data > Display Data > select variables {i.e., K1 and K2}. Click OK.

Note: To find a z score given an area, in Normal dialogue box, check Inverse cumulative probability. Specify Mean: 0 and Standard Deviation: 1. Check Input constant: {type desired area to the left}. Click OK to display z score.

Determining Normality

Graphical Method → Input data in worksheet and label column. Select Stat > Basic Statistics > Graphical Summary. In Variables: double-click column data label. Click OK. *Check for a bell-shaped curve on histogram.

Normal Probability Plot Method → Input data in worksheet and label column. Select Graph > Probability Plot > select Single. In Graph variables: double-click column data label. Click Distribution > Distribution tab > select Normal. Click OK. Click Labels: and input appropriate title and subtitle. Click OK twice. * Check for linearity of point on graph.

Normality Test Method → Input data in worksheet and label column. Select Stat > Basic Statistics > Normality Test . . . > In Variable: double-click column data label. Select desired Tests for Normality. Enter Title. Click OK. * Check for linearity of point on graph.

Confidence Interval Estimate

Normal z Interval (means) → Input data in worksheet and label column. If σ is known, continue to next step*. If σ is not known, select Calc > Column > check Standard deviation > In Input variable: double-click column data > In Store results in: type a variable name (i.e., s). Click OK. *Select Stat > Basic Statistics > 1-Sample Z . . . > In Samples in columns: double-click column data label. In Standard deviation: type σ (if known) or variable for standard deviation {i.e., s). > Click Options . . . > In Confidence level: type desired level of confidence. In Alternative: not equal to. Click OK twice to display results.

t Interval (means) → Input data in worksheet and label column. Select Stat > Basic Statistics > 1-Sample t . . . > In Samples in columns: double-click column data label > Click Options . . . > In Confidence level: type desired level of confidence. In Alternative: not equal to. Click OK twice to display results. *Note:* If data is not given but summary statistics are known, type values for Sample size:, Mean:, and Standard deviation: in appropriate boxes under Summarized data.

Normal z Interval (proportions) → No data will be input in worksheet. Select Stat > Basic Statistics > 1 Proportion . . . > Check Summarized data, input appropriate values for Number of trials: and Number of events: .> Click Options . . . > In Confidence level: type desired level of confidence. In Alternative: not equal to. Click OK twice to display results.

Variance → Minitab Release 14 does not include a confidence interval estimate for variances and standard deviations. This feature will be available in Release 15.

Hypothesis Tests

Normal z Test (means) → Repeat Normal z Interval (means) procedure except in Test mean: type hypothesized mean value > Click Options . . . > In Confidence level: input 1 − significance level (α) (i.e., if $\alpha = 0.05$, $1 − \alpha = 0.95$, use 95). Change Alternative: to less than or not equal or greater than as required. Click OK twice to display results including z-score and *P*-value.

t Test (means) → Repeat t Interval (means) procedure except in Test mean: type hypothesized mean value > Click Options . . . > In Confidence level: input 1 − significance level (α) (i.e., if $\alpha = 0.01$, $1 − \alpha = 0.99$, use 99). Change Alternative: to less than or not equal or greater than as required. Click OK twice to display results including z-score and *P*-value.

Normal z Test (proportions) → Repeat Normal z Interval (proportions) procedure except in Options . . . > Confidence level: input 1 − significance level (α) (i.e. if $\alpha = 0.10$, $1 − \alpha = 0.90$, use 90). In Test proportion: type value for test. Change Alternative: to less than or not equal or greater than as required. Add check to Use test and interval based on normal distribution. Click OK twice to display results including z-score and *P*-value.

Variance → Minitab Release 14 does not include a confidence interval estimate for variances and standard deviations. This feature will be available in Release 15.

Hypothesis Test–Difference Between Two Means

Large Independent Samples → Input two columns of data with headings. Select Stat > Basic Statistics > 2-Sample t. Select Samples in different columns. In First: double-click first column data label. In Second: double-click second column data label. Click Options . . . > In Confidence level: input 1 − significance level (α) (i.e., if $\alpha = 0.05$, $1 - \alpha = 0.95$, use 95). In Test difference: 0.0. In Change Alternative: to less than or not equal or greater than as required. Click OK twice to display results including t-value and P-value.

Small Independent Samples with Equal Variances → Repeat procedure for Large Independent Samples except in dialogue check Assume equal variances.

Small Dependent Samples → Input two columns of data with headings. Select Stat > Basic Statistics > Paired t. Select Samples in columns. In First sample: double-click first column data label. In Second sample: double-click second column data label. Click Options . . . > For Confidence level: input $1 - \alpha$ (as a %), Test mean: 0 and Alternative: less than or not equal or greater than as required. Click OK twice to display results.

Hypothesis Test–Difference Between Two Variances

Input two columns of data with headings. Select Stat > Basic Statistics > 2-Variances. Select Samples in different columns. In First: double-click first column data label. In Second: double-click second column data label. Click Options . . . > In Confidence level: input 1 − significance level (α) (i.e., if $\alpha = 0.05$, $1 - \alpha = 0.95$, use 95). Type appropriate title. Click OK twice. A graph window is displayed. On the right, under F-Test are displayed the values of the test statistic and P-value for a two-tailed test. Divide P-value by 2 for a one-tailed test.

Hypothesis Test–Difference Between Proportions

No worksheet data is required. Select Stat > Basic Statistics > 2-Proportions. Select Summarized data. In First: and Second: input Trials: and Events: data. Click Options . . . > In Confidence level: $1 - \alpha$ (as a %), Test difference: 0 and Alternative: not equal. Check box Use pooled estimate of p for test. Click OK twice to display results.

Scatter Plot

Input two columns of paired data (x,y) with headings. Select Graph > Scatterplot > Simple. For Y variables, double-click second column data label. For X variables, double-click first column data label. Click Data View . . . > Data Display > check Data Display | Symbols box. Click OK. Click Labels > input appropriate Title and Subtitle in Titles/Footnotes. Click OK twice to display graph.

Correlation Coefficient

Input two columns of paired data (x,y) with headings. Select Stat > Basic Statistics > Correlation. For Variables, double-click second column data label (Y Variable), then double-click first column data label (X Variable). Check box Display p-values. Click OK to display result.

Equation of Regression Line

Input two columns of paired data (x,y) with headings. Select Stat > Regression > Regression. For Response:, double-click second column data label (Y Variable) For Predictors: double-click first column data label (X Variable). Click Storage . . . > check boxes Residuals and Fits. Click OK twice to display regression equation. *Note:* Two columns are added to worksheet containing fitted values and residuals.

Multiple Regression

Input columns of data with headings. Click Stat > Regression > Regression. In Response: double-click dependent variable column heading. In Predictors: double-click each independent variable column heading. Click Storage . . . > check box for Residuals and Fits. Click OK twice to display statistics including the multiple regression equation, F (test statistic) and P (P-value).

Chi-Square Hypothesis Test

X^2 Goodness-of-Fit → Input observed counts in C1 and expected counts in C2 with headings O and E respectively. Select Calc > Calculator. In Store result in variable:., type 1st variable name: (i.e., K1). In Expression box, type formula type SUM((O-E)**2/E). Click OK to display result in variable (i.e., K1).

Calculate the P-value. Select Calc > Probability Distributions > Chi-square. Select Cumulative probability, type Degrees of Freedom appropriate to data. In Input Constant, double-click saved variable (i.e., K1) from variable list. In Optional Storage, type 2nd variable name (i.e., K2), which is area to left of test statistic. The P-value is the area to the right. Click OK. Select Calc > Calculator. In Store results in variable: box, type 3rd variable name (i.e., K3). In expression: box, type 1−{2nd variable}, (i.e., 1−K2). Click OK. To display the 3rd variable (i.e., K3) value (P-value), open Window > Project Manager, under Worksheets | Constants.

X^2 Independence Test or Contingency Table Test → Input observed frequencies in columns. Label columns but not rows. Select Stat > Tables > Chi-Square Test. Highlight all columns in list. Click Select to move into columns containing the table box. Click OK to display statistics including Chi-Square test statistic and P-value.

One-Way Analysis of Variance (ANOVA)

Input columns of data with headings. Select Stat > ANOVA > One-Way (Unstacked). Highlight all columns in list. Click Select to copy list to Responses (in separate columns):. Click OK to display results including F (test statistic) and P (P-value).

Two-Way Analysis of Variance

Input column data and label headings. Select Stat > ANOVA > Two-Way . . . In Response: double-click dependent variable column label. In Row factor: double-click 1st independent variable column label. In Column factor: double-click 2nd independent variable column label. Click OK to display results.

To plot data, select Stat > ANOVA > Interactions Plot . . . In Responses: double-click dependent variable column label. In Row factor: double-click independent variable column labels. OK to display results.

The Sign Test

Input column data and label headings. Select Stat > Nonparametrics > 1-Sample Sign . . . In Variables: double-click column label. Click on Test median: input hypothesized value. Alternative: select appropriate test. Click OK to display results including P (P-value).

The Paired-Sample Test

Input two columns of data and label headings (i.e., Before and After). Select Calc > Calculator. In Store result in variable: type variable name (i.e., D for difference). In Expression: double-click 1st (i.e., Before) column, minus, double-click 2nd (i.e., After) column. Click OK to display differences in 3rd or next available column (i.e., column labelled D). Repeat the instruction for the Sign Test on the differences (i.e., D) with hypothesized value of 0.

Wilcoxon Rank Sum Test (Mann-Whitney)

Input two columns of data and label headings. Select Stat > Nonparametric > Mann-Whitney. In First Sample: double-click 1st column label. In Second Sample: double-click 2nd column label. Specify Confidence level: and Alternative:. Click OK to display results.

Wilcoxon Signed-Rank Test

Repeat the Paired-Sample Test procedure except in the final step select Stat > Nonparametric > 1-Sample Wilcoxon. In Variables: select C3 (i.e., D), click Test median: input 0. Click OK to display results including P (P-value).

Kruskal-Wallis Test

Input two columns of data (stacked) with numeric data in one column and associated labels in the second column. Label column headings. Select Stat > Nonparametric > Kruskal-Wallis. In Response: double-click column with numeric data. In Factor: double-click the column with labels. Click OK to display results.

Runs Test for Randomness

Input data in column 1 in the same order collected. Label heading. Select Calc > Column Statistics. Check Median: option. In Input Variable: double-click column label. In Store result in: type appropriate name for data. Click OK. Select Stat > Nonparametric > Runs Test. In Variables: double-click column label. Click above and below, then select name specified in previous step. Click OK to display results including P-value.

Random Sample

With Replacement → Select Calc > Random Data > Integer. Type value in Generate __ rows of data. In Store in column(s):, type a column name. Type desired Minimum value: and Maximum value:. Click OK to display result on worksheet.

Without Replacement → Select Calc > Make Patterned Data > Simple Set of Numbers. In Store patterned data in: type column heading. In From first value: and To last value: type desired range (minimum and maximum). Leave In steps of: 1. Click OK to display values in named column. Select Calc > Random Data > Sample from columns. Sample a portion of the range (i.e., If 50 values, sample 10). In Store sample in: type a new column name. Click OK to display results on worksheet.

Normal Distribution → Select Calc > Random Data > Normal . . . Type value in Generate __ rows of data. In Store in column(s):, type a column name. Type desired values for Mean: and Standard deviation:. Click OK to display results on worksheet.

Note: To display data in session window, select Data > Display data, double-click desired column label. Click OK.

SPSS

Starting SPSS

In Windows XP, click Start > Programs > SPSS for Windows > SPSS for Windows

Opening Screen (Data View)

Variable View

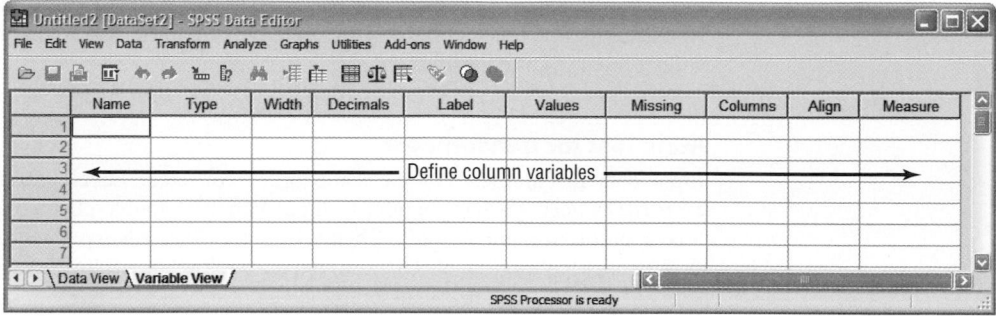

Entering Data

In Data View, input data values in columns under variable names (defined fields).

In Variable View, name variables (column headings or fields), define variables including data type (i.e., string, date, or numeric), measurement level (nominal, ordinal, or scale) and value (descriptive) labels.

The following procedures assume that data variable columns (fields) have been defined and data has been input in data view in rows (records).

Save a Data File

Click 🖫 or File > Save to desired folder. (Default filename extension is .SAV)

Open a Data File

Click 📂 or File > Open > Open Data . . . from saved file folder.

SPSS Commands

Menus or Toolbar buttons may be used to access available commands depending on the desired procedure. SPSS commands may also be entered and run manually by selecting File > New > Syntax to open the Sysntax window. Procedures shown only use menu commands. Results of commands are displayed in the Output – SPSS Viewer window.

Categorical Frequency Table (Qualitative or Discrete Variable)

Select Analyze > Descriptive Statistics > Frequencies. In Descriptives, select appropriate (qualitative or discrete data) label or name in left source list, click ▶ to move variable to right Variable(s) list. Click OK to display output in SPSS Viewer including Frequency, Percent, and Cumulative Percent.

Grouped Frequency Table (Quantitative Variable)

(Manual Coding) In Variable View, define a column variable as numeric and under Values, define classes (i.e., Value: 1, 2, and 3, Labels: Under 20, 20-50, Over 50, respectively). Enter variable name (i.e., AgeGroup) and appropriate label In Data View, code each data value (i.e., 0, 1, or 2) that fits defined variable (i.e., Under 20, 20-50, Over 50) under column label (i.e., AgeGroup). *Note:* Click View > Value Labels to display labels instead of value code in Data View.

(Automatic Coding) Select Transform > Visual Binning . . . In Visual Binning, select appropriate (quantitative data) variable label or name in left source list, click ▶ to move variable to right Variables to bin list. Click Continue. Under Scanned Variable List: Variable, select variable name. With current variable name displayed, type desired new variable name (i.e., AgeGroup) in Binned variable box.   Select Make Cutpoints. Under Equal Width Intervals │ First Cutpoint Location, type upper class limit of lowest bin. Under Number of Cutpoints, type desired number of classes (or bins). Under width, type desired class (bin) width. Click Apply. Click Make labels to automatically generate labels. Click OK, then OK at prompt. Output will be displayed in SPSS Viewer. Note value labels (i.e. 1,2, 3...) beside classes (bins). In Data View, a new column will be created with coded value labels for each class (bin).

To display frequency table, select Analyze > Descriptive Statistics > Frequencies. In Descriptives, select variable label or name containing class (bin) coding in left source list, click ▶ to move variable to right Variable(s) list. Click OK to display output in SPSS Viewer including classes (bins) with frequency, percent, and cumulative percent.

Histograms and Other Charts

To display histogram, select Analyze > Descriptive Statistics > Frequencies. In Descriptives, select variable label or name in left source list, click ▶ to move variable to right Variable(s) list. Click Charts . . . > select Histograms (or desired chart). Click Continue > Click OK to display chart output in SPSS Viewer.

Alternatively, select Graphs > Chart Builder (read pop-up window) > click Gallery > select Histogram (or desired chart) in Choose From: list > drag Simple Histogram (or other chart subtype) icon onto canvas > drag desired variables to the *x*-axis and *y*-axis drop zones. Click OK to display chart in Output: SPSS Viewer.

Descriptive Measures

Define column variable and input data. Select Analyze > Descriptive Statistics > Descriptives. In Descriptives, select variable label or name in left source list, click ▶ to move variable to right Variable(s) list. Click Options and select desired descriptive measures. Click Continue > OK to display output in SPSS Viewer.

Measures of Position

Select Analyze > Descriptive Statistics > Descriptives . . . > In Descriptives, select one or more variable labels or names in left source list, click ▶ to move variable to right Variable(s) list. > Check Save standardized values as variables. > Click OK. In Data View, new column(s) or fields are created containing *z*-scores of selected variable labels with labels prefaced with a *z*. (i.e., Age → zAge).

Relative Frequency (Percentage) Probabilities

Define column variables and input data. Select Transform > Compute variable . . . In dialogue box, under Target Variable: type new variable name (i.e., RelFreq). In source list, click ▶ to move frequency variable to Numeric Expression: box. Type /n (where n is the sum of the frequency column). Click OK to display results in new variable column.

Another method is to repeat the procedure for Categorical Frequency Table using discrete data. In SPSS Viewer, Percent column represents relative frequency probabilities.

Contingency Table

Enter data in two columns and define column variables. Select Analyze > Descriptive Statistics > Crosstabs. . . . In Crosstabs, select variable label or name in left source list, click ▶ to move variable to Row(s):. Repeat to move 2nd variable from source list to Column(s):. Optional: Click Cells . . . and select Percentages | Row, Column and Total. Click Continue. Click OK to display output in SPSS Viewer.

Factorials, Permutations, and Combinations

SPSS does not have built-in functions for Factorials, Permutations, and Combinations.

Binomial Probability Distribution

Define column variables and input data for *X* (i.e., 0, 1, 2...n). Select Transform > Compute variable . . . In dialogue box, under Target Variable: type new variable name (i.e. ProbX). In Numeric Expression, under Function group: | PDF & Noncentral PDF, select under Functions and Special Variables | Pdf.Binom,. Click ▲ to move function to Numeric Expression: box. Replace PDF.BINOM(?,?,?) with values for PDF.BINOM(*X*,*N*,*p*),, (where *X* is column variable name for

X-values, *N* is number of trials, *p* is probability of success for binomial). Click OK to display binomial probabilities in new variable column.

If cumulative probabilities are desired, use new variable name (i.e., CumProbX) and select CDF & Noncentral CDF, select under Functions and Special Variables │ Cdf.Binom using same format as Pdf.Binom.

Graph Binomial Distribution

Create a binomial probability distribution in Data View. Select Graphs > Chart Builder (read, then click OK for displayed dialogue) > Under Choose from: select Histogram │ drag Simple Histogram in into chart preview window. From Variable list: drag variable name (i.e., *X*) to *X*-Axis? and drag variable name (i.e., ProbX) to *Y*-Axis? in preview window. Click OK to display chart in Output │ SPSS Viewer.

To create a line chart, select Line │ Simple type and use either variable for probability of *X* or cumulative probability of *X* as desired.

Poisson Probability Distribution

Define column variables and input data for *X* (i.e., 0, 1, 2…*n*). Select Transform > Compute variable . . . In dialogue box, under Target Variable: type new variable name (i.e., ProbX). In Numeric Expression, under Function group: │ PDF & Noncentral PDF, select under Functions and Special Variables │ Pdf.Poisson. Click ▲ to move function to Numeric Expression: box. Replace PDF.POISSON(?,?) with values for PDF.POISSON(X, mean),, (where *X* is column variable name for *X*-values and mean is the distribution mean). Click OK to display poisson probabilities in new variable column.

If cumulative probabilities are desired, use new variable name (i.e., CumProbX) and select CDF & Noncentral CDF, select under Functions and Special Variables │ Cdf.Poisson using same format as Pdf.Poisson.

Standard Normal Distribution

Refer to Measures of Position for *z*- score conversions of numeric variables.

For cumulative probability distributions, define column variables and input data (*X* values). Select Transform > Compute variable . . . In dialogue box, under Target Variable: type new variable name (i.e., AreaLEFT). In Numeric Expression, under Function group: │ PDF & Noncentral PDF, select under Functions and Special Variables │ Cdf.Normal,. Click ▲ to move function to Numeric Expression: box. Replace CDF.NORMAL(?,?,?) with values for CDF.NORMAL (*X*, mean, standard deviation), (where *X* is column variable name for *X*-values, mean of *X*, standard deviation of *X*). Click OK to display probabilities, cumulative areas, in new variable column.

Note: If column variables represent *z* scores, use mean = 0 and standard deviation = 1 in expression. Alternatively, the CDFNORM function assumes mean = 0 and standard deviation = 1 and returns same value for area to the left.

Note: To calculate area to the right of value, use 1 − Cdf.Normal(value, mean, standard deviation) in Expression: box. To calculate area between, input in Expression: box Cdf.Normal(rightmost value, mean, standard deviation) − Cdf.Normal(leftmost value, mean, standard deviation).

Determining Normality

Graphical Method → define column variables and input data. Select Analyze > Descriptive Statistics > Frequencies. Select desired variable name. Click Charts . . . > select Histograms │ check With normal curve. Click Continue > Click OK to display chart output in SPSS Viewer. *Check for a bell-shaped curve on histogram.

Normal Probability Plot Method → define column variables and input data. Select Analyze > Descriptive Statistic > Explore. Select desired variable name. Under Display: check Both or Plots (as desired). Click Plots . . . > under Descriptive: check Histogram. Check Normality plots with tests. Click Continue > click OK to display chart output in SPSS Viewer. *Check if histogram is bell-shaped, check Normal *Q-Q* Plot for linearity, check Detrended *Q-Q* Plot for equal dispersion of data points above and below line. For Boxplot, check for symmetry and outliers.

Confidence Interval Estimate

Normal z Interval (means) $\rightarrow$ define column variables and input data. Select Analyze > Descriptive Statistics > Explore . . . From source list, select desired variable name and move to Dependent List: box. Under Display, select Both or Statistics (as desired). Click Statistics . . . > Descriptives, | Confidence Interval for Mean: {type desired level of confidence}. Click Continue > OK to display Output in SPSS Viewer including confidence interval for mean (lower and upper bound).

    t Interval (means) $\rightarrow$ define column variables and input data. Select Analyze > Compare Means > One-sample T test . . . From source list, select desired variable name and move to Test Variable(s): box. Click Options . . . and input desired Confidence Interval:. Click Continue > OK to display Output in SPSS Viewer including confidence interval of the difference (lower and upper).

    Normal z Interval (proportions) $\rightarrow$ SPSS does not have a menu procedure for confidence interval estimates for proportion, although there is a procedure for two-variable ratios. Command syntax may be used to manually calculate the lower and upper confidence limits.

    Workaround: Define 7 variables with appropriate names and decimals (i.e., n, x, phat, sterr, z, lower, upper). Input data (i.e., n, x). Select Transform > Compute variable . . . Input appropriate Target variable: name, and use source list variable and Function group | Functions and Special Variables: to create numeric expressions. Click OK twice after creating each expression, then repeat for each variable.

phat $= x / n$

z = Inverse DF | Idf.Normal(prob, mean, stdev), *where prob is cumulative area to left of upper z score, mean* $= 0$, *stdev* $= 1$.

sterr $= z *$ Arithmetic | Sqrt(phat $* (1 - $ phat$) / n$)

lower $=$ phat $-$ sterr

upper $=$ phat $+$ sterr

Variance $\rightarrow$ SPSS does not have a menu procedure confidence interval estimate for variances and standard deviations.

Hypothesis Tests

t Test (means) $\rightarrow$ define column variables and input data. Select Analyze > Compare Means > One-sample T test . . . From source list, select desired variable name and move to Test Variable(s): box. In Test Value: field, type hypothesized value for comparison. . Click Options . . . and input desired Confidence Interval:. *Note:* Confidence level $= 1 - $ significance level. Click Continue > OK to display Output in SPSS Viewer including Sig (2-tailed) or P value and t value under T-test | One-Sample Test.

Hypothesis Test–Difference Between Two Means

t Test (independent samples) $\rightarrow$ define column variables and input data. Select Analyze > Compare Means > Independent-Samples T test . . . From source list, select and move desired variable name to be used as Test Variable(s): and Grouping Variable:, respectively. For numeric grouping variables, click Define Groups . . . and input values to define the groups. Click Options . . . Input desired Confidence Interval:. *Note:* Confidence level $= 1 - $ significance level. Click Continue > OK to display Output in SPSS Viewer including Sig (2-tailed) or P value and t value under T-test | Independent-Samples Test.

    t Test (dependent samples) $\rightarrow$ define column variables and input data. Select Analyze > Compare Means > Paired-sample T test . . . From source list, select two desired variable names so that both variables appear under Current Selections and move to Paired Variables: window. Click Options . . . Input desired value for Confidence Interval:. *Note:* Confidence level $= 1 - $ significance level. Click Continue > OK to display Output in SPSS Viewer including Sig (2-tailed) or P value and t value under T-test | Paired Samples Test.

Hypothesis Test–Difference Between Two Variances

Refer to output in test Between Two Means.

Hypothesis Test–Correlation and Regression

Scatter Plot $\rightarrow$ In data editor, define two variables (i.e., x, y) and input paired data with headings. Select Graphs > Chart Builder (read pop-up window) > click Gallery > select Scatter/Dot in

Choose From: list > drag Simple Scatter icon onto canvas > drag required scale variables to the x-axis and y-axis drop zone on canvas. Click OK to display scatterplot in Output: SPSS Viewer.

Correlation → In data editor, define two variables (i.e., x, y) and input paired data with headings. Select Analyze > Correlate > Bivariate . . . Move two variables (x, y) from source list to Variables: window. Under Correlation Coefficients, check Pearson. Under Test of Significance, check Two-tailed or One-tailed (as required by hypothesis). Click OK to display Output in SPSS Viewer including Sig (2-tailed or 1-tailed), which is the P value for the test.

Regression Equation → In data editor, define two variables (i.e., x, y) and input paired data with headings. Select Analyze > Regression > Linear . . . In Linear Regression dialogue box, move appropriate variable names from source list to Dependent: box and Independent(s): box, respectively. Click OK to display Output in SPSS Viewer including Coefficients table, Sig (P value), and values intersecting Understandardized Coefficients and Models: B and Constants (y-intercept) | B and $x1$ (slope).

Multiple Regression → In data editor, define dependent and independent variables and input data with headings. Select Analyze > Regression > Linear . . . In Linear Regression dialogue box, select preferred variable name from source list to Dependent: field and other variables to Independent(s): field. Click OK to display Output in SPSS Viewer including Sig (P value) under ANOVA and Coefficients which is the P value for the test.

Chi-Square Hypothesis Test

X^2 Goodness-of-Fit → Input observed frequencies in data editor and define and name variable. Select Analyze > Nonparametric Tests > Chi-Square . . . In Chi-Square Tests dialogue box, move the desired variable name from the source list to the Test Variable List:. Under Expected Values, select either All categories equal or if categories are different, input appropriate Values. Click OK to display Output in SPSS Viewer including observed and expected frequencies, χ^2 test statistic and Asymp.Sig or P-value.

X^2 Independence Test or Contingency Table Test → Input observed frequencies in data editor and define and name variables. Select Analyze > Descriptive Statistics > Crosstabs . . . In Crosstabs dialogue box, move one variable name from the source list to the Row(s): window and another variable name to the Column(s): window. Click Statistics . . . In Corsstabs: Statistics dialogue, select Chi-square > Continue. Click Cells . . . In Crosstabs: Cell Display, select desired cell display (i.e., Counts: Observed, Expected; Percentages: Row, Column, Total). Click Continue > OK to display Output in SPSS Viewer including Crosstabulation table and Chi-Square Tests.

One-Way Analysis of Variance

Define column variables and input data. Select Analyze > Compare Means > One-Way ANOVA . . . In dialogue box, select one variable and move to Dependent List: field and select 2nd variable and move to Factor: field. Click Post Hoc . . . In dialogue box, select desired test and significance level. Click Continue. Click Options and select desired Statistics and Plot. Click Continue > OK to display Output results in SPSS Viewer including the Sig (P value), F test value, and Means Plot (if selected).

Two-Way Analysis of Variance

Define column variables and input data into 3 columns. Select Analyze > General Linear Model > Univariate . . . In Univariate dialogue box, select the response variable and move to Dependent Variable: field; select the row and column factor variables and move to Fixed Factor(s): field. Click OK to display Output results in SPSS Viewer including the Sig (P values) and F test values under Test of Between-Subjects Effects.

Signs Test

Define column variables and input data. Select Analyze > Nonparametric Tests > 2-Related-Samples . . . In dialogue box, move two variable names (check both variables are shown under Current Selections) from source list to Test Pair(s) List:. Under Test Type, click Sign. Click OK to display Output in SPSS Viewer including Exact Sig (2-tailed) or P value under Test Statistics.

The Paired-Sample T Test

Define column variables and input data. Select Analyze > Compare Means > Paired Samples T-Test . . . In source list move appropriate variable names (check both variables are shown under Current Selections) to Paired Variables: field. Select 2nd paired variables. Click OK to display Output in SPSS Viewer including Correlation, Sig (P value), and t value.

Wilcoxon Rank Sum Test (Mann-Whitney)

Define column variables and input data. Select Analyze > Nonparametric Tests > 2 Independent Samples . . . In dialogue box, move required variable from source list to Test Variable List:. Under Test Type, select Mann-Whitney U. Under Grouping Variable:, click Define Groups . . . In dialogue box, input appropriate values in Group 1: and Group 2: . Click Continue > OK to display Output in SPSS Viewer including Z and Asymp.Sig (2-tailed) or P value.

Wilcoxon Signed-Rank Test

Define column variables and input data. Select Analyze > Nonparametric Tests > 2-Related-Samples . . . In dialogue box, move two variable names (check both variables are shown under Current Selections) from source list to Test Pair(s) List:. Under Test Type, click Wilcoxon. Click OK to display Output in SPSS Viewer including Exact Sig (2-tailed) or P value under Test Statistics.

Kruskal-Wallis Test

Define column variables and input data. Select Analyze > Nonparametric Tests > K Independent Samples. In dialogue box source list move desired variable to Test Variable List: window. Click Define Range . . . input appropriate values under Range for Grouping Variables: Minimum and Maximum. Click Continue > OK to display Output in SPSS Viewer including test statistic Chi-Square and Asymp.Sig or P value.

Runs Test for Randomness

Define column variables and input data. Select Analyze > Select Nonparametric Test > Runs . . . In dialogue box, select variable name in source list and move to Test Variable List:. Select appropriate Cut Point in dialogue. Click Options . . . Select Statistics | Quartiles. Click Continue > OK to display Output in SPSS Viewer including Asymp.Sig (2-tailed) or P value.

Excel

Excel is a spreadsheet application with basic statistical functions built in and advanced statistical functionality available through the Data Analysis Add-In.

Activate Data Analysis Tool

Open Excel. In worksheet menu, click Tools > Add-Ins and select Analysis Toolpak in Add-Ins dialogue box. Click OK.

Categorical Frequency Table (Qualitative or Discrete Variable)

Type column heading in cell, then input data down column below heading. Input categories in next column with appropriate heading. In next column input heading, such as Count, then move to cell below heading. Click Insert > Function > Statistical category > COUNTIF > OK. Select Range {cells containing data} | Criteria {cell containing adjacent category}. Click OK. Move to next cell and repeat for each category listed. Frequency column may be added with the Sum function.

Grouped Frequency Distribution

Type column heading in cell, then input data down column below heading. Select Tools > Data Analysis > Histogram > OK. Select Input Range {cells containing data} | New Worksheet Ply: | check Cumulative Percentage > OK.

Histogram

Repeat Grouped Frequency Distribution procedure and check Chart Output in last step. Optionally, user-defined bin ranges, in ascending order, may by typed into worksheet to control histogram output. The bin range should then be selected in Histogram dialogue box. The number of data points between the current bin number and the adjoining higher bin are shown in table and chart.

Other Chart Types

Input appropriate data in the worksheet. Use the Chart Wizard to construct a bar chart, line chart, pie chart, Pareto chart, or time series plots. Follow the prompts in the displayed dialogue boxes.

Descriptive Measures

Input data in the worksheet. Move to blank cell. Access the Insert | Function | Statistical menu to select the desired descriptive measures: AVERAGE (mean), MEDIAN, MODE, STDEV (standard deviation), and VAR (variance). Select data range in dialogue box. Click OK. *Note:* Excel functions can be typed manually. Click on cell containing descriptive measure to view function in formula bar.

Alternatively, select Tools > Data Analysis. In Descriptive Statistics dialogue in Input Range, identify data range. Select Summary statistics. Click OK. A table of descriptive statistics will be displayed.

Measures of Position

Input data in the worksheet. Type a single (x) value appropriate to the data set in a cell. Move to blank cell. Access the Insert | Function | Statistical menu and select the STANDARDIZE function. In the Standardize dialogue, fill in cell locations for X value, data range for Mean, and Standard_dev (standard deviation). Click OK.

Factorials, Permutations, and Combinations

Factorial → In a blank cell, access Insert > Function > select Math & Trig category > select FACT function. Type value of n. Click OK.

Permutation → In a blank cell, access Insert > Function > select Statistical category > select PERMUT function. Type value of n in Number box. Type value of r in Number_chosen box. Click OK.

Combination → In a blank cell, access Insert > Function > select Math & Trig category > select COMBIN function. Type value of n in Number box. Type value of r in Number_chosen box. Click OK.

Binomial Probability Distribution and Chart

Type column heading (X) in cell, then input data down column below heading. Label 2nd column P(X). In cell below P(X) heading, using appropriate values, select Insert > Function > Statistical > BINOMDIST. Fill in dialogue box, Number_s {cell with X value, 0}, Trials {value for n}, Probability_s {value for p}, Cumulative {0 or FALSE}. Click OK. *Note:* Formula in formula bar can be typed manually in cell.

Note: If cumulative probabilities are desired, change Cumulative in dialogue to 1 or TRUE and change heading label to P($X<=x$).

Use the Chart Wizard to create a graph. Chart type is Column, first subtype. Click Next. In Data Range tab | Data range: {input range containing P(X) values}. In Series tab, Category (X) axis labels {input range containing X values}. Click Next. Label as desired. Click Next and Finish.

Poisson Probability Distribution

Type column heading (X) in cell, then input data down column below heading. Label 2nd column P(X). In cell below P(X) heading, using appropriate values, select Insert > Function > Statistical > POISSON. Fill in dialogue box X, Mean, Cumulative {0 or FALSE}. Click OK. Copy formula down column to find probabilities of adjacent X values. *Note:* Formula in formula bar can be typed manually in cell.

Note: If cumulative probabilities are desired, change Cumulative in dialogue to 1 or TRUE and change heading label to P($X<=x$).

Normal Distribution

Cumulative area to the left of z score → In blank cell, select Insert > Function > Statistical | NORMSDIST > {type z score or cell reference containing z score}. Click OK.

Note: For areas between and to the right, type z scores on worksheet, use NORMSDIST function to determine given areas to the left. On worksheet, perform arithmetic ($+$ or $-$) calculations to determine required areas.

Find z score given a cumulative area to the left → In blank cell, select Insert > Function > Statistical | NORMSINV > {type cumulative area to the left or cell reference}. Click OK.

Determining Normality: Normal Quantile Plot

Input data on worksheet and label column heading. Sort data in ascending order → In blank cell adjacent to first data value, select Insert > Function > Statistical | NORMSINV > type formula $1/(2*n)$, where n is number of data values. Repeat procedure to find z scores for each data value, changing subsequent formulae to $2/(2*n)$, then $3/(2*n)$, and so on. *Note:* Each z score represents $1/n$th increment of the area under the curve.

Highlight two columns from above. Open the Chart Wizard > select XY Scatter | first Chart sub-type. Label chart appropriately. *Check for linearity to determine normality.

Confidence Interval Estimate

Normal z Interval (means) → *Note:* The Excel CONFIDENCE function returns the maximum error of estimate (E), not the lower and upper confidence limits. *Workaround:* Label column heading (i.e., Data) and input data below heading. Label 4 cells (i.e., Mean, E, LCL, UCL). In cell adjacent to mean, input function =AVERAGE(*data range*). In cell adjacent to E, select Insert > Function > Statistical > CONFIDENCE. In dialogue box, type desired value for Alpha (as decimal); alpha is $1 -$ confidence level. If σ is known, type value. If σ is not known, input function STDEV(*data range*). In Size box, either type in sample size or input function COUNT(*data range*). Click OK to display value for E. In cell adjacent to LCL (*lower confidence limit*) type formula to subtract mean from E. In cell adjacent to UCL (*upper confidence limit*), type cell references that will add mean to E.

t Interval (means) → follow procedure for z Interval above, for σ is not known.

Normal z Interval (proportions) → *Note:* Excel does not include a function for confidence interval estimates for proportions. *Workaround:* Label cells. (i.e., X, n, phat, CI, z score, E, LCL, UCL). Type given data in cells adjacent to X and n. For phat, input formula that references data: =X/n. Type confidence level, as decimal, in cell adjacent to CI. For positive z score, input formula =NORMSINV(1-(1-CI *data cell*)/2). For error of estimate, E, input formula $= z$ *score data cell**SQRT((*phat data cell**$(1 - $ *phat data cell*))/n data cell). In cell adjacent to LCL (*lower confidence limit*) type formula to subtract phat from E. In cell adjacent to UCL (*upper confidence limit*), type cell references that will add phat to E.

Variance → No built-in functions for this procedure. Requires third party add-in or manual workaround.

Hypothesis Tests

Normal z Test (means) → Input data and label heading. Excel will calculate P-values using the ZTEST function in the Insert > Function > Statistical menu but only for a one-tailed hypothesis test. Input appropriate values in the dialogue box or type the function in a blank cell: =ZTEST(*data range*, μ_0, σ). For a two-tailed hypothesis test, type the function =2 * MIN(ZTEST(*data range*, μ_0, σ), 1 - ZTEST(*data range*, μ_0, σ)). *Note:* If σ is unknown, leave blank and Excel will calculate s from data.

t Test (means) → No built-in functions for this procedure. Requires third party add-in or manual workaround.

Normal z Test (proportions) → No built-in functions for this procedure. Requires third party add-in or manual workaround.

Variance → No built-in functions for confidence interval estimates for variance. Requires third party add-in or manual workaround.

Hypothesis Test–Difference Between Two Means

z Distribution → Input 2 data sets and label headings. If variances for two data sets are unknown, in blank cells input =VAR(*data range*) function for each data set. Select Tools > Data Analysis > z-Test: Two Sample for Means. In dialogue box, under Input, Variable 1 Range: select sample 1 data range, Variable 2 Range: select sample 2 data range, Hypothesized Mean Difference: 0,

Variable 1 Variance (known): input known or calculated value for data set 1. Variable 2 Variance (known): input known or calculated value for data set 2. Specify desired Alpha: level. Specify output location. Click OK to display results.

t Distribution (Small Independent Samples) → Input 2 data sets and label headings. Select Tools > Data Analysis > t-Test: Two Sample for Means. Input Variable 1 and Variable 2 data ranges and Hypothesized Mean Difference: 0; specify Alpha: level and output range. Click OK to display results.

t Distribution (Small Dependent Samples) → Input 2 data sets and label headings. Select Tools > Data Analysis > t-Test: Paired Two Sample for Means. Input Variable 1 and Variable 2 data ranges and Hypothesized Mean Difference: 0; specify Alpha: level and output range. Click OK to display results.

Hypothesis Test–Difference Between Two Variances

Input 2 data sets and label headings. Select Tools > Data Analysis > F-Test: Two Sample for Variances. In dialogue box, under Input, Variable 1 Range: select sample 1 data range, Variable 2 Range: select sample 2 data range. Specify desired Alpha: level. Specify output location. Click OK to display results.

Hypothesis Test–Difference Between Two Proportions

No built-in functions for this procedure. Requires third party add-in or manual workaround.

Scatter Plots

Input two columns of paired data (x,y) and label headings. Select paired data range. Click Chart Wizard > XY (Scatter) | first Chart sub-type > click Next twice > enter titles and axis labels and any desired changes > click Next and Finish to display chart.

Correlation Coefficient

Input two columns of paired data (x,y) and label headings. Select a blank cell, then select Insert > Function > Statistical > CORREL. In dialogue box, Array 1: select X values and Array 2: Y values. Click OK to display result.

Correlation and Regression

Input two columns of paired data (x,y) and label headings. For correlation, select Tools > Data Analysis . . . > Correlation. In dialogue box, Input range: select range of both X values and Y values with headings. Grouped by: select Columns (or Rows, if data is in rows). Check box Labels in First Row, if headings are selected with data range. Select desired Output options. Click OK to display resulting correlation.

For regression, select Tools > Data Analysis . . . > Regression . . . In dialogue box, under Input, select appropriate Input Y Range: and Input X Range:. Select desired Output option. Click OK to display resulting statistics, including under Coefficients: Intercept and Slope of regression line.

Multiple Regression

Select Tools > Data Analysis . . . > Regression . . . In dialogue box, under Input, select dependent variable data range in Input Y Range: and data range containing independent variables in Input X Range:. Select desired Output option. Click OK to display resulting statistics, including under Coefficients: Intercept and Slopes for each X Variable of multiple regression line.

Chi-square Hypothesis Test

X^2 Goodness-of-Fit Test → Input observed frequencies and expected frequencies in 2 columns. Label column headings (i.e., O and E). In blank cell, select Input > Function > Statistical > CHITEST. In Acutal_range, input observed frequency data range. In Expected_range, input expected frequency data range. Click OK. The CHITEST result is the P-value.

X^2 Independence Test → No built-in functions for this procedure. Requires third party add-in or manual workaround.

One-Way Analysis of Variance (ANOVA)

Input columns of data and label headings. Select Tools > Data Analysis > Anova: Single Factor. In Input Range: select all column data. Grouped by: Columns. In Alpha: type desired significance level. Specify Output option. Click OK to display results including F (test statistic) and P-value.

Two-Way Analysis of Variance

Input data into columns and rows in contingency table format pairing coded factors with row and column labels. Select Tools > Data Analysis > Anova: Two-Factor With Replication. In dialogue, Input Range: select complete table including labels. Specify an alpha level and output range. Click OK to display results including F (test statistic) and P-value.

Sign Test

No built-in functions for this procedure. Requires third party add-in or manual workaround.

Wilcoxon Mann-Whitney Test

No built-in functions for this procedure. Requires third party add-in or manual workaround.

Kruskal-Wallis Test

No built-in functions for this procedure. Requires third party add-in or manual workaround.

Spearman Rank Correlation Coefficient

No built-in functions for this procedure. Requires third party add-in or manual workaround.

Random Numbers

On a new worksheet, select Tools > Data Analysis > Random Number Generation. Click OK. In dialogue box, fill in desired Number of Variables: value for number of different results. Number of Random Numbers: any desired value. Distribution: select Normal, Bernoulli, Binomial, Poisson, or Patterned Discrete. Parameters: input fields will change according to selected Distribution:. Random seed: any number between 1 and 51. Enter desired Output option. Click OK to display results.

TI-83 Plus

The TI-83 Plus is a multi-function programmable calculator which includes capabilities to edit, describe, graph, and analyze data.

Restore Default Settings

Press ON > 2nd [MEM] > 7 : Reset > 2 : Defaults > 2 : Reset

Clear All Lists

2nd [MEM] > 4 : ClrAllLists > Enter

Input Data

Press STAT > EDIT 1: Edit > {type data in L_1}. Press 2nd [QUIT] when completed.

Histogram (ungrouped data)

Input data in L_1. Press WINDOW. Change Xmin and Xmax (data range), Ymin and Ymax (data frequency) values appropriate to input data. Press 2nd [QUIT]. Press 2nd [STAT PLOT] ENTER twice to turn plot on. Select Histogram symbol, press ENTER. Xlist is L_1 and Freq is 1. Press GRAPH. Press TRACE and ▶ or ◀ keys to display number of data values for each class.

Histogram (grouped data)

Input data midpoints in L_1 and class frequencies in L_2. Press WINDOW and change values appropriate to input data. Press 2nd [QUIT]. Press 2nd [STAT PLOT] ENTER twice to turn plot on. Select Histogram symbol, press ENTER. Xlist is L_1 and Freq is L_2. Press GRAPH. Press TRACE and ▶ or ◀ keys to display number of data values for each class.

Other Chart Types

To construct a frequency polygon, repeat procedure for Histogram (grouped data) except select line chart (2nd) instead of histogram chart (3rd). A time series chart is the same as the frequency polygon except data in L_1 represents a time series.

A boxplot can be created in a similar manner to a Histogram (ungrouped data) except select the boxplot chart (5th).

Measures of Central Tendency

Input data in L_1. Press STAT > CALC > 1:1-Var Stats. Press 2nd [L_1]. The calculator will display the descriptive statistics.

$\bar{x}$	sample mean
Σx	sum of data values
Σx^2	sum of squares of the data values
S_X	sample standard deviation
σ_x	population standard deviation
n	number of data values
minX	smallest data values
Q_1	first quartile
Med	median
Q_3	third quartile
maxX	largest data value

Relative Frequency Probabilities

Input data into L_1 and L_2. Move to L_3 heading. Press 2nd [L_1] / {type sample size}. Press ENTER to display probabilities.

Factorials, Permutations, and Combinations

Factorial → Type value of n. Press MATH > PRB > Select 4:! (factorial). Press ENTER.
Permutation → Type value of n. Press MATH > PRB > Select 2:$_nP_r$. Type value of r. Press ENTER.
Combination → Type value of n. Press MATH > PRB > Select 3:$_nC_r$. Type value of r. Press ENTER.

Discrete Random Variables–Mean and Standard Deviation

* Input x-values (L_1) and probabilities (L_2). Move to L_3 heading. Input formula $L_1 * L_2$. Press ENTER. Move to L_4 heading. Input formula L_1, press x^2, * L_2. Press ENTER. Press 2nd [QUIT]. Pres 2nd [LIST] > MATH > select 5:sum(> L_3. Press ENTER to display the mean. Press 2nd ENTER to display sum(L_3 then select L_4). Press ENTER to display the standard deviation.

Binomial Random Variables

For P(X) → 2nd [DISTR]. Select 0:binompdf(> format is binompdf(n,p,X).
For cumulative P(X) → 2nd [DISTR]. Select A:binomcdf) > format is binomcdf(n,p,X).

Binomial Probability Table

Input X values {0 to n} in L_1. Move to L_2 heading. 2nd [DISTR]. Select 0:binompdf(> format is binomcdf(n,p, L_1). Press ENTER.

Poisson Random Variables

For $P(X)$ → 2nd [DISTR]. Select B:poissondf(> format is poissonpdf(λ, X).
For cumulative P(X) → 2nd [DISTR]. Select C: poissoncdf(> format is poissoncdf(λ, X).

Poisson Probability Table

Input X values in L_1. Move to L_2 heading. 2nd [DISTR]. Select B:poissondf(> format is poissonpdf(λ, X). Press ENTER.

Standard Normal Random Variable

Area between → 2nd [DIST] > 2:normalcdf(> format is normalcdf(lower z score, upper z score).

Area to the left → 2nd [DIST] > 2:normalcdf(> format is normalcdf(lower z score, upper z score). *Note:* For lower z score, use $-\infty$, type (negative) -2nd [EE]99.

Area to the right → 2nd [DIST] > 2:normalcdf(> format is normalcdf(lower z score, upper z score). *Note:* For upper z score, use ∞, type 2nd [EE]99.

To find z score corresponding to a cumulative area to the left. 2nd [DIST] > 3:invNorm(> {type area to the left} to display z score.

Determining Normality: Normal Quantile Plot

Input X values in L_1. Press 2nd [STAT PLOT] > 1:Plot1...> ON > select chart 6 > Xlist: L_1 and Frequ: 1. Press WINDOW > input Xmin and Xmax to appropriate values for data and Ymin $= -3$ and Ymax $= 3$. Press GRAPH. *Check for linearity of points to determine normality.

Confidence Interval Estimate

Normal z Interval (means) → Input data in L_1. Select STATS > TESTS > 7:ZInterval . . . Select Data. If σ is known, type value. If σ is not known, press VARS > 5:Basic Statistics > 3:Sx > ENTER to input standard deviation from L_1. Check List: L_1 and Freq: 1. Indicate desired confidence level as decimal value, C-Level: (i.e., .95). Calculate to display results. *Note:* If summary statistics mean and standard deviation are known, select Stats instead of Data and input appropriate values.

t Interval (means) → Input data in L_1. Select STATS > TESTS > 8:TInterval . . . Select Data. Check List: L_1 and Freq: 1. Indicate desired confidence level as decimal value, C-Level: (i.e., .95). Calculate to display results. *Note:* If summary statistics mean and standard deviation are known, select Stats instead of Data and input appropriate values.

Normal z Interval (proportions) → No data will be input in L_1. Select STATS > TESTS > A:1-PropZInt . . . Type appropriate data for x:, n:, and confidence level as decimal value, C-Level: (i.e., .95). Calculate to display results.

Variance → No built-in functions for confidence interval estimates for variance. Downloadable SDINT program is available from OLC or CD. Follow included instructions.

Hypothesis Tests

Normal z Test (means) → Input data in L_1. Select STATS > TESTS > 1:Z-Test . . . Select Data. In μ_0, input hypothesized mean. If σ is known, input value. If σ is not known, press VARS > 5:Basic Statistics > 3:Sx > ENTER to input standard deviation from L_1. Check List: L_1 and Freq: 1. Select required alternative, μ: $\neq \mu_0$ $<\mu_0$ $>\mu_0$. Select Calculate to display results including z (test statistic) and p (P-value). *Note*: If summary statistics mean and standard deviation are known, select Stats instead of Data and input appropriate values.

t Interval (means) → Input data in L_1. Select STATS > TESTS > 2:T-Test . . . Select Data. In μ_0, input hypothesized mean. Check List: L_1 and Freq: 1. Select required alternative hypothesis, μ: $\neq \mu_0$ $<\mu_0$ $>\mu_0$. Select Calculate to display results including z (test statistic) and p (P-value). *Note*: If summary statistics mean and standard deviation are known, select Stats instead of Data and input appropriate values.

Normal z Interval (proportions) → No data will be input in L_1. Select STATS > TESTS > 5:1-PropZTest . . . In p_0, input hypothesized proportion. Type appropriate data for x: and n:. Select required alternative hypothesis, prop: $\neq p_0$ $<p_0$ $>p_0$. Calculate to display results including z (test statistic) and p (P-value).

Variance → No built-in functions for hypothesis tests for variance. Downloadable SDHYP program is available from OLC or CD. Follow included instructions.

Hypothesis Test–Difference Between Two Means

z Distribution → Input 2 sets of data in L_1 and L_2. Select STATS > TESTS > 3:2-SampZTest . . . Select Data. In μ_0, input hypothesized mean. If $\sigma1$ and $\sigma2$ are known, input values. If $\sigma1$ and $\sigma2$ are not known, calculate $S1_x$ and $S2_x$, then manually input values accordingly. Check List1: L_1, List2: L_2, Freq1:1, and Freq2: 1. Select required alternative, $\mu1$: $\neq\mu2$ $<\mu2$ $>\mu2$. Select Calculate to display results including z (test statistic) and p (P-value). *Note:* If summary statistics mean and standard deviation are known for data sets, select Stats instead of Data and input appropriate values.

Note: A similar procedure for confidence intervals for the difference between two means (z distribution) is available using the STATS > TESTS > 9:2-SampZInt . . . option. Input appropriate values and calculate.

t Distribution → Repeat z Distribution procedure except select STATS > TESTS > 9:2-SampTTest . . . standard deviations are calculated from L_1 and L_2 lists. In Pooled: select No (standard deviations are assumed not equal) or Yes (standard deviations are assumed equal).

Note: A similar procedure for confidence intervals for the difference between two means (t distribution) is available using the STATS > TESTS > 0:2-SampTInt . . . option. Input appropriate values and calculate.

Dependent Samples → Input 2 sets of data in L_1 and L_2. Move to L_3 heading. Type L_1 - L_2. Press ENTER. Select STATS > TESTS > 2:T-Test . . . Input $\mu_0 = 0$, List: L_3, Freq: 1. Check List: L_1 and Freq: 1. Select required alternative, $\mu: \neq \mu_0 < \mu_0 > \mu_0$. Select Calculate to display results.

Note: A similar procedure for confidence intervals for the difference between two means (dependent samples) is available using the STATS > TESTS > 8:TInterval . . . option. Input appropriate values using L_3 and calculate.

Hypothesis Test—Difference Between Two Variances

Input 2 sets of data in L_1 and L_2. Select STATS > TESTS > D:2-SampFTest . . . Select Data. Check List1: L_1, List2: L_2, Freq1:1, and Freq2: 1. Select required alternative, $\sigma 1: \neq \sigma 2 < \sigma 2 > \sigma 2$. Calculate to display results including F (test statistic) and p (P-value). *Note:* If summary statistics mean and standard deviation are known for each data set, select Stats instead of Data and input appropriate values.

Hypothesis Test—Difference Between Two Proportions

No data is required. Select STAT > TESTS > 6:2-PropZTest . . . Type appropriate values for x1:, n1:, x2:, n2:. Select p1:$\neq$2. Press Calculate to display results.

Note: A similar procedure for confidence intervals for the difference between two proportions is available. Select STAT > TESTS > B:2-PropZInt . . . Input appropriate values and calculate.

Scatter Plot

Input x values in L_1 and y values in L_2. Select WINDOW and adjust Xmin, Xmax, Ymin, and Ymax to match data set. Press 2nd [STAT PLOT] > Plot 1 > On. Select: Type: first chart, XList: L_1, Ylist: L_2. Press GRAPH to display scatter plot.

Correlation and Regression

Turn on correlation display. Press 2nd [CATALOG]. Scroll to DiagnosticON. Press ENTER twice. Feature will remain on unless calculator's memory is reset.

Input x values in L_1 and y values in L_2. Press STAT > CALC > LinReg($a + bx$). Press ENTER to display values for a (y-intercept) and b (slope) and r (correlation coefficient).

Plot Regression Equation on Scatter Plot

Follow procedure for Scatter Plot and Correlation and Regression. Press Y= > CLEAR to clear previous equations. Press VARS > 5:Statistics > EQ > 1:RegEQ to display regression equation. Press GRAPH to display resulting graph.

Multiple Regression

No built-in functions for multiple regression. Downloadable MULREG program is available from OLC or CD. Follow included instructions.

Chi-Square Hypothesis Test

X^2 Goodness-of-Fit Test → Input observed frequencies in L_1 and expected L_2. Press 2nd [QUIT] to exit to home screen. To calculate test statistic, press 2nd [LIST] > MATH 5:sum(> input $(L_1-L_2)^2/L_2)$ > ENTER. To calculate P-value, press 2nd [DIST] > 7:X^2cdf(> command format X^2cdf (test statistic, ∞, degrees of freedom). *Note:* Use 2nd [EE], type 99 for ∞.

X^2 Independence Test $\rightarrow$ Press 2nd [MATRX] > EDIT. Input number of rows and columns in contingency table over 1×1 (i.e., 2×3, for 2 rows, 3 columns). Input observed frequencies in displayed matrix (table) pressing ENTER after each data entry. Press STAT > TESTS > C:X^2-Test . . . Check the Observed: [A] and Expected [B]. Select Calculate to display results including X^2 (test statistic) and p (P-value).

One-Way Analysis of Variance (ANOVA)

Input data into L_1, L_2, L_3, etc. Press STAT > TESTS > F:ANOVA(. Type each list followed by a comma (i.e., F:ANOVA(L_1, L_2, L_3). Press ENTER to display F (test statistic) and p (P-value).

Two-Way Analysis of Variance

No built-in functions for two-way analysis of variance. Downloadable TWOWAY program is available from OLC or CD. Follow included instructions.

Random Numbers

To generate a random number from 0 to 1, press MATH > PRB > 1:rand > ENTER to display results. Continue to press ENTER to display more random numbers.

To generate a list of random numbers between specified values, press MATH > PRB > 5:randInt(. Type a desired minimum value, comma, maximum value, comma, number of desired values. (i.e., randInt(1,99,10) will generate 10 random number between 1 and 99.) *Note:* Use arrow ▶ keys to scroll right to see numbers.

Appendix F
Glossary

adjusted R^2 used in multiple regression when n and k are approximately equal, to provide a more realistic value of R^2

alpha the probability of a type I error, represented by the Greek letter α

alternative hypothesis a statistical hypothesis that states a parameter is either less than, not equal to, or greater than a specific value, or states that there is a difference between two parameters

analysis of variance (ANOVA) a statistical technique used to test a hypothesis concerning the means of three or more populations

ANOVA summary table the table used to summarize the results of an ANOVA test

Bayes' theorem a theorem that allows one to compute the revised probability of an event that occurred before another event when the events are dependent

beta the probability of a type II error, represented by the Greek letter β

between-group variance a variance estimate using the means of the groups or between the groups in an F test

biased sample a sample for which some type of systematic error has been made in the selection of subjects for the sample

bimodal a data set with two modes

binomial distribution a discrete probability distribution of the number of successes in a series of n independent trials with each trial having two possible outcomes and a constant probability of success

binomial experiment a probability experiment in which each trial has only two outcomes, there are a fixed number of trials, the outcomes of the trials are independent, and the probability of success remains the same for each trial

boxplot a graph used to represent a data set when the data set contains a small number of values

categorical frequency distribution a frequency distribution used when the data are categorical (nominal)

central limit theorem a theorem that states that as the sample size increases, the shape of the distribution of the sample means taken from the population with mean μ and standard deviation σ will approach a normal distribution; the distribution will have a mean μ and a standard deviation $\sigma/\sqrt{n}$

Chebyshev's theorem a theorem that states that the proportion of values from a data set that fall within k standard deviations of the mean will be at least $1 - 1/k^2$, where k is a number greater than 1

chi-square distribution a probability distribution obtained from the values of $(n - 1)s^2/\sigma^2$ when random samples are selected from a normally distributed population whose variance is σ^2

class a quantitative or qualitative category

class boundaries the upper and lower values of a class for a grouped frequency distribution whose values have one additional decimal place more than the data and end in the digit 5

class midpoint a value for a class in a frequency distribution obtained by adding the lower and upper class boundaries (or the lower and upper class limits) and dividing by 2

class width the difference between the upper class boundary and the lower class boundary for a class in a frequency distribution

classical probability the type of probability that uses sample spaces to determine the numerical probability that an event will happen

cluster sample a sample obtained by selecting a preexisting or natural group, called a cluster, and using the members in the cluster for the sample

coefficient of determination a measure of the variation of the dependent variable that is explained by the regression line and the independent variable; the ratio of the explained variation to the total variation

coefficient of variation the standard deviation divided by the mean; the result is expressed as a percentage

combination a selection of objects without regard to order

complement of an event the set of outcomes in the sample space that are not among the outcomes of the event itself

compound event an event that consists of two or more outcomes or simple events

conditional probability the probability that an event B occurs after an event A has already occurred

confidence interval a specific interval estimate of a parameter determined by using data obtained from a sample and the specific confidence level of the estimate

confidence level the probability that a parameter lies within the specified interval estimate of the parameter

confounded variables two variables confounded when their efects on a response variable cannot be distinguished from each other

consistent estimator an estimator whose value approaches the value of the parameter estimated as the sample size increases

contingency table data arranged in table form for the chi-square independence test, with R rows and C columns

continuous variable a variable that can assume all values between any two specific values; a variable obtained by measuring

control group a group in an experimental study that is not given any special treatment

convenience sample sample of subjects used because they are convenient and available

correction for continuity a correction employed when a continuous distribution is used to approximate a discrete distribution

correlation a statistical method used to determine whether a linear relationship exists between variables

correlation coefficient a statistic or parameter that measures the strength and direction of a linear relationship between two variables

critical or **rejection region** the range of values of the test value that indicates that there is a significant difference and the null hypothesis should be rejected in a hypothesis test

critical value a value that separates the critical region from the noncritical region in a hypothesis test

cumulative frequency the sum of the frequencies accumulated up to the upper boundary of a class in a frequency distribution

data measurements or observations for a variable

data array a data set that has been ordered

data set a collection of data values

data value or **datum** a value in a data set

decile a location measure of a data value; it divides the distribution into ten groups

degrees of freedom the number of values that are free to vary after a sample statistic has been computed; used when a distribution (such as the t distribution) consists of a family of curves

dependent events events for which the outcome or occurrence of the first event affects the outcome or occurrence of the second event in such a way that the probability is changed

dependent samples samples in which the subjects are paired or matched in some way; i.e., the samples are related

dependent variable a variable in correlation and regression analysis that cannot be controlled or manipulated

descriptive statistics a branch of statistics that consists of the collection, organization, summarization, and presentation of data

discrete probability distribution a distribution that consists of the values a random variable can assume and the corresponding probabilities of the values

discrete variable a variable that assumes values that can be counted

disordinal interaction an interaction between variables in ANOVA, indicated when the graphs of the lines connecting the mean intersect

distribution-free statistics *see* nonparametric statistics

double sampling a sampling method in which a very large population is given a questionnaire to determine those who meet the qualifications for a study; the questionnaire is reviewed, a second smaller population is defined, and a sample is selected from this group

element an object contained in a set of data

empirical probability the type of probability that uses frequency distributions based on observations to determine numerical probabilities of events

empirical rule a rule that states that when a distribution is bell-shaped (normal), approximately 68% of the data values will fall within 1 standard deviation of the mean; approximately 95% of the data values will fall within 2 standard deviations of the mean; and approximately 99.7% of the data values will fall within 3 standard deviations of the mean

equally likely events the events in the sample space that have the same probability of occurring

estimation the process of estimating the value of a parameter from information obtained from a sample

estimator a statistic used to estimate a parameter

event outcome of a probability experiment

expected frequency the frequency obtained by calculation (as if there were no preference) and used in the chi-square test

expected value the theoretical average of a variable that has a probability distribution

experimental study a study in which the researcher manipulates one of the variables and tries to determine how the manipulation influences other variables

explanatory variable a variable that is being manipulated by the researcher to see if it affects the outcome variable

exploratory data analysis the act of analyzing data to determine what information can be obtained by using stem and leaf plots, medians, interquartile ranges, and boxplots

extrapolation use of the equation for the regression line to predict y' for a value of x which is beyond the range of the data values of x

F distribution the sampling distribution of the variances when two independent samples are selected from two normally distributed populations in which the variances are equal and the variances s_1^2 and s_2^2 are compared as $s_1^2 \div s_2^2$

F test a statistical test used to compare two variances or three or more means

factors the independent variables in ANOVA tests

five-number summary five specific values for a data set that consist of the lowest and highest values, Q_1 and Q_3, and the median

frequency the number of values in a specific class of a frequency distribution

frequency distribution an organization of raw data in table form, using classes and frequencies

frequency polygon a graph that displays the data by using lines that connect points plotted for the frequencies at the midpoints of the classes

fundamental counting rule in a sequence of n events in which the first one has k_1 possibilities, the second event has k_2 possibilities, the third has k_3 possibilities, etc., the total number possibilities of the sequence will be $k_1 \cdot k_2 \cdot k_3 \cdots k_n$

goodness-of-fit test a chi-square test used to see whether a frequency distribution fits a specific pattern

grouped frequency distribution a distribution used when the range is large and classes of several units in width are needed

Hawthorne effect an effect on an outcome variable caused by the fact that subjects of the study know that they are participating in the study

histogram a bar chart in which vertical bars represent class frequencies

homogeneity of proportions test a test used to determine the equality of three or more proportions

hypergeometric distribution the distribution of a variable that has two outcomes when sampling is done without replacement

hypothesis testing a decision-making process for evaluating claims about a population

independence test a chi-square test used to test the independence of two variables when data are tabulated in table form in terms of frequencies

independent events events for which the probability of the first occurring does not affect the probability of the second occurring

independent samples the measurements in one sample are not related to the measurements in the other sample

independent variable a variable in correlation and regression analysis that can be controlled or manipulated

inferential statistics a branch of statistics that consists of generalizing from samples to populations, performing hypothesis testing, determining relationships among variables, and making predictions

influential observation an observation which when removed from the data values would markedly change the position of the regression line

interaction effect the effect of two or more variables on each other in a two-way ANOVA study

interquartile range $Q_3 - Q_1$

interval estimate a range of values used to estimate a parameter

interval level of measurement a measurement level that ranks data and in which precise differences between units of measure exist. *See also* nominal, ordinal, and ratio levels of measurement

Kruskal-Wallis test a nonparametric test used to compare three or more means

law of large numbers when a probability experiment is repeated a large number of times, the relative frequency probability of an outcome will approach its theoretical probability

least-squares line another name for the regression line

left-tailed test a test used on a hypothesis when the critical region is on the left side of the distribution

level a treatment in ANOVA for a variable

level of significance the maximum probability of committing a type I error in hypothesis testing

lower class limit the lower value of a class in a frequency distribution that has the same decimal place value as the data

lurking variable a variable that influences the relationship between x and y, but was not considered in the study

main effect the effect of the factors or independent variables when there is a nonsignificant interaction effect in a two-way ANOVA study

marginal change the magnitude of the change in the dependent variable when the independent variable changes 1 unit

margin of error the maximum likely difference between the point estimate of a parameter and the actual value of the parameter

mean the sum of the values, divided by the total number of values

mean square the variance found by dividing the sum of the squares of a variable by the corresponding degrees of freedom; used in ANOVA

measurement scales a type of classification that tells how variables are categorized, counted, or measured; the four types of scales are nominal, ordinal, interval, and ratio

median the midpoint of a data array

midrange the sum of the lowest and highest data values, divided by 2

modal class the class with the largest frequency

mode the value that occurs most often in a data set

Monte Carlo method a simulation technique using random numbers

multimodal a data set with three or more modes

multinomial distribution a probability distribution for an experiment in which each trial has more than two outcomes

multiple correlation coefficient a measure of the strength of the relationship between the independent variables and the dependent variable in a multiple regression study

multiple regression a study that seeks to determine if several independent variables are related to a dependent variable

multistage sampling a sampling technique that uses a combination of sampling methods

mutually exclusive events probability events that cannot occur at the same time

negative relationship a relationship between variables such that as one variable increases, the other variable decreases, and vice versa

negatively skewed or left-skewed distribution a distribution in which the majority of the data values fall to the right of the mean

nominal level of measurement a measurement level that classifies data into mutually exclusive (nonoverlapping) exhaustive categories in which no order or ranking can be imposed on them. *See also* interval, ordinal, and ratio levels of measurement

noncritical or nonrejection region the range of values of the test value that indicates that the difference was probably due to chance and the null hypothesis should not be rejected

nonparametric statistics a branch of statistics for use when the population from which the samples are selected is not normally distributed and for use in testing hypotheses that do not involve specific population parameters

nonrejection region *see* noncritical region

normal distribution a continuous, symmetric, bell-shaped distribution of a variable

null hypothesis a statistical hypothesis that states that a parameter is equal to a specific value, or that there is no difference between two parameters

observational study a study in which the researcher merely observes what is happening or what has happened in the past and draws conclusions based on these observations

observed frequency the actual frequency value obtained from a sample and used in the chi-square test

ogive a graph that represents the cumulative frequencies for the classes in a frequency distribution

one-tailed test a test that indicates that the null hypothesis should be rejected when the test statistic value is in the critical region on one side of the mean

one-way ANOVA a study used to test for differences among means for a single independent variable when there are three or more groups

open-ended distribution a frequency distribution that has no specific beginning value or no specific ending value

ordinal interaction an interaction between variables in ANOVA, indicated when the graphs of the lines connecting the means do not intersect

ordinal level of measurement a measurement level that classifies data into categories that can be ranked; however, precise differences between the ranks do not exist. *See also* interval, nominal, and ratio levels of measurement

outcome the result of a single trial of a probability experiment

outcome variable a variable that is studied to see if it has changed significantly due to the manipulation of the explanatory variable

outlier an extreme value in a data set; it is omitted from a boxplot

parameter a characteristic or measure obtained by using all the data values for a specific population

parametric tests statistical tests for population parameters such as means, variances, and proportions that involve assumptions about the populations from which the samples were selected

Pareto chart chart that uses vertical bars to represent frequencies for a categorical variable

Pearson product moment correlation coefficient (PPMCC) a statistic used to determine the strength of a relationship when the variables are normally distributed

percentile a location measure of a data value; it divides a data set into 100 equal parts in which the pth percentile is a value that at most $p\%$ of the observations in the data set are less than this value and the remainder are greater

permutation an arrangement of n objects in a specific order

pie graph a circle that is divided into sections or wedges according to the percentage of frequencies in each category of the distribution

point estimate a specific numerical value estimate of a parameter

Poisson distribution a probability distribution used when n is large and p is small and when the independent variables occur over a period of time

pooled estimate of the variance a weighted average of the variance using the two sample variances and their respective degrees of freedom as the weights

population the totality of all subjects possessing certain common characteristics that are being studied

population correlation coefficient the value of the correlation coefficient computed by using all possible pairs of data values (x, y) taken from a population

positive relationship a relationship between two variables such that as one variable increases, the other variable increases or as one variable decreases, the other decreases

positively skewed or right-skewed distribution a distribution in which the majority of the data values fall to the left of the mean

power of a test the probability of rejecting the null hypothesis when it is false

prediction interval a confidence interval for a predicted value y

probability the chance of an event occurring

probability experiment a chance process that leads to well-defined results called outcomes

proportion a part of a whole, represented by a fraction, a decimal, or a percentage

P-value (or probability value) the probability that a sample statistic (such as the sample mean) could have been selected from the population(s) being tested (or that a more improbable sample could be selected in the direction of the alternative hypothesis) given the assumption that the null hypothesis is true

qualitative variable a variable that can be placed into distinct categories, according to some characteristic or attribute

quantitative variable a variable that is numerical in nature and that can be ordered or ranked

quartile a location measure of a data value; it divides the distribution into four groups

quasi-experimental study a study that uses intact groups rather than random assignment of subjects to groups

random sample a sample obtained by using random or chance methods; a sample for which every member of the population has an equal chance of being selected

random variable a variable whose values are determined by chance; a function that assigns a unique numerical value, determined by chance, to each outcome of an experiment

range the highest data value minus the lowest data value

range rule of thumb dividing the range by 4 given an approximation of the standard deviation

ranking the positioning of a data value in a data array according to some rating scale

ratio level of measurement a measurement level that possesses all the characteristics of interval measurement and a true zero; it also has true ratios between different units of measure. *See also* interval, nominal, and ordinal levels of measurement

raw data data collected in original form

regression a statistical method used to describe the nature of the relationship between variables, that is, a positive or negative, linear or nonlinear relationship

regression line the line of best fit of the data

rejection region *see* critical region

relative frequency graph a graph using proportions instead of raw data as frequencies

relatively efficient estimator an estimator that has the smallest variance from among all the statistics that can be used to estimate a parameter

residual the difference between the actual value of y and the predicted value y' for a specific value of x

resistant statistic a statistic that is not affected by an extremely skewed distribution

right-tailed test a test used on a hypothesis when the critical region is on the right side of the distribution

run a succession of identical letters preceded by or followed by a different letter or no letter at all, such as the beginning or end of the succession

runs test a nonparametric test used to determine whether data are random

sample a group of subjects selected from the population

sample space the set of all possible outcomes of a probability experiment

sampling distribution of sample means a distribution obtained by using the means computed from random samples taken from a population

sampling error the difference between the sample measure and the corresponding population measure due to the fact that the sample is not a perfect representation of the population

scatter plot a graph of the independent and dependent variables in regression and correlation analysis

Scheffé test a test used after ANOVA, if the null hypothesis is rejected, to locate significant differences in the means

sequence sampling a sampling technique used in quality control in which successive units are taken from production lines and tested to see whether they meet the standards set by the manufacturing company

sign test a nonparametric test used to test the value of the median for a specific sample or to test sample means in a comparison of two dependent samples

simple event an outcome that results from a single trial of a probability experiment

simulation techniques techniques that use probability experiments to mimic real-life situations

Spearman rank correlation coefficient the nonparametric equivalent to the correlation coefficient, used when the data are ranked

standard deviation the square root of the variance

standard error of the estimate the standard deviation of the observed y values about the predicted y' values in regression and correlation analysis

standard error of the mean the standard deviation of the sample means for samples taken from the same population

standard normal distribution a normal distribution for which the mean is equal to 0 and the standard deviation is equal to 1

standard score the difference between a data value and the mean, divided by the standard deviation

statistic a characteristic or measure obtained by using the data values from a sample

statistical hypothesis a conjecture about a population parameter, which may or may not be true

statistical test a test that uses data obtained from a sample to make a decision about whether the null hypothesis should be rejected

statistics the science of conducting studies to collect, organize, summarize, analyze, and draw conclusions from data

stem and leaf plot a data plot that uses the stem as the leading part of the data value with the leaf as the remaining part of the data value to form groups or classes

stratified sample a sample obtained by dividing the population into subgroups, called strata, according to various homogeneous characteristics and then selecting members from each stratum

subjective probability the type of probability that uses a probability value based on an educated guess or estimate, employing opinions and inexact information

sum of squares between groups a statistic computed in the numerator of the fraction used to find the between-group variance in ANOVA

sum of squares within groups a statistic computed in the numerator of the fraction used to find the within-group variance in ANOVA

symmetric distribution a distribution in which the data values are uniformly distributed about the mean

systematic sample a sample obtained by numbering each element in the population and then selecting every kth number from the population to be included in the sample

t distribution a family of bell-shaped curves based on degrees of freedom, similar to the standard normal distribution with the exception that the variance is greater than 1; used when one is testing small samples and when the population standard deviation is unknown

t test a statistical test for the mean of a population, used when the population is normally distributed, the population standard deviation is unknown, and the sample size is less than 30

test statistic the numerical value calculated from the sample data in a statistical test

time series graph a graph that represents data that occur over a specific time

treatment group a group in an experimental study that has received some type of treatment

treatment groups the groups used in an ANOVA study

tree diagram a schematic with branches emanating from a starting point showing all possible outcomes of a probability experiment

Tukey test a test used to make pairwise comparisons of means in an ANOVA study when samples are the same size

two-tailed test a test that indicates that the null hypothesis should be rejected when the test value is in either of the two critical regions

two-way ANOVA a study used to test the effects of two or more independent variables and the possible interaction between them

type I error the error that occurs if one rejects the null hypothesis when it is true

type II error the error that occurs if one does not reject the null hypothesis when it is false

unbiased estimator an estimator whose value approximates the expected value of a population parameter, used for the variance or standard deviation when the sample size is less than 30; an estimator whose expected value or mean must be equal to the mean of the parameter being estimated

unbiased sample a sample chosen at random from the population that is, for the most part, representative of the population

ungrouped frequency distribution a distribution that uses individual data and has a small range of data

unimodal a data set that has only one value that occurs with the greatest frequency

upper class limit the upper value of a class in a frequency distribution that has the same decimal place value as the data

variable a characteristic or attribute capable of assuming any value within the data set

variance the average of the squares of the distance that each value is from the mean

Venn diagram a diagram used as a pictorial representative for a probability concept or rule

weighted mean the mean found by multiplying each value by its corresponding weight and dividing by the sum of the weights

Wilcoxon rank sum test a nonparametric test used to test independent samples and compare distributions

Wilcoxon signed-rank test a nonparametric test used to test dependent samples and compare distributions

within-group variance a variance estimate using all the sample data for an F test; it is not affected by differences in the means

z **distribution** *see* standard normal distribution

z **score** *see* standard score

z **test** a statistical test for means and proportions of a population, used when the population is normally distributed and the population standard deviation is known or the sample size is 30 or more

Glossary of Symbols

a	y intercept of a line	F_S	Scheffé test value
α	Probability of a type I error	GM	Geometric mean
b	Slope of a line	H	Kruskal-Wallis test value
β	Probability of a type II error	H_0	Null hypothesis
C	Column frequency	H_1	Alternative hypothesis
cf	Cumulative frequency	HM	Harmonic mean
$_nC_r$	Number of combinations of n objects taking r objects at a time	k	Number of samples
		λ	Number of occurrences for the Poisson distribution
C.V.	Critical value	s_D	Standard deviation of the differences
CVar	Coefficient of variation	s_{est}	Standard error of estimate
D	Difference; decile	SS_B	Sum of squares between groups
$\overline{D}$	Mean of the differences	SS_W	Sum of squares within groups
d.f.	Degrees of freedom	s_B^2	Between-group variance
d.f.N.	Degrees of freedom, numerator	s_W^2	Within-group variance
d.f.D.	Degrees of freedom, denominator	t	t test value
E	Event; expected frequency; maximum error of estimate	$t_{\alpha/2}$	Two-tailed t critical value
		μ	Population mean
$\overline{E}$	Complement of an event	μ_D	Mean of the population differences
e	Euler's constant ≈ 2.7183	$\mu_{\overline{X}}$	Mean of the sample means
$E(X)$	Expected value	w	Class width; weight
f	Frequency	r	Sample correlation coefficient
F	F test value; failure	R	Multiple correlation coefficient
F'	Critical value for the Scheffé test	r^2	Coefficient of determination
MD	Median	ρ	Population correlation coefficient
MR	Midrange	r_S	Spearman rank correlation coefficient
MS_B	Mean square between groups	S	Sample space; success
MS_W	Mean square within groups (error)	s	Sample standard deviation
n	Sample size	s^2	Sample variance
N	Population size	σ	Population standard deviation
$n(E)$	Number of ways E can occur	σ^2	Population variance
$n(S)$	Number of outcomes in the sample space	$\sigma_{\overline{X}}$	Standard error of the mean
O	Observed frequency	$\sum$	Summation notation
P	Percentile; probability	w_s	Smaller sum of signed ranks, Wilcoxon signed-rank test
p	Probability; population proportion		
$\hat{p}$	Sample proportion	X	Data value; number of successes for a binomial distribution
$\overline{p}$	Weighted estimate of p		
$P(B\mid A)$	Conditional probability	$\overline{X}$	Sample mean
$P(E)$	Probability of an event E	x	Independent variable in regression
$P(\overline{E})$	Probability of the complement of E	$\overline{X}_{\text{GM}}$	Grand mean
$_nP_r$	Number of permutations of n objects taking r objects at a time	X_m	Midpoint of a class
		χ^2	Chi-square
π	Pi ≈ 3.14	y	Dependent variable in regression
Q	Quartile	y'	Predicted y value
q	$1 - p$; test value for Tukey test	z	z test value or z score
$\hat{q}$	$1 - \hat{p}$	$z_{\alpha/2}$	Two-tailed critical z value
$\overline{q}$	$1 - \overline{p}$	!	Factorial
R	Range; rank sum		

Appendix G
Bibliography

Aczel, Amir D. *Complete Business Statistics,* 3rd ed. Chicago: Irwin, 1996.

Beyer, William H. *CRC Handbook of Tables for Probability and Statistics,* 2nd ed. Boca Raton, Fla.: CRC Press, 1986.

Brase, Charles, and Corrinne P. Brase. *Understanding Statistics,* 5th ed. Lexington, Mass.: D.C. Heath, 1995.

Chao, Lincoln L. *Introduction to Statistics.* Monterey, Calif.: Brooks/Cole, 1980.

Daniel, Wayne W., and James C. Terrell. *Business Statistics,* 4th ed. Boston: Houghton Mifflin, 1986.

Edwards, Allan L. *An Introduction to Linear Regression and Correlation,* 2nd ed. New York: Freeman, 1984.

Eves, Howard. *An Introduction to the History of Mathematics,* 3rd ed. New York: Holt, Rinehart and Winston, 1969.

Famighetti, Robert, ed. *The World Almanac and Book of Facts 1996.* New York: Pharos Books, 1995.

Freund, John E., and Gary Simon. *Statistics—A First Course,* 6th ed. Englewood Cliffs, N.J.: Prentice-Hall, 1995.

Gibson, Henry R. *Elementary Statistics.* Dubuque, Iowa: Wm. C. Brown Publishers, 1994.

Glass, Gene V., and Kenneth D. Hopkins. *Statistical Methods in Education and Psychology,* 2nd ed. Englewood Cliffs, N.J.: Prentice-Hall, 1984.

Guilford, J. P. *Fundamental Statistics in Psychology and Education,* 4th ed. New York: McGraw-Hill, 1965.

Haack, Dennis G. *Statistical Literacy:* A Guide to *Interpretation.* Boston: Duxbury Press, 1979.

Hartwig, Frederick, with Brian Dearing. *Exploratory Data Analysis.* Newbury Park, Calif.: Sage Publications, 1979.

Henry, Gary T. *Graphing Data: Techniques for Display and Analysis.* Thousand Oaks, Calif.: Sage Publications, 1995.

Isaac, Stephen, and William B. Michael. *Handbook in Research and Evaluation,* 2nd ed. San Diego: EdITS, 1990.

Johnson, Robert. *Elementary Statistics,* 6th ed. Boston: PWS-Kent, 1992.

Kachigan, Sam Kash. *Statistical Analysis.* New York: Radius Press, 1986.

Khazanie, Ramakant. *Elementary Statistics in a World of Applications,* 3rd ed. Glenview, Ill.: Scott, Foresman, 1990.

Kuzma, Jan W. *Basic Statistics for the Health Sciences.* Mountain View, Calif.: Mayfield, 1984.

Lapham, Lewis H., Michael Pollan, and Eric Ethridge. *The Harper's Index Book.* New York: Henry Holt, 1987.

Lipschultz, Seymour. *Schaum's Outline of Theory and Problems of Probability.* New York: McGraw-Hill, 1968.

Marascuilo, Leonard A., and Maryellen McSweeney. *Nonparametric and Distribution-Free Methods for the Social Sciences.* Monterey, Calif.: Brooks/Cole, 1977.

Marzillier, Leon F. *Elementary Statistics.* Dubuque, Iowa: Wm. C. Brown Publishers, 1990.

Mason, Robert D., Douglas A. Lind, and William G. Marchal. *Statistics: An Introduction.* New York: Harcourt Brace Jovanovich, 1988.

MINITAB. *MINITAB Reference Manual.* State College, Pa.: MINITAB, Inc., 1994.

Minium, Edward W. *Statistical Reasoning in Psychology and Education.* New York: Wiley, 1970.

Moore, David S. *The Basic Practice of Statistics.* New York: W. H. Freeman and Co., 1995.

Moore, Davis S., and George P. McCabe. *Introduction to the Practice of Statistics,* 3rd ed. New York: W. H. Freeman, *1999.*

Newmark, Joseph. *Statistics and Probability in Modern Life.* New York: Saunders, 1988.

Pagano, Robert R. *Understanding Statistics,* 3rd ed. New York: West, 1990.

Phillips, John L., Jr. *How to Think about Statistics.* New York: Freeman, 1988.

Reinhardt, Howard E., and Don O. Loftsgaarden. *Elementary Probability and Statistical Reasoning.* Lexington, Mass.: Heath, 1977.

Roscoe, John T. *Fundamental Research Statistics for the Behavioral Sciences,* 2nd ed. New York: Holt, Rinehart and Winston, 1975.

Rossman, Allan J. *Workshop Statistics, Discovery with Data.* New York: Springer, 1996.

Runyon, Richard P., and Audrey Haber. *Fundamentals of Behavioral Statistics,* 6th ed. New York: Random House, 1988.

Shulte, Albert P., 1981 yearbook editor, and James R. Smart, general yearbook editor. *Teaching Statistics and Probability, 1981 Yearbook.* Reston, Va.: National Council of Teachers of Mathematics, 1981.

Smith, Gary. *Statistical Reasoning.* Boston: Allyn and Bacon, 1985.

Spiegel, Murray R. *Schaum's Outline of Theory and Problems of Statistics.* New York: McGraw-Hill, 1961.

Texas Instruments. *TI-83 Graphing Calculator Guidebook.* Temple, Tex.: Texas Instruments, 1996.

Triola, Mario G. *Elementary Statistics,* 7th ed. Reading, Mass.: Addison-Wesley, 1998.

Wardrop, Robert L. *Statistics: Learning in the Presence of Variation.* Dubuque, Iowa: Wm. C. Brown Publishers, 1995.

Warwick, Donald P., and Charles A. Lininger. *The Sample Survey: Theory and Practice.* New York: McGraw-Hill, 1975.

Weiss, Daniel Evan. *100% American.* New York: Poseidon Press, 1988.

Williams, Jack. *The USA Today Weather Almanac 1995.* New York: Vintage Books, 1994.

Wright, John W., ed. *The Universal Almanac 1995.* Kansas City, Mo.: Andrews & McMeel, 1994.

Appendix H
Photo Credits

Appendix I

Credits for Unusual Stats, Interesting Facts, Historical Notes, and Exercises (End-of-Sections and End-of-Chapters)

Chapter 1

p. 2: Unusual Stat: SPCA.com; p. 2: Quick Facts about the Canadian Firearms Program as of March 2007, http://www.cfc-cafc.gc.ca/media/program_statistics/default_e.asp, Canadian Firearms Centre, 2007. Reproduced with the permission of the Minister of Public Works and Government Services Canada, 2007; p. 3: Interesting *Fact: Golf Digest,* September 2005; p. 4: Unusual Stat: Reuters; p. 7: Unusual Stat: Canada World View, Issue 24; p 12: Historical Note: Environics Research Group, July 8, 2004; p. 14: Interesting Fact: www.50plus.com; p. 15: Interesting Fact: ccnmatthews.com, January 25, 2006; p. 15: Unusual Stat: craigmarlatt.com; p. 21: Unusual Stat: *What Canadians Think . . . About Almost Everything,* Darrell Bricker and John Wright; p. 22: #6c: Adapted from Statistics Canada, *The Daily,* March 6, 2006, www.statcan.ca/Daily/English/060306/d060306a.htm; p. 22: #6d: Adapted from Statistics Canada, CANSIM, table (for fee) 252-0021 and Catalogue no. 85-002-X, www40.statcan.ca/I01/cst01/legal20b.htm?sdi=median%20length%20property %20crimes, February 28, 2007; p. 22: #6f: Adapted from Statistics Canada, CANSIM, table (for fee) 052-0004 and Catalogue no. 91-520-X, www40.statcan.ca/I01/cst01/demo08c.htm, February 28, 2007.

Chapter 2

p. 31: Interesting Fact: *Niagara Falls Review,* May 4, 2006; p. 33: Unusual Stat: *Calgary Herald,* April 13, 2006; p. 33: Interesting Fact: Adapted from Statistics Canada, CANSIM, table (for fee) 502-0004 and Catalogue no. 87F0006XIE, www40.statcan.ca/I01/cst01/arts22a.htm, February 28, 2007; p. 40: #14: www.tc.gc.ca/roadsafety/tp/tp3322/2004/page1.htm, reprinted with the permission of the Minister of Public Works and Government Services Canada, 2007; p. 40: #16: Parks Canada, reproduced with permission of the Minister of Public Works and Government Services Canada, 2007; p. 46: Unusual Stat: *National Post,* August 30, 2005; p. 51: #10: www.tc.gc.ca/roadsafety/tp/

tp3322/2004/page10.htm, reprinted with the permission of the Minister of Public Works and Government Services Canada, 2007; p. 53: Source: Youth Smoking Survey, Technical Report, Health Canada, 2002. Adapted and Reproduced with the permission of the Minister of Public Works and Government Services Canada, 2007; p. 65: #2: Adapted from Statistics Canada publication *Juristat,* Crime Statistics in Canada, 2004, Catalogue 85-002, Volume 25, no. 5, page 19; p. 70: #13: Adapted from Statistics Canada publication *Juristat,* Homicide in Canada, 2004, Catalogue 85-002, Volume 26, no. 6, page 17; p. 71: #17: Adapted from Canadian Insolvency Statistics—Up to 2004: Consumer Insolvencies by Major Region, Canada (1987–2004) Table, reproduced with the permission of the Minister of Public Works and Government Services, 2006.

Chapter 3

p. 89: Interesting Fact and Unusual Stat: Adapted from Statistics Canada, Excerpts from *Canadian Agriculture at a Glance 1999,* www.statcan.ca/English/kits/agric/census.htm, February 28, 2007; p. 110: #9: Canadian Climate Normals or Averages 1971–2000, Environment Canada, reproduced with the permission of the Minister of Public Works and Government Services Canada, 2007; p. 113: #41: Adapted from Statistics Canada, Food Statistics, Catalogue 21-020 and also available from Statistics Canada CANSIM Table (for fee) 002-0019, www40.statcan.ca/l01/cst01/famil102a.htm, February 28, 2007; p. 116: Interesting Facts: Goddard Space Flight Center, NASA; p. 132: #11: Adapted from Statistics Canada, excerpts from Police Personnel and Expenditures, www.statcan.ca/Daily/English/051215/d051215d.htm, February 28, 2007; p. 132: #15: Canadian Climate Normals or Averages 1971–2000, Environment Canada, reproduced with the permission of the Minister of Public Works and Government Services Canada, 2007; p. 135: #1: Adapted from Statistics Canada, Excerpt from "Radio Listening," Fall 2004, www.statcan.ca/Daily/English/050708/d050708b.htm,

February 28, 2007; p. 139: #25: Canadian Climate Normals or Averages 1971–2000, Environment Canada, reproduced with the permission of the Minister of Public Works and Government Services Canada, 2007.

Chapter 4

p. 158: #19: Adapted from Statistics Canada, Excerpt of "2001 Census," www40.statcan.ca/l01/cst01/famil50a.htm, February 28, 2007; p. 159: #26: © Correctional Service Canada, 2004, reproduced with the permission of the Minister of Public Works and Government Services Canada, 2007; p. 159: #30: "Where Your Tax Dollar Goes," Finance Canada, 2005, reproduced with the permission of the Minister of Public Works and Government Services, 2007; p. 178: #4: www.tc.gc.ca/roadsafety/tp2436/rs200405/menu.htm, reprinted with the permission of the Minister of Public Works and Government Services Canada, 2007; p. 178: #5: Adapted from Statistics Canada, *Women In Canada Work,* Chapter Updates, 2003, Catalogue 89X0133XIE, also available on Statistics Canada website www.statcan.ca/english/freepub/89F0133XIE/89F0133XIE2003000.pdf, February 28, 2007; p. 178: #6: Adapted from Statistics Canada publication *Adult Correctional Services in Canada, 2003–2004,* Catalogue 85-211, Released date December 2005, page 13 and also available on Statistics Canada website www.statcan.ca/english/freepub/85-211-XIE/0000485-211-XIE.pdf, February 28, 2007; p. 179: #35: CIPO—Annual Report 2004–2005—Data on Trademarks, Copyrights and Patents, reprinted with the permission of the Minister of Public Works and Government Services, 2006; p. 180: #37: Adapted from Statistics Canada, *The Daily,* December 21, 2004: www.statcan.ca/Daily/English/041221/d041221d.htm, February 28, 2007; p. 180: #38: www.tc.gc.ca/roadsafety/tp/tp3322/2004/page3.htm, reprinted with the permission of the Minister of Public Works and Government Services Canada, 2007; p. 180: #41: Adapted from Statistics Canada publication *Canada at a Glance, 2005,* Catalogue 12-581, Released date: March 10, 2006 and also available on Statistics Canada website www.statcan.ca/cgi-bin/downpub/listpub.cgi?catno=12-581-XIE2005001, February 28, 2007; p. 187: Interesting Fact: Adapted from Statistics Canada publication *Canada at a Glance, 2005,* Catalogue 12-581, Released date: March 10, 2006 and also available on Statistics Canada website www.statcan.ca/cgi-bin/downpub/listpub.cgi?catno=12-581-XIE2005001, February 28, 2007; p. 197: #12: Canadian Library Association; p. 198: #26: "It's Your Health: Asthma," Health Canada, May 2006, adapted and reproduced with the permission of the Minister of Public Works and Government Services Canada, 2007.

Chapter 5

p. 216: Historical Note: www.cbc.ca; p. 231: #10: Adapted from Statistics Canada publication *Juristat,* Criminal Victimization in Canada, 2004, Catalogue 85-002, Volume 25, no. 7 and also available from Statistics Canada website www.statcan.ca/english/freepub/85-002-XIE/0070585-002-XIE.pdf, February 28, 2007; p. 231: #11: Canadian Attitudes Towards the Seal

Hunt—Fisheries and Oceans Canada, reproduced with the permission of Her Majesty the Queen in Right of Canada, 2007; p. 231: #15 and #19: Adapted from Statistics Canada, Excerpt of "Viewing Habits of the Average Canadian Family," www.statcan.ca/english/kits/winner/2001/tv/inthelife.htm, February 28, 2007; p. 232: #22: Adapted from Statistics Canada publication *The Daily,* Catalogue 11-001, Released date: April 5, 2006, www.statcan.ca/Daily/English/060405/d060405b.htm, February 28, 2007; p. 231: #27: Adapted from Statistics Canada publication *Juristat,* Crime Statistics in Canada, 2004, Catalogue 85-002, Volume 25, no. 5 and also available from Statistics Canada www.statcan.ca/bsolc/english/bsolc?catno=85-002-X20050058076, February 28, 2007; p. 238: Interesting Fact: CNet news.com; p. 243: #20: Adapted from Statistics Canada publication *Canadian Social Trends,* Catalogue 11-008, no. 80, Spring 2006, www.statcan.ca/english/freepub/11-008-XIE/0040511-008-XIE.pdf; p. 243: #21: Canadian Tobacco Use monitoring Survey (CTUMS), Health Canada, 2005, adapted and reproduced with the permission of the Minister of Public Works and Government Services Canada, 2007.

Chapter 6

p. 265: Interesting Fact: Canadian Centre for Policy Alternatives; p. 267: #2: Adapted from Statistics Canada website http://dissemination.statcan.ca/Daily/English/000808/d000808a.htm, Accessed March 19, 2007; p. 267: #3: © Correctional Service Canada, 2004, reproduced with the permission of the Minister of Public Works and Government Services Canada, 2007; p. 273: Interesting Fact: www.bbc.co.uk/news and www.wikipedia.org; p. 278: #8: Adapted from Statistics Canada publication *Waste Management Industry Survey: Business and Government Sectors, 2002,* Catalogue 16F0023X, Release date: September 24, 2004, www.statcan.ca/english/freepub/16F0023XIE/16F0023XIE2002001.pdf; p. 278: #13: Adapted from Statistics Canada publication *Food Expenditure in Canada, 2001,* Catalogue 62-554, Release date: February 2003 and www.statcan.ca/english/freepub/62-554-XIE/0010162-554-XIE.pdf; p. 278: #17: Health Canada, adapted and reproduced with the permission of the Minister of Public Works and Government Services Canada, 2007; p. 279: #20: Adapted from Statistics Canada, Excerpt of "Back to School . . . by the Numbers," August 29, 2005, www42.statcan.ca/smr08/smr08_009_e.htm, February 28, 2007; p. 279: #25: Adapted from Statistics Canada, CANSIM, table (for fee) 002-0019 and Catalogue no. 21-020-X and www40.statcan.ca/l01/cst01/famil102d.htm?sdi=eggs, February 28, 2007; p. 286: #7: Adapted from Statistics Canada website www40.statcan.ca/l01/cst01/educ42.htm, February 28, 2007; p. 286: #9: Adapted from Statistics Canada, Excerpt from *Update in Education, Canadian Social Trends,* Catalogue 11-008, Winter 2003, no. 71, page 20, www.statcan.ca/english/freepub/11-008-XIE/0030311-008-XIE.pdf; p. 286: #12: Adapted Statistics Canada website www40.statcan.ca/l01/cst01/labor43a.htm, February 28, 2007; p. 288: #3: Adapted from Statistics

Canada, *Earnings of Canadians, 2001 Census,* Catalogue 97F0019XIE2001002, Released date: March 11, 2003; p. 288: #7: Canadian Climate Normals or Averages 1971–2000, Environment Canada, reproduced with the permission of the Minister of Public Works and Government Services Canada, 2007; p. 289: #13: Adapted from Statistics Canada website www40.statcan.ca/l01/cst01/labor44.htm, February 27, 2007; p. 289: #15: Adapted from Statistics Canada publication *Age and Sex, 2001 Census (Age and Sex),* Catalogue 95F0300XIE2001004, Released date: July 16, 2002; p. 290: #20: Canadian Climate Normals or Averages 1971–2000, Environment Canada, reproduced with the permission of the Minister of Public Works and Government Services Canada, 2007; p. 290: #22: Adapted from Statistics Canada publication *Food Consumption in Canada (2002),* Catalogue 32-229, www.statcan.ca/bsolc/english/bsolc?catno=32-229-X; p. 291: #29: Adapted from Statistics Canada publication *The Daily,* Catalogue 11-001, Released date: November 16, 2005, www.statcan.ca/Daily/English/051116/d051116a.htm, February 28, 2007; p. 291: #32: Adapted from Statistics Canada website Experience Labour Force www40.statcan.ca/l01/cst01/labor44.htm, February 27, 2007.

Chapter 7

p. 298: Interesting Fact: www.prevention.com; p. 304: Interesting Fact: Adapted from Statistics Canada publications *Family Expenditure Survey* (1982, 1986, 1992) and *Survey of Household Spending* (1997, 2002); p. 328: #16: Fish and Seafood Survey, Health Canada, 2002, adapted and reproduced with the permission of the Minister of Public Works and Government Services Canada, 2007.

Chapter 8

p. 339: Unusual Stat: Excerpts from "When is Junior Moving Out? Transitions from the Parental Home to Independence," adapted from Statistics Canada publication *Canadian Social Trends,* Catalogue 11-008, No. 82, Released October 3, 2006, pages 28–34, www.statcan.ca/bsolc/english/bsolc?catno=11-008-X; p. 355: #4: Adapted from Statistics Canada publication *Salaries and Salary Scales of Full-time Teaching Staff at Canadian Universities, 2005/2006: Final Report,* Catalogue 81-595, No. 46, Released July 12, 2006, page 31; p. 356: #6: Adapted from Statistics Canada publication *Canadian Potato Production,* Catalogue 22-008, vol. 4 no. 3, www.statcan.ca/bsolc/english/bsolc?catno=22-008-X; p. 356: #11: Excerpts from "Television Viewing–Fall 2004," adapted from Statistics Canada publication *The Daily,* Catalogue 11-001, Released March 31, 2006, www.statcan.ca/Daily/English/060331/d060331b.htm; p. 356: #16: Adapted from Statistics Canada, *Food Consumption in Canada: Part 1,* Catalogue 32-229-XIB, 2002, Released June 27, 2003, page 13, www.statcan.ca/bsolc/english/bsolc?catno=32-229-X; p. 357: #17: © Queen's Printer for Ontario, 2004; p. 357: #21: Adapted from Statistics Canada publication *Farming Facts,* Catalogue 21-522, 2002, Released April 16, 2003,

www.statcan.ca/cgi-bin/downpub/listpub.cgi?catno=21-522-XIE2002001; p. 357: #22: Adapted from Statistics Canada publication *Farming Facts,* Catalogue 21-522, 2002, Released April 16, 2003, www.statcan.ca/cgi-bin/downpub/listpub.cgi?catno=21-522-XIE2002001; p. 363: Interesting Fact: *National Post,* September 2006; p. 365: #5: www.climate.weatheroffice.ec.gc.ca/prods_servs/cdcd_iso_e.html, Environment Canada, reproduced with the permission of the Minister of Public Works and Government Services Canada, 2007; p. 365: #8: Excerpts from "Traffic Report: Weekday Commuting Patterns," adapted from Statistics Canada publication *Canadian Social Trends,* Catalogue 11-008, Spring 2000, No. 56, page 19; p. 366: #14: Source: *Healthy Living: Canada's Guide to Healthy Eating and Physical Activity,* Health Canada, 2004, adapted and reproduced with the permission of the Minister of Public Works and Government Services Canada, 2007; p. 366: #16: Adapted from *Municipal Water Pricing,* 1991-1999, www.ec.gc.ca/water/en/info/pubs/sss/e_price99.htm, Environment Canada, 2001, reproduced with the permission of the Minister of Public Works and Government Services, 2007; p. 366: #18: Adapted from Statistics Canada publication *Changes in Job Tenure and Job Stability in Canada,* Catalogue 11F0019MIE1996095, Table 2, page 9; p. 372: #9: Excerpts from "Telecommunications Statistics," adapted from Statistics Canada publication *The Daily,* Released: May 9, 2006, www.statcan.ca/Daily/English/060509/d060509b.htm; p. 372: #11: www.tc.gc.ca/roadsafety/tp/tp3322/2004/page3.htm, reproduced with the permission of the Minister of Public Works and Government Services Canada, 2007; p. 372: #14: Adapted from Statistics Canada publication *Spending Patterns in Canada,* 2003, Catalogue 62-202; p. 372: #18: Excerpts from "Survey of Earned Doctorates: A Profile of Doctoral Degree Recipients," adapted from Statistics Canada publication *The Daily,* Catalogue 11-001, July 5, 2005, www.statcan.ca/Daily/English/050705/d050705a.htm; p. 376: Interesting Fact: Adapted from Statistics Canada publication *Farming Facts,* 2002, Catalogue 21-522-XIE2002001, page 15; p. 381: #5: Excerpts from "Motor Vehicle Theft in Canada, 2001," adapted from Statistics Canada publication *Juristat,* Catalogue 85-002, Volume 23, No. 1; p. 382: #10: www.climate.weatheroffice.ec.gc.ca/prods_servs/cdcd_iso_e.html, reproduced with the permission of the Minister of Public Works and Government Services Canada, 2007; p. 389: #1: www.climate.weatheroffice.ec.gc.ca/climate_normals/index_e.html, Environment Canada, reproduced with the permission of the Minister of Public Works and Government Services Canada, 2007; p. 390: #5: www.climate.weatheroffice.ec.gc.ca/climate_normals/index_e.html, Environment Canada, reproduced with the permission of the Minister of Public Works and Government Services Canada, 2007; p. 390: #8: Adapted from Statistics Canada publication *Women in Canada: Work chapter updates,* 2003, Catalogue 89F0133XIE.

Chapter 9

p. 410: Unusual Stat: Adapted from Statistics Canada publication *Births–Live Births,* 2005, Catalogue 84F0210XIE, www.statcan.ca/english/freepub/84F0210XIE/ 84F0210XIE2004001.pdf; p. 412: Source: http://www.tc. gc.ca/pol/en/T-Facts3/main.asp?id=43&table=10-Table43& file=air&Lang=&title=AIR%20-%20Passenger%20Traffic. The source of the statistics is Statistics Canada, Air Carrier Statements St. 2, 4 & 6 dated February 2002 and updated September 30th, 2003. Reproduced with the permission of the Minister of Public Works and Government Services Canada, 2007; p. 415: #16: Adapted from Statistics Canada publication *Farm Data for the 2001 Census of Agriculture (Initial Release),* Catalogue 95F0301XIE, www.statcan.ca/ english/freepub/95F0301XIE/tables/pdf/table3Can.pdf; p. 419: Unusual Stat: A Study on the Simulation of Proxemic Behavior; p. 426: Unusual Stat: Adapted from Statistics Canada, *Food Consumption in Canada: Part 1,* Catalogue 32-229-XIB, 2002, Released June 27, 2003, page 13, www.statcan.ca/bsolc/english/bsolc?catno=32-229-X; p. 429: Unusual Stat: "Excerpts from Across the Generations: Grandparents and Grandchildren," adapted from Statistics Canada publication *Canadian Social Trends,* Winter 2003, Catalogue 11-008; p. 439: #16: Excerpts from the "Profile of Labour Force Activity, Class of Worker, Occupation, Industry, Place of Work, Mode of Transportation, Language of Work and Unpaid Work, for Canada, for Urban Areas, 2001 Census," adapted from Statistics Canada publication *Electronic Components of Profiles No. 5,* 2001 Census, Catalogue 95F0490XCB2001009; p. 442: #9: www.climate. weatheroffice.ec.gc.ca/climate_normals/index_e.html, Environment Canada, reproduced with the permission of the Minister of Public Works and Government Services Canada, 2007; p. 445: #24: Adapted from Statistics Canada publication *Employment, Earnings and Hours,* Catalogue 72-002 .

Chapter 10

p. 454: Interesting Fact: *Earthquakes,* published by Public Safety Canada, www.getprepared.gc.ca/risks/earthquakes_e. asp, reproduced with the permission of the Minister of Public Works and Government Services Canada, 2007; p. 467: #17: Adapted from Statistics Canada publication *Juristat,* Catalogue 85-002, Crime Statistics in Canada, 2004, Volume 25 no. 5; p. 467: #21: Excerpts from The Visible Minority Population, by Census Metropolitan Areas (2001 Census)," adapted from Statistics Canada website www40.statcan.ca/l01/cst01/demo53a.htm; p. 467: #23: www.climate.weatheroffice.ec.gc.ca/climate_ normals/index_e.html, Environment Canada, reproduced with the permission of the Minister of Public Works and Government Services Canada, 2007; p. 471: Historical Note: *Encyclopedia Britannica* Online; p. 476: #23: www.climate.weatheroffice.ec.gc.ca/climate_normals/ index_e.html, Environment Canada, reproduced with the permission of the Minister of Public Works and

Government Services Canada, 2007; p. 477: #31: Excerpts from "Head Office Employment in Canada, 1999 to 2005," adapted from Statistics Canada publication *Canadian Economic Observer,* Catalogue 11-010-XIB2006007; p. 493: #2: Adapted from Statistics Canada www40.statcan.ca/ l01/cst01/arts18.htm.

Chapter 11

p. 509: #12: Adapted from Statistics Canada CANSIM Database, Table 153-0034, Using E-STAT (distributor), http://estat.statcan.ca/cgi-win/CNSMCGI.EXE?Lang= E&RootDir=ESTAT/&CANSIMFILE=EStat\English\CII_ 1_E.htm; p. 509: #14: Adapted from Statistics Canada publication *Juristat,* Catalogue 85-002, Adult Correctional Services in Canada, 2003/04, Issue: vol. 25 no. 8, Table 3; p. 509: #15: Adapted from Statistics Canada publication *Juristat,* Catalogue 85-002, Adult Correctional Services in Canada, 2003/04, Vol. 25, no. 8; p. 513: Interesting Fact: U.S. Environmental Protection Agency; p. 516: Interesting Fact: U.S. Center for Health & Athletic Performance, Inc.; p. 519: #10: Canadian Ally.com, www.canadianally.com/ ca/forces-cf-en.asp, 2007, reproduced with the permission of the Minister of Public Works and Government Services, courtesy of the Department of National Defence, 2007; p. 520: #16: Adapted from Statistics Canada publication *The Daily,* Catalogue 11-001, Thursday, July 20, 2006— Crime Statistics, www.statcan.ca/Daily/English/060720/ d060720b.htm; p. 520: #23: Adapted from Statistics Canada publication *The Daily,* Catalogue 11-001, Tuesday, August 22, 2006—Health Reports: Regional Differences in Obesity, www.statcan.ca/Daily/English/060822/d060822b. htm; p. 520: #24: Adapted from Statistics Canada publication *The Daily,* Catalogue 11-001, Thursday, September 23, 2004—E-commerce: Household Shopping on the Internet, www.statcan.ca/Daily/English/040923/ d040923a.htm; p. 521: #25: Adapted from Statistics Canada publication *Perspectives on Labour and Income,* Catalogue 75-001, October 2004; p. 523: #2: Adapted from Statistics Canada website (Population by marital status and sex), www40.statcan.ca/l01/cst01/famil01.htm.

Chapter 12

p. 533: Interesting Fact: www.theweathernetwork.com; p. 534: Unusual Stat: www.nedic.ca/knowthefacts/statistics. shtml; p. 541: #10: Adapted from Statistics Canada CANSIM Database, Table 477-0051, Using E-STAT (distributor), http://estat.statcan.ca/cgi-in/CNSMCGI. EXE?Lang=E&RootDir=ESTAT/&CANSIMFILE=EStat\ English\CII_1_E.htm; p. 542: #15: Adapted from Statistics Canada publication *Farm Data for the 2001 Census of Agriculture,* Catalogue 95F0301XIE, www.statcan.ca/ bsolc/english/bsolc?catno=95F0301X; p. 547: Unusual Stat: World Health Organization; p. 549: Interesting Fact: www. magazine.audubon.org; p. 557: #7: Adapted from Statistics Canada publication *Exploring Crime Patterns in Canada,* Catalogue 85-561-MIE2005005, 2005, No. 5, www.statcan. ca/bsolc/english/bsolc?catno=85-561-M2005005.

Chapter 13

p. 570: Unusual Stat: www.climate.weatheroffice.ec.gc.ca/climate_normals/index_e.html, Environment Canada, reproduced with the permission of the Minister of Public Works and Government Services Canada, 2007; p. 573: #14: Excerpts from "Deaths Involving Firearms," adapted from Statistics Canada publication *Health Reports,* Catalogue 82-003-XPE2004004, Volume 16, No. 4, Released June 28, 2005, www.statcan.ca/bsolc/english/bsolc?catno=82-003-X; p. 580: Interesting Fact: www.tc.gc.ca/roadsafety/tp2436/rs200104/menu.htm, reproduced with the permission of the Minister of Public Works and Government Services Canada, 2007; p. 582: #11: Excerpts from "Television Viewing," adapted from Statistics Canada publication *The Daily,* Friday, March 31, 2006, www.statcan.ca/Daily/English/060331/d060331b.htm; p. 587: #7: Excerpts from "Deaths Involving Firearms," adapted from Statistics Canada publication *Health Reports,* Catalogue 82-003-XPE2004004, Volume 16, No. 4, Released June 28, 2005, www.statcan.ca/bsolc/english/bsolc?catno=82-003-X; p. 590: Unusual Stat: www.tc.gc.ca/roadsafety/tp2436/rs200104/page8.htm, reproduced with the permission of the Minister of Public Works and Government Services Canada, 2007; p. 595: #5: Excerpts from "Forest Fires and Forest Land Burned, by Province and Territory," adapted from Statistics Canada website www40.statcan.ca/l01/cst01/envir02a.htm.

Chapter 14

p. 624: Interesting Fact: Adapted from Statistics Canada publication 2003 *General Social Survey on Social Engagement, Cycle 17: An Overview of Findings,* Catalogue 89-598, www.statcan.ca/english/freepub/89-598-XIE/2003001/Tables/table4.htm.

Appendix J
Selected Answers*

Chapter 1
Review Exercises

1. Descriptive statistics describes a set of data. Inferential statistics uses a set of data to make predictions about a population.

3. Answers will vary.

5. When the population is large, the researcher saves time and money using samples. Samples are used when the units must be destroyed.

7. *a.* ratio   *e.* ratio   *i.* nominal
   b. ordinal   *f.* ordinal   *j.* ratio
   c. ratio   *g.* ratio
   d. interval   *h.* ratio

8. *a.* quantitative   *d.* quantitative   *g.* qualitative
   b. qualitative   *e.* qualitative
   c. quantitative   *f.* quantitative

9. *a.* discrete   *c.* continuous   *e.* discrete
   b. continuous   *d.* continuous   *f.* continuous

11. Random samples are selected by using chance methods or random numbers. Systematic samples are selected by numbering each subject and selecting every kth number. Stratified samples are selected by dividing the population into groups and selecting from each group. Cluster samples are selected by using intact groups called clusters.

12. *a.* cluster   *c.* random   *e.* stratified
    b. systematic   *d.* systematic

13. Answers will vary.

15. Answers will vary.

17. *a.* experimental   *c.* observational
    b. observational   *d.* experimental

19. Answers will vary. Possible answers include:
    a. overall health of participants, amount of exposure to infected individuals through the workplace or home
    b. gender and/or age of driver, time of day
    c. diet, general health, heredity factors
    d. amount of exercise, heredity factors

21. Claims can be proven only if the entire population is used.

23. Since the results are not typical, the advertisers selected only a few people for whom the product worked extremely well.

25. "74% more calories" than what? No comparison group is stated.

27. What is meant by "24 hours of acid control"?

29. Possible reasons for conflicting results: The amount of caffeine in the coffee or tea or the brewing method.

31. Answers will vary.

Chapter Quiz

1. True   2. False
3. False   4. False
5. False   6. True
7. False   8. *c*
9. *b*   10. *d*
11. *a*   12. *c*
13. *a*   14. descriptive, inferential
15. gambling, insurance   16. population
17. sample
18. *a.* saves time   *c.* use when population is infinite
    b. saves money
19. *a.* random   *c.* cluster
    b. systematic   *d.* stratified
20. quasi-experimental   21. random
22. *a.* descriptive   *d.* inferential
    b. inferential   *e.* inferential
    c. descriptive

*Answers may vary due to rounding or use of technology.

Note: These answers to odd-numbered and selected even-numbered exercises include all quiz answers.

23. *a.* nominal   *d.* interval
    b. ratio   *e.* ratio
    c. ordinal

24. *a.* continuous   *d.* continuous
    b. discrete   *e.* discrete
    c. continuous

25. *a.* 47.5–48.5 seconds
    b. 0.555–0.565 centimetres
    c. 9.05–9.15 quarts
    d. 13.65–13.75 pounds
    e. 6.5–7.5 feet

Chapter 2

Exercises 2–2

1. Frequency distributions are used to organize data in a meaningful way, to facilitate computational procedures for statistics, to make it easier to draw charts and graphs, and to make comparisons among different sets of data.

3. *a.* $11.5 - 18.5, \frac{12 + 18}{2} = \frac{30}{2} = 15, 18.5 - 11.5 = 7$
   b. $55.5 - 74.5, \frac{56 + 74}{2} = \frac{130}{2} = 65, 74.5 - 55.5 = 19$
   c. $694.5 - 705.5, \frac{695 + 705}{2} = \frac{1400}{2} = 700,$
     $705.5 - 694.5 = 11$
   d. $13.55 - 14.75, \frac{13.6 + 14.7}{2} = \frac{28.3}{2} = 14.15,$
     $14.75 - 13.75 = 1.2$
   e. $2.145 - 3.935, \frac{2.15 + 3.93}{2} = \frac{6.08}{2} = 3.04,$
     $3.935 - 2.145 = 1.79$

5. *a.* Class width is not uniform.
   b. Class limits overlap, and class width is not uniform.
   c. A class has been omitted.
   d. Class width is not uniform.

7.

Class	Tally	f	Percent
A	////	4	10%
M	ʇʜʜ ʇʜʜ ʇʜʜ ʇʜʜ ʇʜʜ ///	28	70%
H	ʇʜʜ /	6	15%
S	//	2	5%
		40	100%

9.

Class Limits	Class Boundaries	Frequency
70 – 89	69.5 – 89.5	2
90 – 109	89.5 – 109.5	6
110 – 129	109.5 – 129.5	7
130 – 149	129.5 – 149.5	11
150 – 169	149.5 – 169.5	6
170 – 189	169.5 – 189.5	1
190 – 209	189.5 – 209.5	4
210 – 229	209.5 – 229.5	2

11. $H = 780$ $L = 746$
Range $= 780 - 746 = 34$
Width $= 34 \div 6 = 5.\overline{6}$ or 6; round up to 7

Limits	Boundaries	f	cf
745 – 751	744.5 – 751.5	4	4
752 – 758	751.5 – 758.5	5	9
759 – 765	758.5 – 765.5	7	16
766 – 772	765.5 – 772.5	11	27
773 – 779	772.5 – 779.5	2	29
780 – 786	779.5 – 786.5	1	30
		30	

13.

Term (months)	Class Boundaries	Frequency
1 – 48	0.5 – 48.5	9
49 – 96	48.5 – 96.5	4
97 – 144	96.5 – 144.5	4
145 – 192	144.5 – 192.5	2
193 – 240	192.5 – 240.5	1
241 – 288	240.5 – 288.5	1

15.

Class Limits	Class Boundaries	Frequency
63 – 66	62.5 – 66.5	11
67 – 70	66.5 – 70.5	9
71 – 74	70.5 – 74.5	10
75 – 78	74.5 – 78.5	3
79 – 82	78.5 – 82.5	3
83 – 86	82.5 – 86.5	3
87 – 90	86.5 – 90.5	1

17.

Class Limits	Class Boundaries	Frequency
7500 – 7699	7499.5 – 7699.5	14
7700 – 7899	7699.5 – 7899.5	18
7900 – 8099	7899.5 – 8099.5	9
8100 – 8299	8099.5 – 8299.5	4
8300 – 8499	8299.5 – 8499.5	1
8500 – 8699	8499.5 – 8699.5	3
8700 – 8899	8699.5 – 8899.5	1

19. The percents add up to 101%. They should total 100% unless rounding was used.

Exercises 2–3

1.

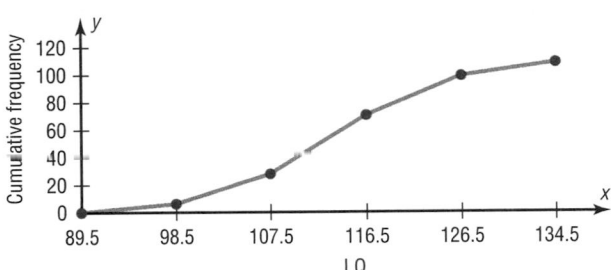

Eighty applicants do not need to enroll in the summer programs.

3.

Histogram

Frequency Polygon

Ogive

5.

Histogram

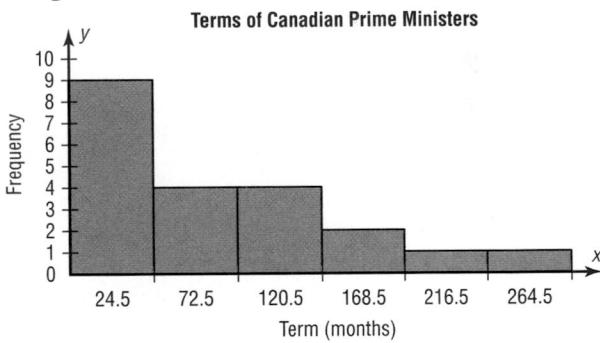

Frequency Polygon

Terms of Canadian Prime Ministers

Ogive

9.

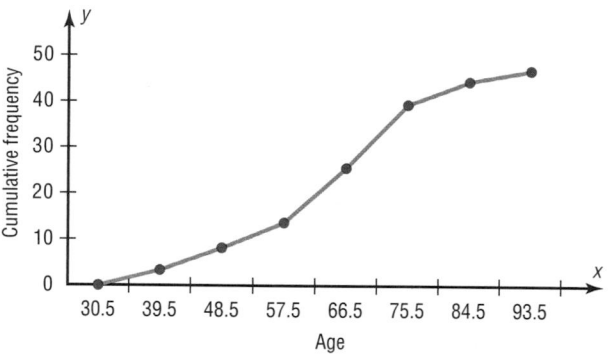

The histogram has a peak at the class of 66.5–75.5 and is somewhat negatively skewed.

7.

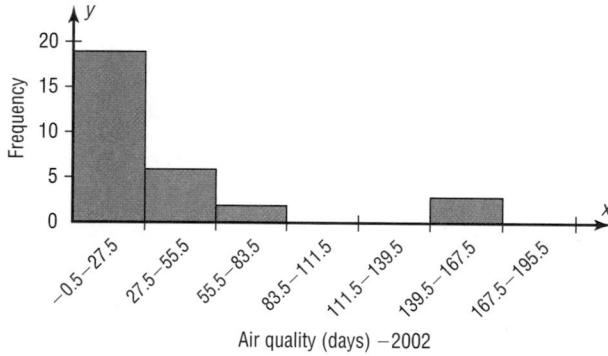

Both graphs are similar in that they are positively skewed. Also, it looks as if the air quality has improved somewhat in that there are slightly more smaller values in 2002, which means fewer days with unacceptable levels of pollution.

11.

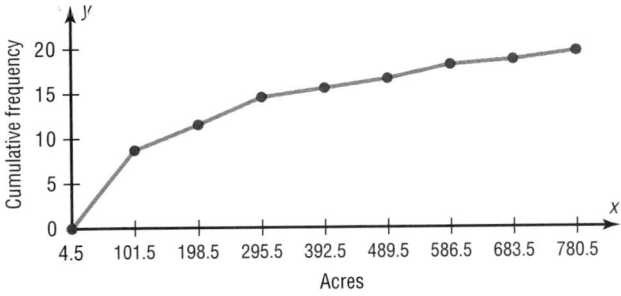

The peak is in the first class, and then the histogram is rather uniform after the first class. Most of the parks have less than 101.5 thousand acres as compared with any other class of values.

13.

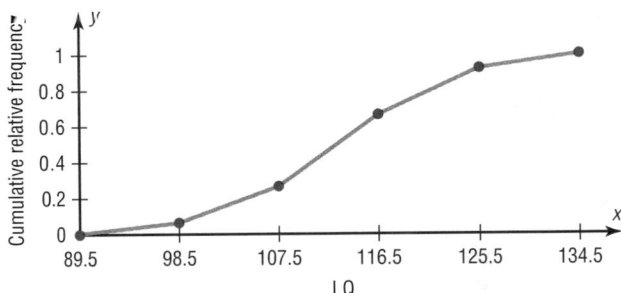

The proportion of applicants who need to enroll in a summer program is 0.26 or 26%.

15. H = 270   L = 80

Range = 270 − 80 = 190

Width = 190 ÷ 7 = 27.1 or 28

Use width = 29 (rule 2)

Limits	Boundaries	f	rf	crf
80 – 108	79.5 – 108.5	8	0.17	0.17
109 – 137	108.5 – 137.5	13	0.28	0.45
138 – 166	137.5 – 166.5	2	0.04	0.49
167 – 195	166.5 – 195.5	9	0.20	0.69
196 – 224	195.5 – 224.5	10	0.22	0.91
225 – 253	224.5 – 253.5	2	0.04	0.95
254 – 282	253.5 – 282.5	2	0.04	0.99*
			0.99	

*due to rounding

The histogram has two peaks.

17.

Boundaries	rf	crf
−0.5 – 27.5	0.63	0.63
27.5 – 55.5	0.20	0.83
55.5 – 83.5	0.07	0.90
83.5 – 111.5	0.00	0.90
111.5 – 139.5	0.00	0.90
139.5 – 167.5	0.10	1.00
167.5 – 195.5	0.00	1.00
	100.0	

19.

Limits	Boundaries	X_m	f	cf
22 – 24	21.5 – 24.5	23	1	1
25 – 27	24.5 – 27.5	26	3	4
28 – 30	27.5 – 30.5	29	0	4
31 – 33	30.5 – 33.5	32	6	10
34 – 36	33.5 – 36.5	35	5	15
37 – 39	36.5 – 39.5	38	3	18
40 – 42	39.5 – 42.5	41	2	20
			20	

Exercises 2–4

1.

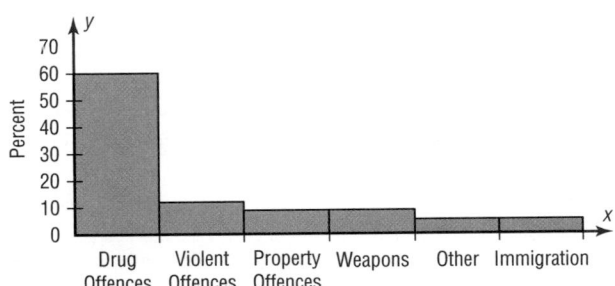

The majority of the money should be spent for drug rehabilitation.

3.

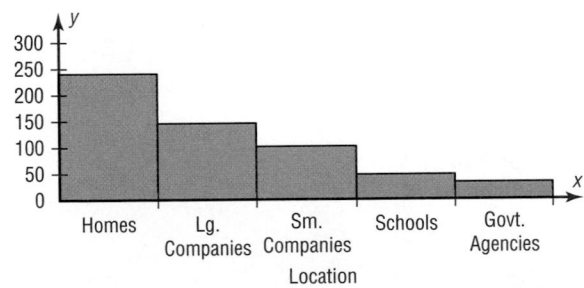

The best place to market products would be to residential users.

5.

7.

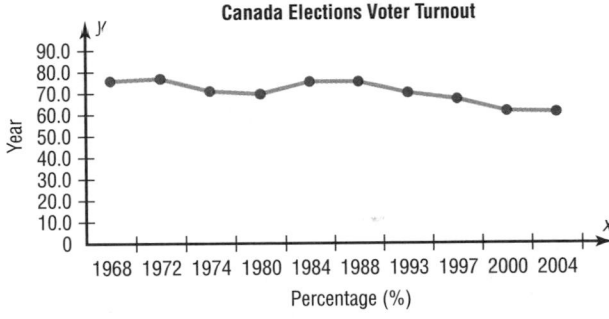

There is a steady increase in consumption of tobacco products.

9. Time-Series Graph

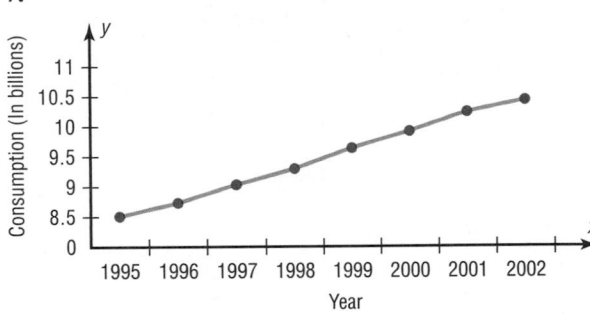

Based on the time-series chart, Canadian voter turnout dropped slightly from 1972 to 1980 then returned to the 1972 levels in the 1984 and 1988 elections. Since 1988, voter turnout has been in a steady decline to the lowest level since 1968 in the 2004 election.

11.

13.
Pie chart:

Pareto chart:

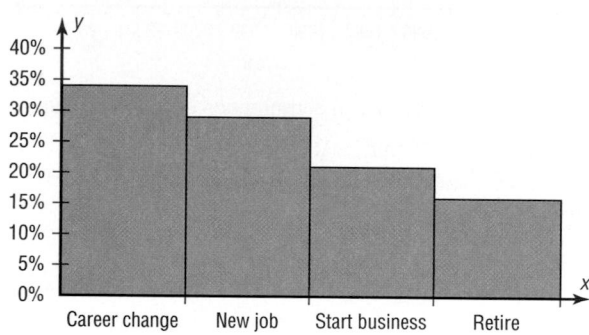

The pie graph better represents the data since we are looking at parts of a whole.

15. Stem and Leaf Plot (Age of Prime Ministers)

Stem	Leaves
3	9
4	5 6 6 6 7 7 8
5	1 2 4 5 7 9
6	0 1 5 6 6 9
7	0 4

17.

```
        Variety 1        |   | Variety 2
                  2 | 1 | 3  8
                3 0 | 2 | 5
          9 8 8 5 2 | 3 | 6  8
              3 3 1 | 4 | 1  2  5  5
9 9 8 5 3 3 2 1 0 | 5 | 0  3  5  5  6  7  9
                    | 6 | 2  2
```

The distributions are similar but variety 2 seems to be more variable than variety 1.

19.

1	3 4 8 9
2	5 8 9
3	2 8
4	1

21.

In 1950, veal production was considerably higher than lamb. By 1970, production was approximately the same for both.

23.

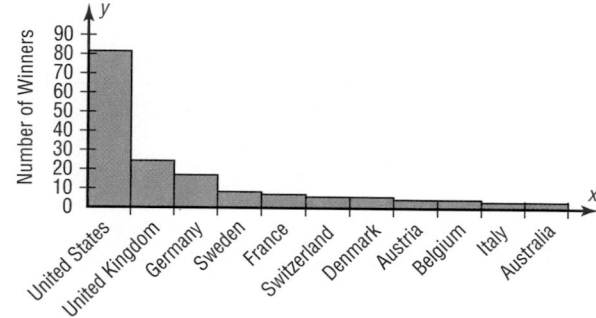

25. The values on the y axis start at 3.5. Also there are no data values shown for the years 2004 through 2011.

Review Exercises

1.

Class	f
Newspaper	10
Television	16
Radio	12
Internet	12
	50

3.

Class	f
baseball	4
golf ball	5
tennis ball	6
soccer ball	5
football	5
	25

5.

Class	f	cf
11	1	1
12	2	3
13	2	5
14	2	7
15	1	8
16	2	10
17	4	14
18	2	16
19	2	18
20	1	19
21	0	19
22	1	20
	20	

7.

Limits	Boundaries	f	cf
85 – 105	84.5 – 105.5	4	4
106 – 126	105.5 – 126.5	7	11
127 – 147	126.5 – 147.5	9	20
148 – 168	147.5 – 168.5	10	30
169 – 189	168.5 – 189.5	9	39
190 – 210	189.5 – 210.5	1	40
		40	

9.

Limits	Boundaries	f	cf
170 – 188	169.5 188.5	11	11
189 – 207	188.5 – 207.5	9	20
208 – 226	207.5 – 226.5	4	24
227 – 245	226.5 – 245.5	5	29
246 – 264	245.5 – 264.5	0	29
265 – 283	264.5 – 283.5	0	29
284 – 302	283.5 – 302.5	0	29
303 – 321	302.5 – 321.5	1	30
		30	

11.

13. Pareto Chart

15.

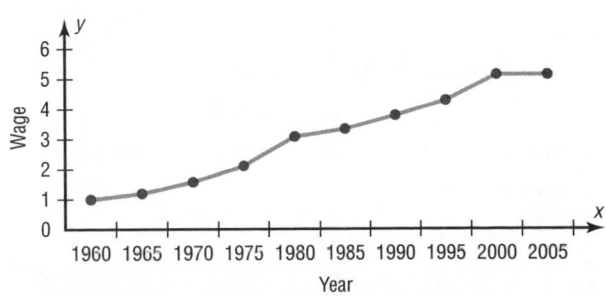

The minimum wage has increased over the years with the largest increase occurring between 1975 and 1980.

17. Time-Series Plot

18.

Class	f	cf
H	6	6
A	5	11
M	6	17
C	8	25
	25	

19.

19.

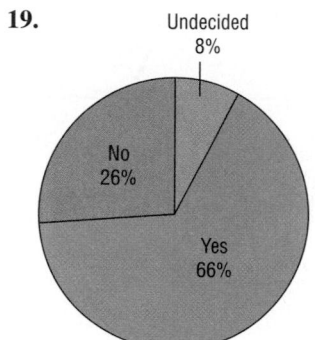

The majority of people surveyed would like to spend the rest of their careers with their present employer.

20.

Class	f	cf
0.5 – 1.5	1	1
1.5 – 2.5	5	6
2.5 – 3.5	3	9
3.5 – 4.5	4	13
4.5 – 5.5	2	15
5.5 – 6.5	6	21
6.5 – 7.5	2	23
7.5 – 8.5	3	26
8.5 – 9.5	4	30
	30	

21.
```
1 | 2  4
1 | 6  7  8  8  9
2 | 0  2  3  4
2 | 5  5  5  6  6  9  9
3 | 2  3
3 | 5  7  8  8  9
```
The peak of the distribution is in the range of 25 – 29.

21.

Chapter Quiz

1. False
2. False
3. False
4. True
5. True
6. False
7. False
8. *c*
9. *c*
10. *b*
11. *b*
12. Categorical, ungrouped, grouped
13. 5, 20
14. categorical
15. time series
16. stem and leaf plot
17. vertical or *y*

22.

Limits	Boundaries	f	cf
27 – 90	26.5 – 90.5	13	13
91 – 154	90.5 – 154.5	2	15
155 – 218	154.5 – 218.5	0	15
219 – 282	218.5 – 282.5	5	20
283 – 346	282.5 – 346.5	0	20
347 – 410	346.5 – 410.5	2	22
411 – 474	410.5 – 474.5	0	22
475 – 538	474.5 – 538.5	1	23
539 – 602	538.5 – 602.5	2	25
		25	

23. The distribution is positively skewed with one more than half of the data values in the lowest class.

24.

25.

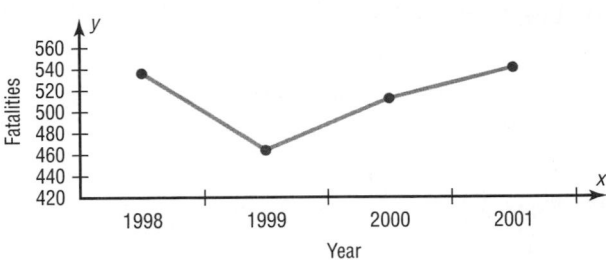

Fatalities decreased in 1999 and then increased the next two years.

26.

1	5	9			
2	6	8			
3	1	5	8	8	9
4	1	7	8		
5	3	3	4		
6	2	3	7	8	
7	6	9			
8	6	8	9		
9	8				

Chapter 3

Note: Answers may vary due to rounding, TI-83s, or computer programs.

Exercises 3–2

1. *a.* 3.724   *b.* 3.73   *c.* 3.74 and 3.70   *d.* 3.715

3. *a.* 16.6   *b.* 8.5   *c.* 13.0   *d.* 37.5

5. 270.75; 209; no mode; 369. It would seem that the average number of identity thefts is not higher than 300.

7. *a.* 6.63   *c.* no mode
    b. 6.45   *d.* 6.7
For the best measure of average, answers will vary.

9. *a.* 5678.9   *c.* 4450
    b. 5342.5   *d.* 5781.5
The distribution is skewed to the right.

11. For Year 1:
    a. 922.6   *b.* 527   *c.* no mode   *d.* 2130.5
    For Year 2:
    a. 911.7   *b.* 485   *c.* 1430   *d.* 2055

The mean, median, and midrange of the traffic fatalities for Year 2 are somewhat less than those for the Year 1 fatalities, indicating that the number of fatalities has decreased.

13. *a.* 291.9   *b.* 292–295

15. *a.* 188.48   *b.* 34–96

Since most of the data is in the lowest class, the mean is probably not the best measure of average. If the individual data values are available, the median may be a better measure of average. A procedure for finding the

approximate median for grouped data is found in
Exercise 42 of this section.

17. *a.* 85.1   *b.* 74.5–85.5

19. *a.* 33.8   *b.* 27–33

21. *a.* 23.7   *b.* 21.5–24.5

23. 44.8; 40.5–47.5

25. 63; 66.5–75.5   **27.** 2.896

29. $545,666.67   **31.** 82.7

33. *a.* Median   *c.* Mode   *e.* Mode
      b. Mean   *d.* Mode   *f.* Mean

35. Both could be true since one could be using the mean
for the average salary, and the other could be using the
mode for the average.

37. 6

39. *a.* 54.55 km/h   *b.* 94.74 km/h   *c.* $8.33

41. 5.48

Exercises 3–3

1. The square root of the variance is equal to the standard
deviation.

3. σ^2, σ

5. When the sample size is less than 30, the formula for
the true standard deviation of the sample will
underestimate the population standard deviation.

7. 48; 254.7; 15.9 (rounded to 16)

9. Data Set 1: Temperatures

$$s = \sqrt{\frac{\Sigma X^2 - [(\Sigma X)^2/n]}{n-1}}$$

$$s = \sqrt{\frac{2604.8 - [(210.7)^2/18]}{18-1}}$$

$$s = 2.85$$

Data Set 2: Precipitation

$$s = \sqrt{\frac{\Sigma X^2 - [(\Sigma X)^2/n]}{n-1}}$$

$$s = \sqrt{\frac{107745.2 - [(1299.1)^2/18]}{18-1}}$$

$$s = 28.68$$

Precipitation data, $s = 28.68$, is more variable than
Temperatures data, $s = 2.85$.

11. Data Set 1: Hong Kong buildings

X	X²
88	7,744
78	6,084
72	5,184
73	5,329
80	6,400
62	3,844
75	5,625
59	3,481
75	5,625
72	5,184
52	2,704
786	57,204

$$s = \sqrt{\frac{\Sigma X^2 - [(\Sigma X)^2/n]}{n-1}}$$

$$s = \sqrt{\frac{57204 - [(786)^2/11]}{11-1}}$$

$$s = 10.2$$

Data Set 2: New York buildings

X	X²
102	10,404
77	5,929
66	4,356
70	4,900
59	3,481
72	5,184
69	4,761
75	5,625
60	3,600
48	2,304
60	3,600
758	54,144

$$s = \sqrt{\frac{\Sigma X^2 - [(\Sigma X)^2/n]}{n-1}}$$

$$s = \sqrt{\frac{54144 - [(758)^2/11]}{11-1}}$$

$$s = 13.8$$

Data set 2, $s = 13.8$, New York buildings, is more variable
than data set 1, Hong Kong buildings, $s = 10.2$.

13. 21; 38.1; 6.2

Using the range rule of thumb, $s \approx \frac{22-1}{4} = 5.25$. The
estimate is close.

15. For 1995:   For 1996:

    R = 4123   R = 3970

    $s^2 = 1,030,817.6$ $s^2 = 1,019,853.8$

    $s = 1015.3$ $s = 1009.9$

The fatalities in 1995 are more variable.

17. R = 11,263; 7,436,475.0; 2727.0

19. 133.6; 11.6   **21.** 27,941.76; 167.2

23. 211.2; 14.5   **25.** 211.2; 14.5;

No, the variability of the lifetimes of the batteries is quite
large.

27. 11.7; 3.4

29. For the West, CVar = 0.464. For the East, CVar = 0.483.
The data for the East is more variable.

31. 23.1%; 12.9%.

The age is more variable.

33. *a.* 96%   *b.* 93.75%

35. $4.84–$5.20   **37.** 89–101

39. 86%   **41.** 2.5%

43. $n = 30$ $\overline{X} = 214.97$ $s = 20.76$.   At least 75% of
the data values will fall between $\overline{X} \pm 2s$.
$\overline{X} - 2(20.76) = 214.97 - 41.52 = 173.45$ and
$\overline{X} + 2(20.76) = 214.97 + 41.52 = 256.49$

In this case all 30 values fall within this range; hence
Chebyshev's Theorem is correct for this example.

45. 56%; 75%; 84%; 88.89%; 92%

47. 4.36

49. It must be an incorrect data value, since is beyond the
range using the formula $s\sqrt{n - 1}$.

Exercises 3–4

1. A z score tells how many standard deviations the data
value is above or below the mean.

3. A percentile is a relative measure while a percent is an
absolute measure of the part to the total.

5. $Q_1 = P_{25}, Q_2 = P_{50}, Q_3 = P_{75}$

7. $D_1 = P_{10}, D_2 = P_{20}, D_3 = P_{30}$, etc.

9. *a.* 1   *b.* -2 *c.* -2.5 *d.* -1.5 *e.* 0.67

11. *a.* 0.075 *b.* -1.25 *c.* 2.25   *d.* -2 *e.* -0.5

13. *a.* 0.75   *b.* 1.67
The score for part *b* is has a higher relative position.

15. *a.* -0.93 *b.* -0.85 *c.* -1.4
The score in part *b* is the highest.

17. *a.* 21st *b.* 58th *c.* 77th *d.* 33rd

19. *a.* 235   *b.* 255   *c.* 261   *d.* 275   *e.* 283

21. Refer to question 20.

   a. 572 km/h   10th percentile
   b. 605 km/h   24th percentile
   c. 671 km/h   48th percentile
   d. 737 km/h   62nd percentile
   e. 803 km/h   90th percentile

23. 82   **25.** 47

27. 2.1   **29.** 12

31. *a.* $Q_1 = 12, Q_2 = 20.5, Q_3 = 32$
   Midquartile $= \frac{12 + 32}{2} = 22$ Interquartile range:
                                              $32 - 12 = 20$

   b. $Q_1 = 62, Q_2 = 94, Q_3 = 99$
   Midquartile $= \frac{62 + 99}{2} = 80.5$ Interquartile range:
                                               $99 - 62 = 37$

Exercises 3–5

1. 6, 8, 12, 19, 27, 32, 54; 24

3. 188, 192, 316, 362, 437, 589; 245

5. 14.6, 15.5, 16.3, 18.2, 19.8; 3.95

7. 11, 3, 8, 5, 9, 4

9. 95, 55, 70, 65, 90, 25

11.

Since the median is to the left of the box centre and the line
to the right of the box is longer than the line to the left of
the box, the distribution is positively skewed.

13.

15.

The median is slightly to the right of the box centre and
the line to the right of the box is longer than the line to
the left of the box which indicates a moderate negative
skew.

17. *a.* May.   *b.* 1999.

   c.

The distribution for 2001 is approximately symmetric while
the distributions for 2000 and 1999 are skewed.

The distribution for 2000 is positively skewed and the
distribution for 1999 is negatively skewed.

The data for the year 2000 is the least variable and has the
smallest median.

Review Exercises

1. *a.* 15.75   *c.* No mode.   *e.* 6.5   *g.* 2.56
     b. 15.15   *d.* 3.25   *f.* 6.57

3. *a.* 8.3   *b.* 7–9 or 6.5–9.5   *c.* 10.0   *d.* 3.2

5. *Note:* Technically the first class should read −0.05, which is redundant. The class limits are 0–2.9, 3–5.9, 6–8.9, etc.
     a. 6.034
     b. 2.95–5.95 (frequency = 7)
     c. 16.318
     d. 4.040

7. 1.1   **9.** 6

11. Magazines: C.Var $= \frac{s}{\bar{X}} = \frac{12}{56} = 0.214$
     Year: C.Var $= \frac{s}{\bar{X}} = \frac{2.5}{6} = 0.417$
     The number of years is more variable.

13. *a.*

     b. 49, 52, 53 (answers are approximate)
     c. 15th; 33rd; 91st (answers are approximate)

15. $0.26–$0.38   **17.** 56%

19. 88.89%

21.

The employees worked more hours before Christmas than after Christmas. Also, the range and variability of the distribution of hours worked before Christmas is greater than that of hours worked after Christmas.

Chapter Quiz

1. True   **2.** True

3. False   **4.** False

5. False   **6.** False

7. False   **8.** False

9. False   **10.** *c*

11. *c*   **12.** *a* and *b*

13. *b*   **14.** *d*

15. *b*   **16.** statistic

17. parameters, statistics   **18.** standard deviation

19. σ **20.** midrange

21. positively   **22.** outlier

23. *a.* 22.7   *c.* 22.9   *e.* 3.9   *g.* 0.995
     b. 22.8   *d.* 1.9   *f.* 0.989

24. *a.* 6.4   *b.* 6–8   *c.* 11.6   *d.* 3.4

25. *a.* 64.4   *b.* 0.5–25.5   *c.* 2167.1   *d.* 46.6

26. *a.* 8.2   *b.* 7–9   *c.* 21.6   *d.* 4.6

27. 1.6

28. 4.46 or 4.5

29. 0.33; 0.162; newspapers

30. 0.3125; 0.229; brands

31. −0.75; −1.67; science

32. *a.* 0.5   *b.* 1.6   *c.* 15, *c* is higher

33. *a.* 5.0; 15.0; 25.0; 35.0; 45.0; 55.0; 65.0; 75.0; 85.0; 95.0
     b. 269.75
     c.

The median is to the left of the box centre and the right tail is longer than the left tail which infers a positively skewed distribution.

34. *a.*

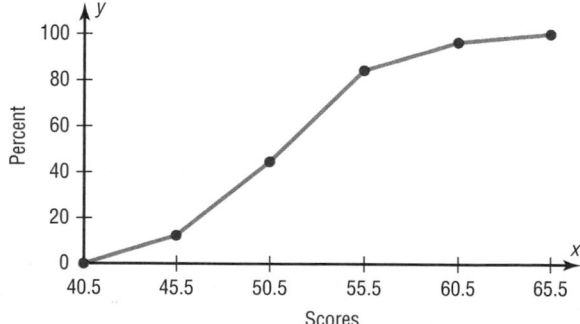

     b. 47; 53; 65
     c. 60th percentile;   6th percentile;   98th percentile

35.

The cost of pre-buy gas is much less than to return the car without filling it with gas. The variability of the return without filling with gas is larger than the variability of the pre-buy gas.

36. 16%; 97.5%

Chapter 4

Note: Answers may vary due to rounding, TI-83s, or computer programs.

Exercises 4–2

1. A probability experiment is a chance process which leads to well-defined outcomes.

3. An outcome is the result of a single trial of a probability experiment, whereas an event can consist of one or more outcomes.

5. The range of values is $0 \leq P(E) \leq 1$.

7. 0

9. 0.80. Since the probability that it won't rain is 80%, you could leave your umbrella at home and be fairly safe.

11. *a.* empirical   *d.* classical   *f.* empirical
    b. classical   *e.* empirical   *g.* subjective
    c. empirical

12. *a.* $\frac{1}{6}$ *c.* $\frac{1}{3}$ *e.* 1   *g.* $\frac{1}{6}$
    b. $\frac{1}{2}$ *d.* 1   *f.* $\frac{5}{6}$

13. There are 6^2 or 36 outcomes.
    a. $\frac{5}{36}$ *b.* $\frac{1}{6}$ *c.* $\frac{2}{9}$ *d.* $\frac{1}{6}$ *e.* $\frac{1}{6}$

14. *a.* $\frac{1}{13}$ *c.* $\frac{1}{52}$ *e.* $\frac{4}{13}$ *g.* $\frac{1}{2}$ *i.* $\frac{7}{13}$
    b. $\frac{1}{4}$ *d.* $\frac{2}{13}$ *f.* $\frac{4}{13}$ *h.* $\frac{1}{26}$ *j.* $\frac{1}{26}$

15. There are 24 possible outcomes.
    a. $\frac{1}{6}$ *b.* $\frac{1}{2}$ *c.* $\frac{1}{2}$

17. *a.* 0.44   *b.* 0.04   *c.* 0.56

19. *a.* 0.52 or 52%   *b.* 0.36 or 36%   *c.* 0.89 or 89%
    d. Probability of less than 3 children, $P(E) = 89\%$, is most likely to occur.

21. *a.* $\frac{1}{8}$ *b.* $\frac{1}{4}$ *c.* $\frac{3}{4}$ *d.* $\frac{3}{4}$

23. $\frac{1}{9}$

25. *a.* $\frac{9}{19}$ *b.* $\frac{9}{38}$ *c.* $\frac{5}{38}$.
    d. The event in part *a* is most likely to occur since it has the highest probability of occurring.

27. 0.54 or 54%

29. *a.*

	1	2	3	4	5	6
1	1	2	3	4	5	6
2	2	4	6	8	10	12
3	3	6	9	12	15	18
4	4	8	12	16	20	24
5	5	10	15	20	25	30
6	6	12	18	24	30	36

   b. $\frac{5}{12}$ *c.* $\frac{17}{36}$

31. Tree Diagram—Outcomes represent the sample space ($n = 16$)

33.

35.

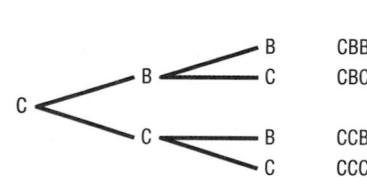

B → B → B → BBB
          → C → BBC
      → C → B → BCB
          → C → BCC

C → B → B → CBB
          → C → CBC
      → C → B → CCB
          → C → CCC

37. *a.* 0.08   *b.* 0.01   *c.* 0.35   *d.* 0.36

39. The statement is probably not based on empirical probability and probably not true.

41. Actual outcomes will vary, however each number should occur approximately $\frac{1}{6}$ of the time.

43. *a.* 1:5, 5:1   *d.* 1:1, 1:1   *g.* 1:1, 1:1
     b. 1:1, 1:1   *e.* 1:12, 12:1
     c. 1:3, 3:1   *f.* 1:3, 3:1

Exercises 4–3

1. Two events are mutually exclusive if they cannot occur at the same time. Examples will vary.

3. $\frac{1}{6}$, $\frac{61}{365}$

Using days makes the probability slightly larger than using months.

5. $\frac{11}{19}$

7. *a.* $\frac{7}{25}$ or 0.28   *b.* $\frac{3}{8}$ or 0.375   *c.* $\frac{17}{100}$ or 0.17
     d. Event *b* has the highest probability so it is most likely to occur.

9. 0.55

11. *a.* $\frac{6}{7}$ *b.* $\frac{4}{7}$ *c.* 1

13. *a.* .7   *b.* 0.0667   *c.* 0.7667

15. *a.* $\frac{38}{45}$ *b.* $\frac{22}{45}$ *c.* $\frac{2}{3}$

17. *a.* $\frac{14}{31}$ *b.* $\frac{23}{31}$ *c.* $\frac{19}{31}$

19. *a.* $\frac{1}{15}$ *b.* $\frac{1}{3}$ *c.* $\frac{5}{6}$ *d.* $\frac{5}{6}$ *e.* $\frac{1}{3}$

21. *a.* $\frac{5}{12}$ *b.* $\frac{1}{8}$ *c.* $\frac{2}{3}$ *d.* $\frac{23}{24}$

23. *a.* $\frac{3}{13}$ *b.* $\frac{3}{4}$ *c.* $\frac{19}{52}$ *d.* $\frac{7}{13}$ *e.* $\frac{15}{26}$

25. $\frac{7}{10}$ **27.** 0.06

29. 0.30

Exercises 4–4

1. *a.* independent   *e.* independent
     b. dependent   *f.* dependent
     c. dependent   *g.* dependent
     d. dependent   *h.* independent

3. 0.706 or 70.6%; the event is likely to occur since the probability is greater than 0.5.

5. 0.437 or 43.7%; the event is unlikely because the probability is less than 0.5.

7. *a.* 0.0954   *b.* 0.9046   *c.* 0.1601

9. 0.154 or 15.4%   **11.** 0.030 or 3.0%

13. 0.498 or 49.8%   **15.** $\frac{243}{1024}$

17. $\frac{5}{28}$

19. 0.210; the event is unlikely to occur since the probability is less than 0.5.

21. 0.116   **23.** 0.03

25. $\frac{49}{72}$ **27.** 0.6

29. 89%   **31.** 70%

33. 82%

35. *a.* 0.108 or 10.8%   *b.* 0.101 or 10.1%

37. *a.* 0.002 or 0.2%   *b.* 0.998

39. 0.8073   **41.** 0.611

43. $\frac{14,498}{20,825}$ **45.** 26.6%

47. $\frac{31}{32}$

49. 0.721; the event is likely to occur since the probability is about 72%.

51. $\frac{7}{8}$

53. No, because $P(A \cap B) = 0$ therefore $P(A \cap B) \neq P(A) \cdot P(B)$

55. Yes.
$P(\text{enroll}) = 0.55$
$P(\text{enroll} \mid \text{DW}) > P(\text{enroll})$ which indicates that DW has a positive effect on enrollment.
$P(\text{enroll} \mid \text{LP}) = P(\text{enroll})$ which indicates that LP has no effect on enrollment.

$P(\text{enroll} \mid \text{MH}) < P(\text{enroll})$ which indicates that MH has a low effect on enrollment.

Thus, all students should meet with DW.

Exercises 4–5

1. 100,000; 30,240   **3.** 5040

5. 40,320   **7.** 120

9. 1000;72   **11.** 10

13. *a.* 40,320   *e.* 2520   *i.* 120
  b. 3,628,800   *f.* 11,880   *j.* 30
  c. 1   *g.* 60
  d. 1   *h.* 1

15. 24   **17.** 120

19. 840   **21.** 151,200

23. 5,527,200   **25.** 300

27. *a.* 10   *c.* 35   *e.* 15   *g.* 1   *i.* 66
  b. 56   *d.* 15   *f.* 1   *h.* 36   *j.* 4

29. 120   **31.** 210

33. 15,504   **35.** 3080

37. 495; 210; 420   **39.** 200

41. 2970   **43.** 136

45. 330   **47.** 125,970

49. 15

51. *a.* 48   *b.* 60   *c.* 72

Exercises 4–6

1. $\frac{11}{221}$

3. *a.* $\frac{4}{35}$ *b.* $\frac{1}{35}$ *c.* $\frac{12}{35}$ *d.* $\frac{18}{35}$

5. *a.* 0.000269 or 0.0269%
  b. 0.00000439 or 0.000439%

7. $\frac{1}{1225}$

9. *a.* $\frac{10}{143}$ *c.* $\frac{15}{1001}$ *e.* $\frac{48}{143}$
  b. $\frac{60}{143}$ *d.* $\frac{160}{1001}$

11. *a.* 0.3216   *b.* 0.1637   *c.* 0.5146
  d. It probably got lost in the wash!

13. $\frac{5}{72}$ **15.** $\frac{1}{60}$

Review Exercises

1. *a.* $\frac{1}{6}$ *b.* $\frac{1}{6}$ *c.* $\frac{2}{3}$

3. $\frac{16}{45}$ **5.** $\frac{17}{30}$

7. *a.* $\frac{1}{10}$ *b.* $\frac{11}{30}$ *c.* $\frac{13}{15}$ *d.* $\frac{13}{15}$

9. 0.98   **11.** 0.006 or 0.6%

13. *a.* $\frac{2}{17}$ *b.* $\frac{11}{850}$ *c.* $\frac{1}{5525}$

15. $\frac{5}{13}$ **17.** 0.4

19. 0.51   **21.** 57.3%

23. *a.* $\frac{19}{44}$ *b.* $\frac{1}{4}$

25. $\frac{31}{32}$

27. 17,576,000; 11,232,000; 12,654,720

29. 350   **31.** 45

33. 26,000   **35.** 495

37. 15,504

39. 456,976,000; 0.00000000219 or 0.000000219%

41. $\frac{2}{7}$

Chapter Quiz

1. False   **2.** False

3. True   **4.** False

5. False   **6.** False

7. True   **8.** False

9. *b*   **10.** *b* and *d*

11. *d*   **12.** *b*

13. *c*   **14.** *b*

15. *d*   **16.** *b*

17. *b*   **18.** sample space

19. zero and one   **20.** zero

21. one   **22.** mutually exclusive

23. *a.* $\frac{1}{13}$ *b.* $\frac{1}{13}$ *c.* $\frac{4}{13}$

24. *a.* $\frac{1}{4}$ *b.* $\frac{4}{13}$ *c.* $\frac{1}{52}$ *d.* $\frac{1}{13}$ *e.* $\frac{1}{2}$

25. *a.* $\frac{12}{31}$ *b.* $\frac{12}{31}$ *c.* $\frac{27}{31}$ *d.* $\frac{24}{31}$

26. *a.* $\frac{11}{36}$ *c.* $\frac{11}{36}$ *e.* 0
  b. $\frac{5}{18}$ *d.* $\frac{1}{3}$ *f.* $\frac{11}{12}$

27. 0.84   **28.** 0.002

29. *a.* $\frac{253}{9996}$ *b.* $\frac{33}{66,640}$ *c.* 0

30. 0.54   **31.** 0.53

32. 0.81   **33.** 0.056

34. *a.* $\frac{1}{2}$ *b.* $\frac{3}{7}$

35. 0.99   **36.** 0.518

37. 0.9999886   **38.** 2,646

39. 40,320   **40.** 1,365

41. 1,188,137,600; 710,424,000

42. 720   **43.** 33,554,432

44. 56   **45.** $\frac{1}{4}$

46. $\frac{3}{14}$ **47.** $\frac{12}{55}$

48.

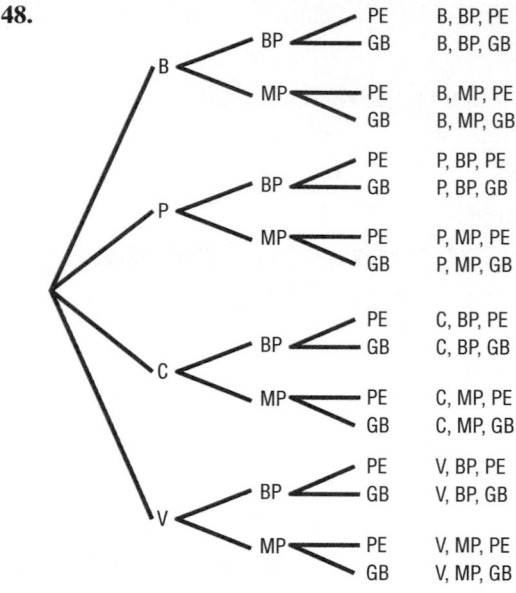

		PE	B, BP, PE
B	BP	GB	B, BP, GB
	MP	PE	B, MP, PE
		GB	B, MP, GB
P	BP	PE	P, BP, PE
		GB	P, BP, GB
	MP	PE	P, MP, PE
		GB	P, MP, GB
C	BP	PE	C, BP, PE
		GB	C, BP, GB
	MP	PE	C, MP, PE
		GB	C, MP, GB
V	BP	PE	V, BP, PE
		GB	V, BP, GB
	MP	PE	V, MP, PE
		GB	V, MP, GB

Chapter 5

Exercises 5–2

1. A random variable is a variable whose values are determined by chance. Examples will vary.

3. The number of commercials a radio station plays during each hour. The number of times a student uses his or her calculator during a mathematics exam. The number of leaves on a specific type of tree.

5. A probability distribution is a distribution which consists of the values a random variable can assume along with the corresponding probabilities of these values.

7. No; probabilities cannot be negative and the sum of the probabilities is not one.

9. Yes

11. No, probability values cannot be greater than 1.

13. Discrete   **15.** Continuous

17. Discrete

19.

X	0	1	2	3
P(X)	$\frac{6}{15}$	$\frac{5}{15}$	$\frac{3}{15}$	$\frac{1}{15}$

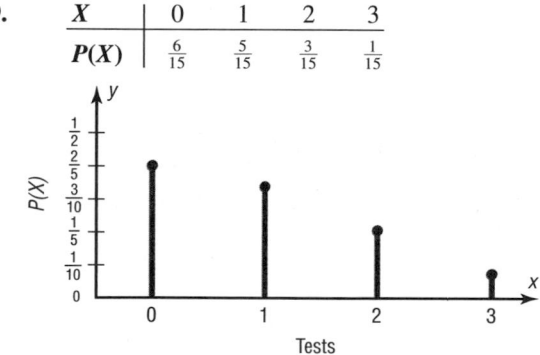

21.

X	0	1	2	3	4	5
P(X)	0.75	0.17	0.04	0.025	0.01	0.005

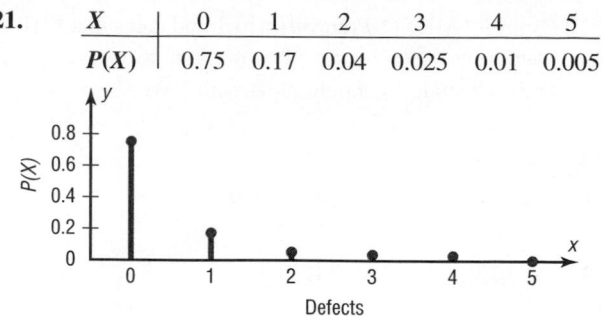

23.

X	1	2	3	4	5	6
P(X)	$\frac{1}{2}$	$\frac{1}{6}$	$\frac{1}{12}$	$\frac{1}{12}$	$\frac{1}{12}$	$\frac{1}{12}$

25.

X	3	4	5	6	7
P(X)	0.15	0.20	0.25	0.2	0.2

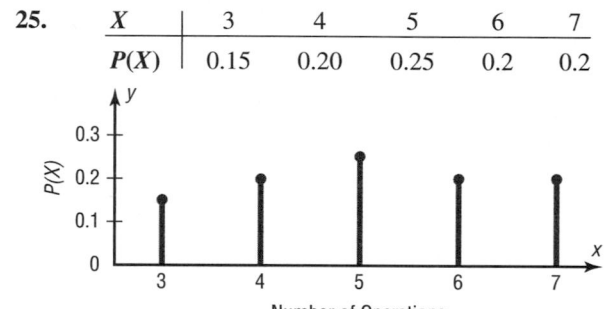

27. Let X = Canadian currency ($bills)

X	f	P(X)
$5	2	0.222
$10	3	0.333
$20	1	0.111
$50	3	0.333
	9	1.000

29.

X	1	2	3	4
P(X)	$\frac{1}{4}$	$\frac{1}{4}$	$\frac{3}{8}$	$\frac{1}{8}$

31.

X	1	2	3
P(X)	$\frac{1}{6}$	$\frac{1}{3}$	$\frac{1}{2}$

Yes.

33.

X	3	4	7
P(X)	$\frac{3}{6}$	$\frac{4}{6}$	$\frac{7}{6}$

No, the sum of the probabilities is greater than one and $P(7) = \frac{7}{6}$ which is also greater than one.

35.

X	1	2	3
P(X)	$\frac{1}{7}$	$\frac{2}{7}$	$\frac{4}{7}$

Yes.

Exercises 5–3

1. 0.2; 0.3; 0.6; 2

3. 1.3; 0.9; 1. No, on average each person has about one credit card.

5. 2.0; 1.6; 1.3; $200   **7.** 6.6; 1.3; 1.1

9. 13.9; 1.3; 1.1   **11.** $260

13. $0.83   **15.** −$1.00

17. −$0.50; − $0.52   **19.** $39,000; yes

21. 10.5   **23.** Answers will vary.

25. Answers will vary.

Exercises 5–4

1. *a.* Yes *c.* Yes *e.* No *g.* Yes *i.* No
   b. Yes *d.* No *f.* Yes *h.* Yes *j.* Yes

2. *a.* 0.420 *c.* 0.590 *e.* 0.000 *g.* 0.418 *i.* 0.246
   b. 0.346 *d.* 0.251 *f.* 0.250 *h.* 0.176

3. *a.* 0.0005 *c.* 0.342 *e.* 0.173
   b. 0.131 *d.* 0.007

5. 0.021; no, it's only about a 2% chance.

7. 0.267

9. 0.071

11. Binomial Distribution
   a. 0.129 *b.* 0.773 *c.* 0.556 *d.* 0.444

13. *a.* 0.121 *b.* 0.088 *c.* 0.967
   d. Event *c* is most likely to occur since it has the highest probability.

15. 8; 7.9; 2.8   **17.** 9; 8.73; 2.95

19. 80; 8.579; 73.6   **21.** 0.199

23. 0.514   **25.** 0.018

27. 0.942

29.

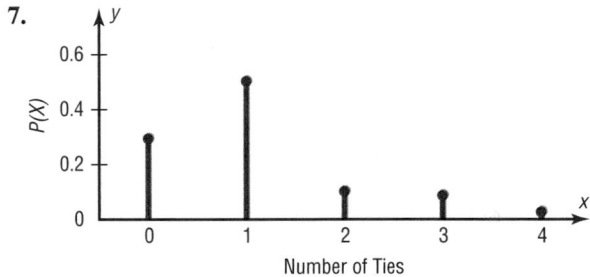

Number of Defective Chips

Exercises 5–5

1. *a.* 0.135 *c.* 0.0096 *e.* 0.0112
   b. 0.0324 *d.* 0.18

3. 0.06

5. $\frac{1}{108}$

7. *a.* 0.1563 *c.* 0.0504 *e.* 0.1241
   b. 0.1465 *d.* 0.071

9. *a.* 0.0183 *c.* 0.1465
   b. 0.0733 *d.* 0.7619

11. 0.3554   **13.** 0.9502

15. 0.1563   **17.** 0.38

19. 0.13   **21.** 0.597

Review Exercises

1. Yes.

3. No, the sum of the probabilities is greater than one.

5.

X	0	1	2	3	4
P(X)	0.05	0.30	0.45	0.12	0.08

Number of Radios

7.

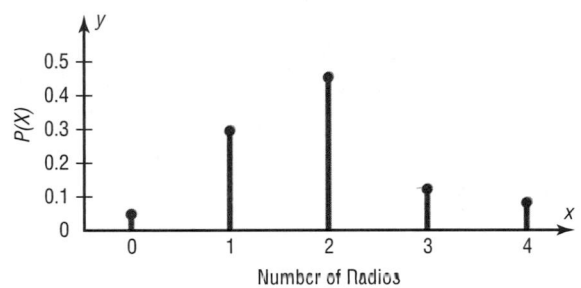

Number of Ties

9. 15.2; 1.6; 1.3   **11.** 24.2; 1.5; 1.2

13. $7.23; to break even, a person should bet $7.23.

15. *a.* 0.122   *b.* 0.989   *c.* 0.043

17. 135; 33.8; 5.8   **19.** 0.967

21. 0.175   **23.** 0.008

25. 0.050

27. *a.* 0.5543   *b.* 0.8488   *c.* 0.4457

29. 0.27

31. *a.* $\frac{21}{44}$ *b.* $\frac{1}{22}$ *c.* $\frac{7}{22}$

Chapter Quiz

1. True   **2.** False

3. False   **4.** True

5. chance   **6.** $\mu = n \cdot p$

7. one   **8.** *c*

9. *c* **10.** *d*

11. No, the sum of the probabilities is greater than one.

12. Yes **13.** Yes

14. Yes

15.

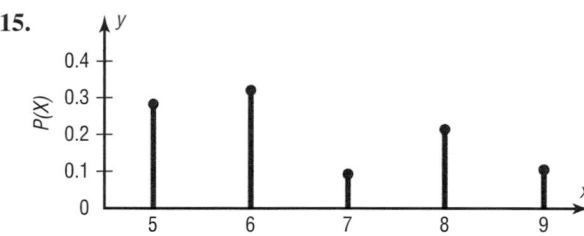

Number of Calls

16.

X	0	1	2	3	4
P(X)	0.02	0.30	0.48	0.13	0.07

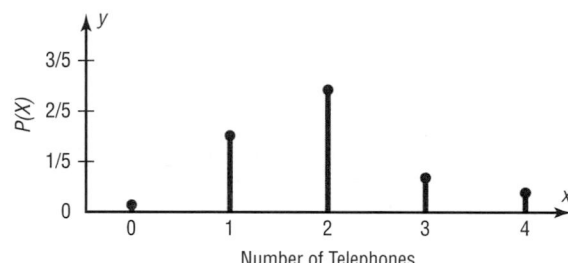

Number of Telephones

17. 2.0; 1.3; 1.1 **18.** 32.2; 1.1; 1.0

19. 5.2 **20.** $9.65

21. 0.124

22. *a.* 0.075 *b.* 0.872 *c.* 0.125

23. 240; 48; 6.9 **24.** 9; 7.9; 2.8

25. 0.0080 **26.** 0.0003

27. 0.061 **28.** 0.122

29. *a.* 0.5471 *b.* 0.9863 *c.* 0.4529

30. 0.128

31. *a.* 0.16 *b.* 0.42 *c.* 0.07

Chapter 6

Exercises 6–3

1. The characteristics of the normal distribution are:
   a. It is bell-shaped.
   b. It is symmetric about the mean.
   c. The mean, median, and mode are equal.
   d. It is continuous.
   e. It never touches the *x*-axis.
   f. The area under the curve is equal to one.
   g. It is unimodal.

3. One or 100%. **5.** 68%, 95%, 99.7%

7. 0.2734 **9.** 0.4808

11. 0.4090 **13.** 0.0764

15. 0.1145 **17.** 0.0258

19. 0.8417 **21.** 0.9826

23. 0.5596 **25.** 0.3574

27. 0.2486 **29.** 0.4418

31. 0.0023 **33.** 0.1131

35. 0.9522 **37.** 0.0706

39. 0.9222 **41.** −1.94

43. −2.13 **45.** −1.26

47. *a.* −2.28 *b.* −0.92 *c.* −0.27

49. *a.* $z = \pm 1.96$, found by: $0.05 \div 2 = 0.025$ is the area in each tail. $0.5 - 0.025 = 0.4750$ is the area needed to determine *z*.
   b. $z = \pm 1.645$, found by: $0.10 \div 2 = 0.05$ is the area in each tail. $0.5 - 0.05 = 0.4500$ is the area needed to determine *z*.
   c. $z = \pm 2.575$, found by: $0.01 \div 2 = 0.005$ is the area in each tail. $0.5 - 0.005 = 0.4950$ is the area needed to determine *z*.

51. 0.6826; 0.9544; 0.9974; they are very close.

53. 2.10 **55.** −1.45 and 0.11

57. $y = \dfrac{e^{\frac{-(x-0)^2}{2(1)^2}}}{1\sqrt{2\pi}} = \dfrac{e^{\frac{-x^2}{2}}}{\sqrt{2\pi}}$

Exercises 6–4

1. 0.0012 or 0.12%

3. *a.* 0.2776 *b.* 0.1518

5. *a.* 0.3023 or 30.23%
   b. 0.0062 or 0.62%

7. *a.* 0.3557 or 35.57%
   b. 0.8389 or 83.89%

9. *a.* 0.0012 *b.* 0.3432 *c.* 0.5
   d. About 0.12% of the ovens would be replaced.

11. *a.* 0.9803 *b.* 0.2514 *c.* 0.3434

13. *a.* 0.9699 *b.* 0.8264
   c. Use the range rule of thumb: If $\frac{\text{Range}}{4} = 16$, then the range is $16.4 = 64$.

15. *a.* 0.3281 *b.* 0.4002
   c. It is not likely that a person would be seated in less than 15 minutes.

17. The prices are between $5518.25 and $7465.75. Yes, a boat priced at $5550 would be sold in this store.

19. The middle 80% means that 40% of the area will be on either side of the mean. The corresponding *z* scores will be ± 1.28. $x = -1.28(92) + 1810 = 1692.24$ sq. ft. $x = 1.28(92) + 1810 = 1927.76$ sq. ft.

21. 0.006; $821

23. The middle 60% means that 30% of the area will be on either side of the mean. The corresponding z scores will be ± 0.84. $x = -0.84(1150) + 8256 = \$7290$ $x = 0.84(1150) + 8256 = \$9222$

25. 4.132 days; 7.04   **27.** $18,840.48

29. 18.6 months.

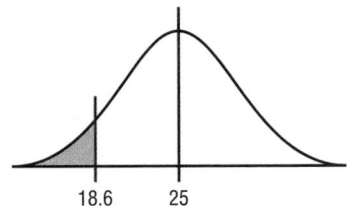

31. *a.* $\mu = 120$, $\sigma = 20$ *b.* $\mu = 15$, $\sigma = 2.5$ *c.* $\mu = 30$, $\sigma = 5$

33. There are several mathematical tests that can be used including drawing a histogram and calculating Pearson's index of skewness.

35. 1.05

37. $\mu = 0.45$ and $\sigma = 1.34$

39. The distribution is not normal.

41. The distribution is not normal.

Exercises 6–5

1. The distribution is called the sampling distribution of sample means.

3. The mean of the sample means is equal to the population mean.

5. The distribution will be approximately normal when the sample size is large.

7. $z = \frac{\bar{x} - \mu}{\sigma/\sqrt{n}}$ **9.** 0.0045 or 0.45%

11. 0.1190; there is an 11.90% probability that the group will exceed 65.5 kg which suggests overweight.

13. 0.0107

15. *a.* 0.3859   *b.* 0.1841
c. Individual values are more variable than means.

17. 0.8965   **19.** 0.9153

21. *a.* 0.3446   *b.* 0.0023
c. Yes, since it is within one standard deviation of the mean.
d. Very unlikely, since the probability would be less than 1%.

23. *a.* 0.3707   *b.* 0.0475

25. 0.8805   **27.** 0.0143

29. $\sigma_x = \frac{\sigma}{\sqrt{n}} = \frac{15}{\sqrt{100}} = 1.5$
$2(1.5) = \frac{15}{\sqrt{n}}$
$3 \cdot \sqrt{n} = 5$
$n = 25.$

Exercises 6–6

1. When p is approximately 0.5, and as n increases, the shape of the binomial distribution becomes similar to the normal distribution. The normal approximation should be used only when np and nq are both greater than or equal to 5. The correction for continuity is necessary because the normal distribution is continuous and the binomial is discrete.

2. *a.* 0.811   *c.* 0.1052   *e.* 0.2327
b. 0.0516   *d.* 0.1711   *f.* 0.9988

3. *a.* Yes   *c.* No   *e.* Yes
b. No   *d.* Yes   *f.* No

5. 0.1660   **7.** 0.4960

9. 0.9998   **11.** 0.4761

13. 0.9951; yes

Review Exercises

1. *a.* 0.4744   *e.* 0.2139   *i.* 0.0183
b. 0.1443   *f.* 0.8284   *j.* 0.9535
c. 0.0590   *g.* 0.0233
d. 0.8329   *h.* 0.9131

3. *a.* 0.500   *b.* 0.2358
c. A salary of $18,000 is the cutoff for the bottom 23.58% of salaries or 76.42% of 15- to 24-year-olds earns a higher salary.

5. 0.9686; 0.9099

7. *a.* 0.6915   *b.* 0.8686

9. The scores should be between 92.2 and 107.8.

11. 0.0023 or 0.23%. Yes, since the probability is less than 1%.

13. 0.8389   **15.** 0.1131

17. The distribution is not normal.

Chapter Quiz

1. False   **2.** True
3. True   **4.** True
5. False   **6.** False
7. *a*   **8.** *a*
9. *b*   **10.** *b*
11. *c*   **12.** 0.5
13. Sampling error.   **14.** The population mean.
15. The standard error of the mean.
16. 5   **17.** 5%
18. *a.* 0.4332   *d.* 0.1029   *g.* 0.0401   *j.* 0.9131
b. 0.3944   *e.* 0.2912   *h.* 0.8997
c. 0.0344   *f.* 0.8284   *i.* 0.017

19. *a.* 0.4846   *d.* 0.0188   *g.* 0.0089   *j.* 0.8461
  b. 0.4693   *e.* 0.7461   *h.* 0.9582
  c. 0.9334   *f.* 0.0384   *i.* 0.9788

20. *a.* 0.4207
  b. 0.3409. Probability of at least 80 mm of rain.
  c. 0.1519
  d. If we use the 90th percentile or top 10% of rainfalls as extremely wet, the top 10% of rainfalls would exceed 101.5 mm.

21. *a.* 0.2090   *b.* 0.2177   *c.* 0.5733
  d. Heights of 154.5 cm and 175.3 cm separate the bottom 5th percentile and top 95th percentile, respectively.

22. *a.* 0.3090   *b.* 0.1711   *c.* 0.9686   *d.* 0.8051

23. *a.* 0.0013   *b.* 0.5   *c.* 0.0081   *d.* 0.5511

24. The probabilities are:
  a. 0.0037   *b.* 0.0228   *c.* 0.5   *d.* 0.3232

25. 8.804 cm

26. The lowest acceptable score is 121.24.

27. 0.015   **28.** 0.9738

29. 0.5793   **30.** 0.0630

31. 0.2177   **32.** 0.7157

33. The distribution is not normal.

34. The distribution is approximately normal.

Chapter 7
Exercises 7–2

1. A point estimate of a parameter specifies a specific value such as $\mu = 87$, whereas an interval estimate specifies a range of values for the parameter such as $84 < \mu < 90$. The advantage of an interval estimate is that a specific confidence level (say 95%) can be selected, and one can be 95% confident that the parameter being estimated lies in the interval.

3. The maximum error of estimate is the likely range of values to the right or left of the statistic in which may contain the parameter.

5. A good estimator should be unbiased, consistent, and relatively efficient.

7. To determine sample size, the maximum error of estimate and the degree of confidence must be specified and the population standard deviation must be known.

9. *a.* 2.575   *c.* 1.96   *e.* 1.88
  b. 2.33   *d.* 1.645

11. *a.* 82   *b.* $77 < \mu < 87$ *c.* $75 < \mu < 89$
  d. The 99% confidence interval is larger because the confidence level is larger.

13. *a.* 12.6   *b.* $11.9 < \mu < 13.3$
  c. It would be highly unlikely since this is far larger than 13.3 minutes.

15. $145,030 < \mu < $154,970

17. $4913 < \mu < 5087$; 4000 hours does not seem reasonable since it is outside this interval.

19. $59.5 < \mu < 62.9$ **21.** 114

23. 25   **25.** 147

Exercises 7–3

1. The characteristics of the *t*-distribution are: It is bell-shaped, symmetrical about the mean, and never touches the *x*-axis. The mean, median, and mode are equal to 0 and are located at the centre of the distribution. The variance is greater than 1. The *t*-distribution is a family of curves based on degrees of freedom. As sample size increases the *t*-distribution approaches the normal distribution.

3. The *t*-distribution should be used when s is unknown and $n < 30$.

4. *a.* 2.898   *c.* 2.624   *e.* 2.093
  b. 2.074   *d.* 1.833

5. $15 < \mu < 17$

7. $\bar{X} = 33.4$; $s = 28.7$; $21.2 < \mu < 45.6$; the point estimate is 33.4 and is close to the actual population mean of 32, which is within the 90% confidence interval. The mean may not be the best estimate since the data value 132 is large and possibly an outlier.

9. We are 90% confident that the average weight of all university wrestlers is between 120.5 kg and 129.5 kg, based on a sample of 6 university wrestlers. Using the upper confidence limit of 129.5 kg as our population mean and assuming a standard deviation of 5.5 kg, a weight of 141 kg would be 2.09 $(141 - 129.5)/$ 5.5 or 2.09 standard deviations above the population mean. Although this value is high, the claim is possible, therefore believable.

11. $13.5 < \mu < 15.1$; the employees should allow about 30 minutes.

13. $17.29 < \mu < $19.77

15. $109 < \mu < 121$

17. $38.8 < \mu < 44.4$

19. $56,466 < \mu < $56,970 ; he should use $56,466.

21. $\bar{X} = 2.175$; $s = 0.585$; $\mu > $1.95 means that one can be 95% confident that the mean revenue is greater than $1.95; $\mu < $2.40 means that one can be 95% confident that the mean revenue is less than $2.40.

Exercises 7–4

1. *a.* 0.5, 0.5   *c.* 0.46, 0.54   *e.* 0.45, 0.55
  b. 0.45, 0.55   *d.* 0.58, 0.42

2. *a.* $\hat{p} = 0.15$; $\hat{q} = 0.85$ *d.* $\hat{p} = 0.51$; $\hat{q} = 0.49$
  b. $\hat{p} = 0.37$; $\hat{q} = 0.63$ *e.* $\hat{p} = 0.79$; $\hat{q} = 0.21$
  c. $\hat{p} = 0.71$; $\hat{q} = 0.29$

3. $0.365 < p < 0.415$

5. 0.09 or 9% $< p <$ 0.15 or 15%
(*Note:* TI-83 answer is $0.092 < p < 0.153$)
11% is contained in the confidence interval.

7. $0.797 < p < 0.883$

9. $0.153 < p < 0.307$
The statement that one in five or 20% of 13- to 14-year-olds is a sometime smoker is within the interval.

11. $0.286 < p < 0.562$; it would not be considered larger since 0.52 is in the interval.

13. $0.419 < p < 0.481$

15. *a.* 3120.1875 or 3121
b. 4160.25 or 4161

17. *a.* 556.97 or 557
b. 663.06 or 664

19. 1067.11 or 1068

21. 1.96 corresponds to a 95% degree of confidence.

Exercises 7–5

1. χ^2

3.

	χ^2 **left**	χ^2 **right**
a.	3.816	21.920
b.	10.117	30.144
c.	13.844	41.923
d.	0.412	16.750
e.	26.509	55.758

5. $8.64 < \sigma^2 < 28.93$
$2.94 < \sigma^2 < 5.38$
Yes. The times deviate between 3 and 5 minutes.

7. $0.40 < \sigma^2 < 2.25$
$0.63 < \sigma < 1.50$

9. $232.1 < \sigma^2 < 691.6$
$15.2 < \sigma^2 < 26.3$

11. $4.1 < \sigma^2 < 7.1$

13. $16.2 < \sigma < 19.8$

Review Exercises

1. $\overline{X} = 12.6$ km/h
We are 90% confident that the population mean of marathon runner speeds is between 12.35 km/h and 12.85 km/h, based on a sample of 36 marathon runners. Minimum speed is the lower confidence limit of 12.35 km/h.

3. $\overline{X} = 13$ days
We are 95% confident that the population mean of hospital stays for seniors who have fallen is between 12.9 and 13.1 days, based on a sample of 1,100 hospital admissions.

5. $25 < \mu < 31$

7. 28

9. $0.434 < p < 0.660$; yes; it seems that as many as 66% were dissatisfied.

11. 460

13. $0.218 < \sigma^2 < 0.435$; yes; it seems that there is a large standard deviation.

15. $5.1 < \sigma^2 < 18.3$

Chapter Quiz

1. True   **2.** True

3. False   **4.** True

5. *b*   **6.** *a*

7. *b*

8. unbiased, consistent, relatively efficient

9. maximum error of estimate

10. point   **11.** 90, 95, 99

12. $23.45; $22.79 < \mu < 24.11

13. $44.80 ; $43.15 < \mu < 46.45

14. $\overline{X} = 1{,}882$ kg
We are 99% confident that the population mean of minivan weights is between 1,793.2 kg and 1,970.8 kg, based on a sample of 40 minivans.

15. $45.7 < \mu < 51.5$ **16.** $418 < \mu < 458$

17. $26 < \mu < 36$ **18.** 180

19. 25   **20.** $0.604 < p < 0.810$

21. $0.295 < p < 0.425$ **22.** $0.342 < p < 0.547$

23. 545   **24.** $7 < \sigma < 13$

25. $30.9 < \sigma^2 < 78.2$ **26.** $1.8 < \sigma < 3.2$
$5.6 < \sigma < 8.8$

Chapter 8
Exercises 8–2

Note: For Chapters 8–13, specific P-values are given in parentheses after the P-value intervals. When the specific P-value is extremely small, it is not given.

1. The null hypothesis states that there is no difference between a parameter and a specific value or that there is no difference between two parameters. The alternative hypothesis states that there is a specific difference between a parameter and a specific value or that there is a difference between two parameters. Examples will vary.

3. A statistical test uses the data obtained from a sample to make a decision about whether the null hypothesis should be rejected.

5. The critical region is the range of values of the test statistic that indicates that there is a significant difference and the null hypothesis should be rejected. The noncritical region is the range of values of the test statistic that indicates that the difference was probably due to chance and the null hypothesis should not be rejected.

7. α, β

9. A one-tailed test should be used when a specific direction, such as greater than or less than, is being hypothesized; when no direction is specified, a two-tailed test should be used.

11. Hypotheses can be proved true only when the entire population is used to compute the test statistic. In most cases, this is impossible.

12. *a.* ±1.96   *d.* +2.33   *g.* +1.645   *i.* −1.75

     b. −2.33   *e.* −1.645   *h.* ±2.575   *j.* +2.05

     c. +2.575   *f.* −2.05

13. *g.* H_0: $\mu = 3.7$ and H_1: $\mu \neq 3.7$

Exercises 8–3

1. H_0: $\mu = \$69.21$ (claim) and H_1: $\mu \neq \$69.21$; C.V. $= \pm 1.96$; $z = -1.15$; do not reject. There is not enough evidence to reject the claim that the average cost of a hotel stay in Atlanta is \$69.21.

3. H_0: $\mu = \$15$ billion and H_1: $\mu < \$15$ billion (claim); C.V. $= -1.645$; $z = -1.40$; do not reject. There is not enough evidence to support the claim that the average revenue of Canadian companies is less than \$15 billion.

5. H_0: $\mu = 9$ and H_1: $\mu < 9$ (claim); C.V. $= -2.33$; $z = -5.67$; reject. There is enough evidence to support the claim that the average age of Air Canada's commercial fleet is less than 9.8 years.

7. H_0: $\mu = 73.7$ and H_1: $\mu \neq 73.7$ (claim); C.V. $= \pm 1.96$; $z = 0.93$; do not reject. There is not enough evidence to support the claim that the average length of 1-year old toddlers is not equal to 73.7 cm.

9. H_0: $\mu = \$19,410$ and H_1: $\mu > \$19,410$ (claim); C.V. $= 2.33$; $z = 2.81$; reject. There is enough evidence to support the claim that the cost of attendance has increased.

11. H_0: $\mu = 21.4$ and H_1: $\mu \neq 21.4$ (claim); C.V. $= \pm 2.575$; $z = 3.51$; reject. There is enough evidence to support the claim that the average Quebec TV viewing hours per week differ than the Canadian national average.

13. H_0: $\mu = \$24.44$ and H_1: $\mu \neq \$24.44$ (claim); C.V. $= \pm 2.33$; $z = -2.28$; do not reject. There is not enough evidence to support the claim that the amount spent at a local mall is not equal to the national average of \$24.44.

15. *a.* Do not reject.   *d.* Reject.

     b. Reject.   *e.* Reject.

     c. Do not reject.

17. H_0: $\mu = 213$ and H_1: $\mu < 213$ (claim); $z = -2.61$; *P*-value > 0.01, do not reject. There is not enough evidence to support the tire manufacturer's claim that the average stopping distance is less than 213 metres.

19. H_0: $\mu = 546$ and H_1: $\mu < 546$ (claim); $z = -2.4$; *P*-value $= 0.008$. Yes, it can be concluded that the number of calories burned is less than originally thought.

21. H_0: $\mu = 246$ and H_1: $\mu > 246$ (claim); $z = 5.99$; *P*-value < 0.01, reject. There is enough evidence to support the claim that the average farm size is larger today than 246 hectares.

23. H_0: $\mu = 48,000$ (claim) and H_1: $\mu \neq 48,000$; $z = 1.71$; *P*-value < 0.10, reject. There is not enough evidence to support the claim that the average vehicle transmission is serviced at 48,000 kilometres.

25. H_0: $\mu = 10$ and H_1: $\mu < 10$ (claim); $z = -8.67$; *P*-value < 0.0001; since *P*-value < 0.05, reject. Yes; there is enough evidence to support the claim that the average number of days missed per year is less than 10.

27. H_0: $\mu = 8.65$ (claim) and H_1: $\mu \neq 8.65$; C.V. $= \pm 1.96$; $z = -1.35$; do not reject. Yes; there is not enough evidence to reject the claim that the average hourly wage of the employees is \$8.65.

Exercises 8–4

1. It is bell-shaped, it is symmetric about the mean, and it never touches the *x*-axis. The mean, median, and mode are all equal to 0, and they are located at the centre of the distribution. The *t* distribution differs from the standard normal distribution in that it is a family of curves and the variance is greater than 1; and as the degrees of freedom increase, the *t* distribution approaches the standard normal distribution.

3. *a.* +1.833   *c.* −3.365   *e.* ±2.145   *g.* ±2.771

     b. ±1.740   *d.* +2.306   *f.* −2.819   *h.* ±2.583

4. Specific *P*-values are in parentheses.

     a. $0.01 < P\text{-value} < 0.025$ (0.018)

     b. $0.05 < P\text{-value} < 0.10$ (0.062)

     c. $0.10 < P\text{-value} < 0.25$ (0.123)

     d. $0.10 < P\text{-value} < 0.20$ (0.138)

     e. $P\text{-value} < 0.005$ (0.003)

     f. $0.10 < P\text{-value} < 0.25$ (0.158)

     g. $P\text{-value} = 0.05$ (0.05)

     h. $P\text{-value} > 0.25$ (0.261)

5. H_0: $\mu = 281.5$ and H_1: $\mu < 281.5$ (claim); C.V. $= -1.833$; $t = -2.962$; reject. There is enough evidence to reject the claim that the average Maritime summer rainfall is equal to 281.5 millimetres.

6. H_0: $\mu = 137.6$ and H_1: $\mu < 137.6$ (claim); C.V. $= -3.747$; $t = -0.205$; do not reject. There is not enough evidence to reject the claim that the average area of British Columbia provincial parks is less than 137.6 square kilometres.

7. H_0: $\mu = \$120,000$ (claim) and H_1: $\mu \neq \$120,000$; C.V. $= \pm 2.776$; $t = -2.286$; do not reject. There is not enough evidence to reject the claim that the average Canadian mayor salary is equal to $120,000.

9. H_0: $\mu = 200$ and H_1: $\mu < 200$ (claim); C.V. $= 3.747$; $t = -0.711$; reject. There is not enough evidence to reject the claim that the average height of Canada's tallest buildings is greater than 200 metres.

11. H_0: $\mu = \$13,252$ and H_1: $\mu > \$13,252$ (claim); C.V. $= 2.539$; d.f. $= 19$; $t = 2.949$; reject. Yes; there is enough evidence to support the claim that the mean cost has increased.

13. H_0: $\mu = \$54.8$ million and H_1: $\mu > \$54.8$ million (claim); C.V. $= 1.761$; d.f. $= 14$; $t = 3.058$; reject. Yes; there is enough evidence to support the claim that the average cost of an action movie is greater than $54.8 million.

15. H_0: $\mu = 132$ (claim) and H_1: $\mu \neq 132$; C.V. $= \pm 2.365$; d.f. $= 7$; $t = -1.7999$; do not reject. Yes; there is not enough evidence to reject the claim that the average time is 132 minutes.

17. H_0: $\mu = 5.8$ and H_1: $\mu \neq 5.8$ (claim); d.f. $= 19$; $t = -3.462$; P-value < 0.01; reject. There is enough evidence to support the claim that the mean number of times has changed.

19. H_0: $\mu = \$15,000$ and H_1: $\mu \neq \$15,000$; d.f. $= 11$; $t = -1.10$; C.V. $= \pm 2.201$; do not reject. There is not enough evidence to conclude that the average stipend differs from $15,000.

Exercises 8–5

1. Answers will vary.

3. $np \geq 5$ and $nq \geq 5$

5. H_0: $p = 0.647$ and H_1: $p \neq 0.647$ (claim); C.V. $= \pm 2.575$; $z = -0.86$; do not reject. No. There is not enough evidence to support the claim that the proportion is different from 0.647.

7. H_0: $p = 0.40$ and H_1: $p \neq 0.40$ (claim); C.V. $= \pm 2.575$; $z = -1.07$; do not reject. No. There is not enough evidence to support the claim that the proportion is different from 0.40.

9. H_0: $p = 0.516$ and H_1: $p \neq 0.516$ (claim); C.V. $= \pm 1.96$; $z = -0.56$; do not reject. There is not enough evidence to reject the claim that 51.6% of Canadians are mobile communication subscribers.

11. H_0: $p = 0.073$ (claim) and H_1: $p \neq 0.073$; C.V. $= \pm 1.96$; $z = 0.19$; do not reject. There is not enough evidence to reject the claim that 74% of vehicle fatalities involve motorcyclists.

13. H_0: $p = 0.133$ (claim) and H_1: $p \neq 0.133$; C.V. $= \pm 2.575$; $z = 0.77$; do not reject. There is not enough evidence to reject the claim that 13.3% of food bank users have jobs.

15. H_0: $p = 0.18$ (claim) and H_1: $p \neq 0.18$; $z = -0.60$; P-value $= 0.5486$; since P-value > 0.05, do not reject. There is not enough evidence to reject the claim that 18% of all high school students smoke at least a pack of cigarettes a day.

17. H_0: $p = 0.44$ (claim) and H_1: $p \neq 0.44$; C.V. $= \pm 1.96$; $z = 3.02$; reject. There is sufficient evidence to reject the claim that 44% of Canadians using library services borrow books.

19. H_0: $p = 0.10$ and H_1: $p < 0.10$ (claim); C.V. $= -1.645$; $z = -0.38$; do not reject. There is not enough evidence to accept the claim that fewer than 10% of injury deaths are firearm-related fatalities.

21. No.

23. $$z = \frac{X - \mu}{\sigma}$$
$$z = \frac{X - np}{\sqrt{npq}} \quad \text{since } \mu = np \text{ and } \sigma = \sqrt{npq}$$
$$z = \frac{X/n - np/n}{\sqrt{npq}/n}$$
$$z = \frac{X/n - np/n}{\sqrt{npq/n^2}}$$
$$z = \frac{\hat{p} - p}{\sqrt{pq/n}} \quad \text{since } \hat{p} = X/n$$

Exercises 8–6

1. *a.* H_0: $\sigma^2 \leq 225$ and H_1: $\sigma^2 > 225$; C.V. $= 27.587$; d.f. $= 17$

b. H_0: $\sigma^2 \geq 225$ and H_1: $\sigma^2 < 225$; C.V. $= 14.042$; d.f. $= 22$

c. H_0: $\sigma^2 = 225$ and H_1: $\sigma^2 \neq 225$; C.V. $= 5.629$; 26.119; d.f. $= 14$

d. H_0: $\sigma^2 = 225$ and H_1: $\sigma^2 \neq 225$; C.V. $= 2.167$; 14.067; d.f. $= 7$

e. H_0: $\sigma^2 \leq 225$ and H_1: $\sigma^2 > 225$; C.V. $= 32.000$; d.f. $= 16$

f. H_0: $\sigma^2 \geq 225$ and H_1: $\sigma^2 < 225$; C.V. $= 8.907$; d.f. $= 19$

g. H_0: $\sigma^2 = 225$ and H_1: $\sigma^2 \neq 225$; C.V. $= 3.074$; 28.299; d.f. $= 12$

h. H_0: $\sigma^2 \geq 225$ and H_1: $\sigma^2 < 225$; C.V. $= 15.308$; d.f. $= 28$

2. *a.* $0.01 < P$-value < 0.025 (0.015)

b. $0.005 < P$-value < 0.01 (0.006)

c. $0.01 < P$-value < 0.025 (0.012)

d. P-value < 0.005 (0.003)

e. $0.025 < P$-value < 0.05 (0.037)

f. $0.05 < P$-value < 0.10 (0.088)

g. $0.05 < P$-value < 0.10 (0.066)

h. P-value < 0.01 (0.007)

3. $H_0: \sigma = 60$ (claim) and $H_1: \sigma \neq 60$; C.V. = 8.672; 27.587; d.f. = 17; $\chi^2 = 19.707$; do not reject. There is not enough evidence to reject the claim that the standard deviation is 60.

5. $H_0: \sigma \geq 500$ and $H_1: \sigma < 500$ (claim); C.V. = 10.851; d.f. = 20; $\chi^2 = 14.211$; do not reject. There is not enough evidence to support the claim that the standard deviation of motor vehicle theft rate per year in Canada is less than 500.

7. $H_0: \sigma \leq 1.2$ (claim) and $H_1: \sigma > 1.2$; $\alpha = 0.01$; d.f. = 14; $\chi^2 = 31.5$; P-value < 0.005 (0.0047); since P-value < 0.01, reject. There is enough evidence to reject the claim that the standard deviation is less than or equal to 1.2 minutes.

9. $H_0: \sigma \leq 20$ and $H_1: \sigma > 20$ (claim); C.V. = 36.191; d.f. = 19; $\chi^2 = 58.5502$; reject. There is enough evidence to support the claim that the standard deviation is greater than 20.

11. $H_0: \sigma \geq 150$ and $H_1: \sigma < 150$ (claim); C.V. = 3.940; d.f. = 10; $\chi^2 = 9.669$; do not reject. There is not enough evidence to support the claim that the standard deviation of annual deaths from fires in Canada is less than 150.

13. $H_0: \sigma^2 \leq 25$ and $H_1: \sigma^2 > 25$ (claim); C.V. = 22.362; d.f. = 13; $\chi^2 = 23.622$; reject. There is enough evidence to support the claim that the variance is greater than 25.

Exercises 8–7

1. $H_0: \mu = 1800$ (claim) and $H_1: \mu \neq 1800$; C.V. = ± 1.96; $z = 0.47$; $1706.04 < \mu < 1953.96$; do not reject. There is not enough evidence to reject the claim that the average of the sales is $1800.

3. $H_0: \mu = 86$ (claim) and $H_1: \mu \neq 86$; C.V. = ± 2.575; $z = -1.29$; $80.00 < \mu < 88.00$; do not reject. There is not enough evidence to reject the claim that the average monthly maintenance is $86.

5. $H_0: \mu = 22$ and $H_1: \mu \neq 22$ (claim); C.V. = ± 2.575; $z = -2.32$; $19.47 < \mu < 22.13$; do not reject. There is not enough evidence to support the claim that the average has changed.

7. The power of a statistical test is the probability of rejecting the null hypothesis when it is false.

9. The power of a test can be increased by increasing α or selecting a larger sample size.

Review Exercises

1. $H_0: \mu = 37°C$ (claim) and $H_1: \mu \neq 37°C$; C.V. = ± 1.96; $z = -2.61$; reject. There is not enough evidence to support the claim that the average Eastern Canada high temperature is equal to 37°C.

3. $H_0: \mu = \$40,000$ and $H_1: \mu > \$40,000$ (claim); C.V. = 1.65; $z = 2.00$; reject. There is enough evidence to support the claim that the average salary is greater than $40,000.

5. $H_0: \mu = 26.8°C$ and $H_1: \mu > 26.8°C$; C.V. = 1.833; d.f. = 9; $t = 1.626$; do not reject. There is not enough evidence to support the claim that the July 2006 was hotter than normal.

7. $H_0: \mu = 6$ and $H_1: \mu \neq 6$ (claim); $t = 1.835$; d.f. = 9; C.V. = ± 2.821; do not reject. There is not enough evidence to support the claim that the attendance has changed.

9. $H_0: p = 0.105$ and $H_1: p > 0.105$ (claim); C.V. = 1.645; $z = 1.47$; do not reject. There is not enough evidence to support the councillor's claim that more than 10.5% of city workers commute to work.

11. $H_0: p = 0.65$ (claim) and $H_1: p \neq 0.65$; $z = 1.17$; P-value = 0.242; since P-value > 0.05, do not reject. There is not enough evidence to reject the claim that 65% of teenagers own their own radios.

13. $H_0: \mu = 10$ and $H_1: \mu < 10$ (claim); $z = -2.22$; P-value = 0.0132; reject. There is enough evidence to support the claim that the average time is less than 10 minutes.

15. $H_0: \sigma = 1.6$ L/100 km and $H_1: \sigma < 1.6$ L/100 (claim); d.f. = 19; $\chi^2 = 6.012$; P-value < 0.05 (0.002); reject. There is enough evidence to support the claim that the standard deviation of automobile fuel consumption is less than 1.6 L/100.

17. $H_0: \sigma = 18$ (claim) and $H_1: \sigma \neq 18$; C.V. = 11.143 and 0.484; d.f. = 4; $\chi^2 = 5.44$; do not reject. There is not enough evidence to reject the claim that the standard deviation is 18 minutes.

19. $H_0: \mu = 10.2$ and $H_1: \mu \neq 10.2$ (claim); C.V. = ± 2.575; $z = 1.49$; do not reject; $9.84 < \mu < 11.56$. There is not enough evidence to support the claim that the average length of leaves has changed from 10.2 cm. Yes, the results agree. The mean is in the interval.

Chapter Quiz

1. True

2. True

3. False

4. True

5. False

6. b

7. d

8. c

9. b

10. Type I

11. β

12. Statistical hypothesis.

13. Right.

14. $n - 1$

15. $H_0: \mu = 28.6$ (claim) and $H_1: \mu \neq 28.6$; $z = 2.14$; C.V. $= \pm 1.96$; reject. There is enough evidence to reject the claim that the average age of the mothers is 28.6 years.

16. $H_0: \mu = \$6500$ (claim) and $H_1: \mu \neq \$6500$; $z = 5.27$; C.V. $= \pm 1.96$; reject. There is enough evidence to reject the agent's claim.

17. $H_0: \mu = 8$ and $H_1: \mu > 8$ (claim); $z = 6$; C.V. $= 1.645$; reject. There is enough evidence to support the claim that the average is greater than 8.

18. $H_0: \mu = 500$ (claim) and $H_1: \mu \neq 500$; d.f. $= 6$; $t = -0.571$; C.V. $= \pm 3.707$; do not reject. There is not enough evidence to reject the claim that the mean is 500.

19. $H_0: \mu = 170$ and $H_1: \mu < 170$ (claim); $t = -3.016$; P-value < 0.01 (0.00355); since P-value < 0.05; reject. There is sufficient evidence to support the claim that the average height of female models is less than 170 cm.

20. $H_0: \mu = 12.4$ and $H_1: \mu < 12.4$ (claim); $t = -2.324$; C.V. $= -1.345$; reject. There is enough evidence to support the claim that the average is less than the company claimed.

21. $H_0: \mu = 63.5$ and $H_1: \mu > 63.5$ (claim); $t = 0.47075$; P-value > 0.25 (0.322); since P-value > 0.05; do not reject. There is not enough evidence to support the claim that the average is greater than 63.5.

22. $H_0: \mu = 26$ (claim) and $H_1: \mu \neq 26$; $t = -1.5$; C.V. $= \pm 2.492$; do not reject. There is not enough evidence to reject the claim that the average is 26.

23. $H_0: p = 0.39$ (claim) and $H_1: p \neq 0.39$; C.V. $= \pm 1.96$; $z = -0.62$; do not reject. There is not enough evidence to reject the claim that 39% took supplements. The study supports the results of the previous study.

24. $H_0: p \geq 0.55$ (claim) and $H_1: p < 0.55$; $z = -0.8989$; C.V. $= -1.28$; do not reject. There is not enough evidence to reject the survey's claim.

25. $H_0: p = 0.35$ (claim) and $H_1: p \neq 0.35$; C.V. $= \pm 2.33$; $z = 0.666$; do not reject. There is not enough evidence to reject the claim that the proportion is 35%.

26. $H_0: p = 0.75$ (claim) and $H_1: p \neq 0.75$; $z = 2.6833$; C.V. $= \pm 2.575$; reject. There is enough evidence to reject the claim.

27. P-value $= 0.0323$

28. P-value $= 0.0001$

29. $H_0: \sigma \leq 6$ and $H_1: \sigma > 6$ (claim); $\chi^2 = 54$; C.V. $= 36.415$; reject. There is enough evidence to support the claim.

30. $H_0: \sigma = 8$ (claim) and $H_1: \sigma \neq 8$; $\chi^2 = 33.2$; C.V. $= 27.991, 79.490$; do not reject. There is not enough evidence to reject the claim that $\sigma = 8$.

31. $H_0: \sigma \geq 2.3$ and $H_1: \sigma < 2.3$ (claim); $\chi^2 = 13$; C.V. $= 10.117$; do not reject. There is not enough evidence to support the claim that the standard deviation is less than 2.3.

32. $H_0: \sigma = 4.1$ (claim) and $H_1: \sigma \neq 4.1$; d.f. $= 9$; $\chi^2 = 13.385$; $0.10 < P$-value < 0.90 (0.146); do not reject. There is enough evidence to support the claim that the standard deviation of wrapping cord strength is equal to 4.1 kg.

33. $28.9 < \mu < 31.2$; no.

34. $\$6562.81 < \mu < \$6637.19$; no.

Chapter 9

Exercises 9–2

1. Testing a single mean involves comparing a sample mean to a specific value such as $\mu = 100$; testing the difference between two means involves comparing the means of two samples, such as $\mu_1 = \mu_2$.

3. The populations must be independent of each other, and they must be normally distributed; s_1 and s_2 can be used in place of σ_1 and σ_2 when σ_1 and σ_2 are unknown and both samples are each greater than or equal to 30.

5. $H_0: \mu_1 = \mu_2$ (claim) and $H_1: \mu_1 \neq \mu_2$; C.V. $= \pm 2.575$; $z = -0.857$; do not reject. There is not enough evidence to reject the claim that the average lengths of the rivers are the same.

7. $H_0: \mu_1 = \mu_2$ and $H_1: \mu_1 > \mu_2$ (claim); C.V. $= +1.645$; $z = 2.56$; reject. Yes; there is enough evidence to support the claim that pulse rates of smokers are higher than pulse rates of nonsmokers.

9. $H_0: \mu_1 = \mu_2$ and $H_1: \mu_1 > \mu_2$ (claim); C.V. $= +2.05$; $z = 1.12$; do not reject. There is not enough evidence to support the claim that the noise levels in the corridors are higher than the noise levels in the clinics.

11. $H_0: \mu_1 = \mu_2$ and $H_1: \mu_1 < \mu_2$ (claim); C.V. $= -1.645$; $z = -2.01$; reject. There is enough evidence to support the claim that the stayers had a higher grade point average.

13. $H_0: \mu_1 = \mu_2$ and $H_1: \mu_1 > \mu_2$ (claim); C.V. $= +2.33$; $z = +1.09$; do not reject. There is not enough evidence to support the claim that colleges spend more money on male sports than they spend on female sports.

15. $H_0: \mu_1 = \mu_2$ and $H_1: \mu_1 \neq \mu_2$ (claim); $z = 1.01$; P-value $= 0.3124$; do not reject. There is not enough evidence to support the claim that there is a difference in self-esteem scores.

17. $2.8 < \mu_1 - \mu_2 < 6.0$ **19.** $-7.3 < \mu_1 - \mu_2 < -1.3$

21. $H_0: \mu_1 - \mu_2 \leq 8$ (claim) and $H_1: \mu_1 - \mu_2 > 8$; C.V. $= +1.645$; $z = -0.73$; do not reject. There is not enough evidence to reject the claim that private school students have exam scores that are at most 8 points higher than those of students in public schools.

Exercises 9–3

1. The variance in the numerator should be the larger of the two variances.

3. One degree of freedom is used for the variance associated with the numerator, and one is used for the variance associated with the denominator.

5. *a.* d.f.N. = 15, d.f.D. = 22; C.V. = 3.36

   b. d.f.N. = 24, d.f.D. = 13; C.V. = 3.59

   c. d.f.N. = 45, d.f.D. = 29; C.V. = 2.03

   d. d.f.N. = 20, d.f.D. = 16; C.V. = 2.28

   e. d.f.N. = 10, d.f.D. = 10; C.V. = 2.98

6. Specific *P*-values are in parentheses.

   a. $0.025 < P\text{-value} < 0.05$ (0.033)

   b. $0.05 < P\text{-value} < 0.10$ (0.072)

   c. $P\text{-value} = 0.05$

   d. $0.005 < P\text{-value} < 0.01$ (0.006)

   e. $P\text{-value} = 0.05$

   f. $P\text{-value} > 0.10$ (0.112)

   g. $0.05 < P\text{-value} < 0.10$ (0.068)

   h. $0.01 < P\text{-value} < 0.02$ (0.015)

7. H_0: $\sigma_1^2 = \sigma_2^2$ and H_1: $\sigma_1^2 \neq \sigma_2^2$ (claim); C.V. = 2.53; d.f.N. = 14; d.f.D. = 14; F = 4.52; reject. There is enough evidence to support the claim that there is a difference in the variances.

9. H_0: $\sigma_1^2 = \sigma_2^2$ and H_1: $\sigma_1^2 \neq \sigma_2^2$ (claim); C.V. = 2.86; d.f.N. = 15; d.f.D. = 15; F = 7.85; reject. There is enough evidence to support the claim that the variances are different. Since both data sets vary greatly from normality, the results are suspect.

11. H_0: $\sigma_1^2 = \sigma_2^2$ and H_1: $\sigma_1^2 \neq \sigma_2^2$ (claim); C.V. = 4.99; d.f.N. = 7; d.f.D. = 7; F = 1; do not reject. There is not enough evidence to support the claim that there is a difference in the variances.

13. H_0: $\sigma_1 = \sigma_2$ and H_1: $\sigma_1 \neq \sigma_2$ (claim); C.V. = 2.27; F = 4.52; reject. There is enough evidence to support the claim that the standard deviations of the ages are different. One reason is that there are many more people who play the slot machines than people who play roulette. This could possibly account for the larger standard deviation in the ages of the players.

15. H_0: $\sigma_1^2 = \sigma_2^2$ and H_1: $\sigma_1^2 \neq \sigma_2^2$ (claim); C.V. = 4.03; d.f.N. = 9; d.f.D. = 9; F = 1.1026; do not reject. There is not enough evidence to support the claim that the variances are not equal.

17. H_0: $\sigma_1^2 = \sigma_2^2$ (claim) and H_1: $\sigma_1^2 \neq \sigma_2^2$; C.V. = 3.44; d.f.N. = 8; d.f.D. = 8; F = 0.251; do not reject. There is not enough evidence to reject the claim that the variance in Montreal and Calgary building heights are different.

19. H_0: $\sigma_1^2 = \sigma_2^2$ (claim) and H_1: $\sigma_1^2 \neq \sigma_2^2$; F = 5.319; d.f.N. = 14; d.f.D. = 14; $P\text{-value} < 0.005$ (0.004); reject. There is enough evidence to reject the claim that the variances in the shoe weights are equal.

Exercises 9–4

1. H_0: $\sigma_1^2 = \sigma_2^2$; C.V. = 4.03; F = 1.93; do not reject. H_0: $\mu_1 = \mu_2$ and H_1: $\mu_1 \neq \mu_2$ (claim); C.V. = ±2.101; d.f. = 18; t = −4.02; reject. There is enough evidence to support the claim that there is a significant difference in the values of the homes based on the appraisers' values. $-\$7762 < \mu_1 - \mu_2 < -\$2434$

3. H_0: $\sigma_1^2 = \sigma_2^2$; C.V. = 3.05; F = 1; do not reject. H_0: $\mu_1 = \mu_2$ (claim) and H_1: $\mu_1 \neq \mu_2$; C.V. = ±2.048; t = −1.61; do not reject. There is not enough evidence to reject the claim that the means are equal.

5. H_0: $\sigma_1^2 = \sigma_2^2$; C.V. = 14.94; F = 1.41; do not reject. H_0: $\mu_1 \leq \mu_2$ and H_1: $\mu_1 > \mu_2$ (claim); C.V. = 2.764; d.f. = 10; t = 1.45; do not reject. There is not enough evidence to support the claim that the average number of family daycare homes is greater than the average number of daycare centres.

7. H_0: $\sigma_1^2 = \sigma_2^2$; C.V. = 4.19; F = 1.70; do not reject. H_0: $\mu_1 = \mu_2$ and H_1: $\mu_1 \neq \mu_2$ (claim); C.V. = ±2.508; d.f. = 22; t = −2.97; reject. There is enough evidence to support the claim that there is a difference in the average times of the two groups. $-11.1 < \mu_1 - \mu_2 < -0.93$

9. H_0: $\sigma_1^2 = \sigma_2^2$; C.V. = 1.98; F = 1.55; do not reject. H_0: $\mu_1 \leq \mu_2$ and H_1: $\mu_1 > \mu_2$ (claim); C.V. = 1.282; d.f. = 48; t = 11.427; reject. There is enough evidence to support the claim that the average cost of a movie ticket in London is greater than the average cost of a movie ticket in New York City. One reason for the difference is the rate of exchange of the money.

11. H_0: $\sigma_1^2 = \sigma_2^2$; C.V. = 7.15; F = 1.23; do not reject. H_0: $\mu_1 = \mu_2$ and H_1: $\mu_1 \neq \mu_2$ (claim); C.V. = ±2.228; d.f. = 10; t = 0.119; do not reject. There is not enough evidence to support the claim that the colour of the mice made a difference. $-5.9 < \mu_1 - \mu_2 < 6.5$

13. $-\$12457.3 < \mu_1 - \mu_2 < -\$3622.4$

Exercises 9–5

1. *a.* Dependent   *d.* Dependent

   b. Dependent   *e.* Independent

   c. Independent

3. H_0: $\mu_D = 0$ and H_1: $\mu_D < 0$ (claim); C.V. = −1.397; d.f. = 8; t = −2.8; reject. There is enough evidence to support the claim that the seminar increased the number of hours students studied.

5. H_0: $\mu_D = 0$ and H_1: $\mu_D \neq 0$ (claim); C.V. = 2.365; d.f. = 7; t = 1.6583; do not reject. There is not enough evidence to support the claim that the means are different.

7. $H_0: \mu_D = 0$ and $H_1: \mu_D > 0$ (claim); C.V. $= 2.571$; d.f. $= 5$; $t = 2.24$; do not reject. There is not enough evidence to support the claim that the errors have been reduced.

9. $H_0: \mu_D = 0$ and $H_1: \mu_D \neq 0$ (claim); d.f. $= 7$; $t = 0.978$; $0.20 < P\text{-value} < 0.50$ (0.361). Do not reject since $P\text{-value} > 0.01$. There is not enough evidence to support the claim that there is a difference in the pulse rates. $-3.23 < \mu_D < 5.73$

11. Using the previous problem $\overline{D} = -1.5625$, whereas the mean of the before values is 95.375 and the mean of the after values is 96.9375; hence, $\overline{D} = 95.375 - 96.9375 = -1.5625$.

Exercises 9–6

1a. *a.* $\hat{p} = \frac{34}{48}, \hat{q} = \frac{14}{48}$ *d.* $\hat{p} = \frac{6}{24}, \hat{q} = \frac{18}{24}$

    b. $\hat{p} = \frac{28}{75}, \hat{q} = \frac{47}{75}$ *e.* $\hat{p} = \frac{12}{144}, \hat{q} = \frac{132}{144}$

    c. $\hat{p} = \frac{50}{100}, \hat{q} = \frac{50}{100}$

1b. *a.* 16   *c.* 48   *e.* 30

    b. 4   *d.* 104

3. $\hat{p}_1 = 0.533$; $\hat{p}_2 = 0.3$; $\overline{p} = 0.44$; $\overline{q} = 0.56$; $H_0: p_1 = p_2$ and $H_1: p_1 \neq p_2$ (claim); C.V. $= \pm 1.96$; $z = 3.64$; reject. There is enough evidence to support the claim that there is a significant difference in the proportions.

5. $\hat{p}_1 = 0.747$; $\hat{p}_2 = 0.75$; $\overline{p} = 0.749$; $\overline{q} = 0.251$; $H_0: p_1 = p_2$ and $H_1: p_1 \neq p_2$ (claim); C.V. $= \pm 1.96$; $z = -0.07$; do not reject. There is not enough evidence to support the claim that the proportions are not equal.

7. $\hat{p}_1 = 0.83$; $\hat{p}_2 = 0.75$; $\overline{p} = 0.79$; $\overline{q} = 0.21$; $H_0: p_1 = p_2$ (claim) and $H_1: p_1 \neq p_2$; C.V. $= \pm 1.96$; $z = 1.39$; do not reject. There is not enough evidence to reject the claim that the proportions are equal. $-0.032 < p_1 - p_2 < 0.192$

9. $\hat{p}_1 = 0.55$; $\hat{p}_2 = 0.45$; $\overline{p} = 0.497$; $\overline{q} = 0.503$; $H_0: p_1 = p_2$ and $H_1: p_1 \neq p_2$ (claim); C.V. $= \pm 2.575$; $z = 1.302$; do not reject. There is not enough evidence to support the claim that the proportions are different. $-0.097 < p_1 - p_2 < 0.297$

11. $\hat{p}_1 = 0.347$; $\hat{p}_2 = 0.433$; $\overline{p} = 0.385$; $\overline{q} = 0.615$; $H_0: p_1 = p_2$ and $H_1: p_1 \neq p_2$ (claim); C.V. $= \pm 1.96$; $z = -1.03$; do not reject. There is not enough evidence to say that the proportion of dog owners has changed $(-0.252 < p_1 - p_2 < 0.079)$. Yes, the confidence interval contains 0. This is another way to conclude that there is no difference in the proportions.

13. $\hat{p}_1 = 0.25$; $\hat{p}_2 = 0.31$; $\overline{p} = 0.286$; $\overline{q} = 0.714$; $H_0: p_1 = p_2$ and $H_1: p_1 \neq p_2$ (claim); C.V. $= \pm 2.575$; $z = -1.45$; do not reject. There is not enough evidence to support the claim that the proportions are different. $-0.165 < p_1 - p_2 < 0.045$

15. $-0.29 < p_1 - p_2 < 0.01$

17. $\hat{p}_1 = 0.43$; $\hat{p}_2 = 0.58$; $\overline{p} = 0.505$; $\overline{q} = 0.495$; $H_0: p_1 = p_2$ and $H_1: p_1 \neq p_2$ (claim); C.V. $= \pm 1.96$;

$z = -2.12$; reject; there is enough evidence to support the claim that the proportions are different.

19. $-0.0631 < p_1 - p_2 < 0.0667$. It does agree with the *Almanac* statistics stating a difference of -0.042 since -0.042 is contained in the interval.

Review Exercises

1. $H_0: \mu_1 = \mu_2$ and $H_1: \mu_1 > \mu_2$ (claim); C.V. $= 2.33$; $z = 0.586$; do not reject. There is not enough evidence to support the claim that single people do more pleasure driving than married people.

3. $H_0: \sigma_1 = \sigma_2$ and $H_1: \sigma_1 \neq \sigma_2$ (claim); C.V. $= 2.77$; $\alpha = 0.10$; d.f.N. $= 23$; d.f.D. $= 10$; $F = 10.365$; reject. There is enough evidence to support the claim that there is a difference in the standard deviations.

5. $H_0: \sigma_1^2 \leq \sigma_2^2$ and $H_1: \sigma_1^2 > \sigma_2^2$ (claim); $\alpha = 0.05$; d.f.N. $= 9$; d.f.D. $= 9$; $F = 5.06$. The P-value for the F test is $0.01 < P\text{-value} < 0.025$ (0.012); reject since $P\text{-value} < 0.05$. There is enough evidence to support the claim that the variance of the number of speeding tickets issued on Route 19 is greater than the variance of the number of speeding tickets issued on Route 22.

7. $H_0: \sigma_1^2 \leq \sigma_2^2$ and $H_1: \sigma_1^2 > \sigma_2^2$ (claim); C.V. $= 1.47$; $\alpha = 0.10$; d.f.N. $= 64$; d.f.D. $= 41$; $F = 2.32$, reject. There is enough evidence to support the claim that the variation in the number of days factory workers miss per year due to illness is greater than the variation in the number of days hospital workers miss per year.

9. $H_0: \sigma_1^2 = \sigma_2^2$; C.V. $= 1.98$; $F = 1.72$; do not reject. $H_0: \mu_1 = \mu_2$ and $H_1: \mu_1 > \mu_2$ (claim); C.V. $= 1.282$. $t = 0.38$.; do not reject. There is not enough evidence to support the claim that it is warmer in Victoria.

11. $H_0: \sigma_1^2 = \sigma_2^2$; $F = 1.12$; do not reject since $p > 0.10$; $H_0: \mu_1 = \mu_2$ and $H_1: \mu_1 \neq \mu_2$ (claim); d.f. $= 7$; $t = -0.828$; do not reject. Since $p > 0.10$, there is not enough evidence to support the claim that the means are different. A cafeteria manager would want to know the results to make a decision on which beverage to serve.

13. $H_0: \mu_D \geq 0$ and $H_1: \mu_D < 0$ (claim); C.V. $= -1.895$; d.f. $= 7$; $t = -2.73$; reject. There is enough evidence to support the claim that the music has increased production.

15. $\hat{p}_1 = 0.15$; $\hat{p}_2 = 0.05$; $\overline{p} = 0.104$; $\overline{q} = 0.896$; $H_0: p_1 = p_2$ and $H_1: p_1 \neq p_2$ (claim); C.V. $= \pm 1.96$; $z = 2.41$; reject. There is enough evidence to support the claim that the proportion has changed. $0.023 < p_1 - p_2 < 0.177$. The confidence level does not contain 0; hence, the null hypothesis is rejected.

Chapter Quiz

1. False   **2.** False

3. True   **4.** False

5. *d*

6. *a*

7. *c*

8. *b*

9. $\mu_1 = \mu_2$

10. Pooled

11. Normal

12. Negative

13. $\dfrac{s_1^2}{s_2^2}$

14. H_0: $\mu_1 = \mu_2$ and H_1: $\mu \neq \mu_2$ (claim); $z = -3.69$; C.V. $= \pm 2.575$; reject. There is enough evidence to support the claim that there is a difference in the cholesterol levels of the two groups. $-10.2 < \mu_1 - \mu_2 < -1.8$

15. H_0: $\mu_1 \leq \mu_2$ and H_1: $\mu > \mu_2$ (claim); C.V. $= 1.28$; $z = 1.60$; reject. There is enough evidence to support the claim that the average rental fees for the apartments in the East are greater than the average rental fees for the apartments in the West.

16. H_0: $\sigma_1^2 = \sigma_2^2$ and H_1: $\sigma_1^2 \neq \sigma_2^2$ (claim); $F = 1.637$; d.f.N. $= 17$; d.f.D. $= 14$; P-value > 0.20 (0.357). Do not reject since P-value > 0.05. There is not enough evidence to support the claim that the variances are different.

17. H_0: $\sigma_1^2 = \sigma_2^2$ and H_1: $\sigma_1^2 \neq \sigma_2^2$ (claim); $F = 1.30$; C.V. $= 1.90$; do not reject. There is not enough evidence to support the claim that the variances in the heights are different.

18. H_0: $\sigma_1 = \sigma_2$ (claim) and H_1: $\sigma_1 \neq \sigma_2$; d.f.N. $= 11$; d.f.D. $= 11$; C.V. $= 3.53$; $F = 1.13$; do not reject. There is not enough evidence to reject the claim that the standard deviations of the number of hours of television viewing are the same.

19. H_0: $\sigma_1^2 = \sigma_2^2$ and H_1: $\sigma_1^2 \neq \sigma_2^2$ (claim); $F = 1.94$; C.V. $= 3.01$; do not reject. There is not enough evidence to support the claim that the variances are not equal.

20. H_0: $\sigma_1^2 = \sigma_2^2$ and H_1: $\sigma_1^2 > \sigma_2^2$ (claim); $F = 1.08$; C.V. $= 5.05$; do not reject. There is not enough evidence to support the claim that the variance of the number of murders committed on the East Coast is greater than the variance of the number of murders committed on the West Coast. One factor that could influence the results is the populations of the cities that were selected.

21. H_0: $\sigma_1 = \sigma_2$ and H_1: $\sigma_1 \neq \sigma_2$ (claim); $F = 1.645$; C.V. $= 2.46$; do not reject. There is not enough evidence to support the claim that the standard deviations are different.

22. H_0: $\sigma_1^2 = \sigma_2^2$; C.V. $= 5.05$; $F = 1.23$; do not reject. H_0: $\mu_1 = \mu_2$ and H_1: $\mu_1 \neq \mu_2$ (claim); $t = 10.922$; C.V. $= \pm 2.779$; reject. There is enough evidence to support the claim that the average prices are different. $0.298 < \mu_1 - \mu_2 < 0.502$

23. H_0: $\sigma_1^2 = \sigma_2^2$; C.V. $= 9.60$; $F = 5.71$; do not reject. H_0: $\mu_1 \geq \mu_2$ and H_1: $\mu_1 < \mu_2$ (claim); C.V. $= -1.860$; d.f. $= 8$; $t = -4.05$; reject. There is enough evidence to support the claim that accidents have increased.

24. H_0: $\sigma_1^2 = \sigma_2^2$; C.V. $= 4.02$; $F = 6.155$; reject. H_0: $\mu_1 = \mu_2$ and H_1: $\mu_1 \neq \mu_2$ (claim); $t = 9.807$; C.V. $= \pm 2.718$; reject. There is enough evidence to support the claim that there is a difference in salaries. $\$6653 < \mu_1 - \mu_2 < -\$11756$

25. H_0: $\sigma_1^2 = \sigma_2^2$; $F = 23.08$; reject since P-value < 0.05. H_0: $\mu_1 \leq \mu_2$ and H_1: $\mu_1 > \mu_2$ (claim); d.f. $= 10$; $t = 0.874$; $0.10 < P$-value < 0.25 (0.198); do not reject since P-value > 0.05. There is not enough evidence to support the claim that the incomes of city residents are greater than the incomes of rural residents.

26. H_0: $\mu_1 \geq \mu_2$ and H_1: $\mu_1 < \mu_2$ (claim); $t = -4.172$; C.V. $= -2.821$; reject. There is enough evidence to support the claim that the sessions improved math skills.

27. H_0: $\mu_1 \geq \mu_2$ and H_1: $\mu_1 < \mu_2$ (claim); $t = -1.714$; C.V. $= -1.833$; do not reject. There is not enough evidence to support the claim that egg production was increased.

28. H_0: $p_1 = p_2$ and H_1: $p_1 \neq p_2$ (claim); $z = -0.69$; C.V. $= \pm 1.645$; do not reject. There is not enough evidence to support the claim that the proportions are different. $-0.105 < p_1 - p_2 < 0.045$

29. H_0: $p_1 = p_2$ and H_1: $p_1 \neq p_2$ (claim); C.V. $= \pm 1.96$; $z = 0.544$; do not reject. There is not enough evidence to support the claim that the proportions have changed. $-0.026 < p_1 - p_2 < 0.0460$. Yes, the confidence interval contains 0; hence, the null hypothesis is not rejected.

Chapter 10

Exercises 10–3

1. Two variables are related when a discernible pattern exists between them.

3. r, ρ (rho)

5. A positive relationship means that as x increases, y increases. A negative relationship means that as x increases, y decreases.

7. Answers will vary.

9. Pearson product moment correlation coefficient.

11. There are many other possibilities, such as chance, or relationship to a third variable.

13. H_0: $\rho = 0$ and H_1: $\rho \neq 0$; $r = -0.832$; C.V. $= \pm 0.811$; reject. There is a significant

relationship between a person's age and the number of hours he or she exercises.

Age vs. Exercise

15. H_0: $\rho = 0$ and H_1: $\rho \neq 0$; $r = -0.883$; C.V. $= \pm 0.811$; reject. There is a significant relationship between the number of years a person has been out of school and his or her contribution.

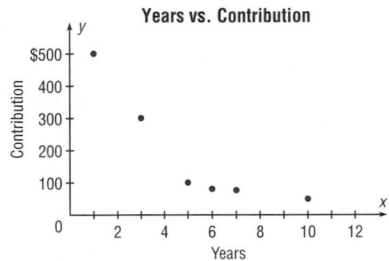

Years vs. Contribution

17. H_0: $\rho = 0$ and H_1: $\rho \neq 0$; $r = 0.893$; C.V. $= \pm 0.754$; reject. There is a significant linear correlation between the robbery and homicide crime rates.

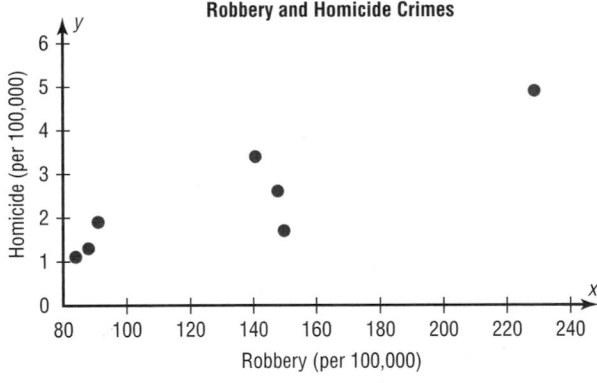

Robbery and Homicide Crimes

19. H_0: $\rho = 0$ and H_1: $\rho \neq 0$; $r = 0.580$; C.V. $= \pm 0.632$; do not reject. There is no significant linear relationship between the number of tornadoes per year and the number of deaths per year from these tornadoes.

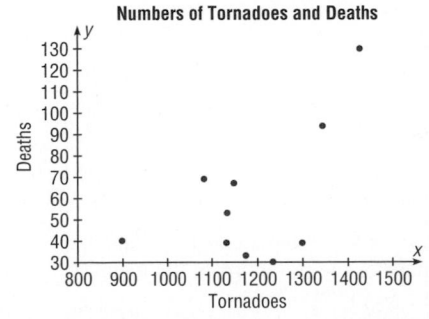

Numbers of Tornadoes and Deaths

21. H_0: $\rho = 0$ and H_1: $\rho \neq 0$; $r = 0.963$; C.V. $= \pm 0.878$; reject. There is a significant linear correlation between the Black and Asian visible minorities.

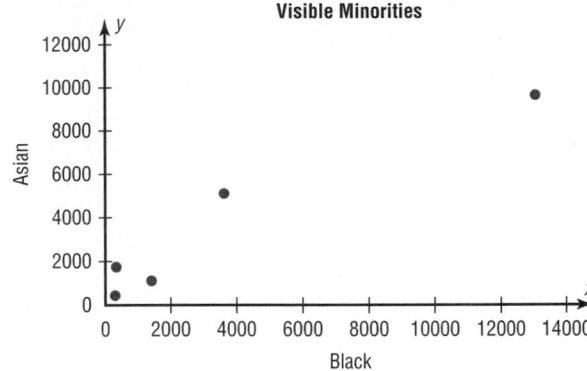

Visible Minorities

23. H_0: $\rho = 0$ and H_1: $\rho \neq 0$; $r = 0.560$; C.V. $= \pm 0.754$; do not reject. There is no significant linear correlation between Canadian city temperatures and average monthly precipitation.

Temperature and Precipitation

25. H_0: $\rho = 0$ and H_1: $\rho \neq 0$; $r = 0.725$; C.V. $= \pm 0.754$; do not reject. There is no significant linear relationship between the number of calories and the cholesterol content of fast-food chicken sandwiches.

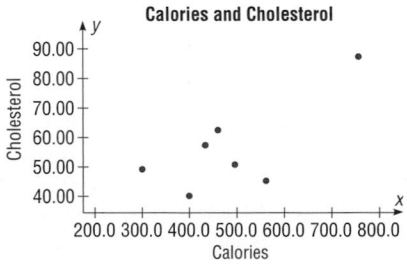

Calories and Cholesterol

27. H_0: $\rho = 0$ and H_1: $\rho \neq 0$; $r = 0.831$; C.V. $= \pm 0.754$; reject. There is a significant linear relationship between the number of licensed beds in a hospital and the number of staffed beds.

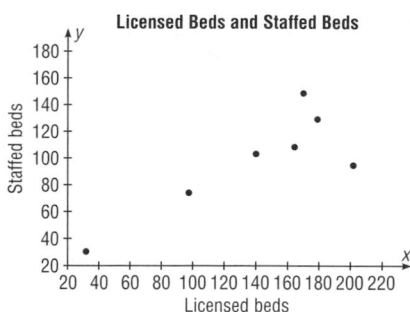

Licensed Beds and Staffed Beds

29. $r = 1.00$: All values fall in a straight line. $r = 1.00$: The value of r between x and y is the same when x and y are interchanged.

Exercises 10-4

1. A scatter plot should be drawn, and the value of the correlation coefficient should be tested to see whether it is significant.

3. $y' = a + bx$

5. It is the line that is drawn through the points on the scatter plot such that the sum of the squares of the vertical distances from each point to the line is a minimum.

7. When r is positive, b will be positive. When r is negative, b will be negative.

9. The closer r is to $+1$ or -1, the more accurate the predicted value will be.

11. When r is not significant, the mean of the y values should be used to predict y.

13. $y' = 10.499 - 0.18x$; 4.2

15. $y' = 453.176 - 50.439x$; 251.42

17. $y' = -0.69 + 0.02x$; 1.64

19. Since r is not significant, no regression should be done.

21. $y' = 1015.2 + 0.7x$; 2730.2

23. Since r is not significant, no regression should be done.

25. Since r is not significant, no regression should be done.

27. $y' = 22.659 + 0.582x$; 48.267

29. $H_0: \rho = 0$ and $H_1: \rho \neq 0$; $r = +0.956$; C.V. $= \pm 0.754$; reject; d.f. $= 5$; $y' = -10.944 + 1.969x$; when $x = 30$, $y' = 48.126$. There is a significant relationship between the amount of lung damage and the number of years a person has been smoking.

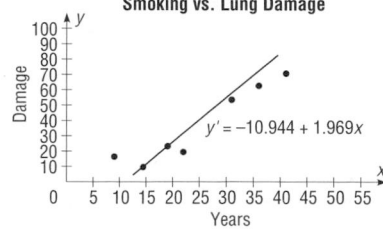

Smoking vs. Lung Damage

$y' = -10.944 + 1.969x$

31. $H_0: \rho = 0$ and $H_1: \rho \neq 0$; $r = 0.987$; C.V. $= \pm 0.754$; reject. $y' = -2.7 + 1.0x$; when $x = 200$, $y' = 205.8$. There is a significant linear correlation between the number of business head offices in 1999 and 2005.

Head Offices (by year)

33. $H_0: \rho = 0$ and $H_1: \rho \neq 0$; $r = -0.981$; C.V. $= \pm 0.811$; reject. There is a significant relationship between the number of absences and the final grade; $y' = 96.784 - 2.668x$.

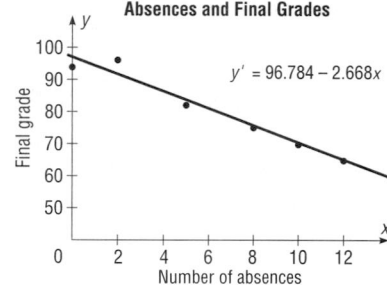

Absences and Final Grades

$y' = 96.784 - 2.668x$

35. $H_0: \rho = 0$ and $H_1: \rho \neq 0$; $r = -0.265$; P-value > 0.05 (0.459); do not reject. There is no significant linear relationship between the ages of billionaires and their net worth. No regression should be done.

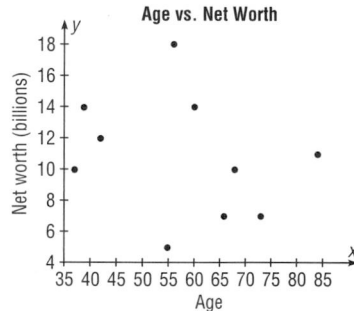

Age vs. Net Worth

37. 453.173; 21.1

Exercises 10-5

1. Explained variation is the variation due to the relationship. It is computed by $\Sigma(y' - \bar{y})^2$.

3. Total variation is the sum of the squares of the vertical distances of the points from the mean. It is computed by $\Sigma(y - \bar{y})^2$.

5. The coefficient of determination is found by squaring the value of the correlation coefficient.

7. The coefficient of nondetermination is found by subtracting r^2 from 1.

9. $r^2 = 0.49$; 49% of the variation of y is due to the variation of x; 51% of the variation of y is due to chance.

11. $r^2 = 0.1369$; 13.69% of the variation of y is due to the variation of x; 86.31% of the variation of y is due to chance.

13. $r^2 = 0.0025$; 0.25% of the variation of y is due to the variation of x; 99.75% of the variation of y is due to chance.

15. 2.092*   **17.** 94.22*

19. $1.59 < y < 12.21$*   **21.** $30.46 < y < 472.38$*

*Answers may vary due to rounding.

Exercises 10–6

1. Simple regression has one dependent variable and one independent variable. Multiple regression has one dependent variable and two or more independent variables.

3. The relationship would include all variables in one equation.

5. They will all be smaller.

7. 3.48 or 3   **9.** $39,390

11. R is the strength of the relationship between the dependent variable and all the independent variables.

13. R^2 is the coefficient of multiple determination. R^2_{adj} is adjusted for sample size and number of predictors.

15. The F test.

Review Exercises

1. H_0: $\rho = 0$ and H_1: $\rho \neq 0$; $r = 0.682$; C.V. $= \pm 0.641$; reject. There is a significant linear relationship between the number of hits and the number of strikeouts. $y' = 7.22 + 0.388x$; 18.9.

Hits vs. Strikeouts

3. H_0: $\rho = 0$ and H_1: $\rho \neq 0$; $r = 0.873$; C.V. $= \pm 0.834$; d.f. $= 6$; reject. There is a significant relationship

between the mother's age and the number of children she has; $y' = -2.457 + 0.187x$; $y' = 3.9$.

Mother's Age and No. of Children

5. H_0: $\rho = 0$ and H_1: $\rho \neq 0$; $r = -0.974$; C.V. $= \pm 0.708$; d.f. $= 10$; reject. There is a significant relationship between speed and time; $y' = 14.086 - 0.137x$; $y' = 4.222$.

Typing Speeds vs. Learning Times

7. H_0: $\rho = 0$ and H_1: $\rho \neq 0$; $r = 0.889$; C.V. $= \pm 0.798$; reject. There is a significant relationship between vehicle's age and repair costs. $y' = 297.6 + 84.6x$; $y' = 890.

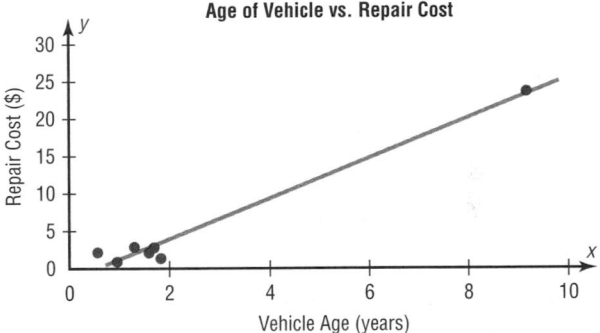

Age of Vehicle vs. Repair Cost

9. 0.468* (TI value 0.513)

11. $3.34 < y < 5.10$*

13. 22.01*

15. $R^2_{adj} = 0.643$*

*Answers may vary due to rounding.

Chapter Quiz

1. False   **2.** True

3. True   **4.** False

5. False   **6.** False

7. *a*   **8.** *a*

9. *d*   **10.** *c*

11. *b*   **12.** Scatter plot

13. Independent

14. $-1, +1$

15. b

16. Line of best fit

17. $+1, -1$

18. H_0: $\rho = 0$ and H_1: $\rho \neq 0$; $r = 0.988$; C.V. $= \pm 0.707$; reject. There is a significant linear relationship between Canada and US drug prices; $y' = -1.44 + 2.70x$; if Canadian drug price is $3.75, US drug price is $8.68.

Canada vs. US Drug Prices

19. H_0: $\rho = 0$ and H_1: $\rho \neq 0$; $r = -0.078$; C.V. $= \pm 0.754$; do not reject. No regression should be done.

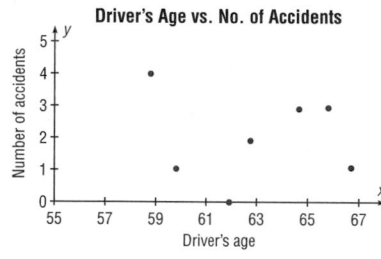

Driver's Age vs. No. of Accidents

20. H_0: $\rho = 0$ and H_1: $\rho \neq 0$; $r = 0.842$; C.V. $= \pm 0.811$; reject. $y' = -1.918 + 0.551x$; 4.14 or 4.

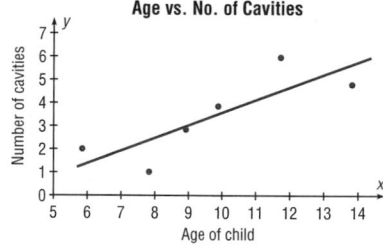

Age vs. No. of Cavities

21. H_0: $\rho = 0$ and H_1: $\rho \neq 0$; $r = 0.602$; C.V. $= \pm 0.707$; do not reject. No regression should be done.

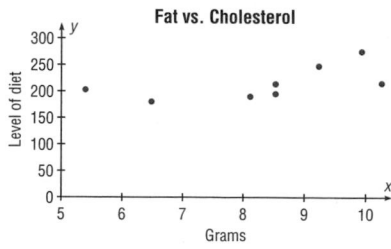

Fat vs. Cholesterol

22. 1.129*

23. 29.5* For calculation purposes only. No regression should be done.

24. $0 < y < 5$*

25. 217.5 (average of y' values is used since there is no significant relationship)

26. 119.9*

27. $R = 0.729$*

28. $R^2_{adj} = 0.439$*

*These answers may vary due to the method of calculation or rounding.

Chapter 11

Exercises 11–2

1. The variance test compares a sample variance with a hypothesized population variance; the goodness-of-fit test compares a distribution obtained from a sample with a hypothesized distribution.

3. The expected values are computed on the basis of what the null hypothesis states about the distribution.

5. H_0: The ages of automobiles are equally distributed over the three categories (claim). H_1: The ages of automobiles are not equally distributed over the three categories. C.V. $= 5.991$; d.f. $= 2$; $\chi^2 = 0.8$; do not reject. There is not enough evidence to reject the claim that the average age of automobiles is equally distributed over the three categories. Tire manufacturers need to make enough tires to fit automobiles of all ages.

7. H_0: New vehicle market share in Canada is General Motors, 29.0%; DaimlerChrysler, 14.3%; Ford, 14.1%; Toyota, 10.2%; Other Manufacturers, 32.4%. H_1: The distribution is different then stated in the null hypothesis (claim). C.V. $= 9.488$; d.f. $= 4$; $\chi^2 = 1.3423$; do not reject. There is not enough evidence to support the claim that the distribution is not the same.

9. H_0: 35% feel that genetically modified food is safe to eat, 52% feel that genetically modified food is not safe to eat, and 13% have no opinion. H_1: The distribution is not the same as stated in the null hypothesis (claim). C.V. $= 9.210$; d.f. $= 2$; $\chi^2 = 1.4286$; do not reject. There is not enough evidence to support the claim that the proportions are different from those reported in the survey.

11. H_0: The types of loans are distributed as follows: 21% for home mortgages, 39% for automobile purchases, 20% for credit card, 12% for real estate, and 8% for miscellaneous (claim). H_1: The distribution is different from that stated in the null hypothesis. C.V. $= 9.488$; d.f. $= 4$; $\chi^2 = 4.786$; do not reject. There is not enough evidence to reject the claim that the distribution is the same as reported in the newspaper.

13. H_0: Cigarette market share in Canada is Rothman's brands with 22%; Imperial Tobacco brands with 59.8%; MacDonald brands with 12.4%; and other brands have 5.8% (claim). H_1: The distribution is different then stated in the null hypothesis. C.V. $= 11.345$; d.f. $= 3$; $\chi^2 = 27.2466$; reject. There is not enough evidence to support the claim that the proportions are the same as stated in the null hypothesis.

15. H_0: Canada's provincial prison population is distributed as crimes of violence, 15.5%; property crimes, 24.1%; impaired driving, 5.5%; drug offences, 4.7%, other criminal code offences, 29.8%; and other statutes, 20.4% (claim). H_1: The distribution is different then stated in the null hypothesis. C.V. $= 11.071$; d.f. $= 5$; $\chi^2 = 5.7804$; do not reject. There is enough evidence to support the claim that the proportions are the same as stated in the null hypothesis.

17. H_0: Distribution of Canadian retail medical prescription payments is 24% out-of-pocket, 34.6% private insurers, and 41.4% public insurance (claim). H_1: The distribution is not the same as stated in the null hypothesis. The d.f. $= 2$; $\chi^2 = 0.4366$; do not reject at $\alpha = 0.05$ since $0.90 < P$-value < 0.10 (0.8039). There is enough evidence to support the claim that the proportions are the same as stated in the null hypothesis.

19. Answers will vary.

Exercises 11–3

1. The independence test and the goodness-of-fit test both use the same formula for computing the test value. However, the independence test uses a contingency table, whereas the goodness-of-fit test does not.

3. H_0: The variables are independent (or not related). H_1: The variables are dependent (or related).

5. The expected values are computed as (row total $\times$ column total) $\div$ grand total.

7. H_0: $p_1 = p_2 = p_3 = p_4 = \cdots = p_n$. H_1: At least one proportion is different from the others.

9. H_0: The type of pet owned is independent of the income of the owners. H_1: The type of pet is dependent upon the income of the owners (claim). C.V. $= 21.026$; d.f. $= 12$; $\chi^2 = 35.1774$; reject. There is enough evidence to support the claim that the type of pet is dependent upon the income of the owner.

11. H_0: The composition of the House of Commons is independent of the province of the Member of Parliament. H_1: The composition of the House of Commons is dependent of the province of the Member of Parliament (claim). C.V. $= 12.592$; d.f. $= 6$; $\chi^2 = 14.675$; reject. There is significant evidence to support the claim that the composition of the House of Commons is dependent of the province of the Member of Parliament.

13. H_0: The number of ads people think that they've seen or heard in the media is independent of the gender of the individual. H_1: The number of ads people think that they've seen or heard in the media is dependent on the gender of the individual (claim). C.V. $= 13.277$; d.f. $= 4$; $\chi^2 = 9.562$; do not reject. There is not enough evidence to support the claim that the number of ads people think they've seen or heard is related to the gender of the individual.

15. H_0: The type of practice of an attorney is independent of the gender of the attorney (claim). H_1: The type of practice of an attorney is dependent upon the gender of the attorney. C.V. $= 5.991$; d.f. $= 2$; $\chi^2 = 7.963$; reject. There is enough evidence to reject the claim that the type of practice is independent of the gender of the attorney.

17. H_0: The type of video rented is independent of the person's age. H_1: The type of video rented is dependent on the person's age (claim). C.V. $= 13.362$; d.f. $= 8$; $\chi^2 = 46.733$; reject. Yes, there is enough evidence to support the claim that the type of movie selected is related to the age of the customer.

19. H_0: The type of snack purchased is independent of the gender of the consumer (claim). H_1: The type of snack purchased is dependent upon the gender of the consumer. C.V. $= 4.605$; d.f. $= 2$; $\chi^2 = 6.342$; reject. There is enough evidence to reject the claim that the type of snack is independent of the gender of the consumer.

21. H_0: The type of book purchased by an individual is independent of the gender of the individual (claim). H_1: The type of book purchased by an individual is dependent on the gender of the individual. The d.f. $= 2$; $\alpha = 0.05$; $\chi^2 = 19.43$; P-value < 0.005; reject since P-value < 0.05. There is enough evidence to reject the claim that the type of book purchased by an individual is independent of the gender of the individual.

23. H_0: $p_1 = p_2 = p_3 = p_4$ (claim). H_1: At least one proportion is different from the others. C.V. $= 11.345$; d.f. $= 3$; $\chi^2 = 1.852$; do not reject. There is not enough evidence to reject the null hypothesis that the proportions of proportions that are obese in each district are equal.

25. H_0: $p_1 = p_2 = p_3 = p_4$ (claim). H_1: At least one proportion is different from the others. C.V. $= 7.815$; d.f. $= 3$; $\chi^2 = 0.017$; There is not enough evidence to reject the null hypothesis that the proportions are the same as they were 20 years ago.

27. H_0: $p_1 = p_2 = p_3 = p_4$ (claim). H_1: At least one proportion is different. C.V. $= 6.251$; d.f. $= 3$; $\chi^2 = 12.755$; reject. There is enough evidence to reject the claim that the proportions are equal.

29. H_0: $p_1 = p_2 = p_3 = p_4$ (claim). H_1: At least one proportion is different. d.f. $= 3$; $\chi^2 = 1.768$; $\alpha = 0.05$; $0.90 < P$-value < 0.10 (0.622); do not reject. There is not sufficient evidence to reject the claim that the proportions are the same.

31. H_0: $p_1 = p_2 = p_3$ (claim). H_1: At least one proportion is different. C.V. $= 4.605$; d.f. $= 2$; $\chi^2 = 2.401$; do not

reject. There is not enough evidence to reject the claim that the proportions are equal.

33. $\chi^2 = 1.075$

Review Exercises

1. H_0: People show no preference for the day of the week that they do their shopping (claim). H_1: People show a preference for the day of the week that they do their shopping. C.V. = 12.592; d.f. = 6; $\chi^2 = 237.15$; reject. There is enough evidence to reject the claim that shoppers have no preference for the day of the week that they do their shopping. Retail merchants should probably plan for more shoppers on Fridays and Saturdays than they will have on the other days of the week.

3. H_0: Opinion is independent of gender. H_1: Opinion is dependent on gender (claim). C.V. = 4.605; d.f. = 2; $\chi^2 = 6.163$; reject. There is enough evidence to support the claim that opinion is dependent on gender.

5. H_0: The type of investment is independent of the age of the investor. H_1: The type of investment is dependent on the age of the investor (claim). C.V. = 9.488; d.f. = 4; $\chi^2 = 28.0$; reject. There is enough evidence to support the claim that the type of investment is dependent on the age of the investor.

7. H_0: $p_1 = p_2 = p_3$ (claim). H_1: At least one proportion is different. $\chi^2 = 4.912$; d.f. = 2; $\alpha = 0.01$; $0.05 < P\text{-value} < 0.10$ (0.086); do not reject since P-value > 0.01. There is not enough evidence to reject the claim that the proportions are equal.

9. H_0: $p_1 = p_2 = p_3 = p_4$ (claim). H_1: At least one proportion is different. C.V. = 6.251; d.f. = 3; $\chi^2 = 6.70$; reject. There is enough evidence to reject the claim that the proportions are equal.

Chapter Quiz

1. False
2. True
3. False
4. *c*
5. *b*
6. *d*
7. 6
8. Independent
9. Right
10. At least five

11. H_0: The reasons why people lost their jobs are equally distributed (claim). H_1: The reasons why people lost their jobs are not equally distributed. C.V. = 5.991; d.f. = $\chi^2 = 2.334$; do not reject. There is not enough evidence to reject the claim that the reasons why people lost their jobs are equally distributed. The results could have been different 10 years ago since different factors of the economy existed then.

12. H_0: Takeout food is consumed according to the following distribution: 53% at home, 19% in the car, 14% at work, and 14% at other places (claim). H_1: The distribution is different from that stated in the null hypothesis. C.V. = 11.345; d.f. = 3; $\chi^2 = 5.271$; do not reject. There is not enough evidence to reject the claim that the distribution is as stated. Fast-food restaurants may want to make their advertisements appeal to those who like to take their food home to eat.

13. H_0: College students show the same preference for shopping channels as those surveyed. H_1: College students show a different preference for shopping channels (claim). C.V. = 7.815; d.f. = 3; $\alpha = 0.05$; $\chi^2 = 21.789$; reject. There is enough evidence to support the claim that college students show a different preference for shopping channels.

14. H_0: The number of commuters is distributed as follows: 75.7%, alone; 12.2%, carpooling; 4.7%, public transportation; 2.9%, walking; 1.2%, other; and 3.3%, working at home. H_1: The proportion of workers using each type of transportation differs from the stated proportions. C.V. = 11.071; d.f. = 5; $\chi^2 = 41.269$; reject. There is enough evidence to support the claim that the distribution is different from the one stated in the null hypothesis.

15. H_0: Ice cream flavour is independent of the gender of the purchaser (claim). H_1: Ice cream flavour is dependent upon the gender of the purchaser. C.V. = 7.815; d.f. = 3; $\chi^2 = 7.198$; do not reject. There is not enough evidence to reject the claim that ice cream flavour is independent of the gender of the purchaser.

16. H_0: The type of pizza ordered is independent of the age of the individual who purchases it. H_1: The type of pizza ordered is dependent on the age of the individual who purchases it (claim). $\chi^2 = 107.3$; d.f. = 9; $\alpha = 0.10$; P-value < 0.005; reject since P-value < 0.10. There is enough evidence to support the claim that the pizza purchased is related to the age of the purchaser.

17. H_0: The colour of the pennant purchased is independent of the gender of the purchaser (claim). H_1: The colour of the pennant purchased is dependent on the gender of the purchaser. $\chi^2 = 5.632$; C.V. = 4.605; reject. There is enough evidence to reject the claim that the colour of the pennant purchased is independent of the gender of the purchaser.

18. H_0: The opinion of the children on the use of the tax credit is independent of the gender of the children. H_1: The opinion of the children on the use of the tax credit is dependent upon the gender of the children (claim). C.V. = 4.605; d.f. = 2; $\chi^2 = 1.534$; do not reject. There is not enough evidence to support the claim that the opinion of the children on the use of the tax is dependent on their gender.

19. H_0: $p_1 = p_2 = p_3$ (claim). H_1: At least one proportion is different from the others. C.V. = 4.605; d.f. = 2; $\chi^2 = 6.711$; reject. There is enough evidence to reject the claim that the proportions are equal. It seems that more women are undecided about their jobs. Perhaps they want better income or greater chances of advancement.

Chapter 12

Exercises 12-3

1. The analysis of variance using the F test can be employed to compare three or more means.

3. The populations from which the samples were obtained must be normally distributed. The samples must be independent of each other. The variances of the populations must be equal.

5. $F = \dfrac{S_B^2}{S_W^2}$

7. The Scheffé test and the Tukey test.

9. H_0: $\mu_1 = \mu_2 = \mu_3$. H_1: At least one mean is different from the others (claim). C.V. = 3.47; $\alpha = 0.05$; d.f.N. = 2; d.f.D. = 21; $F = 1.9912$; do not reject. There is not enough evidence to support the claim that at least one mean is different from the others.

11. H_0: $\mu_1 = \mu_2 = \mu_3$. H_1: At least one mean is different from the others (claim). C.V. = 3.68; d.f.N = 2; d.f.D = 15; $F = 4.620$; reject. There is enough evidence to accept the claim that at least one mean bridge length is different. Scheffé Test: C.V. = 7.78, $\overline{X}_1$ versus $\overline{X}_2$; $F_S = 6.27$; $\overline{X}_1$ versus $\overline{X}_3$; $F_S = 7.00$; $\overline{X}_2$ versus $\overline{X}_3$; $F_S = 0.07$; Scheffé Test reveals no significant differences. (This does occur occasionally.)

13. H_0: $\mu_1 = \mu_2 = \mu_3$. H_1: At least one mean is different from the others (claim). C.V. = 3.89; d.f.N = 2; d.f.D = 12; $F = 39.409$; reject There is sufficient evidence to support the claim that the tuition fees are different. One possible reason for the difference is that provinces may provide different levels of subsidies that support lower tuition fees. Scheffé Test: C.V. = 7.78, $\overline{X}_1$ versus $\overline{X}_2$; $F_S = 0.44$; $\overline{X}_1$ versus $\overline{X}_3$; $F_S = 46.42$; $\overline{X}_2$ versus $\overline{X}_3$; $F_S = 68.12$; There are significant differences between $\overline{X}_1$ versus $\overline{X}_3$ and between $\overline{X}_1$ versus $\overline{X}_3$.

15. H_0: $\mu_1 = \mu_2 = \mu_3$ (claim). H_1: At least one mean is different from the others. C.V. = 3.52; $\alpha = 0.05$; d.f.N = 2; d.f.D = 19; $F = 11.231$; reject. There is enough evidence to reject the claim that the mean number of farms in the Prairie Provinces is the same. Scheffé Test: C.V. = 7.04, $\overline{X}_1$ versus $\overline{X}_2$; $F_S = 0.65$; $\overline{X}_1$ versus $\overline{X}_3$; $F_S = 19.87$; $\overline{X}_2$ versus $\overline{X}_3$; $F_S = 16.30$; There are significant differences between $\overline{X}_1$ versus $\overline{X}_3$ and between $\overline{X}_2$ versus $\overline{X}_3$.

17. H_0: $\mu_1 = \mu_2 = \mu_3$. H_1: At least one mean is different from the others (claim). $F = 10.118$; P-value = 0.00102; reject. Scheffé test: C.V. = 5.22; $\overline{X}_1$ versus $\overline{X}_2$: $F = 2.91$; $\overline{X}_1$ versus $\overline{X}_3$: $F = 19.3$; $\overline{X}_2$ versus $\overline{X}_3$: $F = 8.40$. There is a significant difference between $\overline{X}_1$ and $\overline{X}_3$, and $\overline{X}_2$ and $\overline{X}_3$.

19. H_0: $\mu_1 = \mu_2 = \mu_3 = \mu_4$. H_1: At least one mean is different from the others (claim). C.V. = 5.29; $\alpha = 0.01$;

d.f.N. = 3; d.f.D. = 16; $F = 0.636$; do not reject. There is not enough evidence to support that at least one mean is different from the others. Students may have had discipline problems. Parents may not like the regular school district, etc.

Exercises 12-4

1. The two-way ANOVA allows the researcher to test the effects of two independent variables and a possible interaction effect. The one-way ANOVA can test the effects of only one independent variable.

3. The mean square values are computed by dividing the sum of squares by the corresponding degrees of freedom.

5. *a.* For factor A, d.f.$_A = 2$
   b. For factor B, d.f.$_B = 1$
   c. d.f.$_{A \times B} = 2$
   d. d.f.$_{within} = 24$

7. The two types of interactions that can occur are ordinal and disordinal.

9. *a.* The lines will be parallel or approximately parallel. They may also coincide.
   b. The lines will not intersect and they will not be parallel.
   c. The lines will intersect.

11. H_0: There is no interaction effect between the time of day and the type of diet on a person's sodium level. H_1: There is an interaction effect between the time of day and the type of diet on a person's sodium level.

   H_0: There is no difference between the means for the sodium level for the times of day. H_1: There is a difference between the means for the sodium level for the times of day.

   H_0: There is no difference between the means for the sodium level for the type of diet. H_1: There is a difference between the means for the sodium level for the type of diet.

ANOVA Summary Table

Source	SS	d.f.	MS	F
Time	1800.0	1	1800.000	25.806
Diet	242.0	1	242.000	3.470
Interaction	264.5	1	264.500	3.792
Within	279.0	4	69.750	
Total	2585.5	7		

The critical value at $\alpha = 0.05$ with d.f.N. = 1 and d.f.D. = 4 is 7.71 for F_A, F_B, and $F_{A \times B}$. Since the only F test value that exceeds 7.71 is the one for the time, 25.806, it can be concluded that there is a difference in the means for the sodium level taken at two different times.

13. H_0: There is no interaction effect between the gender of the individual and the duration of the training on the test scores. H_1: There is an interaction effect between the gender of the individual and the duration of the training on the test scores.

H_0: There is no difference between the means of the test scores for the males and females. H_1: There is a difference between the means of the test scores for the males and females.

H_0: There is no difference between the means of the test scores for the two different durations. H_1: There is a difference between the means of the test scores for the two different durations.

ANOVA Summary Table

Source	SS	d.f.	MS	F
Gender	57.042	1	57.042	0.835
Duration	7.042	1	7.042	0.103
Interaction	3978.375	1	3978.375	58.270
Within	1365.500	20	68.275	
Total	5407.959	23		

The critical value at $\alpha = 0.10$ with d.f.N. $= 1$ and d.f.D. $= 20$ is 2.97. Since the F test value for the interaction is greater than the critical value, it can be concluded that gender affects test scores differently for the duration levels.

15. H_0: There is no interaction effect between the ages of the salespeople and the products they sell on the monthly sales. H_1: There is an interaction effect between the ages of the salespeople and the products they sell on the monthly sales.

H_0: There is no difference in the means of the monthly sales of the two age groups. H_1: There is a difference in the means of the monthly sales of the two age groups.

H_0: There is no difference among the means of the sales for the different products. H_1: There is a difference among the means of the sales for the different products.

ANOVA Summary Table

Source	SS	d.f.	MS	F
Age	168.033	1	168.033	1.567
Product	1,762.067	2	881.034	8.215
Interaction	7,955.267	2	3,977.634	37.087
Error	2,574.000	24	107.250	
Total	12,459.367	29		

At $\alpha = 0.05$, the critical values are: for age, d.f.N. $= 1$, d.f.D. $= 24$, C.V. $= 4.26$; for product and interaction, d.f.N. $= 2$ and d.f.D. $= 24$; C.V. $= 3.40$. The null hypotheses for the interaction effect and for the type of product sold are rejected since the F test values

exceed the critical value 3.40. The cell means are as follows:

Product / Age	Pools	Spas	Saunas
Over 30	38.8	28.6	55.4
30 and under	21.2	68.6	18.8

Since the lines cross, there is a disordinal interaction; hence, there is an interaction effect between the ages of salespeople and the type of products sold.

Review Exercises

1. H_0: $\mu_1 = \mu_2 = \mu_3$ (claim). H_1: At least one mean is different from the others. C. V. $= 5.39$; $\alpha = 0.01$; $F = 6.931$; reject. Tukey test; C.V. $= 4.45$; $\overline{X}_1$ versus $\overline{X}_2$; $q = 0.344$; $\overline{X}_1$ versus $\overline{X}_3$; $q = 4.722$; $\overline{X}_2$ versus $\overline{X}_3$; $q = 4.378$. There is a significant difference between $\overline{X}_1$ and $\overline{X}_3$.

3. H_0: $\mu_1 = \mu_2 = \mu_3$. H_1: At least one mean is different from the others (claim). C.V. $= 3.55$; $\alpha = 0.05$; d.f.N. $= 2$; d.f.D. $= 18$; $F = 0.0408$; do not reject. There is not enough evidence to support the claim that at least one mean is different from the others.

5. H_0: $\mu_1 = \mu_2 = \mu_3$. H_1: At least one mean is different from the others (claim). C.V. $= 2.61$; $\alpha = 0.10$; d.f.N. $= 2$; d.f.D. $= 19$; $F = 0.4876$; do not reject. There is not enough evidence to support the claim that at least one mean is different from the others.

7. H_0: $\mu_1 = \mu_2 = \mu_3 = \mu_4$. H_1: At least one mean is different from the other (claim). C.V. $= 3.98$; $\alpha = 0.05$; d. f. N $= 2$; d. f. D $= 11$; $F = 5.166$; reject. Scheffé Test: C.V. $= 3.98$; $\overline{X}_1$ versus $\overline{X}_2$: $F_s = 1.644$; $\overline{X}_1$ versus $\overline{X}_3$: $F_s = 3.175$; $\overline{X}_1$ versus $\overline{X}_4$: $F_s = 0.006$; $\overline{X}_2$ versus $\overline{X}_3$: $F_s = 15.035$; $\overline{X}_2$ versus $\overline{X}_4$: $F_s = 1.856$; $\overline{X}_3$ versus $\overline{X}_4$: $F_s = 4.567$; There is a significant difference between $\overline{X}_2$ and $\overline{X}_3$ and $\overline{X}_3$ and $\overline{X}_4$.

9. H_0: There is no interaction effect between the type of exercise program and the type of diet on a person's glucose level. H_1: There is an interaction effect between type of exercise program and the type of diet on a person's glucose level.

H_0: There is no difference in the means for the glucose levels of the people in the two exercise programs.

H_1: There is a difference in the means for the glucose levels of the people in the two exercise programs.

H_0: There is no difference in the means for the glucose levels of the people in the two diet programs. H_1: There is a difference in the means for the glucose levels of the people in the two diet programs.

ANOVA Summary Table

Source	SS	d.f.	MS	F
Exercise	816.750	1	816.750	60.50
Diet	102.083	1	102.083	7.56
Interaction	444.083	1	444.083	32.90
Within	108.000	8	13.500	
Total	1470.916	11		

At $\alpha = 0.05$, d.f.N. $= 1$, d.f.D. $= 8$, and the critical value is 5.32 for each F_A, F_B, and $F_{A \times B}$. Hence, all three null hypotheses are rejected. The cell means should be calculated.

Exercise \ Diet	A	B
I	64.000	57.667
II	68.333	86.333

Since the means for exercise program I are both smaller than those for exercise program II and the vertical differences are not the same, the interaction is ordinal. Hence one can say that there is a difference for exercise and diet, and that an interaction effect is present.

Chapter Quiz

1. False
2. False
3. False
4. True
5. *d*
6. *a*
7. *a*
8. *c*
9. ANOVA
10. Tukey
11. Two
12. H_0: $\mu_1 = \mu_2 = \mu_3 = \mu_4$. H_1: At least one mean is different from the others (claim). C.V. $= 3.98$; $\alpha = 0.05$; d.f.N $= 2$; d.f.D $= 11$; $F = 3.312$; do not reject. There is not enough evidence to support the claim that at least one mean is different from the others.
13. H_0: $\mu_1 = \mu_2 = \mu_3$. H_1: At least one mean is different from the others (claim). C.V. $= 6.93$; $\alpha = 0.01$; d.f.N. $= 2$; d.f.D. $= 12$; $F = 3.49$. There is not enough evidence to support the claim that at least one mean is different from the others. Writers would want to target their material to the age group of the viewers.
14. H_0: $\mu_1 = \mu_2 = \mu_3$. H_1: At least one mean is different from the others (claim). C.V. $= 3.68$; $\alpha = 0.05$;

d.f.N. $= 2$; d.f.D. $= 15$; $F = 10.494$; reject. Tukey test: C.V. $= 3.67$; $\overline{X}_1 = 47.67$; $\overline{X}_2 = 63$; $\overline{X}_3 = 43.83$; $\overline{X}_1$ versus $\overline{X}_2$, $q = -4.90$; $\overline{X}_1$ versus $\overline{X}_3$, $q = 1.23$; $\overline{X}_2$ versus $\overline{X}_3$, $q = 6.12$. There is a significant difference between $\overline{X}_1$ and $\overline{X}_2$ and between $\overline{X}_2$ and $\overline{X}_3$.

15. H_0: $\mu_1 = \mu_2 = \mu_3$ (claim). H_1: At least one mean is different from the others. C.V. $= 2.70$; $\alpha = 0.10$; d.f.N. $= 2$; d.f.D. $= 15$; $F = 0.670$; do not reject. There is not enough evidence to reject the claim that the means are equal.

16. H_0: $\mu_1 = \mu_2 = \mu_3 = \mu_4$. H_1: At least one mean is different from the others (claim). C.V. $= 3.07$; $\alpha = 0.05$; d.f.N. $= 3$; d.f.D. $= 21$; $F = 0.4564$; do not reject. There is not enough evidence to support the claim that at least one mean is different from the others.

17. a. Two-way ANOVA.

b. Diet and exercise program.

c. 2

d. H_0: There is no interaction effect between the type of exercise program and the type of diet on a person's weight loss. H_1: There is an interaction effect between the type of exercise program and the type of diet on a person's weight loss.

H_0: There is no difference in the means of the weight losses of people in the exercise programs. H_1: There is a difference in the means of the weight losses of people in the exercise programs.

H_0: There is no difference in the means of the weight losses of people in the diet programs. H_1: There is a difference in the means of the weight losses of people in the diet programs.

e. Diet: $F = 21.0$, significant; exercise program: $F = 0.429$, not significant; interaction: $F = 0.429$, not significant.

f. Reject the null hypothesis for the diets.

Chapter 13

Exercises 13–2

1. *Nonparametric* means hypotheses other than those using population parameters can be tested; *distribution-free* means no assumptions about the population distributions have to be satisfied.

3. Nonparametric methods have the following advantages:

a. They can be used to test population parameters when the variable is not normally distributed.

b. They can be used when data are nominal or ordinal.

c. They can be used to test hypotheses other than those involving population parameters.

d. The computations are easier in some cases than the computations of the parametric counterparts.

e. They are easier to understand.

The disadvantages are as follows:

a. They are less sensitive than their parametric counterparts.

b. They tend to use less information than their parametric counterparts.

c. They are less efficient than their parametric counterparts.

5.

Data	22	32	34	43	43	65	66	71
Rank	1	2	3	4.5	4.5	6	7	8

7.

Data	4	6	6	7	8	9	9	10	13	15	16	18
Rank	1	2.5	2.5	4	5	6.5	6.5	8	9	10	11	12

9.

Data	188	188	197	256	321	530	763
Rank	1.5	1.5	3	4	5	6	7

Exercises 13–3

1. The sign test uses only positive or negative signs.

3. The smaller number of positive or negative signs.

5. H_0 : median = 0.9 (claim) and H_1 : median ≠ 0.9; C.V. = 4; test statistic = 8; do not reject. There is not enough evidence to reject the claim that the median is 0.9 metres.

7. H_0: median = 25 (claim) and H_1: median ≠ 25; test value = 7; C.V. = 4; do not reject. There is not enough evidence to reject the claim that the median is 25. School boards could use the median to plan for the costs of cyber school enrollments.

9. H_0: median = \$10.86 (claim) and H_1: median ≠ \$10.86; C.V. = +1.96; z = −0.77; do not reject. There is not enough evidence to reject the claim that the median is \$10.86. Home buyers could estimate the yearly cost of their gas bills.

11. H_0: $p \leq 0.5$ and H_1: $p > 0.5$ (claim); $z = -0.99$; P-value = 0.1611; do not reject. There is not enough evidence to support the claim that more than 50% of the students favour single-room dormitories.

13. H_0: median = 50 (claim) and H_1: median ≠ 50; $z = -2.3$; P-value = 0.0214; reject. There is enough evidence to reject the claim that 50% of the students are against extending the school year.

15. H_0: The medication has no effect on weight loss. H_1: The medication affects weight loss (claim). C.V. = 0; test statistic = 1; do not reject. There is not enough evidence to support the claim that the medication affects weight loss.

17. H_0: Reasoning ability will not be affected by the course and H_1: Reasoning ability increased after the course (claim); C.V. = 1; test value = 1; reject. There is enough evidence to support the claim that reasoning ability has increased after the course.

19. H_0: The number of viewers is the same as last year (claim); H_1: The number of viewers is not the same as

last year; C.V. = 0; test value = 2; do not reject. There is not enough evidence to reject the claim that the number of viewers is the same as last year.

21. 6 ≤ median ≤ 22   **23.** 4.7 ≤ median ≤ 9.3

25. 17 ≤ median ≤ 33

Exercises 13–4

1. n_1 and n_2 are each greater than or equal to 10.

3. The standard normal distribution.

5. H_0: There is no difference in the number of jetplanes grounded for repairs and the number of jetplanes in storage (claim). H_1: There is a difference in the number of planes in each group. C.V. = ±1.96; z = −2.65; reject. There is enough evidence to reject the claim that there is no difference in the number of planes grounded and the number of planes in storage. The airline should plan for more storage facilities.

7. H_0: There is no difference in the stopping distances of the two types of automobiles. (claim). H_1: There is a difference between the stopping distances of the two types of automobiles. C.V. = ±1.645; z = −2.721; reject. There is enough evidence to reject the claim that there is no difference in the stopping distances of the two types of automobiles.

9. H_0: There is no difference in the number of worker fatalities in the two regions. H_1: There is a difference in the number of worker fatalities in the two regions (claim). C.V. = ±1.96; z = 0.128; do not reject. There is enough evidence to reject the claim that there is a difference in the number of worker fatalities in the two regions.

11. H_0: There is no difference in the times needed to assemble the product. H_1: There is a difference in the times needed to assemble the product (claim). C.V. = ±1.96; z = +3.56; reject. There is enough evidence to support the claim that there is a difference in the productivity of the two groups.

Exercises 13–5

1. The t test for dependent samples.

3. Sum of minus ranks is −6; sum of plus ranks is +15. The test value is 6.

5. C.V. = 20; reject.   **7.** C.V. = 130; do not reject.

9. H_0: The human dose is less than or equal to the animal dose. H_1: The human dose is more than the animal dose (claim). C.V. = 6; w_s = 2; reject. There is enough evidence to support the claim that the human dose costs more than the equivalent animal dose. One reason is that some people might not be inclined to pay a lot of money for their pets' medication.

11. H_0: Quebec Francophones watch the same or less TV then Quebec Anglophones. H_1: Quebec Francophones watch more TV then Quebec Anglophones (claim). C.V. = 2; w_x = 0; reject. There is sufficient evidence to support the claim that Quebec Francophones watch more TV than Quebec Angolophones.

13. H_0: The prices of prescription drugs in the United States are greater than or equal to the prices in Canada. H_1: The drugs sold in Canada are cheaper. C.V. $= 11$; $w_s = 3$; reject. There is enough evidence to support the claim that the drugs are less expensive in Canada.

Exercises 13–6

1. H_0: There is no difference in the number of calories. H_1: There is a difference in the number of calories (claim). C.V. $= 7.815$; $H = 2.842$; do not reject. There is not enough evidence to support the claim that there is a difference in the number of calories.

3. H_0: There is no difference in the prices of the three types of lawnmowers. H_1: There is a difference in the prices of the three types of lawnmowers (claim). C.V. $= 4.605$; $H = 1.07$; do not reject. There is not enough evidence to support the claim that the prices are different. No, price is not a factor. Results are suspect since one sample is less than 5.

5. H_0: There is no difference in the number of carbohydrates in one serving of each of the three types of food. H_1: There is a difference in the number of carbohydrates in each of the three types of food (claim). C.V. $= 9.210$; $H = 11.58$; reject. There is enough evidence to say that there is a difference in the number of carbohydrates in the three foods. You should recommend the ice cream.

7. H_0: There is no difference in the number of firearm-related deaths by manner/intent for each age group. H_1: There is a difference in the number of firearm-related deaths by manner/intent for each age group (claim). C.V. $= 4.605$; $H = 8.385$; reject. There is sufficient evidence to support the claim that there is a difference in the number of firearm-related deaths by manner/intent for each age group.

9. H_0: There is no difference in the number of crimes in the five precincts. H_1: There is a difference in the number of crimes in the five precincts (claim). C.V. $= 13.277$; $H = 20.753$; reject. There is enough evidence to support the claim that there is a difference in the number of crimes in the five precincts.

11. H_0: There is no difference in the final exam scores of the three groups. H_1: There is a difference in the final exam scores of the three groups (claim). $H = 1.710$; P-value > 0.10 (0.425); do not reject. There is not enough evidence to support the claim that there is a difference in the final exam scores of the three groups.

Exercises 13–7

1. 0.716

3. 0.648

5. $r_s = 0.286$; H_0: $\rho = 0$ and H_1: $\rho \neq 0$; C.V. $= \pm 0.643$; do not reject. There is not enough evidence to indicate

that there is a correlation between the number of forest fires caused by human activity and lightning.

7. $r_s = 0.943$; H_0: $\rho = 0$ and H_1: $\rho \neq 0$; C.V. $= \pm 0.886$; reject. There is a significant relationship between the sentence and the time period.

9. $r_s = 0.5$; H_0: $\rho = 0$ and H_1: $\rho \neq 0$; C.V. $= \pm 0.738$; do not reject. There is not enough evidence to say that a significant correlation exists.

11. $r_s = 0.6$; H_0: $\rho = 0$ and H_1: $\rho \neq 0$; C.V. $= \pm 0.886$; do not reject. There is not enough evidence to indicate that a correlation exists between monthly fuel prices and monthly prices of a barrel of oil.

13. $r_s = -0.10$; H_0: $\rho = 0$ and H_1: $\rho \neq 0$; C.V. $= \pm 0.900$; do not reject. There is no significant relationship between the number of cyber school students and the cost per pupil. In this case, the cost per pupil is different in each district.

15. H_0: The number of cavities in a person occurs at random. H_1: The null hypothesis is not true. There are 21 runs; the expected number of runs is between 10 and 22. Therefore, do not reject the null hypothesis; the number of cavities in a person occurs at random.

17. H_0: The lotto numbers occur at random. H_1: The null hypothesis is not true. There are 11 runs, and since this is between 9 and 21, do not reject. There is significant evidence that the lottery numbers occur at random.

19. H_0: The number of defective cassette cases manufactured by the machine occurs at random. H_1: The null hypothesis is not true. There are 10 runs; and since this value is between 9 and 20, do not reject the null hypothesis. The number of defective cassette cases manufactured by a machine occurs at random.

21. H_0: The number of absences of employees occurs at random over a 30-day period. H_1: The null hypothesis is not true. There are only 6 runs, and this value does not fall within the 9-to-21 range. Hence, the null hypothesis is rejected; the absences do not occur at random.

23. H_0: The IQs of students who complete the tests are random. H_1: The null hypothesis is not true. Do not reject, since there are 7 runs, and this value is within the 6-to-16 range; the IQs occur at random.

25. ± 0.479

27. ± 0.215

Review Exercises

1. H_0: median $= 5$ (claim) and H_1: median $\neq 5$; test value $= 6$; C.V. $= 2$. Do not reject; there is not enough evidence to reject the claim that the median is 5.

3. H_0: The special diet has no effect on weight. H_1: The special diet increases weight (claim). C.V. $= 1$; test statistic $= 3$; do not reject. There is not enough evidence to support the claim that the special diet increases weight.

5. H_0: There is no difference in the amount of money the groups spent for the textbook. H_1: There is a difference in the amount of money the groups spent for the textbook (claim). C.V. $= \pm1.65$; $z = -3.59$. Reject; there is enough evidence to support the claim that there is a difference in the amount of money the groups spent on the textbooks.

7. H_0: The number of sick days workers used was not reduced. H_1: The number of sick days workers used was reduced (claim). C.V. $= 4$; $w_s = 8.5$. Do not reject; there is not enough evidence to support the claim that the number of sick days was reduced.

9. H_0: The diet has no effect on learning. H_1: The diet affects learning (claim). C.V. $= 5.991$; $H = 8.5$. Reject; there is enough evidence to support the claim that the diets do affect learning.

11. $r_s = 0.891$; H_0: $\rho = 0$ and H_1: $\rho \neq 0$; C.V. $= \pm0.648$; reject. There is a significant relationship in the average number of people who are watching the television shows for both years.

13. H_0: The grades of students who finish the exam occur at random. H_1: The null hypothesis is not true. Since there are 8 runs and this value does not fall in the 9-to-21 interval, the null hypothesis is rejected. The grades do not occur at random.

Chapter Quiz

1. False
2. False
3. True
4. True
5. *a*
6. *c*
7. *d*
8. *b*
9. Nonparametric
10. Nominal, ordinal
11. Sign
12. Sensitive

13. H_0: median $= 300$ (claim) and H_1: median $\neq 300$. There are 7 plus signs. Do not reject since 7 is greater than the critical value of 5. There is not enough evidence to reject the claim that the median is 300.

14. H_0: median $= 1200$ (claim) and H_1: median $\neq 1200$. There are 10 minus signs. Do not reject since the 10 is greater than the critical value 6. There is not enough evidence to reject the claim that the median is 1200.

15. H_0: There will be no change in the weight of the turkeys after the special diet. H_1: The turkeys will weigh more after the special diet (claim). C.V. $= 1$; $+$ signs $= 1$, test statistic $= 1$; reject. There is enough evidence to support the claim that the turkeys gained weight after the special diet.

16. H_0: The distributions are the same. H_1: The distributions are different (claim). $z = -0.05$; C.V. $= \pm1.96$; do not reject the null hypothesis. There is not enough evidence to reject the claim that the distributions are the same.

17. H_0: The distributions are the same. H_1: The distributions are different (claim). $z = -0.14434$;

C.V. $= \pm1.65$; do not reject the null hypothesis. There is not enough evidence to support the claim that the distributions are different.

18. H_0: There is no difference in the GPA of the students before and after the workshop. H_1: There is a difference in the GPA of the students before and after the workshop (claim). Test statistic $= 0$; C.V. $= 2$; reject the null hypothesis. There is enough evidence to support the claim that there is a difference in the GPAs of the students.

19. H_0: There is no difference in the breaking strengths of the tapes. H_1: There is a difference in the breaking strengths of the tapes; $\chi^2 = 5.991$; $H = 29.236$; reject. There is sufficient evidence to support the claim that there is a difference in the breaking strengths of the tapes.

20. H_0: There is no difference in the reaction times of the monkeys. H_1: There is a difference in the reaction times of the monkeys (claim). $H = 6.9$; $0.025 <$ P-value < 0.05 (0.032); reject the null hypothesis. There is enough evidence to support the claim that there is a difference in the reaction times of the monkeys.

21. $r_s = 0.683$; H_0: $\rho = 0$ and H_1: $\rho \neq 0$; C.V. $= \pm0.600$; reject. There is enough evidence to say that there is a significant relationship between the drug prices.

22. $r_s = 0.943$; H_0: $\rho = 0$ and H_1: $\rho \neq 0$; C.V. $= \pm0.829$; reject. There is a significant relationship between the amount of money spent on Head Start and the number of students enrolled in the program.

23. H_0: The births of babies occur at random according to gender. H_1: The null hypothesis is not true. There are 10 runs, and since this is between 8 and 19, the null hypothesis is not rejected. There is not enough evidence to reject the null hypothesis that the gender occurs at random.

24. H_0: There is no difference in the rpm of the motors before and after the reconditioning. H_1: There is a difference in the rpm of the motors before and after the reconditioning (claim). Test statistic $= 0$; C.V. $= 6$; do not reject the null hypothesis. There is not enough evidence to support the claim that there is a difference in the rpm of the motors before and after reconditioning.

25. H_0: The numbers occur at random. H_1: The null hypothesis is not true. There are 16 runs, and since this is between 9 and 21, the null hypothesis is not rejected. There is not enough evidence to reject the null hypothesis that the numbers occur at random.

Chapter 14
Exercises 14–2

1. Random, systematic, stratified, cluster

3. A sample must be randomly selected.

5. Talking to people on the street, calling people on the phone, and asking one's friends are three incorrect ways of obtaining a sample.

7. Random sampling has the advantage that each unit of the population has an equal chance of being selected. One disadvantage is that the units of the population must be numbered; if the population is large, this could be somewhat time-consuming.

9. An advantage of stratified sampling is that it ensures representation for the groups used in stratification; however, it is virtually impossible to stratify the population so that all groups are represented.

11. Answers will vary.   13. Answers will vary.

15. Answers will vary.   17. Answers will vary.

19. Answers will vary.

Exercises 14–3

1. Flaw—asking a biased question. Do you think XYZ Department Store should carry brand name merchandise?

3. Flaw—asking a biased question. Should banks charge a fee to balance their customers' chequebooks?

5. Flaw—confusing words. How many hours did you study for this exam?

7. Flaw—confusing words. If a plane were to crash on the border of New York and New Jersey, where should the victims be buried?

9. Answers will vary.

Exercises 14–5

1. Simulation involves setting up probability experiments that mimic the behavior of real-life events.

3. John Von Neumann and Stanislaw Ulam.

5. The steps are as follows:
   a. List all possible outcomes.
   b. Determine the probability of each outcome.
   c. Set up a correspondence between the outcomes and the random numbers.
   d. Conduct the experiment by using random numbers.
   e. Repeat the experiment and tally the outcomes.
   f. Compute any statistics and state the conclusions.

7. When the repetitions increase, there is a higher probability that the simulation will yield more precise answers.

9. Use two-digit random numbers: 01 through 70 is considered a success and 71 through 99 and 00 a failure. One-digit random numbers can also be used: 1 through 7 as a success and 8, 9, and 0 a miss.

11. Use one-digit random numbers: 1 through 8 would be a hit and 9 and 0 a miss.

13. Let an odd number represent heads and an even number represent tails. Then each person selects a digit at random.

15. Answers will vary.   17. Answers will vary.

19. Answers will vary.   21. Answers will vary.

23. Answers will vary.

Review Exercises

1. Answers will vary.   3. Answers will vary.

5. Answers will vary.   7. Answers will vary.

9. Use one-digit random numbers 1 through 4 for a strikeout and 5 through 9 and 0 represent anything other than a strikeout.

11. In this case, a one-digit random number is selected. Numbers 1 through 6 represent the numbers on the face. Ignore 7, 8, 9, and 0 and select another number.

13. Let the digits 1–3 represent rock, let 4–6 represent paper, let 7–9 represent scissors, and omit 0.

15. Answers will vary.   17. Answers will vary.

19. Flaw—asking a biased question. Have you ever driven through a red light?

21. Flaw—asking a double-barreled question. Do you think all automobiles should have heavy-duty bumpers?

Chapter Quiz

1. True   2. True
3. False   4. True
5. a   6. c
7. c   8. Larger
9. Biased   10. Cluster

11.–14. Answers will vary.

15. Use two-digit random numbers: 01 through 45 means the player wins. Any other two-digit random number means the player loses.

16. Use two-digit random numbers: 01 through 05 means a cancellation. Any other two-digit random number means the person shows up.

17. The random numbers 01 through 13 represent the 13 cards in hearts. The random numbers 14 through 26 represent the 13 cards in diamonds. The random numbers 27 through 39 represent the 13 spades, and 40 through 52 represent the 13 clubs. Any number over 52 is ignored.

18. Use two-digit random numbers to represent the spots on the face of the dice. Ignore any two-digit random numbers with 7, 8, 9, or 0. For cards, use two-digit random numbers between 01 and 13.

19. Use two-digit random numbers. The first digit represents the first player, and the second digit represents the second player. If both numbers are odd or even, player 1 wins. If a digit is odd and the other digit is even, player 2 wins.

20.–24. Answers will vary.

*There are no new Canadian exercise questions in this chapter.

Appendix A

A–1. 362,880

A–3. 120

A–5. 1

A–7. 1320

A–9. 20

A–11. 126

A–13. 70

A–15. 1

A–17. 560

A–19. 2520

A–21. 121; 2181; 14,641; 716.9

A–23. 32; 258; 1024; 53.2

A–25. 328; 22,678; 107,584; 1161.2

A–27. 693; 50,511; 480,249; 2486.1

A–29. 318; 20,150; 101,124; 3296

A–31.

A–33.

A–35.

A–37.

A–39.

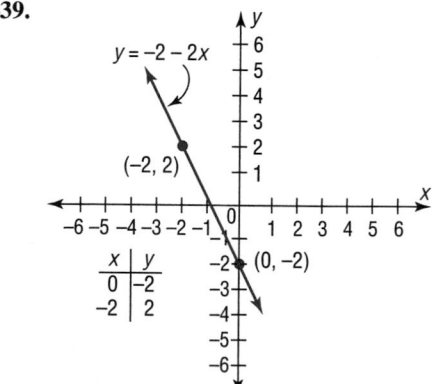

Appendix B-2

B–1. 0.65

B–3. 0.653

B–5. 0.379

B–7. $\frac{1}{4}$

B–9. 0.64

B–11. 0.857

Index

A

Addition rules, 161–165
Adjusted R^2, 489
Alpha, 339
   procedure table, 342
Alternative hypothesis, 335, 399
Ambiguous averages, 17
Analysis of variance (ANOVA),
      530–552
   assumptions, 531, 546
   between-group variance, 531
   degrees of freedom, 531–532, 545
   F-test, 533
   hypotheses, 531, 544–545
   one-way, 531–536
   P-values, 536
   procedure table, 536
   summary table, 533–534, 545
   two-way, 543–552
   within-group variance, 531
Arithmetic average, 80
Assumptions for the use of chi-square
      test, 376, 502
Assumptions for valid predictions in
      regression, 473
Averages, 78–90
   properties and uses, 90

B

Bell curve, 248
Beta, 339, 384
Between-group variance, 531
Biased sample, 607
Bimodal, 49, 85
Binomial distribution, 206, 223–230
   characteristics, 224–225
   mean for, 228
   normal approximation,
      280–285
   notation, 224–225
   standard deviation, 228
   variance, 228–230
Binomial experiment, 224
Binomial probability
      formula, 225

Boundaries, 7
   class, 33
Box-and-whisker plot, 127
Boxplot, 79, 127–130

C

Cardan, Jerome, 147, 161
Categorical frequency distribution,
      32–33
Cauchy, Augustin Louis, 213
Census, 4, 10, 606
Central limit theorem, 249,
      270–276, 350
Chebyshev's theorem, 107–109
Chebyshev, Pafnuty L., 107
Chi-square
   assumptions, 376, 502, 518
   cases, 373
   contingency table, 509–511
   degrees of freedom, 320
   distribution, 320–322
   formula for, 375
   goodness-of-fit test, 501–507
   independence test, 510–512
   procedure table, 503–504
   standard deviation, 373–381
   variance test, 373–381
   variances, 373–381
Class limits, 31
Class(es), 31
   boundaries, 33
   continuity, 34
   exhaustive, 35
   limits, 33
   midpoint, 34
   mutually exclusive, 34
   width, 33–34
Classical probability, 148–152
   formula for, 148
Closed-ended question, 620
Cluster sample, 12, 614–615
Coefficient of determination, 480
Coefficient of multiple
      determination, 489
Coefficient of nondetermination, 477

Coefficient of variation, 105
Combination, 186–188
Combination rule, 187
Complement of an event, 151
Complementary events, 151–152
Compound event, 148
Compound time series graph, 55
Conditional probability, 171, 173–176
Confidence interval, 298
   formula for, 308
   hypothesis testing, 382–384
   mean, 297–311
   means, difference of, 404, 420, 430
   median, 574
   proportions, 313–316
   proportions, differences, 436
   rounding rule, 299–300, 315
   standard deviations and
      variances, 322–324
   variances and standard
      deviations, 322–324
Confidence level, 298
Confounding variable, 15
Consistent estimator, 297
Contingency coefficient, 522
Contingency table, 509–511
Continuous variable, 6, 207, 248
Control group, 14
Convenience sample, 13
Correction factor for continuity, 280
Correlation, 452, 457–465
Correlation coefficient, 457
   formula for, 458
   multiple, 488–489
   Pearson's product moment, 457
   population, 461
   procedure table, 473
   rounding rule, 458
   significance, 460–461
   Spearman's rank, 588–590
Counting rules, summary, 188
Critical region, 340
Critical value, 340
Cumulative frequency, 36
Cumulative frequency graph, 45–47
Cumulative relative frequency, 47

D

Data, 3
Data array, 84
Data collection, 9
Data set, 4
Data value (*datum*), 4
de Fermat, Pierre, 148
de Méré, Chevalier, 148
Deciles, 79, 123
Degrees of freedom, 308
　　F-test, 413
　　t-test, 358, 417
DeMoivre, Abraham, 210, 250, 272
Dependent events, 171
Dependent samples, 423
Dependent variables, 14,
　　　453–454, 543
Descriptive statistics, 4
Detached statistics, 17–18
Difference between two means,
　　　398–405, 416–421, 423–431
　　assumptions for the test to
　　　determine, 399
　　proportions, 433–437
Direct observation, 10
Discrete probability distribution, 208
Discrete variable, 6, 207
Disordinal interaction, 549
Distribution-free statistics
　　　(nonparametric), 564
Distributions, 335
　　bell-shaped, 48, 249
　　bimodal, 85
　　binomial, 206, 223–230
　　chi-square, 320–322
　　F, 408–410
　　frequency, 30, 31
　　hypergeometric, 236–238
　　multimodal, 85
　　multinomial, 233–234
　　negatively skewed, 48, 249
　　normal, 248–253
　　Poisson, 234–236
　　positively skewed, 48, 249
　　probability, 208–211
　　right skewed, 48
　　sampling, 270–276
　　shapes, 48–49, 90
　　standard normal, 251
　　symmetrical, 48, 249, 307
　　uniform, 48
　　unimodal, 85
Double sampling, 13, 615

E

Einstein, Albert, 584
Elements, definition, 3

Empirical probability, 153–155
　　formula for, 153
Empirical rule, 109–110
Equally likely events, 148
Error, 489
Estimation, 296
Estimator, properties of goods, 297
Event, simple, 148
Events
　　complementary, 151–152
　　compound, 148
　　dependent, 171
　　equally likely, 148
　　independent, 168
　　mutually exclusive, 161
Exclusive or, 149
Expectation, 218–220
Expected frequency, 501
Expected value, 218–220
Experimental study, 14
Explained variation, 478
Explanatory variable, 14
Exploratory data analysis, 64, 79,
　　　127–131
Extrapolation, 473

F

F-distribution, characteristics of, 408
F-test, 408–413, 533
　　comparing three or more means,
　　　531–536
　　comparing two variances, 408–413
　　formula for, 316
　　notes for the use of, 410
Factorial notation, 184
Factors, 543
Fair game, 160
Faulty survey questions, 18
Finite population correction factor, 276
Fisher, R. A., 524
Five-number summary, 79, 127–128
Frequency, 31
Frequency distribution, 30, 31
　　categorical, 32–33
　　grouped, 33–37
　　reasons for, 38
　　rules for constructing, 34–35
　　ungrouped, 37
Frequency polygon, 43–44
Fundamental counting rule, 181–184

G

Galileo, 147
Gallup poll, 606
Galton, Francis, 461, 469
Gauss, Carl Friedrich, 248, 250

Gaussian distribution, 248
General rounding rule, 80
Geometric mean, 95
Goodness-of-fit test, 501–507
　　formula for, 501
　　procedure table, 503–504
Gosset, W. S., 234, 307
Grand mean, 532
Grouped data
　　standard deviation, 103–104
　　variance, 103–104
Grouped frequency distribution, 33–37
　　procedure table for, 38

H

H test, 583
Harmonic mean, 95
Hawthorne effect, 15
Hinges, 130
Histogram, 42–43
Homogeneity of proportions test,
　　　516–518
　　assumptions, 518
　　procedure table, 517
Human Development Index, 78
Huygens, Christian, 217
Hypergeometric distribution, 236–238
　　formula for, 234
Hypothesis, 4, 335, 399
Hypothesis testing, 4, 334–345,
　　　398–401
　　alternative, 335, 399
　　common phrases, 336, 401
　　critical region, 340
　　critical value, 340
　　definitions, 335, 399
　　level of significance, 339
　　noncritical region, 340
　　null, 335, 400
　　one-tailed test, 336, 401
　　P-value method, 351–355
　　procedure table, 342
　　statistical, 335, 399
　　statistical test, 337
　　test value, 337
　　traditional method, steps
　　　in, 335–345, 398–401
　　two-tailed test, 335, 399
　　types of errors, 338

I

Implied connections, 18
Inclusive or, 149
Independence test (*chi*-square),
　　　510–512
Independent events, 168

Independent samples, 416
Independent variables, 14,
    453–454, 543
Inferential statistics, 5
Influential observation, 474
Interaction effect, 544
Intercept (*y*), 469–470
    rounding rule, 470
Interquartile range, 123
Intersection, 164
Interval estimate, 297
Interval level of measurement, 8
Ipsos Reid poll, 606

K

Kerrich, John, 210
Kologorov-Smikoriv test, 266
Kramp, Christian, 184
Kruskal-Wallis test, 583–586
    formula for, 583
    procedure for, 585

L

Laplace, Pierre Simon, 10, 210,
    250, 272
Law of large numbers, 155
Least-squares approximation, 471
Least-squares line, 479
Left-skewed distribution, 91
Left-tailed test, 336, 340, 351, 401
Legendre, Adrien-Marie, 469, 471
Level of significance, 337, 339
Levels of measurement, 7–9
    interval, 8
    nominal, 7
    ordinal, 7–8
    ratio, 8
Lilliefoers test, 266
Limits, class, 33
Line of best fit, 469
Lower class boundary, 33
Lower class limit, 33
Lurking variable, 464

M

Main effects, 545
Margin of error, 299
Marginal change, 472
Mathematical expectation, 217
Maximum error of estimate, 299
Mean, 79, 80–83, 213–215
    binomial variable, 228
    definition, 80
    normal distribution, 25, 250
    population, 80

probability distribution, 214
properties of, 90
rounding rule, 81–82, 214
sample, 80
uses of, 90
Mean deviation, 113–114
Mean square, 533
Measurement scales, 7–8
Measurement, levels of, 7–9
Measures of averages, uses of, 90
Measures of central tendency, 79
    properties of, 90
    summary of, 89
    symbols for, 89
    uses of, 90
Measures of dispersion, 79, 96–110
Measures of position, 79, 114–123
    summary of, 123
    symbols, 123
Measures of variance and standard
        deviation,
    uses of, 105
Measures of variation, 79, 96–110
Median, 79, 84–85, 114
    confidence interval for, 574
    defined, 84
    grouped data, for, 96
    properties of, 90
    uses of, 90
Mendel, Gregor, 500
Midquartile, 127
Midrange, 79, 87–88
    properties of, 90
    uses of, 90
Misleading graphs, 18, 58–61
Modal class, 86
Mode, 79, 85–87
    properties of, 90
    uses of, 90
Monte Carlo method, 621–626
Mortality tables, 5
Multimodal, 85
Multinomial distribution, 233–234
Multiple correlation coefficient,
    488–489
Multiple regression, 453, 485–490
    assumptions, 487
    equation, 487
Multiple relationships, 453
Multiplication rules probability,
    168–173
Multistage sampling, 13, 615
Mutually exclusive events, 161

N

Negative relationship, 453
Negatively skewed distribution, 91, 249

Neyman, Jerzy, 298
Nielsen television ratings, 606
Nightingale, Florence, 80
Nominal level of measurement, 7
Noncritical region, 340
Nonparametric statistics, 564–591
    advantages, 565
    disadvantages, 565
Nonrejection region, 340
Nonresistant statistic, 130
Normal approximation to binomial
        distribution, 280–285
Normal distribution, 248–253
    applications of, 260–266
    approximation to the binomial
        distribution, 280–285
    areas under, 253–255
    formula for, 250
    mean, 250
    probability distribution as, 255–256
    properties of, 250
    standard, 251
    standard deviation, 250
Normal Quantile Plot, 266
Normally distributed variables,
    248–253
Norms, 79
Notation for the binomial distribution,
    224–225
Null hypothesis, 335, 400
Numerical frequency, 36

O

Observational study, 13
    advantages, 15
    disadvantages, 15
Observed frequency, 501
Odds, 160
Ogive, 45–46
One-tailed test, 336, 340
    left, 340
    right, 340
One-way analysis of variance, 531–536
Open-ended distribution, 35
Open-ended question, 620
Ordinal interaction, 549
Ordinal level of measurement, 7–8
Outcome, 145
Outcome variable, 14
Outliers, 49, 87, 123, 457
    procedure table, 124

P

P-value, 351
    analysis of variance (ANOVA), 536
    decision rule, 353–354

P-value (*continued*)
    guidelines, 354
    method of hypothesis
        testing, 351–355
    procedure table, 352
    t-test, for, 361–363
    X^2 test, for, 379–381
P-value method
    decision rule, 512–516
    procedure table, 503–504
Paired-sample sign test, 569–571
    procedure table, 571
Parameter, 80
Parametric tests, 564
Pareto chart, 52–54
Pareto, Vilfredo, 54
Partial regression coefficients, 487
Pascal's triangle, 224
Pascal, Blaise, 148, 224
Pearson coefficient of skewness, 114
Pearson product moment correlation
    coefficient, 457
Pearson's index PI of skewness, 266
Pearson, Karl, 250, 461, 469, 480, 501
Percentiles, 79, 115–121
    formula, 119
    procedure table, 121
Permutation, 184
Permutation rule, 185
pi day, 584
Pie graph, 56–58
Playfair, William, 43
Point estimate, 297
Poisson distribution, 234–236
    formula for, 234
Poisson, Simeon D., 234
Pooled estimate of variance, 417
Population, 4, 606
Positive relationship, 453
Positively skewed
    distribution, 90, 249
Power of a test, 384–386
Practical significance, 354
Prediction interval, 483
    formula for, 483
Probability, 4, 144, 145
    addition rules, 161–165
    'at least', 176–177
    binomial, 223–228
    classical, 148–152
    complementary rules, 145
    conditional, 171, 173–176
    counting rules, 191–193
    distribution, 207–211
    empirical, 153–155
    experiment, 145
    multiplication rules, 168–173
    probability distribution, 207–211

    risk taking, 156
    rounding rule for, 149
    rules, 150–151
    subjective, 155–156
Probability distribution of mean, 214
Properties of the distribution of
    sample means, 270
Proportion, 313

Q

Quadratic mean, 96
Qualitative variables, 6
Quantitative variables, 6
Quartiles, 79, 122–123
    procedure table, 121
Quasi-experimental study, 14
Questionnaire, validity, 620
Questionnaire design, 618–620
Quetelet, Adolphe, 80

R

Random numbers, 11, 606, 608–611
Random samples, 10, 607–611
Random sampling, 10–12, 607–611
Random variable, 3, 207
Randomness, 335
Range, 35, 79, 97–98
Range rule of thumb, 106
Rank correlation, Spearman's, 588–590
Ranking, 565
Ratio level of measurement, 8
Raw data, 31
Regression, 452, 468–475
    assumptions for valid prediction, 473
    multiple, 453
Regression line, 468
    equation, 469–470
    formula for, 470
    intercept, 469–470
    line of best fit, 469
    prediction, 472
    slope, 469–470
Regression line equation, procedure
    table, 473
Rejection region, 340
Relationships, 5, 452–453
Relative frequency, 32
Relative frequency graphs, 46–48
Relatively efficient estimator, 297
Requirements for a probability
    distribution, 211
Residual, 479
Residual variation, 489
Resistant statistic, 130
Right-skewed distribution, 90
Right-tailed test, 336, 340, 351, 401

Rounding rule, 80
    confidence interval, 299–300, 315
    correlation coefficient, 458
    intercept, 470
    mean, 81–82, 214
    slope, 470
    standard deviation, 98–99, 214
    variance, 214
Run, 591
Runs test, 591–594

S

Sample, 4, 606
    biased, 607
    cluster, 12, 614–615
    convenience, 13
    random, 10, 607–611
    size for estimating means, 303–305
    size for estimating proportions,
        316–318
    stratified, 12, 612–614
    systematic, 12, 611–612
    unbiased, 607
Sample size, formula for, 316
Sample space, 145
Sampling, 10–13, 601–616
    distribution of sample means,
        270–276
    double, 615
    error, 271
    multistage, 615
    random, 10–12, 607–611
    sequence, 615
Sampling techniques, 9
Scatter plot, 453–457
Scheffé test, 537–538
    formula for, 537
Sequence sampling, 615
Sequential sampling, 13
Short-cut formula for variance and
    standard deviation, 102
Sign test, 567–569
    formula for, 568
    test value for, 567
Significance, level of, 339
Simple event, 148
Simple relationship, 453
Simulation technique, 606, 621
Single sample paired test, procedure
    table, 571
Single sample sign test, 567–569
Skewed distribution, 49, 63
Skewness, 48–49, 249
Slope, 469–470
    rounding rule, 470
Spearman rank correlation coefficient,
    588–590

Standard deviation, 79, 98–104, 216
  binomial distribution, 228
  chi-square, 373–381
  definition, 100
  formula, 100
  grouped data, 103–104
  normal distribution, 250
  population, 100
  rounding rule, 98–99, 214
  sample, 101–102
  short-cut formula, 102
  uses of, 105
Standard error of difference between
    means, 401
Standard error of difference between
    proportions, 434
Standard error of the estimate, 477–482
Standard error of the mean, 272
Standard normal distribution, 251
Standard scores, 79, 114–115
Statistic, 80
Statistical charts, 30
Statistical graphs, 30
Statistical hypothesis, 335, 399
Statistical test, 337
Statistics, 3
  definition, 3
  descriptive, 4
  inferential, 5
  misuses of, 16–19
Stem and leaf plot, 61–65, 127
Stratified sample, 12, 612–614
Student's *t*-distribution, 307
Subjective probability, 155–156
Sum of squares, 533
Surveying records, 10
Surveys, 9–10, 618–620
  mail, 10
  personal interviews, 10
  telephone, 9
Symmetrical distribution, 48, 91, 248
Systematic sampling, 12, 611–612

T

t-distribution, characteristics of, 307
t-test

degrees of freedom, 358
difference of means, for, 416–421,
    423–431
  mean, for, 358–365
Tail, 90, 249
Test value, 337
Time series graph, 54–56
Total variation, 478
Traditional statistics, 79
Treatment groups, 14, 544
Tree diagram, 147, 173, 182, 183
Tukey test, 538–540
  formula for, 537
Two-tailed test, 335, 341, 351, 401
Two-way analysis of variance, 543–552
Type I error, 338, 384–386
Type II error, 338, 384–386

U

Ulam, Stanislaw, 621
Unbiased estimate of population
    variance, 101
Unbiased estimator, 297
Unbiased sample, 607
Unexplained variation, 478
Ungrouped frequency distribution, 37
Uniform distribution, 48, 271
Unimodal, 49, 85
Union, 164
Upper class boundary, 33
Upper class limit, 33

V

Validity, 620
Variable, 3, 207, 248, 453
  confounding, 15
  continuous, 6, 207
  dependent, 14, 453
  discrete, 6, 207
  explanatory, 14
  independent, 14, 453, 543
  outcome, 14
  qualitative, 6
  quantitative, 6
  random, 3, 207

Variance, 79, 98–104, 216
  binomial distribution, 228–230
  chi-square, 373–381
  definition of, 100
  equal, 416
  formula, 100, 216
  grouped data, 103–104
  population, 100
  probability distribution,
      216–218
  rounding rule, 214
  sample, 101–102
  short-cut formula, 102
  unbiased estimate, 102
  unequal, 416
  uses of, 105
  with-in group, 531
Venn diagram, 152–153, 164, 175
Von Neumann, John, 621

W

Weighted estimate of *p*, 434
Weighted mean, 88–89
Wilcoxon rank sum test, 574–577
  formula for, 575
  procedure for, 576
Wilcoxon signed-rank test,
    578–581
  procedure for, 576
Within-group variance, 531

Y

y-intercept, 469–470
Yule, G., 469

Z

z-scores, 79, 114–115, 252
z-test, 346
  formula for, 350
z-test for means, 346–350,
    400–405
z-test for proportions, 366–371,
    433–437
  formula for, 367